D1072363

METABOLISM OF
STEROID HORMONES

Metabolism of Steroid Hormones

BY

RALPH I. DORFMAN

The Worcester Foundation
for Experimental Biology
Shrewsbury, Massachusetts

Presently
Institute of Hormone Biology, Syntex Research
Palo Alto, California

FRANK UNGAR

Department of Biochemistry
University of Minnesota Medical School
Minneapolis, Minnesota

1965

ACADEMIC PRESS New York and London

ACADEMIC PRESS INC.
111 Fifth Avenue, New York, New York 10003

United Kingdom Edition published by
ACADEMIC PRESS INC. (LONDON) LTD.
Berkeley Square House, London W.1

LIBRARY OF CONGRESS CATALOG CARD NUMBER: 65-14644

PRINTED IN THE UNITED STATES OF AMERICA

Preface

Our first monograph on the metabolism of the steroid hormones published in 1953 and reprinted in 1954 represented information obtained from about 1500 reports with a listing of over 400 papers. This publication contains over 2000 literature citations reflecting still a greater number of papers actually consulted. During the intervening period, not only has the literature in the field of steroid hormone metabolism expanded enormously, but also additional areas of steroid research have undergone marked development, and information is constantly being added to swell the total body of knowledge in this field. This monograph presents a reasonably thorough but not necessarily complete coverage of the pertinent literature on the metabolism of the steroid hormones.

The basic plan of this work is to illustrate and tabulate the diverse aspects of steroid metabolism. In those instances where it seemed particularly appropriate we have made certain critical evaluations and have presented some theoretical considerations. In the over-all summaries presented as a complete system in Chapter 7 and in discussions of the tissue hormones and their metabolites we have considered the sum total of both *in vivo* and *in vitro* experiments as a body of composite information obtained from many species of animals. It is to be anticipated that in the near future sufficient information will become available to allow for a more detailed consideration of the comparative aspects of steroid metabolism.

As discussed and illustrated in Chapter 4, almost every position of the steroid molecule may be attacked by enzymes of microbiological origin. The imbalance between the practical and theoretical aspects of the science are striking when it is realized that only relatively few of the microbiological enzymes have been subjected to detailed biochemical study. Yet a few notable exceptions will be found such as the isolation of very active steroid isomerase and dehydrogenase enzymes from a microbiological source. We record with pleasure our indebtedness to Dr. Yuichiro Kurosawa, of the Tsurumi Chemical Research Laboratory, Yokohama, Japan, who so kindly helped search the Japanese literature for important steroid microbiological reactions and presented us with summaries for inclusion in this monograph.

Many steroids have been synthesized which are not naturally occurring and which are particularly important therapeutic agents. The *in vivo* and *in vitro* metabolism of these synthetic steroids has been documented to some extent. The knowledge of synthetic steroid hormone metabolism is expected to grow and become of particular value as it contributes to studies on the mechanism of steroid hormone action and on the relationship between structure and biological activity, two important areas which are not directly covered in the present work.

A particular objective of this form of presentation, which has been clearly one of our primary considerations throughout, was the fashioning of a volume useful to the novice, and for that reason many structural formulas as well as a detailed treatment of the nomenclature have been included. This feature, with the more extensive documentation, we believe will be appreciated equally by the clinician, internist, endocrinologist, gynecologist, obstetrician, pediatrician, psychiatrist, urologist, and by the general practitioner who may desire a firm background in steroid biochemistry.

This publication should be considered to be primarily a qualitative treatment of steroid metabolism. Other reports in recent years have presented certain quantitative aspects of steroid metabolism with the available information on urinary and blood levels. We anticipate that the quantitative aspects and dynamics of metabolism, the relative pathways both of biosynthesis and catabolism, and the levels of steroid hormones and related substances in body fluid will be rapidly forthcoming in some detail and any future revision would deal with these matters at great length.

The staff of Academic Press has been particularly kind and helpful, and the difficult problems created by us were solved efficiently and in a most cooperative manner.

It is possible that in a volume such as this authors by acts of omission as well as commission manage to incorporate in the manuscript an untold number of errors; the bulk of these are detected and brought to our attention by our fellow co-workers and by the secretarial staff. This monograph is no exception and we accept full responsibility for whatever errors remain. To the degree to which the accuracy and the validity of the documentation has been preserved, full praise must go to Mrs. Iola Graton, Mrs. Elaine Joseph, Mrs. Madeline Daley, and Mrs. Marilyn Linn, who in good cheer and with meticulous care did all that was required to assist in preparing the manuscripts. For this we say "many thanks."

Shrewsbury, Massachusetts,
Minneapolis, Minnesota
March, 1965

RALPH I. DORFMAN

FRANK UNGAR

Contents

CHAPTER V

CHAPTER VI

CHAPTER VII

CHAPTER VIII

CHAPTER IX

METABOLISM OF
STEROID HORMONES

CHAPTER I

Introduction

The first steroid hormone, estrone, was isolated in 1929 at a time when the structure of the steroid nucleus was not yet established. Since then, the structure of the steroid nucleus has been elucidated, steroid chemistry has flourished, and four endocrine glands, the testis, the ovary, the adrenal cortex, and the placenta of pregnancy, have been identified as the steroid-producing tissues. In the years that have elapsed since the first crystalline steroid hormones were isolated from human pregnancy urine, many steroids with varying degrees of biological activities have been isolated from tissue sources. These studies have been supplemented with the isolation and identification of over 200 steroids from urine.

The isolation of the steroid hormones and the elucidation of their structure paved the way for intensive steroid metabolic studies. Significant work on steroid metabolism started in the 1930's with the use of the classical technic of administering large doses of known crystalline steroids to human subjects and experimental animals and isolating crystalline metabolites from body fluids, usually the urine. In this way the relationships of pregnanediol to progesterone (Venning and Browne, 1937), androsterone to testosterone (Callow, 1939; R. I. Dorfman and Hamilton, 1939), estradiol-17β to estrone (Fish and R. I. Dorfman, 1941), and deoxycorticosterone to pregnanediol (rabbits: Westphal, 1942; Hoffman *et al.*, 1943; man: Horwitt *et al.*, 1944; chimpanzee: Fish *et al.*, 1943) were established.

An important phase of metabolism considered by early workers was the biosynthesis of the steroid hormones, including the possible conversion of androgens to estrogens. This conversion illustrates very well one aspect of the many problems that exist in the study of biosynthetic pathways.

Conversion of testosterone, the most active naturally occurring male sex hormone, into a substance possessing estrogenic activity was reported by Steinach and Kun (1937) to occur in men. These investigators reported an increase in urinary estrogenic material after the injection of testosterone propionate. In one case they reported a change from 36 to 1200 RU of estrogenic material per liter after the injection of 1 gm of testosterone propionate during a 6-week period. Since the estrogenic assays were made on the crude benzene extracts, there was a possibility that the activity was due to androgens, some of which are known to produce estrogenic or pseudoestrogenic effects on the vaginal epithelium.

R. I. Dorfman and Hamilton (1939), Hoskins *et al.* (1939), and Callow *et al.* (1939) obtained evidence by bioassay procedures for an increase in estrogens in the urine of human subjects with or without gonads after testosterone treatment. R. I. Dorfman and Hamilton (1939) were able to show the same effect in monkeys.

Nathanson *et al.* (1951) reported that the increase in phenolic estrogens after testosterone or dehydroepiandrosterone was actually due to the increased excretion of estrone and estriol, characterized by countercurrent distribution.

The results of these early studies were consistent with a biosynthetic pathway of estrogens from androgens but, since the yields of estrogens were low and many variables were not rigorously controlled, certainty of this biosynthetic route was not attained. It remained for more rigorous experimentation, as described in Chapter III, to establish beyond doubt that the conversion occurred. The decisive demonstration involved the conversion of a radioactively labeled androgen into a labeled estrogen.

In the middle of the 1930's two technical procedures were described which proved to be invaluable for steroid investigation. Girard and Sandulesco (1936) introduced the use of the two reagents known as Girard's reagents T and P, which are trimethylaminoacetohydrazide hydrochloride and pyridylacetohydrazide hydrochloride, respectively. These reagents efficiently separate ketonic steroids from non-ketonic substances, thus aiding immeasurably the fractionation procedures. Reichstein (1936) introduced the use of adsorption column chromatography for the separation of adrenocortical steroids, and Callow and Callow (1939) used this method for the fractionation of urinary steroids. The importance of the introduction of the two methods, the Girard and Sandulesco procedure and adsorption chromatography, can be appreciated from the following illustration. Butenandt (1931), working without these methods, needed about 15,000 liters to isolate 15 mg of androsterone (0.001 mg/liter) from normal men's urine, whereas Callow and Callow (1939) were able to isolate 0.3 mg of androsterone per liter with the use of the newer, more refined technics.

Further improvements in chromatographic technic which followed were adapted for steroid investigation. Paper chromatography, as applied to steroids by Zaffaroni *et al.* (1950), brought a new era of analysis and permitted experimentation at the microgram level. These advances continued with the use of partition columns and thin-layer chromatography. One of the newest and most striking developments concerns gas chromatography, where separations and identifications may soon be possible at the 0.01- to 0.001-μg level.

Countercurrent distribution has been brought to a high level of development for most steroids, starting with the pioneer work of Engel *et al.* (1950) with estrogens.

Structural proof for steroid compounds by physical means has kept pace with developments in separation and fractionation. The development of infrared spectroscopy by Furchgott *et al.* (1946) and by Jones and Dobriner (Dobriner *et al.*, 1948) was an important advance in the field of identification of steroids. Parallel roles have been shared for ultraviolet determinations (L. Dorfman, 1953; Bernstein and Lenhard, 1953), optical rotatory dispersion (Djerassi, 1957), nuclear magnetic resonance (Shoolery and Rogers, 1958), mass spectrometry (Reed, 1958), gas chromatography based on pyrolytic fission (Parsons *et al.*, 1955a, b, 1956, 1957), and X-ray crystallographic analysis (Bernal, 1932; Crowfoot and Dunitz, 1948; Crowfoot *et al.*, 1957).

The early development of certain color reactions, including the Kober reaction (1938), the Zimmermann reaction (1935), and the fluorescence analyses (Cohen and Bates, 1947), hastened progress immensely.

The field of analysis has developed considerably by the use of the technic of double labeling for aldosterone, estrogens, testosterone, cortisol, and progesterone. Methods of analysis have utilized enzymatic procedures (Hurlock and Talalay, 1958) and even steroid biosynthetic enzyme preparations as reagents (Finkelstein *et al.*, 1961, Forchielli *et al.*, 1963).

The metabolism of the steroid hormones and related substances has been studied by a variety of experimental procedures. These procedures have included the perfusion technic and various *in vivo* and *in vitro* preparations. The *in vivo* studies dominated the field at an early period with the administration, usually to humans, of relatively large amounts of steroid hormones and closely related substances. The metabolic products were then isolated from the urine. As the field developed, technics involving the use of perfusion of isolated intact glands, tissue slices, tissue homogenates, and tissue enzyme preparations were utilized.

The perfusion of an isolated single gland for studies on steroid metabolism was carried out by Danby (1940), who showed that liver obtained from a dog and the kidney of the cow could inactivate androgens. Certain C_{19}-steroids (dehydroepiandrosterone and androst-5-ene-3β,17β-diol), perfused through the isolated bull testis, showed increased androgenic activity. This technic was developed to a high degree of proficiency by investigators at the Worcester Foundation for the elaboration of the biosynthetic pathways for the adrenocortical steroids (Hechter *et al.*, 1949, 1951) and for studies of the metabolism by liver tissue of adrenocortical steroids (Caspi *et al.*, 1953).

A great part of our information on the metabolism of the steroid hormones was derived from *in vivo* experiments. This technic has been employed with relatively large doses of the steroid hormones as well as with more physiological concentrations of steroids bearing labeled atoms (C^{14}, deuterium, and tritium) at various points on the steroid nucleus and/or side chain. These *in vivo* studies have had a considerable utility and probably will continue to be of value in specialized types of experiments.

By means of this technic, the interrelationships that exist between certain steroid hormones produced in specific glands and urinary metabolites have been demonstrated. Thus, the determination of the urinary concentration of certain metabolites has made it possible to assess the functional status of a particular endocrine gland. The direct relationship between progesterone, the progestational hormone, and pregnanediol in the urine has been rigidly established. The urinary pregnanediol content during the luteal phase of the menstrual cycle in a nonpregnant woman indicates the quantity of progesterone produced by the ovary. In pregnancy, the massive amount of progesterone produced by the placenta is also converted to and excreted in part as pregnanediol. The concentration of urinary urocortisone plus urocortisol gives a reasonable measure of the cortisol produced by the adrenal cortex. These interrelationships were established by means of *in vivo* experiments. By the use of isotopic technics, *in vivo* studies give more decisive results, since the problems created by the presence of endogenous products are controlled. In addition, the formation of labeled metabolites, with proper specific activities, provide immediate answers to the many tissue hormone–urinary metabolite relationships. The interrelationships between the tissue steroids and their metabolites in blood and urine are considered in detail in Chapter VIII.

The *in vivo* technic has certain limitations, whether or not isotopically labeled hormones are employed. For examples, little can be learned of the intermediate steps in steroid reactions. Neutral steroid hormones which have at least three active centers may undergo reductive or oxidative changes leading to a variety of products. Frequently, alternative pathways are possible. The *in vivo* method of experimentation can only indicate likely possibilities. A further drawback is the fact that the tissue responsible for the transformation cannot be assessed with certainty.

The *in vitro* technic is capable of furnishing us with information, which supplements results obtained with *in vivo* methods, concerning the metabolic pathways of the steroid hormones and the specific tissues involved. Fractionation and purification of specific enzyme systems can provide the means for delineating the individual steps involved in the metabolic pathways of the steroid hormones, and the possible mechanisms involved.

Some of the technics employed in steroid investigation have been presented in order to illustrate their contributions to the understanding of the metabolism of the steroid hormones. By metabolism, we actually mean both the biosynthetic reactions leading to the production of a specific hormone and the transformations that the molecule, once formed, may undergo in peripheral tissues. This volume will be concerned primarily with reactions of the steroids in which the steroid nucleus remains intact. The extensive transformations of the steroid molecule after the disruption of the nucleus are essentially unknown. Studies employing labeled steroids have indicated that a small portion of administered steroids undergo nuclear disruption. The incubation of testosterone-3-C^{14} with human ovarian tissue resulted in the production of a small but significant amount of C^{14}-labeled carbon dioxide (Baggett *et al.*, 1956). Heard *et al.* (1954) have shown that, when estrone-16-C^{14} was administered to a pregnant mare, a portion of the total estrogen administered was converted to $C^{14}O_2$, again demonstrating nuclear disruption.

Since more than 200 different steroids have been identified from tissue and urinary sources and since these compounds undergo many oxidative and reductive reactions, a classification or organization of the many diverse reactions involved becomes desirable. The question arises as to whether this complex of isolated facts may be put into a relatively logical and more useful form. It is the primary purpose of this volume to attempt some unified presentation of the material.

Nomenclature of Steroids

The steroids are a class of organic compounds containing the perhydrocyclopentanophenanthrene nucleus. These substances include such important biological compounds as cholesterol, ergosterol, cardiac glycosides, bile acids, sapogenins, as well as androgens, adrenocortical hormones, estrogens, progesterone, and their metabolites. Figure 1 illustrates the structure of testosterone to indicate the basic common nucleus. The steroid structures are not usually written with all the carbon and hydrogen atoms illustrated, as in Fig. 1 for 5β-pregnane, but rather, as shown in Figs. 1, 2, and 3, with a hexagonal ring for each of the six-carbon rings and a pentagonal ring for the five-carbon ring. The hydrogen atoms are omitted and the representation of the nucleus as such indicates a fully reduced ring structure; that is, each carbon atom has its full complement of valence bonds satisfied by carbon or hydrogen atoms, or both. The carbon atoms represented in the nucleus are of three types: those that are linked to two adjacent carbon atoms and carry two hydrogen atoms; those that are linked to three carbon atoms and are common to two different rings so that they carry only one hydrogen atom; and, finally, the two carbon atoms (numbers 10 and 13) that are linked to four carbon atoms and carry no hydrogen atoms.

Figure 1 also indicates the manner of numbering the carbon atoms and designating the four rings. The carbon atoms are conventionally numbered from 1 to 17 and the rings are referred to by the letters A, B, C, and D. Carbon atoms 18 and 19 are located between rings C and D, and A and B, respectively. The methyl groups, containing carbon atoms 18 and 19, are frequently called angular methyl groups and are represented by solid straight lines between the respective rings. The side chain containing carbons 20 and 21 is attached to carbon 17.

All steroids of the androgenic, estrogenic, adrenocortical, and progestational series may be considered to be derived from the eight basic hydrocarbons represented in Fig. 2. When the steroid molecule is depicted in the usual manner, the angular methyl groups (containing carbon atoms 18 and 19) may be considered to lie above the plane of the paper. Thus, in the pictorial representation of the steroid molecule, the entire nucleus, which is a relatively flat structure with the exception of the angular methyl groups, is considered to lie in the plane of the paper. The methyl groups are joined to the nucleus by means of solid lines designating a β-stereochemical configuration. The angular methyl groups serve as the reference groups for assigning stereochemical configuration. Thus, each time a solid line is used for a substituent group (where stereoisomerism is possible) it will mean that the group is above the plane of the molecule (or paper), it is on the same side of the molecule as the two angular methyl groups, and it has a β-configuration. If a substituent group is connected to the nucleus by means of a dotted line, it will mean that the group is below the plane of the molecule, on the opposite side with respect to the angular methyl groups, and has an α-configuration. When two groups lie on the same side of the molecule they are said to be *cis* to each other and when they lie on opposite sides of the molecule they are referred to as being *trans* to each other.

In Fig. 2 the four-ring structures are modified in four ways. 5β-Gonane is a basic hydrocarbon, with no angular methyl groups, in which the hydrogen atom at carbon 5 projects in front of or above the plane of the molecule while, in 5α-gonane, the hydrogen atom projects in back of or below the plane of the molecule. No naturally occurring derivative of this hydrocarbon is known at this time. The estrane series (5α and 5β) contains only one angular methyl group (carbon number 18) and includes, among its naturally occurring members, 19-norandrost-4-ene-3,17-dione and ring A and ring B unsaturated derivatives.

5β-Androstane and 5α-androstane contain two angular methyl groups (carbon numbers 18 and 19) and differ only by the spatial configuration of the hydrogen attached to carbon atom 5. The 5α-configuration of androstane is designated as "allo" in some of the older system of nomenclature. The 5β-configuration of androstane is sometimes referred to as the "normal" form. The same relationship exists between 5α-pregnane and 5β-pregnane with respect to the spatial configuration of the respective hydrogens at carbon 5.

When 5α-pregnane and 5α-androstane are compared, it is found that the compounds differ in that the former compound has an ethyl (C_2H_5) side chain at carbon 17. A similar relationship exists between 5β-pregnane and 5β-androstane. The side chains in both 5α-pregnane and 5β-pregnane are attached to carbon 17 with a solid line, indicating that the side chain is *cis* to the angular methyl groups and may be considered to lie above the plane of the molecule. This configuration is designated as beta (β), while side chains *trans* to the angular methyl groups are designated as alpha (α). Actually all of the naturally occurring steroids in the sex hormone and adrenocortical hormone series have side chains (when such are present) of the β-configuration. Derivatives of 5α-androstane and 5β-androstane will be encountered among the androgens and their metabolites, while 5α-pregnane and 5β-pregnane are important with respect to the adrenocortical hormones and progesterone.

Changes in stereochemical configuration at carbon 3 are encountered frequently in the steroids. Figure 3 illustrates this type of isomerism. The two compounds 5α-androstan-3α-ol and 5α-androstan-3β-ol differ only in the spatial configuration of the hydroxyl group at carbon atom 3. In 5α-androstan-3α-ol, the hydroxyl group at carbon atom 3 is in a position *trans* to the methyl group on carbon atom 10. This *trans* position is designated as the alpha (α) position, and compounds having this configuration usually do not form insoluble digitonides by the method ordinarily employed. In 5α-androstan-3β-ol, the hydroxyl group is in a position *cis* to the position of the methyl group on carbon atom 10. This position is designated as beta (β), and compounds having a hydroxyl group of this configuration usually do form insoluble digitonides. The precipitation or nonprecipitation of a steroid by digitonin under specific conditions is presumptive, but not conclusive, evidence for the configuration of the hydroxyl group at carbon atom 3.

In addition to the stereoisomers in the steroid series at carbons 3, 5, and 17 which have been discussed, carbon atom 11 frequently carries a hydroxyl group. In the vertebrate animal the hydroxyl group at carbon 11 in all naturally occurring steroids has a β-configuration, i.e., the hydroxyl group is *cis* to the angular methyl groups. It is of interest to note that the 11α-hydroxyl (*trans*) configuration can be formed by the actions of many microorganisms on suitable steroid substrates.

Some order in the nomenclature of the steroid compounds has been finally achieved. The formal form of nomenclature to be discussed is that adopted by Commissions on the Nomenclature of Organic Chemistry and the Nomenclature of Biological Chemistry of the International Union of Pure and Applied Chemistry, 1957. These rules were published in London in 1958 by Butterworth's Scientific Publications under the title *Nomenclature of Organic Chemistry*.

In general, three types of steroid names are used. The common or trivial name has the advantage of simplicity but the disadvantage of not revealing the nature of the substitutions on the steroid nucleus, their position, or their spatial configuration. The second type of name is one which starts with a definite common name of a compound, and designates the compound to be named by changes in the common or trivial name. This practice has occurred particularly in the adrenocortical hormone series. Thus, corticosterone is the trivial name for 11β,21-dihydroxypregn-4-ene-3,20-dione and the name 11-dehydrocorticosterone (or dehydrocorticosterone), which is in common usage, indicates that the new compound is the same as corticosterone except for the loss of two hydrogen atoms at carbon atom

11 (actually one hydrogen is lost from carbon 11 and one is removed from the hydroxy group so the result is the formation of a ketone group). The third type of name emphasizes the parent hydrocarbon and designates the changes in the parent substances by the kind of change, the place of change, and the stereoisomerism involved. Thus, this name rigidly defines the compound in question.

The basic hydrocarbons and the possible stereoisomerism at carbon atoms 3, 5, 11, and 17 have been discussed. Nuclear modification also occurs and requires designation. A common type of nuclear modification is the presence of a double bond. The presence of the double bond is indicated in the spelling of the hydrocarbon. The term androstane represents the fully saturated hydrocarbon. The presence of one double bond changes the suffix "ane" to "ene" so that androstane, for example, becomes androstene. Two double bonds make the suffix "diene," and "triene" indicates three double bonds. Since the bond of unsaturation may occur at a number of places in the steroid, it is important to designate the position. This is done by a number designation and indicates that the double bond is present between the carbon atom named and the next carbon atom in order. Thus, "—3" indicates that the double bond should be placed between carbon atoms 3 and 4. In some instances, such as a double bond between carbon atoms 9 and 11, the double bond does not extend between consecutive carbon atoms. In these cases the numbers of both carbon atoms are used in the form "—9(11)." When more than one bond of unsaturation is present, as for example, between carbon atoms 3 and 4, and 5 and 6, the designation would be "—3,5." In naming compounds with a double bond the following order is used: The first part of the hydrocarbon name, the designation of the position of the double bond(s), followed by the suffix "ene." An example of this is androst-5-ene (Fig. 3). An older form of designation, commonly found in the literature, is the use of the symbol Δ, followed by the carbon number involved, as a prefix to the hydrocarbon name; for example, Δ^5-androstene. This designation is no longer preferred.

A second type of nuclear modification consists of a substitution of oxygen for hydrogen in the hydrocarbon. An alcohol or hydroxyl group is designated either as the suffix "ol" preceded by the number of the carbon atom to which it is attached or by the term hydroxy preceding the hydrocarbon name. An example of one unsaturated group and one alcohol group could be androst-5-ene-3β-ol (Fig. 3). A second type of oxygen substitution is a ketone group designated by the suffix "one" or, when preceding the hydrocarbon name, designated as keto or oxo. Other examples are presented in Fig. 3. Prefixes and suffixes are given in Table 1.

The prefix "nor" is used to designate shortening of the side chain or the elimination of a methyl group (Fig. 4).

Rings may be enlarged or contracted and, to designate these changes, "nor" is used when the ring is decreased, as in *A*-nortestosterone, and "homo" is used when the ring is increased, as in *D*-homotestosterone (Fig. 5). The absence of a ring may be designated as "des" followed by the missing ring, as illustrated in Fig. 6. Here the D ring of the hydrocarbon, 5α-androstane, is absent and the compound is referred to as des-*D*-5α-androstane.

A ring may be opened, as shown in Fig. 7. In this example, the rupture in the steroid 5α-androstane is between carbon atoms 1 and 2 and the designation is 1 : 2-seco-5α-androstane.

Other conventions include a symbol for an unknown configuration which is drawn with a wavy line and designated as ξ (Greek xi); "deoxy," indicating replacement of a hydroxyl group by a hydrogen atom; the prefix "*di*hydro," indicating addition of 2 hydrogen atoms to a double bond; "*de*hydro," indicating the loss of 2 hydrogen atoms; "epi," meaning the inversion of a substituent; and "deoxo," indicating the replacement of an oxo (ketone) group by two hydrogen atoms.

In the interest of efficiency, the common or trivial names have been employed frequently in this book and are given in Table 2 together with their systematic names.

Table 3 lists some general steroid metabolism reviews.

Conformational Analysis

The steroid nucleus is composed of three cyclohexane rings and one cyclopentane ring. The six carbon atoms of the cyclohexane ring are not fixed but can assume various arrangements owing to twisting or turning, with consequent strain on the ring. These different arrangements in space are called conformations. The chair (1) and boat (2) forms of the cyclohexane ring are good examples.

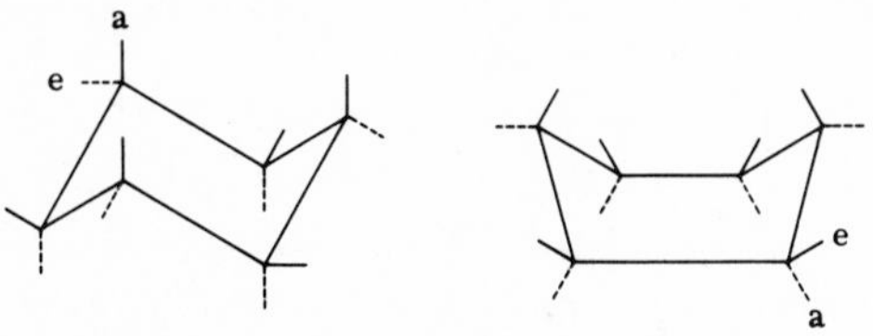

a
e

e
a

Chair
(1)

Boat
(2)

The valencies of the carbon atoms of the cyclohexane ring can exist in the general plane of the ring, and are called equatorial (e); or they are perpendicular to the plane of the ring and are called axial (a). In depicting the equatorial or axial bonds as lying parallel or perpendicular to the plane of the ring, the convention and significance of writing the bonds extending above the plane of the ring as a solid line (β-configuration) and those below the plane of the ring as a broken line (α-configuration) is still retained. The equatorial and axial connotations describe more accurately the spatial relationships of the substituents and the carbon atoms between themselves and the ring system of which they are a part.

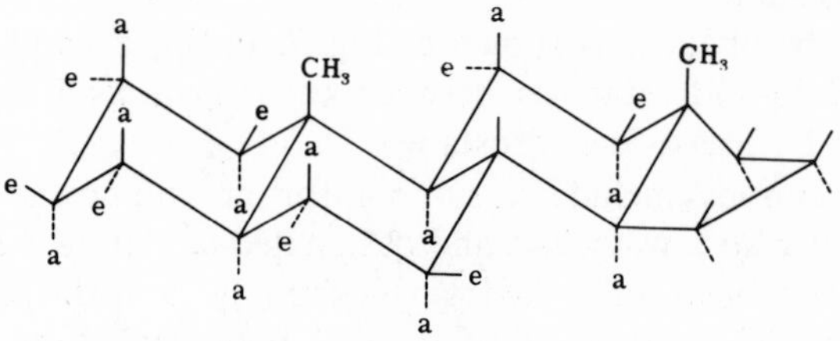

5α -

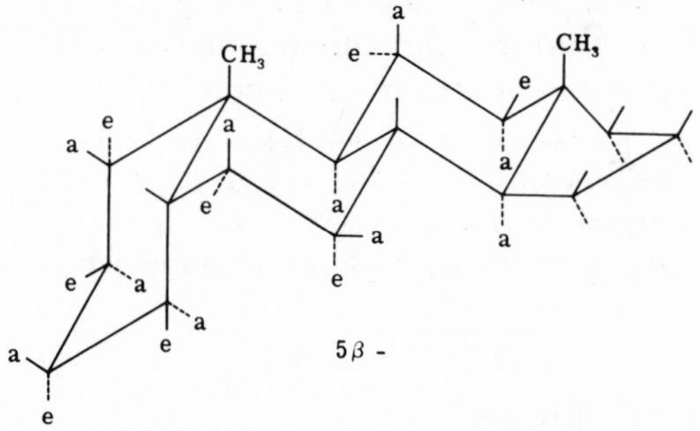

5β -

Carbon	5α (Δ^4 or Δ^5)	5β
1α	a	e
1β	e	a
2α	e	a
2β	a	e
3α	a	e
3β	e	a
4α	e	a
4β	a	e
5α	a	–
5β	–	a

5α – and 5β – Steroids	α	β
6	e	a
7	a	e
8	–	a
9	a	–
10	–	a
11	e	a
12	a	e
13	–	a
14	a	–
15, 16 and 17	indeterminate or quasi –	

The most stable conformation of the cyclohexane ring and of the ring system in steroids is the chair form, and because of the greater interatomic distances, the equatorial substituents on the molecule confer greater stability than do the corresponding axial substituents, owing to differences in repulsion between atoms. The chair forms of the rings A, B, and C can be depicted for 5α- and 5β-steroid forms as shown in the accompanying illustration with the equatorial and axial substituents indicated. Since the conformations on the cyclopentane ring D are nearly at 45° angles, their valencies have been called indeterminate (i), or quasiequatorial or quasi-axial. The conformations for carbons 6 to 17 are the same for steroids with 4- and 5-double bonds as well as for 5α- and 5β-oriented compounds.

Ring A for the 5β-steroids is folded under or below the plane of the remainder of the molecule, and the conformations in ring A differ from those seen in the 5α molecule (or 4- and 5-compounds, as well). A detailed pictorial treatment of the conformations can be found in Fieser and Fieser (1959); original references to the literature will be found in the review by Barton and Cookson (1956).

The concept of conformational analysis has been of inestimable value for the organic chemist in determining the course of synthetic chemical reactions and in describing reaction mechanisms. Some successful attempts have been made to explain characteristics of the steroid compounds in the biochemical field, particularly in the areas of chromatography and spectrophotometry. Continued advances with further applications can be expected which will help to classify much of the empirical data in biochemistry into organized predictable patterns of reactions.

Table 1

NOMENCLATURE[a]

Chemical group	Prefix	Suffix
Double bond	—	ene
Triple bond	—	yne
Acetate	Acetoxy	yl acetate
Hydroxyl	Hydroxy	ol
Benzoate	Benzoyloxy	yl benzoate
Carbonyl	Oxo (formerly keto)	one
Carboxylic acid	Carboxy	oic acid
Carboxylic ester	Methoxycarbonyl (formerly carbomethoxy)	methyloate
Epoxide	Epoxy	—
Amine	Amino	amine

[a] From Klyne (1957).

Table 2

TRIVIAL AND SYSTEMATIC NAMES OF STEROIDS

Common name	Systematic name
Adrenosterone	Androst-4-ene-3,11,17-trione
Aldosterone	11β,21-Dihydroxy-3,20-dioxopregn-4-en-18-al
Allocortol	5α-Pregnane-3α,11β,17α,20α,21-pentol
β-Allocortol	5α-Pregnane-3α,11β,17α,20β,21-pentol
Allocortolone	3α,17α,20α,21-Tetrahydroxy-5α-pregnan-11-one
β-Allocortolone	3α,17α,20β,21-Tetrahydroxy-5α-pregnan-11-one
Androstanedione	5α-Androstane-3,17-dione
Androstenedione	Androst-4-ene-3,17-dione
Androsterone	3α-Hydroxy-5α-androstan-17-one
Corticosterone	11β,21-Dihydroxypregn-4-ene-3,20-dione
Cortisol (hydrocortisone)	11β,17α,21-Trihydroxypregnene-3,20-dione
Cortisone	17α,21-Dihydroxypregn-4-ene-3,11-20-trione
Cortol	5β-Pregnane-3α,11β,17α,20α,21-pentol
β-Cortol	5β-Pregnane-3α,11β,17α,20β,20-pentol
Cortolone	3α,17α,20α,21-Tetrahydroxy-5β-pregnan-11-one
β-Cortolone	3α,17α,20β,21-Tetrahydroxy-5β-pregnan-11-one
11-Dehydrocorticosterone	21-Hydroxypregn-4-ene-3,11,20-trione
Dehydroepiandrosterone	3β-Hydroxyandrost-5-en-17-one
Δ^1-Dehydrotestololactone (Δ^1-testololactone)	13α-Hydroxy-3-keto-13,17-secoandrosta-1, 4-dien-17-oic lactone

Continued on following page

Table 2 *(continued)*

TRIVIAL AND SYSTEMATIC NAMES OF STEROIDS

Common name	Systematic name
Deoxycorticosterone	21-Hydroxypregn-4-ene-3,20-dione
11-Deoxycortisol	17α,21-Dihydroxypregn-4-ene-3,20-dione
21-Deoxycortisol	11β,17α-Dihydroxypregn-4-ene-3,20-dione
Dexamethasone	9α-Fluoro-16α-methyl-11β,17α,21-trihydroxypregna-1,4-diene-3,20-dione
Dromostanolone	2α-Methyl-17β-hydroxy-5α-androstan-3-one
Epiandrosterone	3β-Hydroxy-5α-androstan-17-one
Equilen	3-Hydroxyestra-1,3,5(10),7-tetren-17-one
Equilenin	3-Hydroxyestra-1,3,5(10),6,8-penten-17-one
Estradiol-17β	Estra-1,3,5(10)-triene-3,17β-diol
Estrololactone	13α-Hydroxy-3-keto-13,17-secoestra-1,3,5(10)-trien-17-oic lactone
Estriol	Estra-1,3,5(10)-triene-3,16α,17β-triol
Estrone	3-Hydroxyestra-1,3,5(10)-trien-17-one
Ethynylestradiol	17α-Ethynylestra-1,3,5(10)-triene-3,17β-diol
Etiocholanedione	5β-Androstane-3,17-dione
Etiocholanolone	3α-Hydroxy-5β-androstan-17-one
Fluoxymesterone	9α-Fluoro-11β,17β-dihydroxy-17α-methylandrost-4-en-3-one
11β-Hydroxyandrostenedione	11β-Hydroxyandrost-4-ene-3,17-dione
19-Hydroxyandrostenedione	19-Hydroxyandrost-4-ene-3,17-dione
11β-Hydroxyandrosterone	3α,11β-Dihydroxy-5α-androstan-17-one
18-Hydroxycorticosterone	11β,18,21-Trihydroxypregn-4-ene-3,20-dione
17α-Hydroxy-11-deoxycorticosterone	17α,21-Dihydroxypregn-4-ene-3,20-dione
18-Hydroxy-11-deoxycorticosterone	18,21-Dihydroxypregn-4-ene-3,20-dione
11β-Hydroxyepiandrosterone	3β,11β-Dihydroxy-5α-androstan-17-one
18-Hydroxyestrone	3,18-Dihydroxyestra-1,3,5(10)-trien-17-one
11β-Hydroxyetiocholanolone	3α,11β-Dihydroxy-5β-androstan-17-one
17α-Hydroxypregnenolone	3β,17α-Dihydroxypregn-5-en-20-one
6β-Hydroxyprogesterone	6β-Hydroxypregn-4-ene-3,20-dione
17α-Hydroxyprogesterone	17α-Hydroxypregn-4-ene-3,20-dione
18-Hydroxyprogesterone	18-Hydroxypregn-4-ene-3,20-dione
11-Ketoandrosterone	3α-Hydroxy-5α-androstane-11,17-dione
18-Keto-11-deoxycorticosterone	21-Hydroxy-3,20-dioxopregn-4-en-18-al
11-Ketoetiocholanolone	3α-Hydroxy-5β-androstane-11,17-dione
18-Ketoprogesterone	3,20-Dioxopregn-4-en-18-al
Norethandrolone	17α-Ethyl-17β-hydroxy-19-norandrost-4-en-3-one
Norethindrone (norethisterone)	17α-Ethynyl-17β-hydroxy-19-norandrost-4-en-3-one
Norethynodrel	17α-Ethynyl-17β-hydroxyestr-5(10)-en-3-one
Prednisolone	11β,17α,21-Trihydroxypregna-1,4-diene-3,20-dione
Prednisone	17α,21-Dihydroxypregna-1,4-diene-3,11,20-trione
Pregnanediol	5β-Pregnane-3α,20α-diol

Continued on following page

Table 2 *(continued)*

TRIVIAL AND SYSTEMATIC NAMES OF STEROIDS

Common name	Systematic name
Pregnanetriol	5β-Pregnane-3α,17α,20α-triol
Pregnanolone	3α-Hydroxy-5β-pregnan-20-one
Pregnenolone	3β-Hydroxypregn-5-en-20-one
Progesterone	Pregn-4-ene-3,20-dione
Testololactone	13α-Hydroxy-3-keto-13,17-secoandrost-4-en-17-oic lactone
Testosterone	17β-Hydroxyandrost-4-en-3-one
Tetrahydro A	3α,21-Dihydroxy-5β-pregnane-11,20-dione
Tetrahydro B	3α,11β,21-Trihydroxy-5β-pregnan-20-one
Tetrahydro S	3α,17α,21-Trihydroxy-5β-pregnan-20-one
Triamcinolone	9α-Fluoro-11β,16α,17α,21-tetrahydroxy-pregna-1,4-diene-3,20-dione
Uroaldosterone	3α,11β,21-Trihydroxy-20-keto-5β-pregnan-18-al
Urocortisol (tetrahydro F)	3α,11β,17α,21-Tetrahydroxy-5β-pregnan-20-one
Urocortisone (tetrahydro E)	3α,17α,21-Trihydroxy-5β-pregnane-11,20-dione

Table 3

STEROID METABOLISM REVIEWS

Title	Reference
Biosynthesis of Cholesterol	Gould (1958)
Biosynthesis of Cholesterol and Related Substances	Popjak (1958)
Chemie der Corticosteroide	Neher (1960)
Biochemistry of the Steroid Hormones	R. I. Dorfman (1957)
Metabolism of Androgens	R. I. Dorfman (1959)
Steroid Hormones	Nes (1960)
Über Aldosteron	Wettstein (1959)
Biosynthese des hormones steroides	Wettstein (1961)
Vorkommen, Biogenese, und Stoffwecksel der Ostrogene	Breuer (1960)
Substrate Specificity in the Microbiological Transformation of Steroids	Holmlund *et al.* (1961)
Biochemistry of Steroid Hormones	Engel and Langer (1961)
Steroid Hormone Metabolism	R. I. Dorfman (1961b)
Adrenal Steroidogenesis "In Vitro"; A Review	McCormack and Goldzieher (1961)
Metabolism of Steroid Hormones	R. I. Dorfman and Ungar (1953)
A System for Evaluating the Functional Status of the Adrenal Cortex	R. I. Dorfman (1961a)
Microbiological Transformations of Steroids and their Applications to the Synthesis of Hormones	Eppstein *et al.* (1956)
The Use of Microorganisms in the Synthesis of Steroids, Hormones and Hormone Analogues	Fried *et al.* (1955)

Continued on following page

Table 3 (*continued*)
STEROID METABOLISM REVIEWS

Title	Reference
Metabolism of the Natural Estrogens	Breuer (1962)
Microorganisms and Steroid Transformations	Peterson (1953, 1955)
Transformations of Steroids by Molds	Shull (1956)
Enzymatic Mechanisms in Steroid Metabolism	Talalay (1957)
Enzymatic Transformations of Steroids by Microorganisms	Vischer and Wettstein (1958)
Conversion of Steroids by Microorganisms	Wettstein (1955)
Various reviews, adrenocortical steroids	Short (1960)
Control of Plasma Concentrations of Adrenocortical Hormones	Yates and Urquart (1962)
Oxygenases in Lipid and Steroid Metabolism	Hayano (1962)
Chemical and Biological Factors in the Activity of Adrenocortical Steroids	Bush (1962)
Steroid Hormones in Gynecology	R. I. Dorfman (1963b)
Pituitary–Ovarian Endocrinology	R. I. Dorfman and Castro (1963)
Androgen Biosynthesis and Related Studies	R. I. Dorfman *et al.* (1963)
Chemistry of Androgens and Other C_{19} Steroids	Fujimoto and Ledeen (1963)
Chemistry of Estrogens	Katzman and Elliott (1963)
In Vivo Studies of Steroid Dynamics in Man	Tait and Burstein (1964)
Studies on the Conversion of Squalene to Sterol with Rat Liver Enzymes	Goodman (1963)
Polyisoprenoid Synthesis with Special Reference to the Origin of Squalene	Popjak (1963)
The Biosynthesis of Mevalonate from Acetate	Rudney (1963)
Enzymatic Mechanisms in Steroid Metabolism	Talalay *et al.* (1963)
Biosynthesis of Androgens	Samuels (1963)
Steroid Hormone Biosynthesis	R. I. Dorfman (1963a)
The Biosynthetic Origin of Carbons of Steroid Hormones	Caspi (1963)
Placental Hormones	Diczfalusy and Troen (1961)

I

II

III

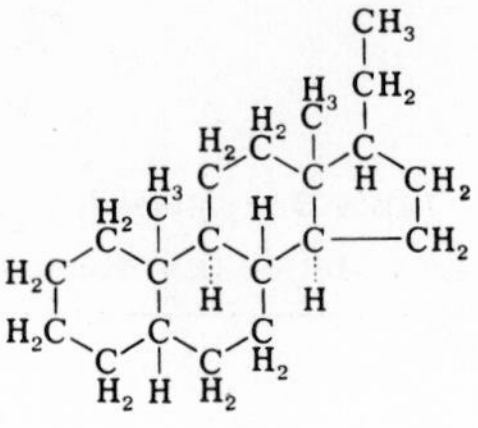

FIG 1. Illustrative steroid structures. I: 5β-Pregnane (showing all carbon and hydrogen atoms). II: 5β-Pregnane (showing conventional representation). III: Testosterone.

I

II

III

IV

V

VI

VII

VIII

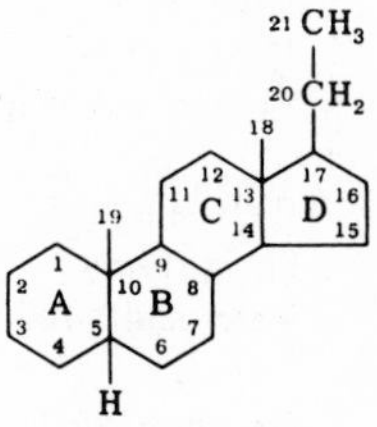

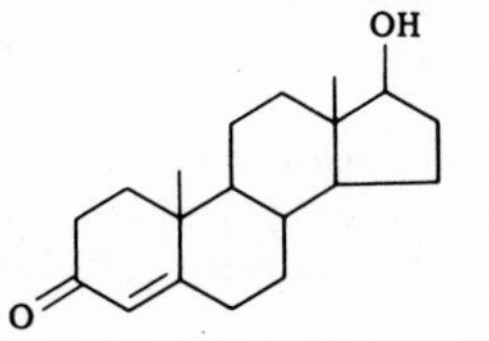

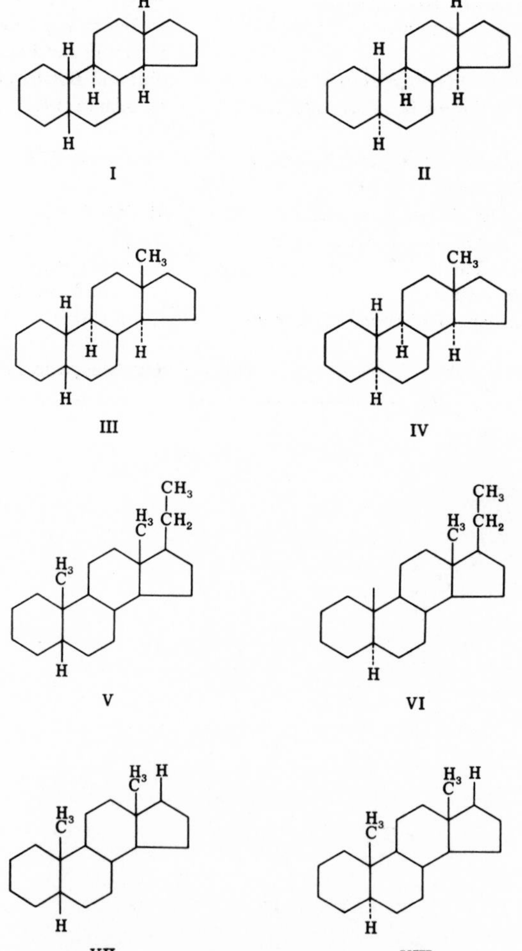

FIG. 2. Basic hydrocarbons. I: 5β-Gonane. II: 5α-Gonane. III: 5β-Estrane. IV: 5α-Estrane. V: 5β-Pregnane. VI: 5α-Pregnane. VII: 5β-Androstane. VIII: 5α-Androstane.

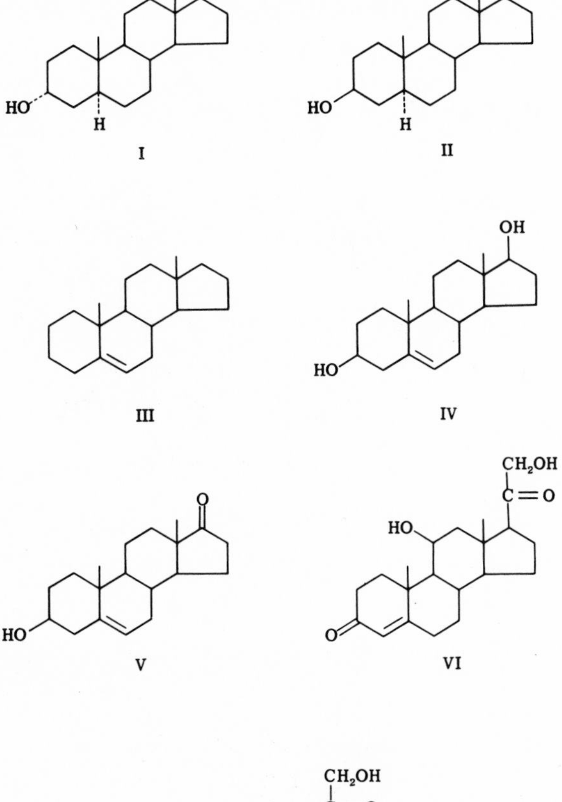

FIG. 3. Illustration of nomenclature rules. I: 5α-Androstan-3α-ol. II: 5α-Androstan-3β-ol. III: Androst-5-ene. IV: Androst-5-ene-3β,17β-diol. V: 3β-Hydroxyandrost-5-en-17-one (dehydroepiandrosterone). VI: 11β-21-Dihydroxypregn-4-ene-3,20-dione (corticosterone). VII: 21-Hydroxypregn-4-ene-3,11,20-trione (11-dehydrocorticosterone).

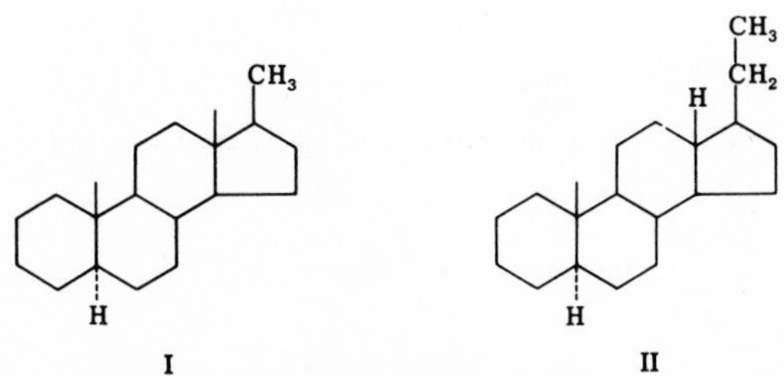

FIG. 4. Illustrations of norsteroids. I: 21-Nor-5α-pregnane. II: 18-Nor-5α-pregnane.

A-Nortestosterone
I

D-Homotestosterone
II

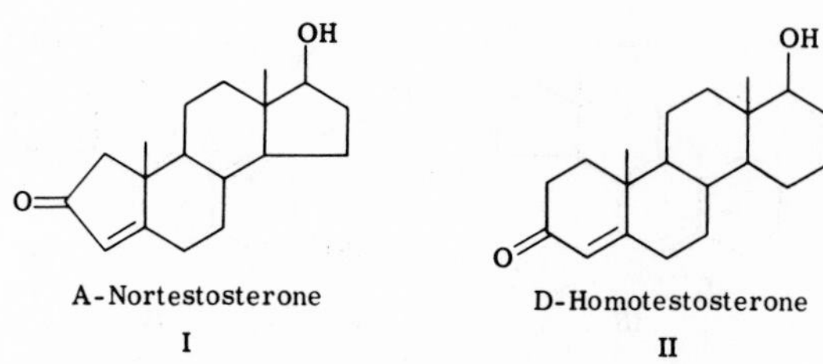

FIG. 5. Illustration of ring contraction or enlargement. I: *A*-Nortestosterone. II: *D*-Homotestosterone.

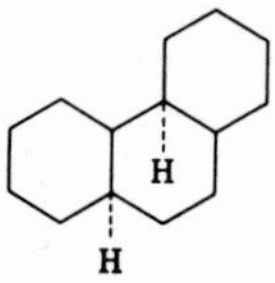

I

FIG. 6. Illustration of a des steroid. I: Des-*D*-5α-androstane.

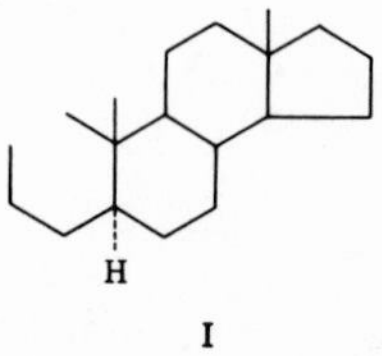

I

FIG. 7. Illustration of a seco steroid. I: 1:2-seco-5α-androstane.

References

Baggett, B., Engel, L. L., Savard, K., and Dorfman, R. I. (1956) *J. Biol. Chem.* **221**: 931.

Barton, D. H. R., and Cookson, R. C. (1956). *Quart. Rev.* (*London*) **10**: 44.

Bernal, J. D. (1932) *Chem. Ind.* (*London*) **51**:466.

Bernstein, S., and Lenhard, R. H. (1953) *J. Org. Chem.* **18**:1146.

Breuer, H. (1960) *Z. Vitamin-, Hormon- Fermentforsch.* **11**:182.

Breuer, H. (1962) *Vitamins Hormones* **20**: 285.

Bush, I. E. (1962) *Pharmacol. Rev.* **14**: 317.

Butenandt, A. (1931) *Z. Angew. Chem.* **44**: 905.

Callow, N. H. (1939) *Biochem. J.* **33**: 559.

Callow, N. H., and Callow, R. K. (1939) *Biochem. J.* **34**: 276.

Callow, N. H., Callow, R. K., and Emmens, C. W. (1939) *J. Endocrinol* **1**: 99.

Caspi, E. (1963) *Proc. Intern. Congr. Biochem. 5th Moscow* 1961, Vol. VII, pp. 347–360. Pergamon Press, New York.

Caspi, E., Levy, H., and Hechter, O. (1953) *Arch. Biochem.* **45**: 169.

Cohen, H., and Bates, R. W. (1947) *J. Clin. Endocrinol.* **7**: 701.

Crowfoot, D., and Dunitz, J. D. (1948) *Nature* **162**: 608.

Crowfoot, D., Hodgkin, D., Webster, M. S., and Dunitz, J. D. (1957) *Chem. Ind.* (*London*) p. 1149.

Danby, M. (1940) *Endocrinology* **27**: 236.

Diczfalusy, E., and Troen, P. (1961) *Vitamins Hormones* **19**: 229.

Djerassi, C. (1957) *Bull Soc. Chim. France,* p. 741.

Dobriner, K., Lieberman, S., Rhoads, C. P., Jones, N. R., Williams, V. Z., and Barnes, R. B. (1948) *J. Biol. Chem.* **172**: 297.

Dorfman, L. (1953) *Chem. Rev.* **53**: 47.

Dorfman, R. I. (1957) *Ann. Rev. Biochem.* **26**: 523.

Dorfman, R. I. (1959) *Proc. Intern. Congr. Biochem. 4th Vienna* 1958, pp. 175–195. Pergamon Press, New York.

Dorfman, R. I. (1961a) *Metabolism* **10**: 902.

Dorfman, R. I. (1961b) *Intern. Congr. Biochem. 5th Moscow*, 1961. Preprint No. 59, p. 1.

Dorfman, R. I. (1961c) *In* "Radioactive Isotopes in Physiology, Diagnostics, and Therapy" (H. Schwiegk and F. Turba, eds.), 2nd ed., pp. 1223–1241. Springer, Berlin.

Dorfman, R. I. (1963a) *Proc. Intern. Congr. Biochem. 5th Moscow* 1961, Vol. VII, pp. 335–347. Pergamon Press, New York.

Dorfman, R. I. (1963b) *Obstet. Gynecol.* **18**: 65.

Dorfman, R. I., and Castro, M. (1963) *In* "Pituitary-Ovarian Endocrinology" (R. I. Dorfman and M. N. Castro, eds.). Holden-Day, San Francisco, California.

Dorfman, R. I., and Hamilton, J. B. (1939) *Endocrinology* **25**: 33.

Dorfman, R. I., and Ungar, F. (1953) "Metabolism of Steroid Hormones." Burgess, Minneapolis, Minnesota.

Dorfman, R. I., Forchielli, E., and Gut, M. (1963) *Recent Progr. Hormone Res.* **19**: 251.

Engel, L. L., and Langer, L. J. (1961) *Ann. Rev. Biochem.* **30**: 499.

Engel, L. L., Slaunwhite, W. R., Jr., Carter, P., and Nathanson, I. T. (1950) *J. Biol. Chem.* **185**: 255.

Eppstein, S. H., Meister, P. D., Murray, H. C., and Peterson, D. H. (1956) *Vitamins Hormones* **14**: 359.

Fieser, L. F., and Fieser, M. (1959) "Steroids." Reinhold, New York.

Finkelstein, M., Forchielli, E., and Dorfman, R. I. (1961) *J. Clin. Endocrinol. Metab.* **21**: 908.

Fish, W. R., and Dorfman, R. I. (1941) *J. Biol. Chem.* **140**: 83.

Fish, W. R., Horwitt, B. N., and Dorfman, R. I. (1943) *Science* **97**: 227.

Forchielli, E., Sorcini, G., Nightingale, M., Brust, N., Dorfman, R. I., Perloff, W. H., and Jacobsen, G. (1963) *Anal. Biochem.* **5**: 416.

Fried, J., Thoma, R. W., Perlman, D., Herz, J. E., and Borman, A. (1955) *Recent Progr. Hormone Res.* **11**: 149.

Fujimoto, G. I., and Ledeen, R. W. (1963) *In* "Comprehensive Biochemistry" (M. Florkin and E. H. Statz, eds.), p. 33. Elsevier, Amsterdam.

Furchgott, R. F., Rosenkrantz, H., and Shorr, E. (1946) *J. Biol. Chem.* **163**: 375.

Girard, A., and Sandulesco, G. (1936) *Helv. Chim. Acta* **19**: 1095.

Goodman, D. S. (1963) *Proc. Intern. Congr. Biochem. 5th Moscow* 1961 Vol. VII, p. 236. Pergamon Press, New York.

Gould, R. G. (1958) *In* "Cholesterol" (R. P. Cook, ed.) p. 209. Academic Press, New York.

Hayano, M. (1962) *In* "Oxygenases" (O. Hayaishi, ed.), pp. 182–237. Academic Press, New York.

Heard, R. D. H., Jacobs, R., O'Donnell, V., Perón, F. G., Saffran, J. C., Solomon, S., Thompson, L. M., Willoughby, H., and Yates, C. H. (1954) *Recent Progress Hormone Res.* **9**: 383.

Hechter, O., Jacobsen, R. P., Jeanloz, R. W., Levy, H., Marshall, C. W., Pincus, G., and Schenker, V. (1949) *J. Am. Chem. Soc.* **71**: 3261.

Hechter, O., Zaffaroni, A., Jacobsen, R. P., Levy, H., Jeanloz, R., Schenker, V., and Pincus, G. (1951) *Recent Progr. Hormone Res.* **6**: 215.

Hoffman, M. M., Kazmin, V. E., and Browne, J. S. L. (1943) *J. Biol. Chem.* **147**: 259.

Holmlund, C. E., Feldman, L. I., Blank, R. H., Balbacci, N., and Nielsen, B. (1961) *Sci. Rept. Ist. Super. Sanita* **1**: 2389.

Horwitt, B. N., Dorfman, R. I., Shipley, R. A., and Fish, W. R. (1944) *J. Biol. Chem.* **155**: 213.

Hoskins, W. H., Coffman, J. R., Koch, F. C., and Kenyon, A. T. (1939) *Endocrinology* **24**: 702.

Hurlock, B., and Talalay, P. (1958) *Endocrinology* **62**: 201.

Katzman, P. A., and Elliott, W. H. (1963) *In* "Comprehensive Biochemistry" (M. Florkin and E. H. Statz, eds.) p. 47. Elsevier, Amsterdam.

Klyne, W. (1957) "The Chemistry of Steroids." Methuen, London.

Kober, S. (1938) *Biochem. J.* **32**: 357.

McCormack, S., and Goldzieher, J. W. (1961) *Pathol. Biol.* **9**: 1343.

Nathanson, I. T., Engel, L. L., Kennedy, B. J., and Kelley, R. M. (1951) *Symp. Steroids Exptl. Clin. Practice, 1st Conf., Cuernevaca, Mex.,* 1951, p. 379.

Neher, R. (1960) *Antibiot. Chemotherap.* **7**: 1.

Nes, W. R. (1960) *In* "Medicinal Chemistry" (A. Burger, ed.), 2nd ed., p. 691. Wiley (Interscience), New York.

Parsons, J., Beher, W. T., and Baker, G. D. (1955a) *Anal. Chem.* **27**: 514.

Parsons, J., Beher, W. T., and Baker, G. D. (1955b) *Anal. Chem.* **27**: 1569.

Parsons, J., Beher, W. T., and Baker, G. D. (1956) *Anal. Chem.* **28**: 1514.

Parsons, J., Beher, W. T., and Baker, G. D. (1957) *Anal. Chem.* **29**: 762.

Peterson, D. H. (1953) *Recent Progr. Hormone Res.* **6**: 309.

Peterson, D. H. (1955) *In* "Perspectives and Horizons in Microbiology" (S. A. Waksman, ed.), p. 121. Rutgers Univ. Press, New Brunswick, New Jersey.

Popjak, G. (1958) *Ann. Rev. Biochem.* **27**: 533.

Popjak, G. (1963) *Proc. Intern. Congr. Biochem. 5th Moscow* 1961 Vol. VII, pp. 205–235. Pergamon Press, New York.

Reed, R. I. (1958) *J. Chem. Soc.* p. 3432.

Reichstein, T. (1936) *Helv. Chim. Acta* **19**: 29.

Rudney, H. (1963) *Proc. Intern. Congr. Biochem. 5th Moscow* 1961 Vol. VII, pp. 254–272. Pergamon Press, New York.

Samuels, L. T. (1963) *Proc. Intern. Congr. Biochem. 5th Moscow* 1961 Vol. VII, pp. 368–380. Pergamon Press, New York.

Shoolery, J. N., and Rogers, M. T. (1958) *J. Am. Chem. Soc.* **80**: 5121.

Short, R. V. (1960) *In* "Biosynthesis and Secretion of Andrenocortical Steroids" (F. Clark and S. K. Grant, eds.), p. 59. Cambridge Univ. Press, London and New York.

Shull, G. M. (1956) *Trans. N.Y. Acad. Sci.* **19(2)**: 147.

Steinach, E., and Kun, H. (1937) *Lancet* **ii**: 845.

Tait, J. F., and Burstein, S. (1964) *In* "The Hormones" (G. Pincus, K. V. Thimann, and E. B. Astwood, eds.), Vol. V, pp. 441–557. Academic Press, New York.

Talalay, P. (1957) *Physiol. Rev.* **37**: 362.

Talalay, P., Kawahara, F. S., and Prairie, R. L. (1963) *Proc. Intern. Congr. Biochem. 5th Moscow* 1961 Vol. VII, pp. 395–404. Pergamon Press, New York.

Venning, E. H., and Browne, J. S. L. (1937) *Endocrinology* **21**: 711.

Vischer, E., and Wettstein, A. (1958) *Advan. Enzymol.* **20**: 237.

Westphal, U. (1942) *Z. Physiol. Chem.* **273**: 13.

Wettstein, A. (1955) *Experientia* **11**: 465.

Wettstein, A. (1959) *In* "Lettre-Inhoffen-Tschesche über Sterine, Gallensaüren, verwandte Naturstoffe." Enke, Stuttgart.

Wettstein, A. (1961) *Experientia* **17**: 329.

Yates, F. E., and Urquhart, J. (1962) *Physiol. Rev.* **42**: 359.

Zaffaroni, A., Burton, R. B., and Keutmann, E. H. (1950) *Science* **111**: 6.

Zimmermann, W. (1935) *Z. Physiol.* **233**: 257.

CHAPTER II

Steroids Isolated from Natural Sources

Steroid hormones have been isolated from marine and terrestrial animals representative of all major classes of vertebrates including fish, amphibians, reptiles, birds, and mammals. The steroid-producing organs or tissues in these species are the ovary, testis, adrenal, and the placenta of primates. Far less is known about the endocrine status of these and other organs in the invertebrate species. Endocrine function is claimed for the gonads of higher forms of crustaceans, and is suspected but not established in annelids. The few hormones, neurohumoral in function, that have been isolated or tentatively identified in insects are not steroid compounds. Sterols of the cholesterol type are present in insects, however. In the plant kingdom sterols of the ergosterol or sitosterol type, but not cholesterol, are present in relatively large amounts. This distribution with many modifications extends to organisms in the yeast and fungi classes. Few or no sterols can be isolated from bacterial sources. In certain unicellular organisms, *Tetrahymena* and *Paramecium*, which may synthesize sterols, a growth factor with the structure of stigmasterol or a related cholesterol derivative has been reported (Conner, 1959).

Secretions of the testis, ovary, and adrenal cortex produce a spectrum of biological effects which can be accounted for by the properties of pure crystalline steroid compounds. In each case, the one steroid compound which exerts the greatest biological activity has been putatively designated the hormone primarily responsible for the observed physiological effects. Testosterone is considered to be the principal hormone of the testis, and compounds which have biological properties of a similar nature or which can be related to testicular activity are called androgens. The biological properties of androgens include effects on the penis, the prostate and seminal vesicles, the body musculature, hair growth patterns, voice timbre, and other secondary features characteristic of the male sex of a species.

Estrogens are substances which are responsible for estrus in animals and can produce uterine hypertrophy, vaginal cornification, mammary gland growth, and other secondary features characteristic of the female sex of a species. Estradiol-17β is considered to be the estrogenic hormone of the ovary. The progestational hormone produced by the corpus luteum of the ovary is progesterone. Progestins are substances which produce characteristic glandular proliferation in the estrogen-primed uterus and mammary gland and are primarily responsible for the maintenance of pregnancy.

The corticoids represent a group of substances produced by the adrenal cortex that are necessary for life maintenance as a result of their participation in the regulation of electrolyte excretion, carbohydrate and protein metabolism, and certain obscure effects involving adaptation of the body's defenses to environmental changes. The mineralocorticoids are compounds that specifically effect electrolyte metabolism. Aldosterone is the most active steroid in this group. Glucocorticoids are substances that primarily influence carbohydrate and protein metabolism. Cortisol is the most active steroid in this group.

Although each of the steroid-producing glands secrete the one or two steroid hormones which give rise to the characteristic biological effects just discussed, the same steroid compounds can be produced by one or all of the other glands to some extent; in addition, there are many related steroid compounds (intermediates, metabolites, or by-products) which possess biological activity. Their contribution to the total physiological state observed in the normal animal has never been properly assessed; however, in abnormal endocrinological states they may play a significant role.

Steroid compounds or the biological activity associated with steroid hormones have been demonstrated in unique instances in certain plant or animal tissues. Butenandt and Jacobi (1933) isolated estrone from palm kernel extract and Skarzynski (1934) isolated estriol from the female willow flower. Levin *et al.* (1951) reported the presence of androgenic activity in wheat germ oil. Androgenic activity in one instance was detected in extracts of pituitary glands (Prelog and Führer, 1945). However, no steroid compounds have ever been isolated from either of these two sources. The placenta, which is known unequivocally to produce estrogens and progesterone in considerable amounts in the later stages of pregnancy, has been suggested to be a source of androgens and glucocorticosteroids, as well as of ACTH, on the basis of demonstrations of biological activity characteristic for these compounds.

The initial steps in the metabolic pathway leading to the formation of the steroid hormones are identical or similar for each steroid-producing tissue (see Chapter III). It is not surprising, therefore, to find the same intermediates or metabolites in each of these tissues in varying amounts. Moreover, our present knowledge of the specific metabolic pathways involved in the biogenesis of each class of steroid hormones offers reasonable explanation for the occurrence of unusual amounts of intermediates or metabolites under certain abnormal conditions, as well as for the paradoxical formation in one tissue of unusual amounts of steroid compounds usually associated with another tissue: i.e., excessive androgen production in the ovary or adrenal, or estrogen formation in a feminizing testicular tumor. The adrenal gland in normal as well as abnormal states is a source of androgens, estrogens, and progesterone, as well as of the typical adrenocortical compounds. To a lesser extent similar conditions probably obtain for the ovary and testis, and possibly the placenta.

The tables in this chapter list the individual steroid hormones, intermediates, and metabolites (or side products) isolated in each of the steroid-producing organs and other tissues. A comparison of the tables will reveal the many steroid compounds found in more than one or in all of these tissues. It is not always possible to assign absolute concentrations or even in some cases to distinguish between major and minor components, since these values will vary with the species studied and the isolation and assay technics employed.

Some difficulties arise in assessing the experimental validation for identification of the microquantities of the steroid compounds usually encountered. In many cases the classical criteria for proof of identity are lacking. Correspondence of rates of migration of unknown material with authentic compounds in chromatographic systems and one or even several nonspecific physical or chemical means of detection often do not provide sufficient criteria for unequivocal identification. Generally, a more rigorous proof of identity has been reported for the identification of the compounds listed in the tables in this chapter.

Testis

Testosterone, the most active of the naturally occurring androgens, has been isolated from the testis gland in the human, bull, stallion, rabbit, and pig (Table 1, Fig. 1). Concentrations in testes are usually of a low order and there appears to be a steady production of the hormone under the influence of the gonadotropic hormones and a steady extrusion into the blood stream. Androst-4-ene-3,17-dione, which differs from testosterone by virtue of a ketone in place of the 17β-hydroxyl group, has been isolated as a companion substance in both the testis tissue and the spermatic venous effluent. A variety of steroids related to the intermediary metabolism of testosterone has been isolated. These compounds include dehydroepiandrosterone, pregnenolone, progesterone, and various 17α-hydroxylated derivatives.

Estrogens have been isolated from the testis of a variety of species. The stallion testis, in fact, has been shown to be the richest tissue source of these hormones (Beall, 1940). Estrone, estradiol, equilin, and equilenin have also been identified from this source.

Evidence for enzymatic activity normally associated with the adrenal cortex, 11β- and 21-hydroxylation, have been found in the testis in presumably normal as well as in abnormal tissue. Compounds bearing these substituents have not yet been isolated directly from normal testis tissue, however.

Ovary

Three types of biologically active compounds, estrogens, progestins, and androgens, are represented in the group of steroids isolated in ovarian tissues (Table 2, Fig. 2). Estradiol-17β, the most active of the estrogens, has been identified in the ovary of the equine, porcine, and human as well as in that of other species. Estrone, which differs from estradiol-17β by virtue of the 17-ketone group, has been isolated as a companion substance to the more active estradiol-17β. The rate of secretion of these compounds is periodic, with peak excretion occurring at the time of ovulation in the human. The 16α-hydroxylated compound, estriol, has been isolated in the ovary but its occurrence in this tissue is probably of minor significance. Other tissues such as the liver are reputed to exert a more important role in the formation and transformation of the 16-oxygenated estrogens.

Progesterone, the most active progestational compound, has been isolated from the ovary, or more specifically the corpus luteum, in a variety of species. Other C_{21}-compounds have been isolated but of these only the 20α- and 20β-hydroxyl derivatives of progesterone have progestational activity.

A number of C_{19}-steroids have been isolated in ovarian tissue, including testosterone, the inactive 17α-hydroxyl isomer of testosterone (epitestosterone), androst-4-ene-3,17-dione, dehydroepiandrosterone, androsterone, and 19-norandrost-4-ene-3,17-dione. Several of these androgenic compounds have been detected in increased amounts in ovarian abnormalities, including Stein–Leventhal disease, Leydig cell tumors, arrhenoblastoma, and in cases of hirsutism.

The presence in the ovary of 11β-hydroxyandrost-4-ene-3, 17-dione and of cortisol, compounds normally associated with the adrenal cortex, is of unknown significance at the present time.

Placenta

Progesterone, estradiol-17β, and various metabolites have been isolated from placental tissue (Table 3, Fig. 3). The amounts produced by the placenta increase gradually and reach a peak during the ninth month of pregnancy. Several reports of isolation of steroids typical of the adrenal cortex and a 16α-hydroxyl derivative of testosterone are included in the list. The actual production or secretion of corticoids and androgens by placental tissue has not been demonstrated, however, and the origin of the substances found in this tissue from the circulating blood or from some other source cannot be discounted.

Adrenal Cortex

A total of 46 steroid compounds have now been isolated from beef or sow adrenal glands. Compounds having the biological activity of each of the major classes of steroids have been isolated, including: estrogens (Table 4; Fig. 4), androgens (Table 5; Fig. 4), progesterone and derivatives (Tables 6 and 7; Fig. 5), and the 21-hydroxy steroids with and without corticoid activity (Tables 8–10; Figs. 6–8).

The adrenal contribution to the total estrogen activity in the normal human is essentially unknown. Isolation of estrogens has been reported only with large-scale extractions of beef adrenals and in certain cases of adrenal carcinoma or tumor in the human (Table 4; Fig. 4). Following ovariectomy, the production of estrogen by the adrenal may increase in some animals and possibly in the human. The increased estrogen titer (presumably estriol) in ovariectomized females reported by Brown (1958) may not be the result of the secretion of the normal estrogens usually encountered (Diczfalusy, 1958). In any case, the efficacy of adrenalectomy for the treatment of breast cancer is well known and is thought to be owing in part to removal of a source of estrogen or estrogen precursors.

The metabolic transformations and the many interesting problems involved in the adrenal production of androgens are discussed in greater detail in Chapter III. A large number of C_{19}-steroids have been isolated from the adrenals of the human, cow, and pig (Table 5; Fig. 4). The C_{19}-compound present in greatest amounts in adrenal tissue and in adrenal venous effluent is 11β-hydroxyandrost-4-ene-3,17-dione. Androst-4-ene-3,17-dione is present in variable amounts. Testosterone and dehydroepiandrosterone have been detected in adrenal tissue by the isotope dilution technic, but amounts sufficient for isolation have occurred only in abnormal situations involving adrenal carcinoma or tumors. Dehydroepiandrosterone has been isolated as the sulfate and glucuronide conjugate from the adrenal venous effluent (Baulieu, 1960a,b) and from adrenal tissue.

19-Hydroxyandrost-4-ene-3,17-dione, an intermediate in the synthesis of estrogen (Chapter III), has been identified following incubation with steroid precursors. Both 6α- and 6β-hydroxyl derivatives of androst-4-ene-3,17-dione were identified in the same series of studies (Meyer, 1955).

Progesterone and derivatives of progesterone have been isolated from the adrenal gland in the human, porcine, and bovine species (Tables 6 and 7; Fig. 5). These derivatives include C_{21}-methyl compounds hydroxylated at the 11β, 17α, 16α, 6β, 20α, or 20β positions. The 21-hydroxylated derivative, deoxycorticosterone, is normally present only in trace amounts in the adrenal. It is increased in amounts in certain cases of adrenogenital syndrome or following the administration of SU-4885 (Metopirone), a drug which can specifically inhibit 11β-hydroxylase activity in the adrenal.

Table 8 (see also Fig. 6) lists corticosterone, 11-deoxycortisol, and similar compounds which have been isolated from adrenal tissue in various species of animals. It is interesting to note that corticosterone, not cortisol, is the major adrenal glucocorticoid in certain species, such as the rat and mouse. Corticosterone is present in the human and bovine adrenal in amounts which are usually less than cortisol concentrations, but occasionally may be elevated, particularly in beef adrenals. 11-Deoxycortisol is normally found only in trace amounts but large increases have been noted in some cases of adrenal carcinoma or following the administration of the drug Metopirone.

Table 9 (see also Fig. 7) lists the steroids, cortisol, cortisone, aldosterone, 18-hydroxycorticosterone, and their derivatives, which have been isolated from a variety of animal species. Cortisol is the major steroid found in the human adrenal, while only minor quantities of cortisone can be detected. Unequivocal proof for the presence of cortisol or other 17-hydroxyl derivatives in the rat or mouse adrenal is lacking. Previous claims for the isolation of cortisol in the rat or mouse are probably owing to the presence of other compounds, such as 18-hydroxycorticosterone, which may be confused with cortisol without suitable isolation and identification procedures.

In addition to 11β-, 17α-, 18- and 21-hydroxylation, steroids isolated from the adrenal contain hydroxyl groups at the 19-, 6β-, and 2α-positions (Tables 9 and 10: Figs. 7 and 8).

The isolation of 20α-hydroxy- and 20α, 22ξ-dihydroxycholesterol in adrenal tissue is of interest since these compounds are suggested intermediates in the conversion of cholesterol to the C_{21}-steroid, pregnenolone.

Bile

The biliary excretion of estrogens and progesterone and their metabolites in conjugated form is well documented. Their involvement in the enterohepatic circulation represents an important consideration with regard to their biological activity and eventual metabolic fate. Whether the bile represents an important route in the circulation and excretion of corticoids and androgens in the human remains to be established. Table 11 (see also Fig. 9) lists the relatively few steroids which have been isolated and identified from the bile.

Blood

A variety of steroid compounds have now been isolated successfully from blood (Tables 12–16; Figs. 10–12). A large number have been recovered from the effluent of the adrenal, testis, or placental tissues where they can be isolated in the free form in relatively high concentrations. The isolation of steroids in peripheral blood has been more difficult because they are present as conjugates to a great extent, and their concentrations in many cases are exceedingly small.

The tables include a few of the steroid compounds isolated and identified in their conjugated form. These examples include isolation from the adrenal venous effluent and umbilical cord blood as well as from peripheral circulation.

Dehydroepiandrosterone is present in peripheral blood in concentrations (~50 μg%) that are higher than for any other single steroid component. Cortisol and corticosterone are present in relatively high concentrations (~10 μg% and 1 μg%, respectively), as are the C_{19}-steroid metabolites, androsterone and etiocholanolone (~20 μg% each). Other steroid hormones, including the estrogens, progesterone, aldosterone, and testosterone, cannot be isolated from peripheral blood without extensive chemical manipulations often involving isotope-carrier technics.

The question of the forms and extent of conjugation present in blood in addition to and including the sulfates and glucuronides has not been completely resolved. Evidence for a phosphorylated form of dehydroepiandrosterone has been reported, and there have been several reports of corticoids conjugated as acetates. The sites of conjugation in the molecule and the possibility of conjugation of ketonic forms (as in progesterone) remain to a large extent unresolved.

Miscellaneous Tissues

Table 17 lists a variety of steroids isolated from miscellaneous tissues or fluids. The steroids isolated from meconium probably represent storage and excretion of substances accumulated by the fetus during the latter stages of its intrauterine existence, since the concentrations fall very rapidly to zero within a few days after birth. The high estriol content, for example, could reflect the large amounts of estriol in maternal blood and in the placenta during the ninth month of pregnancy and at term.

Owing to the fat-soluble characteristics of steroids, it might be expected that traces of these compounds could be detected in adipose tissue, particularly when excessive amounts are administered or secreted. It is, in fact, of interest that in some instances, following the administration of tracer doses of labeled steroid, no steroid or radioactivity could be detected in adipose tissue.

Artifacts in Urinary Extracts

As a result of reactions which occur during the processes of hydrolysis, extraction, and isolation, a number of chemical changes may be produced in the native steroid molecules. Substances which arise as a result of these reactions are called artifacts. The formation of these artifacts, which have been most commonly encountered in urinary extracts, may distort the true picture of the steroid content in three ways. Firstly, when the true metabolite is modified, the concentration of this material may be underestimated. Secondly, the decrease in the concentration of the metabolite is reflected in the formation of a substance or substances not originally present in the urine, and thirdly, the change induced in a metabolite may result in the formation of another compound which is already present as a true metabolite, thus causing overestimates for the latter.

Steroid artifacts or transformation products have been classified in Tables 18–21 according to the alterations produced in the molecule as a result of reactions of substitution, dehydration, rearrangement, and acetylation. Figures 13–16 illustrate typical reactions corresponding to those listed in the Tables. Other transformation products may be produced by degradation, including 17-ketosteroid formation from C_{21}-precursors (Meyer, 1953) and compounds, mainly unknown, as a result of reactions with heavy metals (Lewbart and Mattox, 1960), alkali, and ultraviolet light.

With the improved isolation procedures most commonly employed within recent years, particularly enzyme hydrolysis and solvolysis, the production of artifacts has been greatly minimized. The artifacts listed in the following sections are produced to a large extent under the conditions of heat and acid hydrolysis formerly employed; however, artifact formation is still possible under mild conditions of hydrolysis and extraction and during various chromatographic procedures. The fact that a given substance can be produced under conditions of isolation leading to artifact formation does not negate the possibility that the same compound can also be produced by enzymatic activity within the body or as a result of bacterial action in the gastrointestinal tract or in the urine.

Artifacts of Substitution

Artifacts of substitution are listed in Table 18 (see also Fig. 13). When dehydroepiandrosterone sulfate is heated with hydrochloric acid, a portion of the steroid is converted to the 3-chloro derivative. The reaction was shown indirectly in the early studies of Butenandt and Dannenbaum (1934) and by Venning *et al.* (1942). The 3-chloroandrost-5-en-17β-ol was identified by Ungar and Dorfman (1954) from a urine containing a high concentration of androst-5-ene-3β,17β-diol apparently by a similar mechanism of substitution. However, the isolation of 3-chloroandrost-5-en-17-one by Lieberman *et al.* (1948) and Dobriner *et al.* (1948) was unusual in that, prior to extraction by ether, sulfuric acid rather than hydrochloric acid was employed in the hydrolysis.

Artifacts of Dehydration

The dehydration of androsterone sulfate to 5α-androst-2(or 3)-en-17-one (Table 19; Fig. 14) under the conditions of hydrolysis with hydrochloric acid and heat used for urinary analysis was demonstrated by Venning *et al.* (1942). The androsta-3,5-dien-17-one appears to arise at least in part by the dehydration of dehydroepiandrosterone (Pincus and Pearlman, 1941). Dobriner *et al.* (1944) identified the dienone by its characteristic ultraviolet spectrum, and claimed that the compound was present in extracts of unhydrolyzed urine.

Compounds containing unsaturation at $\Delta^{9(11)}$ represent artifacts resulting from dehydration of the 11β-hydroxyl group. The reaction was demonstrated by Mason and Kepler (1945b) after treatment of 11β-hydroxyandrosterone with a mixture of glacial acetic acid and hydrochloric acid. Analogous reactions appear to occur for 11β-hydroxyetiocholanolone and 3β,11β-dihydroxy-5α-androstan-17-one in urine, since the corresponding $\Delta^{9(11)}$-derivatives have been isolated.

Two other reactions which have been associated with artifact formation are the loss of the 17α-hydroxyl group in C_{21}-steroids and the conversion of a 21-hydroxyl to a 21-methyl group. Since in both cases the transformation products would be identical to metabolites already present in urine, the question of whether these conversions could occur in the body by enzymatic reaction or whether the reactions were a result of artifact formation during the isolation procedures, or possibly a combination of the two, would have an important bearing on the interpretation of steroid metabolic data. In a carefully controlled study, Fukushima and Gallagher (1957a) concluded that the loss of the 17α-hydroxyl group in C_{21}-steroids could be attributed entirely to extraction and isolation procedures rather than to *in vivo* metabolism. The reaction involved the loss of the 17α-hydroxyl group of 3α,17α,20α-trihydroxy-5β-pregnan-11-one to form the 3α-hydroxy-5β-pregnane-11,20-dione. The accompanying conversion of the 20α-hydroxyl group to the 20-ketone during the reaction suggested a mechanism involving an initial dehydration reaction. The conversion of the 21-hydroxyl group to the 21-methyl group has also been suggested to be artifactual; however, the relative contribution of this reaction occurring in the tissues as compared with artifact formation has never been properly assessed.

Artifacts of Rearrangement

The conversion of 3β,17α-dihydroxypregn-5-en-20-one to the *D*-homo compound, 3β,17*a*-dihydroxy-17*a*-methyl-*D*-homoandrost-5-en-17-one (Table 20; Fig. 15) was demonstrated by Hirshmann and Hirshmann (1947) after treatment with alumina, acids, and alkali. The presence of the *D*-homo compounds in human urine and in equine urine, where they were first isolated, is presumed to be a result of artifact formation.

Dehydroepiandrosterone, in addition to conversion to the $\Delta^{3,5}$-derivative, and the 3β-chloro derivative, can form the 3,5-cyclo derivative, *i*-androstenolone, during hydrolysis of the urinary conjugates (Teich *et al.*, 1953). This substance is relatively unstable and will be converted to the original or one of the other forms under acid conditions.

The compound 3α-hydroxy-17-epi-5β-pregnan-20-one was demonstrated by Lieberman *et al.* (1948) in pregnancy urine. It was suggested that this compound was produced by acid-catalyzed epimerization of 3α-hydroxypregnan-20-one.

Artifacts of Acetylation

Lieberman *et al.* (1948) isolated the three acetylated compounds listed in Table 21 (see also Fig. 16) from urinary extracts which had been separated into ketonic and non-ketonic fractions by use of the Girard reagent. It was thought that acetylation could occur during the hydrolysis of the steroid hydrazones in ethereal solution owing to the presence of acetic and hydrochloric acids. Steroid acetates, however, have also been detected in blood (Weichselbaum and Margraf, 1960) under conditions where acetylation would not be likely to occur.

Steroids Isolated from Urine

Tables 22–30 and Figs. 17–24 catalog the large number and variety of steroid compounds isolated from human urine in health and disease and from the urine of many species of animals including the cow, bull, steer, goat, mare, sow, monkey, chimpanzee, rat, guinea pig, and mouse. Although the distribution of urinary metabolites may differ quantitatively insofar as major and minor components are concerned, generally there is a uniform qualitative pattern of similar, reduced, conjugated steroid compounds from one species to another, and in health and disease. In some species, as in the cow and the rat, steroid excretion in the urine is relatively minor as compared with that of the fecal route. In another species, the guinea pig, there is an inordinately high concentration of steroid hormones in the Δ^4-3-keto form, a form present in only trace amounts in the urine of the normal healthy human.

From time to time, the isolation of a particular metabolite from the urine of a patient with a specific disease has been proposed as a diagnostic test for that disease. The subsequent isolation of this apparently unique compound from the urine of healthy individuals or of individuals with other types of disease, which has invariably occurred, greatly decreases the reliability of such a test as a simple diagnostic tool. However, the over-all pattern of the many urinary metabolites as distinguished from an individual compound in several disease states can differ sufficiently from the normal in a quantitative way so as to be highly useful, or even necessary, for a proper diagnosis to be made. The very low titer of 17-ketosteroids and 17-hydroxycorticosteroids in Addison's disease, the high values for 17-hydroxycorticosteroids in Cushing's disease, the high values for 17-ketones (and pregnanetriol, pregnanediol) in the adrenogenital syndrome; all these analyses are now called for by the clinician for a proper diagnosis, and many of these tests have now become standard routine laboratory procedures in most hospital laboratories. The urinary metabolite pattern seen in adrenal cancer can resemble one or have components of many other adrenal abnormalities, so that additional tests for adrenal and pituitary function have to be employed before complete confidence in a diagnosis is possible.

Phenolic Steroids in Urine

The phenolic ring A of estrogens is not altered by metabolism; therefore, estrone, estradiol, estriol, and related substances will be found in the urine in their conjugated form (Table 22). The 16α-hydroxy derivative, estriol, is the major excretory form of the estrogens in the human. In addition, human urine contains other estrogens containing oxygen functions at carbons 16 and 17, particularly 16-epiestriol (16β-hydroxyl) and 16α-hydroxyestrone. Two unusual estrogen compounds isolated from human urine are the 2-methoxyestrone and the 18-hydroxyestrone (Loke and Marrian, 1958). Although the 18-hydroxylated estrogen has been suggested to be of adrenal origin, the significance of the presence of this compound or the 2-methoxy derivative in metabolism remains unsettled. Equine urine contains large amounts of ring B unsaturated estrogens, such as equilin and equilenin. These substances have not been detected in the urine of other species. In addition, equine urine is an unusually rich source for the estrogens, estrone and estradiol.

C_{19}-Steroids in Urine

Tables 23 and 24 (see also Figs. 18 and 19) list the large numbers of C_{19}-compounds isolated from urine of the human and other species. With few exceptions (a notable exception is dehydroepiandrosterone), these compounds are reduced during metabolism in rings A and B and are excreted as conjugates of glucuronic or sulfuric acid. The occasional instances of isolation and identification of these compounds in their conjugate form have been documented. A few of the unusual urinary metabolites isolated contain a Δ^{16}-group, as in 5α-androst-16-en-3α-ol (Brooksbank and Haslewood, 1949); the 7α-hydroxyl group, as in 7α-hydroxydehydroepiandrosterone (Lewbart and Schneider, 1959); the 16α-hydroxyl group, as in androst-5-ene-3β,16α,17β-triol (Hirschmann, 1943); and the 6β-hydroxyl group, as in 6β,11β-dihydroxyandrost-4-ene-3,17-dione (Peron and Dorfman, 1957).

C_{21}-Steroids in Urine

Tables 25–30 (see also Figs. 20–24) list the C_{21}-steroids, isolated from urine of the human and other species, classified according to the number of oxygen functions contained in the molecule (from one to six). With few exceptions (cf., Δ^5-3β-hydroxy steroids), these substances are reduced by metabolism in rings A and B and are excreted as conjugates of glucuronic acid and to a minor extent as conjugates of sulfuric acid.

Small amounts of biologically active substances, including cortisone, cortisol, and aldosterone, are found in urine. An increase in the excretion of Δ^4-3-ketosteroids is seen in severe liver disease as a result of decreased activity of the steroid-reducing enzyme systems normally found in liver. A relatively large proportion of the C_{21}-metabolites are completely reduced and are present in the non-ketonic fraction. Pregnane-3α,20α-diol and pregnane-3α,17α,20α-triol represent the major excretory forms of progesterone and 17-hydroxyprogesterone, respectively. The cortols (20α and 20β) and cortolones (20α and 20β) represent about 30% of the urinary metabolites of cortisol and cortisone. A few examples of the unusual metabolites of C_{21}-steroids in urine include 6β-hydroxycortisol (Burstein *et al.*, 1954), 2α-hydroxycortisol (Burstein, 1956), and 16α-hydroxy steroids such as pregn-5-ene-3β,16α,20α-triol (Hirschmann and Hirschmann, 1949) and 3α,16α-dihydroxy-5β-pregnan-20-one (Neher *et al.*, 1959).

Steroid Conjugates in Blood and Urine

The isolation and identification of steroids in their conjugate form from blood and urine have been documented in Table 31. Some of the steroid conjugate isolations are also listed in the corresponding tables for blood steroids and urinary steroids. Although these isolations demonstrate proof for the existence of the conjugated steroid forms, a critical portion of essential information is lacking concerning the types, amounts, the sites of conjugation, the proportion of the various conjugates as they exist in blood and tissues. Adequate procedures are now available for the separation and isolation of the conjugate forms from biological media, and considerably more information concerning their biochemistry should be available in the near future.

Steroids in Feces

The isolation of steroid compounds from feces (Table 32) has been difficult in spite of the evidence that major portions of these materials are excreted by this route in certain animals, including the cow and the rat. Miller *et al.* (1956) did identify from cow feces, after the administration of progesterone, androst-4-ene-3,17-dione and other C_{19}-fractions; however, the contribution by bacterial action to produce the forms isolated would be difficult to assess.

Table I

Steroids in the Testis

Steroid	Species	Reference
Estrone	Equine	Beall (1940)
	Human (embryonal tumor)	Wotiz *et al.* (1960b)
	Morone labrax	Chieffi (1962)
Estradiol-17β	Equine	Beall (1940)
	Scylliorhinus stellaris	Chieffi (1961, 1962)
	Human	Goldzieher and Roberts (1952); Anliker *et al.* (1957b)
	Bufo vulgaris	Chieffi (1962)
	Human (benign tumor)	Marti and Heusser (1954)
	Human (embryonal tumor)	Wotiz *et al.* (1960b)
Testosterone	Bull	David *et al.* (1935)
	Rat	Savard *et al.* (1956b); Slaunwhite and Samuels (1956)
	Scylliorhinus stellaris	Chieffi (1961, 1962)
	Stallion	Tagmann *et al.* (1946)
	Human	Savard *et al.* (1952, 1956b); Wotiz *et al.* (1955); Anliker *et al.* (1957b)
	Rabbit	Brady (1951)
	Porcine	Brady (1951)
	Human (embryonal tumor)	Wotiz *et al.* (1960b)
	Mouse	Grosso and Ungar (1964)
Androst-4-ene-3,17-dione	Rat	Lynn (1956); Lynn and Brown (1956); Savard *et al.* (1956b) Slaunwhite and Samuels (1956)
	Scylliorhinus stellaris	Chieffi (1961, 1962)
	Human	Anliker *et al.* (1957b)
	Human (embryonal tumor)	Wotiz *et al.* (1960b)
5α-Androst-16-en-3α-ol	Porcine	Ruzicka and Prelog (1943)
5α-Androst-16-en-3β-ol	Porcine	Ruzicka and Prelog (1943)
Adrenosterone	Human (tumor)	Savard *et al.* (1956a)
Adrenosterone	Bovine	Neher and Wettstein (1960c)
11β-Hydroxyandrosta-4-diene-3,17-dione	Human (tumor)	Savard *et al.* (1956a)
11β-Hydroxytestosterone	Human (tumor)	Savard *et al.* (1956a)
Epiandrosterone	Bovine	Neher and Wettstein (1960c)
Epitestosterone		
6β-Hydroxytestosterone		
15α-Hydroxytestosterone		

Continued on following page

Table I *(continued)*

Steroids in the Testis

Steroid	Species	Reference
Dehydroepiandrosterone	Porcine	Neher and Wettstein (1960d)
Testosterone Androst-4-ene-3,17-dione Progesterone	Human embryonal tumor (grown in hamster)	Wotiz *et al.* (1960b)
Pregnenolone	Porcine	Ruzicka and Prelog (1943); Haines *et al.* (1948)
Progesterone	*Bufo vulgaris*	Chieffi (1962)
	Porcine	Neher and Wettstein (1960c)
	Scylliorhinus stellaris	Chieffi (1961, 1962)
	Morone labrax	Chieffi (1961, 1962)
	Human (embryonal tumor)	Wotiz *et al.* (1960b)
3β-Hydroxy-5α-pregnan-20-one	Porcine	Ruzicka and Prelog (1943); Haines *et al.* (1948)
3α-Hydroxy-5α-pregnan-20-one	Porcine	Ruzicka and Prelog (1943); Haines *et al.* (1948)
17α,20β-Dihydroxypregn-4-en-3-one	Bovine	Lynn and Brown (1958a, b); Neher and Wettstein (1960c)
17α,20α-Dihydroxypregn-4-en-3-one	Bovine	Lynn and Brown (1958a, b); Neher and Wettstein (1960c)
17α-Hydroxyprogesterone	Human	Savard *et al.* (1956b)
	Bovine	Neher and Wettstein (1960c)
	Rat	Savard *et al.* (1956b); Slaunwhite and Samuels (1956)
7β-Hydroxycholesterol	Bovine	Neher and Wettstein (1960c)
Estriol	*Morone labrax*	Chieffi (1962)
Testosterone glucuronoside	Salmon (*Oncorhynchus nerka*)	Grajcer and Idler (1963)

Table 2

STEROIDS IN THE OVARY

Steroid	Species	Reference
Estradiol-17β	Porcine	MacCorquodale *et al.* (1936)
	Torpedo marmorata	Chieffi (1962)
	Dogfish (*Squalus suckleyi*)	Wotiz *et al.* (1958)
	Dog	Rabinowitz and Dowben (1955)
	Starfish (*Pisaster ochraceous*)	Botticelli *et al.* (1960)
	Human	Wotiz *et al.* (1956); Smith (1960); Baggett *et al.* (1955, 1956); Zander *et al.* (1959)
	Hen	Layne *et al.* (1958)
	Pecten and sea urchin	Botticelli *et al.* (1961)
	Dogfish (*Squalus suckleyi*)	Wotiz *et al.* (1958)
	Equine (follicular fluid)	Short (1960c)
Estrone	Porcine	Westerfeld *et al.* (1938)
	Bovine	Meyer (1955)
	Dog	Rabinowitz and Dowben (1955)
	Human	Smith (1960); Wotiz *et al.* (1956)
	Hen	Layne *et al.* (1958)
	Dogfish (*Squalus suckleyi*)	Wotiz *et al.* (1958)
	Equine (follicular fluid)	Short (1960c)
Estriol	Human	Wotiz *et al.* (1956); Smith (1960)
	Hen	Layne *et al.* (1958)
	Torpedo marmorata	Chieffi (1962)
Testosterone	Human (arrhenoblastoma)	Anliker *et al.* (1957a); Savard *et al.* (1961a)
	Human (normal)	Kase *et al.* (1961); Mahesh and Greenblatt (1961)
	Human (polycystic ovaries)	Kase *et al.* (1961); O'Donnell and McCaig (1960)
Epitestosterone	Equine (follicular fluid)	Short (1960c)
Androst-4-ene-3,17-dione	Bovine	Solomon *et al.* (1956a)
	Human	Zander (1958); Kase *et al.* (1961); Wiest *et al.* (1959)
	Human (corpus luteum, hilus, cortical-medullary)	Simmer and Voss (1960)
Androst-4-ene-3,17-dione	Human (normal and hirsute)	Mahesh and Greenblatt (1961)
	Human (Stein-Leventhal presumptive)	Lanthier and Sandor (1960)

Continued on following page

Table 2 *(continued)*
STEROIDS IN THE OVARY

Steroid	Species	Reference
	Human (Stein-Leventhal follicular fluid)	Short (1960b)
	Human tumor (Leydig cell)	Cohn and Mulrow (1961)
	Equine (follicular fluid)	Short (1960c)
	Human (arrhenoblastoma)	Savard *et al.* (1961a); Anliker *et al.* (1957a)
19-Norandrost-4-ene-3,17-dione	Equine (follicular fluid)	Short (1960c)
Androsterone	Human (arrhenoblastoma)	Anliker *et al.* (1957a)
Androsterone	Human (corpus luteum)	Simmer and Voss (1960)
Dehydroepiandrosterone	Human (corpus luteum, hilus, cortical-medullary)	Simmer and Voss (1960)
	Human tumor (Leydig cell)	Cohn and Mulrow (1961)
	Human (normal and hirsute)	Mahesh and Greenblatt (1961)
11β-Hydroxyandrost-4-ene-3,17-dione	Human tumor (Leydig cell)	Cohn and Mulrow (1961)
Progesterone	Sow	Wintersteiner and Allen (1934); Butenandt (1934); Slotta *et al.* (1934); Hartmann and Wettstein (1934)
	Rat	Wiest (1959a)
	Dog	Telegdy and Endröczi (1961)
	Whale	Prelog and Meister (1949)
	Bovine	Gorski *et al.* (1958); Bowerman and Melampy (1962)
	Human	Zander (1959)
	Human (presumptive isolation)	Lanthier and Sandor (1960)
	Equine (follicular fluid)	Short (1960c)
	Dogfish (*Squalus suckleyi*)	Wotiz *et al.* (1958)
	Pecten and sea urchin (tentative identification of progesterone)	Botticelli *et al.* (1961)
3β-Hydroxy-5α-pregnan-20-one	Porcine	Slotta *et al.* (1934); Wintersteiner and Allen (1934); Butenandt and Westphal (1934); Heard (1938); Hartmann and Wettstein (1934)
3β-Hydroxy-5α-pregnan-20-one	Whale	Prelog and Meister (1949)
20α-Hydroxypregn-4-en-3-one	Human	Zander (1959)

Continued on following page

Table 2 (*continued*)
STEROIDS IN THE OVARY

Steroid	Species	Reference
20α-Hydroxypregn-4-en-3-one	Rat	Wiest (1959a)
20β-Hydroxypregn-4-en-3-one	Human	Zander (1959)
	Bovine	Gorski *et al.* (1958); Bowerman and Melampy (1962)
	Whale	Kristoffersen *et al.* (1961)
	Pecten and sea urchin (tentative identification of steroid)	Botticelli *et al.* (1961)
17α-Hydroxyprogesterone	Bovine	Solomon *et al.* (1956a)
	Human	Zander (1958); Wiest *et al.* (1959)
	Equine (follicular fluid)	Short (1960c)
	Human (identification presumptive)	Lanthier and Sandor (1960)
	Human (normal and hirsute)	Mahesh and Greenblatt (1961)
17α-Hydroxypregnenolone	Human (normal and hirsute)	Mahesh and Greenblatt (1961)
Cortisol	Equine (follicular fluid)	Short (1960c)
16α-Hydroxyprogesterone	Human	Warren and Salhanick (1961); Zander *et al.* (1962b)
Progesterone	Mare (luteal tissue)	Short (1962a)
20α-Hydroxypregn-4-en-3-one	Mare (luteal tissue)	Short (1962a)
17α-Hydroxyprogesterone (no C_{18} or C_{19} steroids)	Mare (luteal tissue)	Short (1962a)
Pregnenolone Progesterone 20β-Hydroxypregn-4-en-3-one 17α-Hydroxyprogesterone Androst-4-ene-3,17-dione Testosterone Estrone Estradiol-17β	Cow (follicular fluid)	Short (1962b)
Cortisol 19-Norandrost-4-ene-3,17-dione Epitestosterone Dehydroepiandrosterone 6α-Hydroxyestradiol-17β	Equine (follicular fluid)	Short (1962a)
Progesterone	Human Bovine	Short (1962b)

Continued on following page

Table 2 (*continued*)

STEROIDS IN THE OVARY

Steroid	Species	Reference
17α-Hydroxyprogesterone Androst-4-ene-3,17-dione Estradiol-17β Estrone	Equine (principal components of follicular fluid)	Short (1962a)

Table 3

STEROIDS IN THE PLACENTA

Steroid	Species	Reference
Estradiol-17β	Human	Huffman *et al.* (1940)
	Human (170 μg/kg)	Diczfalusy and Lindkvist (1956)
	Human (100 ± 16 μg/kg)	Schmidt-Clemendorff (1961)
	Bovine	Gorski and Erb (1959)
Estrone	Bovine	Gorski and Erb (1959)
	Human	Westerfeld *et al.* (1938)
	Human (41 ± 15 μg/kg)	Schmidt-Clemendorff (1961)
	Human (51 μg/kg)	Diczfalusy and Lindkvist (1956)
Estriol	Human	Browne (1931)
	Human (315 μg/kg)	Huffman *et al.* (1940)
	Human (180 ± 16 μg/kg)	Schmidt-Clemendorff (1961)
Epiestriol (tentative identification)	Human	Diczfalusy and Halla (1958)
Estradiol-17α	Bovine	Gorski and Erb (1959)
16-Ketoestradiol-17β	Human	Diczfalusy and Münstermann (1959)
Progesterone	Human	Salhanick *et al.* (1952); Pearlman and Cerceo (1952a)
	Rhesus monkey	Short and Eckstein (1961)
	Bovine	Bowerman and Melampy (1962)
20β-Hydroxypregn-4-en-3-one	Human	Short (1957a); Zander (1959)
	Equine	Short (1957b)
20α-Hydroxypregn-4-en-3-one	Human	Zander (1959)
	Sheep	Short and Moore (1959)
3β-Hydroxy-5α-pregnan-20-one	Human	Pearlman and Cerceo (1952b)
Pregnanediol	Human	Pearlman and Cerceo (1952b)
5α-Pregnane-3β,20α-diol	Human	Pearlman and Cerceo (1952b)

Continued on following page

Table 3 (*continued*)

STEROIDS IN THE PLACENTA

Steroid	Species	Reference
Cortisol	Human	Berliner *et al.* (1956); Neher and Stark (1961)
Cortisone	Human	Berliner *et al.* (1956); Neher and Stark (1961)
Urocortisone	Human	Berliner *et al.* (1956)
Cortisol Cortisone 11-Deoxycortisol 3α,11β,17α,21-Tetrahydroxy-5β-pregnan-20-one 3α,17α,21-Trihydroxy-5β-pregnane-11,20-dione	Human	Troen (1961)
16α-Hydroxytestosterone 17α,20α,21-Trihydroxypregn-4-ene-3,11-dione 17α,20β,21-Trihydroxypregn-4-ene-3,11-dione	Human	Neher and Stark (1961)

Table 4

C_{18} STEROIDS IN THE ADRENAL

Steroid	Species	Reference
Estrone	Bovine Human (cortical carcinoma)	Beall (1939, 1940) Romanelli *et al.* (1960)
Estrone Estradiol-17β	Human (adrenal adenoma)	Keller *et al.* (1958)
Equilenin (presumptive)	Human (tumor)	Berliner *et al.* (1956)
Estrone 11β-Hydroxyestrone	Human (feminizing tumor)	Mahesh and Herrmann (1963)

Table 5

C_{19} AND C_{20} STEROIDS IN THE ADRENAL

Steroid	Species	Reference
C_{19} Androst-4-ene-3,17-dione	Bovine	Bloch *et al.* (1954); von Euw and Reichstein (1941); Bryson and Sweat (1962)
	Human (normal and abnormal)	Cohn and Mulrow (1961)
	Human	Bloch *et al.* (1956)
	Human (adrenal adenoma)	Keller *et al.* (1958)
	Human (fetal)	Bloch *et al.* (1955); Benirschke *et al.* (1956)
	Human (tumor)	Baulieu (1960a)
	Human (Cushing's syndrome) hyperplasia	Korus *et al.* (1959)
Dehydroepiandrosterone	Human (adrenogenital syndrome)	Bloch *et al.* (1956)
	Human (tumor)	Baulieu (1960a)
	Human (normal and abnormal)	Cohn and Mulrow (1961)
	Human (tumor)	Plantin *et al.* (1957); Keller *et al.* (1958); Revol (1960)
Testosterone	Human (cancer, adreno-genital, and Cushing's syndromes)	Anliker *et al.* (1956)
Andrenosterone	Bovine	Reichstein (1936a, b); Bloch *et al.* (1954)
	Human (Cushing's syndrome hyperplasia)	Korus *et al.* (1959)
11β-Hydroxyandrost-4-ene-3,17-dione	Human (fetal)	Bloch *et al.* (1956)
	Mouse (normal and tumor)	Bloch *et al.* (1960)
	Bovine	Bloch *et al.* (1954); Bryson and Sweat (1962)
	Human (tumor)	Baulieu (1960a)
	Porcine	Wettstein and Anner (1954)
	Human (normal and abnormal)	Cohn and Mulrow (1961)
11β-Hydroxyepiandro-sterone	Bovine	von Euw and Reichstein (1941); Reichstein and von Euw (1938)
11β-Hydroxyandrosterone	Porcine	Neher and Wettstein (1960b)
11β-Hydroxyepitestosterone	Porcine	Neher and Wettstein (1960b)
6β-Hydroxyandrost-4-ene-3,17-dione	Bovine	Meyer *et al.* (1955)

Continued on following page

Table 5 *(continued)*

C_{19} AND C_{20} STEROIDS IN THE ADRENAL

Steroid	Species	Reference
C_{19} 6α-Hydroxyandrost-4-ene-3,17-dione	Bovine	Meyer *et al.* (1955)
19-Hydroxyandrost-4-ene-3,17-dione	Bovine	Meyer (1955)
Androsterone	Human (adrenal tumor)	Keller *et al.* (1958)
Dehydroepiandrosterone sulfate	Human (adrenal tumor)	Baulieu (1960b); Guillon *et al.* (1961)
	Human (normal)	Burstein and Dorfman (1962)
Dehydroepiandrosterone glucuronoside	Human	Baulieu *et al.* (1961a, b)
C_{20} 3-Keto-11β,18-dihydroxy-Δ^4-etienic acid lactone (20 → 18)	Porcine	Neher (1960)

Table 6

$C_{21}O_2$ STEROIDS IN THE ADRENAL

Steroid	Species	Reference
Progesterone	Rat and porcine	Anliker *et al.* (1956)
	Human (adrenogenital syndrome)	Zander (1960)
	Bovine	Beall and Reichstein (1938); Beall (1938); Saba and Hechter (1955); Hayano *et al.* (1956); Bryson and Sweat (1962)
	Human (tumor)	Salhanick and Berliner (1957)
	Dog (ovarian venous)	Telegdy and Endröczi (1961)
20α-Hydroxypregn-4-en-3-one	Porcine	Neher and Wettstein (1960b)
3β-Hydroxy-5α-pregnan-20-one	Bovine	Neher and Wettstein (1960b)
Pregnenolone	Bovine	Staple *et al.* (1956); Saba and Hechter (1955); Hayano *et al.* (1956); Shimizu *et al.* (1961)
	Porcine	Neher and Wettstein (1960b)
	Human (tumor)	Revol (1960)

Table 7

$C_{21}O_3$ Steroids in the Adrenal

Steroid	Species	Reference
21-Hydroxypregn-4-ene-3,20-dione (deoxycorticosterone)	Bovine	Reichstein and von Euw (1939); Bryson and Sweat (1962)
17α-Hydroxypregn-4-ene-3,20-dione (17α-hydroxyprogesterone)	Bovine	Pfiffner and North (1940, 1941); Bryson and Sweat (1962); von Euw and Reichstein (1941)
	Porcine	Heard *et al.* (1956)
	Human (adrenogenital syndrome)	Zander (1960); Bongiovanni (1958)
5α-Pregnane-3β,17α,20β-triol	Bovine	Steiger and Reichstein (1938)
5α-Pregnane-3β,17α,20α-triol	Bovine	Reichstein (1936c)
3β,17α-Dihydroxy-5α-pregnan-20-one	Bovine	Reichstein (1936c); Wintersteiner and Pfiffner (1936)
11-Ketoprogesterone	Porcine	Heard *et al.* (1956); Neher (1960); Neher and Wettstein (1960a)
11β-Hydroxyprogesterone	Bovine	Hayano *et al.* (1956); Bryson and Sweat (1962)
	Porcine	Neher (1960); Neher and Wettstein (1960a)
17α,20α-Dihydroxypregn-4-en-3-one	Porcine	Neher and Wettstein (1960b)
11β,20α-Dihydroxypregn-4-en-3-one	Porcine	Neher and Wettstein (1960b)
17α-Hydroxypregnenolone	Porcine	Neher and Wettstein (1960d)
3α,16α-Dihydroxy-5α-pregnan-20-one	Porcine	Neher *et al.* (1959)
16α-Hydroxyprogesterone	Porcine	Neher and Wettstein (1959)
6β-Hydroxyprogesterone	Bovine	Bryson and Sweat (1962)

Table 8

$C_{21}O_4$ Steroids in the Adrenal

Steroid	Species	Reference
5α-Pregnane-3β,17α,20β,21-tetrol	Bovine	Steiger and Reichstein (1938)
3β,17α,21-Trihydroxy-5α-pregnan-20-one	Bovine	Reichstein and Gatzi (1938b)
17α,21-Dihydroxypregn-4-ene-3,20-dione (11-deoxycortisol)	Bovine	Reichstein and Gatzi (1938b); Reichstein and von Euw (1938)
	Porcine	Dobriner *et al.* (1954)
	Human	Neher (1958)
3β,21-Dihydroxy-5α-pregnane-11,20-dione	Bovine	Mason *et al.* (1937); Steiger and Reichstein (1938)
20β,21-Dihydroxypregn-4-ene-3,11-dione	Bovine	Reichstein and von Euw (1939)
11β,21-Dihydroxypregn-4-ene-3,20-dione (corticosterone)	Bovine	Reichstein (1937b); Mason *et al.* (1937); Hayano *et al.* (1956); Saba and Hechter (1955); Bryson and Sweat (1962)
	Turtle (*Testudo graeco*)	Guillemin *et al.* (1959)
	Fish (*Ictalurus punctalus*)	Guillemin *et al.* (1959)
	Alligator (*Alligator mississippiensis*)	Guillemin *et al.* (1959)
	Rat	Elliot and Schally (1955); Peron (1960); Mialhe-Volloss and Baulieu (1958)
	Porcine	Kuizenga and Cartland (1940); Dobriner *et al.* (1954)
	Porcine (newborn)	Yudaev and Druzhinima (1956)
	Human	Neher (1958); Bailey *et al.* (1960); Liebermann (1959)
	Dog	Reich and Lehninger (1955); de Roos and Bern (1961)
	Rana catesbiana	Carstensen *et al.* (1959a)
	White Leghorn chicken White Keng pigeon Western gull White Pekin duck	de Roos (1961)
	Avian domestic fowl (*Galus domesticus*) Domestic pigeon (*Columbia livia*) Western gull (*Larus occidentalis*)	de Roos (1960a, b)
	California sea lion (*Zalophus californianus*)	Bern and de Roos (1960)

Continued on following page

Table 8 *(continued)*

$C_{21}O_4$ Steroids in the Adrenal

Steroid	Species	Reference
	Mouse (normal and tumor)	Bloch *et al.* (1960)
	Salmon (*Salmo salar*)	Fontaine and Leloup-Hatey (1959)
21-Hydroxypregn-4-ene-3,11,20-trione (11-dehydrocorticosterone)	Bovine	Mason *et al.* (1937); Reichstein and von Euw (1938); Kuizenga and Cartland (1939); Heard *et al.* (1956); Bryson and Sweat (1962)
	Porcine	Dobriner *et al.* (1954)
	Avian domestic fowl Domestic pigeon, Western gull	de Roos (1960a)
	White Leghorn chicken White Keng pigeon Western gull White Pekin duck	de Roos (1961)
19,21-Dihydroxypregn-4-ene-3,20-dione	Bovine	Mattox (1955); Neher and Wettstein (1956); Mattox and Mason (1956)
	Porcine	Neher and Wettstein (1956)
11β,17α,20β-Trihydroxypregn-4-en-3-one 17α,20α,21-Trihydroxypregn-4-en-3-one 17α,20β-Dihydroxypregn-4-ene-3,11-dione 17α,20α-Dihydroxypregn-4-ene-3,11-dione	Porcine	Neher and Wettstein (1960b)
18,21-Dihydroxyprogesterone	Rat	Peron (1961)
11-Deoxycortisol Corticosterone	Human adenoma (primary aldosteronism)	Davignon *et al.* (1961)
Corticosterone	*Rana catesbiana*	Carstensen *et al.* (1961)
6β,21-Dihydroxyprogesterone 11-Deoxycortisol	Bovine	Bryson and Sweat (1962)
11β,18-Dihydroxy-3-keto-4-etienic acid lactone	Bullfrog	Ulick and Kusch (1960)

Table 9

$C_{21}O_5$ Steroids in the Adrenal

Steroid	Species	Reference
5α-Pregnane-3β,11β,17α,20β,21-pentol	Bovine	Wintersteiner and Pfiffner (1935); Steiger and Reichstein (1938); Reichstein and Gatzi (1938a)
3β,11β,17α,21-Tetrahydroxy-5α-pregnan-20-one	Bovine	von Euw and Reichstein (1941)
3α,11β,17α,21-Tetrahydroxy-5α-pregnan-20-one	Bovine	Reichstein (1936b); Kuizenga and Cartland (1939); Mason *et al.* (1936); Wintersteiner and Pfiffner (1935)
11β,17α,20β,21-Tetrahydroxypregn-4-en-3-one	Bovine	Reichstein (1936b, 1937b)
	Human	Touchstone *et al.* (1959a)
17α,20β,21-Trihydroxypregn-4-ene-3,11-dione	Bovine	Reichstein and von Euw (1938)
11β,17α,21-Trihydroxypregn-4-ene-3,20-dione (cortisol)	Bovine	Reichstein (1937b); Mason *et al.* (1938); Kuizenga and Cartland (1939); Caspi (1956); Saba and Hechter (1955); Bryson and Sweat (1962)
	Human Monkey	Lanman and Silverman (1957)
	Human	Liebermann (1959)
	Human (Cushing's syndrome) hyperplasia	Korus *et al.* (1959)
	Human	Davignon *et al.* (1960)
	Human (tumor)	Revol (1960)
	Human (adrenal adenoma)	Keller *et al.* (1958)
	Human (new born)	Gardner and Tice (1957)
	Human	Neher (1958); Bailey *et al.* (1960)
	Avian domestic fowl (*Galus domesticus*) Domestic pigeon (*Columbia livia*) Western gull (*Larus occidentalis*)	de Roos (1960a, b)
	Porcine (newborn)	Yudaev and Druzhinima (1956)
	Porcine	Dobriner *et al.* (1954); Heard *et al.* (1956); Aprile *et al.* (1956)
	California sea lion	de Roos and Bern (1961)

Continued on following page

Table 9 *(continued)*

$C_{21}O_5$ Steroids in the Adrenal

Steroid	Species	Reference
	Salmon (*Salmo salar*) interrenal bodies	Fontaine and Leloup-Hatey (1959)
	Rat	Elliot and Schally (1955); Aprile *et al.* (1956)
	Guinea pig	Burstein and Nadel (1956); Telegdy (1960); Nadel and Burstein (1956)
	Dog	Reich and Lehninger (1955)
	Pacific salmon Rainbow trout	Hane and Robertson (1959)
	Anoplopoma fimbria (sablefish) *Mugil cephalus* (mullet)	Nandi and Bern (1960)
17α,21-Dihydroxypregn-4-ene-3,11,20-trione (cortisone)	Porcine	Dobriner *et al.* (1954)
	Bovine	Bryson and Sweat (1962)
	Mugil cephalus (mullet) *Tilapia mossambica* (cichlid)	Nandi and Bern (1960)
	Pacific salmon Rainbow trout	Hane and Robertson (1959)
	Bovine	Mason *et al.* (1936); Reichstein and von Euw (1938); Kuizenga and Cartland (1939)
	Human (adrenal adenoma)	Keller *et al.* (1958)
	Human	Neher (1958); Liebermann (1959); Lanman and Silverman (1957)
	Human (Cushing's syndrome) hyperplasia	Korus *et al.* (1959)
	Human	Bailey *et al.* (1960); Davignon *et al.* (1960)
	California sea lion (*Zalophus californianus*)	Bern and de Roos (1961)
Aldosterone	Human	Neher (1958); Liebermann (1959)
	Human (adrenal tumor)	Keller *et al.* (1958)
	Bovine	Simpson *et al.* (1954a, b); Harman *et al.* (1954); Mattox and Mason (1956)

Continued on following page

Table 9 *(continued)*

$C_{21}O_5$ STEROIDS IN THE ADRENAL

Steroid	Species	Reference
	Guinea pig	Telegdy (1960)
	Rana catesbiana	Carstensen *et al.* (1959a)
	Rat	Peron (1960); Mialhe-Volloss and Baulieu (1958)
	Mouse	Raman *et al.* (1964)
	White Leghorn chicken	de Roos (1961)
	White Keng pigeon	
	Western gull	
	White Pekin duck	
	Avian domestic fowl (*Galus domesticus*)	de Roos (1960a, b)
	Domestic pigeon (*Columbia livia*)	
	Western gull (*Larus occidentalis*)	
	California sea lion (*Zalophus californianus*)	Bern and de Roos (1960)
19,17α,21-Trihydroxypregn-4-ene-3,20-dione	Porcine and Bovine	Neher and Wettstein (1956)
11β,19,21-Trihydroxypregn-4-ene-3,20-dione	Bovine and Porcine	
6β,21-Dihydroxypregn-4-ene-3,11,20-trione	Bovine	
6β,11β,21-Trihydroxypregn-4-ene-3,20-dione	Bovine and Porcine	
11β,17α,21-Trihydroxy-5α-pregnane-3,20-dione	Bovine and Porcine	
20,20,21-Trihydroxy-18-lactone (18 → 20)-pregn-4-en-3-one	Porcine	
17-Isoaldosterone	Porcine	Neher (1960); Neher and Wettstein (1960d)
18-Hydroxycorticosterone	Rat	Birmingham and Ward (1961); Peron (1961)
3α,17,21-Trihydroxy-5α-pregnane-11,20-dione	Porcine	von Euw *et al.* (1958)
3-Keto-11β,18-dihydroxy-4-etienic acid lactone (20 → 18)		
Cortisol Cortisone Aldosterone	Human adenoma (primary aldosteronism)	Davignon *et al.* (1961)
Aldosterone	*Rana catesbiana*	Carstensen *et al.* (1961)
11β,17α,21-Trihydroxy-5β-pregnane-3,20-dione	Bovine	Bryson and Sweat (1962)

Continued on following page

Table 9 (*continued*)

$C_{21}O_5$ STEROIDS IN THE ADRENAL

Steroid	Species	Reference
18-Hydroxycorticosterone	Bullfrog	Ulick and Kusch (1960)
	Mouse	Raman *et al.* (1964)
6β-Hydroxycorticosterone	Human	Nowaczynski *et al.* (1962)
6β,21-Dihydroxy-pregn-4-ene-3,11,20-trione	Hyperplastic adenoma	

Table 10

$C_{21}O_6$ AND C_{27} STEROIDS IN THE ADRENAL

Steroid	Species	Reference
20α-Hydroxycholesterol	Bovine	Solomon *et al.* (1956b)
Cholestane-3,6-dione	Human (adenoma)	Keller (1956)
6β-Hydroxycortisol (tentative)	Human	Touchstone *et al.* (1959)
20α,22ξ-Dihydroxycholesterol	Bovine	Shimizu *et al.* (1961, 1962)
5α-Cholestan-3β-ol	Guinea pig	Werbin and Chaikoff (1962)
2α-Hydroxycortisol	Guinea pig	Nadel and Burstein (1956)
6β-Hydroxycortisol		

Table 11

STEROIDS IN BILE

Steroid	Species	Reference
Urocortisol	Bovine	Glick (1957)
Urocortisone	Bovine	Glick (1957)
Cortisol	Guinea pig	Eik-nes *et al.* (1957)
Pregnanolone	Bovine (pregnancy)	Pearlman (1948)
5β-Pregnane-3α,20β-diol	Bovine (pregnancy)	Pearlman (1952)
5α-Pregnane-3β,20β-diol	Bovine	Pearlman (1946)
5β-Androstane-3α,17α-diol	Bovine	Pearlman (1952)
Estrone	Bovine (pregnancy)	Pearlman *et al.* (1947)
	Human (pregnancy)	Adlercreutz *et al.* (1960)
Estradiol-17β	Bovine (pregnancy)	Pearlman *et al.* (1948)
Estriol	Human (pregnancy)	Adlercreutz *et al.* (1960)
16-Epiestriol (presumptive)	Human (pregnancy)	Adlercreutz *et al.* (1960); Adlercreutz (1962)
Estradiol-17β (presumptive)	Human (pregnancy)	Adlercreutz *et al.* (1960); Adlercreutz (1962)
Estriol Estrone	Human (post-menopausal women and men)	Adlercreutz (1962)

Table 12

C_{19} Steroids in Blood

Steroid	Species	Reference
Dehydroepiandrosterone	Human	Migeon and Plager (1954); Bush and Mahesh (1959); Clayton and Bongiovanni (1955); Tamm *et al.* (1958); Simmer *et al.* (1959); Oertal and Kaiser (1962)
	Human (tumor adrenal vein and peripheral vein)	Revol (1960)
	Human (adrenal venous)	Lombardo *et al.* (1959); Hirschmann *et al.* (1960)
	Dog	Oertel and Eik-Nes (1959b)
Androst-4-ene-3,17-dione	Human (adrenal venous)	Romanoff *et al.* (1953); Hirschmann *et al.* (1960)
	Dog (spermatic vein)	West *et al.* (1952)
	Bovine	Lindner (1959)
	Bovine (spermatic vein)	Savard *et al.* (1961b)
Androsterone	Human	Migeon (1956); Simmer *et al.* (1959); Oertel (1962); Tamm *et al.* (1958); Oertel and Kaiser (1962); Tamm (1958)
	Human tumor	Revol (1960)
Etiocholanolone	Human	Tamm *et al.* (1958); Oertel (1962); Oertel and Eik-Nes (1961b); Oertel and Kaiser (1962)
Testosterone	Human (cancer prostate)	Lucas *et al.* (1957)
	Human men and women (peripheral)	Finkelstein *et al.* (1961); Oertel (1962)
	Bovine (spermatic vein)	Lindner (1959); Savard *et al.* (1961b)
	Dog (spermatic vein)	Oertel (1961a)
	Salmon (*Oncorhynchus nerka*)	Grajcer and Idler (1961)
	Men treated with human chorionic gonadotropin (peripheral)	Oertel and Eik-Nes (1959a)
Adrenosterone	Salmon plasma	Idler *et al.* (1961b)
11-Ketotestosterone	Salmon	Idler (1961); Idler *et al.* (1960b, 1961a)
11β-Hydroxyandrost-4-ene-3,17-dione	Human (adrenal venous)	Pincus and Romanoff (1955); Romanoff *et al.* (1953);

Continued on following page

Table 12 *(continued)*

C_{19} Steroids in Blood

Steroid	Species	Reference
		Lombardo *et al.* (1959); Hirschmann *et al.* (1960)
	Human (peripheral)	Cooper *et al.* (1958); Tamm *et al.* (1958)
	Rat (adrenal venous)	Longwell *et al.* (1956); Bush (1953)
11β-Hydroxyetiocholanolone	Human	Tamm *et al.* (1958); Savard (1957); Oertel and Eik-Nes (1961b); Oertel (1962)
11-Ketoetiocholanolone	Human	Tamm *et al.* (1958)
11β-Hydroxyandrosterone	Human	Savard (1957)
Dehydroepiandrosterone sulfate	Human (ACTH)	Baulieu (1960a)
	Human (adrenal tumor)	Baulieu (1960b)
	Human	Staib *et al.* (1959a)
Androsterone sulfate	Human (ACTH)	Baulieu (1960a)
	Human	Staib *et al.* (1959a)
Etiocholanolone sulfate	Human (ACTH)	Baulieu (1960a)
Androst-5-ene-3β,17β-diol	Human (adrenal venous)	Hirschmann *et al.* (1960)
Etiocholanolone 11β-Hydroxyetiocholanolone	Human plasma	Oertel and Eik-Nes (1961b)
11β-Hydroxyandrost-4-ene-3,17-dione	Human (adrenal venous)	Bush and Mahesh (1959); Bush *et al.* (1956)
	Dog (adrenal venous)	Hechter *et al.* (1955); Oertel and Eik-Nes (1962)
	Cat (adrenal venous)	Bush (1953)
	Sheep (adrenal venous)	Bush and Fergusen (1953)
	Human (placental)	Zander *et al.* (1962a)
Dehydroepiandrosterone (presumptive)	Man (adrenal venous)	Bush *et al.* (1956)
Adrenosterone (presumptive)	Dog (adrenal venous)	Hechter *et al.* (1955)
Adrenosterone	Human (placental)	Zander *et al.* (1962a)
Androsterone (presumptive)	Man (adrenal venous)	Bush *et al.* (1956)
11β-Hydroxyandrost-4-ene-3,17-dione Dehydroepiandrosterone Androst-4-ene-3,17-dione	Human (adrenal venous after ACTH)	Short (1960a)
3β-Hydroxyandrost-5-ene-7,17-dione	Human	Guillon *et al.* (1961)

Continued on following page

Table 12 (*continued*)

C_{19} STEROIDS IN BLOOD

Steroid	Species	Reference
Dehydroepiandrosterone sulfate	Human (adrenal venous)	Guillon *et al.* (1961)
Testosterone glucuronoside	Salmon (*Oncorhynchus nerka*)	Grajcer and Idler (1963)
Adrenosterone	Human (placental and blood)	Zander *et al.* (1962a)
11β-Hydroxyandrost-4-ene-3,17-dione		

Table 13

$C_{21}O_2$ AND $C_{21}O_3$ STEROIDS IN BLOOD

Steroid	Species	Reference
Progesterone	Rat	Wiest (1958, 1959b)
	Rabbit (ovarian vein)	Hilliard *et al.* (1961); Simmer *et al.* (1963)
	Bovine	Short (1957b)
	Bovine (pregnancy)	Short (1958)
	Sheep	Short (1957b)
	Goat	Short (1957b)
	Dog	Telegdy and Endröczi (1961)
	Porcine	Short (1957b)
	Dog (ovarian vein)	Romanoff *et al.* (1962)
	Sheep (adrenal venous)	Short (1957b)
	Human	Zander and Simmer (1954); Short (1960a); Oertel (1962)
	Human (pregnancy)	Simmer and Simmer (1959)
20β-Hydroxypregn-4-en-3-one	Rat	Wiest (1958); Carstensen *et al.* (1959b)
	Salmon (*Oncorhynchus nerka*)	
Pregnenolone	Canine (adrenal vein)	Oertel and Eik-Nes (1961a)
	Human	Oertel (1962)
20α-Hydroxypregn-4-en-3-one	Human	Forbes and Zander (1957)
	Rat	Wiest (1959b)

Continued on following page

Table 13 (*continued*)

$C_{21}O_2$ AND $C_{21}O_3$ STEROIDS IN BLOOD

Steroid	Species	Reference
	Rabbit (ovarian vein)	Hilliard and Sawyer (1962); Simmer *et al.* (1963)
	Sheep	Short (1957b); Short and Moore (1959)
	Human (placental)	Zander *et al.* (1962c)
Deoxycorticosterone	Dog (adrenal venous)	Farrell *et al.* (1954)
17α-Hydroxyprogesterone	Human (adrenal venous)	Lombardo *et al.* (1959)
	Salmon	Idler *et al.* (1959b)
	Dog (adrenal vein)	Agashe *et al.* (1961)
	Bovine (spermatic vein)	Savard *et al.* (1961b)
17α,20β-Dihydroxypregn-4-en-3-one	*Oncorhynchus nerka* Pacific salmon	Idler *et al.* (1960a)
17α-Hydroxypregnenolone	Human	Oertel (1961a, b); Short (1960a)
16α-Hydroxyprogesterone	Human (placental blood)	Zander *et al.* (1962a)
16α-Hydroxyprogesterone 17α-Hydroxyprogesterone 17α,20α-Dihydroxypregn-4-en-3-one	Human (placental)	Zander *et al.* (1962b)
11-Ketoprogesterone 11β-Hydroxyprogesterone	Canine (adrenal vein)	Oertel and Eik-Nes (1962)
5β-Pregnane-3α,20α-diol 5α-Pregnane-3β,20α-diol 5α-Pregnane-3α,20α-diol	Human	Oertel (1962)
17α-Hydroxypregn-4-ene-3,20-dione 3β-Hydroxypregn-5-en-20-one	Human	Oertel and Eik-Nes (1961c)
Progesterone 20α-Hydroxypregn-4-en-3-one 20β-Hydroxypregn-4-en-3-one	Human (umbilical)	Runnebaum and Zander (1962)
17α-Hydroxyprogesterone 16α-Hydroxyprogesterone 17,20α-Dihydroxypregn-4-en-3-one Progesterone 20α-Hydroxypregn-4-en-3-one 20β-Hydroxypregn-4-en-3-one	Human (placental cord blood)	Zander *et al.* (1962a)

Table 14

$C_{21}O_4$ STEROIDS IN BLOOD

Steroid	Species	Reference
11-Deoxycortisol	Human (congenital adrenal hyperplasia with hypertension)	Eberlein and Bongiovanni (1956)
	Dog (adrenal venous)	Carstensen (1956); Farrell and Lamus (1953)
	Human (adrenal venous)	Touchstone *et al.* (1959a); Lombardo *et al.* (1959)
11-Dehydrocorticosterone	Human	Salvadori *et al.* (1956)
	Rat and rabbit	Reif and Longwell (1958)
	Human (child plus ACTH)	Klein *et al.* (1957)
Corticosterone	Dog	Nelson (1951)
	Dog (adrenal venous)	Reich *et al.* (1950); Zaffaroni and Burton (1953); Farrell and Lamus (1953)
	Salmon	Idler *et al.* (1960b)
	Human	Tamm *et al.* (1958)
	Bull shark	Phillips (1959)
	Brown shark	
	Dusky shark	
	Tiger shark	
	Sting ray	
	Ray	
	Short-nosed sucker	
	Long-nosed sucker	
	Cebus monkey	Aires *et al.* (1962)
	Rat (adrenal venous)	Longwell *et al.* (1955, 1956); Vogt (1957); Afinogenova (1957); Bush (1951, 1953)
	Mouse (strain LAF, adrenal tumor)	Wilson *et al.* (1958)
	Human (peripheral)	Tamm *et al.* (1958); Salvadori *et al.* (1956); Cooper *et al.* (1958); Ayres *et al.* (1957)
	Human (plasma)	Peterson (1957); Short (1960a)
	Rat and rabbit	Reif and Longwell (1958)
	Bovine	Bush (1951, 1953)
	Rabbit	Bush (1951, 1953)
	Ferret	Bush (1951, 1953)
	Human (adrenal venous)	Sweat *et al.* (1953); Romanoff *et al.* (1953); Pincus and Romanoff (1955); Lombardo *et al.* (1959)

Continued on following page

Table 14 *(continued)*

$C_{21}O_4$ STEROIDS IN BLOOD

Steroid	Species	Reference
	Mouse	Southcott *et al.* (1956a, b)
11β,20α,21-Trihydroxy-pregn-4-en-3-one	Mouse	Southcott *et al.* (1956a, b)
3α,17α,21-Trihydroxy-5β-pregnan-20-one	Human (congenital adrenal hyperplasia with hypertension)	Eberlein and Bongiovanni (1956)
3α,11β,21-Trihydroxy-5β-pregnan-20-one 3α,17α,21-Trihydroxy-5β-pregnan-20-one 3α,11β,21-Trihydroxy-5α-pregnan-20-one	Human (plasma)	Gore and Baron (1960)
11-Dehydrocorticosterone acetate	Human (plasma)	Weichselbaum and Margraf (1960); Margraf and Weichselbaum (1962)

Table 15

$C_{21}O_5$ STEROIDS IN BLOOD

Steroid	Species	Reference
Cortisone	Human	de Hachen and Solis (1956); Short (1960a); Cooper *et al.* (1958); Salvadori *et al.* (1956); Savard (1957); Gore and Baron (1960)
	Salmon	Idler *et al.* (1959a, b)
	Human (tumor, adrenal and peripheral vein)	Revol (1960)
	Cebus monkey (adrenal vein)	Aires *et al.* (1962)
Cortisol	Human (adrenal venous)	Sweat *et al.* (1953); Romanoff *et al.* (1953); Pincus and Romanoff (1955); Lombardo *et al.* (1959); Hirschmann *et al.* (1960); Short (1960a)
	Human (peripheral)	de Hachen and Solis (1956); Tamm *et al.* (1958); Cooper *et al.* (1958); Ayres *et al.* (1957)

Continued on following page

Table 15 *(continued)*

$C_{21}O_5$ STEROIDS IN BLOOD

Steroid	Species	Reference
	Human (tumor, adrenal and peripheral vein)	Revol (1960)
	Salmon	Idler *et al.* (1959a, b, 1960b)
	Sharks	Phillips (1959)
	Sting ray	
	Short-nosed sucker	
	Long-nosed sucker	
	Carp flounder	Bondy *et al.* (1957)
	Cebus monkey	Aires *et al.* (1962)
	Ray	Phillips and Chester Jones (1957)
	Dogfish	
	Cod	
	Lungfish	
	Eagle ray	Chester-Jones *et al.* (1959)
	Southern kingfish	
	Channel bass	
	Carp	
	Killifish	
	Dog	Nelson (1951)
	Dog (adrenal venous)	Reich *et al.* (1950); Zaffaroni and Burton (1953); Farrell and Lamus (1953)
	Hamster (adrenal venous)	Schindler and Knigge (1959)
	Bovine	Bush (1951, 1953)
	Rabbit	
	Cat	
	Ferret	
	Guinea pig	Bush (1951, 1953); Fajer and Vogt (1962)
Aldosterone	Monkey (adrenal venous)	Simpson *et al.* (1952)
	Dog (adrenal venous)	Farrell *et al.* (1954)
	Human	Ayres *et al.* (1957)
Urocortisol glucuronoside	Human	Vermeulen (1956a, b, c); Savard (1957); Cohn and Bondy (1959)
Urocortisone glucuronoside	Human	Vermeulen (1956a, b, c); Savard (1957); Cohn and Bondy (1959)

Continued on following page

Table 15 *(continued)*

$C_{21}O_5$ STEROIDS IN BLOOD

Steroid	Species	Reference
Urocortisol	Human	Reddy *et al.* (1955); de Hachen and Solis (1956); Vermeulen (1956a, b, c); Klein *et al.* (1957); Tamm *et al.* (1958); Weichselbaum and Margraf (1960)
Urocortisone	Human	Vermeulen (1956a, b, *c*); Klein *et al.* (1957); Tamm *et al.* (1958); Weichselbaum and Margraf (1960)
Urocortisone Urocortisol 3α,11β,17α,21-Tetrahydroxy-5α-pregnan-20-one	Human (plasma)	Gore and Baron (1960)
17α,20β,21-Trihydroxypregn-4-en-3,11-dione	Salmon (*Oncorhynchus nerka*)	Idler *et al.* (1962)
Cortisol acetate	Man	Margraf and Weichselbaum (1962)

Table 16

C_{18} STEROIDS IN BLOOD

Steroid	Species	Reference
Estrone	Human (pregnancy)	Oertel *et al.* (1959)
Estradiol-17β	Human (pregnancy)	Oertel *et al.* (1959)
Estriol	Human (pregnancy)	Oertel *et al.* (1959)
Estrone Estradiol-17β	Normal men and women	Ichii *et al.* (1962)
Estriol Estriol-3-sulfate Estriol-16(17?)-glucuronoside	Cord blood	Troen *et al.* (1961)
Estrone Estradiol-17β Estriol	Human	Oertel (1962)

Table 17
STEROIDS IN MISCELLANEOUS TISSUES

Steroid	Species	Tissue or fluid	Reference
Cortisol (paper chromatographic evidence)	Human	Synovial fluid	Cope and Sewell (1956)
3,6-Cholestanediol	Human	Adrenal adenoma	Keller (1956)
Glycogenic activity	Porcine	Spleen	Fazekas (1957)
Estriol glucuronoside	Human	Meconium	Menini and Diczfalusy (1960, 1961)
Estradiol-17α	Bovine	Meconium	Velle (1957)
20α-Hydroxypregn-4-en-3-one	Human	Fat tissue	Zander (1959)
	Rat	Fat tissue	Wiest (1959b)
20β-Hydroxypregn-4-en-3-one	Human	Fat tissue	Zander *et al.* (1958)
Dehydroepiandrosterone	Human	Meconium	Francis *et al.* (1960)
Cortisol	Human	Pheochromocytoma	Mulrow *et al.* (1959)
Progesterone	Rat	Fat tissue	Wiest (1959b)
	Bufo vulgaris	Bidder's organs	Chieffi (1962)
Pregnanediol	Human	Liquor amnii feces, bile (after progesterone administration)	Klopper and MacNaughton (1959)
5α-Androstane-3α,17β-diol	Human	Urine + feces	Hirsch *et al.* (1957)
Estrone	Equine	Meconium	Velle and Pigon (1960)
Estradiol-17α			
6"α"-Hydroxyestradiol-17β	Equine	Follicular	Bush *et al.* (1960)
3α-Hydroxy-5β-pregn-16-en-20-one	Human	Meconium	Shen and Kinsella (1961); Francis *et al.* (1962)
Estriol	Human	Amniotic	Troen *et al.* (1961)
Estriol-3-sulfate			
Estriol-16(17?)-glucuronoside			
Estradiol-17β	*Morone labrax*	Bidder's organ	Chieffi (1962)
Estrone			
Estriol			
6α-Hydroxycortisol	Human	Liquor amnii	Lambert and Pennington (1963)
Progesterone	Human	Myometrium (pregnancy)	Keimar *et al.* (1962)

Continued on following page

Table 17 *(continued)*

STEROIDS IN MISCELLANEOUS TISSUES

Steroid	Species	Tissue or fluid	Reference
Estradiol-17β	Bovine	Follicular fluid	Short (1962c)
Progesterone Estradiol-17β 20β-Hydroxypregn-4-en-3-one	Bovine	Ovarian cyst fluid	

Table 18

STEROID ARTIFACTS IN URINE (ARTIFACTS OF SUBSTITUTION)

Artifact	Compound in urine	Reference
3β-Chlorandrost-5-en-17-one	Dehydroepiandrosterone	Butenandt and Dannendaum (1934); Venning *et al.* (1942); Huis In't Veld (1961)
3β-Chloroandrost-5-en-17β-ol	Androst-5-ene-3β,17β-diol	Ungar and Dorfman (1954)

Table 19

STEROID ARTIFACTS IN URINE (ARTIFACTS OF DEHYDRATION)

Artifact	Compound in urine	Reference
5α-Androst-2(or 3)-en-17-one	Androsterone	Hirschmann (1940); Venning *et al.* (1942)
Androsta-3,5-diene-17-one	Dehydroepiandrosterone	Pincus and Pearlman (1941); Dobriner *et al.* (1944)
3α-Hydroxy-5β-androst-9-(11)-en-17-one	11β-Hydroxy-etiocholanolone	Lieberman *et al.* (1951); Peron and Dorfman (1956)
3α-Hydroxy-5α-androst-9(11)-en-17-one	11β-Hydroxy-androsterone	Lieberman *et al.* (1951); Peron and Dorfman (1956)
3β-Hydroxy-5α-androst-9(11)-en-17-one	3β,11β-Dihydroxy-5α-androstan-17-one	Kemp *et al.* (1954)
Pregnanolone	Pregnanetriol	Gallagher (1958)
3α,17α-Dihydroxy-5β-pregnane-11,20-dione	Cortolone	Gallagher (1958)
11β-Hydroxyandrosta-3,5-dien-17-one	3ξ,11β-Dihydroxy-androst-4-en-17-one	Neeman *et al.* (1960)
3α-Hydroxy-5β-pregnane-11,20-dione	3α,17α,20α-Trihydroxy-5β-pregnane-11-one	Fukushima and Gallagher (1957a)
3β-Hydroxy-5α-androst-9(11)-en-17-one	11β-Hydroxy-epiandrosterone	Schubert and Wehrberger (1961, 1962)

Table 20

STEROID ARTIFACTS IN URINE (ARTIFACTS OF REARRANGEMENT)

Artifact	Compound in urine	Reference
3α-Hydroxy-17-epi-5β-pregnan-20-one	Pregnanolone	Lieberman *et al.* (1948)
3β,17α-Dihydroxy-17α-methyl-*D*-homoandrost-5-en-17-one	3β,17α-Dihydroxy-pregn-5-en-20-one	Hirschmann and Hirschmann (1947)
3α,17α-Dihydroxy-17α-methyl-*D*-homo-5β-androstan-17-one	17α-Hydroxy-pregnanolone	Miller and Dorfman (1950)
i-Androstanolone	Dehydroepiandro-sterone	Teich *et al.* (1953)

Table 21

STEROID ARTIFACTS IN URINE (ARTIFACTS OF ACETYLATION)

Artifact	Compound in urine	Reference
3α-Acetoxy-5α-androst-9(11)-en-17-one	11β-Hydroxyandro-sterone	Lieberman *et al.* (1948)
3α-Acetoxy-5β-androstan-17-one	Etiocholanolone	
Androsterone acetate	Androsterone	

Table 22

C_{18} STEROIDS IN URINE

Class	Steroid	Species	Reference
$C_{18}O$	3-Deoxyequilenin	Equine (pregnancy)	Prelog and Führer (1945)
$C_{18}O_2$	Estrone	Human (pregnancy)	Doisy *et al.* (1929); Butenandt (1929); Dingemanse *et al.* (1930, 1938)
		Rhesus monkey (pregnancy)	Short and Eckstein (1961)
		Human (male, adrenal tumor)	Slaunwhite and Buchwald (1960)
		Human (female)	Engel *et al.* (1952); Ladany *et al.* (1962)
		Human (male)	Dingemanse *et al.* (1938)
		Equine (male)	Pigon *et al.* (1961)
		Equine (pregnancy)	de Jongh *et al.* (1931); Savard (1961)
		Bovine (pregnancy)	Klyne and Wright (1959)
		Goat (pregnancy)	Klyne and Wright (1957)

Continued on following page

Table 22 *(continued)*

C_{18} Steroids in Urine

Class	Steroid	Species	Reference
		Equine (stallion)	Deulofev and Ferrari (1934); Haussler (1934)
		Swine (pregnancy)	Bredeck and Mayer (1958); Rombouts (1962)
		Bovine	Marker (1939a, b)
		Porcine	Velle (1958b, 1959)
		Rat	Ketz *et al.* (1961)
		Bovine (pregnancy)	Velle (1958a, c); Pope *et al.* (1957)
		Laying hen	Ainsworth and Common (1962)
$C_{18}O_2$	Estradiol-17β	Human (pregnancy)	Smith *et al.* (1939)
		Rhesus monkey (pregnancy)	Short and Eckstein (1961)
		Human (female)	Engel *et al.* (1952); Ladany *et al.* (1962)
		Human (male adrenal tumor)	Slaunwhite and Buchwald (1960)
		Equine (pregnancy)	Wintersteiner *et al.* (1935)
		Equine (stallion)	Pigon *et al.* (1961)
		Equine (stallion)	Levin (1945)
		Porcine	Velle (1958b)
		Rat	Ketz *et al.* (1961)
$C_{18}O_2$	Mono and diglucuronoside of estriol	Human (pregnancy)	Felger and Katzman (1961)
$C_{18}O_2$	Estradiol-17α	Equine (male)	Pigon *et al.* (1961)
		Equine (pregnancy)	Hirschmann and Wintersteiner (1937)
		Bovine (pregnancy)	Klyne and Wright (1959)
		Bovine (pregnancy)	Velle (1958a)
		Goat (pregnancy)	Klyne and Wright (1957)
		Rat	Ketz *et al.* (1961)
$C_{18}O_2$	3β-Hydroxyestra-5,7,9-trien-17-one	Mare (pregnancy)	Heard and Hoffman (1941): Glen *et al.* (1958)
	Equilin	Equine (pregnancy)	Girard *et al.* (1932)
	Equilenin	Equine (pregnancy)	Savard (1961)
	Hippulin	Equine (pregnancy)	Girard *et al.* (1932)
	Dihydroequilenin	Equine (pregnancy)	Wintersteiner *et al.* (1936)
	Estranediol A	Human (female)	Marker *et al.* (1938c)
	Estranediol B	Human (female)	Marker *et al.* (1938c)
$C_{18}O_3$	Estriol	Human (pregnancy)	Marrian (1930); Doisy *et al.* (1930)
		Human (female)	Engel *et al.* (1952); Ladany *et al.* (1962)

Continued on following page

Table 22 *(continued)*

C_{18} Steroids in Urine

Class	Steroid	Species	Reference
	16-Ketoestradiol-17β	Human	Layne and Marrian (1958b)
	18-Hydroxyestrone	Human	Loke and Marrian (1958)
	16α-Hydroxyestrone	Human	Watson and Marrian (1955); Marrian *et al.* (1957); Layne and Marrian (1958a)
	2-Methoxyestrone	Human	Loke and Marrian (1958); Frandsen (1959); Copenhaven and Gawienowski (1961)
	2-Methoxyestradiol-17β	Human	Frandsen (1959)
	16-Ketoestrone	Human	Serchi (1953)
	16β-Hydroxyestrone	Human	Layne and Marrian (1958b)
	16-Epiestriol	Human	Marrian and Bauld (1955); Correale *et al.* (1962); Watson and Marrian (1956); Breuer and Pangels (1959)
		Human (male adrenal tumor)	Slaunwhite and Buchwald (1960)
	17-Epiestriol	Human (pregnancy)	Breuer (1960); Breuer and Pangels (1961)
	16,17-Epiestriol	Human	Breuer and Pangels (1959, 1961)
	Estriol Estriol-3-sulfate Estriol-16(17?)-glucuronoside	Human (newborn)	Troen *et al.* (1961)
	Estriol-3-glucuronoside	Human (pregnancy)	Beling (1962)
	2-Hydroxyestrone	Human	Fishman (1963); Notchev and Stimmel (1962)
	6-Hydroxyestrone	Human	Loke *et al.* (1957)

Table 23

$C_{19}O$ and $C_{19}O_2$ Steroids in Urine

Class	Steroid	Species	Reference
$C_{19}O$	5α-Androst-16-en-3α-ol	Human	Brooksbank and Haslewood (1949); Mason and Schneider (1950); Miller *et al.* (1953); Burstein and Dorfman (1960, 1962); Engel *et al.* (1953); Kappas *et al.* (1956)

Continued on following page

Table 23 *(continued)*

$C_{19}O$ AND $C_{19}O_2$ STEROIDS IN URINE

Class	Steroid	Species	Reference
$C_{19}O_2$	Androst-4-ene-3,17-dione	Human	Miller *et al.* (1953); Lieberman *et al.* (1948)
	Dehydroepiandrosterone	Human	Butenandt (1931); Callow and Callow (1939, 1940); Engel *et al.* (1941); Hirschmann (1940); Huis In't Veld (1961)
		Bovine	Holtz (1954); Marker (1938a, 1939a)
		Hog (boar)	Clark (1963)
		Rat	Cavina *et al.* (1956); Ketz *et al.* (1961)
		Equine	Oppenauer (1941)
		Ewe (pregnant)	Coulson (1960)
	Androst-5-ene-3β,17β-diol	Human	Hirschmann and Hirschmann (1945); Mason and Kepler (1945a); Schiller *et al.* (1945); Ungar and Dorfman (1953); Fotherby (1958)
	3α-(?)-Hydroxyandrost-5-en-17-one	Human	Keller (1956)
	Androsterone	Human	Butenandt (1932); Butenandt and Westphal (1934); Engel *et al.* (1941); Hirschmann (1941); Callow (1939); Callow and Callow (1939)
		Human (ovariectomized-adrenalectomized)	Bulbrook *et al.* (1960)
		Rat	Cavina *et al.* (1956); Ketz *et al.* (1961); Schubert and Wehrberger (1962)
		Bovine	Marker (1939a, b)
		Ewe (pregnant)	Coulson (1960)
		Hog (boar)	Clark (1963)
	Epiandrosterone	Human	Pearlman (1942); Hirschmann (1941)
		Goat (pregnancy)	Klyne and Wright (1957)
		Equine	Oppenauer (1941)
		Guinea pig	Staib *et al.* (1959b)
		Human	Personen (1962)
	Etiocholanolone	Human	Callow (1939); Callow and Callow (1939, 1940); Hirschmann (1940, 1941); Eberlein and Bongiovanni (1956)

Continued on following page

Table 23 *(continued)*

$C_{19}O$ AND $C_{19}O_2$ STEROIDS IN URINE

Class	Steroid	Species	Reference
		Human (adrenal-ectomized-ovariectomized)	Bulbrook *et al.* (1960)
		Rat	Cavina *et al.* (1956); Schubert and Wehrberger (1962)
		Guinea pig	Peron and Dorfman (1956)
		Bovine	Holtz (1954)
		Ewe (pregnant)	Coulson (1960)
		Hog (boar)	Clark (1963)
	Testosterone	Human	Schubert and Wehrberger (1960b); Camacho and Migeon (1963)
	3β-Hydroxy-5β-androstan-17-one	Human	Dobriner and Lieberman (1952); Fukushima and Gallagher (1957b)
	5β-Androstane-3,17-dione	Human	Lieberman *et al.* (1948); Schubert and Wehrberger (1962)
	5α-Androstane-3,17-dione	Human	Lieberman *et al.* (1948); Schubert and Wehrberger (1962)
	5β-Androstane-3α,17β-diol	Human	Miller and Dorfman (1949); Lieberman *et al.* (1953); Fukushima and Gallagher (1957b)
	5α-Androstane-3α,17β-diol	Human	Lieberman *et al.* (1953); Hirsch *et al.* (1957)
	5α-Androst-1-ene-3,17-dione	Human	Lieberman *et al.* (1948)
	3β-Hydroxy-5α-androstan-16-one	Equine	Heard and McKay (1939); Oppenauer (1941); Huffman and Lott (1951)
	5α-Androstane-3β,16β-diol	Equine	Brooks and Klyne (1956, 1957)
	5α-Androstane-3β,16α-diol	Equine	Brooks and Klyne (1956, 1957)
	5β-Androstene-3α,17α-diol	Bovine (pregnancy)	Klyne and Wright (1959)
	5α-Androstane-3α,17α-diol	Bovine (pregnancy)	Klyne and Wright (1959)
	Dehydroepiandrosterone sulfate	Human	Munson *et al.* (1944); Huis In't Veld (1957); Baulieu (1959)
	Androsterone sulfate	Human	Venning *et al.* (1942)
	Androsterone glucuronide	Human	Pelzer *et al.* (1958)
	Etiocholanolone glucuronide	Human	Pelzer *et al.* (1958)

Table 24

$C_{19}O_3$ AND $C_{19}O_4$ STEROIDS IN URINE

Class	Steroid	Species	Reference
$C_{19}O_3$	11β-Hydroxyetio-cholanolone	Guinea pig	Peron and Dorfman (1956, 1958)
		Human	Lieberman and Dobriner (1948); Plantin and Birke (1955)
		Rat	Schubert and Wehrberger (1962)
		Human (infants)	Birchall *et al.* (1961)
		Hog	Clark (1963)
	11-Ketoetiocholanolone	Guinea pig	Burstein and Dorfman (1958); Peron and Dorfman (1956, 1958)
		Human	Lieberman and Dobriner (1946, 1948)
		Rat	Schubert and Wehrberger (1962)
		Human (infants)	Birchall *et al.* (1961)
		Hog	Clark (1963)
	11β-Hydroxy-androsterone	Guinea pig	Peron and Dorfman (1956)
		Human	Miller and Dorfman (1950); Mason (1945)
		Human (infants)	Birchall *et al.* (1961)
		Human	Lieberman and Dobriner (1948)
		Rat	Schubert and Wehrberger (1962)
	3β-Hydroxyandrost-5-ene-7,17-dione	Human	Baulieu *et al.* (1961a)
	3β-Hydroxy-5α-androstane-11,17-dione	Guinea pig	Schubert and Wehrberger (1961)
		Rat	Schubert and Wehrberger (1962)
	5β-Androstane-3,11,17-trione	Human	Fukushima and Gallagher (1957b)
		Rat	Schubert and Wehrberger (1960a)
		Guinea pig	Schubert and Wehrberger (1961)
	3β-Hydroxyandrost-5-ene-7,17-dione	Human	Fukushima and Gallagher (1957b)
	3β-Hydroxy-5β-androstane-11,17-dione	Human	Fukushima and Gallagher (1957b)
	11β-Hydroxy-5β-androstane-3,17-dione	Human	Fukushima and Gallagher (1957b)
		Guinea pig	Schubert and Wehrberger (1961)
		Rat	Schubert and Wehrberger (1962)
	5β-Androstane-3α,16α,17β-triol	Human	Lieberman *et al.* (1953); Lieberman and Dobriner (1950)
	3α-17β-Dihydroxy-5β-androst-11-one	Human	Dobriner and Lieberman (1952)

Continued on following page

Table 24 (*continued*)

$C_{19}O_3$ AND $C_{19}O_4$ STEROIDS IN URINE

Class	Steroid	Species	Reference
	5α-Androstane-3α,16α,17β-triol	Human	Lieberman and Dobriner (1950); Lieberman *et al.* (1953)
	11-Ketoetiocholanolone glucuronoside	Human	Pelzer *et al.* (1958)
	Androst-5-ene-3β,16α,17β-triol	Human	Hirschmann (1943)
	Androst-5-ene-3β,16α,17β-triol	Human	Finkelstein *et al.* (1953); Marrian (1944); Fotherby *et al.* (1957); Okada *et al.* (1959)
	11β-Hydroxyepi androsterone	Human	Kemp *et al.* (1954)
		Guinea pig	Staib and Doenges (1962); Schubert and Wehrberger (1961)
		Rat	Schubert and Wehrberger (1962)
	3α,18-Dihydroxy-5β-androstan-17-one	Human	Fukushima *et al.* (1962a, b)
	11-Ketoandrosterone	Human	Lieberman *et al.* (1950)
		Guinea pig	Peron and Dorfman (1956)
		Rat	Schubert and Wehrberger (1962)
	7α-Hydroxydehydro-epiandrosterone	Human	Lewbart and Schneider (1959); Okada *et al.* (1959); Starka *et al.* (1962)
	11β-Hydroxyandrost-4-ene-3,17-dione	Human	Salamon and Dobriner (1952, 1953)
		Rat	Schubert and Wehrberger (1960a)
		Guinea pig	Schubert and Wehrberger (1961)
		Bovine	Holtz (1954)
		Mouse (bearing tumor, presumptive isolation)	Wilson *et al.* (1958)
	Androst-5-ene-3β,16β,17β-triol	Human	Fotherby (1957, 1958)
	3β,16α-Dihydroxy-androst-5-en-17-one	Human	Fotherby *et al.* (1957); Bongiovanni (1962)
	11β-Hydroxytestosterone	Mouse (bearing tumor, presumptive)	Wilson *et al.* (1958)
$C_{19}O_4$	6β,11β-Dihydroxy-androst-4-ene-3,17-dione	Guinea pig	Peron and Dorfman (1957, 1958)
	7α,16α-Dihydroxy-dehydroepiandrosterone	Human	Okada *et al.* (1959)
	7-Keto-16α-hydroxy-dehydroepiandrosterone	Human	Okada *et al.* (1959)

Table 25

$C_{21}O$ STEROID IN URINE

Steroid	Species	Reference
5β-Pregnan-3α-ol	Human	Marker and Lawson (1938)

Table 26

$C_{21}O_2$ STEROIDS IN URINE

Steroid	Species	Reference
3α-Hydroxy-5β-pregnan-20-one	Porcine	Marker and Rohrmann (1939c)
	Human	Marker and Kamm (1937); Dobriner (1951); Dobriner *et al.* (1944); van der Molen (1962)
3β-Hydroxy-5α-pregnan-20-one	Human	Pearlman *et al.* (1942)
(Allopregnanolone)	Equine	Marker *et al.* (1938b); Savard *et al.* (1958)
	Porcine	Marker and Rohrmann (1939c)
5β-Pregnane-3α,20α-diol (Pregnanediol)	Human	Engel *et al.* (1941); Eberlein and Bongiovanni (1956); Fukushima and Gallagher (1957b); Heard and Hoffman (1941); Venning and Browne (1937); Marrian (1929); Hirschmann (1940); Butler and Marrian (1937); Mason and Kepler (1945b)
	Bovine	Marker (1938b, c)
	Chimpanzee	Fish *et al.* (1942)
	Equine	Marker *et al.* (1937); Robertson and Coulson (1958)
	Ewe	Robertson and Coulson (1958)
5β-Pregnane-3β,20α-diol	Human	Mason and Kepler (1945b)
3α-Hydroxy-5α-pregnan-20-one	Human	Marker and Kamm (1937); Dobriner *et al.* (1944); Lieberman *et al.* (1948)
5α-Pregnane-3β,20α-diol	Human	Marker *et al.* (1938a)
	Equine	Marker and Rohrmann (1939b)
	Bovine	Marker (1938a, c)
3β-Hydroxy-5β-pregn-16-en-20-one (May be an artifact)	Equine	Klyne and Marrian (1945); Klyne and Patterson (1948)
5α-Pregnane-3α,20α-diol	Human	Lieberman *et al.* (1953); Marker and Kamm (1937); Hartmann and Locher (1935)

Continued on following page

Table 26 *(continued)*

$C_{21}O_2$ STEROIDS IN URINE

Steroid	Species	Reference
	Bovine	Marker (1938b, c)
	Equine	Marker *et al.* (1937); Savard *et al.* (1958)
	Goat (pregnancy)	Klyne and Wright (1957)
Pregn-5-ene-3β,20α-diol	Human	Schiller *et al.* (1945); Jacobson (1962); Mason and Kepler (1945b); Hirschmann and Hirschmann (1945)
	Equine	Marker and Rohrmann (1938)
5α-Pregnane-3β,20β-diol	Equine	Bauld and Heard (1948); Savard *et al.* (1958); Brooks *et al.* (1952)
3α-Hydroxy-5β-pregn-16-en-20-one	Human	Fukushima *et al.* (1954c)
17-Methyl-*D*-homo-5α-androstane-3β,17α-diol	Equine (pregnancy)	Marker and Rohrmann (1939a); Klyne (1950)
5α-Pregnane-3,20-dione	Mare	Marker *et al.* (1938b)
	Human	Dobriner *et al.* (1944); Lieberman *et al.* (1948)
5β-Pregnane-3,20-dione	Mare	Marker *et al.* (1938b)
	Human	Lieberman *et al.* (1948)
Uranolone (17aβ-Hydroxy-17α-methyl-5α-*D*-homoandrostan-3-one)	Equine	Brooks and Klyne (1957)

Table 27

$C_{21}O_3$ STEROIDS IN URINE

Steroid	Species	Reference
3α,17α-Dihydroxy-5β-pregnan-20-one	Human	Lieberman and Dobriner (1948); Eberlein and Bongiovanni (1956); Miller and Dorfman (1950); Dobriner (1951); Mason and Strickler (1947)
5β-Pregnane-3α,17α,20α-triol	Human	Butler and Marrian (1937); Eberlein and Bongiovanni (1956); Miller and Dorfman (1950); Mason and Sprague (1948); Cox and Marrian (1953); Marker *et al.* (1938c); Bongiovanni (1962); Fukushima and Gallagher (1957a, b); Fukushima *et al.* (1962a, b)

Continued on following page

Table 27 (*continued*)

$C_{21}O_3$ STEROIDS IN URINE

Steroid	Species	Reference
	Human (pregnancy)	Ronan *et al.* (1960)
	Human (adrenalectomized, pregnant)	Herrmann and Silverman (1957)
3α,17α-Dihydroxy-5α-pregnan-20-one	Human	Fukushima *et al.* (1954c, 1956)
5α-Pregnane-3α,17α,20α-triol	Human	Fukushima *et al.* (1956); Fukushima and Gallagher (1957a, b)
	Equine	Marker *et al.* (1938a); Haslewood *et al.* (1934); Smith *et al.* (1933); Heard (1938)
5α-Pregnane-3α,17α,20β-triol	Human	Fukushima and Gallagher (1957a, b)
5β-Pregnane-3α,11β,20α-triol	Human	Fukushima *et al.* (1954a, b, c)
3α,11β-Dihydroxy-5β-pregnan-20-one	Human	Fukushima *et al.* (1954a, b, c)
11-Keto-5β-pregnane-3α,20α-diol	Human	Lieberman and Dobriner (1948); Lieberman *et al.* (1953); Fukushima *et al.* (1956); Fukushima and Gallagher (1957a, b)
3α,21-Dihydroxy-5β-pregnan-20-one	Human	Eberlein and Bongiovanni (1956); Richardson *et al.* (1955); Green *et al.* (1960)
3β,17α-Dihydroxypregn-5-en-20-one (17α-Hydroxypregnolone)	Human	Hirschmann and Hirschmann (1947); Bongiovanni (1962)
Pregn-5-ene-3β,16α,20α-triol	Human	Hirschmann and Hirschmann (1949)
Pregn-5-ene-3β,17α,20α-triol	Human	Hirschmann and Hirschmann (1950); Fotherby (1958, 1959); Okada *et al.* (1959); Bongiovanni (1962)
3α,6α-Dihydroxy-5α-pregnan-20-one	Human (pregnancy)	Dobriner *et al.* (1944); Salamon and Dobriner (1952)
3α-Hydroxy-5β-pregnane-11,20-dione	Human	Lieberman and Dobriner (1948)
3α,6α-Dihydroxy-5β-pregnane-20-one	Human	Lieberman *et al.* (1948)
3β,21-Dihydroxypregn-5-en-20-one	Human	Dobriner and Lieberman (1952); Pasqualini and Jayle (1962a)
3α,16α-Dihydroxy-5β-pregnan-20-one 3α,16α-Dihydroxy-5α-pregnan-20-one	Human (adrenogenital salt-losing syndrome)	Neher *et al.* (1959)
5α-Pregnane-3α,16α,20α-triol 5β-Pregnane-3α,16α,20α-triol	Human (pregnancy)	Hirschmann *et al.* (1961)

Continued on following page

Table 27 *(continued)*

$C_{21}O_3$ STEROIDS IN URINE

Steroid	Species	Reference
Pregn-5-ene-3α,16α,20α-triol 5β-Pregnane-3α,16α,20α-triol	Human (adrenal cancer)	Fukushima *et al.* (1960)
3α-Hydroxy-5β-pregnane-(11β-18),(18-20)-dioxide	Human (after aldosterone)	Kelly *et al.* (1962b)
Deoxycorticosterone 3α,17α-21-Trihydroxy-5β-pregnan-20-one	Human	Reynolds and Ulstrom (1962)

Table 28

$C_{21}O_4$ STEROIDS IN URINE

Steroid	Species	Reference
5β-Pregnane-3α,11β,17α,20α-tetrol	Human	Fukushima *et al.* (1956, 1960); Fukushima and Gallagher (1957a, b)
3α,17α,20α-Trihydroxy-5β-pregnan-11-one	Human	Finkelstein *et al.* (1953); Fukushima *et al.* (1956); Bongiovanni (1962)
11-Deoxycortisol	Human	Dyrenfurth *et al.* (1958); Reynolds and Ulstrom (1962)
3α,17α,21-Trihydroxy-5β-pregnan-20-one	Human	Bongiovanni and Eberlein (1955); Rosselet *et al.* (1954a, b); Richardson *et al.* (1955); Ungar and Dorfman (1956); Balls *et al.* (1959); Lipsett and Damast (1958); Dyrenfurth *et al.* (1958); Dohan *et al.* (1955); Eberlein and Bongiovanni (1956); Touchstone *et al.* (1957); Reynolds and Ulstrom (1962); Green *et al.* (1960); Martin (1962)
Corticosterone	Human	Dohan *et al.* (1955); Dyrenfurth *et al.* (1958)
11-Dehydrocorticosterone	Human	Dohan *et al.* (1955)
3α,11β,21-Trihydroxy-5β-pregnan-20-one	Human	Dohan *et al.* (1955); Balls *et al.* (1959); Holness and Gray (1958)
3α,11β,21-Trihydroxy-5α-pregnan-20-one	Human	Dohan *et al.* (1955)
3α,21-Dihydroxy-5β-pregnane-11,20-dione	Human	Dohan *et al.* (1955)
17α,21-Dihydroxy-5β-pregnane-3,20-dione	Human	Lipsett and Damast (1958); Reynolds and Ulstrom (1962)
5β-Pregnane-3α,17α,20α,21-tetrol 5β-Pregnane-3α,17α,20β,21-tetrol	Human	Fukushima *et al.* (1960)

Continued on following page

Table 28 *(continued)*

$C_{21}O_4$ STEROIDS IN URINE

Steroid	Species	Reference
11β,20β,21-Trihydroxypregn-4-en-3-one	Human (after ACTH)	Bulaschenko *et al.* (1960)
3α,21-Dihydroxy-5β-pregnane (11β-18), (18-20)-dioxide	Human (after aldosterone)	Kelly *et al.* (1962a)
Pregn-5-ene-3β,17α,20β,21-tetrol	Human	Bongiovanni (1962)

Table 29

$C_{21}O_5$ STEROIDS IN URINE

Steroid	Species	Reference
Cortisone	Human	Dohan *et al.* (1955); Dyrenfurth *et al.* (1958); Holness *et al.* (1956); Schneider (1950, 1952)
	Guinea pig	Peron and Dorfman (1958)
Cortisol	Human	Mason (1950); Schneider (1952); Mason and Sprague (1948); Holness *et al.* (1956); Dyrenfurth *et al.* (1958)
	Guinea pig	Nadel and Burstein (1956); Burstein and Dorfman (1955)
11β,17α,21-Trihydroxy-5β-pregnane-3,20-dione	Human	Schneider (1952); Pasqualini and Jayle (1962b)
11β,17α,20α,21-Tetrahydroxy-pregn-4-en-3-one	Human	Peterson *et al.* (1957); Kandráč *et al.* (1959); Richardson *et al.* (1958)
	Guinea pig	Peron and Dorfman (1958); Burstein and Dorfman (1955)
11β,17α,20β,21-Tetrahydroxy-pregn-4-en-3-one	Guinea pig	Burstein and Dorfman (1955) Peron and Dorfman (1958)
	Human	Kandráč *et al.* (1959); Richardson *et al.* (1958)
Urocortisone	Human	Dohan *et al.* (1955); Schneider (1952); Dobriner and Lieberman (1952); Holness *et al.* (1956); Dyrenfurth *et al.* (1958)
Urocortisol	Human	Dohan *et al.* (1955); Dobriner and Lieberman (1952); Holness *et al.* (1956); Bush and Willoughby (1957a); Dyrenfurth *et al.* (1958)
Cortol β-Cortol	Human	Fukushima *et al.* (1955)

Continued on following page

Table 29 *(continued)*

$C_{21}O_5$ STEROIDS IN URINE

Steroid	Species	Reference
17α,20β,21-Trihydroxypregn-4-ene-3,11-dione	Human	Holness *et al.* (1956)
Cortolone	Human	Fukushima *et al.* (1955)
β-Cortolone	Human	Fukushima *et al.* (1955); Romanoff *et al.* (1958)
Aldosterone	Human	Majnarich and Dillon (1954); Luetscher (1956); Wettstein *et al.* (1956); Luetscher *et al.* (1954)
17α,21-Dihydroxy-5β-pregnane-3,11,20-trione	Human	Schneider (1952)
3α,11β,17α,21-Tetrahydroxy-5α-pregnan-20-one	Human	Romanoff *et al.* (1958); Bush and Willoughby (1957b)
Allocortol Allocortolone β-Allocortol β-Allocortolone	Human	Gallagher (1958)
17α,20α,21-Trihydroxypregn-4-ene-3,11-dione	Human	Kandráč (1962).
6β-Hydroxycorticosterone 6β,21-Dihydroxypregn-4-ene-3,11,20-trione	Human	Nowaczynski *et al.* (1962)
3α,11β,21-Trihydroxy-18-oxo-5α-pregnan-20-one 3β,11β,21-Trihydroxy-18-oxo-5β-pregnan-20-one 3α,11β,21-Trihydroxy-18-oxo-5β-pregnan-20-one 3β,11β,21-Trihydroxy-18-oxo-5α-pregnan-20-one	Human (after aldosterone)	Kelly *et al.* (1962b)

Table 30

$C_{21}O_6$ STEROIDS IN URINE

Steroid	Species	Reference
6β-Hydroxycortisol	Human	Touchstone and Blakemore (1961); Burstein *et al.* (1954); Nadel *et al.* (1956); Katz *et al.* (1960); Frantz *et al.* (1960)
	Human (newborn)	Ulstrom *et al.* (1960)
	Guinea pig	Burstein and Dorfman (1955); Peron and Dorfman (1958); Nadel and Burstein (1956)
	Human (newborn and pregnancy)	Birchall *et al.* (1961)
2α-Hydroxycortisol	Guinea pig	Burstein (1956); Peron and Dorfman (1956, 1958); Nadel and Burstein (1956)
6β-Hydroxycortisol 2α-Hydroxycortisone 6β-Hydroxycortisone 6β,11β,17α,20,21-Pentahydroxy-pregn-4-en-3-one (Presumptive evidence)	Human	Lipman *et al.* (1961)
6α-Hydroxycortisol	Human	Frantz *et al.* (1961)
6β-Hydroxycortisone	Human (Cushing's disease)	Pasqualini (1962)

Table 31

STEROID CONJUGATES IN BLOOD AND URINE

Conjugate	Species	Reference
Estrone sulfate	Pregnant mare urine	Schachter and Marrian (1935)
17α-Hydroxypregnanolone glucuronoside	Human urine	Mason and Strickler (1947)
Dehydroepiandrosterone glucuronoside	Human urine	Baulieu (1959); Baulieu *et al.* (1961b)
Dehydroepiandrosterone sulfate	Human urine	Malassis *et al.* (1957)
Cortisone glucuronoside Cortisol glucuronoside	Human urine	Brouillet and Mattox (1961)
11-Dehydrocorticosterone sulfate Corticosterone sulfate	Human urine	Pasqualini (1960)

Continued on following page

Table 31 (*continued*)

STEROID CONJUGATES IN BLOOD AND URINE

Conjugate	Species	Reference
7-Keto-dehydroepiandrosterone-3-sulfate	Human blood (virilizing adrenal tumor)	Guillon *et al.* (1961)
Etiocholanolone sulfate Etiocholanolone glucuronoside 3β-Hydroxy-5β-androstan-17-one glucuronide	Human urine	Baulieu and Emiliozzi (1960)
Estrone sulfate	Human plasma	Purdy *et al.* (1961)
Corticosterone-21-sulfate Cortisol-21-sulfate	Human urine	Pasqualini and Jayle (1961)
Dehydroepiandrosterone sulfate Androsterone sulfate	Human urine	Staib (1961)
Testosterone "conjugate" (glucuronoside)	Salmon (*Oncorhynchus nerka*)	Grajcer and Idler (1961, 1963)
Estrone sulfate	Human pregnancy urine	McKenna *et al.* (1961)
Estriol-3-sulfate Estriol-16(17?)-glucuronide	Human cord blood Newborn urine	Troen *et al.* (1961)
3,17β-Dihydroxyestra-1,3,5(10)-trien-16α-yl-β-*D*-glucopyranosiduronic acid	Human pregnancy urine	Neeman and Hashimoto (1962)

Table 32

STEROIDS IN FECES

Steroid	Treatment	Species	Reference
Androgens (not identified)	Progesterone	Ram Castrated male sheep	Raeside (1957)
Androgens (not identified)	Progesterone	Bull	Miller and Turner (1955)
—	Progesterone	Pregnant cow	Miller *et al.* (1956)
Aldosterone	Estradiol-17β	Rat	Llaurado *et al.* (1962)

Table 33

"ANIMAL" STEROIDS IN PLANTS

Steroid	Plant	Reference
Estrone	Palm kernel extract	Butenandt and Jacobi (1933)
Estriol	Female willow flower	Skarzynski (1934)

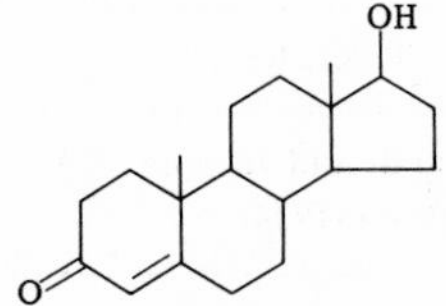

Testosterone

Androst-4-ene-
3, 17-dione

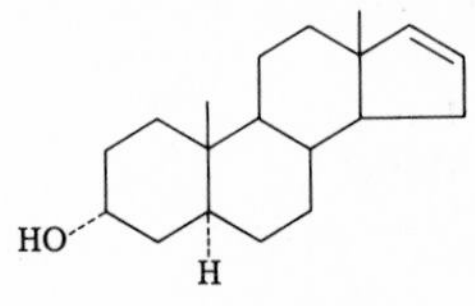

5α-Androst-
16-en-3α-ol

5α-Androst-
16-en-3β-ol

Progesterone

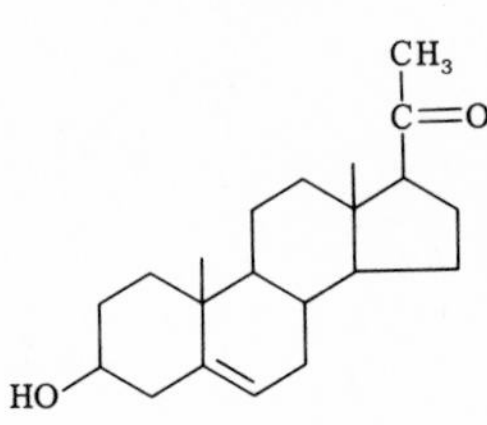

Pregnenolone

3α-Hydroxy-5α-
pregnan-20-one

3β-Hydroxy-5α-
pregnan-20-one

17α-Hydroxy-
progesterone

11β-Hydroxy-
testosterone
(Human tumor)

11β-Hydroxyandrost-
4-ene-3, 17-dione
(Human tumor)

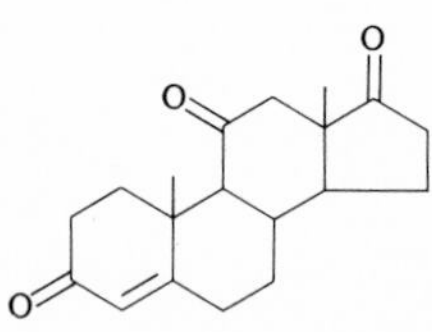

Adrenosterone
(Human tumor)

Estrone

Estradiol-17β

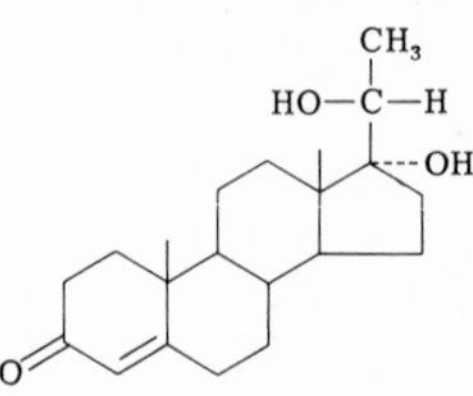

17α, 20β-Dihydroxy-
pregn-4-en-3-one

FIG. 1. Steroids in the testis.

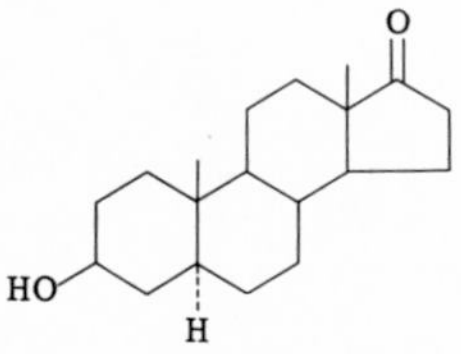

Epiandrosterone

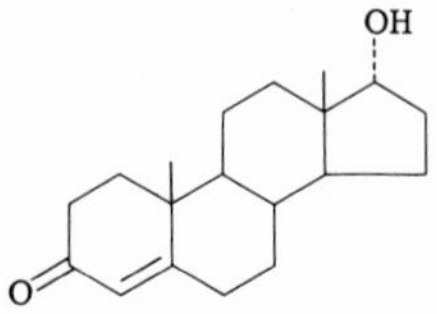

Epitestosterone

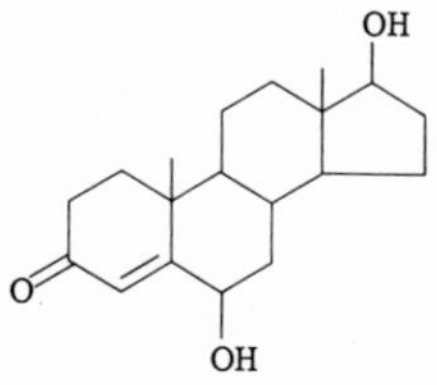

6β-Hydroxytestosterone

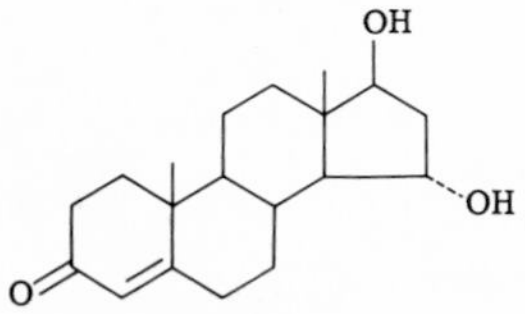

15α-Hydroxy-
testosterone

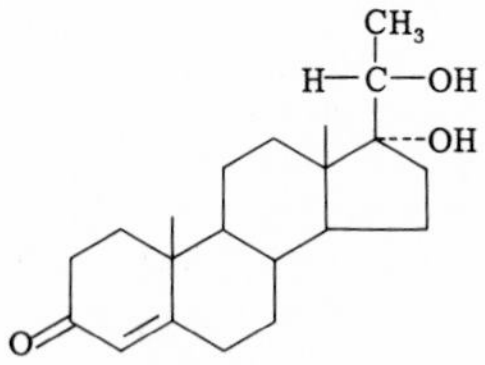

17α, 20α-Dihydroxy-
pregn-4-en-3-one

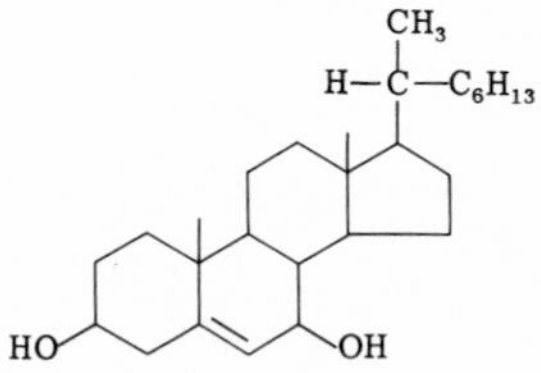

7β-Hydroxycholesterol

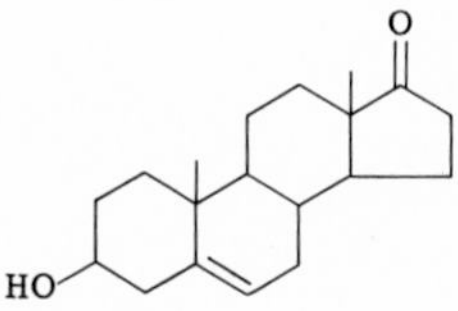

Dehydroepi-
androsterone

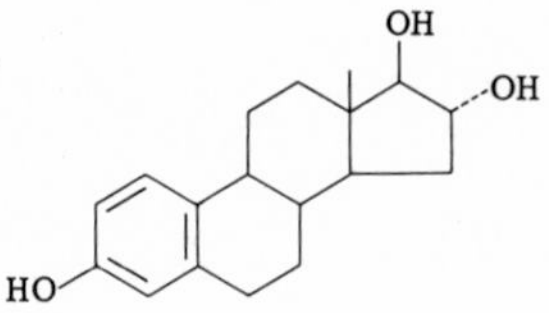

Estriol

FIG. 1. Continued.

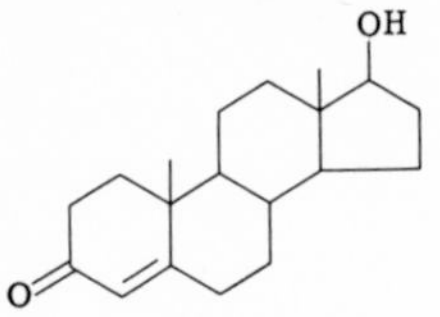

Testosterone

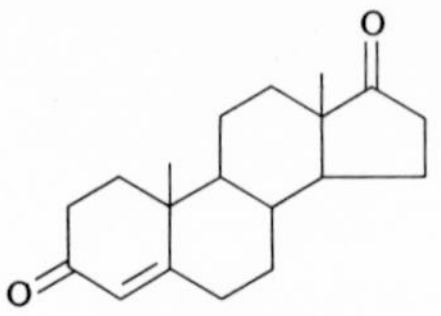

Androst-4-ene-3,17-dione

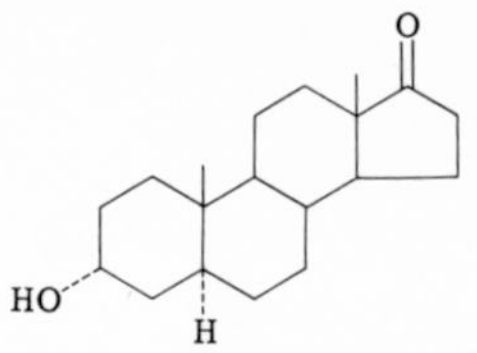

Androsterone

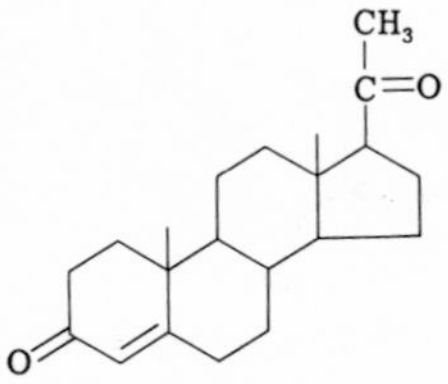

Progesterone

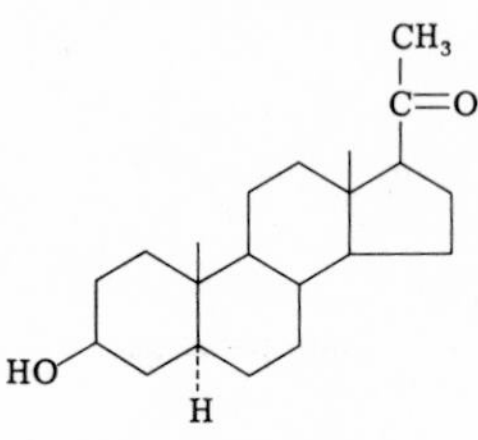

3β-Hydroxy-5α-pregnan-20-one

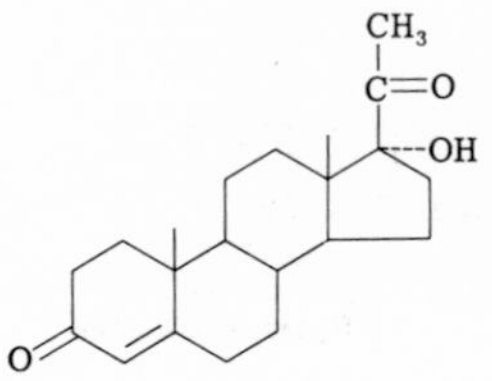

17α-Hydroxy-progesterone

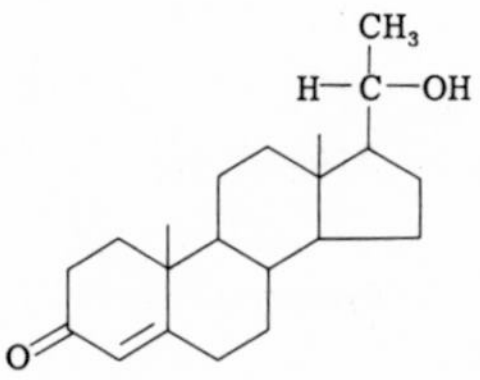

20α-Hydroxy-pregn-4-en-3-one

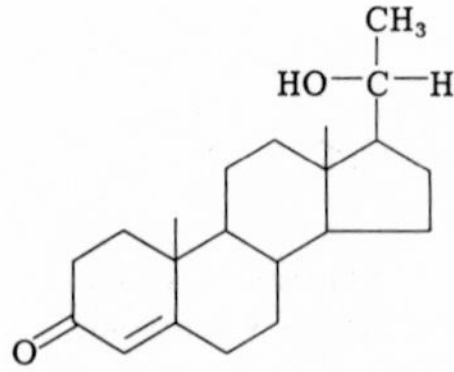

20β-Hydroxy-pregn-4-en-3-one

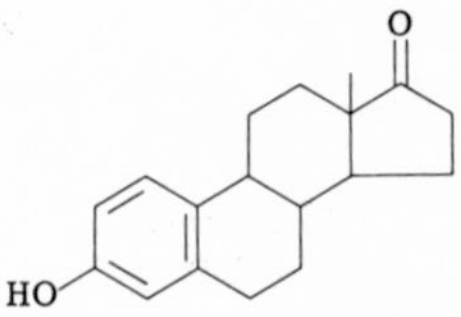

Estrone

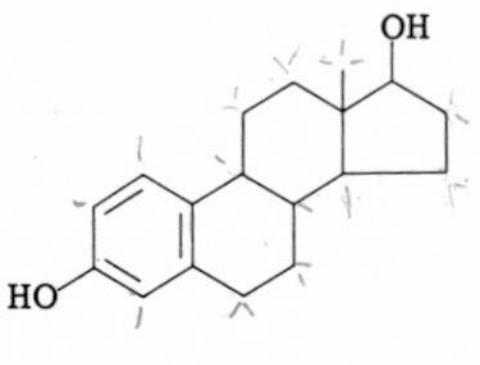

Estradiol-17β

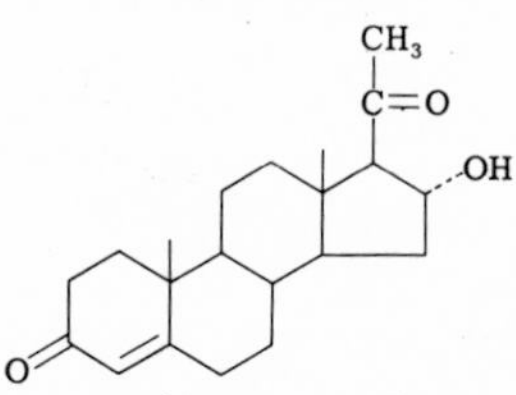

16α-Hydroxy-progesterone

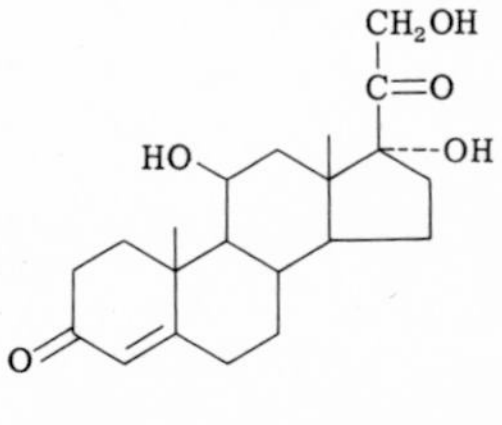

Cortisol

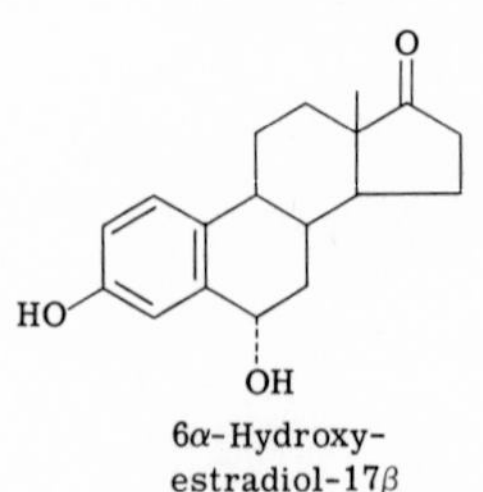

6α-Hydroxy-estradiol-17β

FIG. 2. Steroids in the ovary.

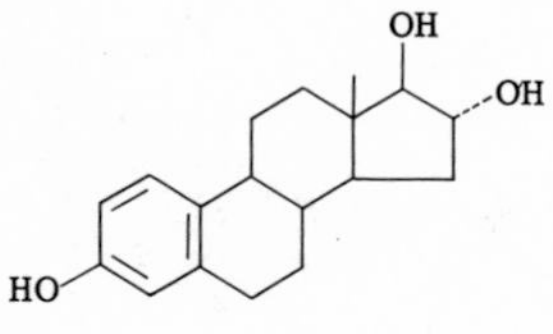

Estriol

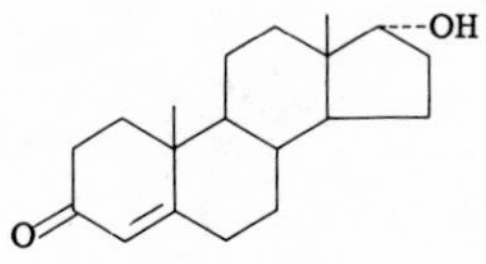

Epitestosterone

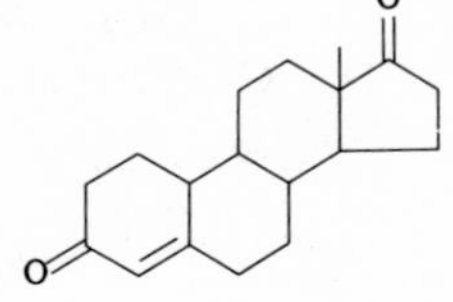

19-Norandrost-4-ene-3, 17-dione

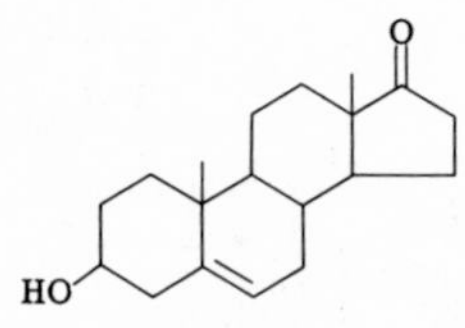

Dehydroepi-androsterone

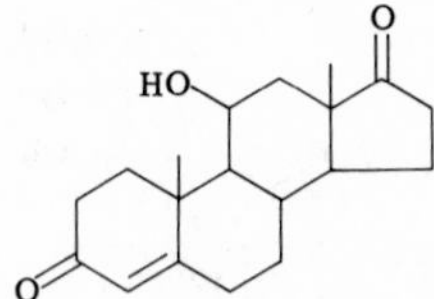

11β-Hydroxyandrost-4-ene-3, 17-dione

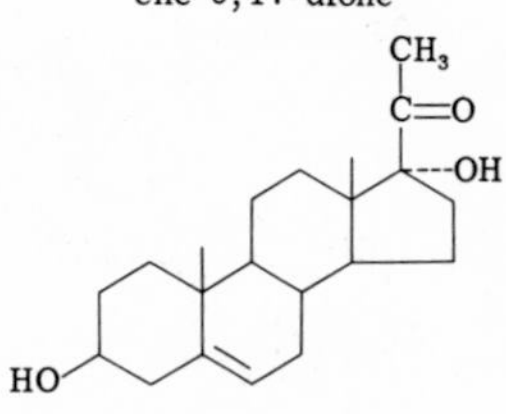

17α-Hydroxy-pregnenolone

FIG. 2. Continued.

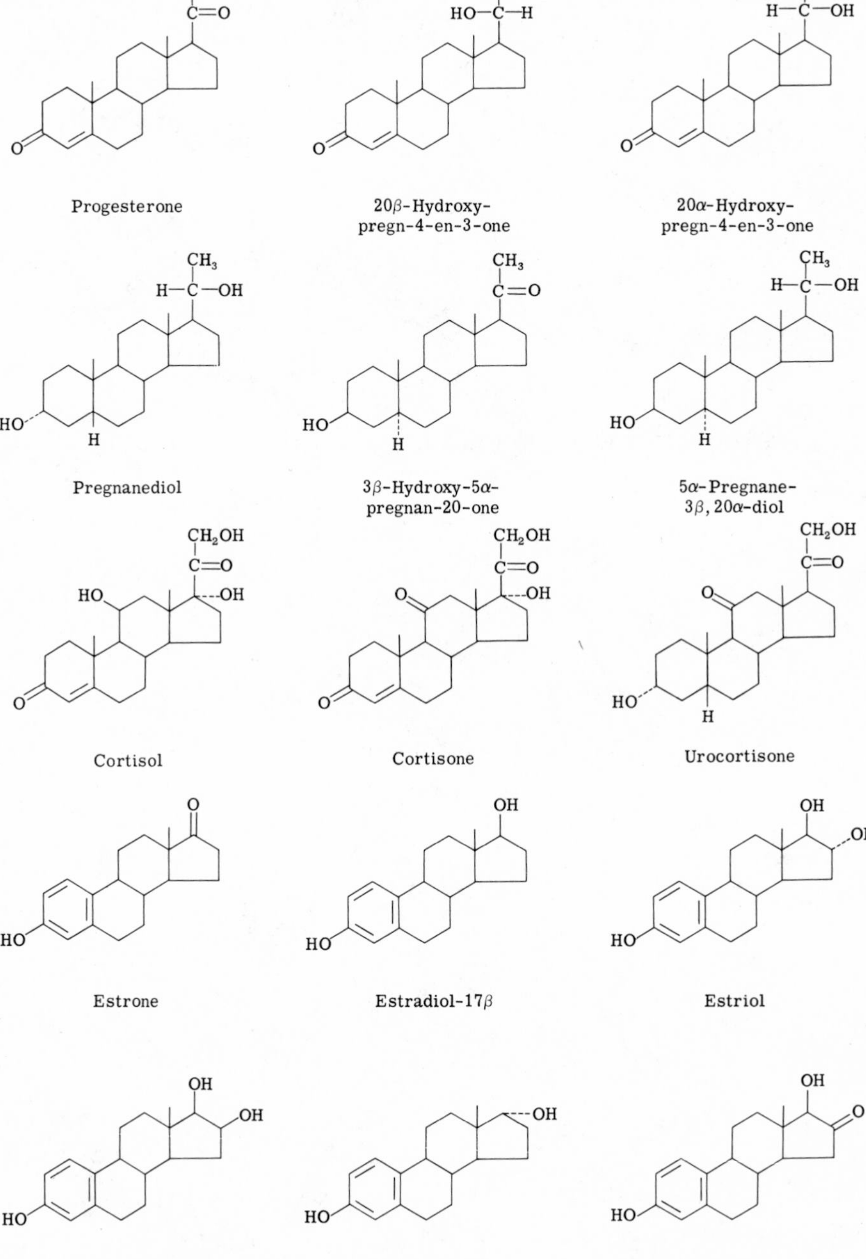

FIG. 3. Steroids in the placenta.

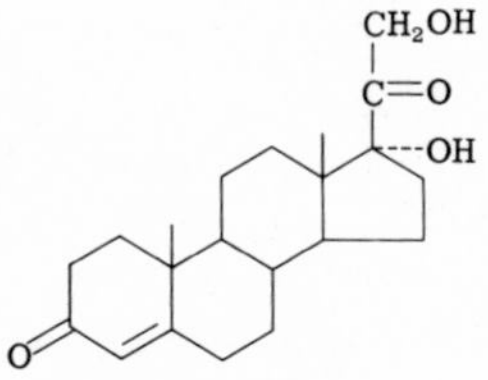

11-Deoxycortisol

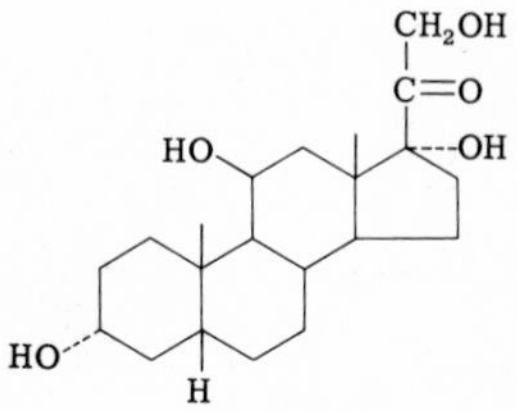

Urocortisol

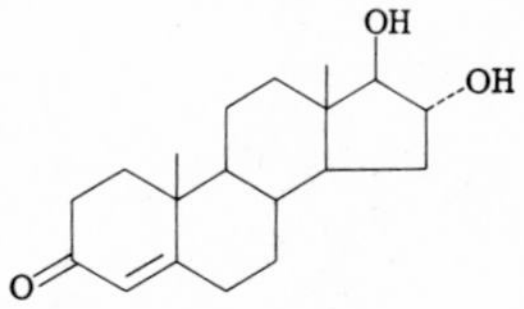

16α-Hydroxy-
testosterone

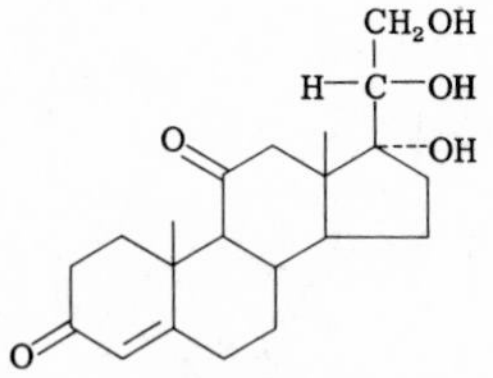

17α, 20α, 21-Tri-
hydroxypregn-4-en-3,11-dione

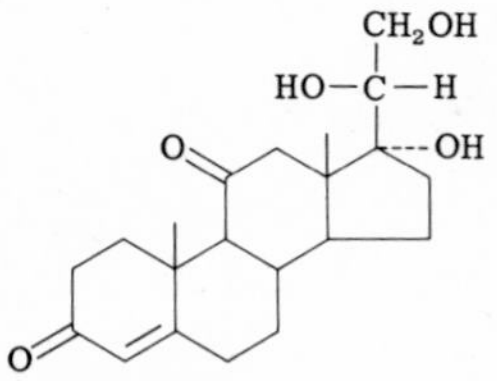

17α, 20β, 21-Tri-
hydroxypregn-4-en-3,11-dione

FIG. 3. Continued.

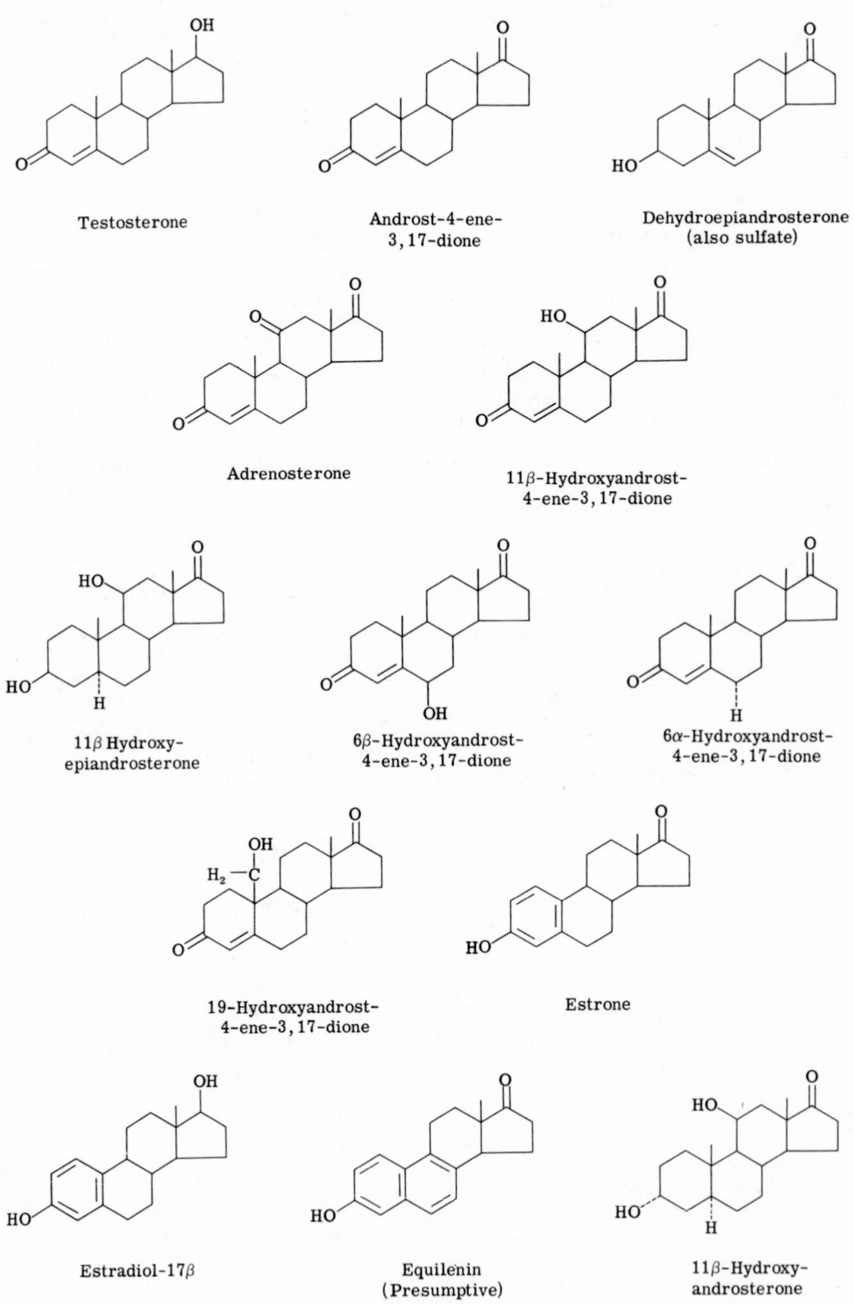

FIG. 4. C_{18} and C_{19} Steroids in the adrenal.

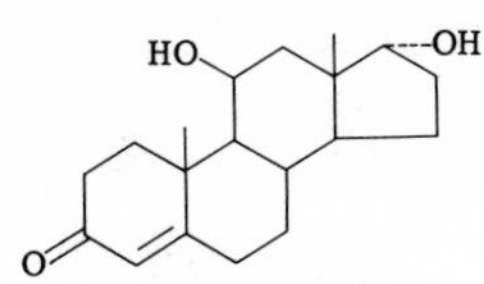

11β-Hydroxyepi-
testosterone

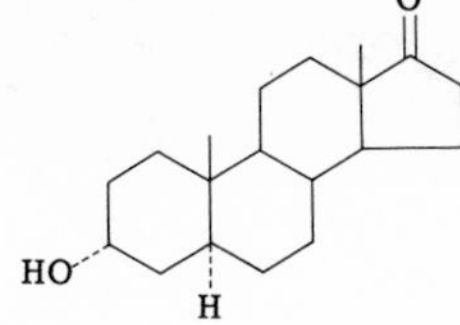

Androsterone

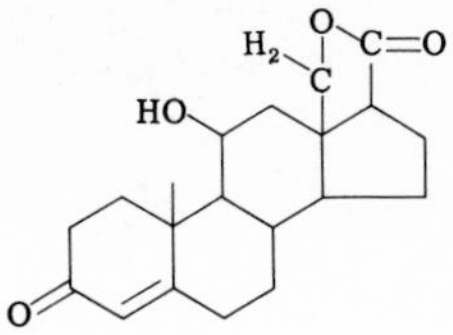

3-Keto-11β, 118-dihydroxy-Δ^4-etienic acid lactone (20→18)

FIG. 4. Continued.

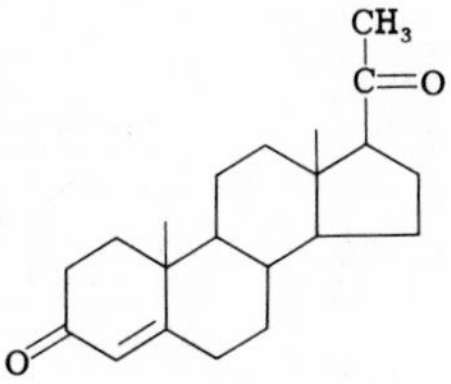

Progesterone

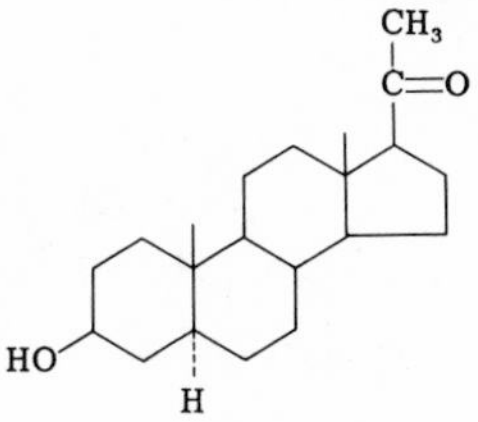

3β-Hydroxy-5α-pregnan-20-one

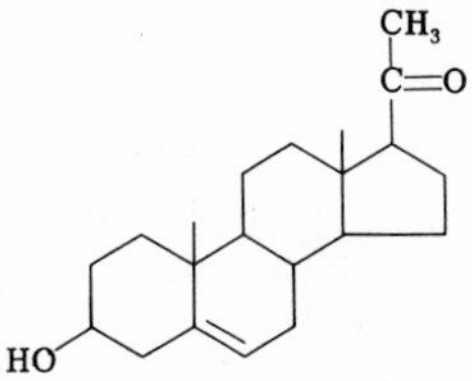

Pregnenolone

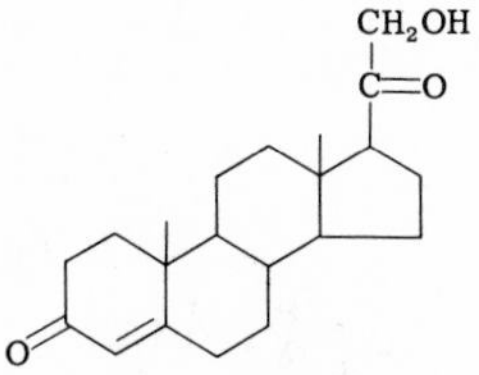

Deoxycorticosterone

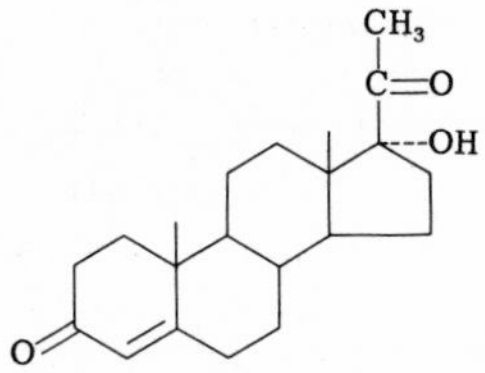

17α-Hydroxy-progesterone

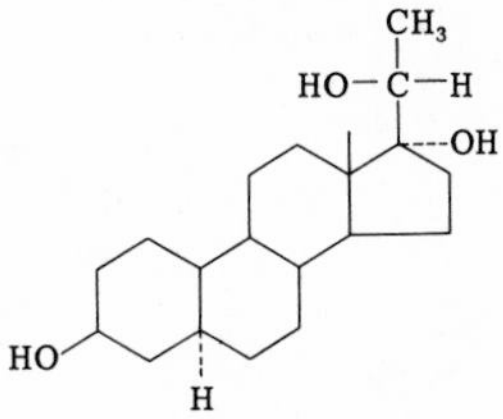

5α-Pregnane-3β, 17α, 20β-triol

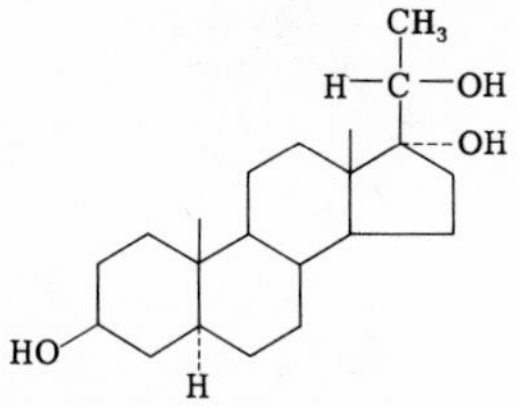

5α-Pregnane-3β, 17α, 20α-triol

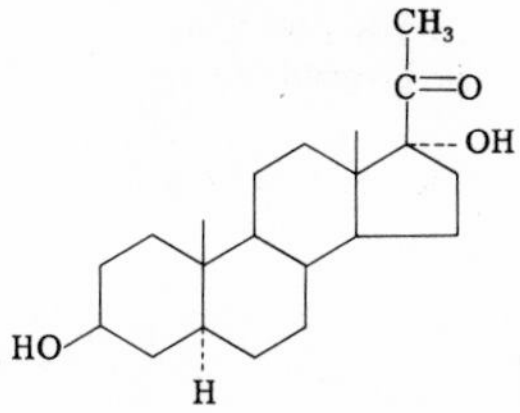

3β, 17α-Dihydroxy-5α-pregnan-20-one

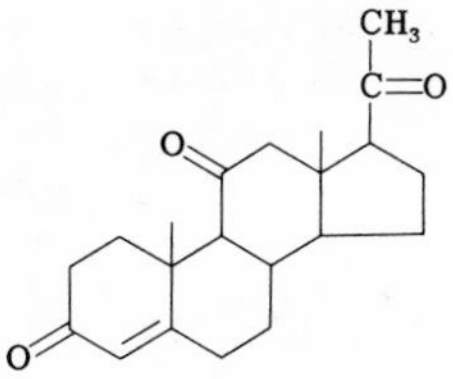

11-Ketoprogesterone

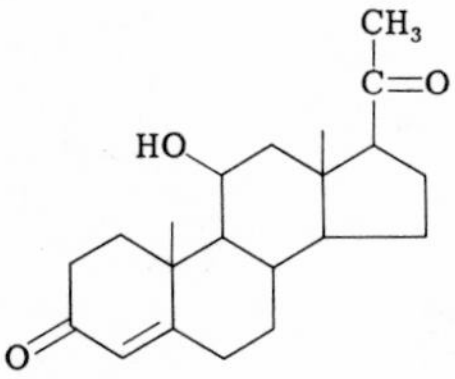

11β-Hydroxy-progesterone

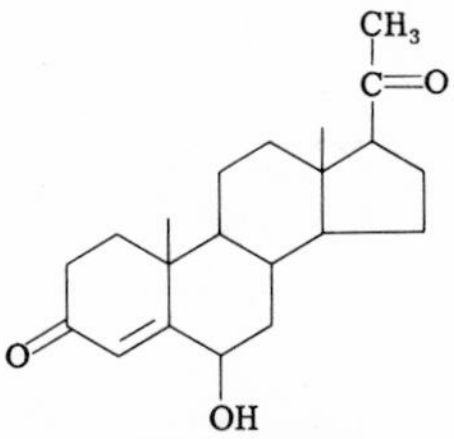

6β-Hydroxy-progesterone

FIG. 5. $C_{21}O_2$ and $C_{21}O_3$ Steroids in the adrenal.

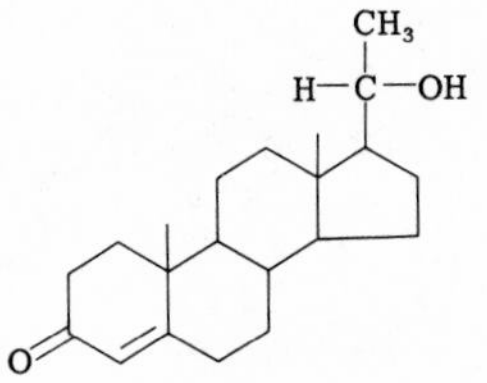

20α-Hydroxypregn-4-en-3-one

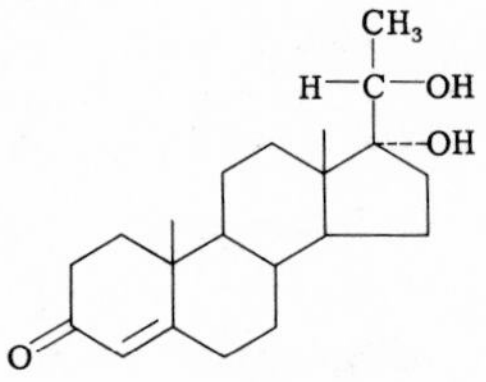

17α,20α-Dihydroxypregn-4-en-3-one

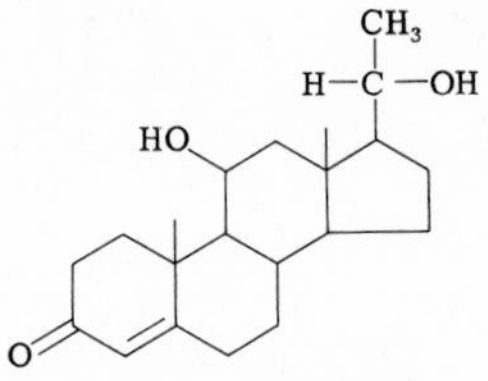

11β, 20α-Dihydroxypregn-4-en-3-one

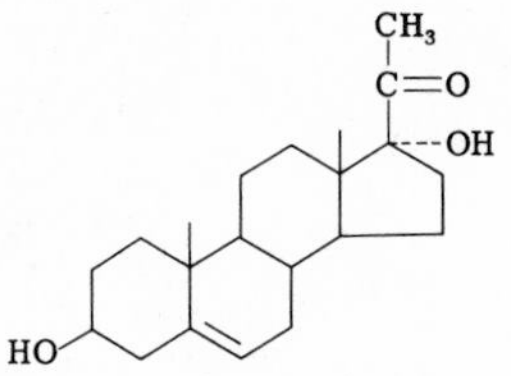

17α-Hydroxypregnenolone

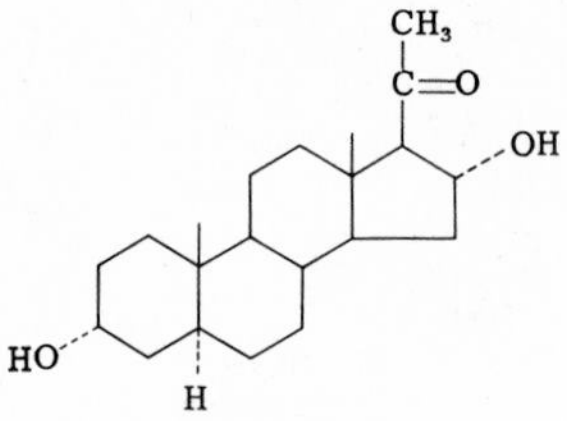

3α, 16α-Dihydroxy-5α-pregnan-20-one

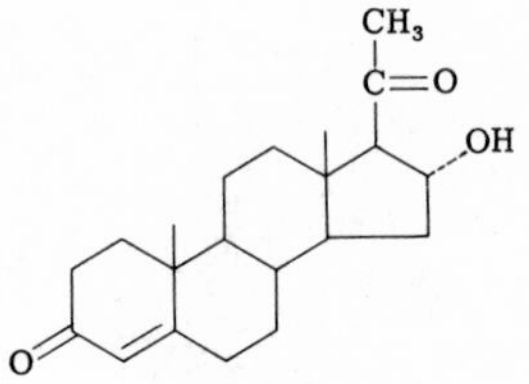

16α-Hydroxyprogesterone

FIG. 5. Continued.

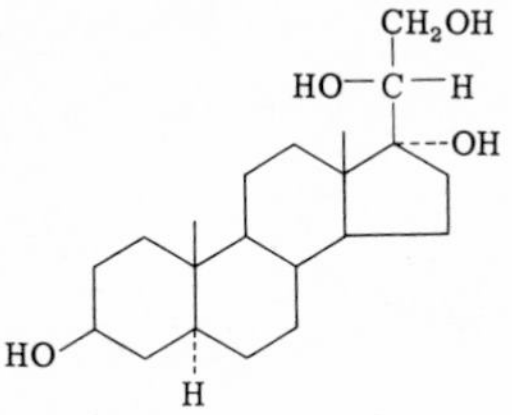

5α-Pregnane-
3β-17α, 20β-21-tetrol

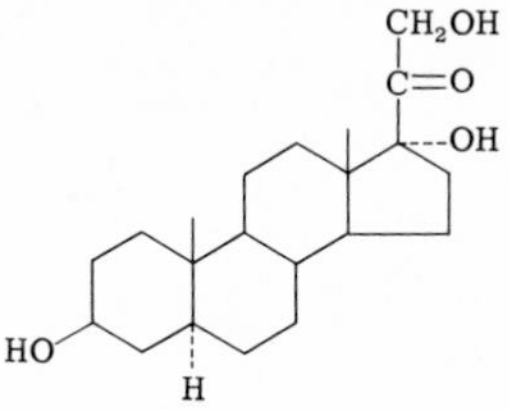

3β, 17α, 21-Trihydroxy-
5α-pregnan-20-one

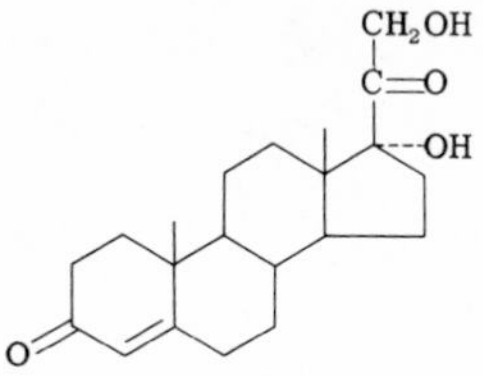

11-Deoxycortisol

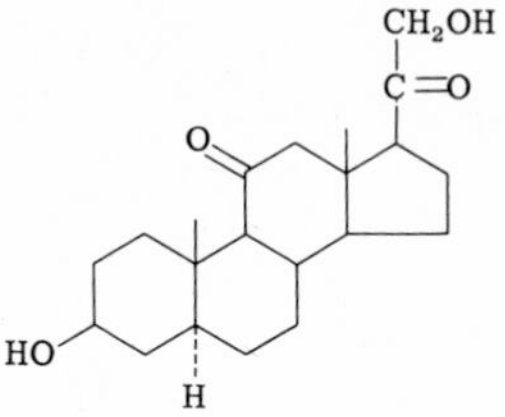

3β, 21-Dihydroxy-5α-
pregnane-11, 20-dione

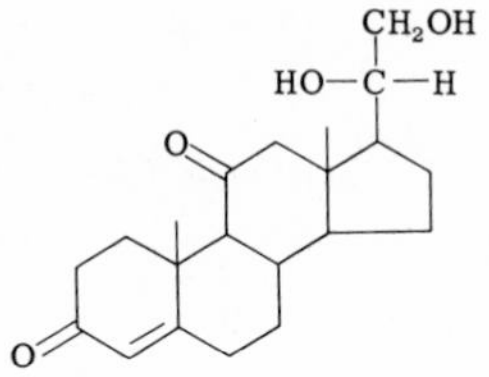

20β, 21-Dihydroxy-
pregn-4-ene-3, 11-dione

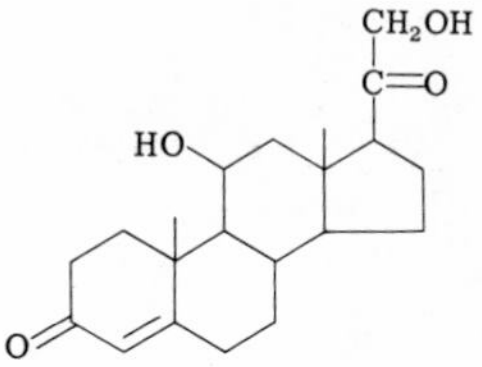

Corticosterone

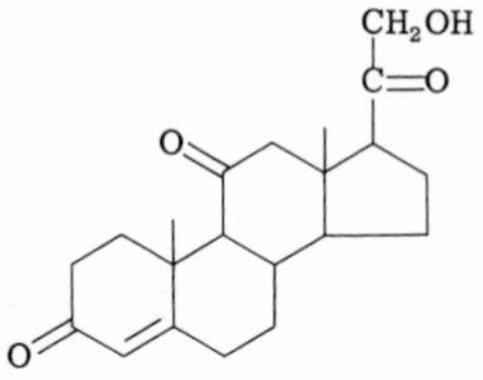

11-Dehydro-
corticosterone

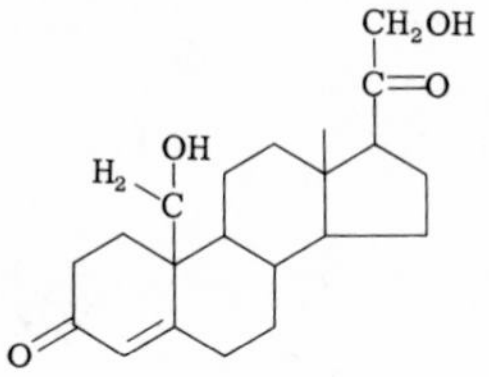

19, 21-Dihydroxy-
pregn-4-ene-3, 20-dione

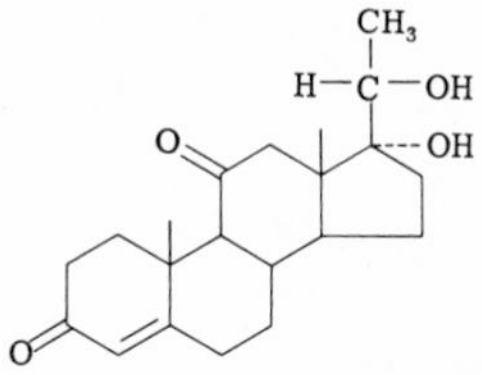

17α, 20α-Dihydroxy-
pregn-4-en-3, 11-dione

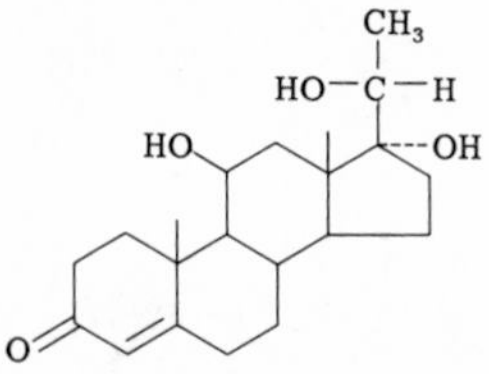

11β, 17α, 20β-Trihydroxy-
pregn-4-en-3-one

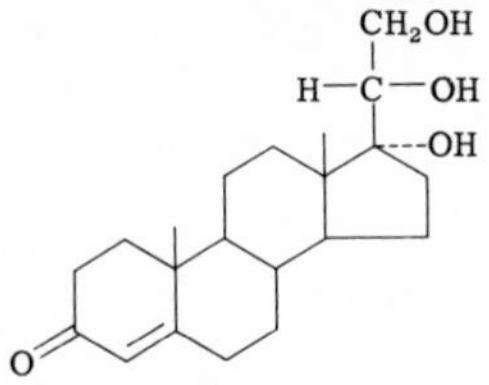

17α, 20α, 21-Trihydroxy-
pregn-4-en-3-one

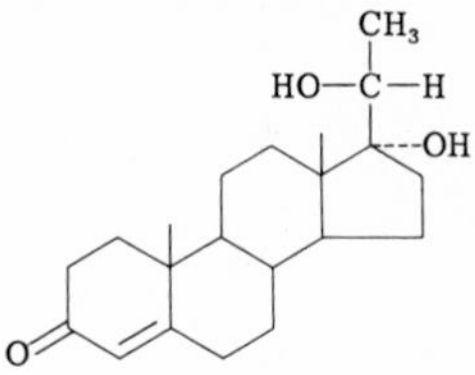

17α, 20β-Dihydroxy-
pregn-4-en-3, 11-dione

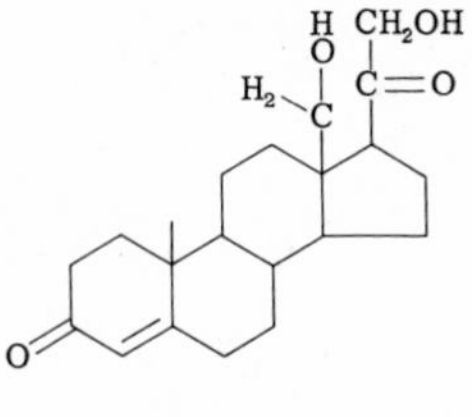

18, 21-Dihydroxy-
progesterone

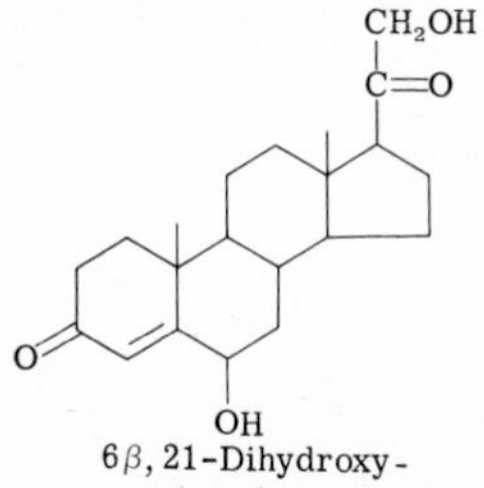

6β, 21-Dihydroxy-
progesterone

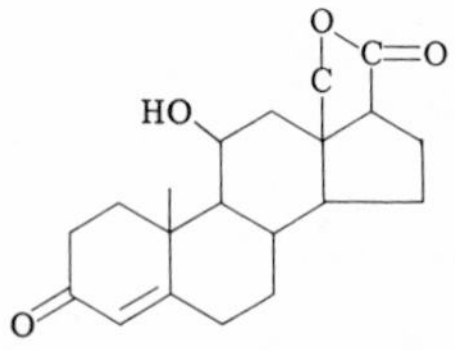

11β, 18-Dihydroxy-3-keto-
4-etienic acid lactone

FIG. 6. $C_{21}O_4$ Steroids in the adrenal.

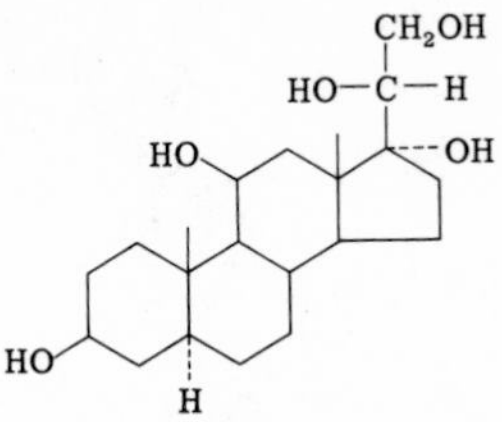

5α-Pregnane-3β, 11β, 17α, 20β, 21-pentol

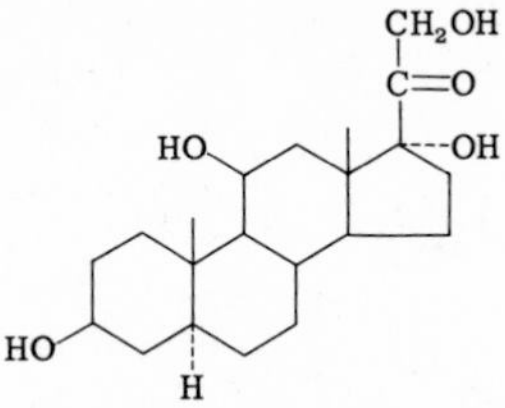

3β, 11β, 17α, 21-Tetrahydroxy-5α-pregnan-20-one

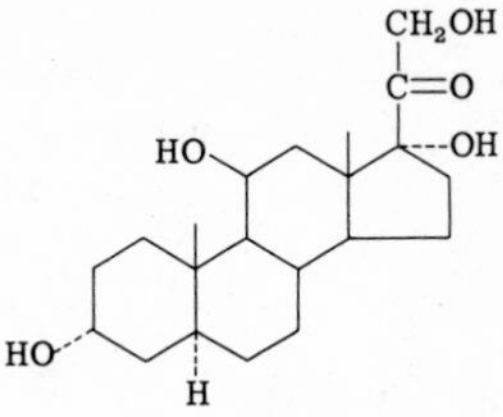

3α, 11β, 17α, 21-Tetrahydroxy-5α-pregnan-20-one

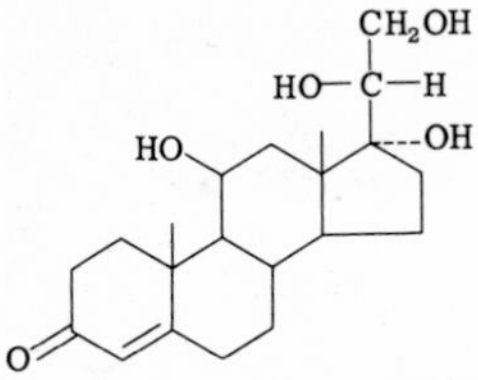

11β, 17α, 20β, 21-Tetrahydroxypregn-4-en-3-one

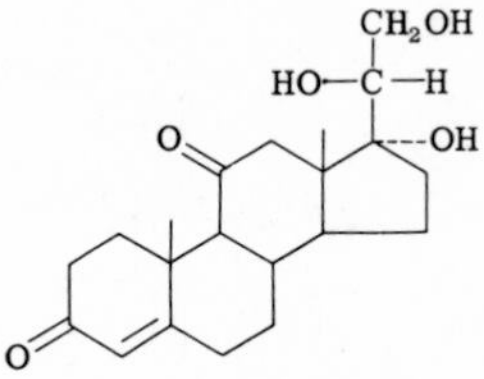

17α, 20β, 21-Trihydroxypregn-4-ene-3, 11-dione

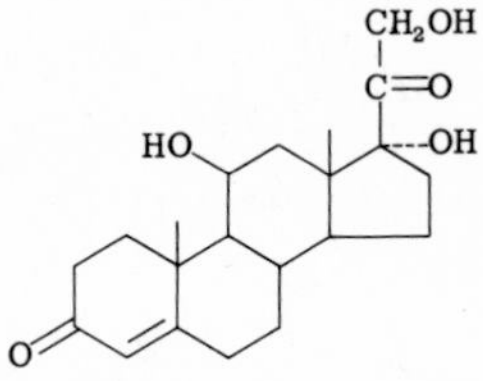

Cortisol

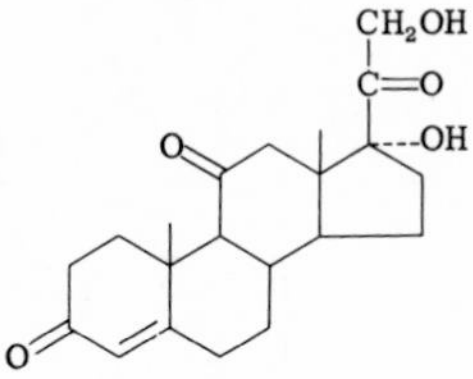

Cortisone

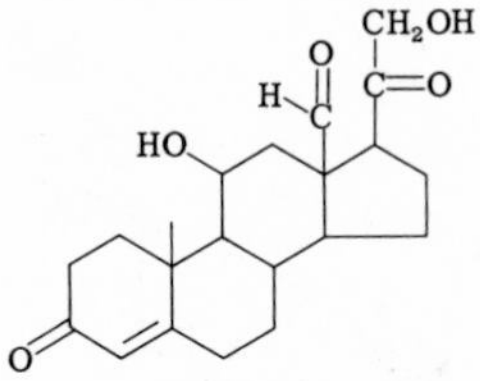

Aldosterone

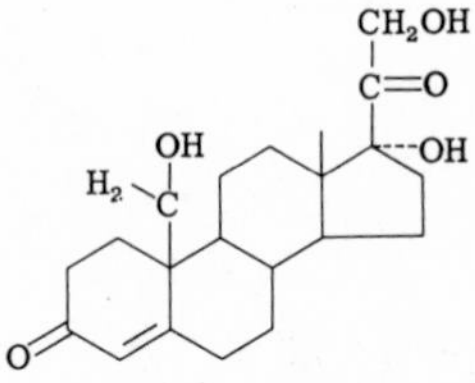

19,17α,21-Trihydroxypregn-4-ene-3,20-dione

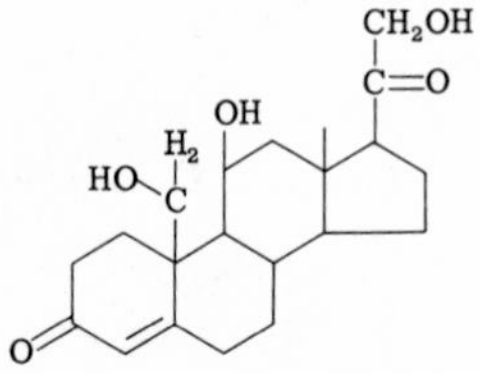

11β, 19, 21-Trihydroxypregn-4-ene-3, 20-dione

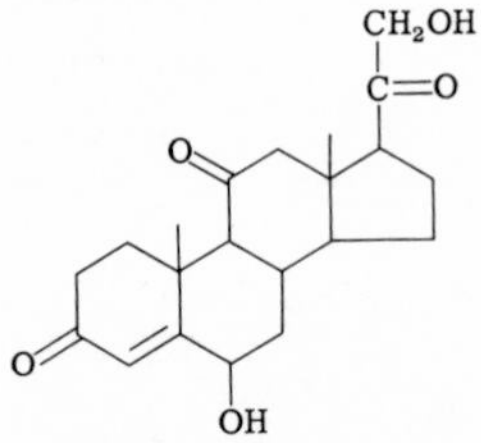

6β, 21-Dihydroxypregn-4-ene-3, 11, 20-trione

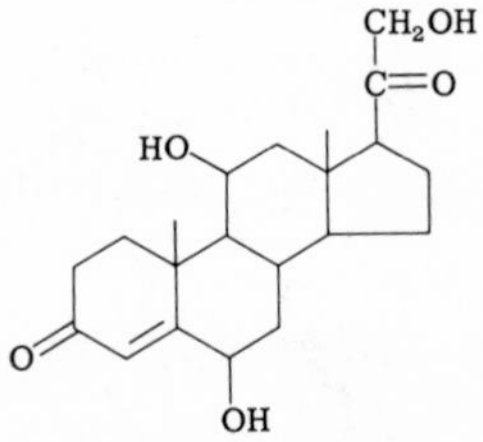

6β, 11β, 21-Trihydroxypregn-4-ene-3, 20-dione

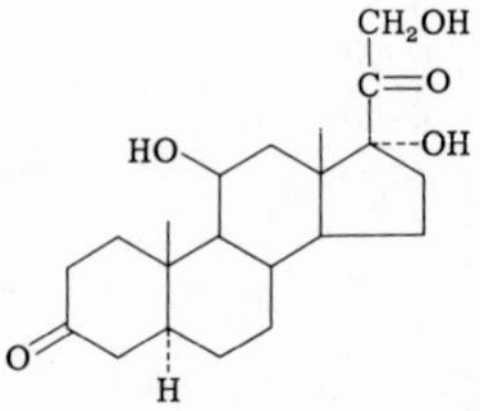

11β, 17α, 21-Trihydroxy-5α-pregnane-3, 20-dione

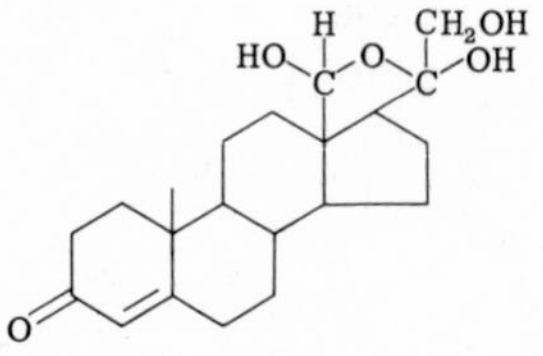

20, 20, 21-Trihydroxy-18-lactone-(18→20)-pregn-4-en-3-one

FIG. 7. $C_{21}O_5$ Steroids in the adrenal.

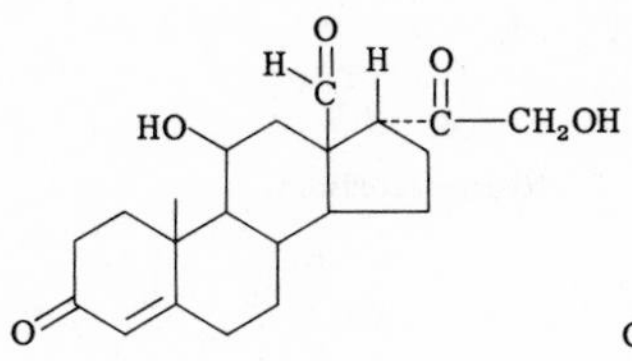

17-Isoaldosterone

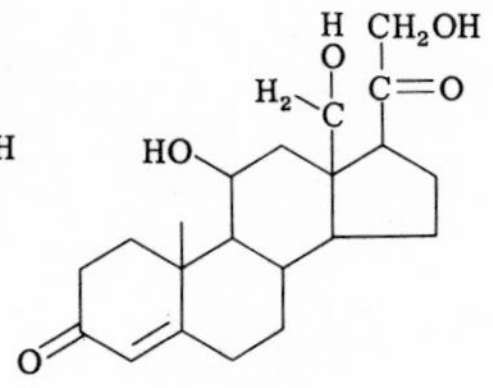

18-Hydroxy-
corticosterone

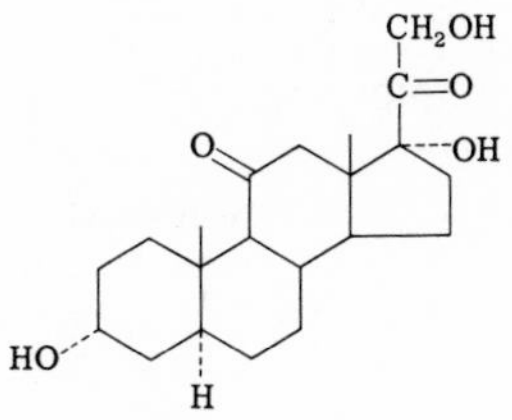

$3\alpha, 17\alpha, 21$-Trihydroxy-
5α-pregnane-11, 20-dione

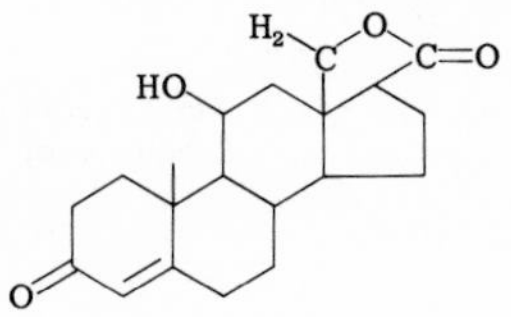

3-Keto-11β, 18-dihydroxy-
4-etienic acid lactone (20→18)

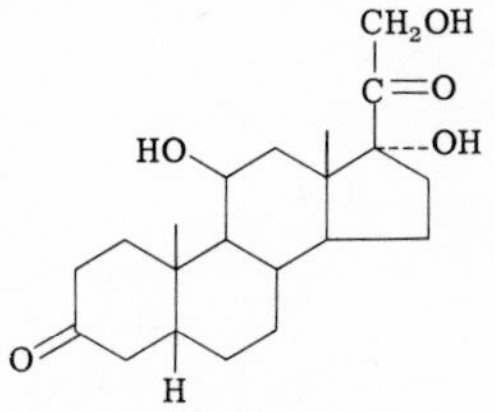

$11\beta, 17\alpha, 21$-Trihydroxy-
5β-pregnane-3, 20-dione

FIG. 7. Continued.

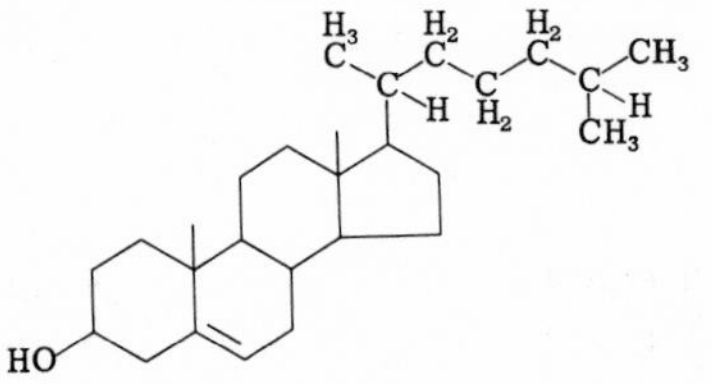

Cholesterol

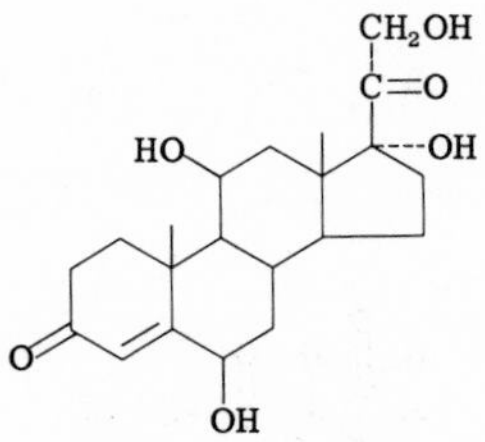

6β-Hydroxycortisol

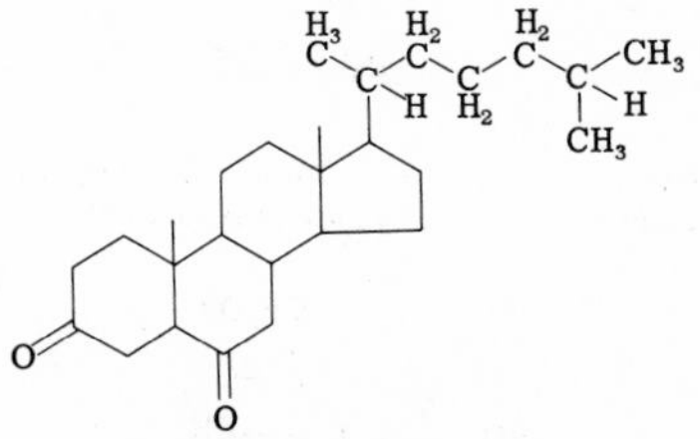

Cholestane-3, 6-dione

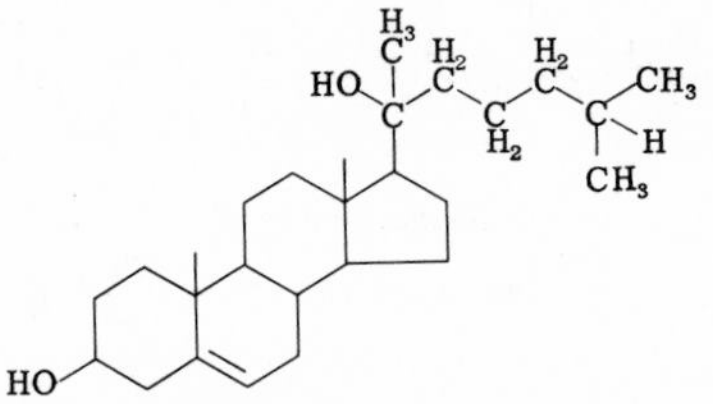

20α-Hydroxy-
cholesterol

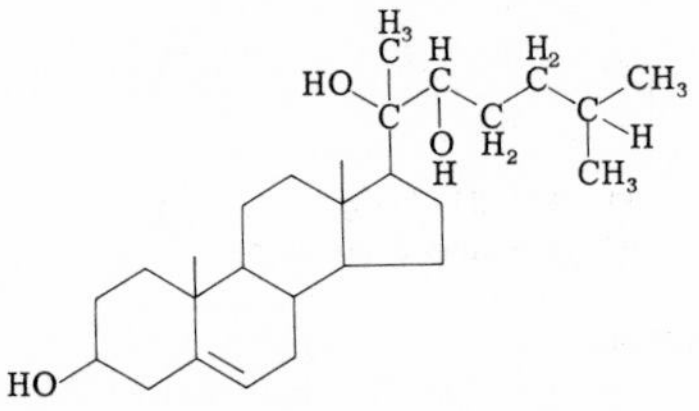

20α, 22ξ-Dihydroxy-
cholesterol

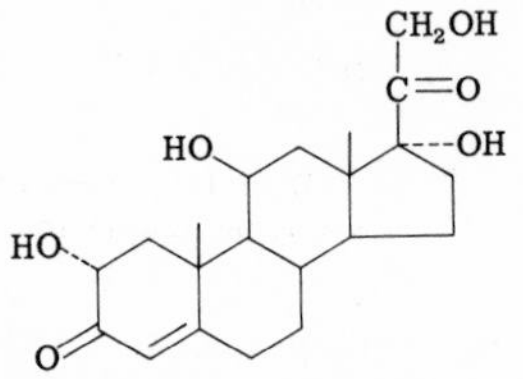

2α-Hydroxycortisol

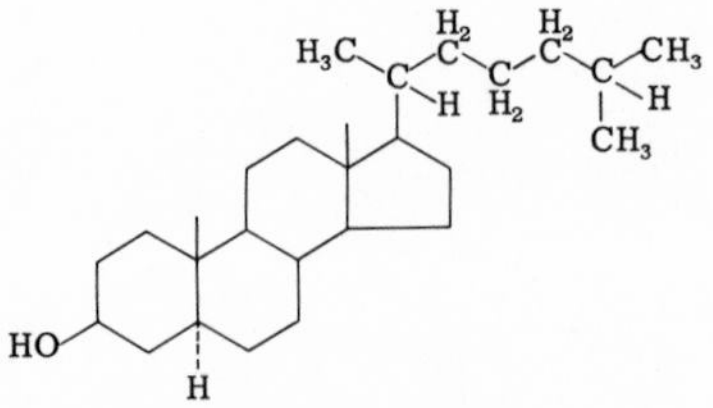

5α-Cholestan-3β-ol

FIG. 8. C_{27} Steroids in the adrenal.

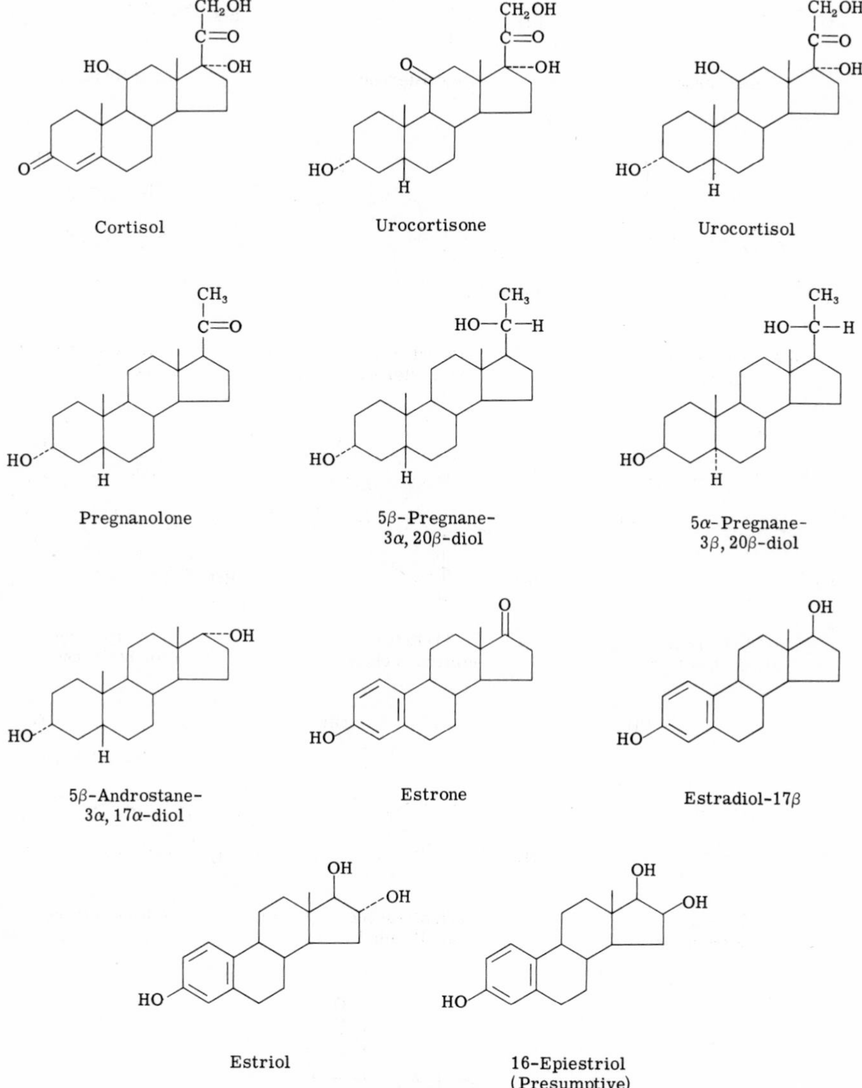

FIG. 9. Steroids in bile.

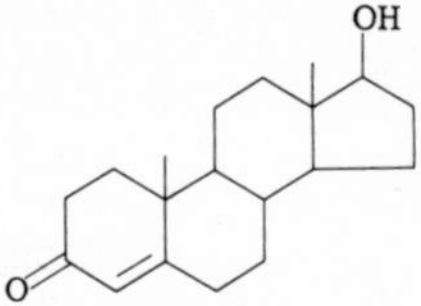

Testosterone

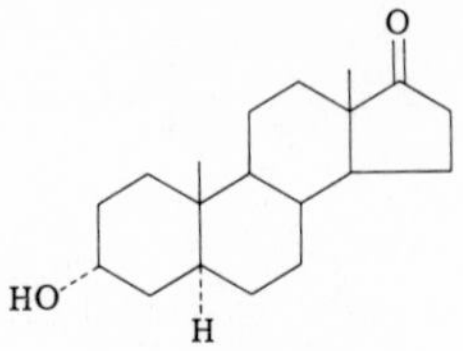

Androsterone

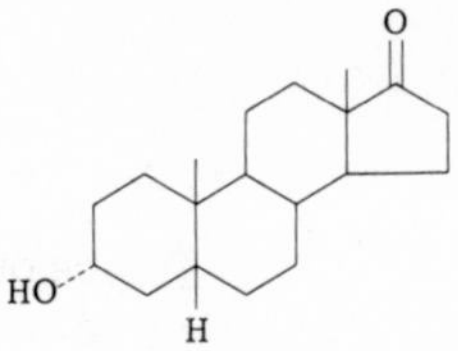

Etiocholanolone

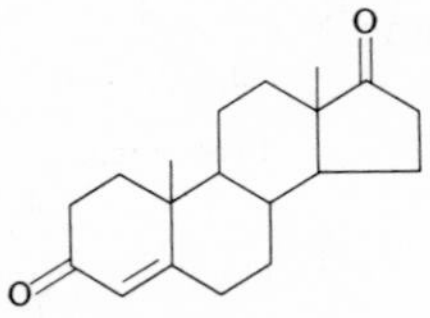

Androst-4-ene-
3, 17-dione

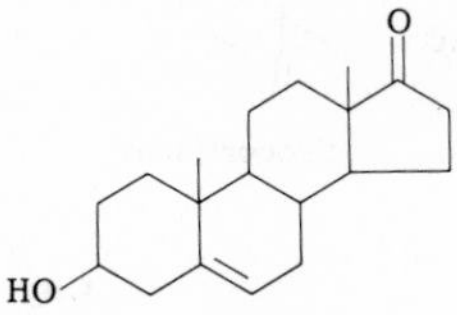

Dehydroepi-
androsterone

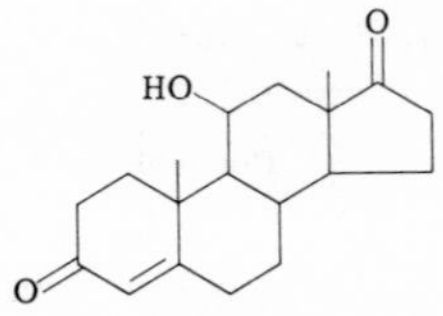

11β-Hydroxyandrost-
4-ene-3, 17-dione

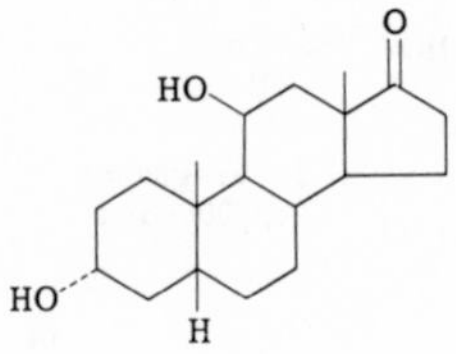

11β-Hydroxy-
etiocholanolone

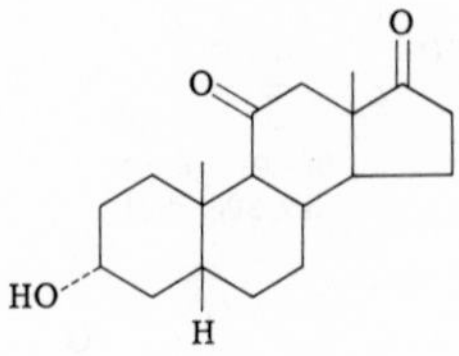

11-Keto-
etiocholanolone

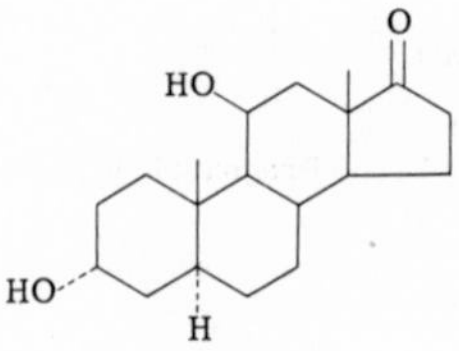

11β-Hydroxy-
androsterone

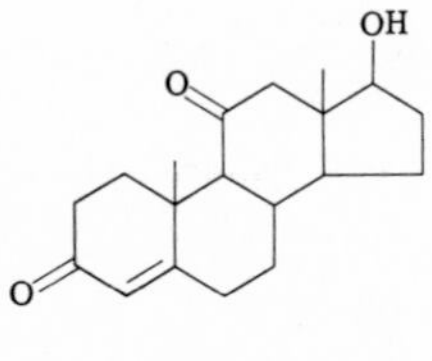

11-Keto-
testosterone

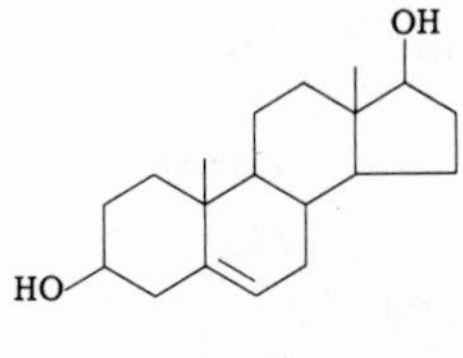

Androst-5-ene-
3β, 17β-diol

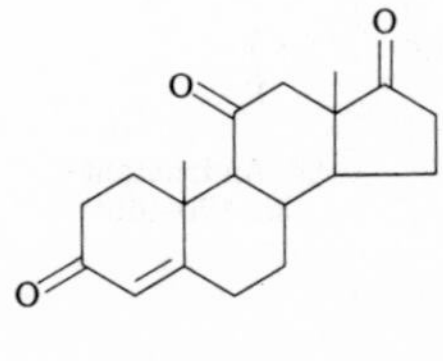

Adrenosterone

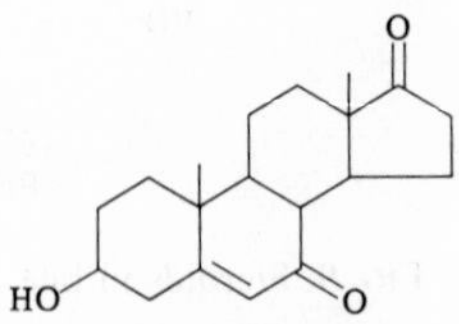

3β-Hydroxyandrost-
5-ene-7, 17-dione

FIG. 10. C_{19} Steroids in blood.

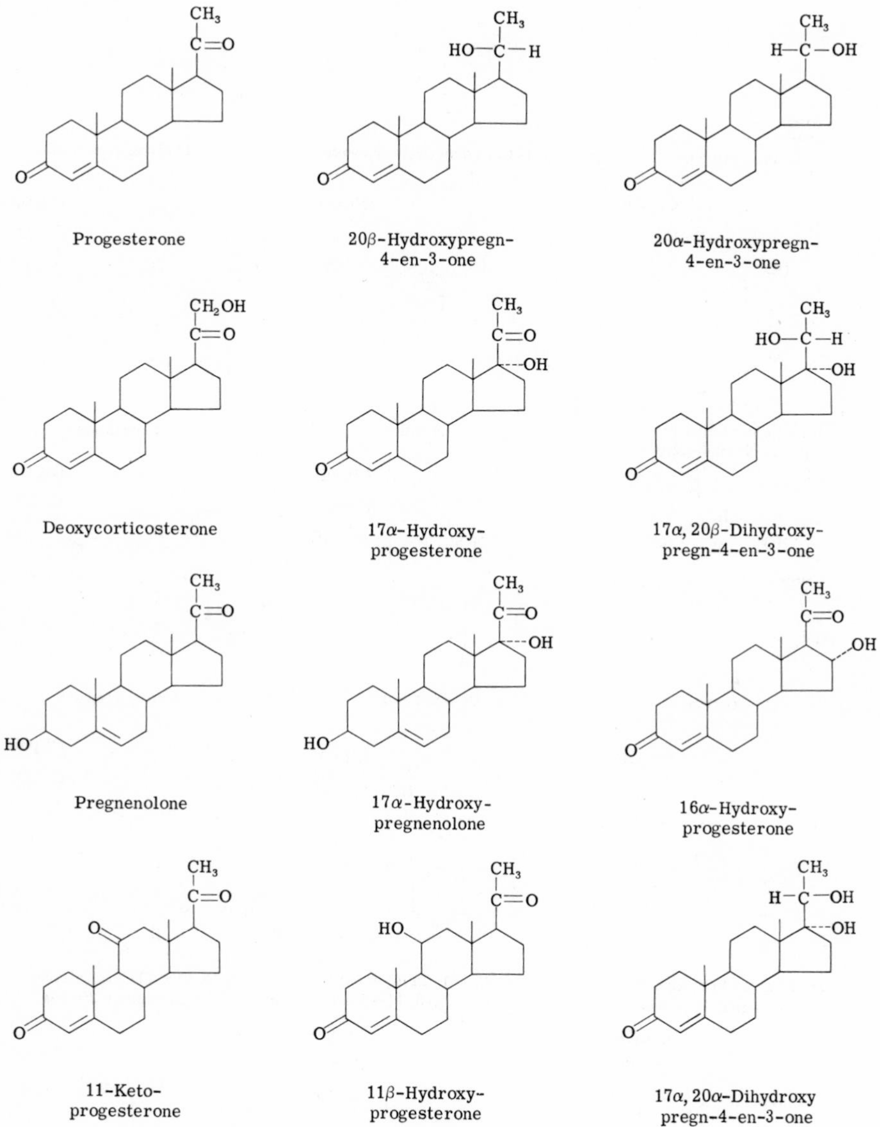

FIG. 11. $C_{21}O_2$ and $C_{21}O_3$ Steroids in blood.

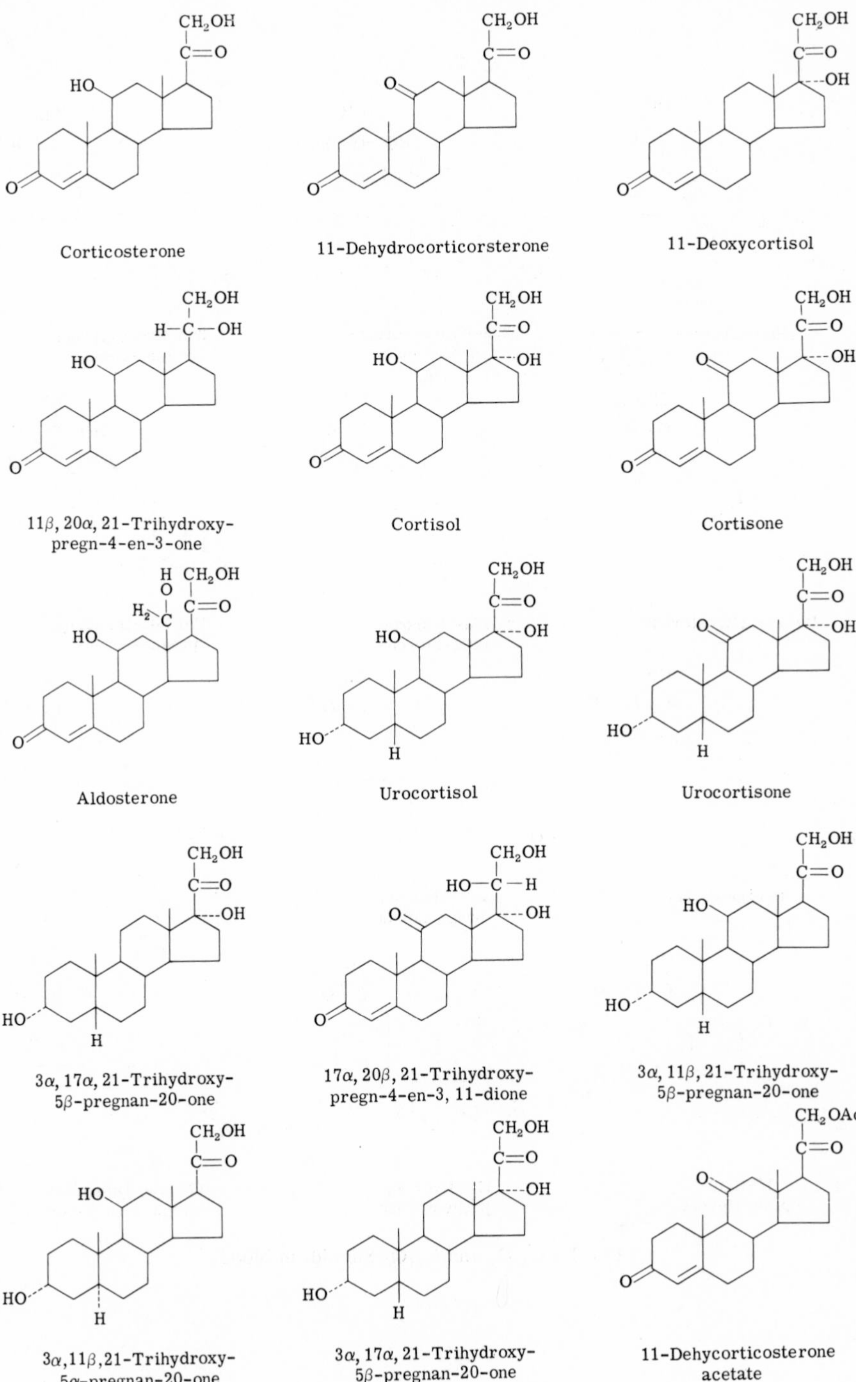

FIG. 12. $C_{21}O_4$ and $C_{21}O_5$ Steroids in blood.

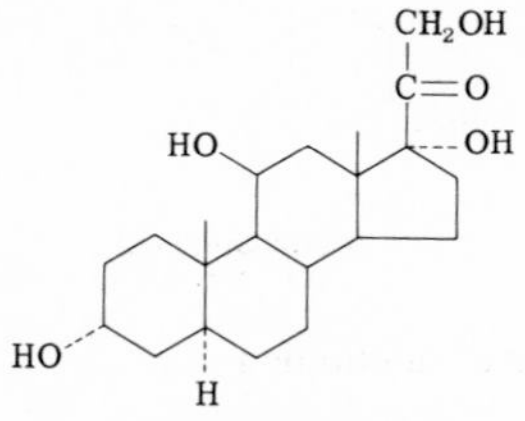

$3\alpha, 11\beta, 17\alpha$, 21-Tetra-hydroxy-$5\alpha$-pregnan-20-one

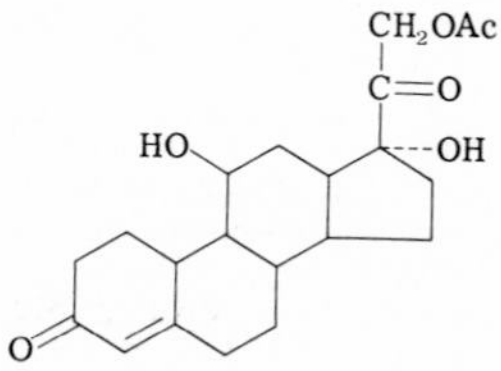

Cortisol acetate

FIG. 12. Continued.

ARTIFACT

ORIGINAL STEROID

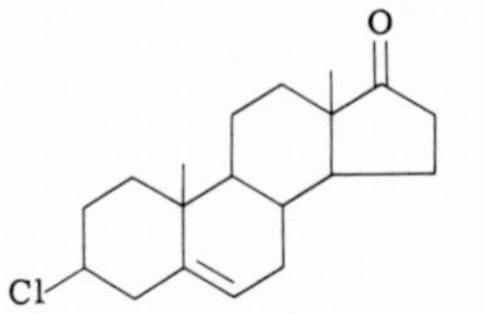

3β-Chloroandrost-5-en-17-one

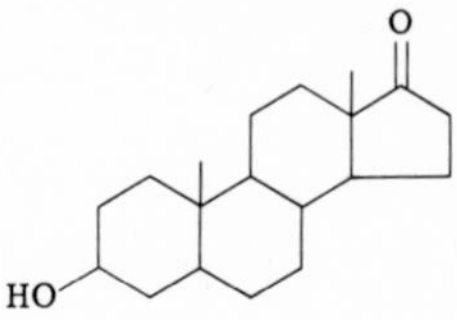

Dehydroepiandrosterone

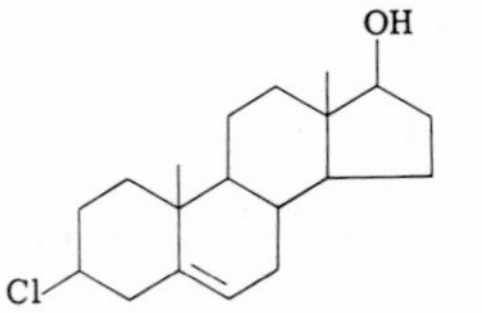

3β-Chloroandrost-5-en-17β-ol

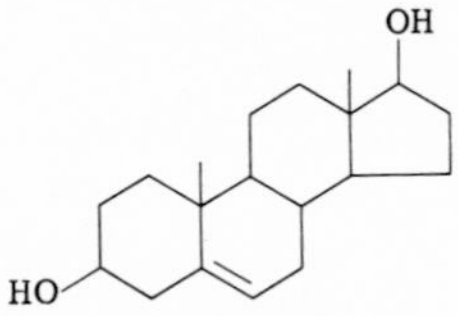

Androst-5-ene-3β, 17β-diol

FIG. 13. Steroid artifacts in urine: artifacts of substitution.

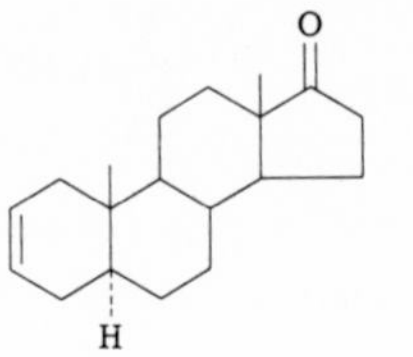

5α-Androst-2 (or 3)-en-17-one

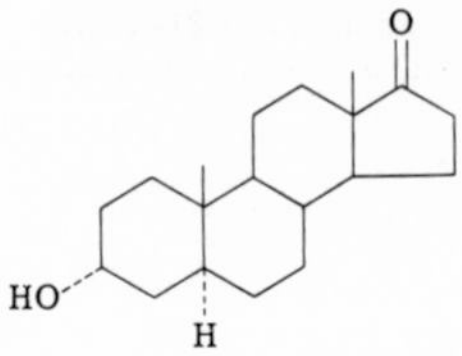

Androsterone

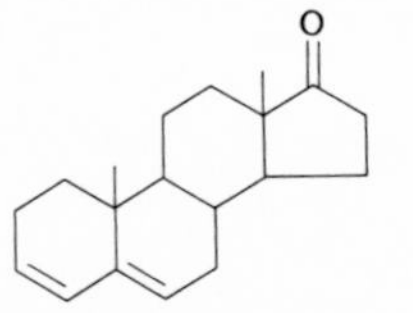

Androst-3, 5-diene-17-one

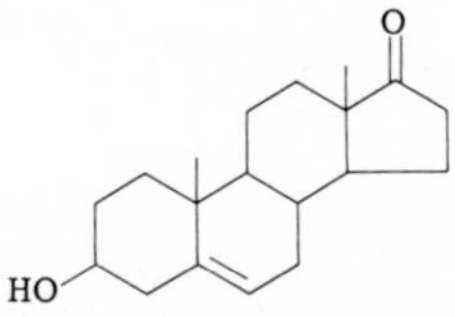

Dehydroepi-androsterone

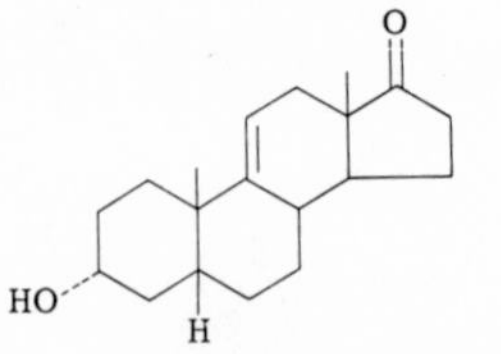

3α-Hydroxy-5β-androst-9(11)-en-17-one

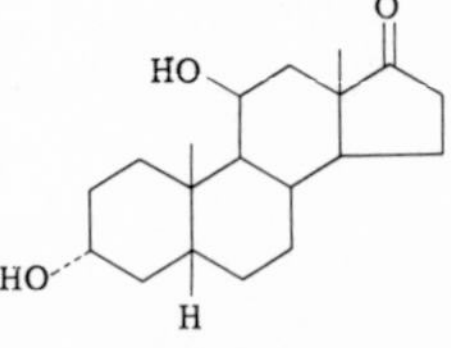

11β-Hydroxy-etiocholanolone

FIG. 14. Steroid artifacts in urine: artifacts of dehydration.

ARTIFACT	ORIGINAL STEROID
3α-Hydroxy-5α-androst-9(11)-en-17-one	11β-Hydroxy-androsterone
3β-Hydroxy-5α-androst-9(11)-en-17-one	3β, 11β-Dihydroxy-5α-androstan-17-one
Pregnanolone	Pregnanetriol
3α, 17α-Dihydroxy-5β-pregnane-11, 20-dione	Cortolone

FIG. 14. Continued.

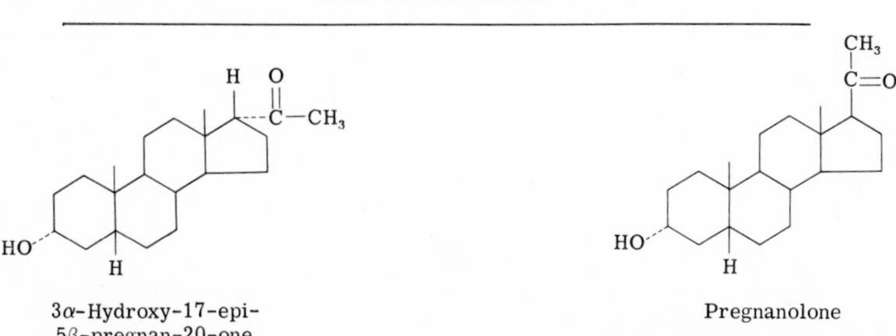

3α-Hydroxy-17-epi-5β-pregnan-20-one	Pregnanolone

FIG. 15. Steroid artifacts in urine: artifacts of rearrangement.

ARTIFACT	ORIGINAL STEROID
3α-Acetoxy-5α-androst-9(11)-en-17-one	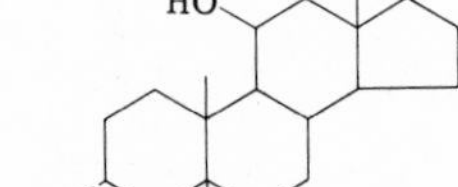 11β-Hydroxyandrosterone
Etiocholanolone acetate	Etiocholanolone
Androsterone acetate	Androsterone

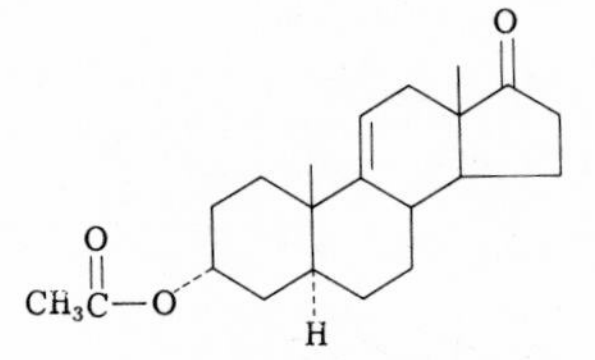

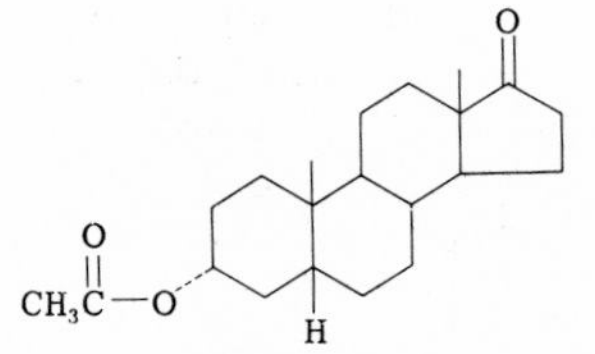

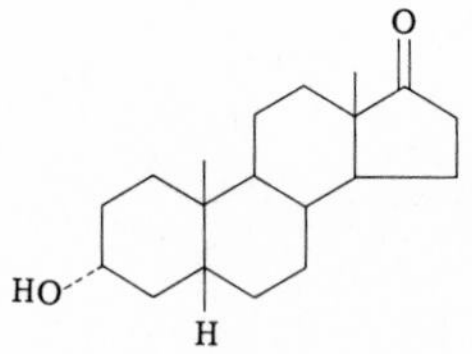

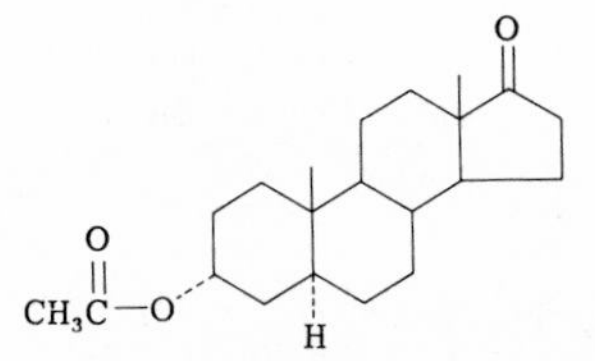

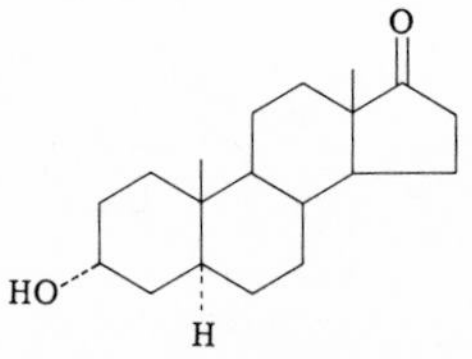

FIG. 16. Steroid artifacts in urine: artifacts of acetylation.

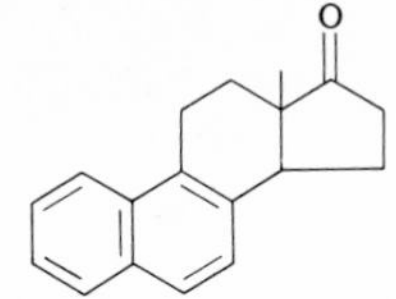

3-Desoxyequilenin

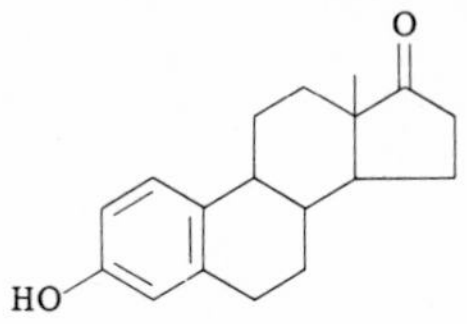

Estrone

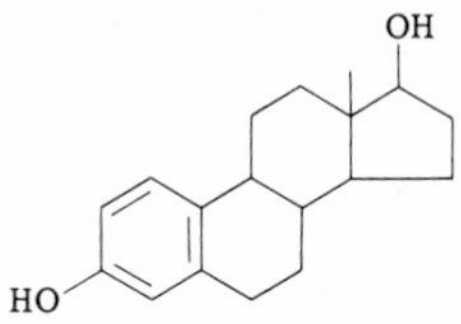

Estradiol-17β

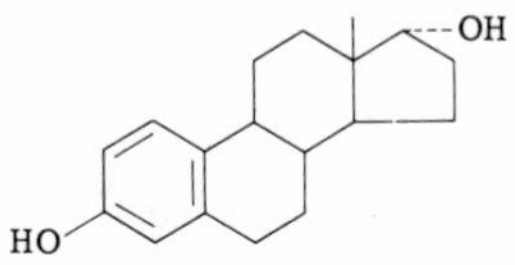

Estradiol-17α

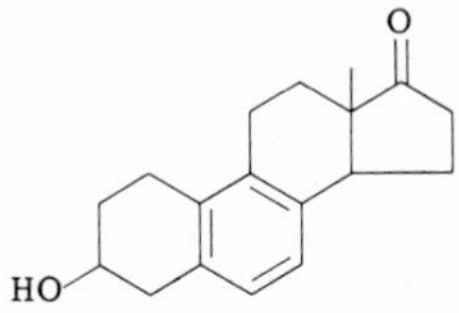

3β-Hydroxyestr-
5, 7, 9-trien-17-one

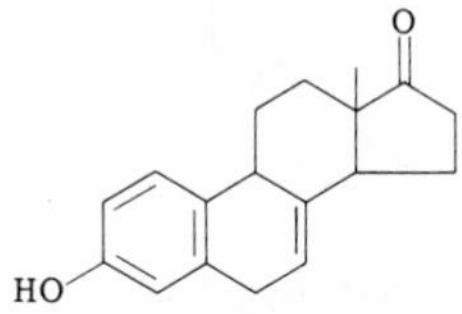

Equilin

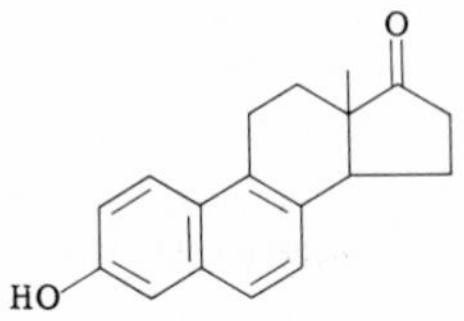

Equilenin

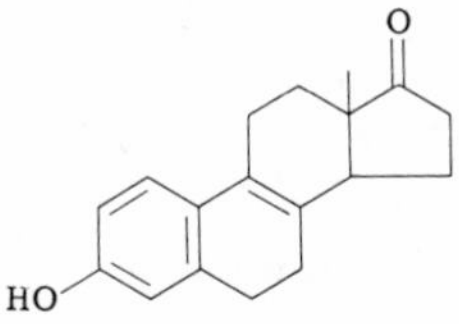

Hippulin

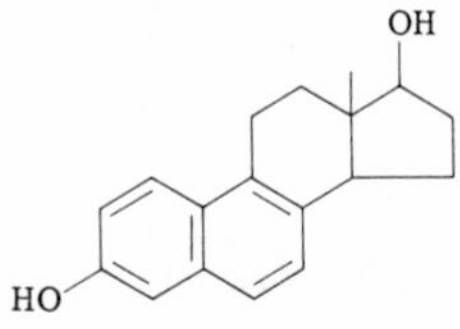

Dihydroequilenin

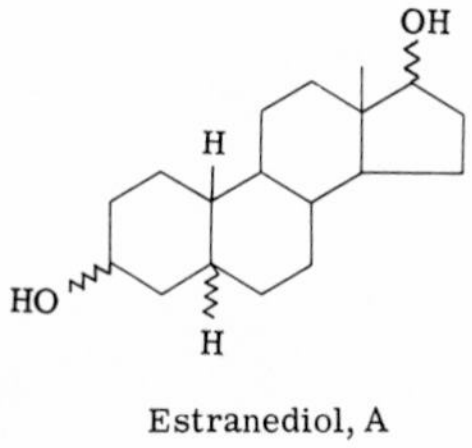

Estranediol, A

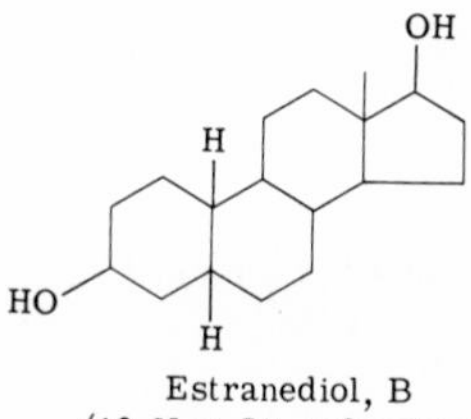

Estranediol, B
(19-Nor-5β-androstane-
3β,17β-diol)

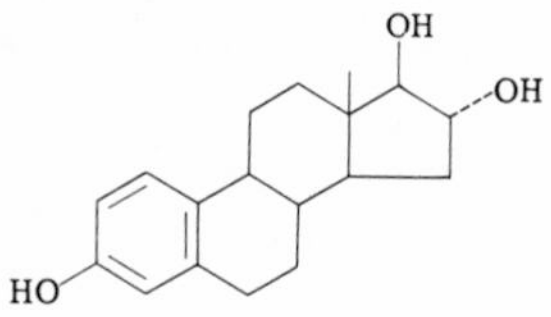

Estriol

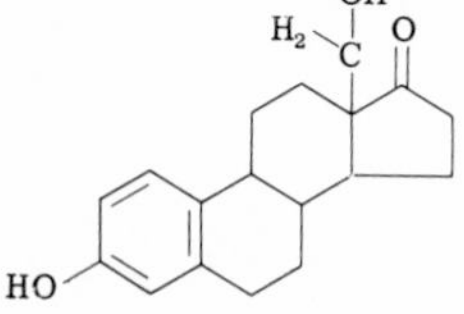

18-Hydroxyestrone

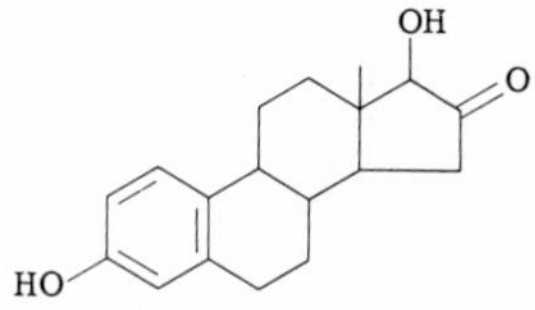

16-Ketoestra-
diol-17β

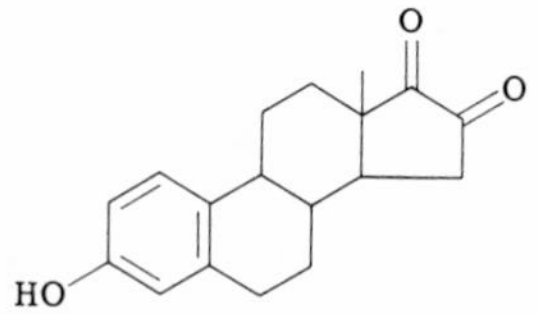

16-Ketoestrone

FIG. 17. C_{18} Steroids in urine.

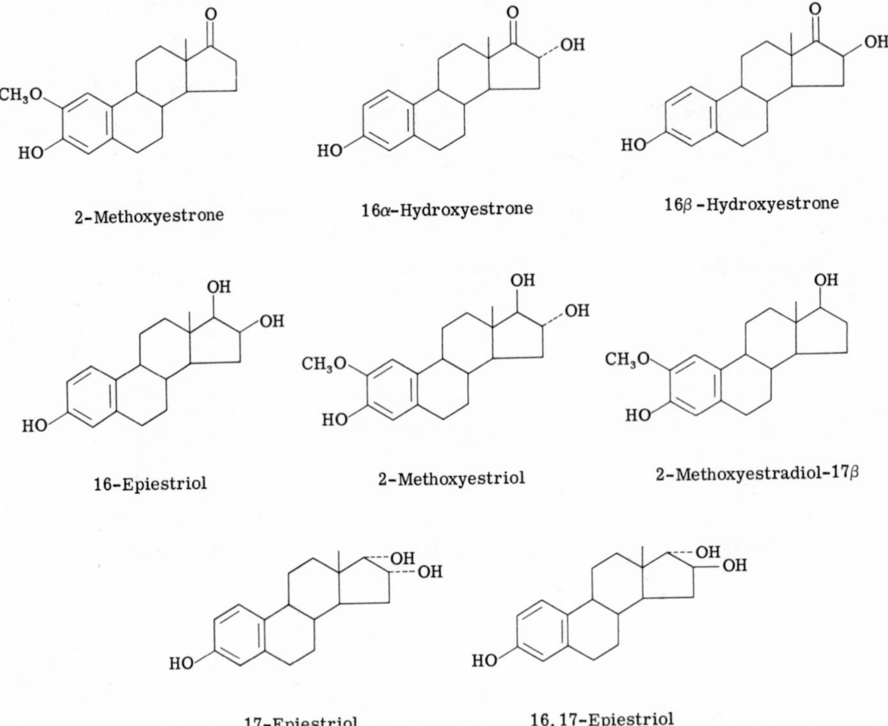

FIG. 17. Continued.

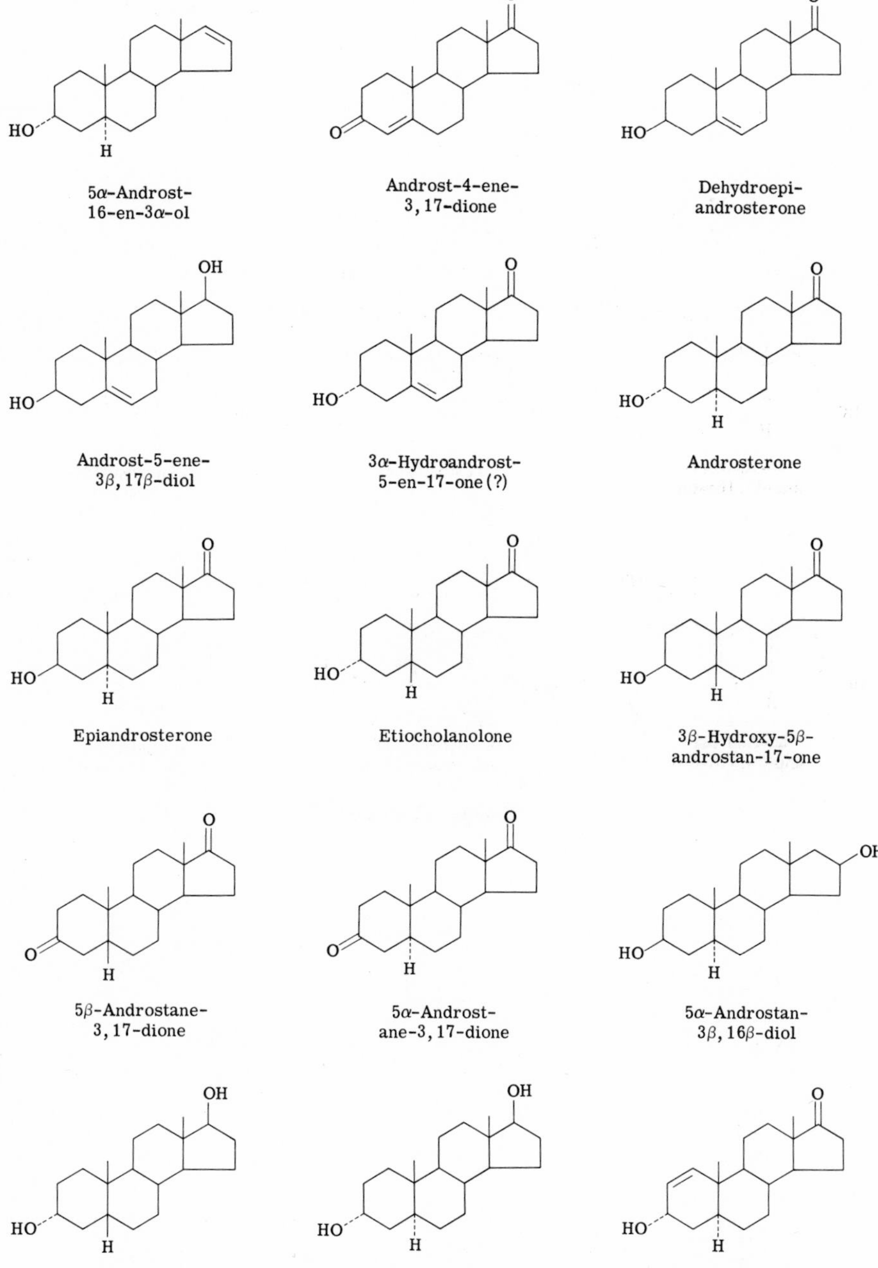

FIG. 18. $C_{19}O$ and $C_{19}O_2$ Steroids in urine.

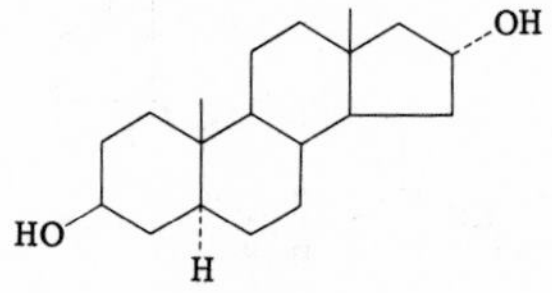

5α-Androst-
ane-3β, 16α-diol

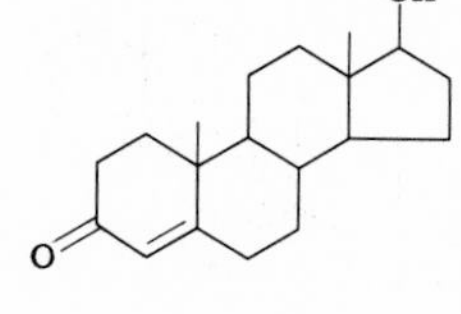

Testosterone

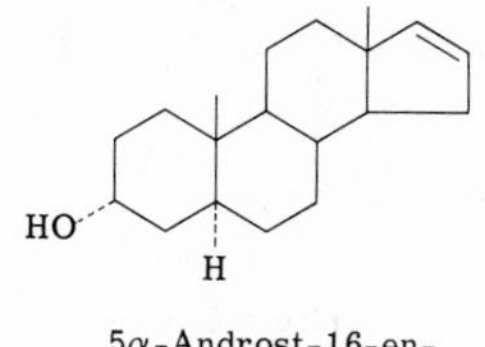

5α-Androst-16-en-
3α-ol

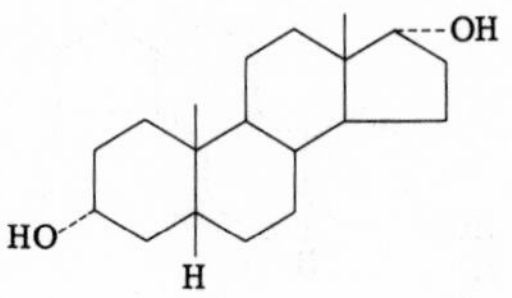

5β-Androst-
ane-3α, 17α-diol

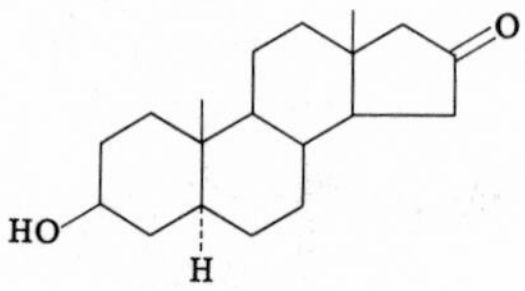

3β-Hydroxy-5α-
androstane-16-one

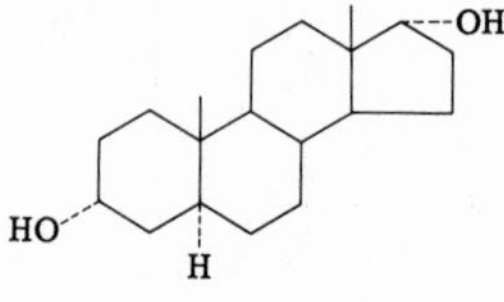

5α-Androstane-
3α, 17α-diol

FIG. 18. Continued.

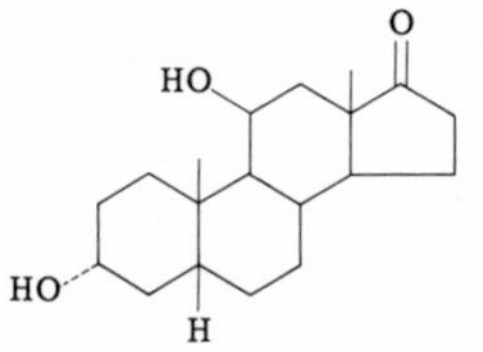

11β-Hydroxy-
etiocholanolone

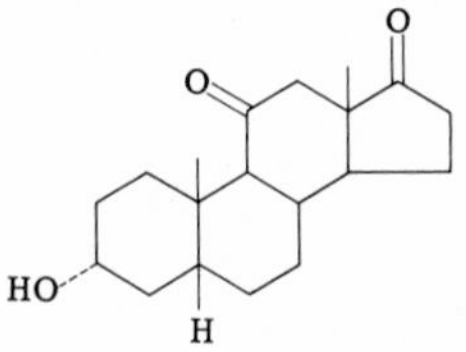

11-Keto-
etiocholanolone

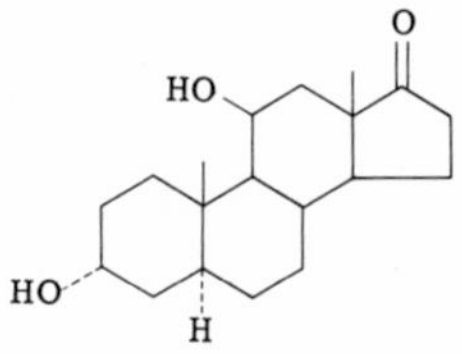

11β-Hydroxy-
androsterone

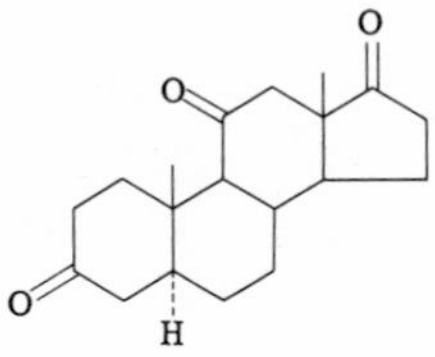

5β-Androstane-
3, 11, 17-trione

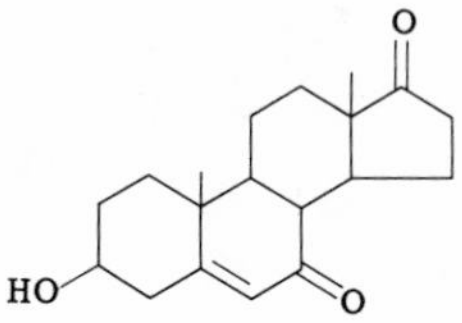

3β-Hydroxyandrost-
5-ene-7, 17-dione

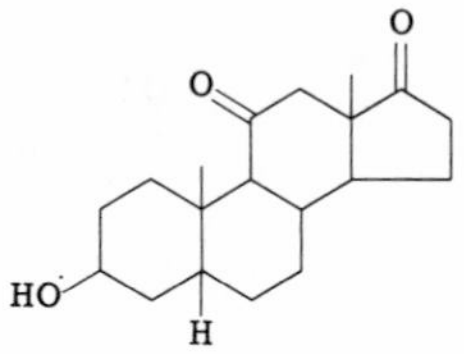

3β-Hydroxy-5β-
androstane-11, 17-dione

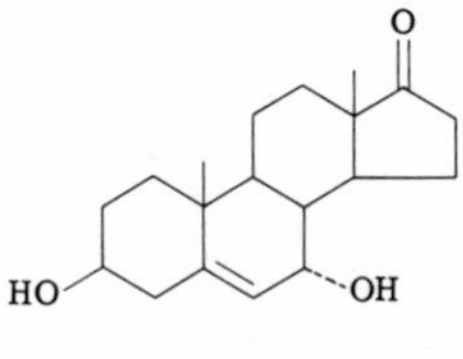

3β,7α-Dihydroxy-
androst-5-en-17-one

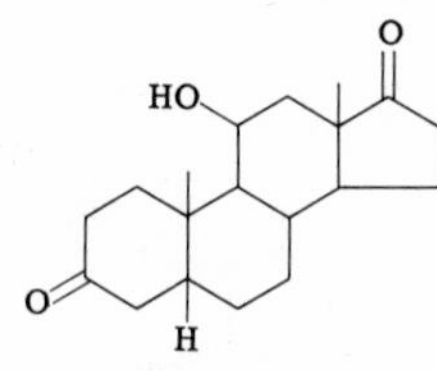

11β-Hydroxy-5β-
androstane-3, 17-dione

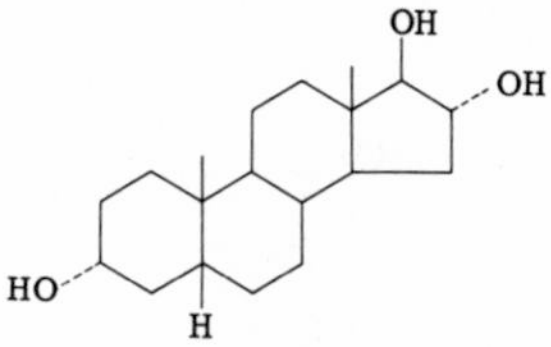

5β-Androstane-
3α, 16α, 17β-triol

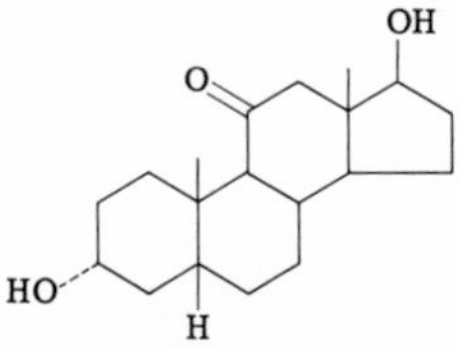

3α, 17β-Dihydroxy-
5β-androst-11-one

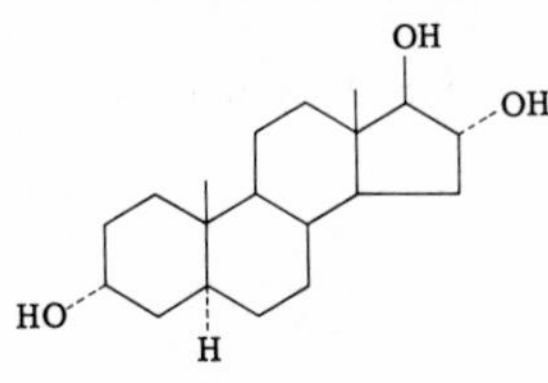

5α-Androstane-
3α, 16α, 17β-triol

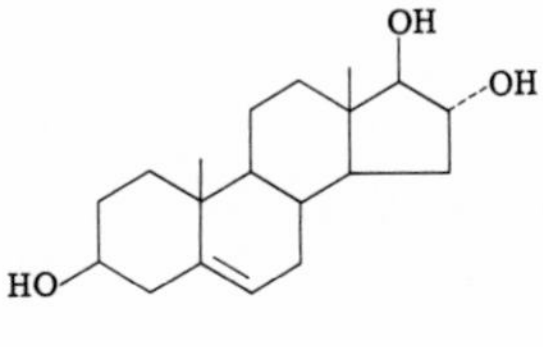

Androst-5-ene-
3β, 16α, 17β-triol

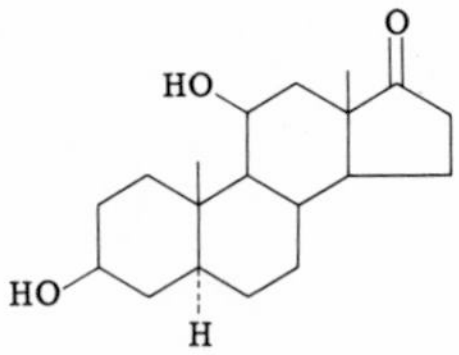

11β-Hydroxy-
epiandrosterone

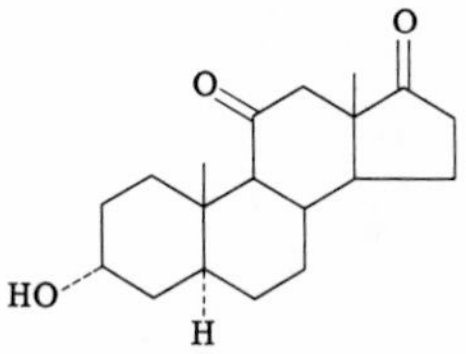

11-Ketoandrosterone

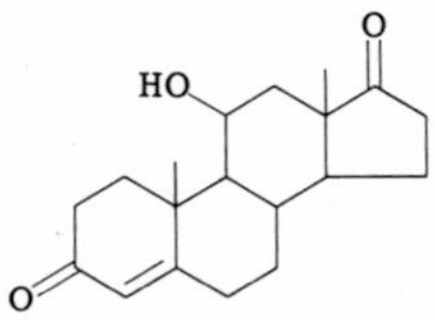

11β-Hydroxyandrost-
4-ene-3, 17-dione

FIG. 19. $C_{19}O_3$ and $C_{19}O_4$ Steroids in urine.

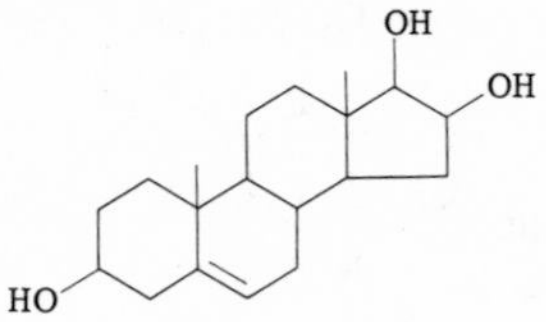

Androst-5-ene-
3β, 16β, 17β-triol

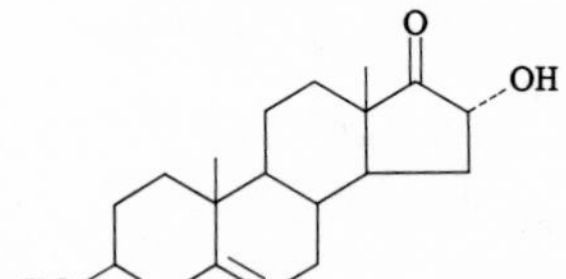

3β, 16α-Dihydroxy-
androst-5-en-17-one

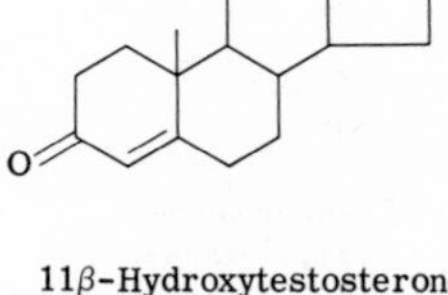

11β-Hydroxytestosterone
(Presumptive identification)

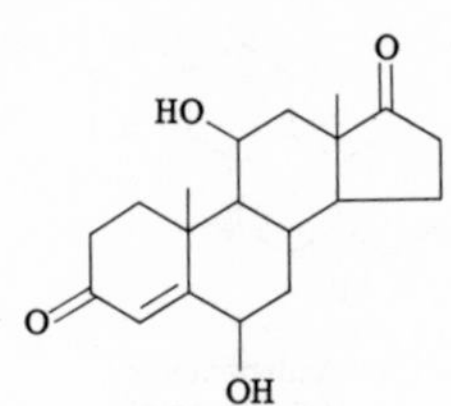

6β, 11β-Dihydroxy-
androst-4-ene-3, 17-dione

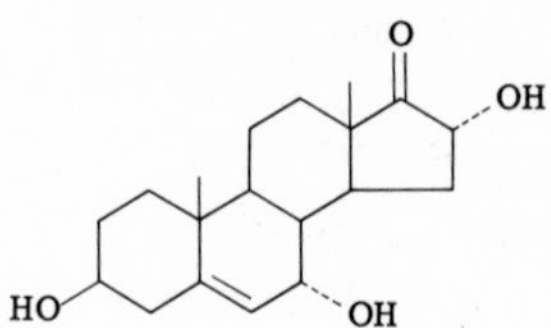

7α, 16α-Dihydroxy-
dehydroepiandrosterone

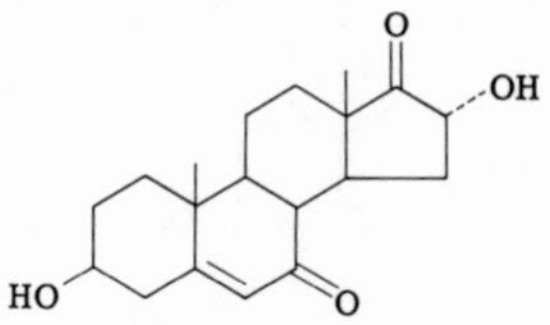

7-Keto, 16α-Hydroxy-
dehydroepiandrosterone

FIG. 19. Continued.

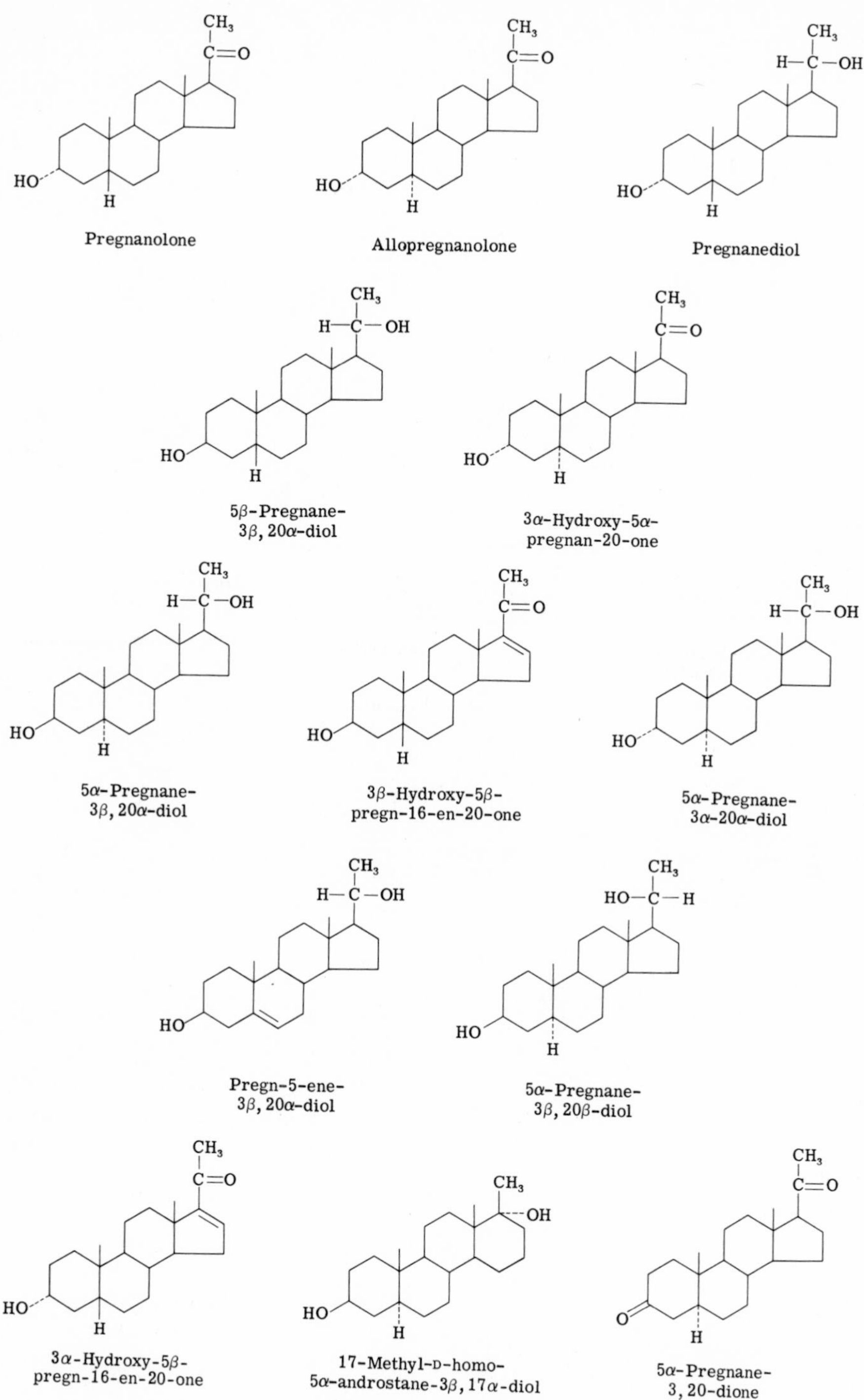

FIG. 20. $C_{21}O$ and $C_{21}O_2$ Steroids in urine.

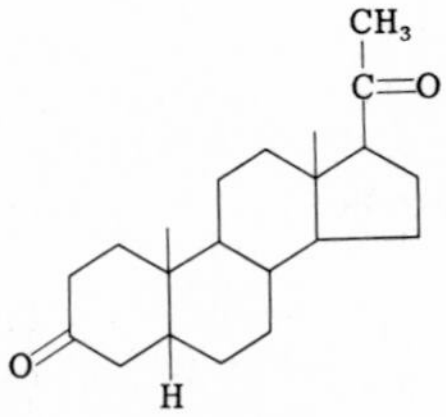

CH3, C=O, O, H

5β-Pregnane-3,20-dione

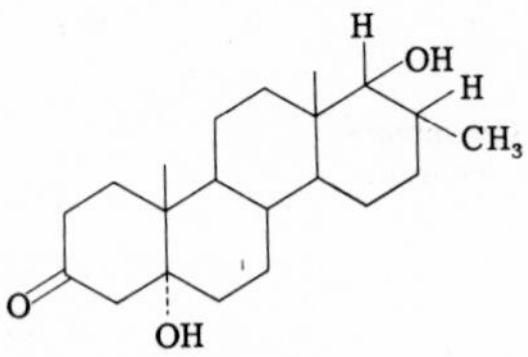

H, OH, H, CH3, O, OH

Uranolone

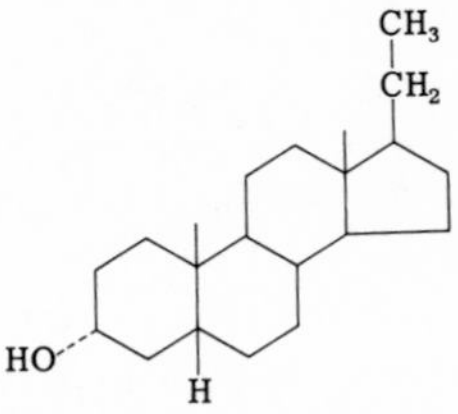

CH3, CH2, HO, H

5β-Pregnan-3α-ol

FIG. 20. Continued.

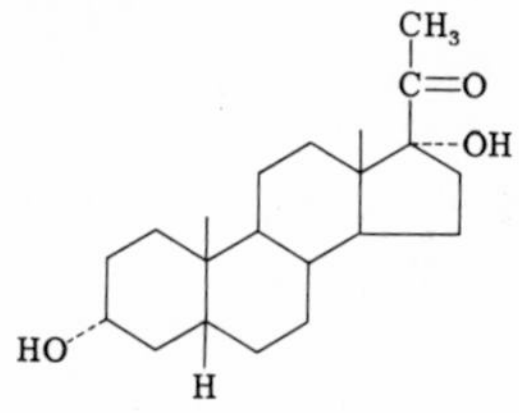

3α, 17α-Dihydroxy-
5β-pregnan-20-one

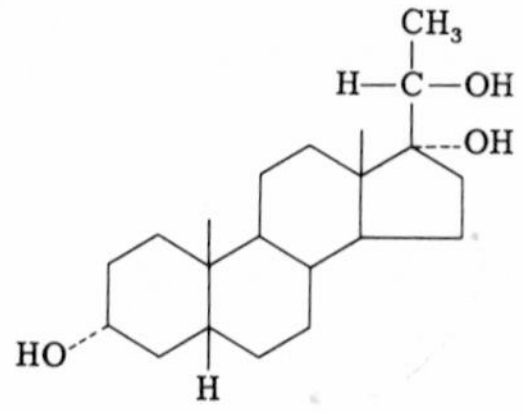

Pregnanetriol

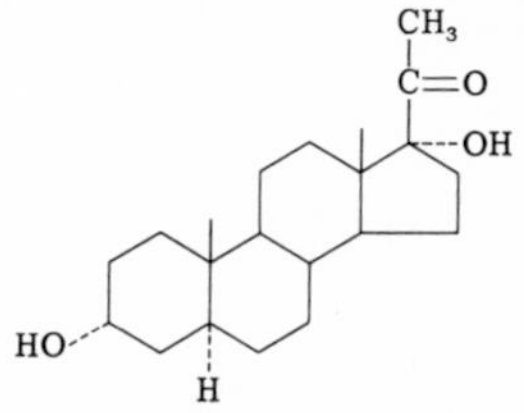

3α, 17α-Dihydroxy-
5α-pregnan-20-one

5α-Pregnane-
3α, 17α, 20α-triol

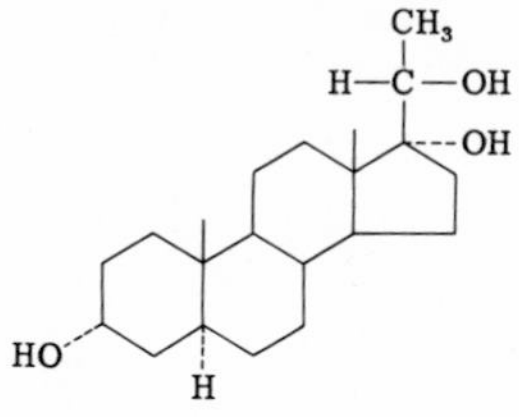

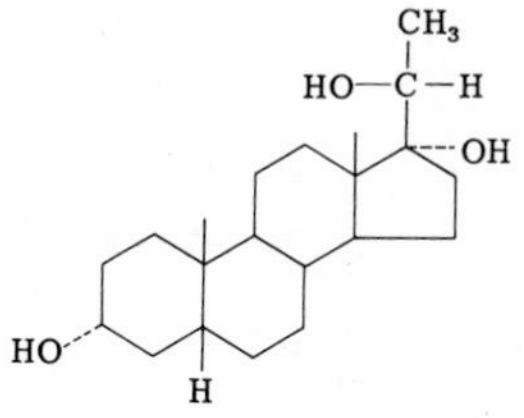

5α-Pregnane-
3α, 17α, 20β-triol

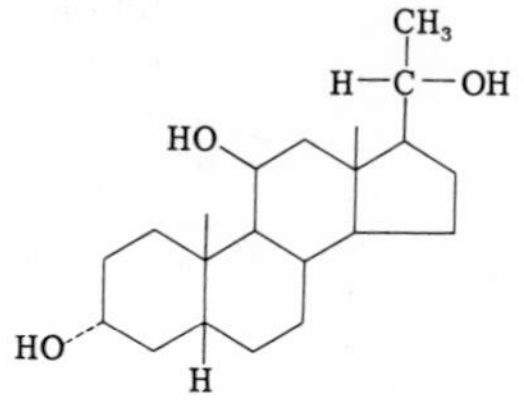

5β-Pregnane-
3α, 11β, 20α-triol

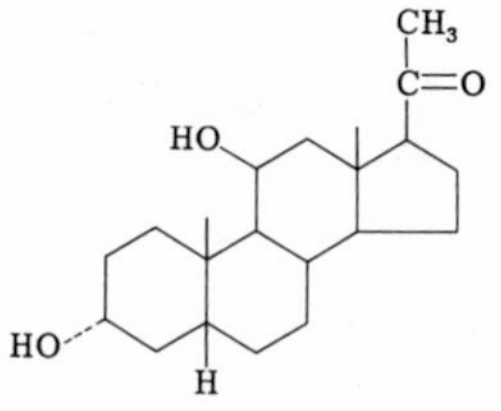

3α, 11β-Dihydroxy-
5β-pregnan-20-one

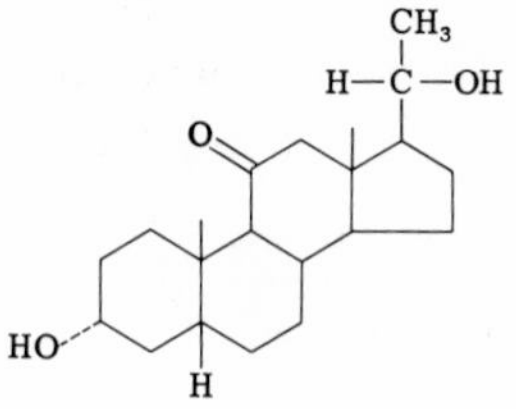

11-Keto-
pregnanediol

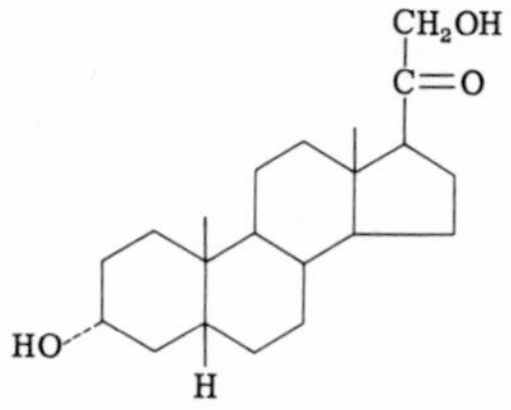

3α, 21-Dihydroxy-
5β-pregnan-20-one

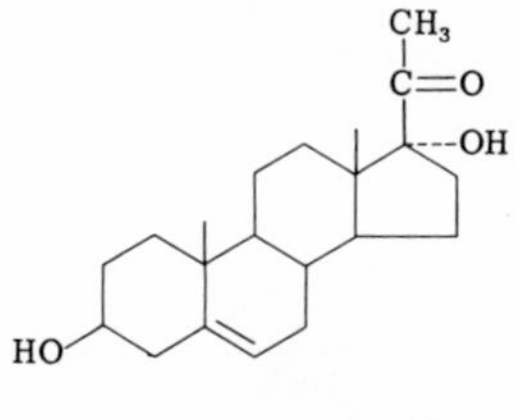

3β, 17α-Dihydroxy-
pregn-5-en-20-one

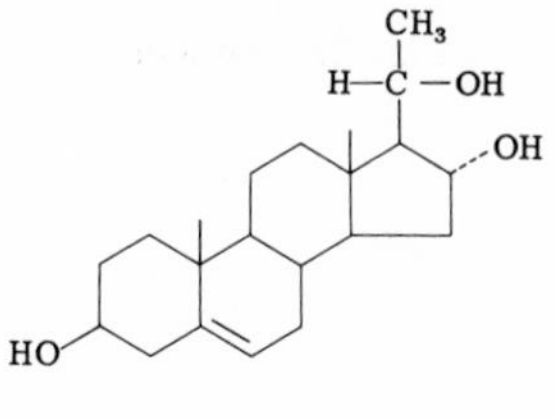

Pregn-5-ene-
3β, 16α, 20α-triol

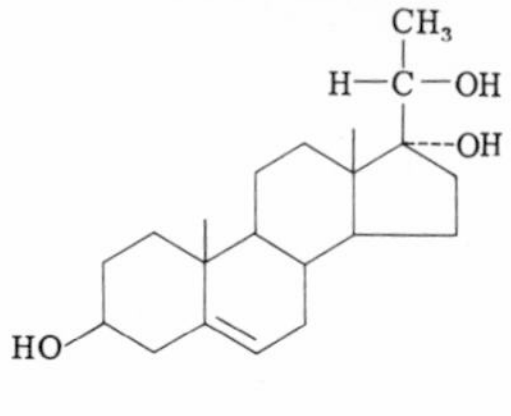

Pregn-5-ene-
3β, 17α, 20α-triol

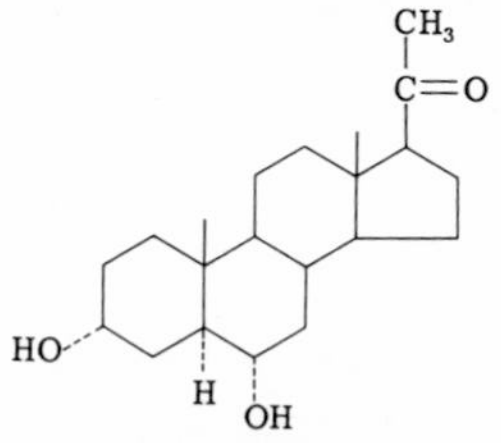

3α, 6α-Dihydroxy-
5α-pregnan-20-one

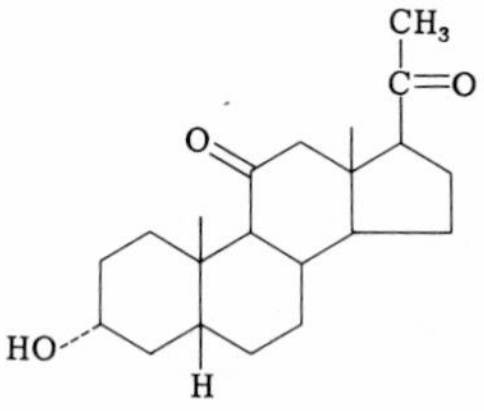

3α-Hydroxy-5β-
pregnane-11, 20-dione

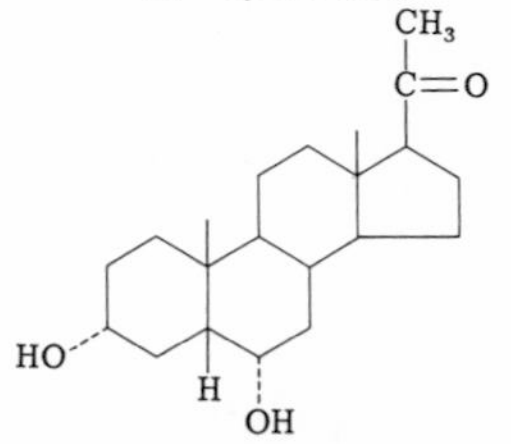

3α, 6α-Dihydroxy-
5β-pregnan-20-one

FIG. 21. $C_{21}O_3$ Steroids in urine.

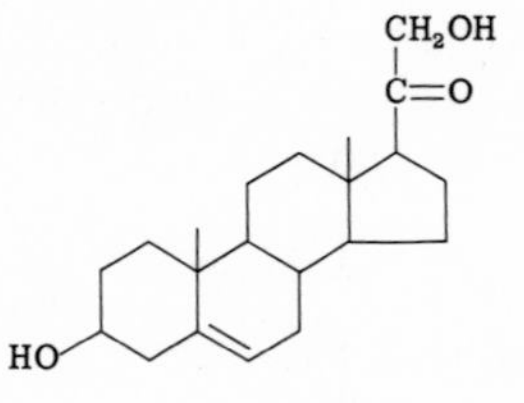

3β, 21-Dihydroxy-pregn-5-en-20-one

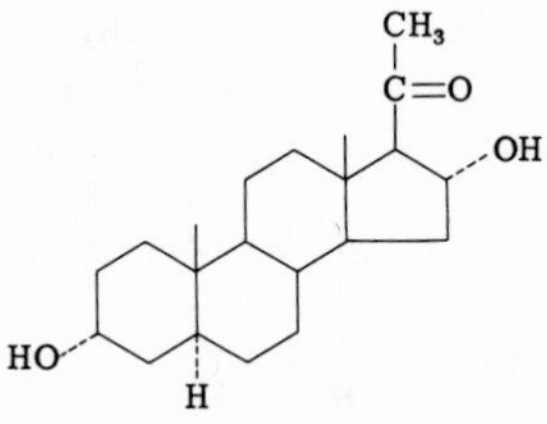

3α, 16α-Dihydroxy-5α-pregnan-20-one

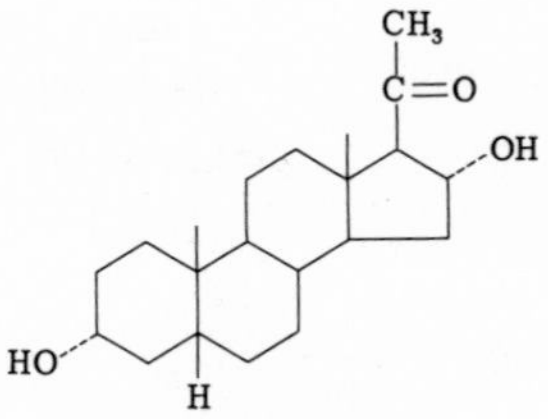

3α, 16α-Dihydroxy-5β-pregnan-20-one

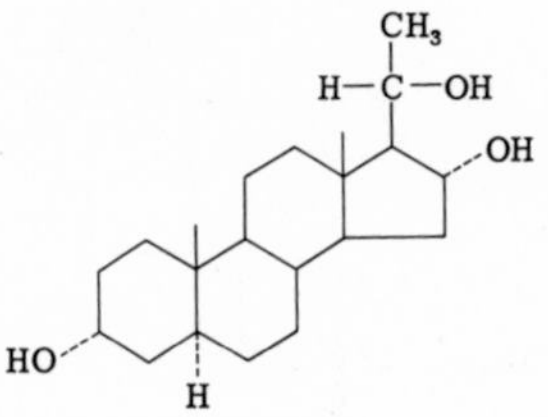

5α-Pregnane-3α, 16α, 20α-triol

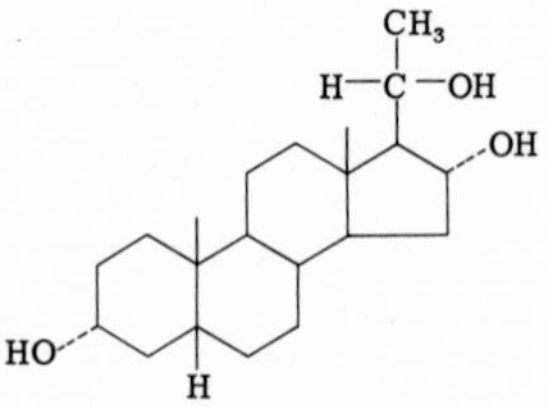

5β-Pregnane-3α, 16α, 20α-triol

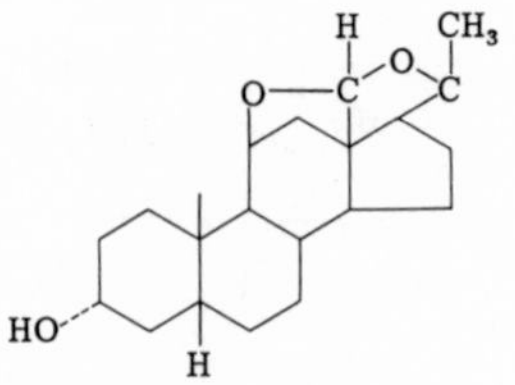

3α-Hydroxy-5β-pregnan-(11β-18), (18-20) dioxide

FIG. 21. Continued.

5β-Pregnane-
3α, 11β, 17α, 20-tetrol

3α, 17α, 20α-Trihydroxy-
5β-pregnan-11-one

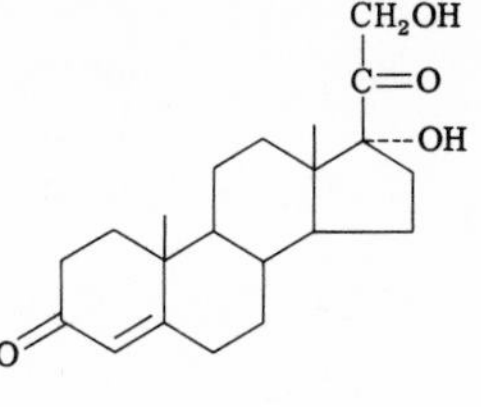

11-Deoxycortisol

3α, 17α, 21-Trihydroxy-
5β-pregnan-20-one

Corticosterone

11-Dehydrocorticosterone

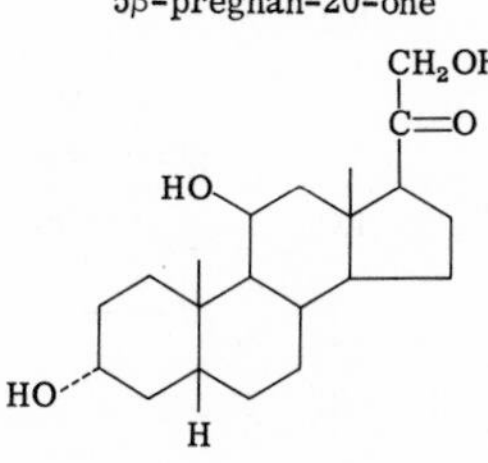

3α, 11β, 21-Trihydroxy-
5β-pregnan-20-one

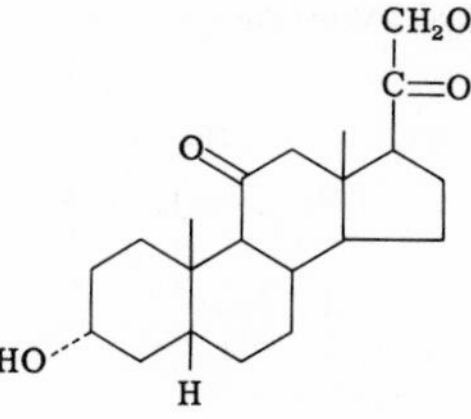

3α, 21-Dihydroxy-5β-
pregnane-11, 20-dione

17α, 21-Dihydroxy-5β-
pregnane-3, 20-dione
(Presumptive)

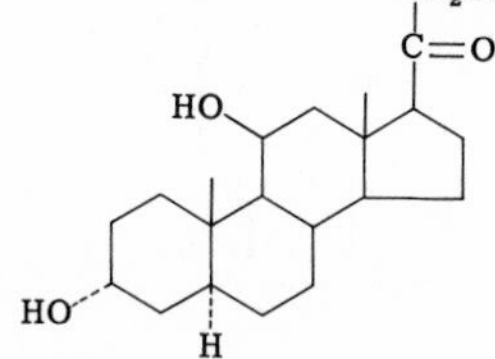

3α, 11β, 21-Trihydroxy-
5α-pregnan-20-one

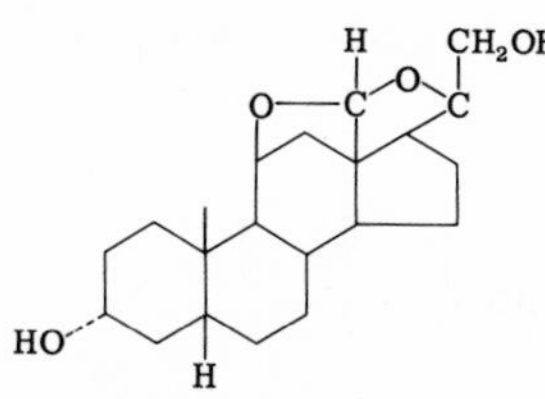

3α, 21-Dihydroxy-5β-pregnane-
(11β-18), (18-20) dioxide

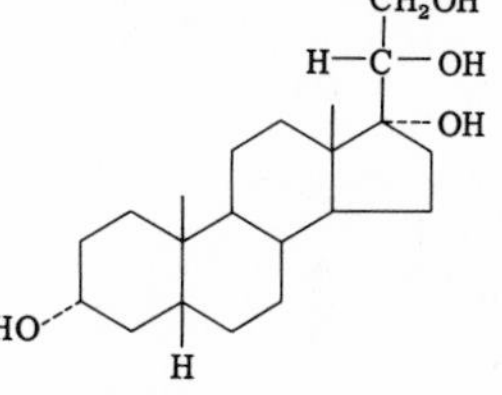

5β-Pregnane-
3α, 17α, 20α, 21-tetrol

5β-Pregnane-
3α, 17α, 20β, 21-tetrol

11β, 20β, 21-Trihydroxy-
pregn-4-en-3-one

FIG. 22. $C_{21}O_4$ Steroids in urine.

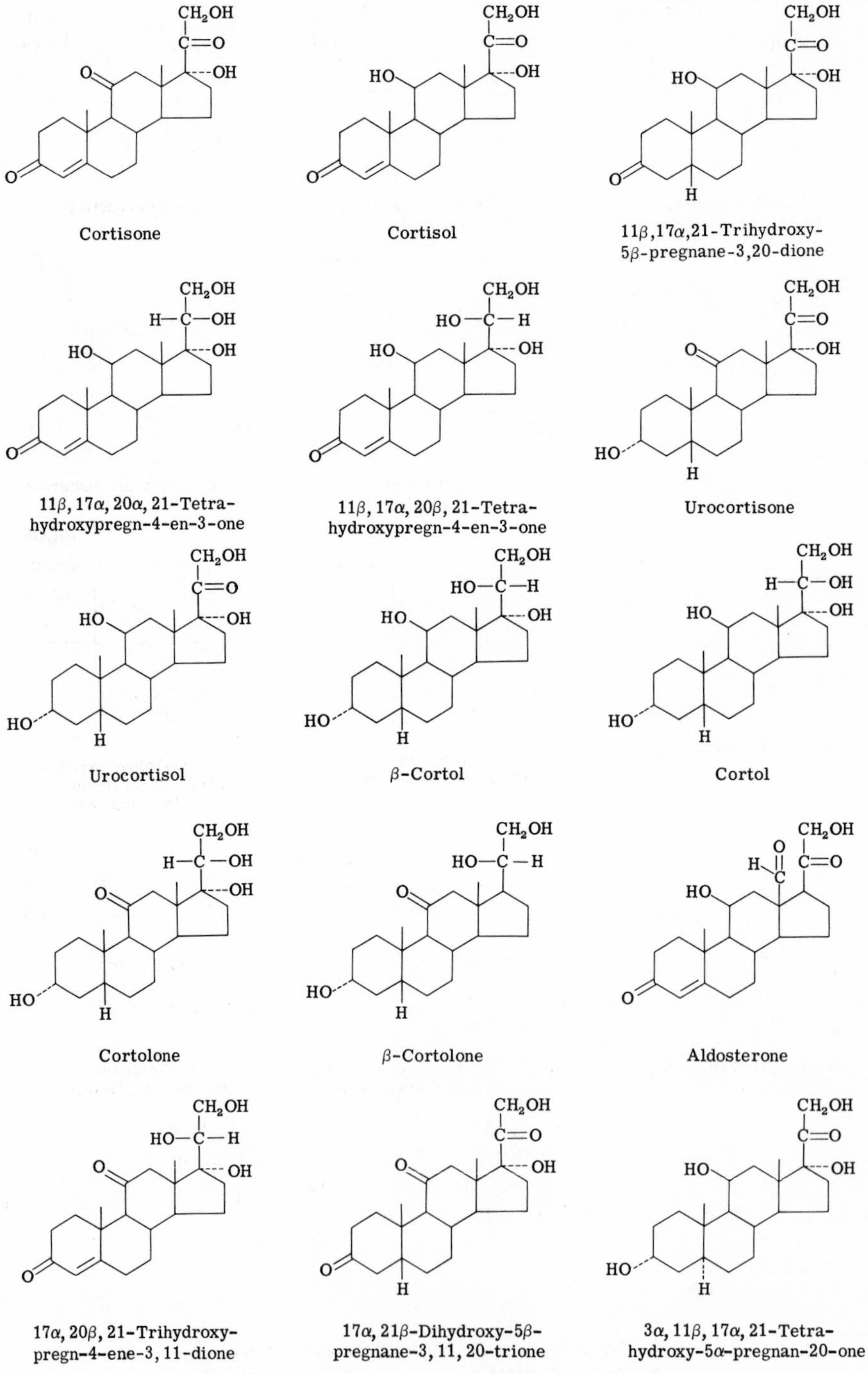

Cortisone

Cortisol

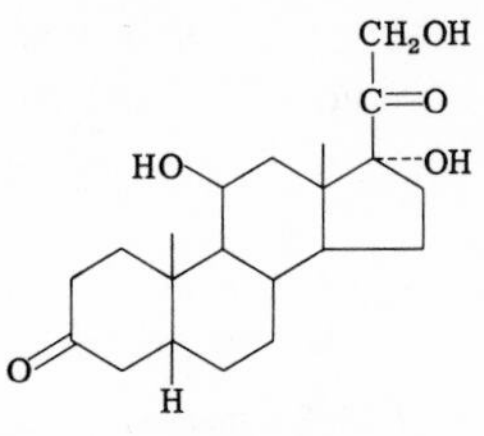

$11\beta,17\alpha,21$-Trihydroxy-5β-pregnane-3,20-dione

$11\beta, 17\alpha, 20\alpha, 21$-Tetrahydroxypregn-4-en-3-one

$11\beta, 17\alpha, 20\beta, 21$-Tetrahydroxypregn-4-en-3-one

Urocortisone

Urocortisol

β-Cortol

Cortol

Cortolone

β-Cortolone

Aldosterone

$17\alpha, 20\beta, 21$-Trihydroxypregn-4-ene-3, 11-dione

$17\alpha, 21\beta$-Dihydroxy-5β-pregnane-3, 11, 20-trione

$3\alpha, 11\beta, 17\alpha, 21$-Tetrahydroxy-$5\alpha$-pregnan-20-one

FIG. 23. $C_{21}O_5$ Steroids in urine.

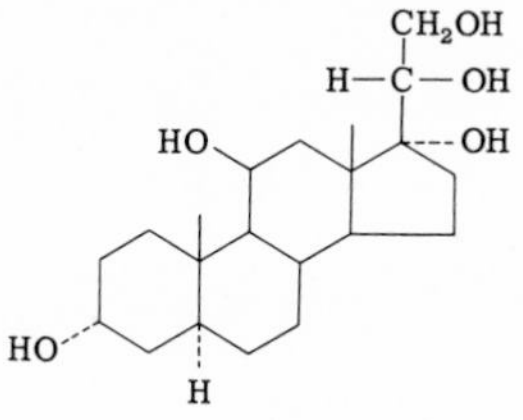

Allocortol

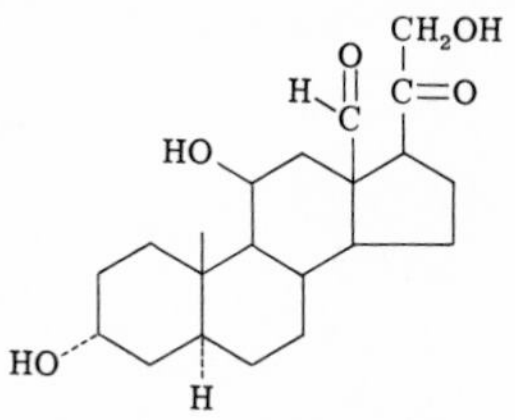

3α,11β,21-Trihydroxy-18-oxo-5α-pregnan-20-one

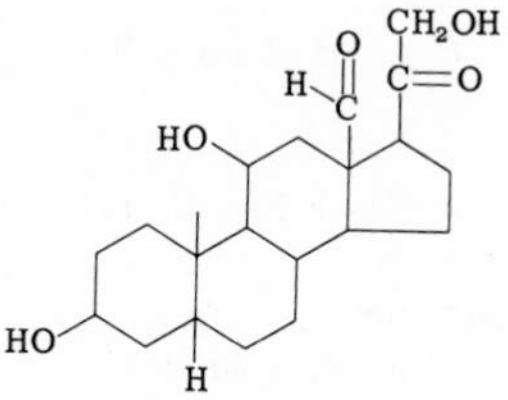

3β, 11β, 21-Trihydroxy-18-oxo-5β-pregnan-20-one

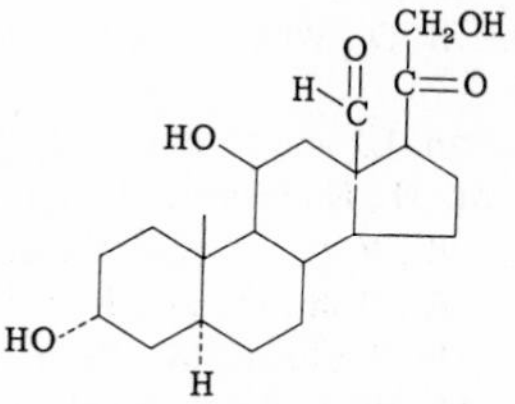

3α, 11β, 21-Trihydroxy-18-oxo-5α-pregnan-20-one

FIG. 23. Continued.

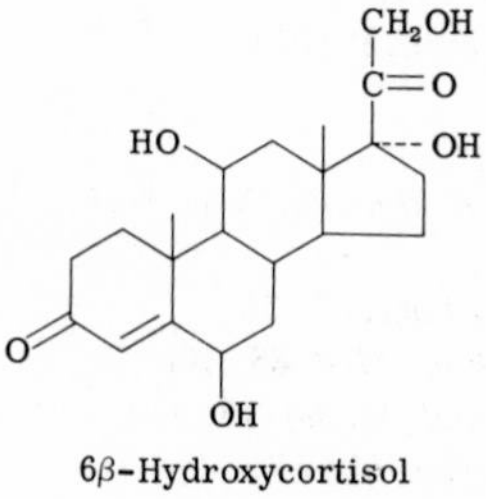

6β-Hydroxycortisol

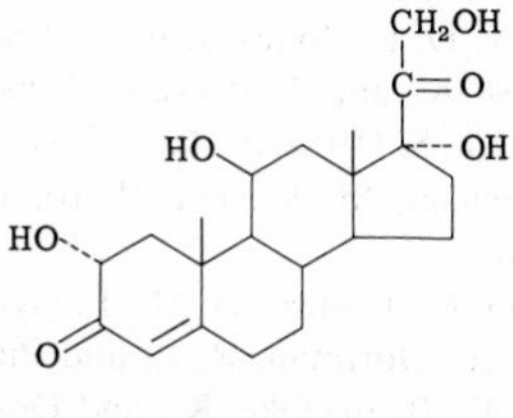

2α-Hydroxycortisol

FIG. 24. $C_{21}O_6$ Steroids in urine.

References

Adlercreutz, H., Sr. (1962) *Acta Endocrinol.* **42** (Suppl.): 72.

Adlercreutz, H., Jr., Diczfalusy, E., and Engstrom, L. (1960) *Endocrinology* **66**: 80.

Afinogenova, S. A. (1957) *Prob. Endokrinol. i. Gormonoterap.* **3**: 36.

Agashe, B. D., Weaver, R. G., and Eik-Nes, K. B. (1961) *Proc. Soc. Exptl. Biol. Med.* **107**: 398.

Ainsworth, L., and Common, R. H. (1962) *Nature* **195**: 4836.

Aires, M. M., Kadekaro, M., and Fajer, A. (1962) *Excerpta Med. Intern. Congr. Ser.* **51**: 141.

Anliker, R., Rohr, O., and Marti, M. (1956) *Helv. Chim. Acta* **39**: 1100.

Anliker, R., Rohr, O., and Ruzicka, L. (1957a) *Ann. Chem. Liebigs* **603**: 109.

Anliker, R., Perlman, M., Rohr, O., and Ruzicka, L. (1957b) *Helv. Chim. Acta* **40**: 1517.

Aprile, M., Bligh, E. G., Webb, J. L., and Heard, R. D. H. (1956) *Rev. Can. Biol.* **15**: 232.

Ayres, P. J., Garrod, O., Tait, S. A. S., Tait, J. F., and Walker, G. (1957) *Ciba Found. Colloq. Endocrinol.* **11**: 309.

Baggett, B., Engel, L. L., Savard, K., and Dorfman, R. I. (1955) *Federation Proc.* **14**: 175.

Baggett, B., Engel, L. L., Savard, K., and Dorfman, R. I. (1956) *J. Biol. Chem.* **221**: 931.

Bailey, R. E., Slade, C. I., Lieberman, A. H., and Luetscher, J. A., Jr. (1960) *Endocrinology* **20**: 457.

Balls, K. F., Nicholson, J. T. L., Goodman, L., and Touchstone, J. C. (1959) *J. Clin. Endocrinol. Metab.* **19**: 1134.

Bauld, W. S., and Heard, R. D. H. (1948) *In* "The Hormones" (G. Pincus and K. V. Thimann, eds.), Vol. I, p. 620, Academic Press, New York.

Baulieu, E. E. (1959) *Compt. Rend.* **248**: 1441.

Baulieu, E. E. (1960a) *J. Clin. Endocrinol. Metab.* **20**: 900.

Baulieu, E. E. (1960b) *Compt. Rend.* **248**: 1421.

Baulieu, E. E., and Emiliozzi, R. (1960) *Compt. Rend.* **251**: 3106.

Baulieu, E. E., Emiliozzi, R., and Corpechot, C. (1961a) *Experientia* **17**: 110.

Baulieu, E. E., Michaud, G., and Benhamon, R. (1961b) *Compt. Rend. Soc. Biol.* **155**: 1003.

Beall, D. (1938) *Biochem. J.* **32**: 1957.

Beall, D. (1939) *Nature* **144**: 76.

Beall, D. (1940) *J. Endocrinol.* **2**: 81.

Beall, D., and Reichstein, T. (1938) *Nature* **142**: 479.

Beling, C. G. (1962) *Acta Endocrinol. Suppl.* **43**: 79.

Benirschke, K., Bloch, E., and Herteg, A. T. (1956) *Endocrinology* **58**: 598.

Berliner, D. L., Jones, J. E., and Salhanick, H. A. (1956) *J. Biol. Chem.* **223**: 1043.

Bern, H. A., and de Roos, C. (1960) *Anat. Record* **138**: 334.

Bernstein, S. (1956) *J. Am. Chem. Soc.* **78**: 1769.

Birmingham, M. K., and Ward, P. (1961) *Proc. Endocrine Soc. 43rd Meeting, New York,* p. 50.

Birchall, K., Cathro, D. M., Forsyth, C. C., and Mitchell, F. L. (1961) *Lancet* **1**: 26.

Bloch, E., Dorfman, R. I., and Pincus, G. (1954) *Proc. Soc. Exptl. Biol. Med.* **85**: 106.

Bloch, E., Benirschke, K., and Dorfman, R. I. (1955) *J. Clin. Endocrinol. Metab.* **15**: 379.

Bloch, E., Dorfman, R. I., and Pincus, G. (1956) *Arch. Biochem. Biophys.* **61**: 245.

Bloch, E., Cohen, A. I., and Furth, J. (1960) *J. Natl. Cancer Inst.* **24**: 97.

Bondy, P. K., Ayston, G. W., and Pickford, G. E. (1957) *Nature* **179**: 1354.

Bongiovanni, A. M. (1958) *J. Clin. Invest.* **37**: 1342.

Bongiovanni, A. M. (1962) *J. Clin. Invest.* **41**: 2086.
Bongiovanni, A. M., and Eberlein, W. R. (1955) *Pediatrics* **16**: 628.
Botticelli, C. R., Hisaw, F. L., Jr., and Wotiz, H. H. (1960) *Proc. Soc. Exptl. Biol. Med.* **103**: 875.
Botticelli, C. R., Hisaw, F. L., Jr., and Wotiz, H. H. (1961) *Proc. Soc. Exptl. Biol. Med.* **106**: 887.
Bowerman, A. M., and Melampy, R. M. (1962) *Proc. Soc. Exptl. Biol. Med.* **109**: 45.
Brady, R. O. (1951) *J. Biol. Chem.* **193**: 145.
Bredeck, H. E., and Mayer, D. T. (1958) *Reprod. Infertility* 3rd *Symp. Fort Collins, Colo.* 1957, p. 157.
Breuer, H. (1960) *Nature* **185**: 613.
Breuer, H., and Pangels, G. (1959) *Biochim. Biophys. Acta* **36**: 572.
Breuer, H., and Pangels, G. (1961) *Z. Chem.* **322**: 177.
Brooks, R. V., and Klyne, W. (1956) *Biochem. J.* **62**: 21P.
Brooks, R. V., and Klyne, W. (1957) *Biochem. J.* **65**: 663.
Brooks, R. V., Klyne, W., Miller, E., and Paterson, J. Y. F. (1952) *Biochem. J.* **51**: 694.
Brooksbank, B. W. L., and Haslewood, G. A. D. (1949) *Biochem. J.* **44**: iii.
Brouillet, J., and Mattox, V. R. (1961) *Federation Proc.* **20**: 179.
Brown, J. B. (1958) *Conf. Endocrine Aspects Breast Cancer, Livingstone, Edinburgh, 1957*, p. 179.
Browne, J. S. L. (1931) Cited by Collip, J. B. *Proc. Calif. Acad. Med.* **1**: 38.
Bryson, M., and Sweat, M. L. (1962) *Arch. Biochem. Biophys.* **96**: 1.
Bulaschenko, H., Richardson, E. M., and Dohan, F. C. (1960) *Arch. Biochem. Biophys.* **87**: 81.
Bulbrook, R. D., Greenwood, F. C., and Thomas, B. S. (1960) *Biochim. Biophys. Acta* **40**: 361.
Burstein, S., and Dorfman, R. I. (1955) *J. Biol. Chem.* **213**: 581.
Burstein, S., Lieberman, S. (1958) *J. Biol. Chem.* **233**: 331.
Burstein, S., and Dorfman, R. I. (1960) *Proc.* 1*st Intern. Congr. Endocrinol. Copenhagen* 1960, p. 689.
Burstein, S., and Dorfman, R. I. (1962) *Acta Endocrinol.* **40**: 188.
Burstein, S., and Nadel, E. (1956) *Federation Proc.* **15**: 228.
Burstein, S., Dorfman, R. I., and Nadel, E. M. (1954) *Arch. Biochem. Biophys.* **53**: 307.
Bush, I. E. (1951) *J. Physiol.* (*London*) **112**: 12.
Bush, I. E. (1953) *J. Endocrinol.* **9**: 95.
Bush, I. E., and Fergusen, K. A. (1953) *J. Endocrinol.* **10**: 1.
Bush, I. E., and Mahesh, V. B. (1959) *Biochem. J.* **71**: 705.
Bush, I. E., and Willoughby, M. (1957a) *Biochem. J.* **66**: 28.
Bush, I. E., and Willoughby, M. (1957b) *Biochem. J.* **67**: 689.
Bush, I. E., Swale, J., and Patterson, J. (1956) *Biochem. J.* **62**: 16P.
Bush, I. E., Klyne, W., and Short, R. V. (1960) *J. Endocrinol.* **20**: 1.
Butenandt, A. (1929) *Naturwissenschaften* **17**: 878.
Butenandt, A. (1931) *Z. Angew. Chem.* **44**: 905.
Butenandt, A. (1932) *Angew. Chem.* **45**: 655.
Butenandt, A. (1934) *Wien. Klin. Wochschr.* **47**: 936.
Butenandt, A., and Dannenbaum, H. (1934) *Z. Physiol. Chem.* **229**: 192.
Butenandt, A., and Jacobi, H. (1933) *Z. Physiol. Chem.* **218**: 104.
Butenandt, A., and Westphal, U. (1934) *Z. Physiol. Chem.* **67**: 1140.
Butler, G. C., and Marrian, G. F. (1937) *J. Biol. Chem.* **119**: 565.
Callow, N. H. (1939) *Biochem. J.* **33**: 559.
Callow, N. H., and Callow, R. K. (1939) *Biochem. J.* **33**: 931.
Callow, N. H., and Callow, R. K. (1940) *Biochem. J.* **34**: 276.
Camacho, A. M., and Migeon, C. J. (1963) *J. Clin. Endocrinol. Metab.* **23**: 301.
Carstensen, H. (1956) *Acta Chem. Scand.* **10**: 474.
Carstensen, H., Burger, A. C., and Li, C. H. (1959a) *J. Am. Chem. Soc.* **81**: 4109.

Carstensen, H., Oertel, G. W., and Eik-Nes, K. B. (1959b) *J. Biol. Chem.* **234**: 2570.
Carstensen, H., Burger, A. C., and Li, C. H. (1961) *Gen. Comp. Endocrinol.* **1**: 37.
Caspi, E. (1956) *J. Org. Chem.* **21**: 814.
Cavina, G., Fidanza, A., and De Cicco, A. (1956) *Quaderni Nutriz.* **16**: 106; (1958) *Chem. Abstr.* **52**: 12055.
Chester-Jones, I., Phillips, J. G., and Holmes, W. N. (1959) *Comp. Endocrinol. Proc. Columbia Univ. Symp. Cold Spring Harbor, N.Y.* 1958 p. 582.
Chieffi, G. (1961) *Nature* **190**: 169.
Chieffi, G. (1962) *Gen. Comp. Endocrinol. Suppl.* **1**: 275–285.
Clark, A. F. (1963) *Federation Proc.* **22**: 468.
Clayton, G. W., and Bongiovanni, A. M. (1955) *J. Clin. Endocrinol. Metab.* **15**: 693.
Cohn, G. L., and Bondy, P. K. (1959) *J. Biol. Chem.* **234**: 31.
Cohn, G. L., and Mulrow, P. J. (1961) *Proc. Endocrine Soc. 43rd Meeting N.Y.* p. 52.
Conner, R. L. (1959) *J. Gen. Microbiol.* **21**: 180.
Cooper, D. Y., Kasparow, M., Blakemore, W. S., and Rosenthal, O. (1958) *Federation Proc.* **17**: 205.
Cope, C. L., and Sewell, C. E. (1956) *Ann. Rheumatic Diseases* **14**: 392.
Copenhaven, J., and Gawienowski, A. M. (1961) *Proc. Am. Chem. Soc. 140th Meeting*, p. 62C.
Correale, L., Balestreri, R., and Arciti, C. (1962) *Arch. "E. Maragliano" Pathol. Clin.* **18**: 97.
Coulson, W. F. (1960) *Nature* **185**: 612.
Cox, R. I., and Marrian, G. F. (1953) *Biochem. J.* **54**: 353.
David, K., Dingemanse, E., Freud, J., and Laqueur, E. (1935) *Z. Physiol. Chem.* **233**: 281.
Davignon, J., Tremblay, G., and Genest, J. (1960) *J. Clin. Endocrinol. Metab.* **20**: 1515.
Davignon, J., Tremblay, G., Nowaczynski, W., Koiw, E., and Genest, J. (1961) *Acta Endocrinol.* **38**: 207.
de Hachen, D. P. C., and Solis, J. (1956) *Rev. Soc. Arg.* **B32**: 23.
de Jongh, S. E., Kober, S., and Laqueur, E. (1931) *Biochem. Z.* **240**: 247.
de Roos, R. (1960a) *Anat. Record* **138**: 343.
de Roos, R. (1960b) *Endocrinology* **67**: 719.
de Roos, R. (1961) *Gen. Comp. Endocrinol.* **1**: 494.
de Roos, R., and Bern, H. A. (1961) *Gen. Comp. Endocrinol.* **1**: 275.
Deulofev, V., and Ferrari, J. (1934) *Z. Physiol. Chem.* **226**: 192.
Diczfalusy, E. (1958) *Conf. Endocrine Aspects Breast Cancer, Livingstone, Edinburgh, 1957.*
Diczfalusy, E., and Halla, M. (1958) *Acta Endocrinol.* **27**: 303.
Diczfalusy, E., and Lindkvist, P. (1956) *Acta Endocrinol.* **22**: 203.
Diczfalusy, E., and Münstermann, A. M. (1959) *Acta Endocrinol.* **32**: 195.
Dingemanse, E., de Jongh, S. E., Kober, S., and Laqueur, E. (1930) *Deut. Med. Wochshr.* **56**: 301.
Dingemanse, E., Laqueur, E., and Muhlboch, O. (1938) *Nature* **141**: 927.
Dobriner, K. (1951) *Symp. Steroids Exptl. Clin. Practice 1st Conf. Cuernavaca, Mex. 1951* p. 130.
Dobriner, K., and Lieberman, S. (1952) *Ciba Found. Colloq. Endocrinol.* **2**: 381.
Dobriner, K., Rhoads, C. P., Lieberman, S., Hill, B. R., and Fieser, L. F. (1944) *Science* **99**: 494.
Dobriner, K., Lieberman, S., and Rhoads, C. P. (1948) *J. Biol. Chem.* **172**: 241.
Dobriner, K., Katzenellenbogen, E. R., and Schneider, R. (1954) *Arch. Biochem. Biophys.* **48**: 167.
Dohan, F. C., Touchstone, J. C., and Richardson, E. M. (1955) *J. Clin. Invest.* **34**: 485.
Doisy, E. A., Veler, C. D., and Thayer, S. A. (1929) *Am. J. Physiol.* **90**: 329.
Doisy, E. A., Thayer, S. A., Levin, L., and Curtis, J. M. (1930) *Proc. Soc. Exptl. Biol. Med.* **28**: 58.
Dyrenfurth, I., Sybulski, S., Notchev, W., Beck, J. C., and Venning, E. H. (1958) *J. Clin. Endocrinol. Metab.* **18**: 391.
Eberlein, W. R., and Bongiovanni, A. M. (1956) *J. Biol. Chem.* **223**: 85.

Eik-Nes, K. B., Demetriou, D. A., Mayne, Y. C., and Jones, R. S. (1957) *Proc. Soc. Exptl. Biol. Med.* **96**: 409.

Elliot, F. H., and Schally, A. V. (1955) *Can. J. Biochem. Physiol.* **33**: 174.

Engel, L. L., Thorn, G. W., and Lewis, R. A. (1941) *J. Biol. Chem.* **137**: 205.

Engel, L. L., Slaunwhite, W. R., Jr., Carter, P., Olmsted, P. C., and Nathanson, I. T. (1952) *Ciba Found. Colloq. Endocrinol.* **2**: 104.

Engel, L. L., Dorfman, R. I., and Abarbanel, A. R. (1953) *J. Clin. Endocrinol. Metab.* **13**: 903.

Fajer, A., and Vogt, M. (1962) *Excerpta Med. Intern. Congr. Ser.* **51**: 141.

Farrell, G. L., and Lamus, B. (1953) *Proc. Soc. Exptl. Biol. Med.* **84**: 89.

Farrell, G. L., Rauschkolb, E. W., Royce, P. C., and Hirschmann, H. (1954) *Proc. Soc. Exptl. Biol. Med.* **87**: 587.

Fazekas, I. G. (1957) *J. Endocrinol.* **15**: 440.

Felger, C. B., and Katzman, P. A. (1961) *Federation Proc.* **20**: 199.

Finkelstein, M., von Euw, J., and Reichstein, T. (1953) *Helv. Chim. Acta* **36**: 1266.

Finkelstein, M., Forchielli, E., and Dorfman, R. I. (1961) *J. Clin. Endocrinol. Metab.* **21**: 98.

Fish, W. R., Dorfman, R. I., and Young, W. C. (1942) *J. Biol. Chem.* **143**: 715.

Fishman, J. (1963) *J. Clin. Endocrinol. Metab.* **23**: 207.

Fontaine, M., and Leloup-Hatey, J. (1959) *J. Physiol.* (*Paris*) **51**: 468.

Forbes, T. R., and Zander, J. (1957) *Recent Progr. Hormone Res.* **13**: 379.

Fotherby, K. (1957) *Biochem. J.* **67**: 25P.

Fotherby, K. (1958) *Biochem. J.* **69**: 596.

Fotherby, K. (1959) *Biochem. J.* **71**: 209.

Fotherby, K., Colás, A., Atherden, S. M., and Marrian, G. F. (1957) *Biochem. J.* **66**: 664.

Francis, F. E., Shen, N.-H. C., and Kinsella, R. A., Jr. (1960) *J. Biol. Chem.* **235**: 1957.

Francis, F. E., Shen, N.-H. C., and Kinsella, R. A., Jr. (1962) *Biochemistry* **1**: 184.

Frandsen, V. A. (1959) *Acta Endocrinol.* **31**: 603.

Frantz, A. G., Katz, F. H., and Jailer, J. W. (1960) *Proc. Soc. Exptl. Biol. Med.* **105**: 41.

Frantz, A. G., Katz, F. H., and Jailer, J. W. (1961) *J. Clin. Endocrinol. Metab.* **21**: 129.

Fukushima, D. K., and Gallagher, T. F. (1957a) *J. Biol. Chem.* **226**: 725.

Fukushima, D. K., and Gallagher, T. F. (1957b) *J. Biol. Chem.* **229**: 85.

Fukushima, D. K., Bradlow, H. L., Dobriner, K., and Gallagher, T. F. (1954a) *J. Biol. Chem.* **206**: 863.

Fukushima, D. K., Dobriner, K., and Gallagher, T. F. (1954b) *J. Biol. Chem.* **206**: 845.

Fukushima, D. K., Kemp, A. D., Schneider, R., Stokem, M. B., and Gallagher, T. F. (1954c) *J. Biol. Chem.* **210**: 129.

Fukushima, D. K., Leeds, N. S., Bradlow, H. L., Kritchevsky, T. H., Stokem, M. B., and Gallagher, T. F. (1955) *J. Biol. Chem.* **212**: 449.

Fukushima, D. K., Meyer, E. D., Ashworth, E., and Gallagher, T. F. (1956) *Federation Proc.* **15**: 257.

Fukushima, D. K., Gallagher, T. F., Greenberg, W., and Pearson, O. H. (1960) *J. Clin. Endocrinol. Metab.* **20**: 1234.

Fukushima, E. K., Bradlow, H. L., Hellman, L., and Gallagher, T. F. (1962a) *J. Biol. Chem.* **237**: 3359.

Fukushima, D. K., Bradlow, H. L., Hellman, L., and Gallagher, T. F. (1962b) *J. Clin. Endocrin. Metab.* **22**: 765.

Gallagher, T. F. (1958) *Proc. Intern. Congr. Biochem. 4th Vienna 1958.*

Gardner, L. I., and Tice, A. A. (1957) *Helv. Paediat. Acta* **12**:147.

Girard, A., Sandulesco, G., Friederson, A., and Rutgers, J. J. (1932) *Compt. Rend.* **195**: 981.

Glen, W. L., Barber, R., and Papineau-Couture, G. (1958) *Nature* **182**: 1308.

Glick, H. J., Jr. (1957) *Endocrinology* **60**: 368.

Goldzieher, J., and Roberts, I. S. (1952) *J. Clin. Endocrinol. Metab.* **12**: 143.

Gore, M. B. R., and Baron, D. N. (1960) *J. Endocrinol.* **21**: 303.

Gorski, J., and Erb, R. E. (1959) *Endocrinology* **64**: 707.

Gorski, J., Dominguez, O. V., Samuels, L. T., and Erb, R. (1958) *Endocrinology* **62**: 234.

Grajcer, D., and Idler, D. R. (1961) *Can. J. Biochem. Physiol.* **39**: 1585.

Grajcer, D., and Idler, D. R. (1963) *Can. J. Biochem. Physiol.* **41**: 23.

Green, O. C., Migeon, C. J., and Wilkins, L. (1960) *J. Clin. Endocrinol. Metab.* **20**: 929.

Grosso, L., and Ungar, F. (1964) *Steroids* **3**: 67.

Guillemin, R., Clayton, G. W., Lipscomb, H. S., and Smith, G. D. (1959) *J. Lab. Clin. Med.* **53**: 830.

Guillon, J., Colas, J., Trichereau, R., Delumeau, G., and Baulieu, E. E. (1961) *Ann. Endocrinol* (*Paris*) **22**: 331.

Haines, W. J., Johnson, R. H., Goodwin, M. P., and Kuizenga, M. H. (1948) *J. Biol. Chem.* **174**: 925.

Hane, S., and Roberston, O. H. (1959) *Proc. Nat. Acad. Sci. U.S.* **45**: 886.

Harman, R. E., Ham, E. A., DeYoung, J. J., Brink, N. G., and Sarett, L. H. (1954) *J. Am. Chem. Soc.* **76**: 5035.

Hartmann, M., and Locher, F. (1935) *Helv. Chim. Acta* **18**: 160.

Hartmann, M., and Wettstein, A. (1934) *Helv. Chim. Acta* **17**: 878.

Haslewood, G. A. D., Marrian, G. F., and Smith, E. R. (1934) *Biochem. J.* **28**: 1316.

Haussler, E. P. (1934) *Helv. Chim. Acta* **17**: 531.

Hayano, M., Saba, N., Dorfman, R. I., and Hechter, O. (1956) *Recent Progr. Hormone Res.* **12**: 79.

Heard, R. D. H. (1938) *J. Am. Chem. Soc.* **60**: 493.

Heard, R. D. H., and Hoffman, M. M. (1941) *J. Biol. Chem.* **138**: 651.

Heard, R. D. H., and McKay, A. F. (1939) *J. Biol. Chem.* **131**: 371.

Heard, R. D. H., Blick, E. G., Cann, M. C., Jellinck, P. H., O'Donnell, V. J., Rao, B. G., and Webb, J. L. (1956) *Recent Progr. Hormone Res.* **12**: 45.

Hechter, O., Macchi, I. A., Korman, H., Frank, E. D., and Frank, H. A. (1955) *Am. J. Physiol.* **182**: 29.

Herrmann, W., and Silverman, L. (1957) *J. Clin. Endocrinol. Metab.* **17**: 1482.

Hilliard, J., and Sawyer, C. H. (1962) *Excerpta Med. Intern. Congr. Ser.* **51**: 26.

Hilliard, J., Endröczi, E., and Sawyer, C. H. (1961) *Proc. Soc. Exptl. Biol. Med.* **108**: 154.

Hirsch, H. S., Berliner, D. L., and Samuels, L. T. (1957) *Arch. Biochem. Biophys.* **71**: 91.

Hirschmann, H. (1940) *J. Biol. Chem.* **136**: 483.

Hirschmann, H. (1941) *Proc. Soc. Exptl. Biol. Med.* **46**:51.

Hirschmann, H. (1943) *J. Biol. Chem.* **150**: 363.

Hirschmann, H., and Hirschmann, F. B. (1945) *J. Biol. Chem.* **157**: 601.

Hirschmann, H., and Hirschmann, F. B. (1947) *J. Biol. Chem.* **167**: 7.

Hirschmann, H., and Hirschmann, F. B. (1949) *Federation Proc.* **8**: 206.

Hirschmann, H., and Hirschmann, F. B. (1950) *J. Biol. Chem.* **187**: 137.

Hirschmann, H., and Wintersteiner, O. (1937) *J. Biol. Chem.* **122**: 303.

Hirschmann, H., DeCourcey, C., Levy, R. P., and Miller, K. L. (1960) *J. Biol. Chem.* **235**: PC48.

Hirschmann, H., Hirschmann, F. B., and Zala, A. P. (1961) *J. Biol. Chem.* **236**: 3141.

Holness, N. J., and Gray, C. H., (1958) *J. Endocrinol.* **17**: 237.

Holness, N. J., Lunnon, J. B., and Gray, C. H. (1956) *J. Endocrinol.* **14**: 138.

Holtz, A. H. (1954) *Nature* **174**: 316.

Huffman, M. N., and Lott, M. H. (1951) *J. Am. Chem. Soc.* **73**: 878.

Huffman, M. N., Thayer, S. A., and Doisy, E. A. (1940) *J. Biol. Chem.* **133**: 567.

Huis In't Veld, L. G. (1957) *Rec. Trav. Chim.* **76**: 622.

Huis In't Veld, L. G. (1961) *Nature* **191**: 175.

Ichii, S., Forchielli, E., Perloff, W. H., and Dorfman, R. I. (1962) *Anal. Biochem.* **5**: 422.

Idler, D. R. (1961) *Can. J. Biochem. Physiol.* **39**: 317.

Idler, D. R., Ronald, A. P., and Schmidt, P. J. (1959a) *J. Am. Chem. Soc.* **81**: 1260.

Idler, D. R., Ronald, A. P., and Schmidt, P. J. (1959*b*) *Can. J. Biochem. Physiol.* **37**: 1227.

Idler, D. R., Fagerlund, V. H. M., and Ronald, A. P. (1960a) *Biochem. Biophys. Res. Commun.* **2**: 133.
Idler, D. R., Schmidt, P. J., and Ronald, A. P. (1960b) *Can. J. Biochem. Physiol.* **38**: 1053.
Idler, D. R., Bitners, I. I., and Schmidt, P. J. (1961a) *Can. J. Biochem. Physiol.* **39**: 1737.
Idler, D. R., Schmidt, P. J., and Bitners, I. (1961b) *Can. J. Biochem. Physiol.* **39**: 1653.
Idler, D. R., Schmidt, P. J., and Ronald, A. P. (1962) *Can. J. Biochem. Physiol.* **40**: 549.
Jacobson, G. M. (1962) *J. Clin. Endocrinol. Metab.* **22**: 859.
Kandráč, M. S., L.Stárka, Z. Zikanová, and Mach, O. (1959) *Chem. Abstr.* **53**: 22411; *Casopis Lekaru Ceskych* **98**: 371.
Kandráč, M. S. (1962) *Chem. Zvesti* **16**: 113.
Kappas, A., Pearson, O. H., West, C. D., and Gallagher, T. F. (1956) *J. Clin. Endocrinol. Metab.* **16**: 517.
Kase, N., Forchielli, E., and Dorfman, R. I. (1961) *Acta Endocrinol.* **37**: 19.
Katz, F. H., Frantz, A. G., and Jailer, J. W. (1960) *Proc. Endocrine Soc. 42nd Meeting, Miami* 35.
Keimar, D., Goodno, J. A., and Barnes, A. C. (1962) *Nature* **195**: 1204.
Keller, M. (1956) *J. Clin. Endocrinol. Metab.* **16**: 1075.
Keller, M., Hauser, A., and Walser, A. (1958) *J. Clin. Endocrinol. Metab.* **18**: 1384.
Kelly, W. G., Bandi, L., Shoolery, J. N., and Lieberman, S. (1962a) *Biochemistry* **1**: 172.
Kelly, W. G., Bandi, L., and Lieberman, S. (1962b) *Biochemistry* **1**: 792.
Kemp, A. D., Kappas, A., Salamon, I. I., Herling, F., and Gallagher, T. F. (1954) *J. Biol. Chem.* **210**: 123.
Ketz, H. A., Witt, H., and Mitzner, M. (1961) *Biochem. Z.* **334**: 73.
Klein, R., Fortunato, J., Laron, Z., and Papadatos, C. (1957) *J. Clin. Endocrinol. Metab.* **17**: 256.
Klopper, A. I., and MacNaughton, M. C. (1959) *J. Endocrinol.* **18**: 319.
Klyne, W. (1950) *Nature* **166**: 559.
Klyne, W., and Marrian, G. F. (1945) *Biochem. J.* **39**: 14.
Klyne, W., and Paterson, J. Y. F. (1948) *Biochem. J.* **42**: 1.
Klyne, W., and Wright, A. A. (1957) *Biochem. J.* **66**: 92.
Klyne, W., and Wright, A. A. (1959) *J. Endocrinol.* **18**: 32.
Korus, W., Schriefers, H., Breuer, H., and Bayer, J. M. (1959) *Acta Endocrinol.* **31**: 529.
Kristoffersen, J., Lunaas, T., and Velle, W. (1961) *Nature* **190**: 1009.
Kuizenga, M. H., and Cartland, G. F. (1939) *Endocrinology* **24**: 526.
Kuizenga, M. H., and Cartland, G. F. (1940) *Endocrinology* **27**: 647.
Ladany, S., Markscheid, L., Beyth, L., and Finkelstein, M. (1962) *Excerpta Med. Intern. Congr. Ser.* **51**: 176.
Lambert, M., and Pennington, G. W. (1963) *Nature* **197**: 391.
Lanman, J. T., and Silverman, L. M. (1957) *Endocrinology* **60**: 443.
Lanthier, A., and Sandor, T. (1960) *Metab. Clin. Exptl.* **9**: 861.
Layne, D. S., and Marrian, G. F. (1958a) *Nature* **182**: 50.
Layne, D. S., and Marrian, G. F. (1958b) *Biochem. J.* **70**: 244.
Layne, D. S., Common, R. H., Maw, W. A., and Fraps, R. M. (1958) *Nature* **181**: 351.
Levin, E., Burn, J. F., and Collins, V. K. (1951) *Endocrinology* **49**: 289.
Levin, L. (1945) *J. Biol. Chem.* **158**: 725.
Lewbart, M. L., and Schneider, J. J. (1959) *Rec. Prog. Hormone Res.* **15**: 201.
Lewbart, M. L., and Mattox, V. R. (1960) *Federation Proc.* **19**: 158.
Lieberman, S., and Dobriner, K. (1946) *J. Biol. Chem.* **166**: 773.
Lieberman, S., and Dobriner, K. (1948) *Recent Progr. Hormone Res.* **3**: 71.
Lieberman, S., and Dobriner, K. (1950) *Proc. Am. Chem. Soc.* 117*th Meeting* p. 19C.
Lieberman, S., Dobriner, K., Hill, B. R., Fieser, L. F., and Rhoads, C. P. (1948) *J. Biol. Chem.* **172**: 263.
Lieberman, S., Fukushima, D. K., and Dobriner, K. (1950) *J. Biol. Chem.* **182**: 299.

Lieberman, S., Hariton, L. B., Stokem, M. B., Studer, P. E., and Dobriner, K. (1951) *Federation Proc.* **10**: 216.

Lieberman, S., Praetz, B., Humphries, P., and Dobriner, K. (1953) *J. Biol. Chem.* **204**: 491.

Liebermann, R. E. (1959) *Schweiz. Med. Wochschr.* **89**: 837.

Lindner, H. R. (1959) *Nature* **183**: 1605.

Lipman, M. M., Katz, F. H., Frantz, A. G., and Jailer, J. W. (1961) *Proc. Endocrine Soc. 43rd Meeting, New York, 1961*, p. 39.

Lipsett, M. B., and Damast, B. (1958) *Proc. Soc. Exptl. Biol. Med.* **99**: 285.

Llaurado, J. G., Claus, J. L., and Trunnell, J. B. (1962) *Endocrinology* **71**: 598.

Loke, K. H., and Marrian, G. F. (1958) *Biochim. Biophys. Acta* **27**: 213.

Loke, K. H., Watson, E. J. D., and Marrian, G. F. (1957) *Biochim. Biophys. Acta* **26**: 230.

Lombardo, M. E., McMorris, C., and Hudson, P. B. (1959) *Endocrinology* **65**: 426.

Longwell, B. B., Reif, A. E., Hansbury, E., and Baker, H. S. (1955) *Federation Proc.* **14**: 246.

Longwell, B. B., Reif, A. E., and Hansbury, E. (1956) *Federation Proc.* **15**: 303.

Lucas, W. M., Whitmore, W. F., Jr., and West, C. D. (1957) *J. Clin. Endocrinol. Metab.* **17**: 465.

Luetscher, J. A., Jr. (1956) *Recent Progr. Hormone Res.* **12**: 175.

Luetscher, J. A., Jr., Neher, R., and Wettstein, A. (1954) *Experientia* **10**: 456.

Lynn, W. S., Jr. (1956) *Federation Proc.* **15**: 305.

Lynn, W. S., Jr., and Brown, R. (1956) *Biochim. Biophys. Acta* **21**: 403.

Lynn, W. S., Jr., and Brown, R. (1958a) *J. Biol. Chem.* **232**: 1005.

Lynn, W. S., Jr., and Brown, R. (1958b) *J. Biol. Chem.* **232**: 1015.

MacCorquodale, D. W., Thayer, S. A., and Doisy, E. A. (1936) *J. Biol. Chem.* **115**: 435.

McKenna, J., Menini, E., and Norymberski, J. K. *Biochem. J.* **79**: 11P.

Mahesh, V. B., and Greenblatt, R. B. (1961) *Proc. Endocrine Soc. 43rd Meeting, New York, 1961*, p. 80.

Mahesh, V. B., and Herrmann, W. (1963) *Steroids* **1**: 51.

Majnarich, J. J., and Dillon, R. N. (1954) *Arch. Biochem. Biophys.* **49**: 247.

Malassis, D., Baulieu, E. E., Weinmann, S., Crepy, O., and Jayle, M. F. (1957) *Compt. Rend. Soc. Biol.* **151**: 447.

Margraf, H. W., and Weichselbaum, T. E. (1962) *Excerpta Med. Intern. Congr. Ser.* **51**: 172.

Marker, R. E. (1938a) *J. Am. Chem. Soc.* **60**: 210.

Marker, R. E. (1938b) *J. Am. Chem. Soc.* **60**: 2442.

Marker, R. E. (1938c) *J. Am. Chem. Soc.* **60**: 2931.

Marker, R. E. (1939a) *J. Am. Chem. Soc.* **61**: 944.

Marker, R. E. (1939b) *J. Am. Chem. Soc.* **61**: 1287.

Marker, R. E., and Kamm, O. (1937) *J. Am. Chem. Soc.* **59**: 1373.

Marker, R. E., and Lawson, E. J. (1938) *J. Am. Chem. Soc.* **60**: 2928.

Marker, R. E., and Rohrmann, E. (1938) *J. Am. Chem. Soc.* **60**: 1565.

Marker, R. E., and Rohrmann, E. (1939a) *J. Am. Chem. Soc.* **61**: 2537.

Marker, R. E., and Rohrmann, E. (1939b) *J. Am. Chem. Soc.* **61**: 2719.

Marker, R. E., and Rohrmann, E. (1939c) *J. Am. Chem. Soc.* **61**: 3476.

Marker, R. E., Kamm, O., and McGrew, R. V. (1937) *J. Am. Chem. Soc.* **59**: 616.

Marker, R. E., Kamm, O., Crooks, H. M., Jr., Oakwood, T. S., Whittle, E. L., and Lawson, E. J. (1938a) *J. Am. Chem. Soc.* **60**: 210.

Marker, R. E., Lawson, E. J., Whittle, E. L., and Crooks, H. M. (1938b) *J. Am. Chem. Soc.* **60**: 1559.

Marker, R. E., Rohrmann, E., Lawson, E. J., and Whittle, E. (1938c) *J. Am. Chem. Soc.* **60**: 1901.

Marker, R. E., Rohrmann, E., Whittle, E. L., and Lawson, E. J. (1938d) *J. Am. Chem. Soc.* **60**: 1512.

Marrian, G. F. (1929) *Biochem. J.* **23**: 1090.

Marrian, G. F. (1930) *Chem. Ind.* (*London*) **49**: 515.

Marrian, G. F. (1944) *Nature* **154**: 19.

Marrian, G. F., and Bauld, W. S. (1955) *Biochem. J.* **59**: 136.
Marrian, G. F., Loke, K. H., Watson, E. J. D., and Panattoni, M. (1957) *Biochem. J.* **66**: 60.
Marti, M., and Heusser, H. (1954) *Helv. Chim. Acta* **37**: 327.
Martin, F. I. R. (1962) *Am. J. Med.* **32**: 795.
Mason, H. L. (1945) *J. Biol. Chem.* **158**: 719.
Mason, H. L., Hehn, W. M., and Kendall, E. C. (1938) *J. Biol. Chem.* **124**: 459.
Mason, H. L. (1950) *J. Biol. Chem.* **182**: 131.
Mason, H. L., and Kepler, E. J. (1945a) *J. Biol. Chem.* **160**: 255.
Mason, H. L., and Kepler, E. J. (1945b) *J. Biol. Chem.* **161**: 235.
Mason, H. L., and Schneider, J. J. (1950) *J. Biol. Chem.* **184**: 593.
Mason, H. L., and Sprague, R. G. (1948) *J. Biol. Chem.* **175**: 451.
Mason, H. L., and Strickler, H. S. (1947) *J. Biol. Chem.* **171**: 543.
Mason, H. L., Meyers, C. S., and Kendall, E. C. (1936) *J. Biol. Chem.* **114**: 613.
Mason, H. L., Hochn, W. M., McKenzie, B. F., and Kendall, E. C. (1937) *J. Biol. Chem.*. **120**: 719.
Mattox, V. R. (1955) *Proc. Staff Meetings Mayo Clinic* **30**: 180.
Mattox, V. R., and Mason, H. L. (1956) *J. Biol. Chem.* **223**: 215.
Menini, E., and Diczfalusy, E. (1960) *Endocrinology* **67**: 500.
Menini, E., and Diczfalusy, E. (1961) *Endocrinology* **68**: 492.
Meyer, A. S. (1953) *J. Biol. Chem.* **203**: 469.
Meyer, A. S. (1955) *Biochem. Biophys. Acta* **24**: 1435.
Meyer, A. S., Hayano, M., Lindberg, M. C., Gut, M., and Rodgers, O. G. (1955) *Acta Endocrinol.* **18**: 148.
Mialhe-Volloss, C., and Baulieu, E. E. (1958) *Compt. Rend.* **246**: 639.
Migeon, C. J. (1956) *J. Biol. Chem.* **218**: 941.
Migeon, C. J., and Plager, J. E. (1954) *J. Biol. Chem.* **209**: 767.
Miller, A. M., and Dorfman, R. I. (1949) *Endocrinology* **42**: 174.
Miller, A. M., and Dorfman, R. I. (1950) *Endocrinology* **46**: 514.
Miller, A. M., Rosenkrantz, H., and Dorfman, R. I. (1953) *Endocrinology* **53**: 238.
Miller, W. R., and Turner, C. W. (1955) *Proc. Soc. Exptl. Biol. Med.* **90**: 142.
Miller, W. R., Turner, C. W., Fukushima, D. K., and Salamon, I. I. (1956) *J. Biol. Chem.* **220**: 221.
Mulrow, P. J., Cohn, G. L., and Yesner, R. (1959) *Yale J. Biol. Med.* **31**: 363.
Munson, P. L., Gallagher, T. F., and Koch, F. C. (1944) *J. Biol. Chem.* **152**: 67.
Nadel, E. M., and Burstein, S. (1956) *J. Natl. Cancer Inst.* **17**: 213.
Nadel, E. M., Burstein, S., and Dorfman, R. I. (1956) *Arch. Biochem. Biophys.* **61**: 144.
Nandi, J., and Bern, H. A. (1960) *Endocrinology* **66**: 295.
Neeman, M., and Hashimoto, Y. (1962) *J. Am. Chem. Soc.* **84**: 2972.
Neeman, M., Slaunwhite, W. R., Jr., Neely, L. M., Colson, J. G., and Sandberg, A. A. (1960) *J. Biol. Chem.* **235**: PC58.
Neher, R. (1958) *Intern. Symp. Aldosterone, Geneva, 1957* p. 11.
Neher, R. (1960) *Folia Endocrinol.* (*Pisa*) **8**: 55.
Neher, R., and Stark, G. (1961) *Experientia* **17**: 1510.
Neher, R., and Wettstein, A. (1956) *Helv. Chim. Acta* **39**: 2062.
Neher, R., and Wettstein, A. (1959) *Helv. Chim. Acta* **42**: 956.
Neher, R., and Wettstein, A. (1960a) *Helv. Chim. Acta* **43**: 623.
Neher, R., and Wettstein, A. (1960b) *Helv. Chim. Acta* **43**: 1171.
Neher, R., and Wettstein, A. (1960c) *Helv. Chim. Acta* **43**: 1628.
Neher, R., and Wettstein, A. (1960d) *Acta Endocrinol.* **35**: 1.
Neher, R., Meystre, C., and Wettstein, A. (1959) *Helv. Chim. Acta* **42**: 132.
Nelson, D. H. (1951) *In* "Adrenal Cortex," Vol. 3. Josiah Macy Jr. Foundation, New York.
Notchev, V. D., and Stimmel, B. F. (1962) *Excerpta Med. Intern. Congr. Ser.* **51**: 175.
Nowaczynski, W., Koiw, E., and Genest, J. (1962) *Can. J. Biochem. Physiol.* **40**: 1779.
O'Donnell, V. J., and McCaig, J. G. (1960) *Biochem. J.* **71**: 9P.

Oertel, G. W. (1961a) *Acta Endocrinol.* **37**: 237.
Oertel, G. W. (1961b) *Acta Endocrinol.* **37**: 301.
Oertel, G. W. (1962) *Fortschr. Med.* **80**: 291.
Oertel, G., and Eik-Nes, K. B. (1959a) *Proc. Soc. Exptl. Biol. Med.* **102**: 553.
Oertel, G. W., and Eik-Nes, K. B. (1959b) *Endocrinology* **65**: 766.
Oertel, G. W., and Eik-Nes, K. B. (1961a) *Acta Endocrinol.* **37**: 305.
Oertel, G. W., and Eik-Nes, K. B. (1961b) *Arch. Biochem. Biophys.* **92**: 150.
Oertel, G. W., and Eik-Nes, K. B. (1961c) *Arch. Biochem. Biophys.* **93**: 392.
Oertel, G. W., and Eik-Nes, K. B. (1962) *Endocrinology* **16**: 313.
Oertel, G. W., and Kaiser, E. (1962) *Clin. Chim. Acta* **7**: 221.
Oertel, G. W., West, C. D., and Eik-Nes, K. B. (1959) *J. Clin. Endocrinol. Metab.* **19**: 1619.
Okada, M., Fukushima, D. K., and Gallagher, T. F. (1959) *J. Biol. Chem.* **234**: 1688.
Oppenauer, R. (1941) *Z. Physiol. Chem.* **270**: 97.
Pasqualini, J. R. (1960) *Acta Physiol. Latinoam.* **10**: 135.
Pasqualini, J. R. (1962) *Compt. Rend.* **255**: 3258.
Pasqualini, J. R., and Jayle, M. F. (1961) *Biochem. J.* **81**: 147.
Pasqualini, J. R., and Jayle, M. F. (1962a) *J. Clin. Invest.* **41**: 981.
Pasqualini, J. R., and Jayle, M. F. (1962b) *Experientia* **18**: 273.
Pearlman, W. H. (1942) *Endocrinology* **30**: 270.
Pearlman, W. H. (1946) *J. Biol. Chem.* **166**: 473.
Pearlman, W. H. (1948) *Federation Proc.* **7**: 178.
Pearlman, W. H. (1952) *Ciba Found. Colloq. Endocrinol.* **2**: 309.
Pearlman, W. H., and Cerceo, E. (1952a) *J. Biol. Chem.* **198**: 79.
Pearlman, W. H., and Cerceo, E. (1952b) *J. Biol. Chem.* **194**: 807.
Pearlman, W. H., Pincus, G., and Werthesen, N. T. (1942) *J. Biol. Chem.* **142**: 649.
Pearlman, W. H., Rakoff, A. E., Cantarow, A., and Paschkis, K. E. (1947) *J. Biol. Chem.* **170**: 173.
Pearlman, W. H., Rakoff, A. E., Paschkis, K. E., Cantarow, A., and Walkling, A. A. (1948) *J. Biol. Chem.* **173**: 175.
Pelzer, H., Staib, W., and Dietrich, O. (1958) *Z. Physiol. Chem.* **312**: 15.
Peron, F. G. (1960) *Endocrinology* **66**: 458.
Peron, F. G. (1961) *Endocrinology* **69**: 39.
Peron, F. G., and Dorfman, R. I. (1956) *J. Biol. Chem.* **223**: 877.
Peron, F. G., and Dorfman, R. I. (1957) *Arch. Biochem. Biophys.* **67**: 490.
Peron, F. G., and Dorfman, R. I. (1958) *Endocrinology* **62**: 1.
Personen, S. (1962) *Acta Endocrinol.* **40**: 387.
Peterson, R. E. (1957) *J. Biol. Chem.* **225**: 25.
Peterson, R. E., Pierce, C. E., and Kliman, B. (1957) *Arch. Biochem. Biophys.* **70**: 614.
Pfiffner, J., and North, H. B. (1940) *J. Biol. Chem.* **132**: 459.
Pfiffner, J., and North, H. B. (1941) *J. Biol. Chem.* **139**: 855.
Phillips, J. G. (1959) *J. Endocrinol.* **18**: xxxvii.
Phillips, J. G., and Chester-Jones, I. (1957) *J. Endocrinol.* **16**: iii.
Pigon, H., Lunaas, T., and Velle, W. (1961) *Acta Endocrinol.* **36**: 131.
Pincus, G., and Pearlman, W. H. (1941) *Endocrinology* **29**: 413.
Pincus, G., and Romanoff, E. B. (1955) *Ciba Found. Colloq. Endocrinol.* **8**: 97.
Plantin, L. O., and Birke, G. (1955) *Acta Endocrinol.* **10**: 8.
Plantin, L. O., Diczfalusy, E., and Birke, G. (1957) *Nature* **179**: 421.
Pope, G. S., McNaughter, M. L., and Jones, M. E. H. (1957) *Biochem. J.* **66**: 206.
Prelog, V., and Führer, J. (1945) *Helv. Chim. Acta* **28**: 583.
Prelog, V., and Meister, P. (1949) *Helv. Chim. Acta* **32**: 2435.
Purdy, R. H., Engel, L. L., and Oncley, L. L. (1961) *J. Biol. Chem.* **236**: 1043.
Rabinowitz, J. L., and Dowben, R. M. (1955) *Biochem. Biophys. Acta* **16**: 96.
Raeside, J. F. (1957) *Proc. Soc. Exptl. Biol. Med.* **95**: 300.
Raman, P., Ertel, R. J., and Ungar, F. (1964) *Endocrinology* **74**: 865.

Reddy, W. J., Haydar, N. A., and Laidlaw, J. C. (1955) *J. Clin. Endocrinol. Metab.* **15**: 891.

Reich, E., and Lehninger, A. L. (1955) *Biochim. Biophys. Acta* **17**: 136.

Reich, H., Nelson, D. H., and Zaffaroni, A. (1950) *J. Biol. Chem.* **187**: 411.

Reichstein, T. (1936a) *Helv. Chim. Acta* **19**: 223.

Reichstein, T. (1936b) *Helv. Chim. Acta* **19**: 29.

Reichstein, T. (1936c) *Helv. Chim. Acta* **19**: 402.

Reichstein, T. (1937a) *Helv. Chim. Acta* **20**: 253.

Reichstein, T. (1937b) *Helv. Chim. Acta* **20**: 953.

Reichstein, T., and von Euw, J. (1938) *Helv. Chim. Acta* **21**: 1197.

Reichstein, T., and von Euw, J. (1939) *Helv. Chim. Acta* **22**: 1222.

Reichstein, T., and Gatzi, K. (1938a) *Helv. Chim. Acta* **21**: 1185.

Reichstein, T., and Gatzi, K. (1938b) *Helv. Chim. Acta* **21**: 1490.

Reif, A. E., and Longwell, B. B. (1958) *Endocrinology* **62**: 573.

Revol, A. (1960) *Ann. Biol. Clin.* (*Paris*) **18**: 565.

Reynolds, J. W., and Ulstrom, R. A. (1962) *J. Clin. Endocrinol. Metab.* **23**: 191.

Richardson, E. M., Touchstone, J. C., and Dohan, F. C. (1955) *J. Clin. Invest.* **34**: 285.

Richardson, E. M., Bulaschenko, H., and Dohan, F. C. (1958) *J. Clin. Endocrinol. Metab.* **18**: 1399.

Robertson, H., and Coulson, W. F. (1958) *Nature* **182**: 1512.

Romanelli, R., Biancalana, D., and Neher, R. (1960) *Proc. 1st Intern. Congr. Endocrinol. Copenhagen* 1960, p. 383.

Romanoff, E. B., Hudson, P., and Pincus, G. (1953) *J. Clin. Endocrinol. Metab.* **13**: 1546.

Romanoff, E. B., Deshpande, N., and Pincus, G. (1962) *Endocrinology* **70**: 532.

Romanoff, L. P., Rodriguez, R. M., Seelye, J. M., Parent, C., and Pincus, G. (1958) *J. Clin. Endocrinol. Metab.* **17**: 1285.

Rombouts, P. (1962) *Ann. Biol. Animale. Biochim. Biophys.* **2**: 151.

Ronan, F. F., Parsons, L., Namiot, R., and Wotiz, H. H. (1960) *J. Clin. Endocrinol. Metab.* **20**: 355.

Rosselet, J. P., Furman, M., Lieberman, S., and Jailer, J. W. (1954a) *Science* **120**: 788.

Rosselet, J. P., Overland, L., Jailer, J. W., and Lieberman, S. (1954b) *Helv. Chim. Acta* **37**: 1933.

Runnebaum, B., and Zander, J. (1962) *Klin. Wochschr.* **40**: 453.

Ruzicka, L., and Prelog, V. (1943) *Helv. Chim. Acta* **26**: 975.

Saba, N., and Hechter, O. (1955) *Federation Proc.* **14**: 775.

Salamon, I. I., and Dobriner, K. (1952) *J. Clin. Endocrinol. Metab.* **12**: 967.

Salamon, I. I., and Dobriner, K. (1953) *J. Biol. Chem.* **204**: 487.

Salhanick, H. A., and Berliner, D. L. (1957) *J. Biol. Chem.* **227**: 583.

Salhanick, H. A., Noall, M. W., Zarrow, M. X., and Samuels, L. T. (1952) *Science* **115**: 708.

Salvadori, B., Leone, U., and Cassano, F. (1956) *Quaderni Clin. Obstet. Ginecol* **11**: 261.

Savard, K. (1957) *Ciba Found. Colloq. Endocrinol.* **11**: 252.

Savard, K. (1961) *Endocrinology* **68**: 411.

Savard, K., Dorfman, R. I., and Poutasse, E. (1952) *J. Clin. Endocrinol. Metab.* **12**: 935.

Savard, K., Dorfman, R. I., Baggett, B., Engel, L. L., Lester, L. M., and Engel, F. L. (1956a) *J. Clin. Endocrinol. Metab.* **16**: 970.

Savard, K., Dorfman, R. I., Baggett, B., and Engel, L. L. (1956b) *J. Clin. Endocrinol. Metab.* **16**: 1629.

Savard, K., Andrec, K., Brooksbank, B. W. L., Reyneri, C., Dorfman, R. I., Heard, R. D. H., Jacobs, R., and Solomon, S. S. (1958) *J. Biol. Chem.* **231**: 765.

Savard, K., Gut, M., Dorfman, R. I., Gabrilove, J. L., and Soffer, L. J. (1961a) *J. Clin. Endocrinol. Metab.* **21**: 165.

Savard, K., Mason, N. R., Ingram, J. T., and Gassner, F. X. (1961b) *Endocrinology* **69**: 324.

Schachter, B., and Marrian, G. F. (1935) *J. Biol. Chem.* **126**: 663.

Schiller, S., Miller, A. M., Dorfman, R. I., Sevringhaus, E. H., and McCullough, E. P. (1945) *Endocrinology* **27**: 262.

Schindler, W. J., and Knigge, K. M. (1959) *Endocrinology* **65**: 739.

Schmidt-Clemendorff, H. W. (1961) *Acta Endocrinol.* **38**: 527.

Schneider, J. J. (1950) *J. Biol. Chem.* **183**: 365.

Schneider, J. J. (1952) *J. Biol. Chem.* **194**: 337.

Schubert, K., and Wehrberger, K. (1960a) *Z. Physiol. Chem.* **321**: 71.

Schubert, K., and Wehrberger, K. (1960b) *Naturwissenschaften* **47**: 281.

Schubert, K., and Wehrberger, K. (1961) *Z. Physiol. Chem.* **326**: 242.

Schubert, K., and Wehrberger, K. (1962) *Z. Physiol. Chem.* **328**: 173.

Serchi, G. (1953) *Chimica (Milan)* **8**: 9.

Shen, N.-H. C., and Kinsella, R. A., Jr. (1961) *Proc. Am. Chem. Soc. 140th Meeting* p. 62C.

Shimizu, K., Hayano, M., Gut, M., and Dorfman, R. I. (1961) *J. Biol. Chem.* **236**: 695.

Shimizu, K., Gut, M., and Dorfman, R. I. (1962) *J. Biol. Chem.* **237**: 699.

Short, R. V. (1957a) *J. Endocrinol.* **15**: i.

Short, R. V. (1957b) *Ciba Colloq. Endocrinol.* **11**: 362.

Short, R. V. (1958) *J. Endocrinol.* **16**: 426.

Short, R. V. (1960a) *Biochem. Soc. Symp. (Cambridge, Engl.)* **18**: 59.

Short, R. V. (1960b) *Proc. Roy. Soc. Med.* **53**: 42.

Short, R. V. (1960c) *J. Endocrinol.* **20**: 147.

Short, R. V. (1962a) *J. Endocrinol.* **24**: 59.

Short, R. V. (1962b) *J. Endocrinol.* **23**: 401.

Short, R. V. (1962c) *J. Reprod. Fertility* **4**: 27.

Short, R. V., and Eckstein, P. (1961) *J. Endocrinol.* **22**: 15.

Short, R. V., and Moore, N. W. (1959) *J. Endocrinol.* **19**: 288.

Simmer, H., and Simmer, I. (1959) *Klin. Wochschr.* **37**: 971.

Simmer, H., and Voss, H. E. (1960) *Klin. Wochschr.* **38**: 819.

Simmer, H., Simmer, I., and Zellmar, O. (1959) *Klin. Wochschr.* **37**: 966.

Simmer, H., Hilliard, J., and Archibald, D. (1963) *J. Clin. Endocrinol. Metab.* **72**: 67.

Simpson, S. A., Tait, J. F., and Bush, I. E. (1952) *Lancet* **263**: 226.

Simpson, S. A., Tait, J. F., Wettstein, A., Neher, R., von Euw, J., Schindler, O., and Reichstein, T. (1954a) *Helv. Chim. Acta* **37**: 1163.

Simpson, S. A., Tait, J. F., Wettstein, A., Neher, R., von Euw, J., Schindler, O., and Reichstein, T. (1954b) *Experientia* **10**: 132.

Skarzynski, B. (1934) *Chem. Abstr.* **28**: 4755.

Slaunwhite, W. R., Jr., and Buchwald, K. W. (1960) *J. Clin. Endocrinol. Metab.* **20**: 786.

Slaunwhite, W. R., Jr., and Samuels, L. T. (1956) *J. Biol. Chem.* **220**: 341.

Slotta, K. H., Rushing, H., and Fels, E. (1934) *Ber. Deut. Chem. Ges.* **67**: 1270.

Smith, E. R., Hughes, D., Marrian, G. F., and Haslewood, G. A. D. (1933) *Nature* **132**: 102.

Smith, G. V. S., Smith, O. W., Huffman, M. N., Thayer, S. A., MacCorquodale, D. W., and Doisy, E. A. (1939) *J. Biol. Chem.* **130**: 431.

Smith, O. W. (1960) *Endocrinology* **67**: 698.

Solomon, S., Vande Wiele, R., and Lieberman, S. (1956a) *J. Am. Chem. Soc.* **78**: 5453.

Solomon, S., Levitan, P., and Lieberman, S. (1956b) *Rev. Can. Biol.* **15**: 282.

Southcott, C. M., Bandy, H. E., Newson, S. E., and Darrach, M. (1956a) *Can. J. Biochem. Physiol.* **34**: 913.

Southcott, C. M., Gandossi, S. K., Barker, A. D., Bandy, H. E., McIntosh, H., and Darrach, M. (1956b) *Can. J. Biochem. Physiol.* **34**: 146.

Staib, W. (1961) *Z. Physiol. Chem.* **325**: 177.

Staib, W., and Doenges, K. (1962) *Experientia* **18**: 223.

Staib, W., Teller, W., and Pelzer, H. (1959a) *Biochim. Biophys. Acta* **31**: 591.

Staib, W., Teller, W., and Schmidt, W. (1959b) *Experientia* **15**: 188.

Staple, E., Lynn, W. S., Jr., and Gurin, S. (1956) *J. Biol. Chem.* **219**: 845.

Stárka, L., Šulcova, J., and Šilink, K. (1962) *Clin. Chim. Acta* **7**: 309.
Steiger, M., and Reichstein, T. (1938) *Helv. Chim. Acta* **21**: 546.
Sweat, M. L., Abbott, W. E., Jefferies, W. McK., and Bliss, E. L. (1953) *Federation Proc.* **12**: 141.
Tagmann, E., Prelog, V., and Ruzicka, L. H. (1946) *Chem. Abstr.* **29**: 440.
Tamm, J. (1958) *Symp. Deut. Ges. Endokrinol.* **5**: 290.
Tamm, J., Beckmann, I., and Voigt, K. D. (1958) *Acta Endocrinol.* **27**: 403.
Teich, S., Rogers, J., Lieberman, S., Engel, L. L., and Davis, J. W. (1953) *J. Am. Chem. Soc.* **75**: 2523.
Telegdy, G. (1960) *Acta Physiol. Acad. Sci. Hung.* **18**: 211.
Telegdy, G., and Endröczi, E. (1961) *Acta Physiol. Acad. Sci. Hung.* **20**: 277.
Touchstone, J. C., and Blakemore, W. S. (1961) *J. Clin. Endocrinol. Metab.* **21**: 263.
Touchstone, J. C., Bulaschenko, H., Richardson, E. M., and Dohan, F. C. (1957) *J. Clin. Endocrinol. Metab.* **17**: 250.
Touchstone, J. C., Cooper, V., and Blakemore, W. S. (1959a) *J. Clin. Endocrinol. Metab.* **19**: 812.
Touchstone, J. C., Kasparow, M., and Rosenthal, O. (1959b) *Federation Proc.* **18**: 340.
Troen, P. (1961) *J. Clin. Endocrinol. Metab.* **21**: 1511.
Troen, P., Nilsson, B., Wilgrist, N., and Diczfalusy, E. (1961) *Acta Endocrinol.* **38**: 361.
Ulick, S., and Kusch, K. (1960) *J. Am. Chem. Soc.* **82**: 6421.
Ulstrom, R. A., Colle, E., Burley, J., and Gunville, R. (1960) *J. Clin. Endocrinol. Metab.* **20**: 1080.
Ungar, F., and Dorfman, R. I. (1953) *J. Biol. Chem.* **205**: 125.
Ungar, F., and Dorfman, R. I. (1954) *J. Biol. Chem.* **206**: 597.
Ungar, F., and Dorfman, R. I. (1956) *J. Clin. Endocrinol. Metab.* **16**: 920.
van der Molen, H. J. (1962) *Acta Endocrinol.* **41**: 247.
Velle, W. (1957) *Acta Chem. Scand.* **11**: 1793.
Velle, W. (1958a) *Acta Endocrinol.* **27**: 64.
Velle, W. (1958b) *Acta Endocrinol.* **28**: 255.
Velle, W. (1958c) *Am. J. Vet. Res.* **19**: 405.
Velle, W. (1959) *Acta Vet. Scand.* **1**: 19.
Velle, W., and Pigon, H. (1960) *Proc. 1st Intern. Congr. Endocrinol. Copenhagen 1960*: 1117.
Venning, E. H., and Browne, J. S. L. (1937) *Endocrinology* **21**: 711.
Venning, E. H., Huffman, M. N., and Browne, J. S. L. (1942) *J. Biol. Chem.* **146**: 369.
Vermeulen, A. (1956a) *Acta Endocrinol.* **22**: 115.
Vermeulen, A. (1956b) *Acta Endocrinol.* **23**: 113.
Vermeulen, A. (1956c) *J. Clin. Endocrinol. Metab.* **16**: 163.
Vogt, M. (1957) *Ciba Found. Colloq. Endocrinol.* **11**: 193.
von Euw, J., and Reichstein, T. (1941) *Helv. Chim. Acta* **24**: 879.
von Euw, J., Meystre, C., Neher, R., Reichstein, T., and Wettstein, A. (1958) *Helv. Chim. Acta* **41**: 1516.
Warren, J. C., and Salhanick, H. A. (1961) *J. Clin. Endocrinol. Metab.* **21**: 1218.
Watson, E. J. D., and Marrian, G. F. (1955) *Biochem. J.* **61**: 64.
Watson, E. J. D., and Marrian, G. F. (1956) *Biochem. J.* **63**: 64.
Weichselbaum, T. E., and Margraf, H. W. (1960) *J. Clin. Endocrinol. Metab.* **20**: 1341.
Werbin, H., and Chaikoff, I. L. (1962) *Biochim. Biophys. Acta* **57**: 150.
West, C. D., Hollander, V. P., Kritchevsky, T. H., and Dobriner, K. (1952) *J. Clin. Endocrinol. Metab.* **12**: 915.
Westerfeld, W. W., MacCorquodale, D. W., Thayer, S. A., and Doisy, E. A. (1938) *J. Biol. Chem.* **126**: 195.
Wettstein, A., and Anner, G. (1954) *Experientia* **10**: 397.
Wettstein, A., Neher, R., and Llaurado, J. G. (1956) *Proc. Univ. Otago Med. School, New Zealand* **34**: 7.
Wiest, W. G. (1958) *Federation Proc.* **17**: 335.

Wiest, W. G. (1959a) *J. Biol. Chem.* **234**: 3115.

Wiest, W. G. (1959b) *Endocrinology* **65**: 825.

Wiest, W. G., Zander, J., and Holmstrome, E. G. (1959) *J. Clin. Endocrinol. Metab.* **19**: 297.

Wilson, H., Borris, J. J., and Bahn, R. C. (1958) *Endocrinology* **62**: 135.

Wintersteiner, O., and Allen, W. M. (1934) *J. Biol. Chem.* **107**: 321.

Wintersteiner, O., and Pfiffner, J. J. (1935) *J. Biol. Chem.* **111**: 599.

Wintersteiner, O., and Pfiffner, J. J. (1936) *J. Biol. Chem.* **116**: 291.

Wintersteiner, O., Schwenk, E., and Whitman, B. (1935) *Proc. Soc. Exptl. Biol. Med.* **32**: 1087.

Wintersteiner, O., Schwenk, E., Hirschmann, H., and Whitman, B. (1936) *J. Am. Chem. Soc.* **58**: 2652.

Wotiz, H. H., Davis, J. W., and Lemon, H. M. (1955) *J. Biol. Chem.* **216**: 677.

Wotiz, H. H., Davis, J. W., Lemon, H. M., and Gut, M. (1956) *J. Biol. Chem.* **222**: 487.

Wotiz, H. H., Botticelli, C., Hisaw, F. L., Jr., and Ringler, I. (1958) *J. Biol. Chem.* **231**: 589.

Wotiz, H. H., Botticelli, C. R., Hisaw, F. L., Jr., and Olsen, A. G. (1960a) *Proc. Natl. Acad. Sci. U.S.* **46**: 580.

Wotiz, H. H., Ziskind, B. S., and Lemon, H. M. (1960b) *Cancer Res.* **20**: 34.

Yudaev, N. A., and Druzhinima, K. V. (1956) *Prob. Endokrinol. Gormonoterap.* **2**: 3.

Zaffaroni, A., and Burton, R. B. (1953) *Arch. Biochem. Biophys.* **42**: 1.

Zander, J. (1958) *J. Biol. Chem.* **232**: 117.

Zander, J. (1959) *Recent Progr. Endocrinol. Reprod., Proc. Conf. Syracuse, 1958*, p. 255.

Zander, J. (1960) *Klin. Wochschr.* **38**: 5.

Zander, J., and Simmer, H. (1954) *Klin. Wochschr.* **32**: 529.

Zander, J., Brendle, E., Münstermann, A. M., Diczfalusy, E., Martinsen, B., and Tillinger, K. G. (1959) *Acta Obstet. Gynecol. Scand.* **38**: 725.

Zander, J., Forbes, T. R., Münstermann, A. M. V., and Neher, R. (1958) *J. Clin. Endocrinol. Metab.* **18**: 337.

Zander, J., Münstermann, A. M., and Runnebaum, B. (1962a) *Klin. Wochschr.* **40**: 436.

Zander, J., Thyssen, J., and Münstermann, A. M. (1962b) *J. Clin. Endocrinol. Metab.* **22**: 861.

Zander, J., Münstermann, A. M., and Runnebaum, B. (1962c) *Acta Endocrinol.* **41**: 507.

CHAPTER III

Biosynthesis of Steroid Hormones

Formation of Cholesterol

At the present time the primary route to the steroid hormones is considered to involve the same biosynthetic intermediates leading to the formation of cholesterol, including acetic acid, mevalonic acid, and squalene. The evidence for this route is nearly complete for the biosynthesis of cholesterol and there has been no contraindication for a similar pathway leading to the formation of the steroid hormones. Added assurance that similar pathways exist would result if it could be shown that the type of carbon distribution originating from acetic acid in the steroid hormones would be the same as that found in cholesterol, or in a compound similar to cholesterol which would, in turn, most likely be a precursor of cholesterol.

It has been demonstrated by both *in vivo* and *in vitro* technics that C^{14}-labeled acetate and cholesterol are efficient precursors of the steroid hormones. In these studies it was considered most unlikely that cholesterol-4-C^{14} was degraded to simpler C^{14}-containing compounds which were then converted to steroids without going through cholesterol. To study this relationship more closely, carbon atoms 1, 2, 3, 4, 5, 6, 7, 20, and 21 of cortisol-C^{14} biosynthesized from acetate-1-C^{14} were isolated by precise chemical degradation (Caspi *et al.*, 1962). In the same paper, carbons 3, 4, 6, and 7 of cholesterol-C^{14} biosynthesized from acetate-1-C^{14} were also studied. It was concluded from this study that the individual carbon atoms of cortisol and the adrenal cholesterol could be biosynthesized by the same route. The study did not exclude the possibility that the steroid hormone biosynthesis may proceed through a steroid intermediate similar to cholesterol.

The biosynthetic steps to cholesterol formation are illustrated in a series of figures. In Fig. 1, it is seen that the coenzyme A (CoA) form of acetate is converted to acetoacetyl-CoA, which in turn forms the intermediate 3-hydroxy-3-methylglutaryl-CoA. Of particular importance in this pathway is the fact that fatty acids may also enter into this scheme at the acetyl-CoA stage or at the next step on the pathway and that the 3-hydroxy-3-methyglutaryl-CoA (HMG-CoA) can also originate from leucine and isovalerate. HMG-CoA is converted successively to mevaldic acid, mevaldic acid-CoA, and mevalonic acid. This last compound is converted to squalene, as illustrated in Fig. 2. The step, squalene to lanosterol, involves a hydroxylation at what becomes carbon atom 3 (steroid numbering), and the four condensed rings are formed with the migration of one carbon atom (Fig. 3).

The conversion of lanosterol to cholesterol essentially consists in the reduction of the double bond in carbon 24 of the side chain, the rearrangement of the double bond between carbons 8 and 9 to 5,6, and the removal of three methyl groups, the two gemdimethyl groups at carbon 4, and the methyl group at carbon 14. Figure 4 illustrates one of several possible sequences in the transformation of lanosterol to cholesterol (Popjak and Cornforth, 1960). The exact order of the latter reactions, and the mechanisms involved, require further experimental verification.

Cholesterol need not be the obligatory intermediate for steroid hormone formation. It is unlikely that compounds I, II, and III (Fig. 4) would, in fact, be direct precursors. Even compounds IV and V (Fig. 4) are somewhat unlikely possible precursors because of the presence of the methyl groups at carbons 4 and 14. However, the compounds zymosterol (compound VI, Fig. 4) and desmosterol (compound VII, Fig. 4) seem to be excellent possible candidates for steroid biosynthesis. Compounds IX and X (Fig. 4) might be considered in the same category. The 24,25-dihydrozymosterol (compound IX, Fig. 4) is an even more likely intermediate because the side chain is precisely that of cholesterol and one could easily visualize that a 20,22-dihydroxy derivative of this compound may be handled by a 20,22-desmolase. Similarly, lathosterol, containing a double bond at carbons 7,8, could serve as a direct intermediate.

Figure 5 deals with the distribution of carbon atoms as derived from the methyl and carboxyl carbons of acetic acid.

The biosynthetic steps leading to the formation of all the steroid hormones are documented by a series of comprehensive tables containing the experimental tissues employed and the references. The information in the tables is translated to the figures which present the best available, plausible schemes of biosynthesis.

Tables 1, 2, and 3 are concerned with the biosynthesis of cholesterol, which is considered to be an important although not necessarily an obligatory component in the biosynthetic scheme. Table 1 lists the many compounds which may be converted to cholesterol. Table 2 deals with the biosynthesis of direct and indirect cholesterol intermediates; i.e., those that may be converted to compounds, which in turn, can be changed to cholesterol by enzymatic means. These compounds are also precursors, in the strictest sense, of cholesterol. Table 3 is a summation of those studies which led to the establishment of the relationship between acetic acid and cholesterol, and indicates which of the cholesterol carbons are derived from either the carboxyl carbon or the methyl carbon of acetic acid.

Formation of Pregnenolone

The biosynthesis of pregnenolone and progesterone *in vivo* is summarized in Table 4. Pregnenolone is one, if not the exclusive, primary steroid on the route to steroid hormone formation. Progesterone in addition to being a biosynthetic intermediate also is an important hormone. In two perfusion experiments using the human placenta (Table 5), cholesterol has yielded pregnenolone and progesterone. Both studies were reported by the group of Solomon *et al.* (1954, 1956–1957). Further advances in the problem of pregnenolone and progesterone formation were accomplished by using *in vitro* technics (Table 6).

Solomon *et al.* (1956–1957) suggested that cholesterol can be converted to 20β-hydroxycholesterol, with the implication that this sterol may be a biosynthetic intermediate. Actually, the nomenclature used at that time was incorrect and the compound discussed was the 20α-hydroxycholesterol. Shimizu *et al.* (1960) demonstrated that 20α-hydroxycholesterol could be cleaved at the side chain to give isocaproic acid. The C_{21} steroid nuclear moiety, pregnenolone, was subsequently demonstrated by use of adrenal homogenate preparations. The human placenta and the rat testes performed these transformations as well (Shimizu *et al.*, 1961). Rat liver homogenates were not capable of performing this reaction. The reaction was also demonstrated with a bovine corpus luteum homogenate (Tomaoki and Pincus, 1961). 20α,22*x*-Dihydroxycholesterol, when incubated with the adrenal homogenate, was converted into pregnenolone. In another study, Chaudhuri *et al.* (1962) showed that a 22-hydroxycholesterol could also serve as a precursor of pregnenolone. These studies were confirmed by Constantopoulos and Tchen (1961).

Figure 6 presents the formation of intermediates between cholesterol and pregnenolone. Two monohydroxy derivatives of cholesterol are illustrated, one with the hydroxyl group in the 20α position and one with a hydroxyl group in the 22 position. It appears that either monohydroxylated intermediate could be further hydroxylated to the dihydroxy compound 20α,22*x*-dihydroxycholesterol which, with the action of the 20,22-desmolase, forms pregnenolone and isocaproic aldehyde. In many of the systems in which this reaction has been shown to take place *in vitro*, the isocaproic aldehyde is oxidized further to the acid.

Figure 7 considers the possible formation of 17α-hydroxypregnenolone from cholesterol without the necessity of pregnenolone being an intermediate. This reaction has not been demonstrated, but cannot be excluded on theoretical grounds.

The adrenocorticotropic hormone (ACTH) stimulates corticoid production in adrenal slices (Haynes *et al.*, 1952b) and bisected rat adrenals (Saffran *et al.*, 1952), as well as in the perfusion of the isolated bovine adrenal (Hechter *et al.*, 1951). On the basis of these last findings, Hechter and co-workers suggested (Stone and Hechter, 1951) that an action of ACTH could be placed between cholesterol and pregnenolone.

Recently, Shimizu and Dorfman (1962) have reported the stimulation by ACTH of the formation of isocaproic acid from cholesterol and 20α-hydroxycholesterol using a cell-free enzyme system derived from the bovine adrenal. This finding as well as other evidence suggests that perhaps one of the important limiting steps in the synthesis of steroid hormones by the adrenal (and perhaps the gonads and placenta as well) is the supply of available pregnenolone and, further, that, as part of its main function, the tropic hormone ACTH (and the gonadotropic hormones) supplies adequate concentrations of pregnenolone. If one can assume from *in vitro* experience, where concentrations of nicotinamide adenine dinucleotide phosphate, reduced form ($NADPH_2$) are not limiting, that the hydroxylation reactions beyond the progesterone stage are not dependent upon ACTH, the idea is favored that the ACTH stimulation may well be concerned with the desmolase reaction involving the rupture of the carbon-carbon bond at C-20, C-22.

Biosynthesis of Androgens

Experimental data dealing with the biosynthesis of androgens are considered in Tables 7–9. The many biosynthetic reactions that have been observed using *in vitro*, *in vivo*, and perfusion methods in normal and abnormal tissues are classified. It is on the basis of this information that pathways of androgen formation may be suggested.

Early studies of the biosynthesis of androgens frequently involved *in vivo* methods and acetate as a precursor. Ungar and Dorfman (1953) administered acetic acid labeled with C^{14} in the carboxyl position and proved that C^{14} was present in the androsterone, dehydroepiandrosterone, and androst-5-ene-3β,17β-diol isolated from the urine of a patient bearing an adrenal cancer. Similarly labeled products were found after cholesterol administration to the same patient. Since then, many experiments of this type have been reported, and the list of substrates has been significantly expanded. Studies by perfusion of the isolated intact gland were also productive, as illustrated by the studies of Kushinsky (1955). The perfusion of dehydroepiandrosterone led to the formation of 11β-hydroxyandrost-4-ene-3,17-dione (Rosenfeld *et al.*, 1955). The conversion of acetic acid to testosterone and androst-4-ene-3,17-dione was demonstrated by perfusion of the human (Savard *et al.*, 1952) and stallion (Savard and Goldzieher, 1960) testis gland. These experiments are documented in Table 9. On the basis of experiments in this table, as well as those in Tables 7 and 8, a series of biosynthetic pathways may be suggested.

Six routes for androgen biosynthesis have been established or indicated. A mechanism, which has been described for all steroid-producing tissues and which was first reported by Slaunwhite and Samuels (1956) and soon thereafter by Savard *et al.* (1956), involves 17α-hydroxyprogesterone, the formation of androst-4-ene-3,17-dione by a desmolase reaction, and the reduction of the 17-keto group to testosterone (Fig. 8). This path is known for the testis (Slaunwhite and Samuels, 1956; Savard *et al.*, 1956), for the ovary (Solomon *et al.*, 1956, Kase *et al.*, 1961), and for the adrenal (Rao and Heard, 1957a).

The second pathway (Fig. 9), involving the formation of dehydroepiandrosterone, rests on secure evidence. Incubations of a homogenate prepared from a human adrenal adenoma with pregnenolone-7-H^3 resulted in the formation of dehydroepiandrosterone-H^3 (Goldstein *et al.*, 1960). The same conversion was reported by Burstein and Dorfman (1962), who injected the tritium-labeled substrate into a virilized woman bearing an adrenal adenoma and isolated tritiated dehydroepiandrosterone from her urine in good yield. The step 17α-hydroxypregnenolone to dehydroepiandrosterone has been established by Solomon *et al.* (1960). The direct isolation of dehydroepiandrosterone from testis tissue by Neher and Wettstein (1960) disproved the thesis that this androgen is exclusively of adrenal origin.

The third pathway for androgen biosynthesis (Fig. 10) involves the conversion of progesterone to testosterone acetate and then to testosterone. In a study by Kase *et al.* (1962), the incubation of progesterone-7H^3 and 17α-hydroxyprogesterone-4-C^{14}, with a homogenate prepared from human polycystic ovaries, yielded testosterone containing a higher ratio of H^3/C^{14} than that found for androst-4-ene-3,17-dione simultaneously formed. This finding suggested the possibility that testosterone could be formed from progesterone without the prior formation of androst-4-ene-3,17-dione. The existence of this pathway has been demonstrated by Fonken *et al.* (1960), who isolated the necessary testosterone acetate intermediate in the transformation of progesterone to testosterone by *Cladosporium resinae*. It is possible that this direct pathway is of some importance in supplying a highly biologically active androgen, testosterone, in ovaries and adrenals in hirsute or virilized women, as well as in normal testis tissue.

A fourth mechanism (Fig. 11), which can be suggested on theoretical grounds, is the direct formation of dehydroepiandrosterone from cholesterol without the necessity of a C-21 intermediate. In this pathway, a 17α,20α-dihydroxycholesterol derivative would be the intermediate. The possibility of such a pathway is suggested on the basis of *in vivo* (Burstein and Dorfman, 1962) and *in vitro* (Gual *et al.*, 1962a) studies.

Recent evidence indicates that the bulk of dehydroepiandrosterone is secreted by the adrenal conjugated as the sulfate, and even the portion secreted into the blood as the free compound would be converted rapidly to the conjugate. As the conjugate, this compound may be considered to be a relatively inert androgen. However, the administration of tritiated dehydroepiandrosterone sulfate to human males *in vivo* resulted in the excretion of labeled androsterone and etiocholanolone, demonstrating the reversible nature of the free and conjugate forms (Roberts *et al.*, 1961a). Other unpublished studies have indicated that the intravenous administration of tritiated dehydroepiandrosterone resulted in the appearance of testosterone-H^3 and androst-4-ene-3,17-dione-H^3 in the blood. This transformation occurs in men in the absence of the testis and in women in the absence of the ovary. Proof is not absolute that the reactions take place solely in the adrenal and it is quite likely that this biosynthetic route to testosterone and androst-4-ene-3,17-dione (Fig. 12) may take place in the gonads and adrenal, and in peripheral tissues.

In Fig. 13 we have an analogous situation to that indicated in Fig. 10. In Fig. 10 progesterone is routed to testosterone acetate and here pregnenolone goes directly to the Δ^5-3β-hydroxy,17β-acetoxy compound and then through androst-5-ene-3β,17β-diol to testosterone and androst-4-ene-3,17-dione. This mechanism is yet to be demonstrated.

Another pathway is related to peripheral formation of androgens from non-androgenic compounds by enzymes in such tissues as liver and muscle (Fig. 14). Examples of these reactions include the well-documented formation of C_{19}- and C_{21}-steroids with liver preparations. C_{21} compounds having oxygen functions at C-17 and C-20 are metabolized to 17-ketosteroids (Dorfman, 1957). Many *in vivo* experiments have been reported that used the following substrates: cortisone, cortisol, 21-deoxycortisone, 21-deoxycortisol, 11-deoxycortisol, and 17α-hydroxyprogesterone. The yield of 17-ketosteroids from C_{21}-steroids possessing the Δ^5-3β-hydroxyl groups is severely reduced. *In vitro* methods have been quite illuminating, such as those of Caspi and Hechter (1954, 1956), Forchielli and Dorfman (1956), and Forchielli *et al.* (1955), where 11-deoxycortisol incubated with liver homogenates has yielded androsterone, androstane-3,17-dione, androst-4-ene-3,17-dione, and etiocholanolone. The cellular location of the desmolase has not been established.

Figure 15 illustrates the formation by 11β-hydroxylation of the 11-oxygenated androgens from three $C_{19}O_2$ androgens, dehydroepiandrosterone, androst-4-ene-3,17-dione, and testosterone. This reaction is specific for the adrenal cortex. However, 11β-hydroxylation has been observed in certain types of interstitial cell tumors of the testes (Savard *et al.*, 1960) and in certain types of ovarian tumors of the luteoma or the adrenal rest type (Dorfman, 1960).

Compounds of the cortisol and 21-deoxycortisol type (Fig. 16) may undergo the side chain removal reaction in the presence of a desmolase, resulting in the formation of 11β-hydroxyandrost-4-ene-3,17-dione, which in turn could be oxidized to adrenosterone.

Figure 17 gives a summary of the various androgen biosynthetic reactions that have been discussed.

Biosynthesis of Adrenal Hormones

Documentation of the biosynthetic pathways of corticoids is presented in Tables 10–12 and illustrated by Figs. 18–21. The ability of the adrenal gland to hydroxylate the steroid nucleus was first demonstrated with a perfusion technic by Hechter and Pincus (1954), and Hayano and Dorfman (1953) reported similar reactions using *in vitro* cell-free systems. Previously described evidence for the conversion of acetate and cholesterol to steroid hormones includes the important finding (Table 11) by Zaffaroni *et al.* (1951) that both acetate-1-C^{14} and cholesterol-4-C^{14} perfused through a bovine adrenal formed the C^{14}-labeled corticoids, cortisol and corticosterone. These reactions were confirmed by Solomon *et al.* (1954) using labeled cholesterol and by Caspi *et al.* (1956) using acetate-1-C^{14}.

In addition to the biosynthetic studies using acetate and cholesterol, an intriguing observation was made by Werbin *et al.* (1960), who found that when β-sitosterol, labeled with tritium, was administered to guinea pigs, cortisol containing the tritium was isolated. This finding would suggest that cholesterol need not be an obligatory intermediate. If β-sitosterol can, in fact, be converted to the steroid hormones without prior formation of cholesterol, it would be possible also for a 20,22-dihydroxy intermediate to be formed with other sterols such as lanosterol, lathosterol, zymosterol, and desmosterol.

A key compound found as a result of the adrenal perfusion technic was pregnenolone, which could be converted to progesterone by virtue of the Δ^5-3β-ol-dehydrogenase. The key role of pregnenolone and progesterone in the formation of the adrenal steroids first reported by Levy *et al.* (1950) has been discussed in detail by Hechter *et al.* (1951) and Levy *et al.* (1954). When progesterone was perfused through the adrenal, excellent yields of corticosterone, cortisol, and many other steroids were obtained (Table 11, see Levy and Kushinsky, 1955).

The perfusion technic with the isolated bovine adrenal has been of value for the study of aldosterone (Ungar *et al.*, 1954; Rosemberg *et al.*, 1956) and for the demonstration of aldosterone formation from steroid precursors (Chen *et al.*, 1958).

A variety of substrates have been perfused through the adrenal (Table 11), including 11β-hydroxyprogesterone which is converted to both cortisol and corticosterone (Eichhorn and Hechter, 1958) and 17α-hydroxyprogesterone which only forms cortisol since the 17-hydroxy group is not removed. Deoxycorticosterone is converted to corticosterone and to aldosterone but not to cortisol. Other transformations of interest that have been demonstrated include 21-deoxycortisol to cortisone and cortisol, corticosterone to aldosterone, and testosterone acetate undergoing 11β-hydroxylation to form 11β-hydroxytestosterone with the hydrolysis of the acetate group. Even 17α-ethnyltestosterone, 17α-vinyltestosterone, and other unusual compounds have been shown to be hydroxylated.

Acetate and cholesterol have been used as substrates for corticoid synthesis with *in vitro* technics as listed in Table 12. This extensive table also indicates that progesterone, deoxycorticosterone, 11-deoxycortisol, 17α-hydroxyprogesterone, corticosterone, 11β-hydroxyprogesterone, pregnenolone, 11-ketoprogesterone, and 17α-hydroxypregnenolone are converted to corticoids under *in vitro* conditions. For the purpose of this table those modifications of progesterone or pregnenolone which involve the addition of a hydroxyl group, as in the conversion of progesterone to 17α-hydroxyprogesterone, are listed (Table 12).

The biogenetic pathways leading to the formation of cortisol and corticosterone are represented in Fig. 18. The arrows indicate the known pathways between pregnenolone, progesterone, and the corticoids. Between progesterone and cortisol there are four intermediates. These are numbered III, IV, V, and VI in Fig. 18 and are, respectively, 17α-hydroxyprogesterone, 11β-hydroxyprogesterone, 11-deoxycortisol, and 21-deoxycortisol. The single intermediate to corticosterone is deoxycorticosterone.

Several studies based on equivocal evidence have suggested the possibility that corticosterone could be converted to cortisol, but in one extensive study by Eichhorn and Hechter (1957), directed specifically to this problem, the conversion of corticosterone to cortisol could not be demonstrated.

The pathways in Fig. 18 need not be the only pathways for the biosynthesis of corticoids. Pregnenolone can also serve as a basic precursor going through 17α-hydroxypregnenolone and then on to cortisol (Weliky and Engel, 1961). Figure 19 outlines such potentialities, starting, for example, with 17α-hydroxypregnenolone. The 17-hydroxylated compound is immediately converted into 17α-hydroxyprogesterone, which may be 21-hydroxylated, and then is converted to cortisol by 11β-hydroxylation. On the other hand, an alternative pathway route may be considered. The 17α-hydroxypregnenolone could be hydroxylated at carbon 21, yielding the 3β,17α,21-trihydroxypregn-5-en-3-one which would form 11-deoxycortisol (Berliner *et al.*, 1962) or this compound (IV, Fig. 15) in turn could be converted into the Δ^5-3β-hydroxy analog of cortisol, which on simple oxidation at carbon 3 would give rise to cortisol. These potentialities deserve further investigation.

Figure 20 considers pathways to corticosterone from pregnenolone. Two alternative routes are indicated in the diagram. A route from pregnenolone to 21-hydroxypregnenolone to deoxycorticosterone has been demonstrated by Berliner *et al.* (1962). Alternatively, 21-hydroxypregnenolone could be 11β-hydroxylated and the compound would then, in turn, form corticosterone under the action of the Δ^5-3β-ol-dehydrogenase.

Biosynthesis of Aldosterone

Figure 21 deals with the biosynthesis of aldosterone. Aldosterone formation has been demonstrated by a variety of procedures from such steroid substrates as progesterone, deoxycorticosterone, and corticosterone. Some discrepancies occur in the literature as to which one of the three steroids mentioned is the most immediate precursor; however, the bulk of these investigations indicate that progesterone → deoxycorticosterone → corticosterone → aldosterone is a likely pathway. In terms of yield, progesterone by the perfusion technic (Rosemberg *et al.*, 1956) or by incubation with adrenal capsule strippings (Ayres *et al.*, 1975a, Travis and Farrell, 1958a) gave the largest conversion to aldosterone. However, the relative specific activity of the isolated aldosterone from these steroids labeled with C^{14} was lowest for progesterone and highest for corticosterone in the work of Ayres *et al.* (1957a), whereas the specific activity was lowest for corticosterone and highest with progesterone as substrate in the work of Travis and Farrell (1958a). Deoxycorticosterone gave values intermediate in range in these cases. In the work of Wettstein *et al.* (1955) deoxycorticosterone-21-C^{14} was converted to aldosterone in high yields, whereas progesterone was not, using adrenal gland homogenates. In this study the 18-aldehyde derivative of deoxycorticosterone was isolated and this compound was suggested to be a direct intermediate in aldosterone biosynthesis. More detailed experiments using bovine capsule strippings by Ayres *et al.* (1960), while not discounting the presence of other pathways, strongly suggest that the major conversion to aldosterone occurs by a sequence involving cholesterol–progesterone–deoxycorticosterone–corticosterone–aldosterone.

The mechanism for the formation of the 18-aldehyde (free or in the hemiacetal form) in aldosterone remains to be demonstrated. Aldosterone is unique among the adrenal steroids not only owing to the presence of the 18-aldehyde group but in addition because it is not primarily stimulated by ACTH and it is formed exclusively in the zona glomerulosa of the cortex. The preparations used by Ayres *et al.* (1957a) and by Giroud *et al.* (1958) employed strippings of the adrenal capsule to which the zona glomerulosa adheres. This preparation is very efficient for the study of aldosterone biosynthesis and at the same time forms only negligible amounts of cortisol, owing to a deficiency or absence of the 17α-hydroxylating system. Corticosterone on the other hand is efficiently synthesized in both the fasciculata and glomerulosa zones. A likely route to the aldehyde form is via 18-hydroxylation. The 18-hydroxyl derivatives of corticosterone and/or deoxycorticosterone have been isolated from rat adrenals (Ward and Birmingham, 1962; Peron, 1962), frog adrenals (Ulick and Solomon, 1960), beef adrenals (Kahnt *et al.*, 1961), and mouse adrenals (Raman *et al.*, 1964). These substances have been synthesized *in vitro* from steroid precursors, progesterone, deoxycorticosterone, and corticosterone, and it has been suggested that the 18-hydroxy derivatives take the role of intermediates to aldosterone formation. The tetrahydro derivative of 18-hydroxycorticosterone isolated from human urine has been shown by Ulick and Kusch (1960) to be solely a metabolite of 18-hydroxycorticosterone and not of aldosterone. The pathways of catabolism for the two compounds apparently are completely independent. It remains to be proved whether in biosynthesis the 18-hydroxyl group of 18-hydroxycorticosterone is converted to the 18-aldehyde form in aldosterone.

Biosynthesis of Estrogens

Estrogen biosynthesis begins historically with the observations by Zondek (1934), Nathanson and Towne (1937), Steinach and Kun (1937), and Dorfman and Hamilton (1939) that indicated the possible conversion of androgens, administered *in vivo* to humans, to estrogens. These studies could never produce definitive nor precise information dealing with the question of estrogen biosynthesis. The major difficulties that could not be overcome with these types of studies included the normally low titer of estrogens in the body and the fact that the yield of estrogens from androgens was exceedingly low. The possibility existed that the injected androgens stimulated the *de novo* synthesis of estrogen in some gland in the body. It was for these reasons that radioisotopic technics were necessary to solve this problem. When labeled steroid precursors became available, Heard *et al.* (1955), Baggett *et al.* (1955, 1956), and Wotiz *et al.* (1956) were able to show that testosterone-C^{14} was, in fact, converted to estrone-C^{14} or estradiol-17β-C^{14}. These experiments paved the way for a breakthrough in the understanding of estrogen biosynthesis. Acetate-1-C^{14} could also serve as an efficient precursor for estrone, as demonstrated in the pregnant mare by Heard *et al.* (1956). Werbin *et al.* (1957b) demonstrated that cholesterol-4-C^{14} administered to a human resulted in the isolation of urinary radioactive estrogens.

A major discovery in elucidating the estrogen biosynthetic pathways was that provided by Meyer, who in 1955 isolated and identified the 19-hydroxy derivative of androst-4-ene-3,17-dione (Meyer, 1955b). The correct hypothesis was made by assigning for this compound the role of an intermediate in estrogen biosynthesis. Meyer incubated the 19-hydroxyandrost-4-ene-3, 17-dione with various enzyme preparations from the ovary, the adrenal, and the placenta and demonstrated the formation of estrogenic compounds (Meyer, 1955a).

Ryan (1959) prepared human placental microsomal fractions and obtained a highly effective estrogen-forming enzyme preparation. Up to the time of this important finding, all of the previous studies gave conversions of androgens to estrogens of only a few per cent. By taking advantage of centrifugation and the preparation of a supernatant microsomal preparation, Ryan was able to obtain an enzyme preparation which, when the proper enzyme-substrate ratios were observed, gave yields of the order of 50 to 70%.

Additional evidence for the role of the 19-hydroxy derivative as an intermediate in estrogen synthesis was provided by the studies of Longchampt *et al.* (1960) who, after incubating androst-4-ene-3,17-dione with the placental system, were able to isolate the 19-hydroxy intermediate.

Table 16 summarizes the compounds that have been studied for aromatization of ring A en route to the estrogens. Most of these compounds were not converted by the placental enzyme preparation. There were, however, a few which were converted to the natural estrogens, estrone and estradiol-17β. 19-Norandrost-4-ene-3,17-dione was converted to estrone in a low yield. This substance has been shown to be present in large amounts in mare follicular fluid and may be a significant source of body estrogens. The route has not been studied extensively, since a dehydrogenation of ring A is involved and no enzyme system has yet been prepared which is highly efficient in this respect. Androst-4-ene-3,17-dione, 19-hydroxyandrost-4-ene-3,17-dione, previously discussed, and 19-oxoandrost-4-ene-3,17-dione yielded trace amounts of estrogens. The 19-oxo compound was active probably by virtue of its rapid decarboxylation to 19-norandrost-4-ene-3,17-dione. Dehydroepiandrosterone also yields estrone, probably by way of an initial oxidation to androst-4-ene-3,17-dione. Androsta-1,4-diene-3,17-dione is another possible substrate for estrogen biosynthesis, but its presence in the tissues of the body is yet to be proved.

Tables 13–15 record the studies on estrogen biosynthesis. Acetate, cholesterol, testosterone, and progesterone have been demonstrated to be precursors of estrogenic compounds in the *in vivo* studies listed in Table 13. The conversion of cortisone to the 11β-hydroxyestrone and the 11β-hydroxyestradiol-17β (Table 13) is indeed unique. This finding by Chang and Dao (1961) could be accounted for by the cleavage of the side chain of cortisone to form adrenosterone, which could be aromatized to give an 11-keto estrogen and, by reduction, the 11β-hydroxy form.

Perfusion of the isolated human placenta has proved of value in demonstrating the conversion of acetate and steroid precursors to estrogens as shown by the studies of Levitz *et al.* (1955) and Troen (1961a). The equine testis (Nyman *et al.*, 1959) and bovine ovary (Romanoff and Pincus, 1962) have been employed with the perfusion technic in the investigation of estrogen biosynthesis.

The large number of *in vitro* studies listed in Table 15 documents the role of acetate, testosterone, androst-4-ene-3,17-dione, and related compounds as intermediates in estrogen formation. Mevalonic acid was shown to be converted to estradiol-17β by human testis homogenates (Rabinowitz and Ragland, 1958). Cholesterol and progesterone also can serve as precursors of estrogens under suitable *in vitro* conditions.

The metabolic pathways of estrogen biosynthesis are summarized in Figs. 22–26. An important observation by Breuer and Grill (1961) was the identification of formaldehyde as the volatile component split out during the aromatization step in the conversion of androst-4-ene-3,17-dione and 19-hydroxyandrost-4-ene-3,17-dione to estrone by a human placental preparation. Morato *et al.* (1961), in confirming the observation that formaldehyde is liberated from the 19-hydroxy compound, also showed that the 19-oxo compound yields formic acid in addition to the estrogen. Figure 22 illustrates the estradiol-17β formation from testosterone. Estrone would be formed if androst-4-ene-3,17-dione were the substrate. After the

19-hydroxylation of testosterone, the product may be oxidized to the 19-oxo derivative which yields estradiol-17β and formic acid (Fig. 23).

Estrogens may be formed from 19-nortestosterone or 19-norandrost-4-ene-3,17-dione. The sequence of this pathway as shown in Fig. 24 indicates hydroxylation of testosterone followed successively by oxidation to the 19-aldo and 19-carboxylic acid derivatives. This latter intermediate is decarboxylated and the resulting 19-nortestosterone is converted to estradiol-17β by a mechanism involving the removal of hydrogen at carbons 1,2. The exact order of sequence in the latter reactions has not been established.

There is a theoretical possibility of a 1-2 dehydrogenation yielding the 17β-hydroxyandrosta-1,4-dien-3-one. This compound, if hydroxylated at 19 with subsequent splitting out of the one carbon unit, would spontaneously yield estradiol-17β as indicated in Fig. 25.

A summary of the various individual biosynthetic pathways to estradiol-17β is presented in Fig. 26. The transformation of androst-4-ene-3,17-dione to estrogen involves the elimination of the C-19 group and hydrogen from C-1 and C-2. The loss of the C-2 hydrogen could be conveniently explained by a simple enolization of the C-3 oxygen to form a Δ^2-double bond since this structure would also favor the removal of a C-1 group in a later step. The problem of C-1 hydrogen removal involves the questions of when in the reaction sequence it is eliminated and how it is eliminated. With regard to the first point, the hydrogen is undoubtedly removed after the oxidation of the C-19 methyl group to the hydroxy or oxo compound and before or during the elimination of this group, since androsta-1,4-diene-3,17-dione, 19-norandrost-4-ene-3,17-dione, and 19-norandrost-5(10)-ene-3,17-dione do not appear to be good substrates for conversion to estrogen (Table 16).

The dehydrogenation step at carbons 1–2 in the process of aromatization has been investigated in two laboratories with divergent results. Axelrod and Goldzieher (1962) studied the conversion of androst-4-ene-3,17-dione to estrone by incubation with human and baboon ovaries. On the basis of assumptions concerning the stability and distribution of tritium label in their steroid precursor, they concluded that the 1α-hydrogen is eliminated in the dehydrogenation step together with the loss of carbon 19.

Morato *et al.* (1962) studied the same reaction by use of the human placental preparation and concluded that the 1β-hydrogen is eliminated. Two samples of androst-4-ene-3,17-dione were prepared with tritium label distributed 25% to 1α and 75% to 1β for compound I, and 93% to 1α and 7% to 1β for compound II (Brodie *et al.*, 1962). The results are shown in Table 17. When compound I with tritium predominantly in the 1β position (75%) was incubated, 83% of the tritium label in the isolated estrone was lost, whereas when compound II with tritium predominantly in the 1α position (93%) was incubated, only 15% of the label in the isolated estrone was lost. The results from this laboratory therefore indicate a preferential elimination of the 1β-hydrogen during aromatization.

After the oxidation of the C-19 group, there are three general ways in which removal of the C-1 hydrogen can take place. These are illustrated in the Fig. 27. Modifications of the general types shown to involve different reaction sequences and enolization forms can be visualized. Pathway I shows a 1,2-dehydrogenation followed by the spontaneous elimination of the C-19 group. This pathway is not favored because a 1,2-dehydrogenation does not now appear likely, at least by the mechanism operating in microorganisms. With the Δ^1-dehydrogenase from *Bacillus sphaericus* (ATCC 7055), the C-1α-hydrogen is eliminated (Ringold *et al.*, 1962); further, there is no requirement for $NADPH_2$ and oxygen, which are essential in the placental aromatization process (Morato *et al.*, 1962).

The more likely pathway for C-1 hydrogen elimination would involve either displacing it by an activated group "Y" (for example, hydroxyl) which can later be eliminated (pathway II) or eliminating it as a hydride ion concerted with the removal of the C-19 oxygenated group (pathway III). This latter pathway could take place either through the mechanism shown or by a four-center type (cyclic) elimination involving an activated C-19 oxonium ion intermediate (not shown). From present knowledge, these types of reactions could reasonably be expected to involve $NADPH_2$ and oxygen and the 1β-hydrogen.

Formation of Steroid Conjugates

The presence of steroid conjugates in the bile and the possible consequences of such an enterohepatic circulation, in addition to the more recent demonstrations of steroid conjugation in tissues other than liver, suggest that this form of the steroid hormones may have a greater significance in the areas of biogenesis and biological activity than had been considered previously. Heretofore, the role of the conjugation reaction had been relegated as an essential step in the catabolic process necessary for the more efficient excretion of steroids in urine. The enzyme systems involved in the formation of steroid conjugates are discussed in more detail in Chapter VI.

A list of the sulfuric and glucuronic acid conjugates of androgens, estrogens, corticoids, and progesterone intermediates which have been isolated under *in vivo* and *in vitro* conditions is presented in Table 18. Among the interesting forms isolated are the 21-sulfates of cortisol and corticosterone (Pasqualini and Jayle, 1961a), testosterone glucuronide (Fishman and Sie, 1956), and the 3,17-disulfate form of androst-5-ene-3β, 17β-diol. Wengle and Bostrom (1962) separated the 3β-ol and 17β-ol sulfokinase in a preparation obtained from a female rat liver supernatant.

Inhibitors of Steroid Biogenesis

The synthetic compounds shown in Fig. 28A, including amphenone, SU-4885, MER-29, and others, demonstrate the interesting property of interfering with the biosynthesis of the steroid hormones. There are apparent differences in the type of inhibition produced by these substances, although their exact mode of action remains essentially unknown. The compound MER-29 (triparanol) interferes with the formation of cholesterol at a stage in the synthesis involving the reduction of the Δ^{24}-double bond. Following the administration of MER-29, levels of cholesterol in blood and tissues fall markedly, with a corresponding increase in the levels of desmosterol and other Δ^{24}-containing sterol intermediates. Amphenone and *o,p′* DDD cause a general decrease in the production of adrenal steroids. Other inhibitors when administered in the proper dose will selectively inhibit a specific enzyme involved in steroid hydroxylation. The compound SU-4885 (Metopirone) will specifically inhibit 11β-hydroxylation at one dosage level, and at higher doses other hydroxylating enzymes will be affected as well. Similarly, the drugs SU-8000 and SU-9055 will selectively inhibit the 17α-hydroxylating reaction (see Fig. 28B).

Hertz (1955) discovered that the compound amphenone was capable of producing changes in adrenal, thyroid, and pituitary glands of the rat. The alterations seen in the thyroid were similar to those obtained by use of other goitrogenic compounds. The adrenal glands were enlarged and highly colored and showed histological evidence of marked fat accumulation, especially in the enlarged cells of the zona fasiculata and zona reticularis, while the zona glomerulosa appeared to be unaffected. The adrenal and thyroid effects were entirely absent in the hypophysectomized rat. The thyroid response was suppressed by thyroxin without any impairment to the adrenal effect, and, conversely, the adrenal effect was suppressed by cortisone without any concommitant reduction in the goitrogenic action of the compound. When amphenone was administered intravenously, at about three times the dose necessary for characteristic endocrinological effects, amphenone exerted an anesthetic action in dogs, rats, and rabbits. Chemically, the adrenals of the amphenone-treated rat contained about three times the normal concentration of cholesterol and about 70% of the normal concentration of ascorbic acid. When these animals were subjected to the stimulation of endogenous ACTH by exposure to cold, or by administration of exogenous ACTH, the ascorbic acid was depleted but the cholesterol concentration did not appear to change significantly. Amphenone-treated rats tolerated cold exposure as well as normal rats and they required no salt supplementation for survival.

Amphenone exhibited progestational activity in the ovariectomized rabbit but not in the adrenalectomized–ovariectomized rabbit. The mechanism of the progestational action was presumably owing to the interference with the hydroxylation of progesterone to form corticoids, thus resulting in the accumulation of excess amounts of progesterone. Amphenone changes in the adrenal involved inhibition of corticoid biosynthesis leading to a compensatory increase in ACTH which, in turn, would produce an abnormally large adrenal.

The action of amphenone is as striking when administered to humans as it is in other species (Table 19). When dose is adequate, cortisol synthesis can be depressed. Aldosterone, androgen, and estrogen biosynthesis have also been shown to be decreased.

Studies by Tullner *et al.* (1956) indicated that the rate of corticoid production in the hypophysectomized rat stimulated with exogenous ACTH was suppressed by amphenone. Gallagher and his co-workers (1956, 1957) administered amphenone to patients with adrenal cancer and measured the excretion of 17-ketosteroids. Dehydroepiandrosterone was dramatically decreased and some order of lowering of the excretion of other $C_{19}O_2$ and $C_{19}O_3$ steroids was in evidence. Thorn *et al.* (1956) found an irregular decrease in urinary corticoid in some patients. Peterson and his co-workers (1957), in a detailed study, demonstrated inhibition of corticoid biosynthesis with amphenone. These results were confirmed by McCullagh and Tretbar (1958). Even the aldosterone biosynthesis was modified by this inhibitor as reported by Renold *et al.* (1957) and Hernando *et al.* (1957). In some instances when the concentration of amphenone was high enough, complete inhibition in aldosterone production was shown. Mach and Muller (1957) showed that administration of 4–6 gm of this compound for three days caused essentially a complete disappearance of aldosterone.

Chart *et al.* (1962) has reported a variety of tetralones (example, SU-9055), indenes (example, SU-8000), dihydronaphthalenes, *N*-acetylated amphenones, and 3-pyridyl substituted nitrites, all of which have a rather important effect on 17α-hydroxylation (Table 19). Other inhibitors, including 4,4′-methylenedianiline, when administered *in vivo* to rats, dogs, and rabbits inhibited corticoid production (Tullner, 1960).

The compound op′DDD, which also caused marked decreases in corticoid production, is particularly toxic and causes necrosis of the adrenal cortical tissue. On this basis, Hertz (1960) has suggested that it perhaps has some usefulness in human adrenal carcinoma. The compound causes a decrease in 17-ketosteroids and corticoids and, in some instances, there could be some beneficial effect on adrenal tumors. The high toxicity, however, limits the usefulness of the compound.

The actions of these compounds have proved to be of great value in the study of the biosynthetic pathways leading to the steroid hormones. In addition, several compounds have been tested clinically and may prove to be potentially useful as therapeutic agents. MER-29 was employed experimentally as a drug for lowering blood cholesterol until it was recognized that serious side effects could ensue which largely limit its usefulness as a general clinical agent.

SU-4885 has received particular attention as a special diagnostic tool for the assessment of the pituitary reserve for ACTH. Since the drug inhibits 11β-hydroxylation and, therefore, the formation of cortisol, the effective blood levels of cortisol are lowered, causing an increased secretion of ACTH. The adrenal glands respond by increasing in size and activity with the result that excessive amounts of 11-deoxysteroids, particularly 11-deoxycortisol, are produced. The measurement of 11-deoxycortisol in the blood, or S metabolites in the urine, therefore, reflect the capacity of the pituitary to secrete ACTH.

Increased levels of naturally occurring steroids have been shown to exert an inhibitory effect on specific tissue enzyme systems. Sharma *et al.* (1962) have shown that androst-4-ene-3,17-dione is a competitive inhibitor of 11β-hydroxylase activity in the bovine adrenal. Also shown in these studies is an effect of testosterone, dehydroepiandrosterone, and the sulfate conjugate of the latter compound. Since these compounds will inhibit 11β-hydroxylase activity, this raises the question of whether the level of androgens in the adrenal could possibly interfere or modulate the corticoid production. In a similar fashion, progesterone *in vitro* has been shown by Mahajan and Samuels (1962) to inhibit the reaction of 17α-hydroxyprogesterone to androstenedione and also the 17β-reduction of androstenedione. This appears to be a very precise mechanism for influencing the biosynthesis of androgens. Layne *et al.* (1962) discussed the decreased secretion rate of cortisol and increased secretion rate of aldosterone as a result of the administration of the estrogen ethynylestradiol-17β-3-methylether. Fukuii *et al.* (1961) described the inhibition of corticosterone production by cortisol and prednisolone being added *in vitro* to adrenal sections. Similar effects had been noted by Peron *et al.* (1960) in a series of *in vivo* and *in vitro* experiments.

Stimulation of Steroid Biogenesis

Table 20 lists examples of demonstrated stimulatory effects on steroid biogenesis owing to various agents other than ACTH. The action of ACTH on the adrenal and the stimulatory effect on steroidogenesis is well documented. An increase in progesterone biosynthesis has been demonstrated by Marsh *et al.* (1961) by the addition of follicle-stimulating hormone (FSH) or luteinizing hormone (LH), but not prolactin, to an *in vitro* preparation of bovine corpus luteum tissue. The suggestion is inescapable that the action of gonadotropin in the ovary and testis is quite comparable with that of ACTH in the adrenal. An ascorbic acid depletion assay in the ovary, for example, has been found to be a reliable index of gonadotropic activity just as the assay in the adrenal reflects ACTH activity.

Some progress has been made during the past few years on the mechanism of ACTH action. The early observations by Stone and Hechter (1951) place the site of action of ACTH at the biogenetic steps involved in the cleavage of the cholesterol side change via the 20,22-dihydroxy form (see p. 125) to form the C_{21} steroid, pregnenolone. An alternative hypothesis was proposed by Haynes and Berthet (1957) in which ACTH was thought to increase phosphorylase activity in the adrenal cortex specifically. The resulting increase in glucose metabolism would cause increased levels of $NADPH_2$ which is a necessary cofactor for steroid hydroxylation. The phosphorylase activator, adenosine-3′,5′-monophosphate (3′,5′-AMP) when tested in this *in vitro* system elicited a response in corticosteroid production equal to or greater than that produced by ACTH (Haynes *et al.*, 1959). The fact that hydroxylation reactions beyond the pregnenolone stage were not stimulated by ACTH was noted by Stone and Hechter in advancing their thesis, and cannot be satisfactorily explained by the theory advanced by Haynes. An effect of freezing and thawing adrenal slices or homogenates and by the addition of Ca^{++} ions was observed by Koritz and Peron (1959) to result in a threefold increase in corticosteroid production. Under these conditions, nicotinamide-adenine dinucleotide phosphate (NADP) and glucose-6-phosphate were necessary additions to the incubation medium. Apparently only the step, cholesterol to pregnenolone, in the corticoid biosynthetic sequence is stimulated by the freezing or by the presence of Ca^{++} ions. In whole homogenates at pH 7.5, calcium ions stimulate the transformation of 20α-hydroxycholesterol to corticoids (Koritz, 1962b). It was suggested that the step, cholesterol to 20α-hydroxycholesterol, is rate limiting. The role of Ca^{++} is unknown, although it appears to be specifically involved in the action of ACTH (Peron and Koritz, 1958); however, adrenal sections maximally stimulated with Ca^{++} still respond to ACTH with a further increase in corticoid production. The action of ACTH on adrenal production of steroids has been considered to require the intact cell preparation, slice or quartered adrenal.

Factors involved in the stimulation of aldosterone production and secretion at the present time can be listed as (1) sodium depletion (Denton *et al.*, 1959a, b); (2) thoracic caval constriction (Yankopoulos *et al.*, 1959); (3) a pineal factor (Farrell, 1959); and (4) a kidney renin-angiotensin system (Tobian, 1960) and conditions such as hemorrhage, edema, hypertension, etc. The preparations of Denton and colleagues (Blair-West *et al.*, 1963) involving the Merino sheep with permanent, unilateral, parotid fistula and/or with a left adrenal transplant in a combined carotid artery–jugular vein skin loop, have been very valuable for the study of aldosterone regulation. Their studies confirm, but cannot exclude, any of the four mechanisms just listed as evoking aldosterone secretion. An infusion of angiotensin II at a rate of 0.1–0.5 μg/hr evoked an increase in aldosterone with no consistent change in cortisol or corticosterone secretion.

Aldosterone biosynthesis may be increased selectively by the total intravenous injection of 40–50 μg of angiotensin II per 100 gm of rat body weight, but under these conditions corticosterone production did not rise (Glaz, 1962). A similar experiment was reported by Mulrow *et al.* (1962). Injections of small doses of renin-containing extracts of dog kidneys and synthetic angiotensin II stimulated aldosterone secretion in hypophysectomized, nephrectomized dog, while cortisol secretion was not stimulated. Some increment in corticosterone and blood pressure was observed in these experiments. Kaplan and Bartter (1962) claim, however, an increase in corticoid secretion at all doses of angiotensin which stimulate aldosterone.

Biological Rhythms

It has become increasingly evident that an adequate understanding of the processes involved in production and secretion of the steroid hormones cannot be obtained by using a simple model based merely on a description of a tropic hormone stimulation and of the enzymatic make-up of the target organ, as in the fundamental feedback mechanism proposed for the adrenal by Sayers and Sayers (1947). The role of the hypothalamus in modifying the secretion of the pituitary tropic hormones is now generally accepted, owing to the work of Harris, Porter, and others (See Harris, 1955). In addition, both inhibitory and stimulatory nerve pathways in the higher centers of the brain have been described (Egdahl, 1960, 1961) which can affect tropic hormone secretions.

The *in vitro* Saffran technic that uses quartered rat adrenals (Saffran and Schally, 1955) has been of great value not only for the assessment of ACTH action in steroid biogenesis but, in addition, as an assay procedure for the hypothalamic factor which stimulates ACTH release, or possibly production, by the pituitary gland (Saffran *et al.*, 1955; Guillemin and Schally, 1959; Fortier, 1958). Periodic cyclic phenomena also affect the endocrine systems just as they do other biological systems. The estrus cycle in mammals and the menstrual cycle in primates are perhaps the best known examples of rhythmical behavior. The reader is referred to the Cold Spring Harbor Symposium of 1960 for an introduction to the rapidly advancing field of biological rhythms.

In 1943, Pincus reported a difference in the steroid content of urine excreted during the early morning hours as compared with the afternoon or evening hours. These differences seen in the steroid levels in the blood and urine of normal individuals has been referred to as "diurnal variation." This concept has found clinical application owing to the fact that in Cushing's disease the evening samples of blood or urine are as high as the early morning samples and a diurnal variation is not evident (Doe *et al.*, 1954; Mijeon *et al.*, 1955). These variations have been documented in many species, including the mouse (Halberg *et al.*, 1959) where the peak steroid levels occur at 4 p.m. (under usual lighting schedules) for this nocturnally active rodent. Many of the periodic cyclic rhythms demonstrated for a good number of biological phenomena, including the pituitary–adrenal system, are nearly, but not exactly, 24 hours in length. The term "circadian (*circa*, about; *dies*, day) rhythm" has been applied to these variations and is to be preferred to the earlier designation of "diurnal variation."

The circadian rhythm of adrenal steroid content and production has been demonstrated to persist under *in vitro* conditions by use of the Saffran technic in the mouse adrenal. Ungar and Halberg (1962) have shown that the responsiveness of adrenal corticosterone production to ACTH added *in vitro* depends upon the time of gland removal and that peak production occurs at 0400 (under usual lighting schedules) at a time when serum corticosterone levels in the mouse are at their lowest. The pituitary content of ACTH also manifests a circadian rhythm which shows a lead-in-phase to the blood corticosterone rhythm (Ungar and Halberg, 1963). Finally, a cyclic contribution by the hypothalamus to the pituitary–adrenal relationship has been assessed under the same *in vitro* conditions. These *in vitro* results are in excellent agreement with similar observations obtained under *in vivo* conditions, so that the technic provides an unusual opportunity to examine the periodic behavior of the adrenal and pituitary in terms of biogenesis and secretion under rigidly controlled conditions (Ungar, 1964) (see Fig. 29).

Table I

Conversion of Various Compounds to Cholesterol

Substrate	Reference
Acetate	Bloch, K., and Rittenberg (1942)
	Frantz and Bucher (1954)
	Bucher (1953)
	Zabin and Barker (1953)
	Eidinoff *et al.* (1954)
	Hellman *et al.* (1954)
	Rosenfeld *et al.* (1954)
	Rabinowitz and Gurin (1954a)
	Bucher and McGarrahan (1956)
Pyruvate	Bloch, K., and Rittenberg (1944)
	Popjak *et al.* (1953)
	Brady and Gurin (1950)
	Rittenberg and Schoenheimer (1937)
Ethanol	Bloch, K., *et al.* (1954)
	Rittenberg and Schoenheimer (1937)
	Curran and Rittenberg (1951)
	Bloch, K., and Rittenberg (1944)
Butyric acid	Rittenberg and Schoenheimer (1937)
	Bloch, K. (1944, 1951)
	Brady and Gurin (1950)
	Zabin and Bloch (1951a)
Valeric acid	Rittenberg and Schoenheimer (1937)
	Bloch, K., and Rittenberg (1942)
	Zabin and Bloch (1950a)
Hexanoic acid	Brady and Gurin (1950)
Acetaldehyde	Bloch, K., *et al.* (1943)
	Brady and Gurin (1951)
Acetone	Borck and Rittenberg (1949)
	Price and Rittenberg (1950)
	Zabin and Bloch (1950a, b)
	Brady and Gurin (1951)
Acetoacetic acid	Zabin and Bloch (1950a, b)
	Brady and Gurin (1951)
	Curran (1951)
	Blecher and Gurin (1954)
Valine	Bloch, K. (1951)
Leucine	Rittenberg and Schoenheimer (1937)
	Bloch, K. (1944)

Continued on following page

Table I *(continued)*

CONVERSION OF VARIOUS COMPOUNDS TO CHOLESTEROL

Substrate	Reference
Isovaleric acid	Rittenberg and Schoenheimer (1937)
	Bloch, K. (1944, 1951)
	Zabin and Bloch (1950a, b, 1951a, b)
	Brady and Gurin (1951)
Mevalonic acid	Tavormina *et al.* (1956)
	Gould and Popjak (1957)
Octanoic acid	Lyon *et al.* (1956)
Isobutyric acid	Bloch, K. (1944)
	Kritchevsky and Gray (1951)
Glucose	Popjak *et al.* (1953)
β-Hydroxy-β-methylglutaric acid	Rabinowitz and Gurin (1954b)
Dimethylacrylic acid	Bloch, K., *et al.* (1954)
Squalene	Langdon and Bloch (1952, 1953b)
	Schwenk *et al.* (1955a)
	Dituri *et al.* (1956)
	Nicolaides *et al.* (1955)
Cholestenone	Anker and Bloch (1949)
Lanosterol	Clayton and Bloch (1956b)
	Olson and Bloch (1956)
Zymosterol	Schwenk *et al.* (1955a)
	Johnston and Bloch (1957)
Lathosterol (Δ^7-cholesterol)	Biggs *et al.* (1954)
	Davidson *et al.* (1957)
Δ^7-Dehydrocholesterol	Cook *et al.* (1954)
Mevalonic acid	Folkers *et al.* (1959)
Squalene→lanosterol→4,4-dimethylcholesta-8,24-dien-3β-ol→4,4-dimethylcholesta-8,24-dien-3-one→4α-methylcholesta-8,24-dien-3-one→zymosterol→desmosterol→cholesterol	Bloch, K. (1959)
	Cornforth (1959)
24,25-Dehydrolanosterol	Kandutsch and Russell (1960)
4α-Methyl-Δ^8-cholesterol	
Δ^7-Cholesterol	
7-Dehydrocholesterol	
Methosterol (4α-methyl-Δ^7-cholesten-3β-ol)	Wells and Lorah (1960)
Desmosterol	Stokes *et al.* (1958)
β,β-Dimethylacrylic acid (yes)	Sandermann and Stockmann (1956)
Geraniumic acid (no)	
Farnesylic acid (no)	
Geranylgeranidimic acid (no)	
Deuterium oxide (cholesterol-D)	Rittenberg and Schoenheimer (1937)
Cholestenone	Rosenfeld *et al.* (1962)
Mevaldic acid	Folkers *et al.* (1959)

Continued on following page

Table 1 *(continued)*

CONVERSION OF VARIOUS COMPOUNDS TO CHOLESTEROL

Substrate	Reference
24,25-Dehydrolanosterol 4α-Methyl-Δ^8-cholesterol Δ^7-Cholesterol 7-Dehydrocholesterol	Kandutsch and Russell (1960)
Methosterol	Neiderhiser and Wells (1959)
Mevalonic acid	Dituri *et al.* (1957)
β-Hydroxy-β-methyl-α-valerolactone	Isler *et al.* (1957)
Squalene	Tchen and Bloch (1957)
Lanosterol	Olson *et al.* (1957)
4α-Methylcholest-8-en-3-one	Bloch, K. (1959)
Zymosterol	Johnston and Bloch (1957)
Δ^7-Cholestenol	Frantz *et al.* (1959)
Δ^7-Cholestenol 7-Dehydrocholesterol	Schroepfer and Frantz (1961)
Zymosterol Zymostenol	Schroepfer (1961)

Table 2

BIOSYNTHESIS OF DIRECT AND INDIRECT CHOLESTEROL INTERMEDIATES

Substrate	Product	Reference
Acetate-2-C^{14}	Squalene-C^{14}	Eidinoff *et al.* (1954)
Acetate-1-C^{14}	Dimethylacrylic acid Senecioic acid-C^{14}	Rabinowitz (1954)
Acetate-C^{14} Pyruvate-C^{14}	β-Hydroxy-β-methyl-glutaric acid-C^{14}	Rabinowitz and Gurin (1954a)
β-Hydroxy-β-methylglutaric acid-C^{14}	β-Methylcrotonic acid-C14 β-Methylglutaconic acid-C^{14}	Rabinowitz and Gurin (1954b)
Acetate-C^{14}	Dimethylacrylic acid-C^{14}	Rudney (1954)
Squalene	Lanosterol Agnosterol	Clayton and Bloch (1956a)
Acetate-C^{14}	Lanosterol-C^{14}	Clayton and Bloch (1955, 1956a)
Acetate-1-C^{14}	Squalene-C^{14}	Schwenk *et al.* (1955b)
Acetate-1-C^{14}	Zymosterol	Schwenk *et al.* (1955a)

Continued on following page

Table 2 *(continued)*

Biosynthesis of Direct and Indirect Cholesterol Intermediates

Substrate	Product	Reference
Acetate-C^{14} β-Hydroxy-β-methyl-glutaric acid-C^{14}	Squalene-C^{14}	Dituri *et al.* (1955); Rabinowitz *et al.* (1955)
Acetate-C^{14}	Squalene	Langdon and Bloch (1953a); Popjak (1954); Cornforth and Popjak (1954)
β-Hydroxy-β-methyl-glutaric acid-C^{14}	Farnesinic acid-C^{14} (no farnesol-C^{14})	Rabinowitz *et al.* (1955); Dituri *et al.* (1956)
β-Hydroxyisovaleric acid-C^{14}	Squalene-C^{14}	Rabinowitz *et al.* (1955); Dituri *et al.* (1956)
Mevalonic acid	Squalene	Amdur *et al.* (1957); Cornforth *et al.* (1958); Dituri *et al.* (1957)
Acetate	Mevalonic acid	Knauss *et al.* (1959); Brodie and Porter (1960)
Mevaldic acid (3-hydroxy-3-methylglutaraldehydic acid)	Mevalonic acid	Knauss *et al.* (1959)
β-Hydroxy-β-methylglutaryl coenzyme A	Mevalonic acid	Durr and Rudney (1960)
Mevalonic acid	Squalene	Wright (1961)
Acetate	Methostenol	Wells and Lorah (1960)
Mevalonate Farnesyl pyrophosphate	Squalene	Popjak *et al.* (1961)
Farnesyl pyrophosphate	Squalene	Lynen *et al.* (1958); Popjak (1959); Goodman and Popjak (1960)
β,β-Dimethylacrylic acid (yes) Geraniumic acid (no) Farnesylic acid (no) Geranylgeraniumic acid (no)	Squalene	Sandermann and Stockmann (1956)
Acetate	Squalene Mevalonic acid	Knauss *et al.* (1959)
Mevaldic acid	Mevalonic acid	Wright *et al.* (1957); Durr *et al.* (1959); Lynen *et al.* (1959)
Mevaldic acid	Squalene	Lynen *et al.* (1959)
Acetate	Mevalonic acid	Brodie and Porter (1960)
β-Hydroxy-β-methylglutaryl coenzyme A	Mevalonic acid	Durr and Rudney (1960)
Mevalonic acid	Mevalonic acid-5-phosphate	Markley and Smallman (1960); Levy and Popjak (1959)
Mevalonic acid-5-phosphate	Mevalonic acid-5-pyrophosphate	Waard and Popjak (1959); Henning *et al.* (1959)
Mevalonic acid-5-pyrophosphate	Isopentenyl pyrophosphate	Lynen *et al.* (1959); Chaykin *et al.* (1958)

Continued on following page

Table 2 (*continued*)

BIOSYNTHESIS OF DIRECT AND INDIRECT CHOLESTEROL INTERMEDIATES

Substrate	Product	Reference
Isopentenyl pyrophosphate	Dimethylallyl pyrophosphate	Agranoff *et al.* (1960)
Acetate	Methostenol (4α-methyl-Δ^7-cholesten-3β-ol)	Neiderhiser and Wells (1959)
Acetate	Squalene	Eidinoff *et al.* (1954)
Squalene	Lanosterol	Tchen and Bloch (1957)
3-Hydroxy-3-methylglutaryl-CoA	Mevalonate	Ferguson *et al.* (1959); Lynen *et al.* (1959)
Acetoacetyl-CoA and acetyl-CoA	3-Hydroxy-3-methyl-glutaryl-CoA	Ferguson and Rudney (1959)
Mevalonic acid	5-Phosphomevalonic acid	Levy and Popjak (1959); Tchen (1958); Waard and Popjak (1959)
5-Phosphomevalonic acid	5-Diphosphomevalonic acid	Chaykin *et al.* (1958); Levy and Popjak (1959)
5-Diphosphomevalonic acid	Isopentyl pyrophosphate	Chaykin *et al.* (1958); Lynen *et al.* (1958); Waard and Popjak (1959)
Isopentyl pyrophosphate	Dimethylallyl pyrophosphate	Agranoff *et al.* (1960)
Farnesyl pyrophosphate	Nerolidyl pyrophosphate	Popjak (1959)

Table 3

ORIGIN OF CARBON ATOMS IN CHOLESTEROL BIOSYNTHESIZED FROM ACETATE

Cholesterol carbon atom number	Origin		Reference
	From methyl carbon of acetate	From carboxyl carbon of acetate	
1	+		Cornforth *et al.* (1953)
2		+	
3	+		
4		+	
5	+		
6		+	
7	+		Bloch, K. (1953); Dauben and Takemura (1953)
8		+	Cornforth *et al.* (1956, 1957)
9	+		
10		+	Cornforth *et al.* (1953)
11		+[a]	Cornforth *et al.* (1956, 1957)
12		+[a]	

Continued on following page

Table 3 (*continued*)

Origin of Carbon Atoms in Cholesterol Biosynthesized from Acetate

Cholesterol carbon atom number	Origin: From methyl carbon of acetate	Origin: From carboxyl carbon of acetate	Reference
13	+		Woodward and Bloch (1953); Cornforth and Popjak (1954)
14		+	Cornforth *et al.* (1956, 1957)
15	+		
16		+	
17	+		Wuersch *et al.* (1952)
18	+		
19	+		Cornforth *et al.* (1953)
20		+	Wuersch *et al.* (1952)
21	+		
22	+		
23		+	
24	+		
25		+	
26	+		
27	+		

[a] Dauben and Hutton (1956) demonstrated that these two carbon atoms originated from the carboxyl carbon of acetate which was used to biosynthesize ergosterol.

Table 4

Biosynthesis of Pregnenolone and of Progesterone, *In Vivo*

Substrate	Product	Species	Reference
Cholesterol	Pregnanediol	Human (pregnancy)	Bloch, K. (1945); Davis *et al.* (1956)
	Pregn-5-ene-3β,20α-diol	Human (adrenal cancer)	Ungar and Dorfman (1953)
Acetate	Pregnanediol Pregnanolone	Human (pregnancy)	Davis *et al.* (1956)
	3β-Hydroxy-5α-pregnan-20-one	Mare (pregnancy)	Heard *et al.* (1956); Savard *et al.* (1958)

Table 5

BIOSYNTHESIS OF PREGNENOLONE AND PROGESTERONE BY PERFUSION

Substrate	Product	Species (tissues)	Reference
Cholesterol	Progesterone	Human (placenta)	Solomon *et al.* (1954)
	Pregnenolone Progesterone	Human (placenta)	Solomon *et al.* (1956)

Table 6

BIOSYNTHESIS OF PREGNENOLONE AND PROGESTERONE, *In Vitro*

Substrate	Product	Test system	Species	Reference
Cholesterol	Pregnenolone	Adrenal homogenate	Bovine	Saba *et al.* (1954)
	Progesterone	Corpora lutea	Bovine	Solomon *et al.* (1956)
	Pregnenolone Progesterone	Adrenal homogenate	Bovine	Staple *et al.* (1956); Hayano *et al.* (1956)
Acetate	Progesterone	Adrenal slices and cell-free preparation	Rat Porcine	Aprile *et al.* (1956–1957)
		Ovary mince	Human Bovine	Sweat *et al.* (1960)
Pregnenolone	Progesterone	Adrenal homogenate	Bovine	Plager and Samuels (1952)
β,β-Dimethyl-acrylate	Progesterone	Adrenal slices and cell-free preparation	Rat Porcine	Aprile *et al.* (1956–1957)
Acetate	Pregnenolone	Adrenal slices (fetal)	Human	Bloch, E., and Benirschke (1959)
	Progesterone	Testis (tumor slices)	Human (grown in hamster)	Wotiz *et al.* (1960)
20α-Hydroxy-cholesterol	Pregnenolone Progesterone	Adrenal homogenate	Bovine	Shimizu *et al.* (1961)
		Placental homogenate	Human	
		Testis homogenate	Rat	
	Pregnenolone	Adrenal homogenate	Bovine	Constantopoulos and Tchen (1961)

Continued on following page

Table 6 *(continued)*

Biosynthesis of Pregnenolone and Progesterone, *In Vitro*

Substrate	Product	Test system	Species	Reference
20α,22*x*-Dihydroxy-cholesterol	Pregnenolone	Adrenal homogenate	Bovine	Shimizu *et al.* (1962)
20α-Hydroxy-cholesterol	Pregnenolone	Corpus luteum	Bovine	Tomaoki and Pincus (1961)
Acetate	Progesterone Pregnenolone	Ovary (follicular cyst linings, minced)	Human	Ryan and Smith (1961c)
	Progesterone	Adrenal homogenate	Bovine	Bryson and Sweat (1962)
Pregnenolone	Progesterone	Placental slices	Human	Nissim and Robson (1951); Pearlman (1954)
22-Hydroxy-cholesterol	Pregnenolone	Adrenal mitochondria	Bovine	Chaudhuri *et al.* (1962)
Acetate	Progesterone 20α-Hydroxy-pregn-4-en-3-one	Ovarian (pseudo-pregnant), slices	Rabbit	Pearlman and Huang (1962)
Progesterone	20α-Hydroxy-pregn-4-en-3-one	Adrenal tumor homogenate	Human	Neher *et al.* (1962)
Cholesterol Pregnenolone	Progesterone	Placental slices	Rat Human	Venning and Sybulski (1962)
Acetate	Pregnenolone	Fetal (12–23 weeks) adrenal slices	Human	Bloch, E., and Benirschke (1962)
Cholesterol 20α,22ξ-Dihydroxy-cholesterol	Pregnenolone plus isocaproaldehyde	Adrenal cortex	Bovine	Constantopoulos *et al.* (1962)
Acetate; progesterone	20α-Hydroxy-pregn-4-en-3-one	Ovaries	Rat	Huang and Pearlman (1962)

Table 7

BIOSYNTHESIS OF ANDROGENS, *In Vivo*

Substrate	Product	Species	Reference
Acetate	Androsterone Etiocholanolone Dehydroepiandrosterone Androst-5-ene-3β,17β-diol	Human (adrenal cancer)	Ungar and Dorfman (1953)
Cholesterol	Androsterone Etiocholanolone Dehydroepiandrosterone Androst-5-ene-3β,17β-diol	Human (adrenal cancer)	Ungar and Dorfman (1953)
Cholesterol	Androsterone Etiocholanolone 11-Ketoetiocholanolone	Human	Werbin and Le Roy (1954, 1955); Werbin *et al.* (1957b)
17α-Hydroxy-pregnenolone	Dehydroepiandro-sterone Androsterone Etiocholanolone	Human	Solomon *et al.* (1960)
Pregnenolone	Dehydroepiandro-sterone	Dog Castrated Adrenal-ectomized Hepatectomized	Oertel and Eik-Nes (1959)
Progesterone	Androsterone	Human (chorio-epithelioma)	Plotz (1959)
Pregnenolone Cholesterol	Dehydroepiandro-sterone Androsterone	Human (adrenal adenoma)	Burstein and Dorfman (1962)
17α-Hydroxy-pregnenolone	Dehydroepiandro-sterone Androsterone Etiocholanolone	Human (adrenal adenoma)	Roberts *et al.* (1961b)
Acetate (spermatic artery infusion)	Testosterone (peripheral vein)	Dog	Mason and Samuels (1961)
Cholesterol-4-C^{14} (infused in spermatic artery)	Dehydroepiandro-sterone-C^{14} (from spermatic vein)	Dog	Eik-Nes and Hall (1962)
3β,17α-Dihydroxy-pregn-5-en-20-one (infused in spermatic artery)	17α-Hydroxy-progesterone Dehydroepiandrosterone Testosterone	Dog	Hagen and Eik-Nes (1963)

Continued on following page

Table 7 (*continued*)

Biosynthesis of Androgens, *In Vivo*

Substrate	Product	Species	Reference
	Androst-4-ene-3,17-dione (From spermatic vein)		
Dehydroepiandrosterone	Testosterone Androst-4-ene-3,17-dione	Human	Mahesh and Greenblatt (1962)
HCG and FSH treatment	Androst-4-ene-3,17-dione	Dog (female)	Telegdy and Huszan (1962)

Table 8

Biosynthesis of Androgens by Perfusion

Substrate	Product	Species (gland)	Reference
Androst-4-ene-3,17-dione	11β-Hydroxyandrost-4-ene-3,17-dione	Bovine (adrenal)	Jeanloz *et al.* (1950, 1953)
Progesterone	11β-Hydroxyandrost-4-ene-3,17-dione	Bovine (adrenal)	Kushinsky (1955)
Dehydroepiandrosterone	11β-Hydroxyandrost-4-ene-3,17-dione	Bovine (calf) (adrenal)	Rosenfeld *et al.* (1955)
Acetate	Androst-4-ene-3,17-dione Testosterone (Also 17α-hydroxyprogesterone and progesterone	Stallion (testis)	Savard and Goldzieher (1960)
9α-Fluoroandrost-4-ene-3,17-dione	19-Hydroxy-9α-fluoroandrost-4-ene-3,17-dione	Bovine (adrenal)	Bergstrom and Dodson (1960)
Cholesterol (*in vivo* perfusion)	Dehydroepiandrosterone	Dog (testis)	Eik-Nes and Hall (1962)
Acetate	Testosterone Androst-4-ene-3,17-dione	Human (testis)	Savard *et al.* (1952)

Table 9

Biosynthesis of Androgens, *In Vitro*

Substrate	Product	Test system	Species	Reference
Androst-4-ene-3,17-dione	11β-Hydroxyandrost-4-ene-3,17-dione	Adrenal homogenate	Bovine	Hayano and Dorfman (1953)
	11β-Hydroxyandrost-4-ene-3,17-dione Adrenosterone 6α-Hydroxyandrost-4-ene-3,17-dione 6β,11β-Dihydroxy-androst-4-ene-3,17-dione	Adrenal homogenate	Bovine	Meyer *et al.* (1955)
	Testosterone	Ovarian slices	Human	Sandor and Lanthier (1960)
	19-Hydroxyandrost-4-ene-3,17-dione	Adrenal homogenate Placental microsomes	Bovine Human	Meyer (1955b) Longchampt *et al.* (1960)
Dehydroepiandrosterone	11β-Hydroxyandrost-4-ene-3,17-dione	Adrenal homogenate	Bovine	Meyer *et al.* (1955)
Progesterone	Androst-4-ene-3,17-dione	Testis homogenate Adrenal cell-free extract	Rat Mouse Porcine	Dominguez *et al.* (1960) Rao and Heard (1957)
Acetate	Androst-4-ene-3,17-dione Testosterone	Adrenal homogenate Testis tumor slices	Porcine Human (grown in hamster)	Bligh *et al.* (1955); Heard *et al.* (1956) Wotiz *et al.* (1960)
	Dehydroepiandrosterone Androst-4-ene-3,17-dione 11β-Hydroxyandrost-4-ene-3,17-dione	Adrenal slice	Human	Bloch, E., *et al.* (1956)
	Dehydroepiandrosterone Androst-4-ene-3,17-dione 11β-Hydroxyandrost-4-ene-3,17-dione	Adrenal slices (fetal)	Human	Bloch, E., and Benirshke (1959)

Continued on following page

Table 9 (*continued*)

Biosynthesis of Androgens, *In Vitro*

Substrate	Product	Test system	Species	Reference
Progesterone	Testosterone	Testis homogenate	Rat Mouse	Dominguez *et al.* (1960)
	Androst-4-ene-3,17-dione	Arrheno-blastoma	Human	Wiest *et al.* (1959)
17α-Hydroxy-pregnenolone	Dehydroepiandro-sterone	Testis adrenal (homogenates)	Bovine	Kahnt *et al.* (1961)
Pregnanolone and 17α-hydroxypro-gesterone	Androst-4-ene-3,17-dione (presumptive)	Ovary (normal and Stein-Leventhal)	Human	Lanthier and Sandor (1960a)
Androst-4-ene-3,17-dione	11β-Hydroxytesto-sterone 11β-Hydroxyandrost-4-ene-3,17-dione Testosterone Adrenosterone(?)	Adrenal tumor (slices)	Mice	Bloch *et al.* (1960)
Dehydroepian-drosterone	Androst-4-ene-3,17-dione			
Cholesterol	Dehydroepiandro-sterone	Fetal adrenal homogenate	Human	Villee *et al.* (1959b)
Progesterone	Androst-4-ene-3,17-dione Testosterone	Fetal testis mince	Human	Acevedo *et al.* (1961b)
Progesterone	19-Hydroxyandrost-4-ene-3,17-dione Testosterone	Polycystic ovaries (pre-paration not specified)	Human	Axelrod and Goldzieher (1962)
Pregnenolone	19-Hydroxyandrost-4-ene-3,17-dione Dehydroepiandro-sterone			
Testosterone	19-Hydroxyandrost-4-ene-3,17-dione			
Progesterone	Testosterone (not through 17α-hydroxyproge-sterone)	Rat testis homogenate	Human	Forchielli and Dorfman (1961)
Acetate	Testosterone	Testis slices	Rabbit	Hall and Eik-Nes (1961)
17α-Hydroxy-pregnenolone	11β-Hydroxy-androsta-4-diene-	Adrenal tumor	Human	Weliky and Engel (1961)

Continued on following page

Table 9 (*continued*)

BIOSYNTHESIS OF ANDROGENS, *In Vitro*

Substrate	Product	Test system	Species	Reference
Progesterone	3,17-dione	(Cushing's Syndrome) slices		
Progesterone	Corticosterone Cortisol	Adrenal (neonatal)	Human	Lanman and Silverman (1957)
Pregnenolone	Dehydroepiandrosterone	Adrenal homogenate	Human	Goldstein *et al.* (1960)
17α-Hydroxy-progesterone	Androst-4-ene-3,17-dione	Ovarian slices	Human	Lanthier and Sandor (1960b)
Progesterone	17α-Hydroxy-progesterone Testosterone Androst-4-ene-3,17-dione	Ovary (idiopathic hirsutism)	Human	Goldzieher and Axelrod (1960)
Cholesterol Pregnenolone	Dehydroepiandrosterone	Adrenal homogenate (adenoma)	Human	Gual *et al.* (1962a)
Pregnenolone	Testosterone Androst-4-ene-3,17-dione	Fetal testis	Human	Acevedo *et al.* (1961b)
Progesterone	Androst-4-ene-3,17-dione	Minced ovary	Human	Warren and Salhanick (1961a)
Progesterone 17α-Hydroxy-progesterone	Testosterone Androst-4-ene-3,17-dione	Ovarian homogenate	Human	Kase *et al.* (1961)
Progesterone	Androsta-1,4-diene-3,17-dione	Ovary (polycystic) (normal, no product)	Bovine	Gawienowski *et al.* (1961)
17α-Hydroxy-pregnenolone	Testosterone Androst-4-ene-3,17-dione	Testis mince	Rat	Carstensen (1961)
	Testosterone	Testis mince	Human	
Acetate	5α-Androst-16-en-3α-ol	Testicular slices		Gower and Haslewood (1961–1962)
Progesterone	Testosterone Androst-4-ene-3,17-dione	Testicular tumor homogenate	Human	Dominguez (1961)

Continued on following page

Table 9 (*continued*)

BIOSYNTHESIS OF ANDROGENS, *In Vitro*

Substrate	Product	Test system	Species	Reference
17α-Hydroxy-progesterone	Androst-4-ene-3,17-dione			
Acetate	Testosterone	Ovarian slices (Stein-Leventhal)	Human	Leon *et al.* (1962)
Testosterone	Androstane-3α,17β-diol Etiocholane-3α,17β-diol Androstane-3β,17β-diol 16α-Hydroxytestosterone Androsta-4,16-dien-3-one Androst-16-en-3β-ol	Testis homogenate	Rat	Stylianou *et al.* (1961)
Acetate	Androst-4-ene-3,17-dione Dehydroepiandrosterone	Ovary (follicular cyst linings) minced	Human	Ryan and Smith (1961c)
	Androst-4-ene-3,17-dione 11β-hydroxyandrost-4-ene-3,17-dione	Adrenal homogenate	Bovine	Bryson and Sweat (1962)
Progesterone	Androst-4-ene-3,17-dione	Ovarian homogenate	Bovine	Solomon *et al.* (1956)
Acetate	(Preliminary) Testosterone Androst-4-ene-3,17-dione (Also 17α-hydroxy-progesterone)	Stein–Leventhal ovary	Human	O'Donnell and McCaig (1959)
Progesterone	Androst-4-ene-3,17-dione (Also 17α-hydroxy-progesterone)	Adrenal fetal zone	Human	Solomon *et al.* (1958)
Acetate	Testosterone	Testis homogenate	Various	Rabinowitz (1956)
Progesterone	Testosterone (Also 17α-hydroxy-progesterone)	Testis homogenate	Guinea pig rat	Lynn and Brown (1958)

Continued on following page

Table 9 (*continued*)

BIOSYNTHESIS OF ANDROGENS, *In Vitro*

Substrate	Product	Test system	Species	Reference
Progesterone	Androst-4-ene-3,17-dione Testosterone Also 17α-Hydroxy-progesterone 20α-Hydroxypregn-4-en-3-one 20β-Hydroxypregn-4-en-3-one	Ovarian arrheno-blastoma	Human	Savard *et al.* (1961)
Acetate	Dehydroepiandro-sterone	Testis slice	Rabbit	Hall *et al.* (1963)
	Testosterone	Testis slice	Rabbit Porcine	Brady (1951)
Dehydroepi-androsterone	Androst-4-ene-3,17-dione Testosterone	Ovarian folli-cular slices	Equine	West and Naville (1962)
Progesterone 17α-Hydroxy-progesterone	Androst-4-ene-3,17-dione Testosterone	Testis homogenate	Human Klinefelter syndrome 47 chromosomes XXY	Slaunwhite *et al.* (1962a)
Testosterone	Androst-4-ene-3,17-dione	Interstitial cell tumor of testis homo-genate	Human	Gual *et al.* (1962c)
Pregnenolone	Dehydroepiandro-sterone Androst-4-ene-3,17-dione Testosterone			
ACTH stimu-lation	Dehydroepiandro-sterone Androst-4-ene-3,17-dione 11β-Hydroxyandrost-4-ene-3,17-dione	Adrenal (normal and abnormal) slices	Human	Cohn and Mulrow (1963)
Testosterone	Androst-4-ene-3,17-dione 11β-Hydroxyandrost-4-ene-3,17-dione	Normal adrenal	Human	Chang *et al.* (1963)

Continued on following page

Table 9 *(continued)*

BIOSYNTHESIS OF ANDROGENS, *In Vitro*

Substrate	Product	Test system	Species	Reference
	11β-Hydroxytestosterone			
Progesterone	Various androgens	Homogenates of ovarian follicular cells	Equine	Mahajan and Samuels (1963)
Progesterone	Testosterone Androst-4-ene-3,17-dione	Corpus luteum		
17α-Hydroxyprogesterone	Testosterone Androst-4-ene-3,17-dione	Corpus luteum follicles Corpus hemorrhagicum		
Acetate	Dehydroepiandrosterone	Ovarian slices	Human	Noall *et al.* (1962)
Progesterone 17α-Hydroxyprogesterone	Testosterone Androst-4-ene-3,17-dione	Testis (Klinefelter type)	Human	Slaunwhite *et al.* (1962a)
Progesterone	Testosterone Androst-4-ene-3,17-dione	Normal adrenal and virilizing adenoma	Human	Ichii *et al.* (1962)
Acetate	Testosterone	Testis slices stimulated by ICSH and FSH	Rabbit	Hall and Eik-Nes (1962)
Cholesterol	Testosterone	Testis homogenate	Rabbit	Hall and Eik-Nes (1962)
Progesterone 17α-Hydroxyprogesterone	Testosterone Androst-4-ene-3,17-dione	Normal adrenal homogenate	Human	Kase and Kowal (1962)
Progesterone	17α-Hydroxyprogesterone Androst-4-ene-3,17-dione Testosterone	Testis homogenate (normal and cryptorchid)	Rat	Llaurado and Dominguez (1963)
Progesterone	Testosterone Androst-4-ene-3,17-dione	Fetal (15 weeks) testis mince	Human	Bloch, E., *et al.* (1962)

Continued on following page

Table 9 *(continued)*

Biosynthesis of Androgens, *In Vitro*

Substrate	Product	Test system	Species	Reference
Androst-5-ene-3β,17β-diol-17α-H^3	Testosterone-17α-H^3 (without androst-4-ene-3,17-dione as intermediate)	Placenta and adrenal tumor homogenate	Human	Baulieu *et al.* (1963)
Acetate-1-C^{14}	Dehydroepiandrosterone Androst-4-ene-3,17-dione 11β-Hydroxy-androst-4-ene-3,17-dione	Fetal (12–23 weeks) adrenal slices	Human	Bloch, E., and Benirschke (1962)
Progesterone Androst-4-ene-3,17-dione 17α-Hydroxy-progesterone	Testosterone Androst-4-ene-3,17-dione	Lipoid cell tumor (ovarian homogenate)	Human	Sandberg *et al.* (1962)
Progesterone	17α-Hydroxy-progesterone			
None	Testosterone (in presence of HCG)	Testis slices	Rat	Suzuki *et al.* (1962)
Androst-4-ene-3β,17β-diol Pregnenolone	Testosterone	Testis	Mouse	Grosso and Ungar (1964)

Table 10

Biosynthesis of Corticoids, *In Vivo*

Substrate	Product	Species	Reference
Acetate	3α,17α,21-Trihydroxy-5β-pregnan-20-one	Human (adrenal cancer)	Caspi *et al.* (1957)
	Cortisol	Guinea pig adrenal	Burstein and Nadel (1956)
	Cortisol	Hamster	Schindler and Knigge (1959)
Cholesterol	Urocortisone	Human	Werbin and Le Roy (1954, 1955)
	Urocortisol	Human	Werbin *et al.* (1957b)
	Cortisol	Guinea pig	Werbin *et al.* (1958, 1959)
β-Sitosterol-H^3	Cortisol	Guinea pig	Werbin *et al.* (1960)

Table II

BIOSYNTHESIS OF CORTICOIDS BY PERFUSION[a]

Substrate	Product	Species	Reference
Cholesterol	Cortisol Corticosterone	Bovine	Zaffaroni *et al.* (1951); Solomon *et al.* (1954)
Acetate	Cortisol Corticosterone	Bovine	Zaffaroni *et al.* (1951); Capsi *et al.* (1956)
Pregnenolone	Progesterone Corticosterone Cortisol	Bovine	Levy *et al.* (1950, 1954); Hechter *et al.* (1951)
Progesterone	Progesterone	Bovine	Kushinsky (1955)
	20β-Hydroxy-Δ^4-pregnen-3-one Allopregnane-3,20-dione 3β-Hydroxypregnan-20-one 17α-Hydroxyallopregnane-3,20-dione 3β,17α-Dihydroxy-allopregnan-20-one 17α-Hydroxyprogesterone 11β-Hydroxyprogesterone 6β-Hydroxyprogesterone 11-Deoxycortisol Corticosterone 19-Hydroxydeoxy-corticosterone Cortisol 3α,17α,11β,21-Tetra-hydroxyallopregnan-20-one 6β,17α,21-Trihydroxy-Δ^4-pregnene-3,20-dione 3β,17α,11β,21-Tetra-hydroxyallopregnan-20-one 17α,19,21-Trihydroxy-Δ^4-pregnene-3,20-dione	Bovine	Levy and Kushinsky (1955)
	6β-Hydroxyprogesterone	Bovine	Levy *et al.* (1954)
	17α-Hydroxyprogesterone 11β-Hydroxyprogesterone Corticosterone Cortisol 11-Deoxycortisol	Bovine	Levy *et al.* (1950, 1954); Hechter *et al.* (1951)

Continued on following page

Table 11 (*continued*)

BIOSYNTHESIS OF CORTICOIDS BY PERFUSION[a]

Substrate	Product	Species	Reference
	Cortisol Corticosterone	Bovine	Eichhorn and Hechter (1958)
	Cortisol Aldosterone	Bovine (calf) Bovine	Rosenfeld *et al.* (1955) Chen *et al.* (1958)
11β-Hydroxy-progesterone	Cortisol Corticosterone	Bovine	Eichhorn and Hechter (1958)
17α-Hydroxy-progesterone	Cortisol	Bovine	Levy *et al.* (1950, 1954); Hechter *et al.* (1951)
Deoxycorticosterone	Corticosterone	Bovine Bovine (calf) Bovine	Hechter *et al.* (1949, 1951); Levy *et al.* (1953) Rosenfeld *et al.* (1955) Eichhorn and Hechter (1958)
	Corticosterone 11-Deoxycortisol	Human (Cushing's syndrome hyperplasia)	Korus *et al.* (1959)
11-Deoxycortisol	Cortisol	Bovine Bovine (calf)	Hechter *et al.* (1949, 1951) Rosenfeld *et al.* (1955)
21-Deoxycortisol Corticosterone	Cortisol Aldosterone	Bovine (calf) Bovine	Rosenfeld *et al.* (1955) Chen *et al.* (1958)
Progesterone	Cortisol Cortisone Corticosterone	Human placenta	Troen (1961a, b)
Testosterone acetate Ethynyltestosterone Vinyltestosterone	11β-Hydroxytestosterone 11β-Hydroxyethynyltestosterone 11β-Hydroxyvinyltestosterone	Bovine	Marshall *et al.* (1957)
None	Cortisone Cortisol 11-Deoxycortisol Urocortisone Urocortisol	Human (placenta)	Troen (1962)

Continued on following page

Table 11 (*continued*)

BIOSYNTHESIS OF CORTICOIDS BY PERFUSION[a]

Substrate	Product	Species	Reference
17α-Hydroxy-progesterone	17α,20α-Dihydroxypregn-4-en-3-one 3α,17α-Dihydroxypregn-4-en-3-one	Bovine (adrenal and ovary)	Levy *et al.* (1963)

[a] Adrenal tissue was used except where otherwise specified.

Table 12

BIOSYNTHESIS OF CORTICOIDS, *In Vitro*

Substrate	Product	Test system	Species	Reference
Cholesterol	Cortisol Corticosterone	Adrenal homogenate	Bovine Dog	Reich and Lehninger (1955)
	Cortisol Corticosterone	Adrenal homogenate	Bovine	Staple *et al.* (1956)
	Cortisol Corticosterone 11β-Hydroxyprogesterone	Adrenal mito-chondrial preparation	Bovine	Hayano *et al.* (1956)
	Aldosterone	Adrenal capsule strippings	Bovine	Ayres *et al.* (1957a); Hechter (1958)
	Cortisol	Adrenal	Bovine	Ganis and Radakovich (1958)
	Cortisol Cortisone Corticosterone 11-Dehydrocorticosterone	Adrenal homogenate	Hamster	Schindler and Knigge (1959)
Acetate	Cortisol	Adrenal slice	Bovine	Haynes *et al.* (1952a, 1954)
	Cortisol Cortisone Corticosterone Deoxycorticosterone	Adrenal slice	Porcine	Haines (1952)
	Cortisol	Adrenal slice (fetal)	Human	Bloch, E., and Benirschke (1959)

Continued on following page

Table 12 (*continued*)
BIOSYNTHESIS OF CORTICOIDS, *In Vitro*

Substrate	Product	Test system	Species	Reference
Progesterone	Aldosterone	Adrenal capsule strippings	Bovine	Ayres *et al.* (1956, 1957a, b, 1958); Hechter (1958); Travis and Farrell (1958a, b); Giroud *et al.* (1958)
	Aldosterone	Adrenal mince	American bullfrog	Ulick and Solomon (1960)
	17α-Hydroxy-progesterone	Testis homogenate	Rat Mouse	Dominguez *et al.* (1960)
	Cortisol	Adrenal slice	Human	Lombardo *et al.* (1956)
	Corticosterone Aldosterone	Adrenal slice	Mouse	Carstensen (1961) Raman *et al.* (1964)
	18-Hydroxycorti-costerone 18-Hydroxydeoxy-corticosterone	Adrenal sections	Rat	Peron (1962)
	17α,20β-Dihydroxy-pregn-4-en-3-one	Testis homogenate	Rat	Dominguez *et al.* (1960)
	Deoxycorticosterone	Adrenal homogenate	Bovine	Ryan (1956)
	11β-Hydroxy-progesterone	Adrenal mitochondria	Bovine	Saba and Hechter (1955); Brownie *et al.* (1954)
	17α-Hydroxy-progesterone	Arrheno-blastoma homogenate	Human	Wiest *et al.* (1959)
	Cortisol	Adrenal tumor (Cushing's syndrome) slices	Human	Weliky and Engel (1961)
	Deoxycorticosterone Corticosterone	Homogenate (adrenal tumor)	Mouse	Hofmann *et al.* (1960)
	18-Aldo-21-hydroxy-pregn-4-ene-3,20-dione	Adrenal	Rat	Dominguez *et al.* (1961)
	Cortisol Cortisone Corticosterone	Placental homogenate	Human	Endroczi *et al.* (1958)

Continued on following page

Table 12 (*continued*)
BIOSYNTHESIS OF CORTICOIDS, *In Vitro*

Substrate	Product	Test system	Species	Reference
	16α-Hydroxy-progesterone 3β,16α-Dihydroxy-5α-pregnan-20-one	Adrenal homogenate	Bovine	Wettstein *et al.* (1959)
	11-Deoxycortisol	Adrenal homogenate	Bovine	Plager and Samuels (1954)
	11-Deoxycortisol	Testis homogenate	Rat	Dominguez *et al.* (1960)
	Cortisol Corticosterone	Adrenal homogenate	Bovine	Plager and Samuels (1952)
	Cortisol Cortisone Aldosterone 11-Deoxycortisol Corticosterone 16α-Hydroxyprogesterone 11-Dehydrocorticosterone 11β-Hydroxyprogesterone 17α-Hydroxyprogesterone 11-Ketoprogesterone	Adrenal cell-free extract	Porcine	Rao and Heard (1957)
	Cortisol	Fetal adrenal homogenate	Human	Villee *et al.* (1959a)
Deoxycorti-costerone	Corticosterone 11-Dehydrocorticosterone 6β-Hydroxydeoxy-corticosterone	Adrenal slices	Porcine	Haines (1952)
	Deoxycorticosterone	Testis homogenate	Mice Rats	Dominguez *et al.* (1960)
	6β,17β,21-Trihydroxy-progesterone 11β,19,21-Trihydroxy-progesterone 6β,11β,21-Trihydroxy-progesterone	Adrenal brei	Bovine Porcine	Neher and Wettstein (1956)
	19,21-Dihydroxy-progesterone	Adrenal brei	Porcine	Neher and Wettstein (1956)
	Corticosterone	Adrenal homogenate	Bovine	Hayano *et al.* (1956); Sweat *et al.* (1960)

Continued on following page

Table 12 (*continued*)

Biosynthesis of Corticoids, *In Vitro*

Substrate	Product	Test system	Species	Reference
	18,21-Dihydroxy-progesterone 19,21-Dihydroxy-progesterone	Adrenal homogenate	Bovine	Kahnt *et al.* (1961)
	19,21-Dihydroxy-progesterone	Adrenal homogenate	Bovine	Hayano and Dorfman (1955)
	6β,21-Dihydroxy-progesterone	Adrenal brei	Porcine	Haines (1952)
	Corticosterone	Adrenal homogenate	Bovine	Hayano and Dorfman (1953)
	Aldosterone	Adrenal homogenate	Bovine	Kahnt *et al.* (1961)
	18-Aldodeoxycortico-sterone	Adrenal	Rat	Dominguez *et al.* (1961)
	Aldosterone	Adrenal (zona glomerulosa)	Bovine	Ayres *et al.* (1957a, b); Hechter (1958); Giroud *et al.* (1958); Travis and Farrell (1958a)
11-Deoxy-cortisol	Cortisol Cortisone	Adrenal slices	Porcine	Haines (1952)
	Cortisol	Adrenal homogenate	Bovine	Hayano and Dorfman (1953)
	Cortisol	Adrenal homogenate	Bovine	McGinty *et al.* (1950); Savard *et al.* (1950)
17α-Hydroxy-progesterone	Cortisol	Adrenal slices	Human	Lombardo *et al.* (1956)
	Cortisol	Fetal adrenal homogenate	Human	Villee *et al.* (1959a)
	11-Deoxycortisol	Adrenal homogenate	Bovine	Ryan and Engel (1956)
	Cortisol	Adrenal homogenate	Bovine	Hayano and Dorfman (1952)
	17α,20α-Dihydroxy-pregn-4-en-3-one	Ovarian slice	Human	Sandor and Lanthier (1961)
21-Deoxy-cortisol	Cortisol	Adrenal homogenate	Bovine	Ryan and Engel (1956)

Continued on following page

Table 12 (*continued*)

BIOSYNTHESIS OF CORTICOIDS, *In Vitro*

Substrate	Product	Test system	Species	Reference
Corticosterone	Aldosterone	Adrenal capsule	Bovine	Travis and Farrell (1958a, b); Ayres *et al.* (1957a, b); Hechter (1958); Giroud *et al.* (1958)
		Adrenal slices	Human	Mulrow and Cohn (1959)
11β-Hydroxy-progesterone	Aldosterone	Adrenal (zona glomerulosa)	Bovine	Giroud *et al.* (1958)
None	Corticosterone 11-Dehydrocorticosterone Aldosterone	Quarter adrenals	Rat	Roche (1959)
Pregnenolone	17α-Hydroxy-pregnenolone	Adrenal testis (homogenates)	Bovine	Kahnt *et al.* (1961)
Progesterone	11β-Hydroxy-progesterone	Adrenal tumor	Mice	Bloch, E., *et al.* (1960)
16-Ketoproge-sterone	11β-Hydroxy-progesterone			
17α-Hydroxy-progesterone	Cortisol			
Progesterone	17α-Hydroxy-progesterone Deoxycorticosterone 11-Deoxycortisol 20α-Hydroxypregn-4-en-3-one 20β-Hydroxypregn-4-en-3-one 17α,20α-Dihydroxypregn-4-en-3-one 17α,20β-Dihydroxypregn-4-en-3-one	Fetal testis	Human	Acevedo *et al.* (1961a)
	17α-Hydroxy-progesterone	Placenta	Human	Little and Shaw (1961)
17α-Hydroxy-pregnenolone	Cortisol	Adrenal tumor (Cushing's syndrome) slices	Human	Weliky and Engel (1961)

Continued on following page

Table 12 (*continued*)

BIOSYNTHESIS OF CORTICOIDS, *In Vitro*

Substrate	Product	Test system	Species	Reference
Progesterone	17α-Hydroxy-progesterone 2α-Hydroxypregn-4-en-3-one 17α,20α-dihydroxypregn-4-en-3-one	Minced ovary	Human	Warren and Salhanick (1961a)
	Deoxycorticosterone 17α-Hydroxyprogesterone 16α-Hydroxyprogesterone	Fetal adrenal slices	Human	Villee *et al.* (1961)
Acetate Mevalonic acid Cholesterol	No products	Fetal adrenal slices	Human	Villee *et al.* (1961)
Progesterone	18-Hydroxycortico-sterone	Adrenal slice	*Rana catesbiana*	Ulick and Kusch (1960)
	17α-Hydroxy-progesterone	Placental homogenate	Human	Little and Shaw (1961)
	Deoxycorticosterone	Testis homogenate (normal and tumor)	Mouse	Dominguez (1960)
Acetate	17α-Hydroxy-progesterone (17α-Hydroxypregnenolone less vigorous)	Ovary (follicular cyst lining minces)	Human	Ryan and Smith (1961c)
	Cortisol 11β,17α,21-Trihydroxy-5β-pregnane-3,20-dione 11-Dehydrocorticosterone 6β,21-Dihydroxyprogesterone 11-Deoxycortisol 6β-Hydroxyprogesterone 11β-Hydroxyprogesterone 17α-Hydroxyprogesterone Deoxycorticosterone	Adrenal homogenate	Bovine	Bryson and Sweat (1962)
Progesterone	Cortisol Cortisone Corticosterone 11-Deoxycortisol Aldosterone	Adrenal slices (malignant hypertension; Cushing's syndrome; adenoma)	Human	Mulrow and Cohn (1961)

Continued on following page

Table 12 (*continued*)

Biosynthesis of Corticoids, *In Vitro*

Substrate	Product	Test system	Species	Reference
17α-Hydroxyprogesterone	Cortisol Cortisone 11-Deoxycortisol	Adrenals and adrenal tumors	Mouse	Hofmann and Christy (1961)
Progesterone	17α,20α-Dihydroxy-pregn-4-en-3-one 17α,20β-Dihydroxy-pregn-4-en-3-one 6β-Hydroxyprogesterone 17α-Hydroxyprogesterone 11-Deoxyprogesterone	Testicular tumor	Human	Dominguez (1961)
17α-Hydroxyprogesterone	17α,20α-Dihydroxy-pregn-4-en-3-one 17α,20β-Dihydroxy-pregn-4-en-3-one 17α-Hydroxyprogesterone			
11-Deoxycorticosterone	6β-Hydroxy-11-deoxycorticosterone Corticosterone			
Androst-4-ene-3,17-dione	11β-Hydroxyandrost-4-ene-3,17-dione Adrenosterone 5α-Androstane-3,17-dione			
Testosterone	6β-Hydroxytestosterone 11β-Hydroxytestosterone Adrenosterone Androst-4-ene-3,17-dione			
17α-Hydroxypregnenolone	Cortisol 17α-Hydroxyprogesterone 11-Deoxycortisol Dehydroepiandrosterone (not in rat adrenal experiment)	Adrenal slices	Human Rat Guinea pig	Lipsett and Hökfelt (1961)
Progesterone	17α-Hydroxyprogesterone	Ovarian	Bovine	Solomon *et al.* (1956)
Progesterone and deoxycorticosterone	Corticosterone Aldosterone	Transplanted adrenal tumor slices Normal adrenal slices	Rat	Johnson *et al.* (1961)

Continued on following page

Table 12 (*continued*)

BIOSYNTHESIS OF CORTICOIDS, *In Vitro*

Substrate	Product	Test system	Species	Reference
Progesterone	16α-Hydroxy-progesterone	Ovarian mince	Human	Warren and Salhanick (1961b)
Progesterone Pregnenolone	6-Ketoprogesterone 6β-Hydroxyprogesterone	Placental villi	Human	Iwata (1959)
11-Deoxy-cortisol	Cortisol 6β-Hydroxy-11-deoxycortisol			
21-Deoxy-cortisol	Cortisol Cortisone			
Progesterone Pregnenolone Cholesterol	No corticoids	Placental mince	Human	Sybulski and Venning (1961)
Pregnenolone Cholesterol	Progesterone			
Cortisol	6β-Hydroxycortisol	Slices of liver, adrenal, kidney, placenta, skeletal muscle	Human	Lipman *et al.* (1962)
Progesterone or none	Corticosterone Cortisol	Fetal adrenal slices	Bovine	Druzhinina (1958)
	Corticosterone Cortisol	Adrenal slices	Pig	
Deoxycorti-costerone	Corticosterone 18-Hydroxycorticosterone (20–18 hemiketal)	Quartered adrenals	Rat	Ward and Birmingham (1962)
Progesterone	11β-Hydroxy-progesterone Corticosterone Aldosterone Cortisol	Adrenal homogenate	Bovine	Ayres *et al.* (1960)
Cholesterol	Corticosterone Cortisol	Adrenal mitochondria		
	Aldosterone Cortisol Corticosterone	Glomerulosa homogenate		
	Cortisol Corticosterone	Fasciculata plus reticularis		

Continued on following page

Table 12 (*continued*)

BIOSYNTHESIS OF CORTICOIDS, *In Vitro*

Substrate	Product	Test system	Species	Reference
Progesterone	Aldosterone Corticosterone Cortisol	Glomerulosa		
Deoxycorticosterone	Corticosterone Aldosterone	Glomerulosa		
Corticosterone	Aldosterone	Glomerulosa		
Deoxycorticosterone 11-Deoxycortisol	Corticosterone Cortisol	Soluble purified adrenal preparation	Bovine	Sharma *et al.* (1962)
Progesterone	Cortisol Cortisone 6β-Hydroxyprogesterone	Placental homogenate Placenta	Human Human	Polvani *et al.* (1962) Berliner and Salhanick (1956)
Progesterone Corticosterone	18-Hydroxycorticosterone	Zona glomerulosa	Bovine	Sandor and Lanthier (1962)
18-Hydroxycorticosterone	Aldosterone			
Pregnenolone Progesterone	Deoxycorticosterone 16α-Hydroxyprogesterone	Fetal adrenal Fetal adrenal (anecephalic)	Human	Villee *et al.* (1962)
18-Hydroxycorticosterone Corticosterone	Aldosterone	Adrenal (bovine) zona glomerulosa	Bullfrog Bovine	Nicolis and Ulick (1962)
Progesterone	Cortisol Cortisone Corticosterone 17α-Hydroxyprogesterone	Adrenal tumor homogenate	Human	Neher *et al.* (1962)
Cholesterol	Cortisol	Adrenal	Bovine	Kurath *et al.* (1957)
Progesterone	Aldosterone Corticosterone	Adrenal	Lizard (*Lacenta vividis* L) Snakes (*Matrix matrix* L)	Phillips *et al.* (1962)

Continued on following page

Table 12 (*continued*)

Biosynthesis of Corticoids, *In Vitro*

Substrate	Product	Test system	Species	Reference
Progesterone Corticosterone	18-Hydroxy-corticosterone	Adrenal zona glomerulosa slices	Bovine Human	Sandor *et al.* (1963)
Progesterone Corticosterone	Aldosterone		Human	
18-Hydroxy-corticosterone	Aldosterone		Bovine	
3β,21-Di-hydroxypregn-5-en-20-one	Deoxycorticosterone	Adrenal homogenate	Bovine	Berliner *et al.* (1962)
3β,17α,21-Tri-hydroxypregn-5-en-20-one	11-Deoxycortisol			
Progesterone	17α-Hydroxy-progesterone	Fetal (15 weeks) testis mince	Human	Bloch, E., *et al.* (1962)
		Hypertrophied adrenal after unilateral adrenalectomy	Rat	Brownell *et al.* (1963)
Acetate	Cortisol	Fetal adrenal slices	Human	Bloch, E., and Benirschke (1962)
Progesterone 17α-Hydroxy-pregnenolone	Cortisol	Adrenal cortical tumor slices	Human	Weliky and Engel (1962)
Progesterone	Cortisol Cortisone Tentative identification as follows: 6β-Hydroxycortisol 11-Deoxycortisol 6β-Hydroxyprogesterone 11-Oxoprogesterone	Testicular tumor, frozen and minced	Human	Besch *et al.* (1963)
11β-Hydroxy-progesterone Deoxycortico-sterone	Corticosterone	Adrenal (quartered)	Rat	Kraulis and Birmingham (1963)

Continued on following page

Table 12 (*continued*)

BIOSYNTHESIS OF CORTICOIDS, *In Vitro*

Substrate	Product	Test system	Species	Reference
3β,17α-Dihydroxypregn-5-en-20-one	Cortisol	Normal and hyperplastic adrenal slices	Human	Mulrow *et al.* (1962a)
Progesterone	Cortisol (trace) Corticosterone 18-Hydroxycorticosterone Aldosterone Deoxycorticosterone	Adrenal slices	Domestic duck pond turtle	Sandor *et al.* (1963)
	17α-Hydroxy-progesterone 11-Deoxycortisol	Adrenal cortex after enucleation	Rat	Brownell *et al.* (1963)
	Corticosterone	Adrenal cortex (mitochondria) (microsomes suppress)	Guinea pig	Hofmann (1962)
	17α-Hydroxy-progesterone Cortisol	Normal adrenal and virilizing adenoma	Human	Ichii *et al.* (1962)
	Cortisol	Adrenal mince	Human	Ungar *et al.* (1962)
	Corticosterone	Hyperplasia and normal		
Dehydroepiandrosterone	11β-Hydroxyandrost-4-ene-3,17-dione	Hyperplasia and normal	Human	Ungar *et al.* (1962)

Table 13

BIOSYNTHESIS OF ESTROGENS, *In Vivo*

Substrate	Product	Species	Reference
Cholesterol	Estrogens	Human	Werbin *et al.* (1957b)
Acetate	Estrone Equilin Equilenin	Mare (pregnancy)	Heard *et al.* (1956); Savard *et al.* (1958)

Continued on following page

Table 13 (*continued*)

BIOSYNTHESIS OF ESTROGENS, *In Vivo*

Substrate	Product	Species	Reference
Testosterone	Estrone	Mare (pregnancy) Human	Heard *et al.* (1955) West *et al.* (1956)
Progesterone	Estrone	Human (chorio-epithelioma)	Plotz (1959)
Cortisone	11β-Hydroxyestrone 11β-Hydroxyestradiol-17β	Human	Chang and Dao (1961)
Testosterone Androsta-1,4-diene-3,17-dione	Estradiol-17β	Human	Breuer (1962)
19-Nortestosterone 19-Nortestosterone phenyl propionate	Estrone Estriol		
Cortisone acetate	11β-Hydroxyestrone	Human (ovariectomized–adrenalectomized) women	Chang *et al.* (1962)

Table 14

BIOSYNTHESIS OF ESTROGENS BY PERFUSION

Substrate	Product	Species (organ)	Reference
Acetate	Estrone Estradiol-17β	Human (placenta) Equine (testis)	Levitz *et al.* (1955) Nyman *et al.* (1959)
Estradiol-17β	Estriol (with HCG) 2-Methoxyestrone Estrone 16-Epiestriol (with HCG)	Human (placenta)	Troen (1961a)
16α-Hydroxyestrone 16α-Hydroxytesto-sterone 16α-Hydroxyandrost-4-ene-3,17-dione	Estriol	Human (placenta)	Varangot *et al.* (1962)
Estradiol-17β	Estrone Estriol 2-Methoxyestrone 16-Epiestriol	Human (placenta) +HCG	Troen (1962)

Table 15

Biosynthesis of Estrogens, *In Vitro*

Substrate	Product	Test system	Species	Reference
Acetate	Estrone Estradiol-17β	Ovarian homogenate	Dog	Rabinowitz and Dowben (1955)
	Estradiol-17β	Testis homogenate	Various	Rabinowitz and Oleksyshyn (1956)
	Estrone Estradiol-17β	Testicular carcinoma (embryonal)	Human	Wotiz *et al.* (1955)
	Estrone Estradiol-17β	Ovarian homogenate	Human	Ryan and Smith (1961a)
Testosterone	Estradiol-17β	Ovarian tissue slices	Human	Baggett *et al.* (1955, 1956)
		Placental microsomes	Human	Ryan (1959)
	Estrone Estradiol-17β Estriol	Ovary (cortical stromal hyperplasia)	Human	Wotiz *et al.* (1956)
	Estradiol-17β	Testis homogenate	Various	Rabinowitz (1958)
	Estradiol-17β	Placental microsomes	Human	Ryan (1958)
	Estradiol-17β	Ovary	Mouse	Hollander and Hollander (1959)
Androst-4-ene-3,17-dione	Estrone	Placenta (homogenate) Ovarian follicular fluid	Human Bovine	Meyer (1955a)
		Placental microsomes	Human	Breuer and Ortlepp (1960); Ryan (1958, 1959); Longchampt *et al.* (1960)
			Marmoset	Ryan *et al.* (1961)
19-Hydroxyandrost-4-ene-3,17-dione	Estrone	Placenta (homogenate) Ovarian follicular fluid	Human Bovine	Meyer (1955a)
		Placental microsomes	Human	Ryan (1959)

Continued on following page

Table 15 (*continued*)

BIOSYNTHESIS OF ESTROGENS, *In Vitro*

Substrate	Product	Test system	Species	Reference
Androsta-1,4-diene-3,17-dione	Estrone	Placenta (homogenate) Ovarian follicular fluid	Human Bovine	Meyer (1955a)
		Placental microsomes	Human	Ryan (1959)
19-Norandrost-4-ene-3,17-dione	Estrone	Placenta (homogenate) Ovarian follicular fluid	Human Bovine	Meyer (1955a)
		Placental microsomes	Human	Ryan (1959)
Androst-5-ene-3β,16α,17β-triol	Estriol	Placental microsomes	Human	Ryan (1958)
6α-Hydroxyandrost-4-ene-3,17-dione 6β-Hydroxyandrost-4-ene-3,17-dione	6α-Hydroxyestrone 6β-Hydroxyesterone	Placental microsomes	Human	Breuer (1960)
Dehydroepiandrosterone	Estrone	Placental microsomes	Human	Ryan (1959)
Mevalonic acid	Estradiol-17β	Testis homogenate	Human	Rabinowitz and Ragland (1958)
Testosterone	Estrone Estradiol-17β	Granulosa cell tumor slices	Human	Marsh *et al.* (1961)
Progesterone	Estrone Estradiol-17β	Ovary (minced)	Human	Ryan and Smith (1961a)
	Estradiol-17β	Testis homogenate	Various	Rabinowitz (1958)
	Estrone Estradiol-17β	Ovary (idiopathic hirsutism)	Human	Goldzieher and Axelrod (1960)
Cholesterol	Estradiol-17β	Testis homogenate	Various	Rabinowitz (1958)
Androst-4-ene-3,17-dione 19-Hydroxyandrost-4-ene-3,17-dione	Estrone + formaldehyde	Placenta	Human	Breuer and Grill (1961)
Androst-4-ene-3,17-dione Testosterone	Corresponding ring A aromatic compounds	Placental microsomes	Human	Ryan (1961)

Continued on following page

Table 15 (*continued*)
BIOSYNTHESIS OF ESTROGENS, *In Vitro*

Substrate	Product	Test system	Species	Reference
19-Hydroxyandrost-4-ene-3,17-dione				
19-Nortestosterone				
Androst-1,4-diene-3,17-dione				
17β-Hydroxyandrosta-1,4-dien-3-one				
1β-Hydroxytestosterone				
2β-Hydroxyandrost-4-ene-3,17-dione				
(2α-Hydroxyandrost-4-ene-3,17-dione: negative)				
6β-Hydroxyandrost-4-ene-3,17-dione	6β-Hydroxyestrone			
11α-Hydroxytestosterone	11α-Hydroxyestrone			
11β-Hydroxytestosterone	No product			
17β-Hydroxyandrostan-3-one	No product			
5α-Androst-1-ene-3,17-dione	No product			
17α-Methyltestosterone	17α-Methylestradiol-17β			
Epitestosterone	Estradiol-17α			
Cholesterol	Estrone	Ovary (mince of follicular cyst linings)	Human	Ryan and Smith (1961b)
Androst-4-ene-3,17-dione	Estrone Estradiol-17β	Ovarian follicular cyst linings homogenized	Human	Smith and Ryan (1961)
6α-Hydroxyandrost-4-ene-3,17-dione	6α-Hydroxyestrone	Placental microsomes	Human	Breuer (1960)
6β-Hydroxyandrost-4-ene-3,17-dione	6β-Hydroxyestrone			
19-Hydroxyandrost-4-ene-3,17-dione	Estrone	Placenta	Human	Morato *et al.* (1961)
19-Aldoandrost-4-ene-3,17-dione				
10β-Carboxyestr-4-ene-3,17-dione				

Continued on following page

Table 15 (*continued*)

Biosynthesis of Estrogens, *In Vitro*

Substrate	Product	Test system	Species	Reference
Testosterone	Estradiol-17β	Ovarian slice	Dog	Hollander and Hollander (1958)
Acetate	(*Preliminary*) Estrone Estradiol-17β	Stein–Leventhal ovary	Human	O'Donnell and McCaig (1959)
Acetate	Estradiol-17β	Ovarian homogenate	Various	Rabinowitz and Oleksyshyn (1956)
	Estradiol-17β	Testis homogenate	Various	
Dehydroepiandrosterone	Estradiol-17β Estrone	Ovarian follicular slices	Equine	West and Naville (1962)
Estradiol-17β	Estrone	Placental slice	Human	Pearlman (1954)
Testosterone	Estradiol-17β	Ovarian slices	Rats	Stitch *et al.* (1962)
Androst-4-ene-3,17-dione	Estradiol-17β Estrone	Corpus luteum	Human	Pearlman and Huang (1962)
Cortisone acetate	11β-Hydroxyestrone 11β-Hydroxyestradiol-17β	Mammary tumor tissue	Human	Chang *et al.* (1962)
19-Hydroxyandrost-4-ene-3,17-dione	Estrone Estradiol-17β	Placental microsomes	Human	Gual *et al.* (1962b)
Androst-4-ene-3,17-dione				
Testosterone				
Dehydroepiandrosterone				
Androsta-1,4-diene-3,17-dione				
19-Norandrost-4-ene-3,17-dione				
9α-Fluoroandrosta-1,4-diene-3,17-dione	9α-Fluoroestrone			
11α-Hydroxyandrost-4-ene-3,17-dione	11α-Hydroxyestrone			
B-Nortestosterone	*B*-Norestradiol-17β			
2β-Hydroxyandrostene-3,17-dione	2-Hydroxyestrone			
Estrone	11β-Hydroxyestrone 16α-Hydroxyestrone	Adrenal mince	Bovine	Knuppen and Breuer (1962)
Testosterone Androst-4-ene-3,17-dione	Estrone Estradiol-17β	Placental homogenate	Human	Amatsu (1963)

Continued on following page

Table 15 (*continued*)
BIOSYNTHESIS OF ESTROGENS, *In Vitro*

Substrate	Product	Test system	Species	Reference
Dehydroepiandrosterone				
19-Nortestosterone	Estradiol-17β			
Androsta-4,16-dien-3-one	Estra-1,3,5(10),16-tetren-3-ol	Placental homogenate supernatant	Human	Knuppen and Breuer (1963)
Testosterone	Estradiol-17β Estrone			
6α-Hydroxyandrost-4-ene-3,17-dione 6β-Hydroxyandrost-4-ene-3,17-dione	6α-Hydroxy-estrone 6β-Hydroxyestrone	Placental homogenate	Human	Breuer *et al.* (1962)
Estradiol-17β	6α-Hydroxy-estradiol-17β 6β-Hydroxy-estradiol-17β	Liver microsomes	Rat	Breuer *et al.* (1962)
Testosterone	Estradiol-17β Estrone	Ovarian granulosa cell tumor	Human	Marsh *et al.* (1961)
Testosterone Androst-4-ene-3,17-dione	Estrogens	Corpus luteum	Equine	Mahajan and Samuels (1963)
Acetate Cholesterol Progesterone	Estrogens	Placental slices	Human	Suzuki *et al.* (1962)
None Addition of human pregnancy serum	Estrone Estradiol-17β Estriol	Placental slices	Human	
Pregnenolone Testosterone Estrone	Estradiol-17β	Ovary	Porcine	

Table 16

CONVERSIONS OF VARIOUS STEROIDS TO ESTROGENS[a]

		Per cent conversion
C_{18}	19-Norandrost-4-ene-3,17-dione	10
	17β-Hydroxy-5α,10β-estran-3-one	0
	5α,10α-Estrane-3,17-dione	0
	17α-Ethynyl-10β,17β-dihydroxyandrost-4-ene-3,17-dione	0
	17α-Ethynyl-17β-hydroxy-19-nor(10β)-androst-5(10)-en-3-one	0
C_{19}	Androst-4-ene-3,17-dione	40
	19-Hydroxyandrost-4-ene-3,17-dione	60
	19-Oxoandrost-4-ene-3,17-dione	80
	10β-Carboxyestr-4-ene-3,17-dione	1
	17β-Hydroxyandrost-4-en-3-one(testosterone)	40
	3β-Hydroxyandrost-5-en-3-one(dehydroepiandrosterone)	30
	Androsta-1,4-diene-3,17-dione	25
	5α-Androst-1-ene-3,17-dione	0
	1α-Hydroxyandrost-4-ene-3,17-dione	0
	1α,3β-Dihydroxyandrost-5-en-17-one	0
	1α-Methyl-17β-hydroxyandrost-4-en-3-one	0
	2β-Hydroxyandrost-4-ene-3,17-dione	10
	2-Hydroxymethylene-17α-methyl-17β-hydroxyandrost-4-en-3-one	0
	2β-Methyl-17β-hydroxyandrost-4-en-3-one	0
	2-Formyl-17α-methyl-17β-hydroxyandrosta-1,4-dien-3-one	0
	Androsta-4,6-diene-3,17-dione	0
	Androsta-1,4,6-triene-3,17-dione	0
	Androst-4-ene-3,11,17-trione	0
	11β-Hydroxyandrost-4-ene-3,17-dione	0
	11α-Hydroxyandrost-4-ene-3,17-dione	40
	6α-Fluoro-17β-hydroxyandrost-4-en-3-one	0
	6β-Fluoro-17β-hydroxyandrost-4-en-3-one	0
	5α-Androstane-3,17-dione(androsterone)	0
	9α-Fluoroandrosta-1,4-diene-3,17-dione	35
	17β-Acetoxyandrosta-4,7-dien-3-one	15
C_{21}	Pregn-4-ene-3,20-dione(progesterone)	0
	17α,19,21-Trihydroxypregn-4-ene-3,20-dione	0
	6β-Fluoro-16α-methyl-21-acetoxy-11β,17α-dihydroxypregnane-1,4-diene-3,20-dione	0

[a] Data of Gual *et al.* (1962b).

Table 17

CONVERSION OF ANDROST-4-ENE-3,17-DIONE TO ESTROGEN

	Substrate	Product	Per cent loss of activity
Experiment 1	Androst-4-ene-3,17-dione (25% 1α-H^3, 75% 1β-H^3)	Estrone	
	dpm/μmole	*dpm*/μmole	
	Expt. (1) 9.45×10^4	1.74×10^4	81.6
	(2) 11.6×10^4	2.07×10^4	82.2
Experiment 2	Androst-4-ene-3,17-dione (93% 1α-H^3, 7% 1β-H^3)		
	dpm/μmole	*dpm*/μmole	
	2.23×10^7	1.89×10^7	15.3

Table 18

BIOSYNTHESIS OF STEROID CONJUGATES, *In Vitro* AND *In Vivo*

Substrate	Product	Test system	Species	Reference
Androsterone	Androsterone glucuronoside	Kidney perfusion	Dog	Cohn and Hume (1960)
Etiocholanolone	Etiocholanolone glucuronoside			
Dehydroepiandrosterone	Dehydroepiandrosterone sulfate	*In vivo*	Human	Staib *et al.* (1960)
Epiandrosterone	Epiandrosterone sulfate			
Androsterone	Androsterone glucuronoside (major) Androsterone sulfate (minor)			
Androsterone	Androsterone sulfate	Liver (soluble fraction)	Rat	Roy (1956)
Dehydroepiandrosterone	Dehydroepiandrosterone sulfate			
Etiocholanolone	Etiocholanolone glucuronoside	*In vivo*	Human	Schenker *et al.* (1961)
Cortisol	Cortisol sulfate	*In vivo*	Human	Pasqualini (1960)
Dehydroepiandrosterone	Dehydroepiandrosterone sulfate	*In vivo*	Human	Roberts *et al.* (1961b)
Etiocholanolone	Sulfate and glucuronoside	*In vivo*	Human	Baulieu and Emiliozzi (1960)

Continued on following page

Table 18 (*continued*)

BIOSYNTHESIS OF STEROID CONJUGATES, *In Vitro* AND *In Vivo*

Substrate	Product	Test system	Species	Reference
Estrone	Estrone sulfate	*In vitro* placental homogenate	Guinea pig	Levitz *et al.* (1961)
Estriol	Sodium estriol-16(17?)-glucosiduronate	Intestinal	Human	Diczfalusy *et al.* (1961b)
Estradiol-17β	Sodium estradiol-17β-3-sulfate	Fetus	Human	Diczfalusy (1961a)
	Sodium estrone sulfate			
Estriol	Sodium estriol-3-sulfate			
Cortisol	Cortisol-21-sulfate	*In vivo*	Human	Pasqualini and Jayle (1961a)
Corticosterone	Corticosterone-21-sulfate			
Deoxycorticosterone	3α,21-Dihydroxy-5β-pregnan-20-one glucuronoside	*In vivo*	Human	Pasqualini and Jayle (1961b)
		In vitro		Schneider and Lewbart (1956)
Urocortisol	Urocortisol glucuronoside	*In vitro* microsomes	Guinea pig liver	Isselbacher and Axelrod (1955)
Androsterone 5α-Pregnane-3β,20β-diol Stilbestrol	Glucuronosides	*In vitro* microsomes	Mouse liver	Dutton (1956)
Androst-5-ene-3β,17β-diol	Disulfate	*In vitro* supernatant female liver	Rat	Wengle and Bostrom (1962)
21-Hydroxy-pregnenolone	Disulfate	*In vitro* liver	Rat	Pasqualini (1962)
Testosterone	Glucuronoside	Liver slices	Hamster Rat Mouse Dog Rabbit Guinea pig	Fishman and Sie (1956)
1-Methyl-17β-hydroxy-5α-androst-1-en-3-one	Glucuronoside	*In vivo*	Human	Langecker and Kramer (1962)

Continued on following page

Table 18 (*continued*)

BIOSYNTHESIS OF STEROID CONJUGATES, *In Vitro* AND *In Vivo*

Substrate	Product	Test system	Species	Reference
Estradiol-17β	Estrone glucuronoside Estradiol-17β-3-glucuronoside (tentative)	Intestinal tract	Human	Diczfalusy *et al.* (1962)
Dehydroepiandrosterone	Dehydroepiandrosterone sulfate	Virilizing adrenal cancer homogenate	Human	Wallace and Lieberman (1963)

Table 19

INHIBITION OF STEROID BIOSYNTHESIS

Inhibitor	Test system	Species	Result	Reference
Metopirone (SU-4885, 2-methyl-1:2-bis(3-pyridyl)-1-propanone)	*In vitro* adrenal slices	Rats	Decreased corticosterone	Roche *et al.* (1960)
	In vivo adrenal slices	Rats	Up to 50% reduction in corticosterone	
4,4′-Methylenedianiline	*In vivo*	Rat, dog, rabbit	Inhibit corticoid product	Tullner (1960)
o,p′DDD[(2,2-bis(2-chlorophenyl, 4-chlorophenyl)-1,1-dichloroethane)]	*In vivo*	Dog	Markedly decreased corticoid production	Tullner and Hertz (1960)
Amphenone	*In vivo*	Human (adrenal cancer)	Cortisol synthesis depressed; other adrenal steroids variably depressed	Gallagher (1958)
		Human (neperotic syndrome)	Aldosterone excretion severely depressed	Luetscher and Lieberman (1958)
		Human (feminizing adrenal cancer)	Decrease in estrogens, corticoids, aldosterone	Biancalana and Romanelli (1958)

Continued on following page

Table 19 (*continued*)

INHIBITION OF STEROID BIOSYNTHESIS

Inhibitor	Test system	Species	Result	Reference
*o,p'*DDD	*In vivo* (adrenal cancer)	Human	Decreased 17-ketosteroids and corticoids	Bergenstal *et al.* (1959, 1960a, b)
Amphenone	Injected into dorsal lymphatic sac	*Rana temporaria*	Increase in size and lipid level of interrenal gland	Dluzniewski (1959)
SU-4885 (Metopirone)	*In vitro* *In vivo*	Rat	Approximately 50% reduction in corticoid biosynthesis	Roche *et al.* (1960)
Mer-29	Pretreatment *in vivo* with Mer-29 then *in vitro* (adrenal)	Rat	Inhibition of corticosterone, deoxycorticosterone, aldosterone	Melby *et al.* (1961a)
SU-8000[3-(chloro-3-methyl-2-indenyl)-pyridine] SU-9055[3-(1,2,3,4-tetrahydro-1-oxo-2-naphthyl)-pyridine]	Adrenal venous blood	Dog	Corticosterone increased, decreased cortisol, no increase in deoxycortisol, apparent inhibition in 17α-hydroxylation	Chart and Sheppard (1959, 1961); Chart *et al.* (1958); Sheppard and Chart (1961)
SU-4885	Adrenal vein	Dog	Low doses of 11β-hydroxylation inhibited	Jenkins *et al.* (1959a)
Amphenone	Adrenal vein	Dog	Cortisol and corticosterone decreased	
SU-4885	*In vivo*	Human	Increased amounts of 11-deoxycortisol and 3α,5β-tetrahydro derivative	
SKF-6296A [2-amino-4-(*p*-trifluoromethylanilino)-*s*-triazine] and SKF-3195A [2-amino-4-(*p*-chloroanilin)-*s*-triazine]	*In vivo*	Guinea pig	Decreased urinary corticoids and 17-ketosteroids	Costa (1960)
SU-4885	*In vivo*	Human	Decrease in 11β-hydroxylated steroids	Coppage *et al.* (1959)

Continued on following page

Table 19 (*continued*)

INHIBITION OF STEROID BIOSYNTHESIS

Inhibitor	Test system	Species	Result	Reference
SU-4885	*In vivo*	Human adrenal cancer	Decrease in 11β-hydroxy steroids	Fukushima *et al.* (1960)
Triparanol (Mer-29)	*In vivo*	Rat	Decreased corticosterone secretion	Holloszy and Eisenstein (1961)
*o,p′*DDD	*In vivo*	Human Cushing's nontumorous adrenal hyperfunction	Decreased urinary 17-ketosteroids and corticoids Decreased plasma corticoids	Southren *et al.* (1961)
Cortisol and prednisolone	*In vitro* adrenal quarters with added ACTH	Rat	Decreased corticosterone production	Fukuii *et al.* (1961)
Triparanol (Mer-29)	*In vivo*	Human	Cortisol and aldosterone production decreased	Melby *et al.* (1961b)
SU-4885	*In vivo*	Human	Reversibility of inhibition *in vivo*	Ungar *et al.* (1962)
Androst-4-ene-3,17-dione	*In vitro*	Bovine 11β-hydroxylase preparation	Competitive inhibitor	Sharma *et al.* (1963)
Testosterone Dehydroepiandrosterone Dehydroepiandrosterone sulfate	*In vitro*	Bovine 11β-hydroxylase preparation	Inhibitor	
Progesterone	*In vitro*		Inhibits reaction of 17α-hydroxyprogesterone to androst-4-ene-3,17-dione and reduction of latter compound	Mahajan and Samuels (1962)
*o,p′*DDD	*In vivo*	Man (adrenal cortical carcinoma)	Decrease in urinary corticoid, 17-ketosteroid, and pregnanetriol	Verdon *et al.* (1962)
Ethynylestradiol-17β-3-methyl ether	*In vivo*	Human	Decrease secretion rate of cortisol and increase secretion rate of aldosterone	Layne *et al.* (1962)

Continued on following page

Table 19 (*continued*)

INHIBITION OF STEROID BIOSYNTHESIS

Inhibitor	Test system	Species	Result	Reference
*o,p′*DDD	*In vivo* treatment *In vitro* test	Dog	Decreased corticoid production in presence or absence of ACTH	Cazorla and Moncloa (1962)
2,2-Bis(*p*-ethylphenyl)-2,2-diphenyl 2,2-Bis(*p*-bromophenyl)-1,1-dichloroethane 2,2-Bis(*p*-chlorophenyl)-1,1-dichloroethane 2,2-Bis(*p*-chlorophenyl)-2-hydroxy-1,1-dichloroethane	ACTH stimulation	Dog	Decrease	Cobey *et al.* (1958)
Cholesterone	*In vivo*	Dog	Increased adrenal size 6–8 times normal; corticosterone and aldosterone decreased	Fredrickson *et al.* (1958); Steinberg *et al.* (1958)
SU-9055	*In vivo*	Dog	Decrease in cortisol and 11-deoxycortisol and increase in corticosterone and deoxycorticosterone in adrenal venous blood	Chart *et al.* (1962)
SU-9055	*In vitro*	Guinea pig	Decreased conversion of progesterone-16-H^3 to 17α-hydroxylated corticoids using adrenal slices	Chart *et al.* (1962)
Chlorpromazine	*In vivo*	Human	Suppressed 17-hydroxycorticoids in urine and response to methopyrapone	Feldschuh *et al.* (1961)
Diphenylhydantoin	*In vivo*	Human	Decreases magnitude of corticoid response to methopyrapone; perhaps blocks pituitary release of ACTH	Krieger (1962)
DPNH	*In vitro* adrenal homogenate	Rat	Inhibited corticoid production (perhaps product of inhibition of 3β-ol dehydrogenase)	Koritz (1962b)

Continued on following page

Table 19 (*continued*)
INHIBITION OF STEROID BIOSYNTHESIS

Inhibitor	Test system	Species	Result	Reference
Estrogen	*In vitro*	Human	*In vitro* conversion of androst-4-ene-3,17-dione to testosterone by testis is inhibited, but not conversion of 17α-hydroxy-progesterone to androst-4-ene-3,17-dione; HCG reverses estrogen effect	Slaunwhite *et al.* (1962a)
Stilbestrol	*In vivo* treatment, prostate cancer patient	Human	Prevented androst-4-ene-3,17-dione conversion to testosterone but did not affect significantly 17α-hydroxyprogesterone androsten-4-ene-3,17-dione	Slaunwhite *et al.* (1962b)
Triparanol		Human		Ney *et al.* (1962)
SU-4885	Bovine adrenal homogenate *In vivo* rat adrenal	Bovine Rat	Blocks, in following decreasing order: Aldosterone 19-Hydroxylation 11β-Hydroxylation	Kahnt and Neher (1962)
SU-8000			Blocks, in following decreasing order: 17α-Hydroxylation Aldosterone 18-Hydroxylation	
SU-9055	Bovine adrenal homogenate *In vivo* rat adrenal	Bovine Rat	Blocks, in following: decreasing order: Aldosterone 17α-Hydroxylation 19-Hydroxylation	
SU-10,603			Blocks, in following order: 17α-Hydroxylation Aldosterone 18-Hydroxylation	
Amphenone	Progesterone and adrenal	Lizards Snakes	Transformations inhibited	Phillips *et al.* (1962)

Continued on following page

Table 19 (*continued*)

INHIBITION OF STEROID BIOSYNTHESIS

Inhibitor	Test system	Species	Result	Reference
L-Phenylalanyl Puromycin	*In vitro* adrenal slices	Bovine	Inhibition of leucine-C^{14} incorporation and steroid biosynthesis to ACTH *Also*: Inhibition to 3′,5′ cyclic AMP but not to $NADPH_2$	Ferguson (1962, 1963)
o,p′DDD	*In vivo*	Human	Decreased urinary corticoid and androgen metabolites	Gallagher *et al.* (1962)
Chloramphenicol Puromycin	Testis slices, FSH and ICSH	Rabbit	Decreases stimulation	Hall and Eik-Nes (1962)
Adrenal microsomes	Adrenal mitochondria Progesterone to corticosterone	Guinea pig	Microsomes inhibit progesterone to corticosterone	Hofmann (1962)
SU-4885	*In vitro*	Mouse	Blocks adrenal corticosterone and more polar steroids	Ertel and Ungar (1964)

Table 20

STIMULATION OF STEROID BIOSYNTHESIS

Stimulation (substrate)	Product	Test system	Reference
Pregnant mare's serum (PMS) (pregnenolone)	Estradiol-17β(?) (about 100% increase)	Swine ovary slice	Susuki *et al.* (1961)
Human ICSH (17α-hydroxypregnenolone)	Testosterone (threefold increase)	Human testis mince	Carstensen (1961)
Human ICSH (17α-hydroxyprogesterone)	Testosterone (no increased formation)		
Human ICSH (17α-hydroxyprogesterone)	Androst-4-ene-3,17-dione (tenfold increase) Testosterone (150% increase)	Rat testis mince	Carstensen (1961)
Human ICSH (17α-hydroxypregnenolone)	No increase in C_{19} steroid production		

Continued on following page

Table 20 *(continued)*

STIMULATION OF STEROID BIOSYNTHESIS

Stimulation (substrate)	Product	Test system	Reference
Estradiol-17β (none added)	Increased corticocosterone production	Rat adrenal quarters	Fukuii *et al.* (1961)
Ascorbic acid (11-deoxycortisol) (limited NADP)	Cortisol	Bovine adrenal homogenate	Jenkins (1962)
Serotonin (no added substrate)	Cortisol Corticosterone	Perfusion, dog adrenal	Verdesca *et al.* (1961)
Angiotensin	Aldosterone	Infusion into dog (nephrectomized, hypophysectomized) adrenal artery	Ganong *et al.* (1962)
Estradiol-17β	Aldosterone	Rat *in vivo*	Llaurado *et al.* (1962)
Angiotensin	Increase in aldosterone corticosterone	Dog (hypophysectomized and nephrectomized)	Ganong and Mulrow (1961)
LH, FSH, HCG, PMS, Cu salts	Increase in progesterone 20α-Hydroxypregn-4-en-3-one	Rabbit	Hilliard and Sawyer (1962)
Angiotensin II	Increased aldosterone production; chlorpromazine interfered with this effect	Rat	Glaz and Sugar (1962)
HCG	Estriol production stimulated; substrates present were 16α-hydroxytestosterone, 16α-hydroxy-androst-4-ene-3,17-dione	Perfused human placenta	Varangot *et al.* (1962)
Angiotensin II	Aldosterone increased; corticosterone not increased	*In vivo* rat	Glaz and Sugar (1962)
Renin extract and synthetic angiotensin II	Aldosterone secretion stimulated; cortisol secretion not stimulated; some increment in corticosterone secretion	*In vivo* hypophysectomized, nephrectomized dog	Mulrow *et al.* (1962b)
Reserpine	Corticosterone increase in adrenal and plasma in 3 hours after treatment	*In vivo* cockerels	Newcomer (1962)

Table 21

The Concentration of Steroid Sulfatase and a Steroid Sulfate-Forming Enzyme in Various Rodent Livers[a]

Species	Sex	Status	Steroid sulfatase hydrolyzed (μmoles of ester $\pm$ SD)	Dehydroepiandrosterone sulfate formed (μmoles $\pm$ SD)
Rat	M	Intact	403 $\pm$ 91	53 $\pm$ 22
	M	Castrate	279	72
	F	Intact	187 $\pm$ 62	149 $\pm$ 37
	F	Spayed	182	152
Mouse	M	Intact	1.5 $\pm$ 0.4	7 $\pm$ 4
	F	Intact	1.6 $\pm$ 0.4	34 $\pm$ 18
Guinea pig	M	Intact	0	72 $\pm$ 9
	F	Intact	0	78 $\pm$ 11

[a] After Roy (1958).

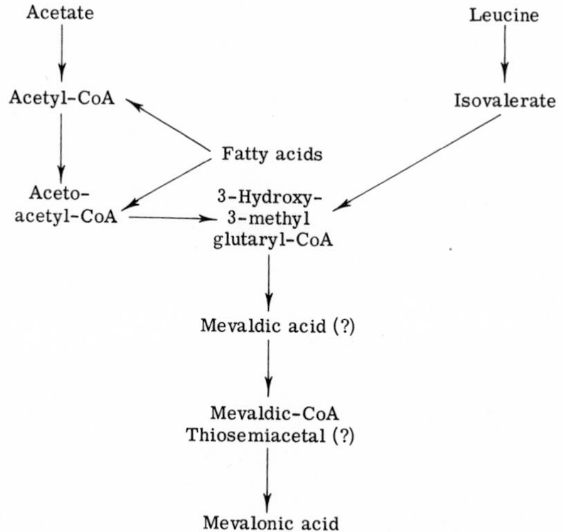

FIG. 1. Biosynthesis of cholesterol. Formation of mevalonic acid. (After Popjak and Cornforth, 1960.)

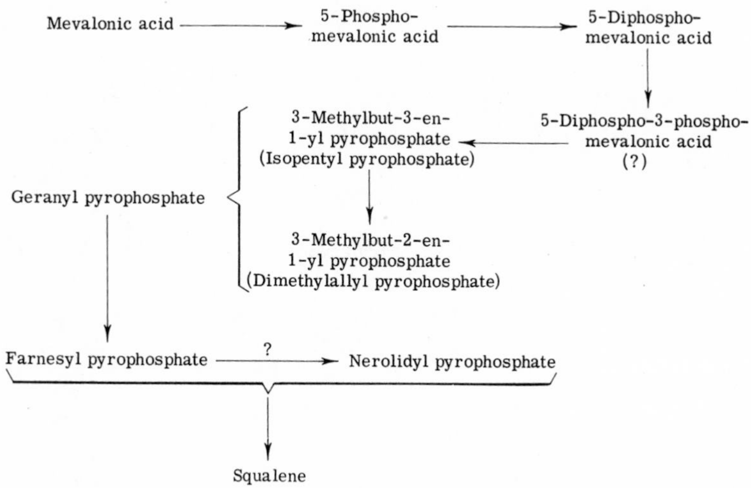

FIG. 2. Biosynthesis of cholesterol. Formation of squalene.

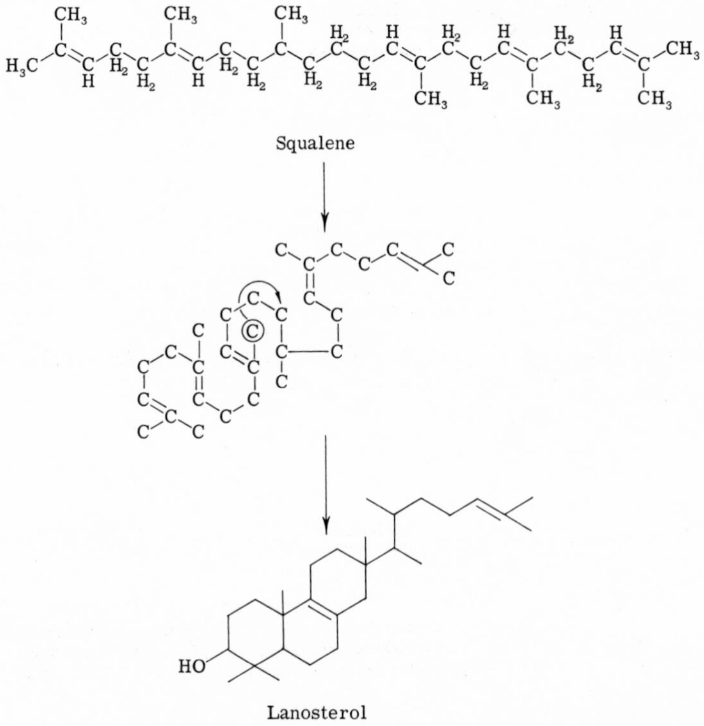

Squalene

Lanosterol

FIG. 3. Biosynthesis of cholesterol. Formation of lanosterol.

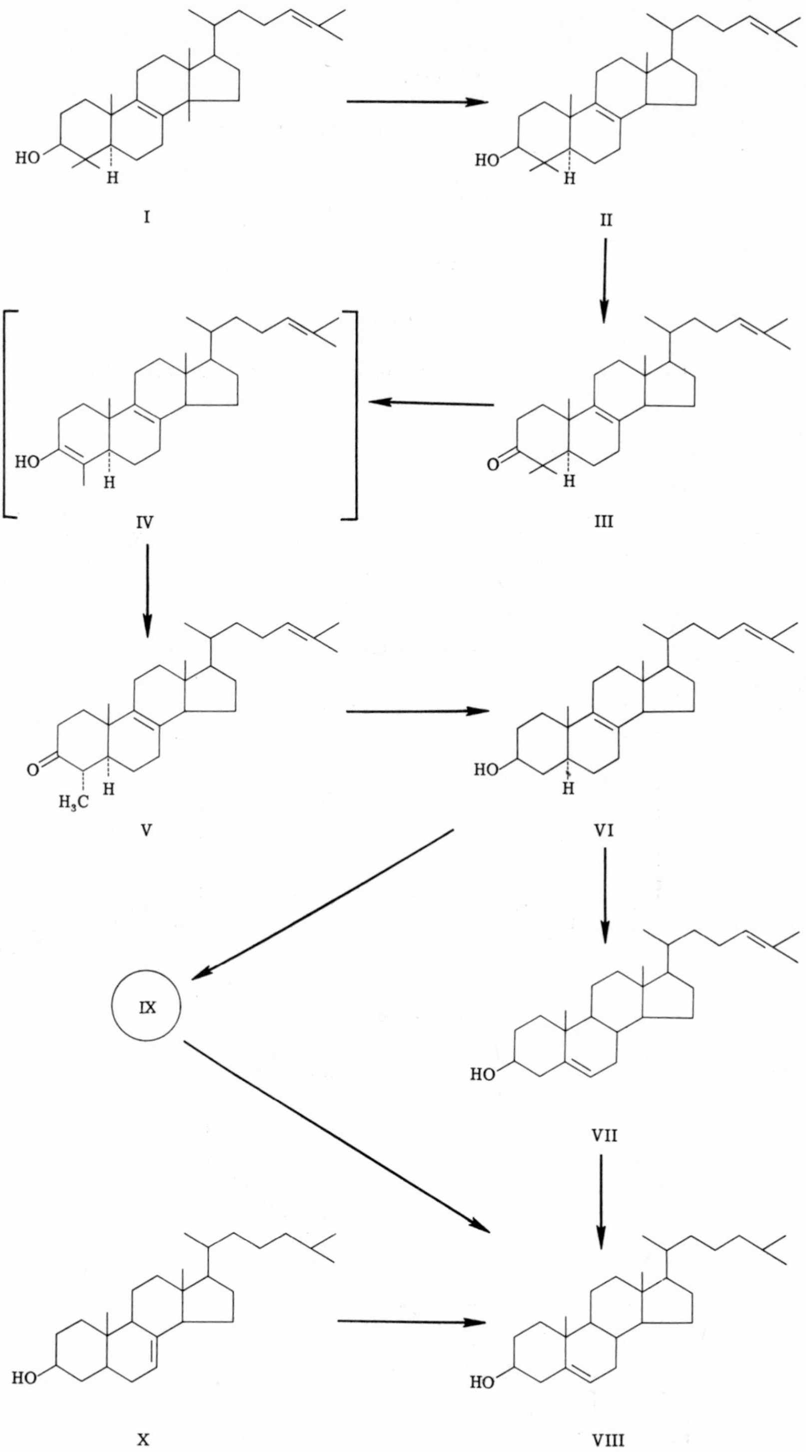

FIG. 4. Biosynthesis of cholesterol from lanosterol. (After Popjak and Cornforth, 1960.)

I. Lanosterol	VI. Zymosterol
II. 4,4-Dimethylcholesta-8,24-dien-3β-ol	VII. Desmosterol
III. 4,4-Dimethylcholesta-8,24-dien-3-one	VIII. Cholesterol
IV. 4-Methylcholesta-3,8,24-trien-3β-ol	IX. 24,25-Dihydroxyzymosterol
V. 4α-Methylcholesta-8,24-dien-3-one	X. Lathosterol

Key: $H_3C—COOH=H_3M—COOH$

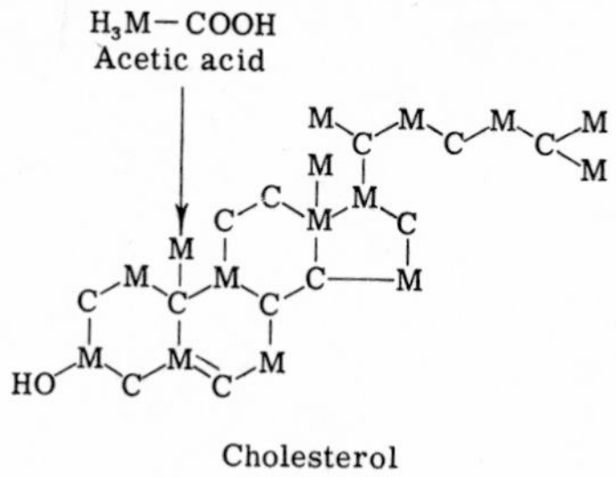

$H_3M—COOH$
Acetic acid

Cholesterol

FIG. 5. Relation of carbons in cholesterol to carbons of acetic acid.

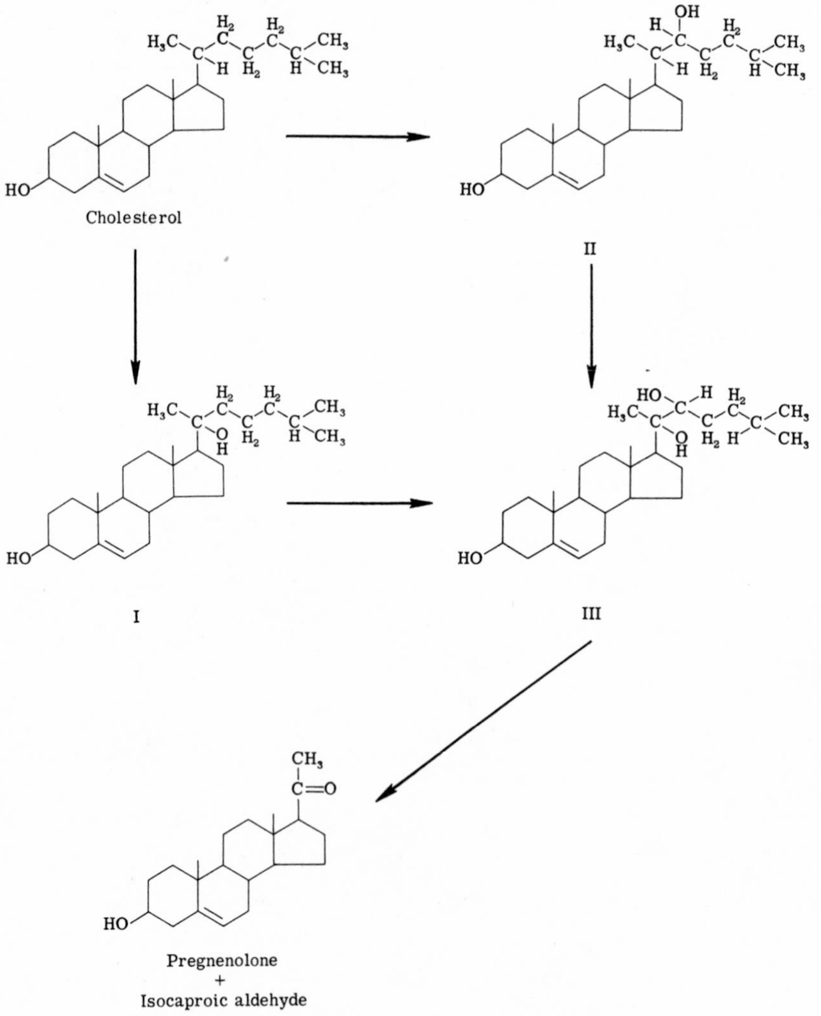

Cholesterol

II

I

III

Pregnenolone
+
Isocaproic aldehyde

FIG. 6. Biosynthesis of pregnenolone.
I. 20α-Hydroxycholesterol
II. 22R-Hydroxycholesterol
III. 20α,22R-Dihydroxycholesterol

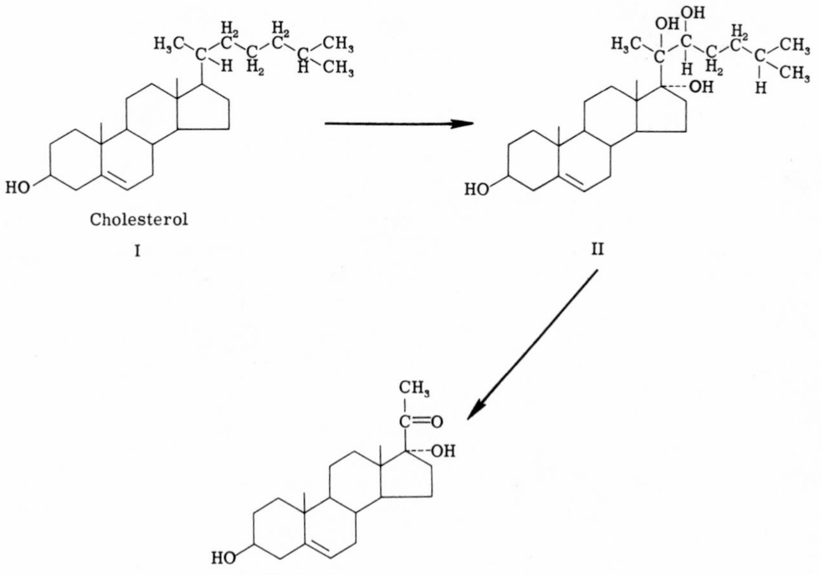

Cholesterol
I

II

17α-Hydroxypregnenolone
III

FIG. 7. Possible biosynthesis of 17α-hydroxypregnenolone. II. 17α,20α-Dihydroxycholesterol.

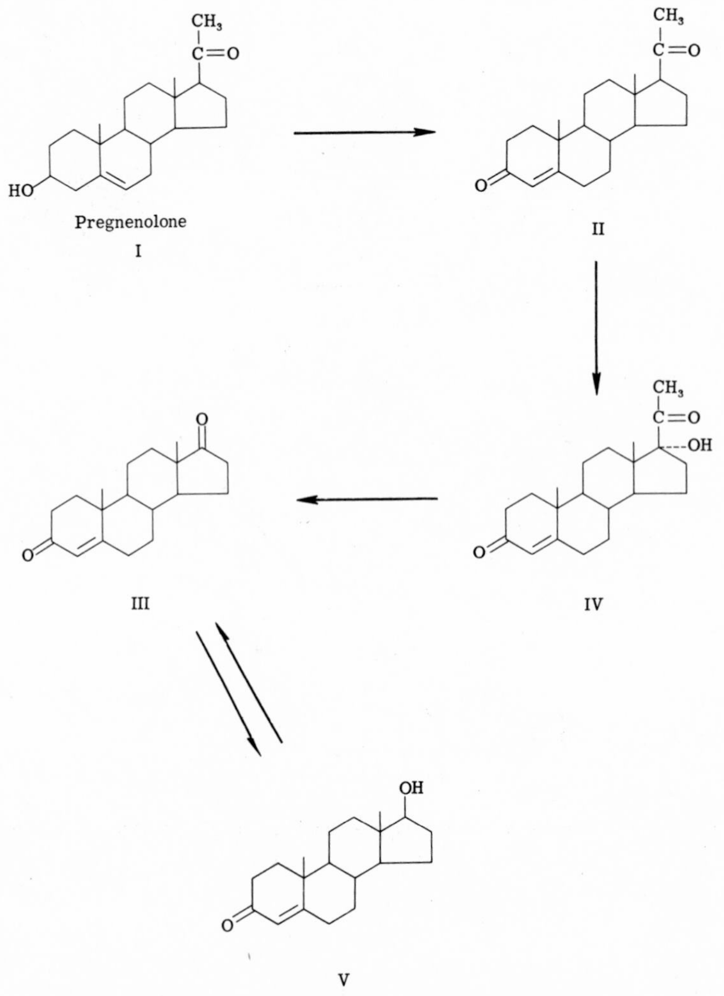

CH3
C=O
HO
Pregnenolone
I

CH3
C=O
O
II

CH3
C=O
---OH
O
IV

O
O
III

OH
O
V

Fig. 8. Biosynthesis of androgens through 17α-hydroxyprogesterone.

II. Progesterone
III. Androst-4-ene-3,17-dione
IV. 17α-Hydroxyprogesterone
V. Testosterone

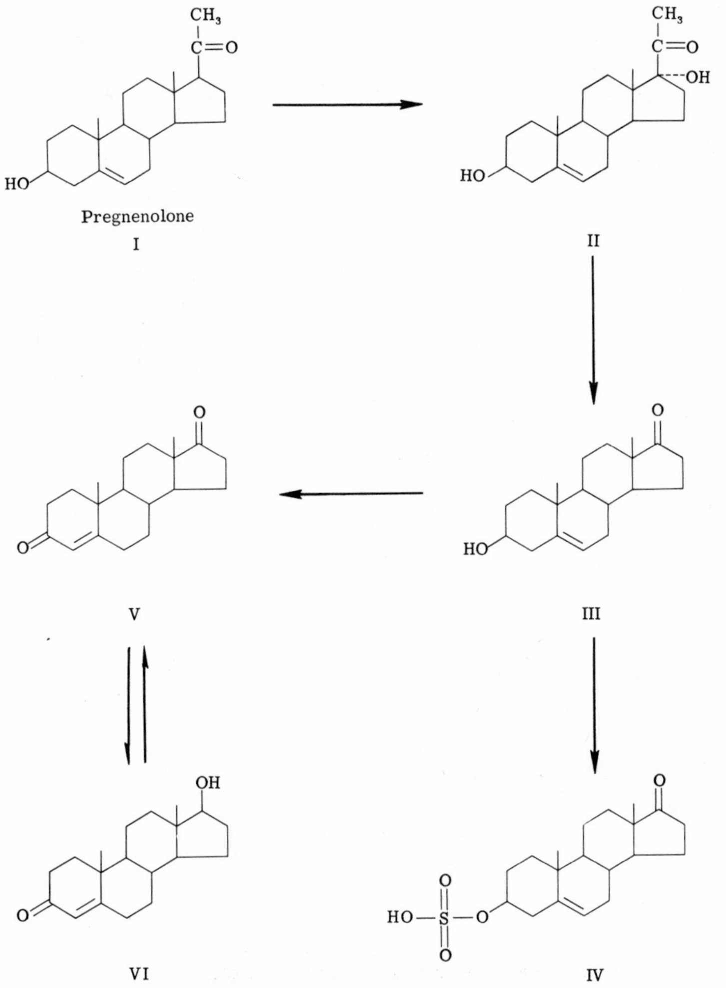

CH$_3$
C=O
HO
Pregnenolone
I

CH$_3$
C=O
OH
HO
II

O
O
V

O
HO
III

OH
O
VI

O
O
HO—S—O
O
IV

FIG. 9. Biosynthesis of androgens through 17α-hydroxypregnenolone.

II. 17α-Hydroxypregnenolone
III. Dehydroepiandrosterone
IV. Dehydroepiandrosterone Sulfate
V. Androst-4-ene-3,17-dione
VI. Testosterone

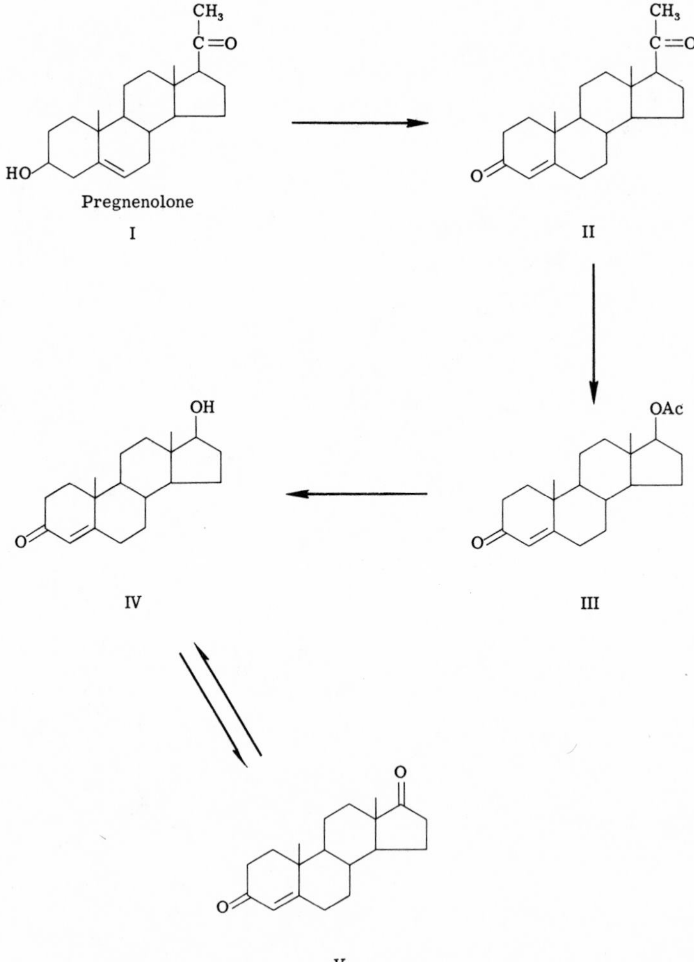

FIG. 10. Biosynthesis of androgens through testosterone acetate.

II. Progesterone
III. Testosterone acetate
IV. Testosterone
V. Androst-4-ene-3,17-dione

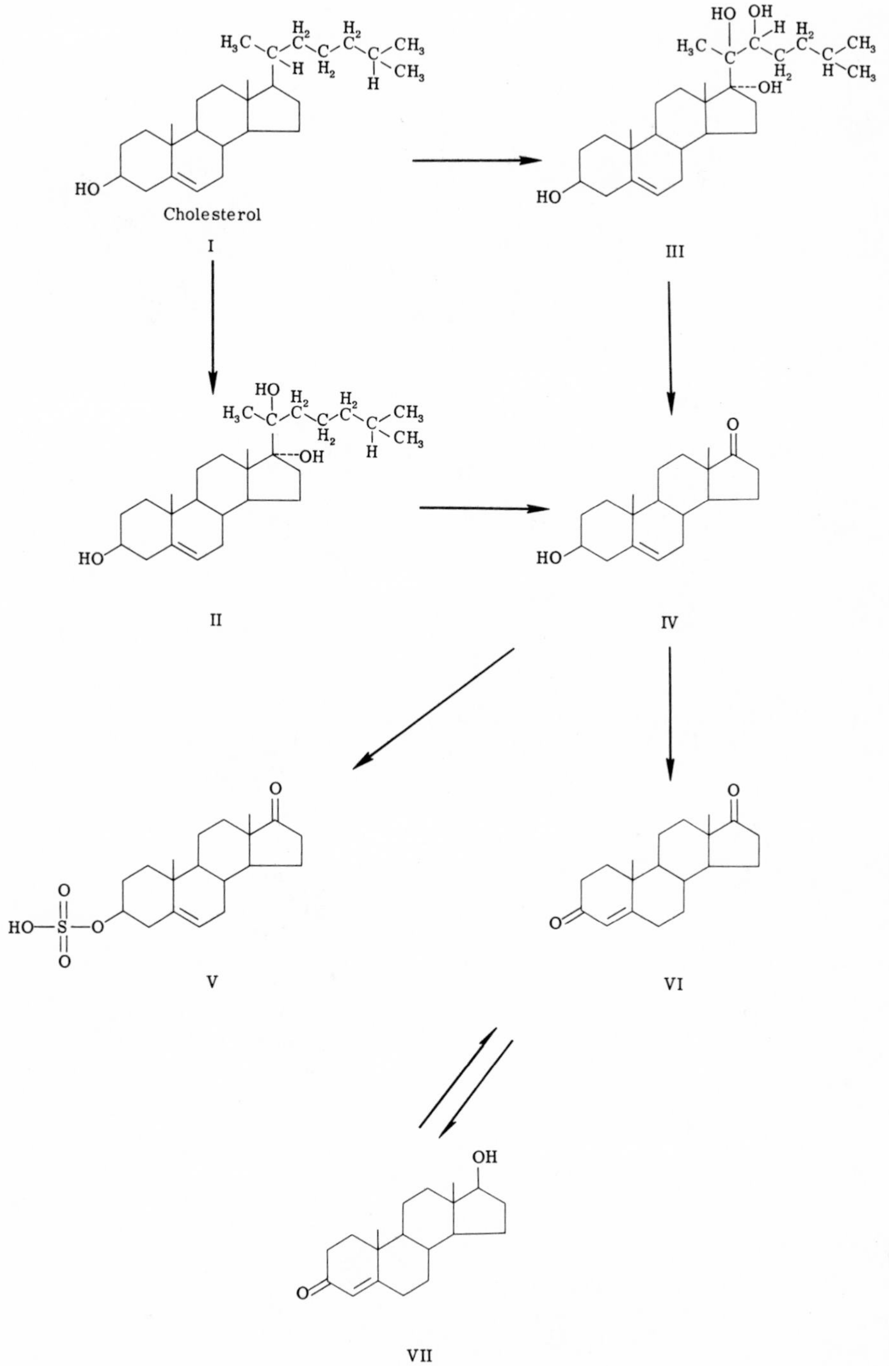

Cholesterol

I

II

III

IV

V

VI

VII

FIG. 11. Biosynthesis of androgens through 17α-20α-dihydroxycholesterol (II) or 17α,20α,22-Trihydroxycholesterol (III).

IV. Dehydroepiandrosterone

V. Dehydroepiandrosterone sulfate

VI. Androst-4-ene-3,17-dione

VII. Testosterone

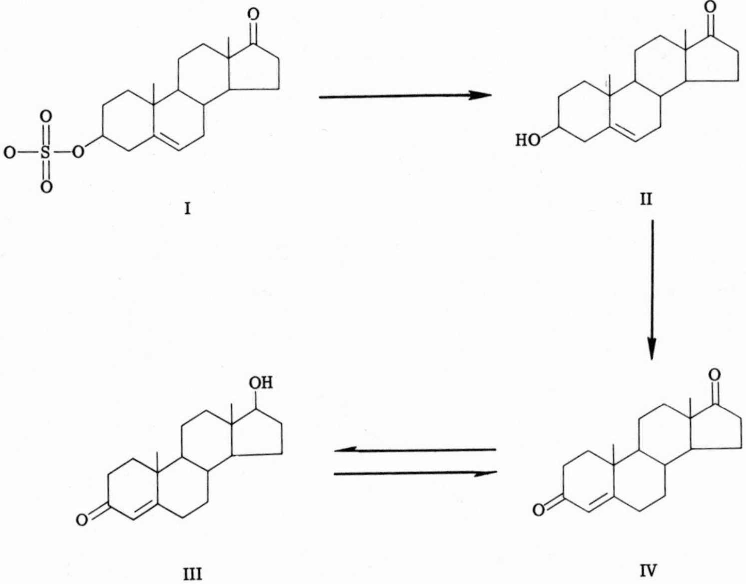

FIG. 12. Biosynthesis of androgens through dehydroepiandrosterone sulfate.

I. Dehydroepiandrosterone sulfate
II. Dehydroepiandrosterone
III. Androst-4-ene-3,17-dione
IV. Testosterone

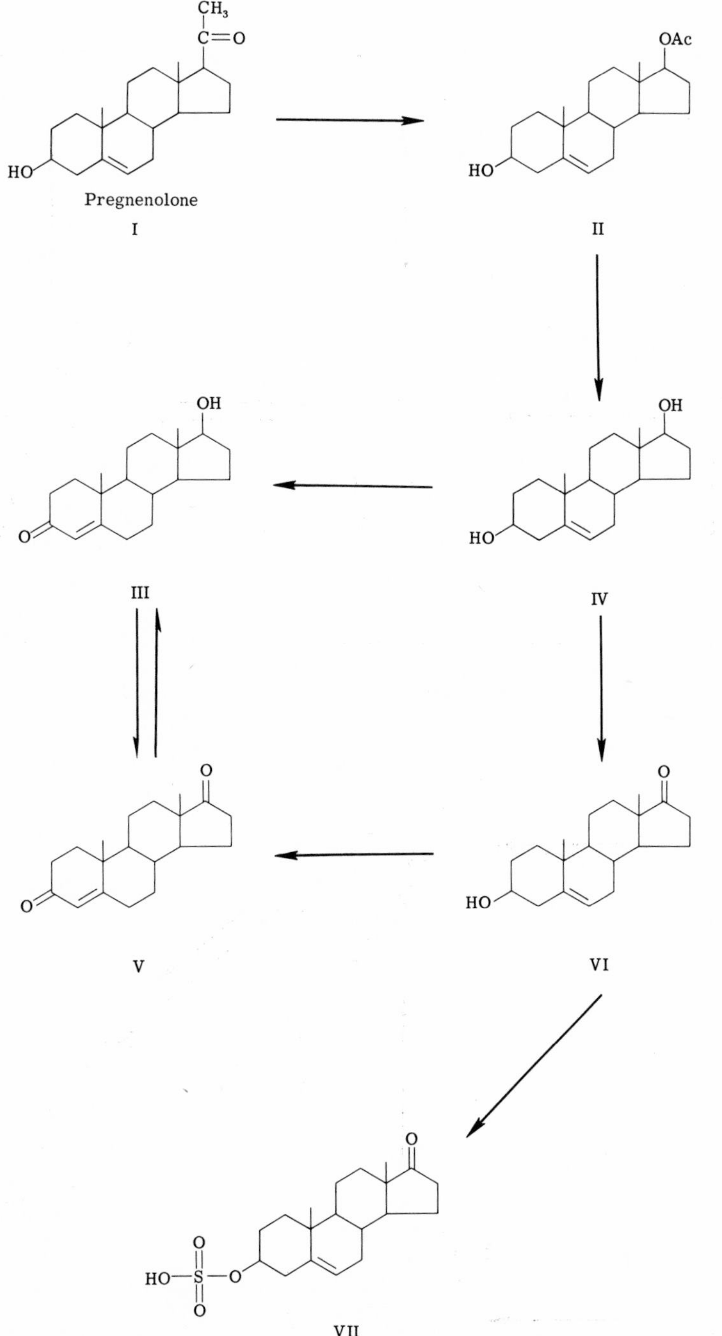

FIG. 13. Biosynthesis of androgens through androst-5-ene-3β,17β-diol-17β-acetate.

II. Androst-5-ene-3β,17β-diol-17-acetate
III. Testosterone
IV. Androst-5-ene-3β,17β-diol
V. Androst-4-ene-3,17-dione
VI. Dehydroepiandrosterone
VII. Dehydroepiandrosterone sulfate

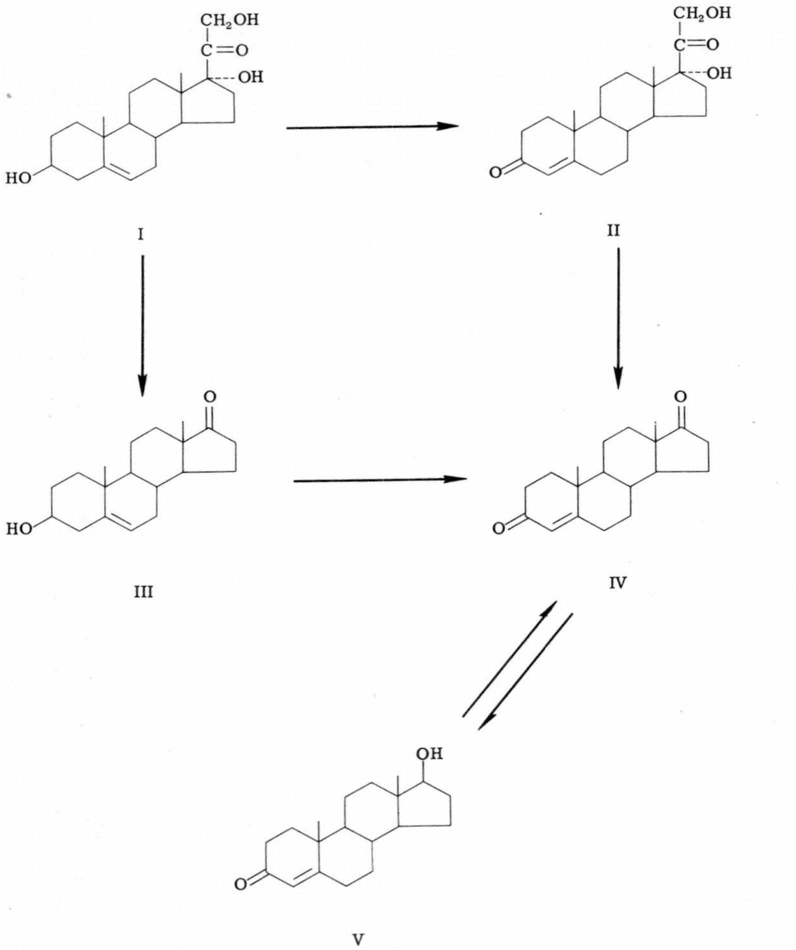

FIG. 14. Possible biosynthesis of androgens through 21-hydroxylated derivatives.

I. $3\beta,17\alpha$,21-Trihydroxypregn-5-en-20-one
II. 11-Deoxycortisol
III. Dehydroepiandrosterone
IV. Androst-4-ene-3,17-dione
V. Testosterone

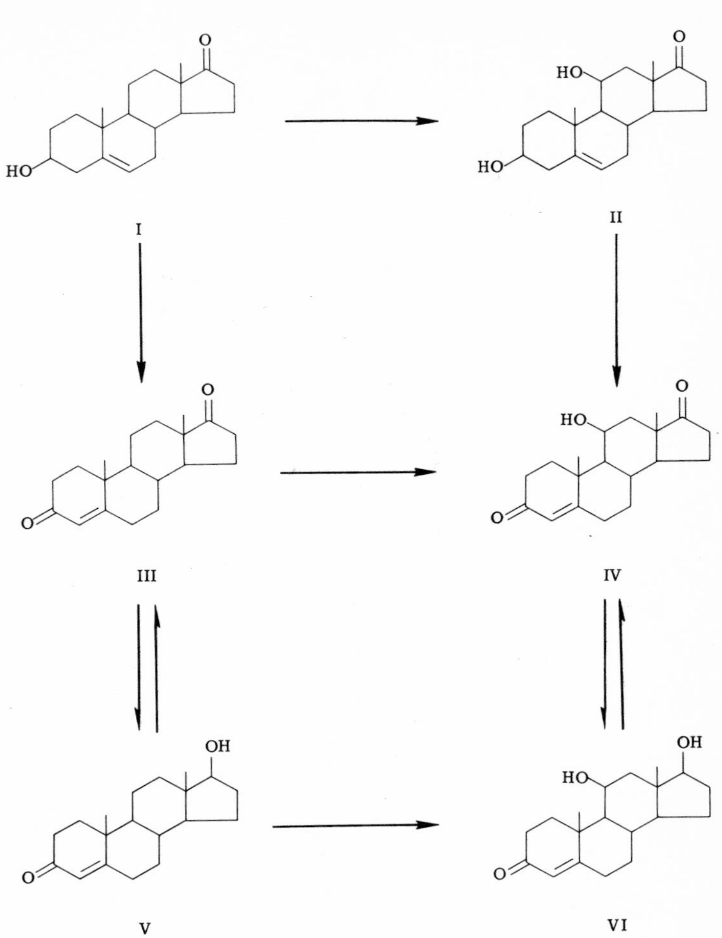

FIG. 15. Biosynthesis of some adrenal androgens.

I. Dehydroepiandrosterone
II. $3\beta,11\beta$-Dihydroxyandrost-5-en-17-one
III. Androst-4-ene-3,17-dione
IV. 11β-Hydroxyandrost-4-ene-3,17-dione
V. Testosterone
VI. 11β-Hydroxytestosterone

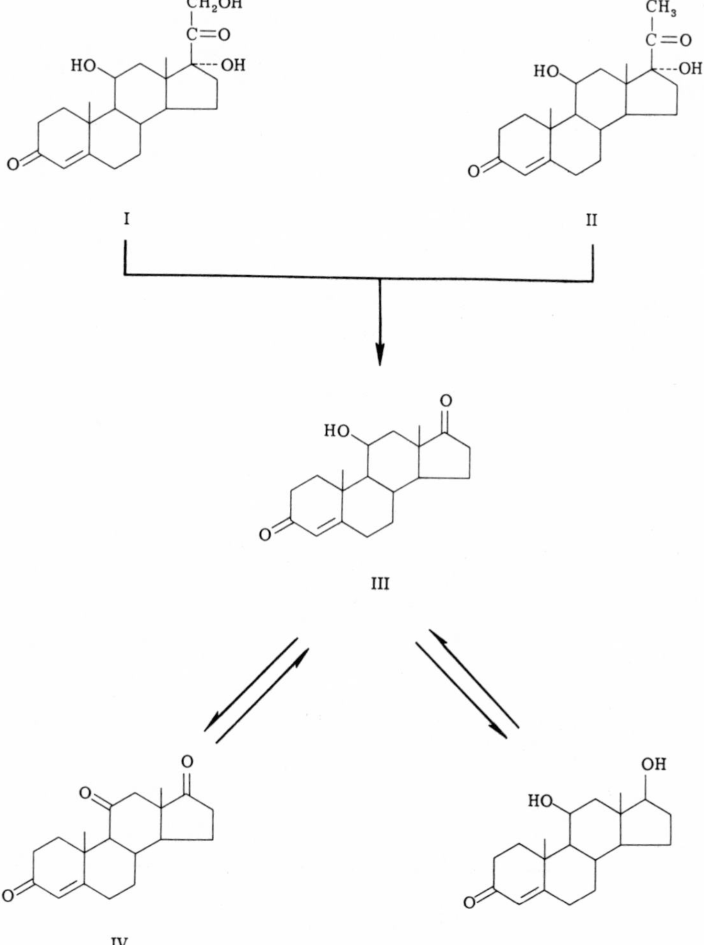

FIG. 16. Biosynthesis of some adrenal androgens.

I. Cortisol
II. 21-Deoxycortisol
III. 11β-Hydroxyandrost-4-ene-3,17-dione
IV. Adrenosterone
V. 11β-Hydroxytestosterone

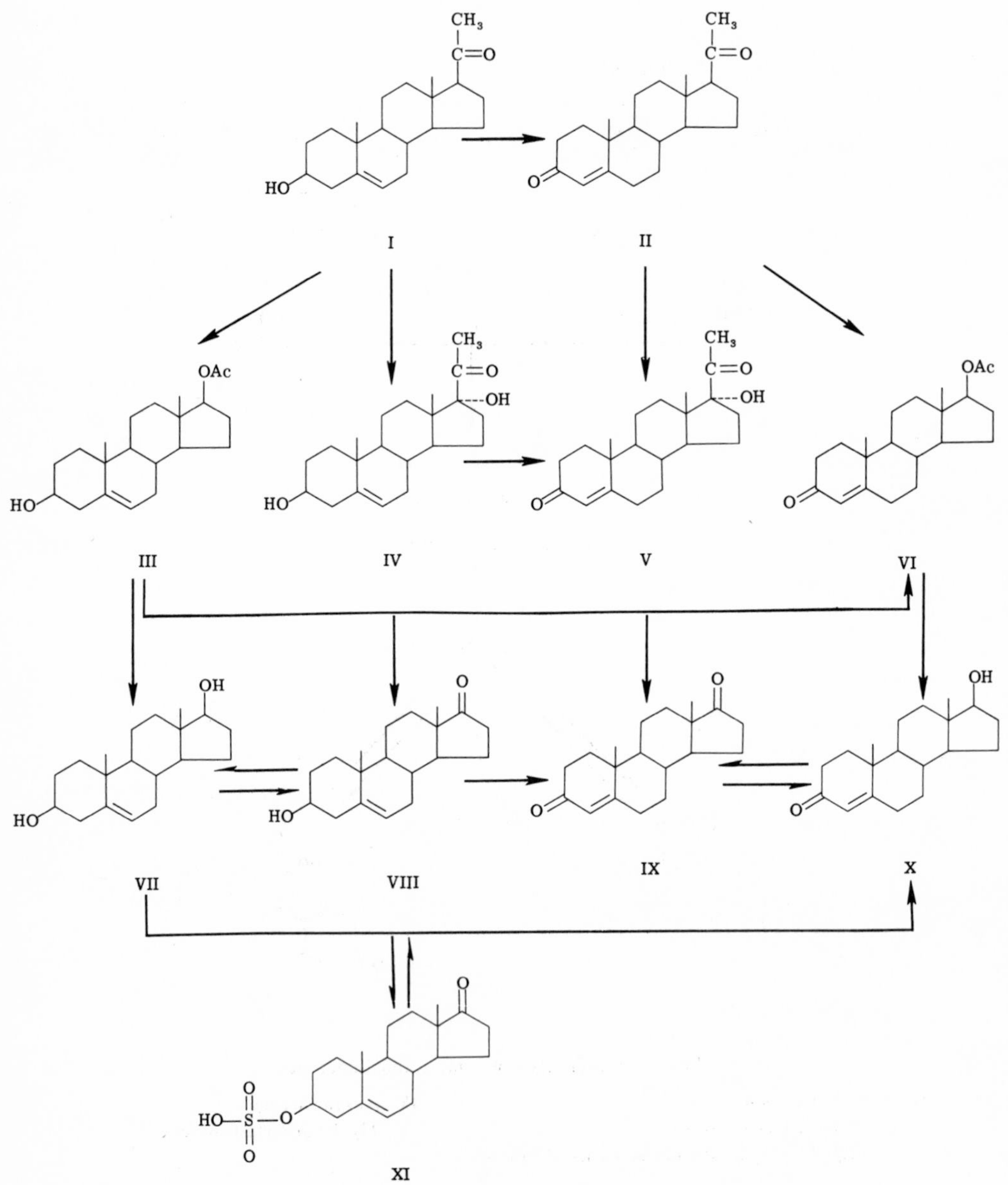

FIG. 17. Summary of androgen biosynthetic pathways.

I. Pregnenolone
II. Progesterone
III. Androst-5-ene-3β,17β-diol-17-acetate
IV. 17α-Hydroxypregnenolone
V. 17α-Hydroxyprogesterone
VI. Testosterone acetate
VII. Androst-5-ene-3β,17β-diol
VIII. Dehydroepiandrosterone
IX. Androst-4-ene-3,17-dione
X. Testosterone
XI. Dehydroepiandrosterone sulfate

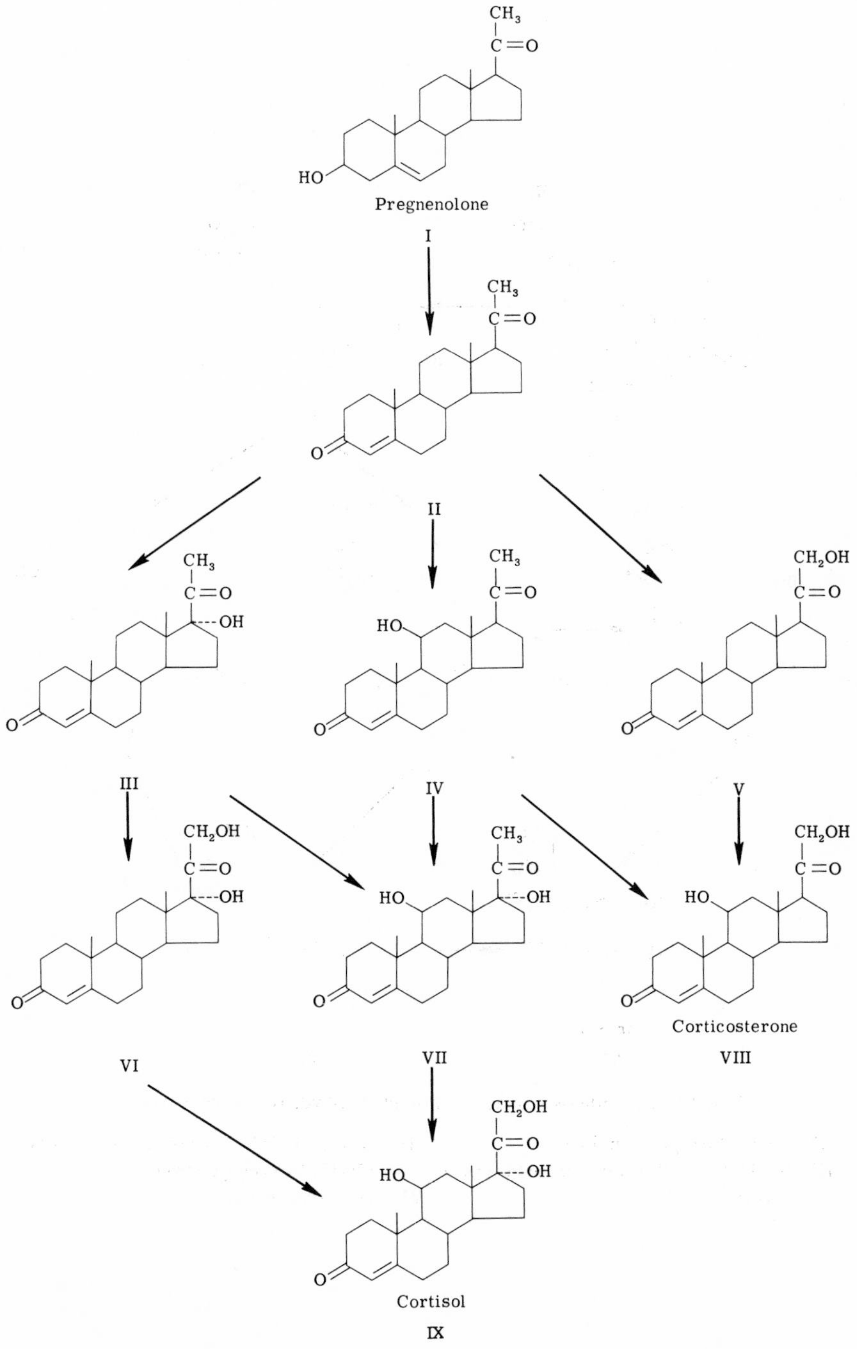

CH$_3$
C=O
HO
Pregnenolone
I

CH$_3$
C=O
O

II

CH$_3$
C=O
OH
O

CH$_3$
C=O
HO
O

CH$_2$OH
C=O
O

III

IV

V

CH$_2$OH
C=O
OH
O

CH$_3$
C=O
HO
OH
O

CH$_2$OH
C=O
HO
O
Corticosterone
VIII

VI

VII

CH$_2$OH
C=O
HO
OH
O
Cortisol
IX

FIG. 18. Biosynthesis of cortisol and corticosterone.

II. Progesterone
III. 17α-Hydroxyprogesterone
IV. 11β-Hydroxyprogesterone
V. Deoxycorticosterone
VI. 11-Deoxycortisol
VII. 21-Deoxycortisol

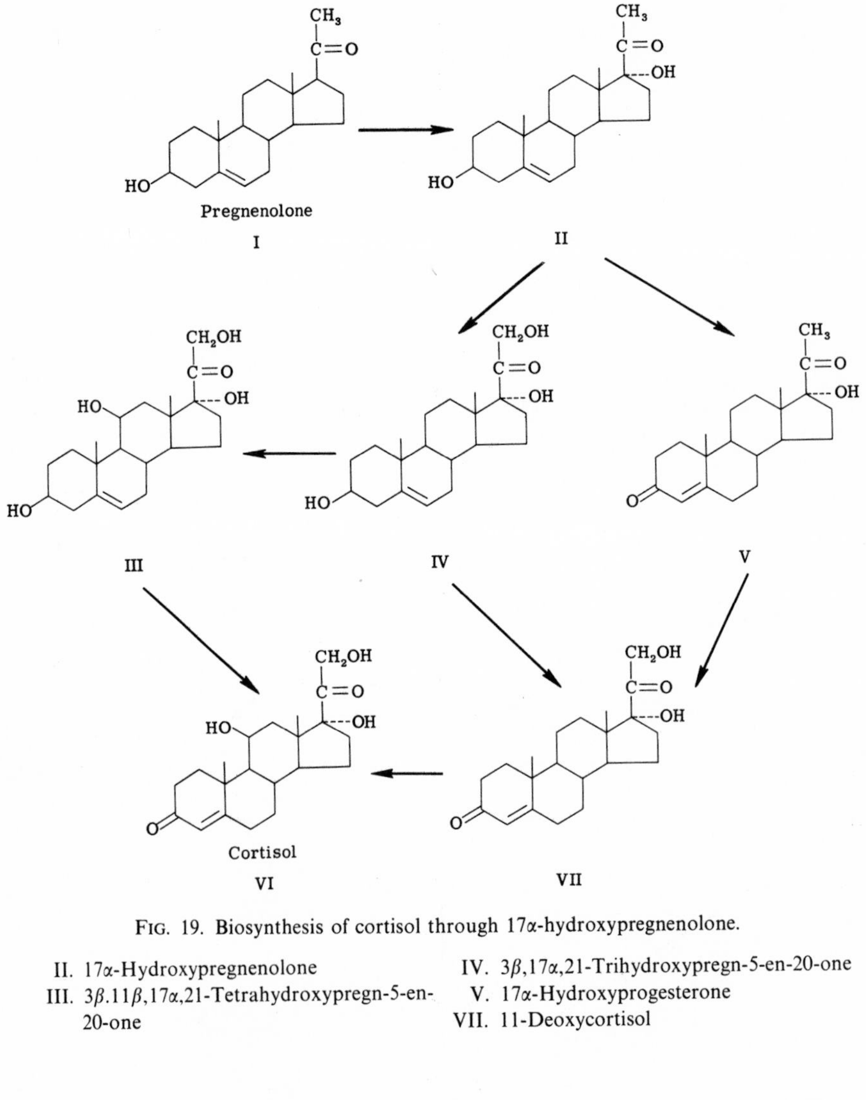

Pregnenolone

I

II

III

IV

V

Cortisol

VI

VII

FIG. 19. Biosynthesis of cortisol through 17α-hydroxypregnenolone.

II. 17α-Hydroxypregnenolone

III. 3β.11β,17α,21-Tetrahydroxypregn-5-en-20-one

IV. 3β,17α,21-Trihydroxypregn-5-en-20-one

V. 17α-Hydroxyprogesterone

VII. 11-Deoxycortisol

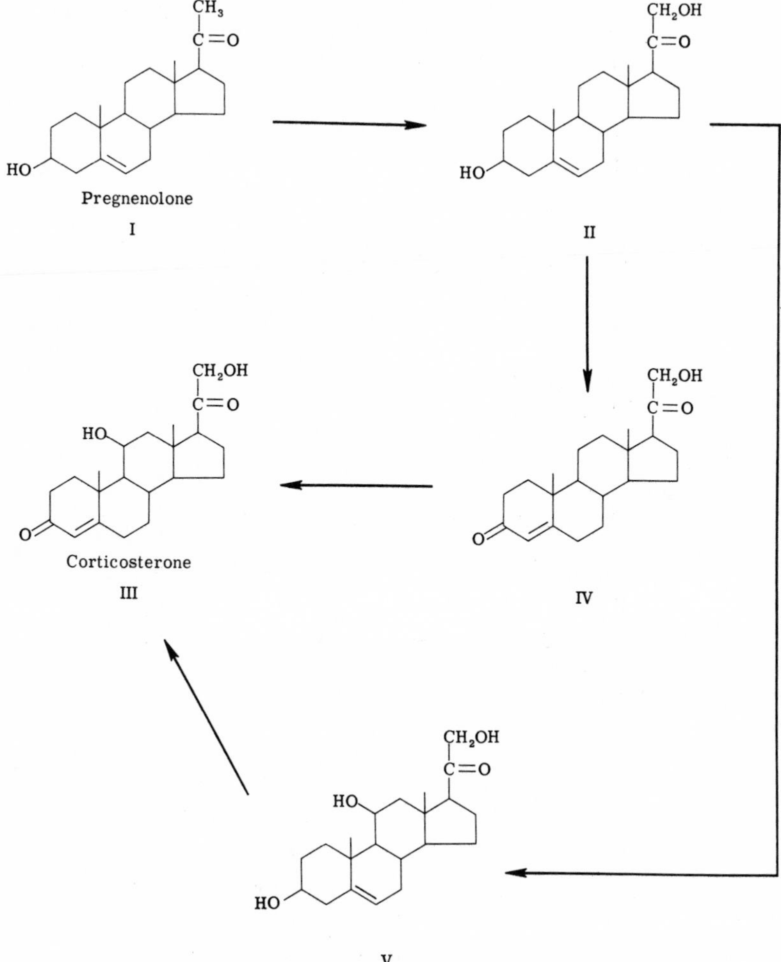

FIG. 20. Biosynthesis of corticosterone through 21-Hydroxypregnenolone.

II. 21-Hydroxypregnenolone
IV. Deoxycorticosterone
V. $3\beta,11\beta$,21-Trihydroxypregn-5-en-20-one

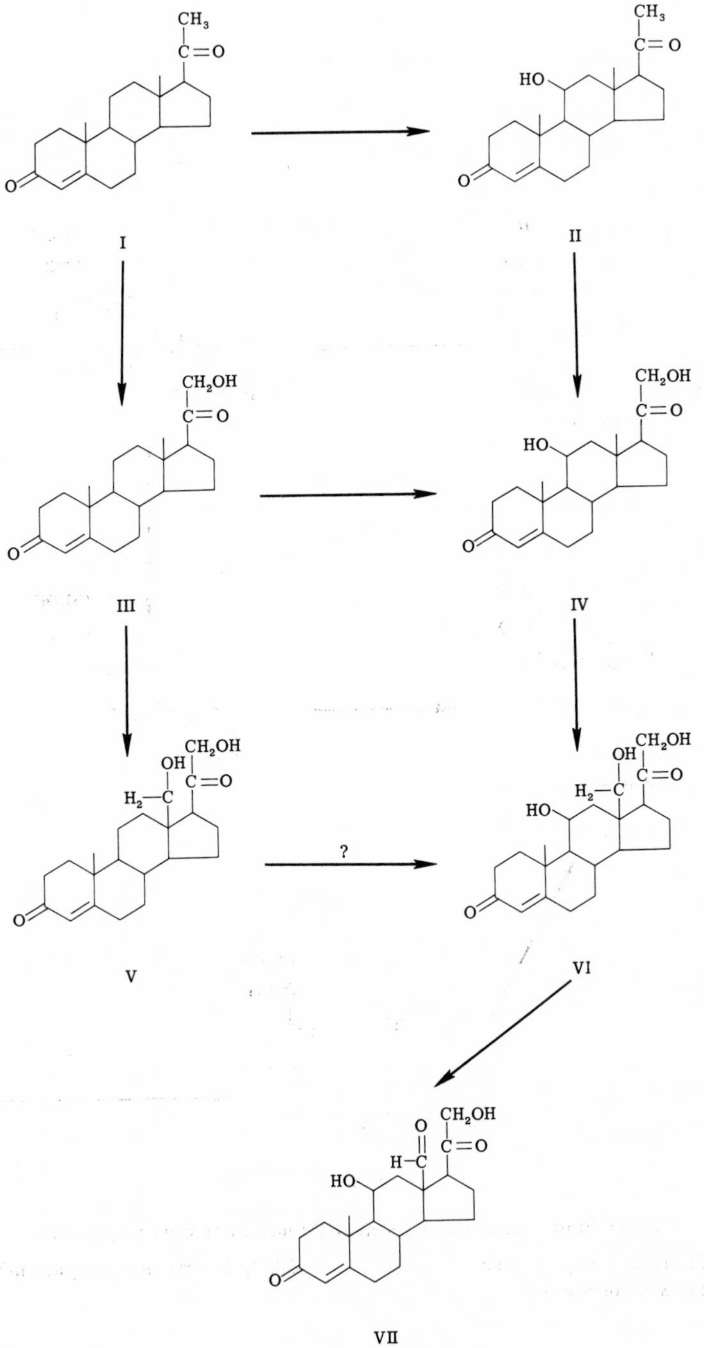

I

II

III

IV

V

VI

VII

FIG. 21. Biosynthesis of aldosterone.

I. Progesterone
II. 11β-Hydroxyprogesterone
III. Deoxycorticosterone
IV. Corticosterone
V. 18,21-Dihydroxyprogesterone
VI. 18-Hydroxycorticosterone
VII. Aldosterone

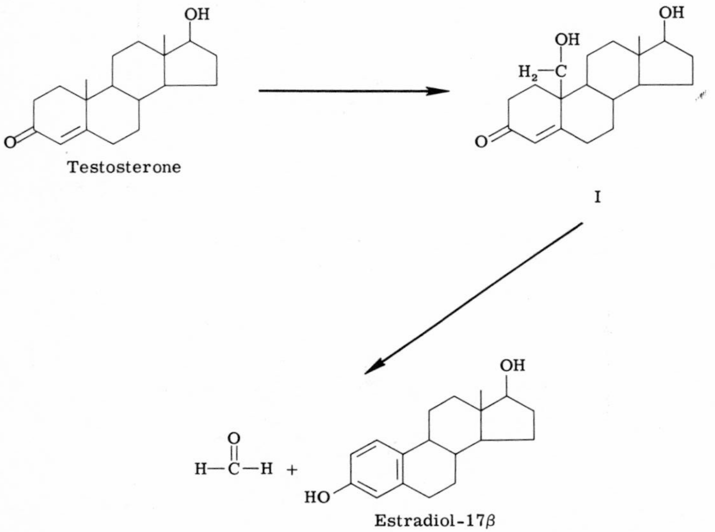

Testosterone

I

$H{-}C({=}O){-}H$ + Estradiol-17β

FIG. 22. Biosynthesis of estrogens through 19-hydroxy-C_{19} steroids.

I. 19-Hydroxytestosterone

Testosterone

I

II

III

$H{-}C({=}O){-}OH$ + Estradiol-17β

IV

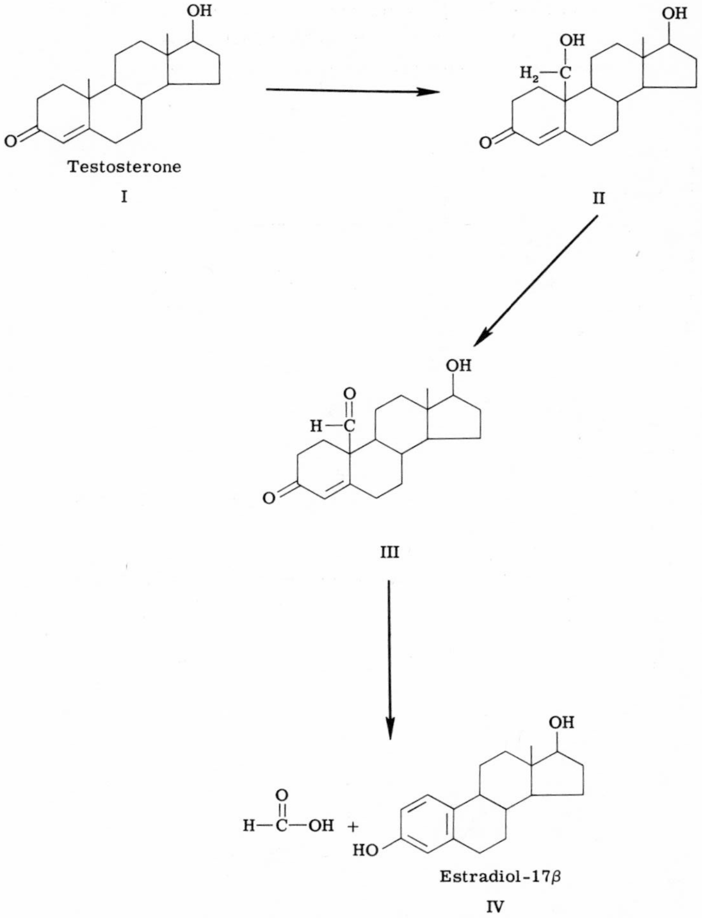

FIG. 23. Biosynthesis of estrogens through 19-oxo-C_{19} steroids.

II. 19-Hydroxytestosterone III. 19-Oxotestosterone

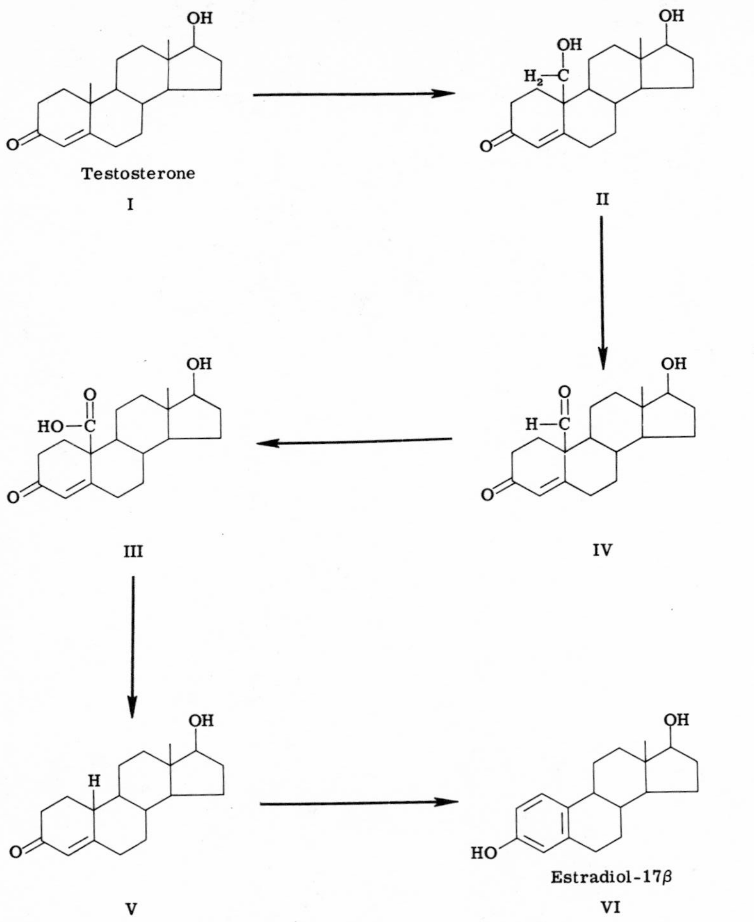

Testosterone

I

II

III

IV

V

Estradiol-17β

VI

FIG. 24. Biosynthesis of estrogens through 19-carboxy-C_{19} steroids.

II. 19-Hydroxytestosterone
III. 19-Carboxytestosterone
IV. 19-Oxotestosterone
V. 19-Nortestosterone

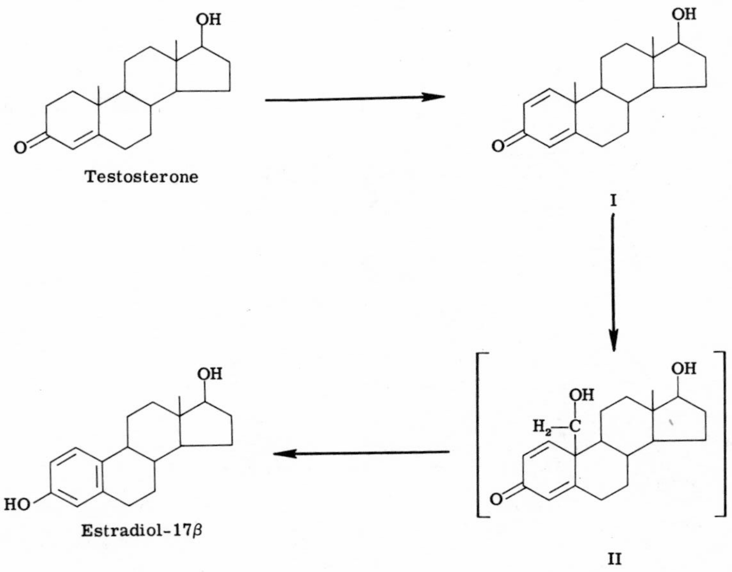

Testosterone

I

II

Estradiol-17β

FIG. 25. Biosynthesis of estrogens through Δ^1-C_{19} steroids.

I. 17β-Hydroxyandrosta-1,4-dien-3-one
II. 17β-Hydroxy-19-carboxyandrosta-1,4-dien-3-one

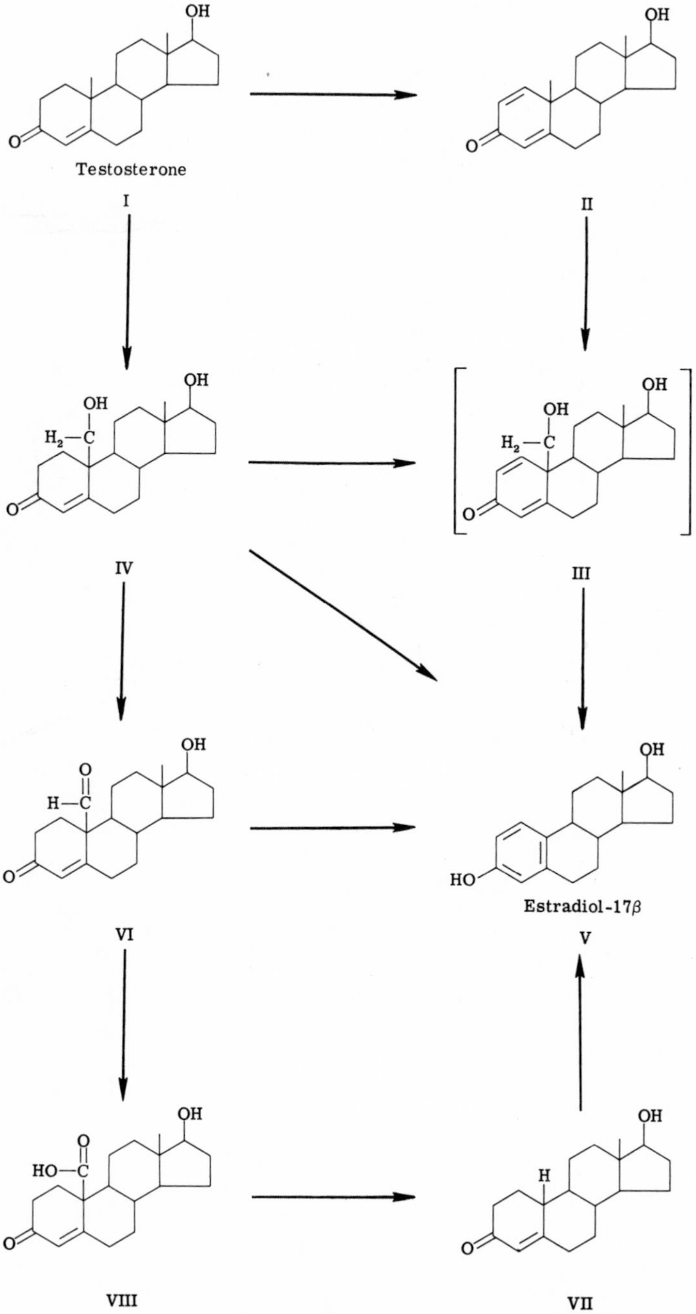

Testosterone

I

II

IV

III

VI

Estradiol-17β

V

VIII

VII

FIG. 26. Biosynthesis of estrogens: summary.

II. 17β-Hyroxyandrosta-1,4-dien-3-one
III. 17β,19-Dihydroxyandrosta-1,4-dien-3-one
IV. 19-Hydroxytestosterone
VI. 19-Oxotestosterone
VII. 19-Nortestosterone
VIII. 19-Carboxytestosterone

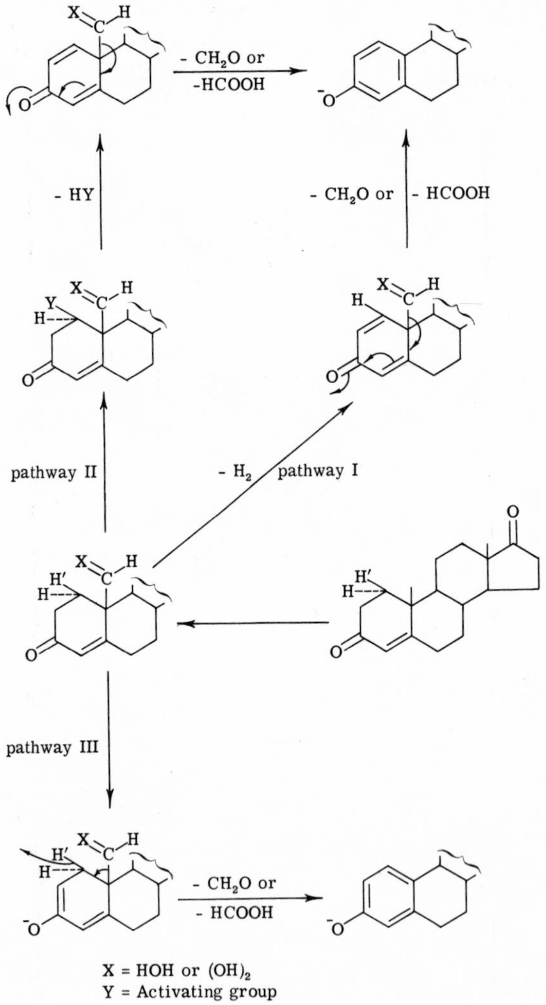

- CH_2O or -HCOOH

- HY

- CH_2O or - HCOOH

pathway II

- H_2 pathway I

pathway III

- CH_2O or - HCOOH

X = HOH or $(OH)_2$
Y = Activating group

FIG. 27. Specifically labeled estrogen biosynthesis substrate.

Synthetic Blocking Agents

Amphenone B
3, 3-bis (p-aminophenyl)-
2-butanone

D.D.D.
2,2-bis (p-chlorophenyl)
1,1-dichloroethane

SU-4885
2, methyl-1, 2-bis-
(3-pyridyl)-propanone

MER-29
1- 4(-diethylamino ethoxy) phenyl -
1-(p-totyl)-2-(p-chlorophenyl)-ethanol

FIG. 28. (A) Structure and names of steroid inhibitors.

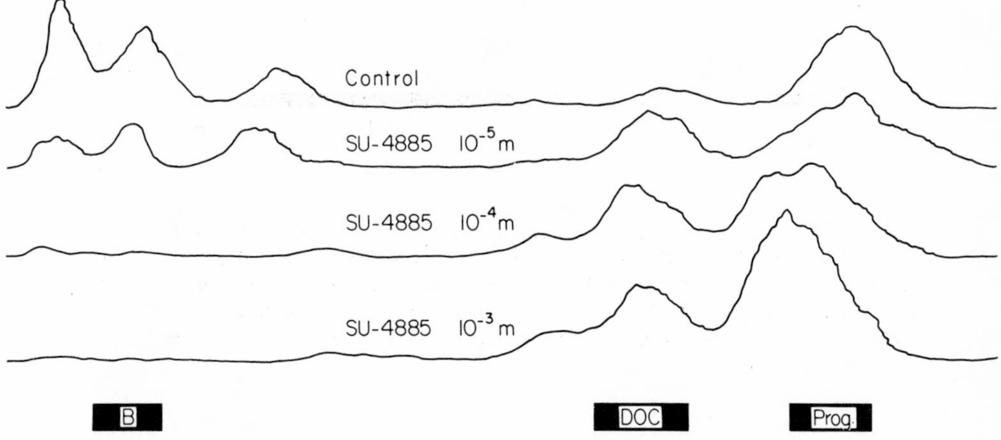

(B) Tracings obtained with a strip counter on paper chromatograms illustrating the inhibitory effect of SU-4885 when added to incubation medium containing quartered rat adrenal glands and progesterone-4-C^{14}. The top line contains no inhibitor. With increasing concentrations of SU-4885, there is a gradual loss of polar (hydroxylated) steroids and a corresponding increase in less polar compounds such as deoxycortisol (DOC) and progesterone. [After Ertel and Ungar (1964).]

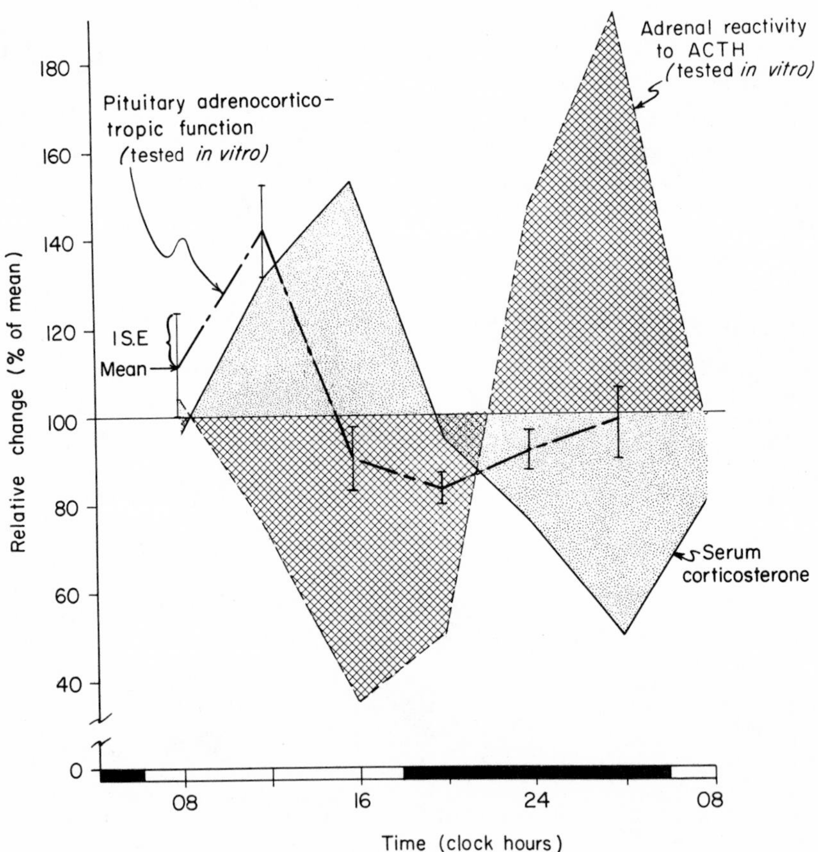

FIG. 29. Quartered adrenal glands removed at four hourly intervals show a variation in their capacity to produce corticosterone by the addition of ACTH. Their peak activity occurs at a time when blood corticosterone values are lowest. The dotted line represents corticosterone values produced by the addition of pituitary glands removed at four hourly intervals to quartered adrenal glands which had been removed at one time point (0400). [From Ungar and Halberg (1963).]

References

Acevedo, H. F., Axelrod, L. R., Ishikawa, E., and Takaki, F. (1961a) *Abstr. Endocrine Soc. 43rd Ann. Meeting N.Y.* p. 22.

Acevedo, H. F., Axelrod, L. R., Ishikawa, E., and Takaki, F. (1961b) *J. Clin. Endocrinol. Metab.* **21**: 1611.

Agranoff, B. W., Eggerer, H., Henning, U., and Lynen, F. (1960) *J. Biol. Chem.* **235**: 326.

Amatsu, M. (1963) *Japan. J. Endocrinol.* **38**: 1164.

Amdur, B. H., Rilling, M., and Bloch, K. (1957) *J. Am. Chem. Soc.* **79**: 2646.

Anker, H. S., and Bloch, K. (1949) *J. Biol. Chem.* **178**: 971.

Aprile, M. E., Bligh, E. G., Webb, J. L., and Heard, R. D. H. (1956–57) *Rev. Can. Biol.* **15**: 232.

Axelrod, L., and Goldzieher, J. (1962) *J. Clin. Endocrinol. Metab.* **22**: 537.

Ayres, P. J., Gould, R. P., Simpson, S. A., and Tait, J. F. (1956) *Biochem. J.* **63**: 19P.

Ayres, P. J., Hechter, O., Saba, N., Simpson, S. A., and Tait, J. F. (1957a) *Biochem. J.* **65**: 22P.

Ayres, P. J., Garrod, O., Tait, S. A. S., Tait, J. F., Walker, G., and Pearlman, W. H. (1957b) *Ciba Found. Colloq. Endocrinol.* **11**: 309.

Ayres, P. J., Pearlman, W. H., Tait, J. F., and Tait, S. A. S. (1958) *Biochem. J.* **70**: 230.

Ayres, P. J., Eichhorn, J., Hechter, O., Saba, N., Tait, J. F., and Tait, S. A. S. (1960) *Acta Endocrinol.* **33**: 37.

Baggett, B., Engel, L. L., Savard, K., and Dorfman, R. I. (1955) *Federation Proc.* **14**: 175.

Baggett, B., Engel, L. L., Savard, K., and Dorfman, R. I. (1956) *J. Biol. Chem.* **221**: 931.

Baulieu, E. E., and Emiliozzi, R. (1960) *Compt. Rend.* **251**: 3106.

Baulieu, E. E., Wallace, E., and Lieberman, S. (1963) *J. Biol. Chem.* **238**: 1316.

Bergenstal, D. M., Lipsett, M. B., May, R. H., and Hertz, R. (1959) *Trans. Assoc. Am. Physicians* **72**: 341.

Bergenstal, D. M., Lipsett, M. B., May, R. H., and Hertz, R. (1960a) *In* "Biological Activities of Steroids in Relation to Cancer" (G. Pincus and E. P. Vollmer, eds.), p. 463. Academic Press, New York.

Bergenstal, D. M., Hertz, R., Lipsett, M. B., and May, R. H. (1960b) *Ann. Internal Med.* **53**: 672.

Bergstrom, C. G., and Dodson, R. M. (1960) *J. Am. Chem. Soc.* **82**: 3480.

Berliner, D. L., and Salhanick, H. A. (1956) *J. Clin. Endocrinol. Metab.* **16**: 903.

Berliner, D. L., Cazes, D. M., and Nabors, C. J., Jr. (1962) *J. Biol. Chem.* **237**: 2478.

Besch, P. K., Watson, D. J., Barry, R. D., Hamwi, G. J., Mostow, J., and Gwinup, G. (1963) *Steroids* **1**: 644.

Biancalana, D., and Romanelli, R. (1958) *Folia. Endocrinol. (Pisa)* **11**: 1.

Biggs, M. W., Lemmon, R. M., and Pierce, F. T., Jr. (1954) *Arch. Biochem. Biophys.* **51**: 155.

Blair-West, J. R., Coghlan, J. P., Denton, D. A., Goding, J. R., Munro, J. A., Peterson, R. E., and Wintour, M. (1963) *J. Clin. Invest.* **41**: 1606.

Blecher, M., and Gurin, S. (1954) *J. Biol. Chem.* **209**: 953.

Bligh, E. G., Heard, R. D. H., O'Donnell, V. J., Webb, J. L., Saffran, M., and Schonbaum, E. (1955) *Arch. Biochem. Biophys.* **58**: 249.

Bloch, E., and Benirschke, K. (1959) *J. Biol. Chem.* **234**: 1085.

Bloch, E., and Benirschke, K. (1962) *Human Adrenal Cortex, Proc. Conf. Glasgow, 1960* p. 589.

Bloch, E., Dorfman, R. I., and Pincus, G. (1956) *Arch. Biochem. Biophys.* **61**: 245.

Bloch, E., Cohen, A. I., and Furth, J. (1960) *J. Nat. Cancer Inst.* **24**: 97.

Bloch, E., Tissenbaum, B., and Benirschke, K. (1962) *Biochim. Biophys. Acta* **60**: 182.
Bloch, K. (1944) *J. Biol. Chem.* **155**: 255.
Bloch, K. (1945) *J. Biol. Chem.* **157**: 661.
Bloch, K. (1951) *Recent Progr. Hormone Res.* **6**: 11.
Bloch, K. (1953) *Helv. Chim. Acta* **36**: 1611.
Bloch, K. (1959) *In* "Biosynthesis of Terpenes and Sterols" (G. E. W. Wolstenholme and M. O'Conner, eds.), pp. 4–19. Little, Brown, Boston, Massachusetts.
Bloch, K., and Rittenberg, D. (1942) *J. Biol. Chem.* **145**: 625.
Bloch, K., and Rittenberg, D. (1944) *J. Biol. Chem.* **155**: 243.
Bloch, K., Berg, B. N., and Rittenberg, D. (1943) *J. Biol. Chem.* **149**: 511.
Bloch, K., Clark, C., and Harrary, I. (1954) *J. Biol. Chem.* **211**: 687.
Borck, E., and Rittenberg, D. (1949) *J. Biol. Chem.* **179**: 843.
Brady, R. O. (1951) *J. Biol. Chem.* **193**: 145.
Brady, R. O., and Gurin, S. (1950) *J. Biol. Chem.* **186**: 461.
Brady, R. O., and Gurin, S. (1951) *J. Biol. Chem.* **189**: 371.
Breuer, H. (1960) *Symp. Deut. Ges. Endokrinol.* **7**: 273.
Breuer, H. (1962) *Acta Endocrinol.* **40**: 111.
Breuer, H., and Grill, P. (1961) *Z. Physiol. Chem.* **324**: 254.
Breuer, H., and Ortlepp, R. (1960) *Acta Endocrinol.* **35**: 508.
Breuer, H., Knuppen, R., and Pangels, G. (1962) *Biochim. Biophys. Acta* **65**: 1.
Brodie, J., and Porter, J. W. (1960) *Biochem. Biophys. Res. Commun.* **3**: 173.
Brodie, H. J., Hayano, M., and Gut, M. (1962) *J. Am. Chem. Soc.* **84**: 3766.
Brownell, K. A., Lee, S. L., Beck, R. R., and Besch, P. K. (1963) *Endocrinology* **72**: 167.
Brownie, A. C., Grant, J. K., and Davidson, D. W. (1954) *Biochem. J.* **58**: 218.
Bryson, M. J., and Sweat, M. L. (1962) *Arch. Biochem. Biophys.* **96**: 1.
Bucher, N. L. R. (1953) *J. Am. Chem. Soc.* **75**: 498.
Bucher, N. L. R., and McGarrahan, K. (1956) *J. Biol. Chem.* **222**: 1.
Burstein, S., and Dorfman, R. I. (1962) *Acta Endocrinol.* **40**: 188.
Burstein, S., and Nadel, E. M. (1956) *Federation Proc.* **15**: 228.
Carstenson, H. C. H. (1961) *Acta Soc. Med. Upsalien.* **66**: 129.
Caspi, E., and Hechter, O. (1954) *Arch. Biochem. Biophys.* **52**: 478.
Caspi, E., and Hechter, O. (1956) *Arch. Biochem. Biophys.* **61**: 299.
Caspi, E., Rosenfeld, G., and Dorfman, R. I. (1956) *J. Org. Chem.* **21**: 814.
Caspi, E., Ungar, F., and Dorfman, R. I. (1957) *J. Org. Chem.* **22**: 326.
Caspi, E., Dorfman, R. I., Khan, B. T., Rosenfeld, G., and Schmid, W. (1962) *J. Biol. Chem.* **237**: 2085.
Cazorla, A., and Moncloa, F. (1962) *Science* **136**: 47.
Chang, E., and Dao, D. F. (1961) *J. Clin. Endocrinol. Metab.* **21**: 624.
Chang, E., Mittelman, A., and Dao, T. L. (1962) *Excerpta Med. Intern. Congr. Ser.* **51**: 237.
Chang, E., Mittelman, A., and Dao, T. L. (1963) *J. Biol. Chem.* **238**: 913.
Chart, J. J., and Sheppard, H. (1959) *J. Med. Pharm. Chem.* **1**: 407.
Chart, J. J., and Sheppard, H. (1961) *Abstr. Endocrine Soc. 43rd Ann. Meeting N.Y.* p. 20.
Chart, J. J., Sheppard, H., Allen, M. J., Bencze, W. L., and Gaunt, R. (1958) *Experientia* **14**: 151.
Chart, J. J., Sheppard, H., Mowles, T., and Howie, N. (1962) *Endocrinology* **71**: 479.
Chaudhuri, A. C., Harada, Y., Shimizu, K., Gut, M., and Dorfman, R. I. (1962) *J. Biol. Chem.* **237**: 703.
Chaykin, S., Law, J., Phillips, A. H., Tchen, T. T., and Bloch, K. (1958) *Proc. Natl. Acad. Sci. U.S.* **44**: 998.
Chen, P. S., Jr., Schedl, H. P., Rosenfeld, G., and Bartter, F. C. (1958) *Proc. Soc. Exptl. Biol. Med.* **97**: 683.
Clayton, R. B., and Bloch, K. (1955) *Federation Proc.* **14**: 194.
Clayton, R. B., and Bloch, K. (1956a) *J. Biol. Chem.* **218**: 305.

Clayton, R. B., and Bloch, K. (1956b) *J. Biol. Chem.* **218**: 319.

Cobey, F. A., Taliaferro, I., and Haag, H. B. (1958) *Proc. Soc. Exptl. Biol. Med.* **97**: 491.

Cohn, G. L., and Hume, M. (1960) *J. Clin. Invest.* **39**: 1584.

Cohn, G. L., and Mulrow, P. J. (1963) *J. Clin. Invest.* **42**: 64.

Constantopoulos, G., and Tchen, T. T. (1961) *Am. Chem. Soc., St. Louis, 1941 Abstr.* p. 31C.

Constantopoulos, G., Satoh, P. S., and Tchen, T. T. (1962) *Biochem. Biophys. Res. Commun.* **8**: 50.

Cook, R. P., Kliman, A., and Fieser, L. F. (1954) *Arch. Biochem. Biophys.* **52**: 439.

Coppage, W. S., Jr., Island, D., Smith, M., and Liddle, G. W. (1959) *J. Clin. Invest.* **38**: 2101.

Cornforth, J. W. (1959) *J. Lipid Res.* **1**: 3.

Cornforth, J. W., and Popjak, G. (1954) *Biochem. J.* **58**: 403.

Cornforth, J. W., Hunter, G. D., and Popjak, G. (1953) *Biochem. J.* **54**: 597.

Cornforth, J. W., Popjak, G., and Gore, I. Y. (1956) "Biochemical Problems of Lipids" (G. Popjak and E. Le Breton, eds.), p. 216. Butterworths, London.

Cornforth, J. W., Gore, I. Y., and Popjak, G. (1957) *Biochem. J.* **65**: 94.

Cornforth, J. W., Cornforth, R. H., Popjak, G., and Gore, I. Y. (1958) *Biochem. J.* **69**: 146.

Costa, P. J. (1960) *J. Pharmacol. Exptl. Therap.* **129**: 214.

Curran, G. L. (1951) *J. Biol. Chem.* **191**: 775.

Curran, G. L., and Rittenberg, D. (1951) *J. Biol. Chem.* **190**: 17.

Dauben, W. G., and Takemura, K. H. (1953) *J. Am. Chem. Soc.* **75**: 6302.

Davidson, A. G., Dulit, E. G., and Frantz, I. D., Jr. (1957) *Federation Proc.* **16**: 169.

Davis, M. E., Plotz, E. J., LeRoy, G. V., and Gould, R. G. (1956) *Am. J. Obstet. Gynecol.* **72**: 740.

Denton, D. A., Goding, J. R., and Wright, R. D. (1959a) *Brit. Med. J.* **2**: 447.

Denton, D. A., Goding, J. R., and Wright, R. D. (1959b) *Brit. Med. J.* **2**: 522.

Diczfalusy, E., Cassmer, O., Alonson, C., and de Miguel, M. (1961a) *Acta Endocrinol.* **38**: 31.

Diczfalusy, E., Franksson, C., and Martinsen, B. (1961b) *Acta Endocrinol.* **38**: 59.

Diczfalusy, E., Franksson, C., Lisboa, B. P., and Martinsen, B. (1962) *Acta Endocrinol.* **40**: 537.

Dituri, F., Cobey, F., Warms, J. V. B., and Gurin, S. (1955) *Federation Proc.* **14**: 203.

Dituri, F., Cobey, F. A., Warms, J. V. B., and Gurin, S. (1956) *J. Biol. Chem.* **221**: 181.

Dituri, F., Gurin, S., and Rabinowitz, J. L. (1957) *J. Am. Chem. Soc.* **79**: 2650.

Dluzniewski, A. (1959) *Endokrynol. Polska* **10**: 259.

Doe, R. P., Flink, E. B., and Flint, M. G. (1954) *J. Clin. Endocrinol. Metab.* **14**: 774.

Dominguez, O. V. (1960) *J. Biol. Chem.* **235**: 2608.

Dominguez, O. V. (1961) *J. Clin. Endocrinol. Metab.* **21**: 663.

Dominguez, O. V., Acevedo, H. F., Huseby, R. A., and Samuels, L. T. (1960) *J. Biol. Chem.* **235**: 2608.

Dominguez, O. V., Urry, D. W., and Samuels, L. T. (1961) *Federation Proc.* **20**: 180.

Dorfman, R. I. (1957) *Ann. Rev. Biochem.* **26**: 523.

Dorfman, R. I. (1960) *In* "Biological Activities of Steroids in Relation to Cancer" (G. Pincus and E. P. Vollmer, eds.), p. 456. Academic Press, New York.

Dorfman, R. I., and Hamilton, J. B. (1939) *Endocrinology* **25**: 33.

Druzhinima, K. V. (1958) *Probl. Endokrinol. i Gormonoterap.* **4**: 23.

Durr, I. F., and Rudney, H. (1960) *J. Biol. Chem.* **235**: 2572.

Durr, I. F., Rudney, H., and Ferguson, J. J., Jr., (1959) *Federation Proc.* **18**: 219.

Dutton, G. J. (1956) *Biochem. J.* **64**: 693.

Egdahl, R. H. (1960) *Endocrinology* **66**: 200.

Egdahl, R. H. (1961) *Endocrinology* **68**: 574.

Eichhorn, J., and Hechter, O. (1957) *Proc. Soc. Exptl. Biol. Med.* **95**: 311.

Eichhorn, J., and Hechter, O. (1958) *Proc. Soc. Exptl. Biol. Med.* **97**: 614.

Eidinoff, M. L., Rosenfeld, R. S., Knoll, J. E., Marano, B. J., and Hellman, L. (1954) *J. Clin. Invest.* **33**: 333.

Eik-Nes, K. B., and Hall, P. F. (1962) *Proc. Soc. Exptl. Biol. Med.* In press, *Proc. Soc. Exptl. Biol. Med.* **111**: 280.
Endroczi, E., Telegdy, G., and Martin, J. (1958) *Acta Physiol. Acad. Sci. Hung.* **14**: 311.
Ertel, R. J., and Ungar, F. (1964) *Abstr. Endocrinol. Soc. 45th Ann. Meeting, San Francisco* p. 74.
Farrell, G. (1959) *Endocrinology* **65**: 239.
Feldschuh, S., Musacchio, I., and Kupperman, H. S. (1961) *Abstr. Endocrine Soc. 43rd Ann. Meeting N.Y.* p. 57.
Ferguson, J. J., Jr. (1962) *Biochim. Biophys. Acta* **57**: 616.
Ferguson, J. J., Jr. (1963) *Federation Proc.* **22**: 53.
Ferguson, J. J., Jr., and Rudney, H. (1959) *J. Biol. Chem.* **234**: 1076.
Ferguson, J. J., Jr., Durr, I. F., and Rudney, H. (1959) *Proc. Natl. Acad. Sci. U.S.* **45**: 499.
Fishman, W. H., and Sie, H. G. (1956) *J. Biol. Chem.* **218**: 335.
Folkers, K., Shunk, C. H., Linn, B. O., Robinson, F. M., Wittreich, P. E., Huff, J. W., Gilfillan, J. L., and Skeggs, H. R. (1959) *In* "Biosynthesis of Terpenes and Sterols" (G. E. W. Wolstenholme and M. O'Connor, eds.), pp. 20–45. Little, Brown, Boston, Massachusetts.
Fonken, G. S., Murray, H. C., and Reineke, L. M. (1960) *J. Am. Chem. Soc.* **82**: 5507.
Forchielli, E., and Dorfman, R. I. (1956) *J. Biol. Chem.* **223**: 443.
Forchielli, E., and Dorfman, R. I. (1961) *Abstr. Endocrinol. Soc. 43rd Ann. Meeting, N.Y.*, p. 25.
Forchielli, E., Rosenkrantz, H., and Dorfman, R. I. (1955) *J. Biol. Chem.* **215**: 713.
Fortier, C. (1958) *Proc. Soc. Exptl. Biol. Med.* **99**: 628.
Frantz, I. D., Jr., and Bucher, N. L. R. (1954) *J. Biol. Chem.* **206**: 471.
Frantz, I. D., Jr., Davidson, A. G., Dulit, E., and Mobberley, M. L. (1959) *J. Biol. Chem.* **234**: 2240.
Fredrickson, D. S., Gemzell, G., Peterson, R. E., and Steinberg, D. (1958) *Science* **127**: 704.
Fukuii, S., Takeuchi, K., Watanabe, F., Kumagi, A., Yano, S., and Nishino, K. (1961) *Endocrinol. Japon.* **8**: 43.
Fukushima, D. K., Gallagher, T. F., Greenberg, W., and Pearson, O. H. (1960) *J. Clin. Endocrinol. Metab.* **20**: 1234.
Gallagher, T. F. (1957) *Cancer Res.* **17**: 520.
Gallagher, T. F. (1958) *J. Clin. Endocrinol. Metab.* **18**: 937.
Gallagher, T. F., Kappas, A., Spencer, H., and Lazlo, D. (1956) *Science* **124**: 487.
Gallagher, T. F., Fukushima, D. K., and Hellman, L. (1962) *Metab. Clin. Exptl.* **11**: 1155.
Ganis, F. M., and Radakovich, M. (1958) *Federation Proc.* **17**: 226.
Ganong, W. F., and Mulrow, P. J. (1961) *Nature* **190**: 1115.
Ganong, W. F., Mulrow, P. J., Boryczka, A., and Cera, G. (1962) *Proc. Soc. Exptl. Biol. Med.* **109**: 381.
Gawienowski, A. M., Lee, S. L., and Marion, G. B. (1961) *Endocrinology* **69**: 388.
Giroud, C. J. P., Stachenko, J., and Piletta, P. (1958) *In* "Aldosterone" (A. F. Muller and C. M. O'Conner, eds.), p. 56. Little, Brown, Boston, Massachusetts.
Glaz, E. (1962) *J. Endocrinol.* **24**: 299.
Glaz, E., and Sugar, K. (1962) *Excerpta Med. Intern. Congr. Ser.* **51**: 221.
Goldstein, M., Gut, M., and Dorfman, R. I. (1960) *Biochim. Biophys. Acta* **38**: 190.
Goldzieher, J. W., and Axelrod, L. R. (1960) *Intern. Congr. Endocrinol., 1st, Copenhagen, 1960* p. 617.
Goodman, De W. S., and Popjak, G. (1960) *J. Lipid Res.* **1**: 286.
Gould, R. G., and Popjak, G. (1957) *Biochem. J.* **66**: 51P.
Gower, D. E., and Haslewood, G. A. (1961–62) *J. Endocrinol.* **23**: 253.
Grosso, L., and Ungar, F. (1964) *Steroids* **3**: 67.
Gual, C., Lemus, A. E., Kline, I. T., Gut, M., and Dorfman, R. I. (1962a) *J. Clin. Endocrinol. Metab.* In press.
Gual, C., Morato, T., Hayano, M., Gut, M., and Dorfman, R. I. (1962b) *Endocrinology* **71**: 920.
Gual, C., Sanchez, J., Dorfman, R. I., and Rosenthal, I. M. (1962c) *J. Clin. Endocrinol. Metab.* **22**: 1040.
Guillemin, R., and Schally, A. V. (1959) *Endocrinology* **65**: 555.

Hagen, A. A., and Eik-Nes, K. B. (1963) *Federation Proc.* **22**: 330.
Haines, W. J. (1952) *Recent Progr. Hormone Res.* **7**: 255.
Halberg, F., Peterson, R. E., and Silber, R. H. (1959) *Endocrinology* **64**: 222.
Halkerston, I. D. K. (1961) *J. Biol. Chem.* **236**: 374.
Hall, P. F., and Eik-Nes, K. B. (1961) *Abstr. Endocrine Soc., 43rd Ann. Meeting. N.Y.* p. 26.
Hall, P. F., and Eik-Nes, K. B. (1962) *Biochim. Biophys. Acta* **63**: 411.
Hall, P. F., Sozer, C., and Eik-Nes, K. B. (1963) *Endocrinology*. In press.
Harris, G. W. (1955) "Neural Control of the Pituitary." Arnold, London.
Hayano, M., and Dorfman, R. I. (1952) *Arch. Biochem. Biophys.* **36**: 237.
Hayano, M., and Dorfman, R. I. (1953) *J. Biol. Chem.* **201**: 175.
Hayano, M., and Dorfman, R. I. (1955) *Arch. Biochem. Biophys.* **55**: 289.
Hayano, M., Saba, N., Dorfman, R. I., and Hechter, O. (1956) *Recent Progr. Hormone Res.* **12**: 79.
Haynes, R. C., and Berthet, L. (1957) *J. Biol. Chem.* **225**: 115.
Haynes, R. C., Savard, K., and Dorfman, R. I. (1952a) *J. Clin. Endocrinol. Metab.* **12**: 972.
Haynes, R. C., Savard, K., and Dorfman, R. I. (1952b) *Science* **116**: 690.
Haynes, R. C., Savard, K., and Dorfman, R. I. (1954) *J. Biol. Chem.* **207**: 925.
Haynes, R. C., Koritz, S. B., and Peron, F. G. (1959) *J. Biol. Chem.* **234**: 1959.
Heard, R. D. H., Jellinck, P. H., and O'Donnell, V. J. (1955) *Endocrinology* **57**: 200.
Heard, R. D. H., Bligh, E. G., Cann, M. C., Jellinck, P. H., O'Donnell, V. J., Rao, B. G., and Webb, J. L. (1956) *Recent Progr. Hormone Res.* **12**: 45.
Hechter, O. (1958) *In* "Cholesterol" (R. P. Cook, ed.), p. 309. Academic Press, New York.
Hechter, O., and Pincus, G. (1954) *Physiol. Rev.* **34**: 459.
Hechter, O., Jacobsen, R. P., Jeanloz, R. W., Levy, H., Marshall, C. W., Pincus, G., and Schenker, V. (1949) *J. Am. Chem. Soc.* **71**: 3261.
Hechter, O., Zaffaroni, A., Jacobsen, R. P., Levy, H., Jeanloz, R. W., Schenker, V., and Pincus, G. (1951) *Recent Progr. Hormone Res.* **6**: 215.
Hellman, L., Rosenfeld, R. S., and Gallagher, T. F. (1954) *J. Clin. Invest.* **33**: 142.
Henning, U., Moslein, E. M., and Lynen, F. (1959) *Arch. Biochem. Biophys.* **83**: 259.
Hernando, L., Crabbe, J., Ross, E. J., Reedy, W. J., Renold, A. E., Nelson, D. H., and Thorn, G. W. (1957) *Metab. Clin. Exptl.* **6**: 518.
Hertz, R. (1955) *Recent Progr. Hormone Res.* **11**: 119.
Hertz, R. (1960) *Endocrinology* **66**: 494.
Hilliard, J., and Sawyer, C. H. (1962) *Excerpta Med. Intern. Congr. Ser.* **51**: 26.
Hofmann, F. G. (1962) *Biochim. Biophys. Acta* **65**: 13.
Hofmann, F. G., and Christy, N. P. (1961) *Biochim. Biophys. Acta* **54**: 354.
Hofmann, F. G., Dickie, M. M., and Christy, N. P. (1960) *Acta Endocrinol.* **34**: 84.
Hollander, N., and Hollander, V. P. (1958) *J. Biol. Chem.* **233**: 1097.
Hollander, N., and Hollander, V. P. (1959) *Cancer Res.* **19**: 290.
Holloszy, J., and Eisenstein, A. B. (1961) *Proc. Soc. Exptl. Biol. Med.* **107**: 347.
Huang, W. Y., and Pearlman, W. H. (1962) *J. Biol. Chem.* **237**: 1060.
Ichii, S., Forchielli, E., Cassidy, C. E., Rosoff, C. B., and Dorfman, R. I. (1962) *Biochem. Biophys. Res. Commun.* **9**: 344.
Isler, O., Ruegg, R., Wursh, J., Gey, K. F., and Pletscher, A. (1957) *Helv. Chim. Acta* **40**: 2369.
Isselbacher, K. J., and Axelrod, J. (1955) *J. Am. Chem. Soc.* **77**: 1070.
Iwata, K. (1959) *Tokyo Jikeikai Ika Daigaku Zasshi* **74**: 927.
Jeanloz, R. W., Levy, H., Jacobsen, R. P., Hechter, O., Schenker, V., and Pincus, G. (1950) (*Abstr. Am. Chem. Soc. 118th Meeting, Chicago, Ill., 1950* p. 12C.
Jeanloz, R. W., Levy, H., Jacobsen, R. P., Hechter, O., Schenker, V., and Pincus, G. (1953) *J. Biol. Chem.* **203**: 453.
Jenkins, J. S. (1962) *Endocrinology* **70**: 267.
Jenkins, J. S., Meakin, J. W., and Nelson, D. H. (1959a) *Endocrinology* **64**: 572.

Jenkins, J. S., Pothier, L., Reddy, W. J., Nelson, D. H., and Thorn, G. W. (1959b) *Brit. Med. J.* **1**: 398.
Johnson, D. F., Snell, K. C., Francois, D., and Heftmann, E. (1961) *Acta Endocrinol.* **37**: 329.
Johnston, J. D., and Bloch, K. (1957) *J. Am. Chem. Soc.* **79**: 1145.
Kahnt, F. W., and Neher, R. (1962) *Experientia* **18**: 499.
Kahnt, F. W., Neher, R., Schmid, K., and Wettstein, A. (1961) *Experientia* **17**: 19.
Kandutsch, A. A., and Russell, A. E. (1960) *Federation Proc.* **19**: 237.
Kaplan, N. M., and Bartter, F. C. (1962) *J. Clin. Invest.* **41**: 715.
Kase, N., and Kowal, J. (1962) *J. Clin. Endocrinol. Metab.* **22**: 925.
Kase, N., Forchielli, E., and Dorfman, R. I. (1961) *Acta Endocrinol.* **37**: 19.
Kase, N., Forchielli, E., and Dorfman, R. I. (1962) Unpublished data.
Knauss, H. J., Porter, J. W., and Wasson, G. (1959) *J. Biol. Chem.* **234**: 2835.
Knuppen, R., and Breuer, H. (1962) *Biochim. Biophys. Acta* **58**: 147.
Knuppen, R., and Breuer, H. (1963) *Acta Endocrinol.* **42**: 129.
Koritz, S. B. (1962a) *Biochim. Biophys. Acta* **56**: 63.
Koritz, S. B. (1962b) *Biochim. Biophys. Acta* **59**: 326.
Koritz, S. B., and Peron, F. G. (1959) *J. Biol. Chem.* **234**: 3122.
Korus, W., Schriefers, H., Breuer, H., and Bayer, J. M. (1959) *Acta Endocrinol.* **31**: 529.
Kraulis, I., and Birmingham, M. K. (1963) *Federation Proc.* **22**: 530.
Krieger, D. T. (1962) *J. Clin. Endocrinol. Metab.* **22**: 490.
Kritchevsky, D., and Gray, I. (1951) *Experientia* **7**: 183.
Kurath, P., Ganis, F. M., and Radakovich, M. (1957) *J. Am. Chem. Soc.* **79**: 5323.
Kushinsky, S. (1955) PhD Thesis, Boston Univ., Boston, Massachusetts.
Langdon, R. G., and Bloch, K. (1952) *J. Am. Chem. Soc.* **74**: 1869.
Langdon, R. G., and Bloch, K. (1953a) *J. Biol. Chem.* **200**: 129.
Langdon, R. G., and Bloch, K. (1953b) *J. Biol. Chem.* **200**: 135.
Langecker, H., and Kramer, M. (1962) *Excerpta Med. Intern. Congr. Ser.* **51**: 210.
Lanman, J. T., and Silverman, L. M. (1957) *Endocrinology* **60**: 443.
Lanthier, A., and Sandor, T. (1960a) *Metabolism Clin. Exptl.* **9**: 861.
Lanthier, A., and Sandor, T. (1960b) *Laval Med.* **30**: 624.
Layne, D. S., Meyer, C. J., Vaishwaner, P. S., and Pincus, G. (1962) *J. Clin. Endocrinol. Metab.* **22**: 107.
Leon, N., Castro, M. N., and Dorfman, R. I. (1962) *Acta Endocrinol.* **39**: 411.
Levitz, M., Condon, G. P., and Dancis, J. (1955) *Federation Proc.* **14**: 245.
Levitz, M., Condon, G. P., and Dancis, J. (1961) *Endocrinology* **68**: 825.
Levy, H., and Kushinsky, S. (1955) *Arch. Biochem. Biophys.* **55**: 290.
Levy, H., Jeanloz, R. W., Jacobsen, R. P., Hechter, O., Schenker, V., and Pincus, G. (1950) *Abstr. Am. Chem. Soc., 118th Meeting, Chicago, Ill., 1950* p. 29C.
Levy, H., Jeanloz, R. W., Marshall, C. W., Jacobsen, R. P., Hechter, O., Schenker, V., and Pincus, G. (1953) *J. Biol. Chem.* **203**: 433.
Levy, H., Jeanloz, R. W., Jacobsen, R. P., Hechter, O., Schenker, V., and Pincus, G. (1954) *J. Biol. Chem.* **211**: 867.
Levy, H., Saito, T., Takeyama, S., Merrill, A. P., and Schepis, J. P. (1963) *Biochim. Biophys. Acta* **69**: 198.
Levy, H. R., and Popjak, G. (1959) *Biochem. J.* **72**: 35P.
Lipman, M. M., Katz, F. H., and Jailer, J. W. (1962) *J. Clin. Endocrinol. Metab.* **22**: 268.
Lipsett, M. B., and Hökfelt, B. (1961) *Experientia* **17**: 449.
Little, B., and Shaw, A. (1961) *Acta Endocrinol.* **36**: 455.
Llaurado, J. G., and Dominguez, O. V. (1963) *Endocrinology* **72**: 292.
Llaurado, J. G., Claus, S. L., and Trunnell, J. B. (1962) *Endocrinology* **71**: 598.
Lombardo, M. E., Roitman, E., and Hudson, P. B. (1956) *J. Clin. Endocrinol. Metab.* **16**: 1283.
Longchampt, J. E., Gual, C., Ehrenstein, M., and Dorfman, R. I. (1960) *Endocrinology* **66**: 416.

Luetscher, J. A., Jr., and Lieberman, A. H. (1958) *A. M. A. Arch. Internal Med.* **102**: 314.

Lynen, F., Eggerer, H., Henning, U., and Kessel, I. (1958) *Angew. Chem.* **70**: 739.

Lynen, F., Eggerer, H., Henning, U., Knappe, J., Kessel, I., and Ringelmann, E. (1959) *In* "Biochemistry of Terpenes and Sterols" (G. E. W. Wolstenholme and M. O'Connor, eds.), p. 95. Little, Brown, Boston, Massachusetts.

Lynn, W. S., Jr., and Brown, R. H. (1958) *J. Biol. Chem.* **232**: 1015.

Lyon, I., Geyer, R. P., and Marshall, L. D. (1956) *J. Biol. Chem.* **217**: 757.

McCullagh, E. P., and Tretbar, H. A. (1958) *J. Clin. Endocrinol. Metab.* **18**: 134.

McGinty, D. A., Smith, G. N., Wilson, M. L., and Warrel, C. S. (1950) *Science* **112**: 506.

Mach, R. S., and Muller, A. F. (1957) *Schweiz. Med. Wochschr.* **87**: 406.

Mahajan, D. K., and Samuels, L. T. (1962) *Federation Proc.* **21**: 209.

Mahajan, D. K., and Samuels, L. T. (1963) *Federation Proc.* **22**: 531.

Mahesh, V. B., and Greenblatt, R. B. (1962) *Acta Endocrinol.* **41**: 400.

Markley, K., and Smallman, E. (1960) *Federation Proc.* **19**: 240.

Marsh, J. M., Mason, N. R., and Savard, K. (1961) *Federation Proc.* **20**: 187.

Marshall, C. W., Ralls, J. W., Saunders, F. J., and Riegel, B. (1957) *J. Biol. Chem.* **228**: 339.

Mason, N. R., and Samuels, L. T. (1961) *Endocrinology* **68**: 899.

Melby, J. C., Dale, S. L., and St. Cyr, M. (1961a) *Abstr. Endocrine Soc., 43rd Ann. Meeting, N.Y.* p. 19.

Melby, J. C., St. Cyr, M., and Dale, S. L. (1961b) *New Engl. J. Med.* **264**: 583.

Meyer, A. S. (1955a) *Biochim. Biophys. Acta* **24**: 1435.

Meyer, A. S. (1955b) *Experientia* **11**: 99.

Meyer, A. S., Hayano, M., Lindberg, M. C., Gut, M., and Rodgers, O. G. (1955) *Acta Endocrinol.* **18**: 148.

Migeon, C. J., French, A. B., Samuels, L. T., and Bowers, J. Z. (1955) *Am. J. Physiol.* **182**: 462.

Morato, T., Hayano, M., Dorfman, R. I., and Axelrod, L. R. (1961) *Biochem. Biophys. Res. Commun.* **6**: 334.

Morato, T., Raab, K., Brodie, H. J., Hayano, M., and Dorfman, R. I. (1962) *J. Am. Chem. Soc.* **84**: 3764.

Mulrow, P. J., and Cohn, G. L. (1959) *Proc. Soc. Exptl. Biol. Med.* **101**: 731.

Mulrow, P. J., and Cohn, G. L. (1961) *J. Clin. Invest.* **40**: 1250.

Mulrow, P. J., Cohn, G. L., and Kuljian, A. (1962a) *J. Clin. Invest.* **41**: 1584.

Mulrow, P. J., Ganong, W. F., Cera, G., and Kuljian, A. (1962b) *J. Clin. Invest.* **41**: 505.

Nathanson, I. T., and Towne, L. E. (1937) *Endocrinology* **25**: 488.

Neher, R., and Wettstein, A. (1956) *Helv. Chim. Acta* **39**: 2062.

Neher, R., and Wettstein, A. (1960) *Acta Endocrinol.* **35**: 1.

Neher, R., Roversi, G. D., Polvani, F., and Bompiani, A. (1962) *Excerpta Med. Intern. Congr. Ser.* **51**: 237.

Neiderhiser, D. H., and Wells, W. W. (1959) *Arch. Biochem. Biophys.* **81**: 300.

Newcomer, W. S. (1962) *Am. J. Physiol.* **202**: 337.

Ney, R. L., Coppage, W. S. Jr., Shimizu, N., Island, D. P., Zukoski, C. F., and Liddle, G. W. (1962) *J. Clin. Endocrinol. Metab.* **22**: 1057.

Nicolaides, N., Reiss, O. K., and Langdon, R. G. (1955) *J. Am. Chem. Soc.* **77**: 1535.

Nicolis, G., and Ulick, S. (1962) *Excerpta Med. Intern. Congr. Ser.* **51**: 218.

Nissim, J. A., and Robson, J. M. (1951) *J. Physiol.* **114**: 12P.

Noall, M. W., Alexander, I., and Allen, W. M. (1962) *Biochim. Biophys. Acta* **59**: 520.

Nyman, M. A., Geiger, J., and Goldzieher, J. W. (1959) *J. Biol. Chem.* **234**: 16.

O'Donnell, V. J., and McCaig, J. G. (1959) *Biochem. J.* **71**: 9P.

Oertel, G. W., and Eik-Nes, K. B. (1959) *Endocrinology* **65**: 766.

Olson, J. A., and Bloch, K. (1956) *Federation Proc.* **15**: 323.

Olson, J. A., Lindberg, M., and Bloch, K. (1957) *J. Biol. Chem.* **226**: 941.

Pasqualini, J. R. (1960) *Compt. Rend.* **251**: 1236.

Pasqualini, J. R. (1962) *Excerpta Med. Intern. Congr. Ser.* **51**: 177.

Pasqualini, J. R., and Jayle, M. F. (1961a) *Biochem. J.* **81**: 147.
Pasqualini, J. R., and Jayle, M. F. (1961b) *Experientia* **17**: 450.
Pearlman, W. H. (1954) *Acta Endocrinol.* **17**: 321.
Pearlman, W. H., and Huang, W. Y. (1962) *Excerpta Med. Intern. Congr. Ser.* **51**: 193.
Peron, F. G. (1962) *Endocrinology* **70**: 386.
Peron, F. G., and Koritz, S. B. (1958) *J. Biol. Chem.* **223**: 256.
Peron, F. G., Moncloa, F., and Dorfman, R. I. (1960) *Endocrinology* **67**: 379.
Peterson, R. E., Hertz, R., and Lubs, H. A. (1957) *Proc. Soc. Exptl. Biol. Med.* **94**: 421.
Phillips, J. G., Jones, I. C., and Bellamy, D. (1962) *J. Endocrinol.* **25**: 233.
Pincus, G. (1943) *J. Clin. Endocrinol.* **3**: 195.
Plager, J. E., and Samuels, L. T. (1952) *Federation Proc.* **11**: 383.
Plager, J. E., and Samuels, L. T. (1954) *J. Biol. Chem.* **211**: 21.
Plotz, E. J. (1959) *Arch. Gynaekol.* **193**: 317.
Polvani, F., Roversi, G. D., Silvestrini, R., and Bompiani, A. (1962) *Excerpta Med. Intern. Congr. Ser.* **51**: 268.
Popjak, G. (1954) *Arch. Biochem. Biophys.* **48**: 102.
Popjak, G. (1959) *Tetrahedron Letters* **19**: 19.
Popjak, G., and Cornforth, J. W. (1960) *Advan. Enzymol.* **22**: 281.
Popjak, G., Hunter, G. D., and French, T. H. (1953) *Biochem. J.* **54**: 238.
Popjak, G., Goodman, DeW. S., Cornforth, J. W., Cornforth, R. H., and Ryhage, R. (1961) *Biochem. Biophys. Res. Commun.* **4**: 138.
Price, T. D., and Rittenberg, D. (1950) *J. Biol. Chem.* **185**: 449.
Rabinowitz, J. L. (1954) *J. Am. Chem. Soc.* **76**: 3037.
Rabinowitz, J. L. (1956) *Arch. Biochem. Biophys.* **64**: 285.
Rabinowitz, J. L. (1958) *Atompraxis* **4**: 85.
Rabinowitz, J. L., and Dowben, R. M. (1955) *Biochim. Biophys. Acta* **16**: 96.
Rabinowitz, J. L., and Gurin, S. (1954a) *J. Biol. Chem.* **208**: 307.
Rabinowitz, J. L., and Gurin, S. (1954b) *J. Am. Chem. Soc.* **76**: 5168.
Rabinowitz, J. L., and Oleksyshyn, O. (1956) *Arch. Biochem. Biophys.* **64**: 285.
Rabinowitz, J. L., and Ragland, J. B. (1958) *Federation Proc.* **17**: 293.
Rabinowitz, J. L., Dituri, F., Cobey, F., and Gurin, S. (1955) *Federation Proc.* **14**: 760.
Raman, P. B., Ertel, R. J., and Ungar, F. (1964) *Endocrinology* **74**: 865.
Rao, B. G., and Heard, R. D. H. (1957) *Arch. Biochem. Biophys.* **66**: 504.
Reich, E., and Lehninger, A. L. (1955) *Biochim. Biophys. Acta* **17**: 136.
Renold, A. E., Crabbe, J., Hernando-Avendano, L., Nelson, D. H., Ross, E. J., Emerson, K., Jr., and Thorn, G. W. (1957) *New Engl. J. Med.* **256**: 16.
Ringold, H. J., Gut, M., Hayano, M., and Turner, A. (1962) *Tetrahedron Letters* **18**: 835.
Rittenberg, D., and Schoenheimer, R. (1937) *J. Biol. Chem.* **121**: 235.
Roberts, K. D., Vande Wiele, R. L., and Lieberman, S. (1961a) *Federation Proc.* **20**: 180.
Roberts, K. D., Vande Wiele, R. L., and Lieberman, S. (1961b) *J. Clin. Endocrinol. Metab.* **21**: 1522.
Roche, J. (1959) *Compt. Rend. Soc. Biol.* **153**: 1147.
Roche, J., Michel, R., Jouan, P., and Cormier, M. (1960) *Bull. Soc. Chim. Biol.* **42**: 913.
Romanoff, E. B., and Pincus, G. (1962) *Endocrinology* **71**: 752.
Rosemberg, E., Rosenfeld, G., Ungar, F., and Dorfman, R. I. (1956) *Endocrinology* **58**: 708.
Rosenfeld, G., Ungar, F., Dorfman, R. I., and Pincus, G. (1955) *Endocrinology* **56**: 24.
Rosenfeld, R. S., Hellman, L., Considine, W. J., and Gallagher, T. F. (1954) *J. Biol. Chem.* **208**: 73.
Rosenfeld, R. S., Zumoff, B., and Hellman, L. (1962) *Arch. Biochem. Biophys.* **96**: 84.
Roy, A. B. (1956) *Biochem. J.* **63**: 294.
Rudney, H. (1954) *Federation Proc.* **13**: 286.
Ryan, K. J. (1956) *Federation Proc.* **15**: 344.

Ryan, K. J. (1958) *Biochim. Biophys. Acta* **27**: 658.
Ryan, K. J. (1959) *J. Biol. Chem.* **234**: 268.
Ryan, K. J. (1961) *Intern. Congr. Biochem. 5th, Moscow, 1961 Reprint* 61.
Ryan, K. J., and Engel, L. L. (1956) *J. Am. Chem. Soc.* **78**: 2654.
Ryan, K. J., and Smith, O. W. (1961a) *J. Biol. Chem.* **236**: 705.
Ryan, K. J., and Smith, O. W. (1961b) *J. Biol. Chem.* **236**: 2204.
Ryan, K. J., and Smith, O. W. (1961c) *J. Biol. Chem.* **236**: 2207.
Ryan, K. J., Benirschke, K., and Smith, O. W. (1961) *Endocrinology* **69**: 613.
Saba, N., and Hechter, O. (1955) *Federation Proc.* **14**: 775.
Saba, N., Hechter, O., and Stone, D. (1954) *J. Am. Chem. Soc.* **76**: 3862.
Saffran, M., and Schally, A. V. (1955) *Endocrinology* **56**: 523.
Saffran, M., Grad, M. J., and Bayliss, M. J. (1952) *Endocrinology* **50**: 639.
Saffran, M., Schally, A. V., and Benfey, B. G. (1955) *Endocrinology* **52**: 439.
Sandberg, A. A., Slaunwhite, W. R., Jr., Jackson, J. E., and Frawley, T. F. (1962) *J. Clin. Endocrinol. Metab.* **22**: 929.
Sandermann, W., and Stockmann, H. (1956) *Naturwissenschaften* **43**: 581.
Sandor, T., and Lanthier, A. (1960) *Rev. Can. Biol.* **19**: 445.
Sandor, T., and Lanthier, A. (1961) *Can. J. Biochem. Physiol.* **39**: 973.
Sandor, T., and Lanthier, A. (1962) *Excerpta Med. Intern. Congr. Ser.* **51**: 139.
Sandor, T., Lanthier, A., and Lamoureux, J. (1963) *Federation Proc.* **22**: 270.
Savard, K., and Goldzieher, J. W. (1960) *Endocrinology* **66**: 617.
Savard, K., Green, A. A., and Lewis, L. A. (1950) *Endocrinology* **47**: 418.
Savard, K., Dorfman, R. I., and Poutasse, E. (1952) *J. Clin. Endocrinol. Metab.* **12**: 935.
Savard, K., Dorfman, R. I., Baggett, B., and Engel, L. L. (1956) *J. Clin. Endocrinol. Metab.* **16**: 1629.
Savard, K., Andrec, K., Brooksbank, B. W. L., Reyneri, C., Dorfman, R. I., Heard, R. D. H., Jacobs, R., and Solomon, S. S. (1958) *J. Biol. Chem.* **231**: 765.
Savard, K., Dorfman, R. I., Baggett, B., Fielding, L. L., Engel, L. L., McPherson, H. T., Lister, L. M., Johnson, D. S., Hamblen, E. C., and Engel, F. L. (1960) *J. Clin. Invest.* **39**: 534.
Savard, K., Gut, M., Dorfman, R. I., Gabrilove, J. L., and Soffer, L. J. (1961) *J. Clin. Endocrinol. Metab.* **21**: 165.
Sayers, G., and Sayers, M. A. (1947) *Endocrinology* **40**: 265.
Schenker, S., Wilson, H., and Spickard, A. (1961) *Abstr. Endocrine Soc. 43rd Meeting N.Y. 1961* p. 97.
Schindler, W. J., and Knigge, K. M. (1959) *Endocrinology* **65**: 739.
Schneider, J. J., and Lewbart, M. L. (1956) *J. Biol. Chem.* **222**: 787.
Schroepfer, G. J., and Frantz, I. D., Jr. (1961) *J. Biol. Chem.* **236**: 3137.
Schroepfer, G. J., (1961) *J. Biol. Chem.* **236**: 1668.
Schwenk, E., Alexander, G. J., Stoudt, T. H., and Fish, C. A. (1955a) *Arch. Biochem. Biophys.* **55**: 274.
Schwenk, E., Alexander, G. J., Fish, C. A., and Stoudt, T. H. (1955b) *Federation Proc.* **14**: 752.
Sharma, D. C., Forchielli, E., and Dorfman, R. I. (1962) *J. Biol. Chem.* **237**: 1495.
Sharma, D., Forchielli, E., and Dorfman, R. I. (1963) *J. Biol. Chem.* In press.
Sheppard, H., and Chart, J. J. (1961) *Biochem. Pharmacol.* **8**: 431.
Shimizu, K., Dorfman, R. I., and Gut, M. (1960) *J. Biol. Chem.* **235**: PC25.
Shimizu, K., Gut, M., and Dorfman, R. I. (1962) *J. Biol. Chem.* **237**: 699.
Shimizu, K., and Dorfman, R. I. (1962) Unpublished data.
Shimizu, K., Hayano, M., Gut, M., and Dorfman, R. I. (1961) *J. Biol. Chem.* **236**: 695.
Slaunwhite, W. R., Jr., and Samuels, L. T. (1956) *J. Biol. Chem.* **220**: 341.
Slaunwhite, W. R., Jr., Sandberg, A. A., Staubitz, W. J., Jackson, J. E., and Koepf, G. I. (1962a) *J. Clin Endocrinol. Metab.* **22**: 989.

Slaunwhite, W. R., Jr., Sandberg, A. A., Jackson, J. E., and Staubitz, W. J. (1962b) *J. Clin. Endocrinol. Metab.* **22**: 992.

Smith, O. W., and Ryan, K. J. (1961) *Endocrinology* **69**: 869.

Solomon, S., Lenz, A. L., Van de Wiele, R., and Lieberman, S. (1954) *Abstr. Am. Chem. Soc., 126th Meeting, N.Y. 1954* p. 29C.

Solomon, S., Van de Wiele, R., and Lieberman, S. (1956) *J. Am. Chem. Soc.* **78**: 5453.

Solomon, S., Levitan, P., and Lieberman, S. (1956–1957) *Rev. Can. Biol.* **15**: 282.

Solomon, S., Lanman, J. T., Lind, J., and Lieberman, S. (1958) *J. Biol. Chem.* **233**: 1084.

Solomon, S., Carter, A. C., and Lieberman, S. (1960) *J. Biol. Chem.* **235**: 351.

Southren, A. L., Weisenfeld, S., Laufer, A., and Goldner, M. G. (1961) *J. Clin. Endocrinol. Metab.* **21**: 201.

Staib, W., Teller, W., and Scharf, F. (1960) *Z. Physiol. Chem.* **318**: 163.

Staple, E., Lynn, W. S., Jr., and Gurin, S. (1956) *J. Biol. Chem.* **219**: 845.

Steinach, E., and Kun, H. (1937) *Lancet* **ii**: 845.

Steinberg, D., Fredrickson, D. S., and Avigan, J. (1958) *Proc. Soc. Exptl. Biol. Med.* **97**: 784.

Stitch, S. R., Oakey, R. E., and Eccles, S. S. (1962) *Excerpta Med. Intern. Congr. Ser.* **51**: 145.

Stokes, W. M., Hickey, F. C., and Fish, W. A. (1958) *J. Biol. Chem.* **232**: 347.

Stone, D., and Hechter, O. (1951) *Arch. Biochem. Biophys.* **51**: 457.

Stylianou, M., Forchielli, E., and Dorfman, R. I. (1961) *J. Biol. Chem.* **236**: 1318.

Suzuki, M., Takahashi, K., and Murakami, Y. (1961) *Tohoku J. Exptl. Med.* **74**: 28.

Suzuki, M., Takahashi, K., Hirano, M., and Shindo, K. (1962) *Tohoku J. Exptl. Med.* **76**: 89.

Sweat, M. L., Berliner, D. L., Bryson, M. J., Nabors, C., Jr., Haskell, J., and Holmstrome, E. G. (1960) *Biochim. Biophys. Acta* **40**: 289.

Sybulski, S., and Venning, E. H. (1961) *Can. J. Biochem. Physiol.* **39**: 203.

Tavormina, P. A., Gibbs, M. H., and Huff, J. W. (1956) *J. Am. Chem. Soc.* **78**: 4498.

Tchen, T. T. (1958) *J. Biol. Chem.* **233**: 1100.

Tchen, T. T., and Bloch, K. (1957) *J. Biol. Chem.* **226**: 921.

Telegdy, G., and Huszan, L. (1962) *Acta Physiol. Acad. Sci. Hung.* **21**: 339.

Thorn, G. W., Renold, A. E., Goldfien, A., Nelson, D. H., Reedy, W. J., and Hertz, R. (1956) *New Engl. J. Med.* **254**: 547.

Tobian, L. (1960) *Physiol. Rev.* **40**: 280.

Tomaoki, B. I., and Pincus, G. (1961) *Endocrinology* **69**: 527.

Travis, R. H., and Farrell, G. L. (1958a) *Endocrinology* **63**: 882.

Travis, R. H., and Farrell, G. L. (1958b) *Federation Proc.* **17**: 324.

Troen, P. (1961a) *J. Clin. Endocrinol. Metab.* **21**: 895.

Troen, P. (1961b) *J. Clin. Endocrinol. Metab.* **21**: 1511.

Troen, P. (1962) *Excerpta Med. Intern. Congr. Ser.* **51**: 269.

Tullner, W. W. (1960) *Endocrinology* **66**: 470.

Tullner, W. W., and Hertz, R. (1960) *Endocrinology* **66**: 494.

Tullner, W. W., Graff, M. M., and Hertz, R. (1956) *Endocrinology* **58**: 802.

Ulick, S., and Kusch, K. (1960) *J. Am. Chem. Soc.* **82**: 6421.

Ulick, S., and Solomon, S. (1960) *J. Am. Chem. Soc.* **82**: 249.

Ungar, F. (1964) *Ann. N.Y. Acad. Sci.* (Symposium, Photo-Neuro-Endocrine Effects, June 1963) **117** (Art. 1), 374.

Ungar, F., and Dorfman, R. I. (1953) *J. Biol. Chem.* **205**: 125.

Ungar, F., and Halberg, F. (1962) *Science* **137**: 1058.

Ungar, F., and Halberg, F. (1963) *Experentia.* **19**: 158.

Ungar, F., Rosenfeld, G., Rosemberg, E., and Dorfman, R. I. (1954) *Proc. Soc. Exptl. Biol. Med.* **87**: 653.

Ungar, F., Doe, R. P., and Moran, W. H. (1962) *Abstr. Endocrine Soc. 44th Ann. Meeting, Chicago 1962* p. 87.

Varangot, J., Cedard, L., and Yannotti, S. (1962) *Excerpta Med. Intern. Congr. Ser.* **51**: 270.

Venning, E. H., and Sybulski, S. (1962) *Excerpta Med. Intern. Congr. Ser.* **51**: 267.

Verdesca, A. S., Westermann, C. D., Crompton, R. S., Block, W. C., Nedeljkovic, R. I., and Hilton, J. G. (1961) *Am. J. Physiol.* **201**: 1065.

Verdon, T. A., Bruton, J., Herman, R. H., and Beisel, W. R. (1962) *Metabolism* **11**: 226.

Villee, C. A., Loring, J., and Villee, D. B. (1962) *Excerpta Med. Intern. Congr. Ser.* **51**: 143.

Villee, D. B., Engel, L. L., and Villee, C. A. (1959a) *Endocrinology* **65**: 465.

Villee, D. B., Loring, J. M., and Villee, C. A. (1959b) *Federation Proc.* **18**: 344.

Villee, D. B., Engel, L. L., Loring, J. M., and Villee, C. A. (1961) *Endocrinology* **69**: 354.

Waard, A. de, and Popjak, G. (1959) *Biochem. J.* **73**: 410.

Wallace, E. Z., and Lieberman, S. (1963) *J. Clin. Endocrinol. Metab.* **23**: 90.

Ward, P. J., and Birmingham, M. K. (1962) *Acta Endocrinol.* **39**: 110.

Warren, J. C., and Salhanick, H. A. (1961a) *J. Clin. Endocrinol. Metab.* **21**: 1218.

Warren, J. C., and Salhanick, H. A. (1961b) *J. Clin. Endocrinol. Metab.* **21**: 1376.

Weliky, I., and Engel, L. L. (1961) *Federation Proc.* **20**: 179.

Weliky, I., and Engel, L. L. (1962) *J. Biol. Chem.* **237**: 2089.

Wells, W. W., and Lorah, C. L. (1960) *J. Biol. Chem.* **235**: 978.

Werbin, H., Plotz, E. J., LeRoy, G. V., and Davis, M. E. (1957b) *Federation Proc.* **16**: 346.

Werbin, H., Chaikoff, I. L., and Jones, E. E. (1958) *Federation Proc.* **17**: 333.

Werbin, H., and LeRoy, G. V. (1955) *Federation Proc.* **14**: 303.

Werbin, H., Bergenstal, D. M., Gould, R. G., and LeRoy, G. V. (1957a) *J. Clin. Endocrinol. Metab.* **17**: 337.

Werbin, H., Plotz, E. J., LeRoy, G. V., and Davis, M. E. (1957b) *Federation Proc.* **16**: 346.

Werbin, H., Chaikoff, I. L., and Jones, E. E. (1958) *Federation Proc.* **17**: 333.

Werbin, H., Chaikoff, I. L., and Jones, E. E. (1959) *J. Biol. Chem.* **234**: 282.

Werbin, H., Chaikoff, I. L., and Jones, E. E. (1960) *J. Biol. Chem.* **235**: 1629.

West, C. D., Damast, B. L., Sarro, S. D., and Pearson, O. H. (1956) *J. Biol. Chem.* **218**: 409.

West, C. D., and Naville, A. H. (1962) *Biochemistry* **1**: 645.

Wettstein, A., Kahnt, F. W., and Neher, R. (1955) *Ciba Found. Colloq. Endocrinol.* **8**: 170.

Wettstein, A., Neher, R., and Urech, H. J. (1959) *Helv. Chim. Acta* **42**: 956.

Wiest, W. G., Zander, J., and Holmstrome, E. G. (1959) *J. Clin. Endocrinol. Metab.* **19**: 297.

Woodward, R., and Bloch, K. (1953) *J. Am. Chem. Soc.* **75**: 2023.

Wotiz, H. H., Davis, J. W., and Lemon, H. M. (1955) *J. Biol. Chem.* **216**: 677.

Wotiz, H. H., Davis, J. W., Lemon, H. M., and Gut, M. (1956) *J. Biol. Chem.* **222**: 487.

Wotiz, H. H., Ziskind, B. S., and Lemon, H. M. (1960) *Cancer Res.* **20**: 34.

Wright, L. D. (1961) *Ann. Rev. Biochem.* **30**: 525.

Wright, L. D., Cleland, M., Dutta, B. N., and Norton, J. S. (1957) *J. Am. Chem. Soc.* **79**: 6572.

Wuersch, J., Huang, R. L., and Bloch, K. (1952) *J. Biol. Chem.* **195**: 439.

Yankopoulos, N. A., Davis, J. O., Kliman, B., and Peterson, R. E. (1959) *J. Clin. Invest.* **38**: 1278.

Zabin, I., and Barker, W. F. (1953) *J. Biol. Chem.* **205**: 633.

Zabin, I., and Bloch, K. (1950a) *J. Biol. Chem.* **185**: 117.

Zabin, I., and Bloch, K. (1950b) *J. Biol. Chem.* **185**: 131.

Zabin, I., and Bloch, K. (1951a) *J. Biol. Chem.* **192**: 261.

Zabin, I., and Bloch, K. (1951b) *J. Biol. Chem.* **192**: 267.

Zaffaroni, A., Hechter, O., and Pincus, G. (1951) *J. Am. Chem. Soc.* **73**: 1390.

Zondek, B. (1934) *Nature* **133**: 494.

CHAPTER IV

Steroid Transformations by Microorganisms

The announcement by Hench and Kendall in 1949 of the dramatic effects of cortisone administration to rheumatoid arthritic patients resulted in a great effort by many laboratories to find practical procedures for the introduction of an 11-oxygen function on the steroid nucleus. Successful chemical and biological methods evolved from these investigations which made possible for the first time the production of 11-oxygenated steroids in relatively large quantities. One of the more novel approaches to the problem was the search for microorganisms which would perform this function.

The introduction of an 11α-hydroxyl group on the steroid nucleus was reported by Murray and Peterson at the Upjohn Laboratories in 1952, using the organism *Rhizopus arrhizus*, which had been isolated following the exposure of an agar plate to air. In addition to 11-hydroxylation, a wide variety of steroid reactions by microorganisms was subsequently demonstrated by these investigators and other groups, including Fried *et al.* (1952) at the Squibb Laboratories; Mancera *et al.* (1952) at the Syntex Laboratories; and Kahnt *et al.* (1952) at the Ciba Laboratories. The reactions of microorganisms on steroid compounds have been valuable in the study of specific problems in steroid metabolism, and in conjunction with chemical syntheses, in the commercial production of useful and complex corticosteroids from readily available raw materials.

The demonstrations of the variability and specificity of the alterations on the steroid molecule made possible by the use of microorganisms, surprising as they are in scope and utility, were not entirely unexpected. Generally, it had been assumed that the absence of steroidal substances in the soil, expected to be present from the excreta of animals, was the result of microbial action. The few early studies of microbial action on steroids were limited, however, to simple oxidative and reductive changes. Mamoli and co-workers (Mamoli, 1938a; Mamoli and Vercellone, 1938) demonstrated the reduction of double bonds and ketones and the oxidation of alcohol groups in naturally occurring steroids. Turfitt (1948) obtained a species of proactinomyces from soil which could convert Δ^4-cholestenone to the 3-keto-Δ^4-etiocholenic acid. Further oxidative changes in ring A could be demonstrated.

The unusual feature of the microbiological hydroxylation reaction reported by Murray and Peterson was the fact that the 11α-hydroxyl group was formed rather than the 11β-isomer, the only form in which it occurs in mammals. The organism used, *Rhizopus arrhizus*, converted progesterone to 11α-hydroxyprogesterone in yields which were eventually raised to 50%. Another organism, *Rhizopus nigricans*, produced the same product in even more impressive yields. Fried *et al.* (1952) reported 11α-hydroxylation using *Aspergillus niger*. Although microorganisms have subsequently been found which formed the 11β-isomer, the 11α-hydroxylation still has great utility in the commercial preparation of steroid analogs. Hydroxylations by microbiological systems in addition to or in conjunction with 11α-hydroxylation were generally observed and eventually identified. The 16α-hydroxylation of progesterone, for example, was reported in 1952 by Tollman *et al.* (1952).

One of the obvious applications of the stereospecific reactions of microorganisms that has been utilized is the resolution of the *dl*-mixtures of steroids obtained by total synthesis. Vischer *et al.* (1956) reduced *dl*-estrone microbiologically and obtained only the natural *d*-estradiol-17β; the *l*-estrone did not react. This group of investigators achieved a similar type of resolution by forming *d*-aldosterone from *dl*-21-deoxyaldosterone using *Ophiobolus herpotrichus.* Similarly, an organism that performed a Δ^1-dehydrogenation, reacted with the *d*-form of *dl*-aldosterone, and only the *d*-form of *dl*-cortisone, was dehydrogenated in a similar microbiological reaction. The resolution of the *d*- from the *l*-form of testosterone was achieved by Talalay (1957) by using a β-hydroxy steroid dehydrogenase isolated from a species of *Pseudomonas* which oxidized the *d*-form to *d*-androst-4-ene-3,17-dione, leaving the *l*-testosterone form unchanged.

Two other useful applications of stereospecific microbiological reactions has been the determination of the spatial configuration of the H atoms in the steroid nucleus when deuterium or tritium are incorporated into the molecule, and the elucidation of the mechanism of the reaction involved in a biosynthetic pathway. The introduction of a hydroxyl group, for example, has been shown to involve removal of a hydrogen atom without change of spatial configuration, and this information has been of value in the chemical synthesis of deuterated or tritiated steroids containing specific spatial configurations. Possible intermediates containing a label at specific sites have been employed in the investigations dealing with the reaction mechanisms for estrogen biosynthesis (see Chapter III).

The tables and figures in this chapter are organized on the basis of the specific reactions that have been observed with the various microorganisms. For example, Table 1 lists the published data for microbiological hydroxylation at carbon 1α and 1ξ. 1α-Hydroxylation has been established by certain *Penicillium* species, while a 1-hydroxylated product of unknown configuration has been observed for the *Streptomyces* species, *Rhizoctonia ferrugena*, and *Flavobacterium dehydrogenans.* These reactions are shown in Fig. 1. Figures 1 through 17 correspond, respectively, to the microbiological hydroxylation reactions listed in Tables 1 through 17. Hydroxylations have been demonstrated at every carbon in the steroid nucleus that is capable of accepting a hydroxyl group. Carbons 3, 4, 5, 10, 13, and 20 contain a substituent (carbonyl, methyl, or double bond) in the steroid compounds usually encountered, and it is not unlikely that hydroxylations could be demonstrated at these positions if suitable steroid substrates were used. For example, Peterson (1955; Pederson *et al.*, 1956) demonstrated a 10β-hydroxylation in a 19-nor compound, 19-nortestosterone (Table 7). The C-10 position normally could not be hydroxylated due to the presence of either the C_{19}-methyl group in the neutral steroids or the double bond at C-10 in the estrogen series.

Table 18 lists examples of, and Fig. 18 illustrates, the oxidative conversion of the Δ^5-3β-hydroxy steroids to the corresponding Δ^4-3-ketosteroids. The enzyme system involved has been called the 3β-ol dehydrogenase. This enzyme system should be designated more exactly as the Δ^5-3β-ol dehydrogenase to distinguish this reaction from the reactions involved in the oxidation of the 3β-hydroxyl group to the 3-ketone (Table 19, Fig. 19) without involvement of a ring A double bond. In mammalian systems, the enzymes involved in the latter reaction will not react with the Δ^5-3β-hydroxyl group (see Chapter VI).

The introduction of a Δ^4-bond in a 5α-saturated steroid by a microbiological system has been reported by Vischer and Wettstein (1953) (Table 20, Fig. 20). This unique reaction has not been observed in mammalian tissue.

Tables 21–23 list examples of specific oxidative-reductive reactions at carbon 3 first reported by Mamoli and co-workers. The 3α- and 3β-hydroxy steroid dehydrogenases and the isomerase isolated by Talalay from a species of *Pseudomonas* are probably in the purest state of any of the enzymes involved in steroid reactions that have been investigated to this time.

The many instances of reduction of the Δ^4-bond to the 5β and 5α forms by microorganisms are listed in Tables 24 and 25 and illustrated in the corresponding figures.

The 11β-hydroxyl group can be oxidized to the 11-keto form by microbiological oxidation (Table 26, Fig. 26). The reversible oxidation-reduction at carbon 17 has been demonstrated for estrogens as well as for the C_{19}-compounds (Tables 27 and 28, Figs. 27 and 28). The formation of 20β-hydroxy and 20α-hydroxy steroids from the 20-ketosteroids are listed in Tables 29 and 30 (see also Figs. 29 and 30).

The conversion of a 21-aldehyde group to a 21-alcohol by *Streptomyces roseochromogenes* was reported by Smith *et al.* (1962) (Table 31, Fig. 31).

The introduction of a Δ^1-group in ring A of many active steroid hormones produces a significant increase in biological activity, particularly in the glucocorticoid series. For this reason great effort has been expended in searching for microorganisms which can perform this reaction. Table 32 (see also Fig. 32) lists the many species that have been found capable of forming the Δ^1-bond. The Δ^1-bond can be formed in steroids of the C_{19}

and C_{21} series and even in the 19-nor series, as demonstrated by the conversion of 19-nortestosterone to estrone (Levy and Talalay, 1957; Meeks *et al.*, 1958) and to estradiol-17β (Meeks *et al.*, 1958).

Microorganisms can convert C_{21}-steroids to C_{19}-steroids with lactone formation (Table 33, Fig. 33) or without the presence of a lactone (Table 34, Fig. 34). It is quite conceivable that, in the two conversions, analogous reactions are involved in which progesterone is converted to testosterone acetate and then to testosterone by the Beyer-Williger reaction as demonstrated by Fonken *et al.* (1960). The formed testosterone is oxidized to androst-4-ene-3,17-dione which is converted to a ring D lactone by the same Beyer-Williger reaction.

An unusual acetylation of a complex progesterone derivative by *Trichoderma glaucum* has been reported (Table 35, Fig. 35) (Holmund *et al.*, 1961). Conversely, steroid acetates have been deacetylated by microbiological action (Table 36, Fig. 36). Epoxidation has been observed in steroid substrates containing unsaturation at $\Delta^{9(11)}$, Δ^{11}, and Δ^{14} sites (Table 37, Fig. 37), probably due to the action of specific hydroxylase enzymes present in microorganisms.

The formation of a 9, 10-seco compound by opening of ring B is documented in Table 38 (see also Fig. 38). The 16α, 17α-epoxide derivatives of progesterone have been cleaved by incubation with fermenting yeast as reported by Camerino and co-workers (Table 39).

Table 1

CARBONS 1α AND 1ξ

Substrate	Product	Microorganism	Reference
Androst-4-ene-3,17-dione	1α-Hydroxyandrost-4-ene-3,17-dione	*Penicillium* sp.	Dodson and Muir (1957); Dodson *et al.* (1957)
Progesterone	1ξ-Hydroxy-progesterone	*Flavobacterium dehydrogenans*	Nussbaum *et al.* (1957)
Dehydroepi-androsterone	1α-Hydroxydehydro-epiandrosterone	*Penicillium* sp.	Dodson *et al.* (1957)
11-Deoxycortisol	1ξ,17α,21-Tri-hydroxyprogesterone	*Rhizoctonia ferrugena*	Greenspan *et al.* (1957)
9α-Fluorocortisol	1ξ-Hydroxy-9α-fluorocortisol	*Streptomyces* sp.	McAleer *et al.* (1958b)
5α-Androstane-3,17-dione	1α-Hydroxy-5α-androstane-3,17-dione	*Penicillium* sp. (ATCC 12,556)	Dodson *et al.* (1960)
Androst-4-ene-3,17-dione	1α-Hydroxyandrost-4-ene-3,17-dione		
Dehydroepi-androsterone	1α-Hydroxydehydro-epiandrosterone		

Table 2

MICROBIOLOGICAL HYDROXYLATIONS AT CARBON 2β

Substrate	Product	Microorganism	Reference
Corticosterone	2β-Hydroxycortico-sterone	*Sclerotinia libertiana*	Shirasaka (1961a)
11-Deoxycortisol	2β,17α,21-Trihydroxy-progesterone	*Sclerotinia libertiana*	Shirasaka *et al.* (1959b)
11-Deoxycortisol	2β,17α,21-Trihydroxy-progesterone	*Helminthosporium tritici-vulgaris* (H-25)	Kondo (1960)
17α-Hydroxy-progesterone	2β,17α-Dihydroxy-progesterone	*Sclerotinia libertiana*	Shirasaka *et al.* (1959b)
Progesterone	2β,15β-Dihydroxy-progesterone	*Sclerotinia libertiana*	Shirasaka *et al.* (1959b)
Deoxycorticosterone acetate	2β,15β,21-Trihydroxy-progesterone	*Sclerotinia libertiana*	Shirasaka (1961a)
Androst-4-ene-3,17-dione	2β-Hydroxyandrost-4-ene-3,17-dione	*Penicillium* sp.	Dodson and Muir (1957); Dodson *et al.* (1957)
11-Deoxycortisol	2β,17α,21-Tri-hydroxyprogesterone	*Rhizoctonia*	Herzog *et al.* (1957); Greenspan *et al.* (1957)
9α-Fluorocortisol	2β-Hydroxy-9α-fluorocortisol	*Streptomyces roseochromogenes*	Smith *et al.* (1961)
Androst-4-ene-3,17-dione	2β-Hydroxyandrost-4-ene-3,17-dione	*Penicillium* sp. (ATCC 12,556)	Dodson *et al.* (1960)

Table 3

MICROBIOLOGICAL HYDROXYLATIONS AT CARBON 6β

Substrate	Product	Microorganism	Reference
Testerosterone	6β-Hydroxytestosterone	Rhizopi	Eppstein *et al.* (1954)
	6β-Hydroxyandrost-4-ene-3,17-dione	*Fusarium* sp.	Eppstein *et al.* (1956)
	17β-Hydroxyandrost-4-ene-3,6-dione (probably derived from 6β-hydroxy derivative)	*Rhizopus nigricans*	Eppstein *et al.* (1954)
Androst-4-ene-3,17-dione	6β-Hydroxyandrost-4-ene-3,17-dione	*Rhizopus nigricans*	Eppstein *et al.* (1954)
		Aspergillus niger	Fried *et al.* (1955a)
19-Nortestosterone	6β-Hydroxy-19-nortestosterone	*Rhizopus nigricans*	Pederson *et al.* (1956); Peterson (1958)
14α-Hydroxyprogesterone	$6\beta,14\alpha$-Dihydroxyprogesterone	*Naematblama sublateritium*	Schubert *et al.* (1960a)
Progesterone	$6\beta,14\alpha$-Dihydroxyprogesterone	*Naematblama sublateritium*	
Progesterone	$6\beta,11\alpha$-Dihydroxyprogesterone	*Rhizopus kansho Yamamoto*	Asai *et al.* (1958a)
		Aspergillus saitoi	Iizuka *et al.* (1958)
		Aspergillus usamii mutant	Iizuka *et al.* (1958)
		Gloeosporium kaki	Shirasaka and Tsuruta (1961a)
		Sclerotium hydrophilium	Shirasaka and Tsuruta (1961b)
		Aspergillus ochraceus	Dulaney *et al.* (1955)
	$6\beta,14\alpha$-Dihydroxyprogesterone	*Absidia regnieri*	Tanabe *et al.* (1959); Shirasaka *et al.* (1959a)
		Achromobacter sp.	Iizuka *et al.* (1960a,b)
	$6\beta,11\alpha$-Dihydroxyprogesterone	*Aspergillus niger*	Fried *et al.* (1952)
		Rhizopi	Peterson *et al.* (1952)
	6β-Hydroxyprogesterone	*Streptomyces aureofaciens*	Fried *et al.* (1955b)
		Penicillium urticae	Murray and Peterson (1953); Eppstein *et al.* (1956)
	6β-Hydroxyandrost-4-ene-3,17-dione	*Gliocladium catenulatum*	Peterson *et al.* (1953a)

Continued on following page

Table 3 (*continued*)

MICROBIOLOGICAL HYDROXYLATIONS AT CARBON 6β

Substrate	Product	Microorganism	Reference
	6β,15α-Dihydroxy-progesterone	*Fusarium lini*	Gubler and Tamm (1958)
Deoxycorticosterone	6β,21-Dihydroxy-progesterone	*Cephalothecium roseum*	Meister *et al.* (1954)
		Trichothecium roseum	Meystre *et al.* (1954)
		Rhizopi	Eppstein *et al.* (1953)
		Rhizopus arrhizus	Hayano *et al.* (1956)
Deoxycorticosterone acetate	6β,11α,21-Trihydroxy-progesterone	*Sclerotium hydrophilium*	Shirasaka and Tsuruta (1961b)
17α-Hydroxy-progesterone	6β,17α-Dihydroxy-progesterone	Rhizopi	Meister *et al.* (1953b)
16α-Hydroxy-progesterone	6β,16α-Dihydroxy-progesterone	*Aspergillus nidulans*	Fried *et al.* (1955b)
11α-Hydroxy-progesterone	6β,11α-Dihydroxy-progesterone	*Cunninghamella blakesleeana*	Eppstein *et al.* (1956)
Methyltestosterone	6β-Hydroxymethyl-testosterone	Rhizopi	Eppstein *et al.* (1954)
Pregnenolone	6ξ-Hydroxy-pregnenolone	*Serratia marcescens* Bizio	Narita *et al.* (1958)
11-Deoxycortisol	6β,14α,17α,21-Tetrahydroxy-progesterone	*Curvularia lunata* (No. 49)	Kondo and Mitsugi (1961)
		C. geniculata (1FO-6284)	
		C. trifolii (1FO-6241)	
11-Deoxycortisol	6β,17α,21-Trihydroxy-progesterone	Rhizopi	Peterson *et al.* (1953b)
11β-Hydroxy-androst-4-ene-3,17-dione	6β,11β-Dihydroxy-androst-4-ene-3,17-dione	*Rhizoctonia solani*	Urech *et al.* (1960)
17α,21-Dihydroxy-pregna-1,4-diene-3,11,20-trione	6β,17α,21-Trihydroxy-pregna-1,4-diene-3,11,20-trione	*Chaetomium*	Cervajal (1960)

Table 4

MICROBIOLOGICAL HYDROXYLATIONS AT CARBONS 7α AND 7β

Substrate	Product	Microorganism	Reference
Progesterone	7α-Hydroxy-progesterone	*Phycomyces blakesleeanus*	Fried and Sabo (1953); Fried *et al.* (1955b)
		Helminthosporium	McAleer *et al.* (1958a)
	7α,14α,-Dihydroxy-progesterone	*Absidia regnieri*	Tanabe *et al.* (1959; Shirasaka *et al.* (1959a)
	7α,14α,15β-Trihydroxy-progesterone	*Absidia regnieri*	Tanabe *et al.* (1959); Shirasaka *et al.* (1959a)
		Syncephalastrum racemosum	Asai *et al.* (1959); Tsuda *et al.* (1960)
Deoxycortico-sterone	7α-Hydroxydeoxy-corticosterone	*Curvularia* sp.	Meystre *et al.* (1955)
		Peziza sp.	
		Helminthosporium	McAleer *et al.* (1958a)
11-Deoxycortisol	7α,14α-Dihydroxy-11-deoxycortisol	*Curvularia lunata*	Agnello *et al.* (1955)
		Cephalosporium sp. (Lederle Z-164)	Bernstein *et al.* (1959)
Androst-4-ene-3,17-dione	7β-Hydroxyandrost-4-ene-3,17-dione	*Rhizopus nigricans*	Peterson (1958)
Pregnenolone	7β-Hydroxy-pregnenolone	*Rhizopus nigricans*	Eppstein *et al.* (1956)
	7β,11α-Dihydroxy-pregnenolone	*Rhizopus arrhizus*	Eppstein *et al.* (1956); Murray and Peterson (1955a)
	7β,15β-Dihydroxy-progesterone	*Diplodia tubericola*	Asai *et al.* (1961)
3β-Hydroxy-5α-pregnan-20-one	3β,7β-Dihydroxy-5α-pregnan-20-one	*Rhizopus arrhizus*	Eppstein *et al.* (1956); Murray and Peterson (1952)
3β,21-Dihydroxy-5α-pregnan-20-one	7β,3β,21-Trihydroxy-5α-pregnan-20-one	*Rhizopus* sp.	Kahnt *et al.* (1952)
Progesterone	7ξ-Hydroxyprogesterone	*Phycomyces blakesleeanus*	Fried *et al.* (1955b)
	7α,15β-Dihydroxy-progesterone	*Syncephalastrum racemosum*	Asai *et al.* (1959); Tsuda *et al.* (1960)
	7β,15β-Dihydroxy-progesterone	*Diplodia tubericola*	Asai *et al.* (1961)

Continued on following page

Table 4 (*continued*)

Microbiological Hydroxylations at Carbons 7α and 7β

Substrate	Product	Microorganism	Reference
Dehydroepi-androsterone	7β-Hydroxydehydro-epiandrosterone	*Rhizopus arrhizus*	Schneider and Lewbart (1959); Dodson *et al.* (1959)
		Rhizopus	
	7α-Hydroxydehydroepi-androsterone	*Rhizopus fusidium* (*M*61-1)	Dodson *et al.* (1959)
Cholesterol	7ξ-Hydroxychol-esterol	*Proactinomyces roseus*	Kramli and Horvath (1948, 1949)
Progesterone	7β-Hydroxy-progesterone	*Diplodia tubericola*	Asai *et al.* (1961)
		Cladosporium	McAleer *et al.* (1958a)
11-Deoxycortisol	7β,17α,21-Trihydroxy-progesterone	*Diplodia tubericola*	Asai *et al.* (1961)
Deoxycortico-sterone	7β,21-Dihydroxy-progesterone	*Cladosporium*	McAleer *et al.* (1958a)

Table 5

Microbiological Hydroxylations at Carbon 8β or 9α

Substrate	Product	Microorganism	Reference
Progesterone	8- or 9-Hydroxy-progesterone	*Streptomyces aureofaciens*	Eppstein *et al.* (1956); Fried *et al.* (1955b)
	9α,14α-Dihydroxy-progesterone	*Absidia regnieri*	Tanabe *et al.* (1959); Shirasaka *et al.* (1959a)
Deoxycorti-costerone	8- or 9-Hydroxy-deoxycorticosterone	*Neurospora crassa*	Stone *et al.* (1955)
		Mucors, *Helicostylum piriforme*	Eppstein *et al.* (1956); Murray and Peterson (1955c)
	(8-14α) or (9α-14α) Dihydroxydeoxycorti-costerone	*Helicostylum piriforme* (AT 8992)	Eppstein *et al.* (1958)
11-Deoxycortisol	8- or 9-Hydroxy-11-deoxycortisol	Mucors, *Helicostylum piriforme*	Eppstein *et al.* (1956); Murray and Peterson (1952)

Table 6

MICROBIOLOGICAL HYDROXYLATIONS AT CARBON 9α

Substrate	Product	Microorganism	Reference
11-Deoxycortisol	9α,17α,21-Trihydroxy-progesterone	*Curvularia lunata*	Kondo and Mitsugi (1961)
Progesterone	2ξ,9α-Dihydroxypro-gesterone	*Circinella* strain	Schubert (1959)

Table 7

MICROBIOLOGICAL HYDROXYLATIONS AT CARBON 10β

Substrate	Product	Microorganism	Reference
19-Nortestosterone	10β-Hydroxy-19-nortestosterone	*Rhizopus nigricans*	Pederson *et al.* (1956) Peterson (1958)

Table 8

MICROBIOLOGICAL HYDROXYLATIONS AT CARBON 11α

Substrate	Product	Microorganism	Reference
Testosterone	11α-Hydroxy-testosterone	Rhizopi	Eppstein *et al.* (1954)
		Metarrhizium anisopliae	Kurosawa (1958)
Androst-4-ene-3,17-dione	11α-Hydroxyandrost-4-ene-3,17-dione	*Rhizopus nigricans*	Dulaney *et al.* (1955); Eppstein *et al.* (1954)
19-Nortestosterone	11α-Hydroxy-19-nortestosterone	*Rhizopus nigricans*	Pederson *et al.* (1956); Peterson (1958)
Methyltestosterone	11α-Hydroxymethyl-testosterone	Rhizopi	Eppstein *et al.* (1954)
Progesterone	11α-Hydroxy-progesterone	*Pestalotia foedans*	Shull *et al.* (1954, 1955b)
		Neurospora sitophila	Murray and Peterson (1954)
		Aspergilli	Fried *et al.* (1952); Murray and Peterson (1953); Weisz *et al.* (1956); Dulaney *et al.* (1955)
		Gloeosporium kaki	Shirasaka and Tsuruta (1961a)
		Metarrhizium	Nishikawa *et al.* (1959)

Continued on following page

Table 8 (*continued*)

MICROBIOLOGICAL HYDROXYLATIONS AT CARBON 11α

Substrate	Product	Microorganism	Reference
		Rhizopus chinensis Saito	Asai *et al.* (1958a)
		R. nigricans Yamazaki	
		R. kansho Yamamoto	
		Rhizopus nigricans	Barmenkov *et al.* (1961)
		Aspergillus usamii, mutant	Iizuka *et al.* (1958)
		Aspergillus usamii, mutant *shirousamii*	
		Aspergillus awamori	
		Aspergillus saitoi	
		Serratia marcescens Bizio	Narita *et al.* (1958)
		Rhizopus sp. (*R. chinensis* Saito 10-10)	Asai *et al.* (1958b)
		Metarrhizium anisopliae	Kurosawa (1958)
Progesterone	6β,11α-Dihydroxy-progesterone	*Rhizopus kancho* Yamamoto	Asai *et al.* (1958a)
		Aspergillus saitoi	Iizuka *et al.* (1958)
		Aspergillus usamii mutant	
		Gloeosporium kaki	Shirasaki and Tsuruta (1961a)
		Sclerotium hydrophilium	Shirasaka and Tsuruta (1961b)
Progesterone	11α-Hydroxy-progesterone	*Rhizopus* sp.	Kahnt *et al.* (1952); Mancera *et al.* (1952)
		Rhizopi	Peterson and Murray (1952); Peterson *et al.* (1952)
		Bacillus cereus	McAleer *et al.* (1958b)
		Gloeosporium kaki	Shirasaka and Tsuruta (1961a)

Continued on following page

Table 8 *(continued)*

MICROBIOLOGICAL HYDROXYLATIONS AT CARBON 11α

Substrate	Product	Microorganism	Reference
		Dactylium dendroides	Dulaney *et al.* (1955)
	11α-,21-Dihydroxy-progesterone	*Aspergillus niger*	Weisz *et al.* (1956)
	11α,17α-Dihydroxy-progesterone	*Cephalothecium roseum*	Meister *et al.* (1954)
		Dactylium dendroides	Dulaney *et al.* (1955)
	11α-Hydroxy-5α-pregnane-3,20-dione	*Rhizopus nigricans*	Peterson *et al.* (1952)
	11α-Hydroxy-progesterone	*Eurotium chevalieri*	Pfizer & Co. (1955)
19-Norprogesterone	11α-Hydroxy-19-norprogesterone	*Rhizopus nigricans*	Bowers *et al.* (1958)
6-Dehydro-progesterone	11α-Hydroxy-6-dehydroprogesterone	*Rhizopus nigricans*	Peterson *et al.* (1953c)
16,17-Oxido-progesterone	11α-Hydroxy-progesterone	Rhizopi	Peterson *et al.* (1955)
16-Dehydro-progesterone	11α,17α-Dihydroxy-progesterone	*Rhizopus nigricans*	Meister *et al.* (1953a)
Pregnenolone	3β,11α-Dihydroxy-pregn-5-ene-7,20-dione	*Rhizopus arrhizus*	Eppstein *et al.* (1956); Murray and Peterson (1955b)
	11α-Hydroxy-pregnenolone	*Metarrhizium anisopliae*	Kurosawa (1958)
		Pseudomonas fluorescens migula, *Serratia marcescens* Bizio	Narita *et al.* (1958)
	7β,11α-Dihydroxy-pregn-5-en-20-one	*Rhizopus arrhizus*	Eppstein *et al.* (1956); Murray and Peterson (1955a)
3β-Hydroxy-5α-pregnan-20-one	3β,11α-Dihydroxy-5α-pregnan-20-one	*Rhizopus nigricans*	Eppstein *et al.* (1956)
5β-Pregnane-3,20-dione	11α-Hydroxy-5β-pregnane-3,20-dione	*Rhizopus nigricans*	Eppstein *et al.* (1953b)
5α-Pregnane-3,20-dione	11α-Hydroxy-5α-pregnane-3,20-dione	*Rhizopus nigricans*	Eppstein *et al.* (1953)
Deoxycortico-sterone	11α,17α-Dihydroxy-deoxycorticosterone	*Cephalothecium roseum*	Meister *et al.* (1954)

Continued on following page

Table 8 (*continued*)

MICROBIOLOGICAL HYDROXYLATIONS AT CARBON 11α

Substrate	Product	Microorganism	Reference
Deoxycorticosterone	Epicorticosterone	*Rhizopus nigricans*	Hayano *et al.* (1956)
		Sclerotium hydrophilium	Shirasaka and Tsuruta (1961a)
		Aspergilli	Eppstein *et al.* (1956); Fried *et al.* (1952); Murray and Peterson (1953)
		Glomerella lagearium	Shirasaka and Tsuruta (1961a)
11-Deoxycortisol	11-Epicortisol	*Helicostylum piriforme*	Eppstein *et al.* (1956)
		Helminthosporium sigmoideum (H-37, H-39)	Kondo (1960)
		Aspergillus nidulans	Fried *et al.* (1955a)
		Absidia regnieri	Shirasaka (1961b)
		Gloeosporium folliicolum *Glomerella mume* *Glomerella cingulata*	Kondo and Masuo (1960)
11-Deoxycortisol	Epicortisol	*Cercospora scirpicola* *Cercospora melongerae* *Cercospora zinniae*	Kondo *et al.* (1960)
		Sclerotinia sp.	Shirasaka *et al.* (1958)
		Syncephalastrum racemosum	Tsuda *et al.* (1960); Asai *et al.* (1959)
		Corticium sasakii	Nishikawa and Hagiwara (1958b); Hasegawa and Takahashi (1958)
		Curvularia lunata (No. 49) *Curvularia geniculata* (IFO6284) *Curvularia trifolii* (IFO6241)	Kondo and Mitsugi (1961)

Continued on following page

Table 8 (*continued*)

MICROBIOLOGICAL HYDROXYLATIONS AT CARBON 11α

Substrate	Product	Microorganism	Reference
		Glomerella lagearium	Shirasaka and Tsuruta (1961a)
		Sclerotium hydrophilium	Shirasaka and Tsuruta (1961b)
		Absidia glauca	Schmidt–Thomé (1957)
11-Deoxycorticosol	11-Epicortisol	*Aspergillus niger*	Fried *et al.* (1952); Murray and Peterson (1952)
		Rhizopus sp.	Kahnt *et al.* (1952)
		Rhizopus nigricans	Peterson *et al.* (1953b)
11-Deoxycortisol	$11\alpha,17\alpha,21$-Trihydroxy-5β-pregnane-3,20-dione	*Rhizopus nigricans*	Peterson *et al.* (1953b)
$17\alpha,21$-Dihydroxy-5β-pregnane-3,20-dione	$11\alpha,17\alpha,21$-Trihydroxy-5β-pregnane-3,20-dione	*Rhizopus nigricans*	Peterson *et al.* (1953b)
16α-Hydroxy-progesterone	$11\alpha,16\alpha$-Dihydroxy-progesterone	*Aspergillus niger*	Fried *et al.* (1955b)
17α-Hydroxy-progesterone	$11\alpha,17\alpha$-Dihydroxy-progesterone	Rhizopi	Meister *et al.* (1953b)
		Aspergillus niger	Fried *et al.* (1952)
	$11\alpha,17\alpha$-Dihydroxy-17α-methyl-*D*-homoandrost-4-ene-3,17-dione	*Aspergillus niger*	Fried *et al.* (1952)
	$11\alpha,17\alpha$-Dihydroxy-progesterone	*Absidia regnieri*	Shirasaka (1961b)
		Gloeosporium kaki	Shirasaka and Tsuruta (1961a)
		Sclerotium hydrophilium	Shirasaka and Tsuruta (1961b)
		Sclerotinia libertiana	Shirasaka *et al.* (1959b)
3,5-Cyclo-6β-hydroxypregnan-20-one	3,5-Cyclo-$6\beta,11\alpha$-dihydroxypregnan-20-one	*Metarrhisium anisopliae*	Kurosawa (1958)
$17\alpha,21$-Dihydroxy-pregna-1,4-diene-3,20-dione	$11\alpha,17\alpha,21$-Trihydroxy-pregna-1,4-diene-3,20-dione	*Delacroixia coronata*	Testa (1957)
$17\alpha,21$-Dihydroxy-pregna-1,4-diene-3,20-dione	$11\alpha,17\alpha,21$-Trihydroxy-pregna-1,4-diene-3-20-dione	*Delacroixia coronata*	Lepetit (1957)

Table 9

MICROBIOLOGICAL HYDROXYLATIONS AT CARBON 11β

Substrate	Product	Microorganism	Reference
Progesterone	11β-Hydroxy-progesterone	*Cunninghamella blakesleeana*	Eppstein *et al.* (1956)
		Curvulariae	Shull and Kita (1955); Shull *et al.* (1955a)
		Monascus	Hasegawa and Takahashi (1958)
	Corticosterone	*Curvularia lunata*	Rubin *et al.* (1956)
19-Norprogesterone	11β-Hydroxy-19-norprogesterone	*Curvularia lunata*	Bowers *et al.* (1958)
17α-Hydroxy-progesterone	11β,17α-Dihydroxy-progesterone	*Curvulariae*	Shull and Kita (1955)
	11β,14α,17α-Tri-hydroxyprogesterone	*Curvularia lunata*	Shull and Kita (1955); Shull *et al.* (1955a, b)
Deoxycorticosterone	Corticosterone	*Cunninghamella blakesleeana*	Mann *et al.* (1955a, b); Hayano *et al.* (1956)
		Curvulariae	Shull and Kita (1955)
		Stachylidium bicolor	Shirasaka (1961d)
		Serratia marcescens Bizio	Narita *et al.* (1958)
		Pseudomonas fluorescens migula	
11-Deoxycortisol	Cortisol	*Cunninghamella blakesleeana* (also cortisone)	Hanson *et al.* (1953)
		Streptomyces fradiae	Colingsworth *et al.* (1952)
		Absidia glauca	Schmidt-Thomé (1957)
		Pycnosporium sp.	Pfizer & Co. (1957)
		Curvulariae (also cortisone)	Shull and Kita (1955)
		Coniothyrium sp.	Fried *et al.* (1955b)
		Trichothecium roseum	Shull *et al.* (1956)
11-Deoxycortisol	11β,17α,20β,21-Tetrahydroxypregn-4-en-3-one	*Curvularia lunata*	Shull (1956)
	Prednisolone	*Pseudomonas* mutant sp. 109	Uchibayashi (1960b)

Continued on following page

Table 9 (*continued*)

MICROBIOLOGICAL HYDROXYLATIONS AT CARBON 11β

Substrate	Product	Microorganism	Reference
11-Deoxycortisol	Cortisol	*Sclerotinia* sp.	
		Helminthosporium sigmoideum (H-40)	
		Cercospora zinniae	Kondo and Mitsugi (1961)
		Botrytis cineres	Shirasaka (1961c)
		Corticium sasakii	Nishikawa and Hagiwara (1958a); Hasegawa and Takahashi (1958)
		Pseudomonas sp. 109	Uchibayashi (1960a)
		Stachylidium bicolor	Shirasaka (1961d)
		Pycnosporium sp.	Shull (1956)
		Rhodoseptoria sp.	
		Dothichiza sp.	
14α,21-Dihydroxy-progesterone	14α-Hydroxy-corticosterone	*Stachylidium bicolor*	Shirasaka (1961c)
15α-Hydroxy-androst-4-ene-3,17-dione	11β,15α-Dihydroxy-androst-4-ene-3,17-dione	*Cunninghamella elegans*	Urech *et al.* (1960)
11-Deoxycortisol	Cortisol	*Curvularia lunata* homogenate supernatant (30 min, 25,000*g*)	Zuidweg *et al.* (1962)

Table 10

MICROBIOLOGICAL HYDROXYLATIONS AT CARBON 12β

Substrate	Product	Microorganism	Reference
Progesterone	12β,15α-Dihydroxy-progesterone	*Calonectria decora*	Schubert *et al.* (1957); Hayano *et al.* (1959); Kurosawa *et al.* (1961b)
5β-Pregnane-3,20-dione	12β,15α-Dihydroxy-5β-pregnane-3,20-dione	*Calonectria decora*	Schubert and Siebert (1958)
5α-Pregnane-3,20-dione	12β,15α-Dihydroxy-5α-pregnane-3,20-dione	*Calonectria decora*	Schubert and Siebert (1958)
Pregnenolone	12β,15α-Dihydroxy-progesterone	*Calonectria decora*	Schubert and Siebert (1958)

Table II

MICROBIOLOGICAL HYDROXYLATIONS AT CARBON 14α

Substrate	Product	Microorganism	Reference
Testosterone	14α-Hydroxytestosterone	Mucors	Meister *et al.* (1953c); Eppstein *et al.* (1956)
		Fusaria	Eppstein *et al.* (1956)
Androst-4-ene-3,17-dione	14α-Hydroxyandrost-4-ene-3,17-dione	Mucors, *Helicostylum piriforme*	Meister *et al.* (1953c); Eppstein *et al.* (1956)
Progesterone	9α,14α-Dihydroxyprogesterone	*Absidia regnieri*	Tanabe *et al.* (1959)
	7α,14α,15β-Trihydroxyprogesterone	*Absidia regnieri*	Shirasaka *et al.* (1959a)
	14α-Hydroxyprogesterone	Mucors, *Helicostylum piriforme*	Meister *et al.* (1953c); Eppstein *et al.* (1956)
		Bacillus cereus	Fried *et al.* (1955b)
		Absidia regnieri	Tanabe *et al.* (1959); Shirasaka *et al.* (1959a)
		Circinella strain	Schubert (1959)
		Stemphylium botryosum	Nishikawa and Hagiwara (1958a)
	6β,14α-Dihydroxyprogesterone	*Absidia regnieri*	Tanabe *et al.* (1959); Shirasaka *et al.* (1959a)
		Achromobacter sp.	Iizuka *et al.* (1960a)
	7α,14α,15β-Trihydroxyprogesterone	*Syncephalastrum racemosum*	Asai *et al.* (1959); Tsuda *et al.* (1960)
	7α,14α-Dihydroxyprogesterone	*Absidia regnieri*	Tanabe *et al.* (1959); Shirasaka *et al.* (1959a)
	11β,14α-Dihydroxyprogesterone	*Curvularia lunata*	Shull *et al.* (1955a)
	6β,14α-Dihydroxyprogesterone	*Naematblama sublateritium*	Schubert et al. (1960a)
17α-Hydroxyprogesterone	14α,17α-Dihydroxyprogesterone	*Stemphylium botryosum*	Nishikawa and Hagiwara (1958a)
Corticosterone	11β,14α,21-Trihydroxyprogesterone	*Absidia regnieri*	Shirasaka (1961b)
Deoxycorticosterone	14α-Hydroxydeoxycorticosterone	Mucors, *Helicostylum piriforme*	Meister *et al.* (1953c); Murray and Peterson (1955c)
		Stachylidium bicolor	Shirasaka (1961d)

Continued on following page

Table 11 (*continued*)

MICROBIOLOGICAL HYDROXYLATIONS AT CARBON 14α

Substrate	Product	Microorganism	Reference
		Cunninghamella blakesleeana	Mann *et al.* (1955a, b)
		Absidia regnieri	Shirasaka (1961b)
11-Deoxycortisol	14α,17α,21-Trihydroxyprogesterone	*Cunninghamella blakesleeana*	Eppstein *et al.* (1956)
		Mucors, *Helicostylum piriforme*	Meister *et al.* (1953c); Eppstein *et al.* (1956)
		Curvularia sp.	Wettstein (1955)
	7α,14α,17α,21-Tetrahydroxyprogesterone	*Curvularia lunata*	Agnello *et al.* (1955)
	14α,17α,21-Trihydroxyprogesterone	*Absidia regnieri*	Shirasaka (1961b)
		Helminthosporium avenae (H-9)	Kondo (1960)
	14α,17α,21-Trihydroxyprogesterone	*Curvularia lunata* (No. 49)	Kondo and Mitsugi (1961)
		Curvularia lunata (IFO 6280)	
		Curvularia geniculata (IFO 6284)	
		Curvularia trifolii (IFO 6241)	
	6β,14α,17α,21-Tetrahydroxyprogesterone	*Curvularia lunata* (No. 49)	Kondo and Mitsugi (1961)
		Curvularia geniculata (IFO 6248)	
		Curvularia trifolii (IFO 6241)	

Table 12

MICROBIOLOGICAL HYDROXYLATION AT CARBON 15α

Substrate	Product	Microorganism	Reference
Testosterone	15α-Hydroxytestosterone	*Fusarium* sp.	Eppstein *et al.* (1956); Peterson (1958)
		Fusarium lini	Gubler and Tamm (1958)
	15α-Hydroxyandrost-4-ene-3,17-dione	*Fusarium* sp.	Peterson (1958)
Androst-4-ene-3,17-dione	15α-Hydroxyandrost-4-ene-3,17-dione	*Fusarium* sp.	Eppstein *et al.* (1956)
		Fusarium lini	Gubler and Tamm (1958)
		Gibberella saubinetti	Urech *et al.* (1960)
Progesterone	15α-Hydroxyprogesterone	*Penicillium urticae*	Eppstein *et al.* (1956); Murray and Peterson (1953)
		Penicillium notatum	Camerino *et al.* (1956)
		Gibberellae	Eppstein *et al.* (1956)
		Fusaria	Eppstein *et al.* (1956)
		Bacillus cereus	Fried *et al.* (1955b)
		Streptomyces aureus	Fried *et al.* (1956)
		Bacillus megaterium	McAleer (1958)
		Colletotrichum antirrhini	Fried *et al.* (1955b)
		Fusarium culmorum and other fusaria	Klüger *et al.* (1957)
		Fusarium lini	Gubler and Tamm (1958)
Progesterone	6β,15α-Dihydroxyprogesterone	*Fusarium lini*	Gubler and Tamm (1958)
Deoxycorticosterone	15α,21-Dihydroxyprogesterone	*Fusarium* sp.	Vischer and Wettstein (1958)
		Fusaria	Eppstein *et al.* (1956)
		Gibberellae	Eppstein *et al.* (1956); Meystre *et al.* (1955)
		Fusarium lini	Gubler and Tamm (1958)
		Gibberella baccata	Urech *et al.* (1960); Wettstein (1955)
11α-Hydroxyprogesterone	11α,15α-Dihydroxyprogesterone	*Calonectria decora*	Schubert *et al.* (1957)

Continued on following page

Table 12 (*continued*)

MICROBIOLOGICAL HYDROXYLATION AT CARBON 15α

Substrate	Product	Microorganism	Reference
5β-Pregnane-3,20-dione	12β,15α-Dihydroxy-5β-pregnane-3,20-dione	*Calonectria decora*	Schubert and Siebert (1958)
5α-Pregnane-3,20-dione	12β,15α-Dihydroxy-5α-pregnane-3,20-dione		
Pregnenolone	12β,15α-Dihydroxy-progesterone		
11-Deoxycortisol	15α,17α,21-Trihydroxy-progesterone	*Gibberella baccata*	Urech *et al.* (1960)
		Hormodendrum olivaceum (AT 13,596)	Bernstein *et al.* (1956)

Table 13

MICROBIOLOGICAL HYDROXYLATION AT CARBON 15β

Substrate	Product	Microorganism	Reference
7β-Hydroxy-progesterone	7β,15β-Dihydroxy-progesterone	*Diplodia tubericola*	Asai *et al.* (1961)
Progesterone	7α,15β-Dihydroxy-progesterone	*Syncephalastrum racemosum*	Asai *et al.* (1959); Tsuda *et al.* (1960)
		Diplodia tubericola	Asai *et al.* (1961)
	7β,15β-Dihydroxy-progesterone	*Diplodia tubericola*	Asai *et al.* (1961)
	2β,15β-Dihydroxy-progesterone	*Sclerotinia libertiana*	Shirasaka *et al.* (1959b)
	15β-Hydroxyproge-sterone	*Bacillus megaterium*	McAleer *et al.* (1958b)
		Phycomyes blakesleeanus	Fried *et al.* (1955b)
		Chrysosporium pannorum	Kurosawa *et al.* (1961b)
	7α,14α,15β-Trihydroxy-progesterone	*Absidia regnieri*	Tanabe *et al.* (1959); Shirasaka *et al.* (1959a)
		Syncephalastrum racemosum	Asai *et al.* (1959); Tsuda *et al.* (1960)

Continued on following page

Table 13 (*continued*)

MICROBIOLOGICAL HYDROXYLATION AT CARBON 15β

Substrate	Product	Microorganism	Reference
	12β,15β-Dihydroxyprogesterone	*Calonectria decora*	Schubert *et al.* (1957)
Deoxycorticosterone	15β,21-Dihydroxyprogesterone	*Lenzites abietina*	Meystre *et al.* (1955); Wettstein (1955)
		Fusarium sp.	Vischer and Wettstein (1958)
		Botrytis cinerea	Shirasaka (1961c)
11-Deoxycortisol	15β,17α,21-Trihydroxyprogesterone	*Spicaria* sp. *Spicaria simplicissima* (AT 13,595)	Bernstein *et al.* (1956)
Corticosterone	15β,21-Dihydroxypregn-4-ene-3,11,20-trione	*Sclerotium hydrophilium*	Shirasaka and Tsurata (1961b)
	15β-Hydroxycorticosterone	*Sclerotinia libertiana*	Shirasaka (1961a)
		Botrytis cinerea	Shirasaka (1961c)
17α-Hydroxyprogesterone	15β,17α-Dihydroxyprogesterone	*Sclerotinia libertiana*	Shirasaka (1961a)
Deoxycorticosterone acetate	2β,15β,21-Trihydroxyprogesterone	*Sclerotinia libertiana*	Shirasaka (1961a)
Pregnenolone	7β,15β-Dihydroxyprogesterone	*Diplodia tubericola*	Asai *et al.* (1961)
15β-Hydroxyprogesterone 11α-Hydroxyprogesterone	12β,15β-Dihydroxyprogesterone	*Calonectria decora*	Schubert *et al.* (1957)

Table 14
MICROBIOLOGICAL HYDROXYLATION AT CARBON 16α

Substrate	Product	Microorganism	Reference
Testosterone	16α-Hydroxytestosterone	*Streptomyces* sp.	Perlman *et al.* (1955); Underkofler and Hickey (1954)
		Streptomyces roseochromogenes	Fried *et al.* (1955b)
Androst-4-ene-3,17-dione	16α-Hydroxyandrost-4-ene-3,17-dione	*Streptomyces roseochromogenes*	Fried *et al.* (1955b)
Progesterone	16α-Hydroxyprogesterone	*Streptomyces* sp.	Perlman *et al.* (1952)
		Actinomyces globosus	Vondrova and Hanc (1960)
	16α-Hydroxy-5β-pregnane-3,20-dione	*Streptomyces* sp.	Perlman *et al.* (1952, 1955)
Deoxycorticosterone	16α,21-Dihydroxyprogesterone	*Streptomyces* sp.	Fried *et al.* (1955b); Vischer *et al.* (1954)
		Streptomyces roseochromogenes	Fried *et al.* (1955b)
9α-Fluorocortisol	16α-Hydroxy-9α-fluorocortisol	*Streptomyces roseochromogenes*	Thoma *et al.* (1957)
9α-Fluoroprednisolone	16α-Hydroxy-9α-fluoroprednisolone		Thoma *et al.* (1957)
Estrone	16α-Hydroxyestrone	*Streptomyces*	Stimmel (1955)
Estradiol-17β	Estriol		
Estradiol-17α	17-Epiestriol		
9α-Fluoroprednisolone	11β,16α,17α,20β,21-Pentahydroxy-9α-fluoropregn-4-en-3-one	*Streptomyces roseochromogenes*	Smith *et al.* (1962)
Estrone	16α-Hydroxyestrone	*Streptomyces halstedii*	Kita *et al.* (1961)
Estradiol-17β	Estriol	*Streptomyces mediocidicus*	
9α-Fluorocortisol	9α-Fluoro-16α-hydroxycortisol	*Streptomyces halstedii*	Kita *et al.* (1961)
Cortisol	16α-Hydroxycortisol		
A-Norprogesterone	16α-Hydroxy-*A*-norprogesterone	*Streptomyces roseochromogenes*	Lerner (1962)

Table 15

MICROBIOLOGICAL HYDROXYLATION AT CARBON 17α

Substrate	Product	Microorganism	Reference
Progesterone	17α-Hydroxyprogesterone	*Cephalothecium roseum*	Hayano *et al.* (1956)
		Trichoderma viride	McAleer and Dulaney (1956)
	11α,17α-Dihydroxyprogesterone	*Dactylium dendroides*	Dulaney *et al.* (1955)
Deoxycorticosterone	11-Deoxycortisol	*Cephalothecium roseum*	Peterson (1955)
		Trichothecium roseum	Meystre *et al.* (1954)
	16β,17α,21-Trihydroxyprogesterone	*Cephalothecium roseum*	Meister *et al.* (1954)
	Epicortisol	*Cephalothecium roseum*	Meister *et al.* (1954)
Corticosterone	Cortisol	*Trichothecium roseum*	Meystre *et al.* (1954)
		Cephalothecium roseum	Meister *et al.* (1954)
	Cortisone (probably through cortisol)	*Trichothecium roseum*	Meystre *et al.* (1954)
		Cephalothecium roseum	Meister *et al.* (1954)
11-Dehydrocorticosterone	Cortisone (probably through cortisol)	*Trichothecium roseum*	Meystre *et al.* (1954)
		Cephalothecium roseum	Meister *et al.* (1954)
11α-Hydroxyprogesterone	11α,17α-Dihydroxyprogesterone	*Cephalothecium roseum*	Murray and Reineke (1911)

Table 16

MICROBIOLOGICAL HYDROXYLATION AT CARBON 19

Substrate	Product	Microorganism	Reference
11-Deoxycortisol	17α,19,21-Trihydroxyprogesterone	*Corticium sasakii*	Nishikawa and Hagiwara (1958b); Hasegawa and Takahashi (1958)

Table 17

MICROBIOLOGICAL HYDROXYLATION AT CARBON 21

Substrate	Product	Microorganism	Reference
Progesterone	Deoxycorticosterone	*Ophiobolus herpotrichus*	Meystre *et al.* (1954); Hayano *et al.* (1956)
		Aspergillus niger	Zaffaroni *et al.* (1955)
		Wojnowicia graminis	McAleer and Dulaney (1956)
	Corticosterone	*Curvularia lunata*	Rubin *et al.* (1956)
	Epicorticosterone	*Aspergillus niger*	Weisz *et al.* (1956)
19-Norprogesterone	19-Nordeoxycorticosterone	*Aspergillus niger*	Zaffaroni *et al.* (1955)
6β-Hydroxyprogesterone	6β,21-Dihydroxyprogesterone	*Aspergillus niger*	Zaffaroni *et al.* (1955)
11α-Hydroxyprogesterone	11α,21-Dihydroxyprogesterone	*Dactylium dendroides*	Dulaney *et al.* (1955)
		Aspergillus niger	Zaffaroni *et al.* (1955)
11β-Hydroxyprogesterone	Corticosterone	*Aspergillus niger*	Zaffaroni *et al.* (1955)
		Hendersonia aricola	Merck & Co. (1956)
14α-Hydroxyprogesterone	14α,21-Dihydroxyprogesterone	*Aspergillus niger*	Zaffaroni *et al.* (1955)
11-Ketoprogesterone	11-Dehydrocorticosterone	*Ophiobalus herpotrichus*	Meystre *et al.* (1954)
		Aspergillus niger	Zaffaroni *et al.* (1955)
17α-Hydroxyprogesterone	11-Deoxycortisol	*Ophiobolus herpotrichus*	Meystre *et al.* (1954)
19-Nor-17α-hydroxyprogesterone	19-Nor-11-deoxycortisol	*Ophiobolus herpotrichus*	Zaffaroni *et al.* (1954)

Table 18

MICROBIOLOGICAL OXIDATION OF Δ^5-3β-OH TO Δ^4-3-KETO GROUPING

Substrate	Product	Microorganism	Reference
Androst-5-ene-3β,17β-diol	Testosterone	*Acetobacter pasteurianum*	Koester *et al.* (1941)
		Corynebacterium mediolanum	Ercoli and Molina (1944)
		Flavobacteria	Molina and Ercoli (1944)
		Proactinomyces erythropolis	Turfitt (1946)

Continued on following page

Table 18 *(continued)*

MICROBIOLOGICAL OXIDATION OF Δ^5-3β-OH TO Δ^4-3-KETO GROUPING

Substrate	Product	Microorganism	Reference
	Androst-4-ene-3,17-dione	Yeast	Koester *et al.* (1941)
		Proactinomyces erythropolis	Turfitt (1946)
		Flavobacteria	Ercoli and Molina (1944)
		Corynebacterium mediolanum	Arnaudi (1942b); Ercoli (1941); Vercellone and Mamoli (1938)
Androst-5-ene-3β,17β-diol-17-benzoate	Testosterone benzoate	*Proactinomyces erythropolis*	Turfitt (1946)
Dehydroepi-androsterone	Testosterone	Yeast	Koester *et al.* (1941)
	Androst-4-ene-3,17-dione	*Proactinomyces erythropolis*	Turfitt (1946)
		Bacillus pulvifaciens	Iizuka *et al.* (1960a)
		Flavobacterium carbonilicum	Molina and Ercoli (1944)
		Cornynebacterium mediolanum	Arnaudi (1939); Mamoli (1938b)
		Acetobacter pasteurianum	Koester *et al.* (1941)
	Androsta-1,4-diene-3,17-dione	Fusaria	Vischer and Wettstein (1953)
Pregnenolone	Progesterone	Yeast plus *Cornynebacterium mediolanum*	Mamoli (1938b)
		Cornynebacterium mediolanum	Arnaudi (1942b); Ercoli (1941)
		Penicillium chrysogenum	Perlman (1952)
		Streptomycetes	Perlman (1952)
		Phycomyces blakesleeanus	Perlman (1952)
		Aspergillus niger	Perlman (1952)
		Eremothecium ashbyii	Perlman (1952)
		Bacillus pulvifaciens	Iizuka *et al.* (1960b)
		Ustilago zeae	Perlman (1952); Schubert and Siebert (1958)

Continued on following page

Table 18 (*continued*)

MICROBIOLOGICAL OXIDATION OF Δ^5-3β-OH TO Δ^4-3-KETO GROUPING

Substrate	Product	Microorganism	Reference
	Androsta-1,4-dione-3,17-dione	Fusaria	Vischer and Wettstein (1953)
	7β,15β-Dihydroxy-progesterone	*Diplodia tubericola*	Asai *et al.* (1961)
17-Ethynylandrost-5-ene-3β,17β-diol	17β-Hydroxy-17-ethynylandrost-4-en-3-one	*Corynebacterium mediolanum*	Arnaudi (1942b)
17-Methylandrost-5-ene-3β,17β-diol	Methyltestosterone	*Corynebacterium*	Arnaudi (1942b); Mamoli (1939b)
3β,21-Dihydroxy-pregn-5-en-20-one-21-acetate	Deoxycorticosterone	*Corynebacterium mediolanum*	Mamoli (1939a)

Table 19

MICROBIOLOGICAL OXIDATION OF 3β-OH TO 3-KETO

Substrate	Product	Microorganism	Reference
3β-Hydroxy-5α-pregnan-20-one-3-acetate	Androsta-1,4-dione-3,17-dione	Fusaria	Vischer and Wettstein (1953)

Table 20

MICROBIOLOGICAL INTRODUCTION OF THE Δ^4-DOUBLE BOND IN 5α STEROIDS

Substrate	Product	Microorganism	Reference
5α-Pregnane-3,20-dione	Androsta-1,4-diene-3,17-dione	Fusaria	Vischer and Wettstein (1953)
5α-Androstane-3,17-dione			
3β-Hydroxy-5α-pregnan-20-one-3-acetate			

Table 21

MICROBIOLOGICAL REDUCTION OF THE 3-KETO GROUP TO 3α-OH

Substrate	Product	Microorganism	Reference
5α-Androstane-3,17-dione	Androsterone	*Pseudomonas* sp.	Talalay and Marcus (1954)
		Putrefactive bacteria	Mamoli and Schramm (1938)
Testosterone	5β-Androstane-3α,17β-diol	Putrefactive bacteria	Mamoli and Schramm (1938)
5β-Androstane-3,17-dione	5β-Androstane-3α,17β-diol	Putrefactive bacteria	Ercoli (1938)
5α-Pregnane-3,11,20-trione	3α-Hydroxy-5α-pregnane-11,20-dione	Yeast	Camerino *et al.* (1953)
5β-Pregnane-3,11,20-trione	3α-Hydroxy-5α-pregnane-11,20-dione	Yeast	Camerino *et al.* (1953)
Androst-4-ene-3,17-dione	5β-Androstane-3α,17β-diol	*Bacillus putrificus*	Mamoli *et al.* (1939)
17β-Hydroxy-5β-androstan-3-one	5β-Androstane-3α,17β-diol	Putrefactive bacteria	Ercoli (1938)
Progesterone	3α-Hydroxy-5β-pregnan-20-one	*Alternaria bataticola*	Shirasaka and Tsuruta (1959)
Deoxycorticosterone	3α,21-Dihydroxy-5β-pregnan-20-one	*Alternaria bataticola*	Shirasaka and Tsuruta (1959)
11-Deoxycortisol	3α,17α,21-Trihydroxy-5β-pregnan-20-one	*Alternaria bataticola*	Shirasaka and Tsuruta (1959)

Table 22

MICROBIOLOGICAL REDUCTION OF THE 3-KETO GROUP TO THE 3β-HYDROXY FORM

Substrate	Product	Microorganism	Reference
Progesterone	3β-Hydroxy-5β-pregnan-20-one	*Alternaria bataticola*	Shirasaka and Tsuruta (1959)
Deoxycorticosterone	3β,21-Dihydroxy-5β-pregnan-20-one	*Alternaria bataticola*	Shirasaka and Tsuruta (1959)
11-Deoxycortisol	3β,17α,21-Trihydroxy-5β-pregnan-20-one	*Alternaria bataticola*	Shirasaka and Tsuruta (1959)
5α-Androstane-3,17-dione	3β-Hydroxy-5α-androstan-17-one	Putrefactive bacteria	Mamoli *et al.* (1939); Mamoli and Schramm (1938)
11α-Hydroxy-5α-pregnane-3,20-dione	3β,11α-Dihydroxy-5α-pregnan-20-one	Yeast	Camerino *et al.* (1953)

Table 23

MICROBIOLOGICAL OXIDATION OF THE 3α-OH GROUP TO THE 3-KETONE

Substrate	Product	Microorganism	Reference
Androsterone	5α-Androstane-3,17-dione	*Pseudomonas* sp.	Talalay and Marcus (1954)

Table 24

MICROBIOLOGICAL REDUCTION OF THE Δ^4-DOUBLE BOND TO THE 5β FORM

Substrate	Product	Microorganism	Reference
Testosterone	17β-Hydroxy-5β-androstane-3-one	*Bacillus putrificus*	Ercoli (1938); Mamoli *et al.* (1939)
	5β-Androstane-3α,17β-diol	Putrefactive bacteria	Mamoli and Schramm (1938)
Androst-4-ene-3,17-dione	5β-Androstane-3,17-dione	*Bacillus putrificus*	Mamoli *et al.* (1939)
	17β-Hydroxy-5β-androstan-3-one	*Bacillus putrificus*	Mamoli *et al.* (1939)
	5β-Androstane-3α,17β-diol	*Bacillus putrificus*	Mamoli *et al.* (1939)
11α-Hydroxy-progesterone	11α-Hydroxy-5β-pregnane-3,20-dione	Unknown anaerobe	Eppstein *et al.* (1956)
Progesterone	5β-Pregnane-3,20-dione	*Bacillus putrificus*	Mamoli *et al.* (1939)
	3β-Hydroxy-5β-pregnan-20-one 3α-Hydroxy-5β-pregnan-20-one	*Alternaria bataticola*	Shirasaka and Tsuruta (1959)
Deoxycorticosterone	3α,21-Dihydroxy-5β-pregnan-20-one 3β,21-Dihydroxy-5β-pregnan-20-one	*Alternaria bataticola*	Shirasaka and Tsuruta (1959)
11-Deoxycortisol	3α,17α,21-Trihydroxy-5β-pregnan-20-one 3β,17α,21-Trihydroxy-5β-pregnan-20-one	*Alternaria bataticola*	Shirasaka and Tsuruta (1959)

Table 25

MICROBIOLOGICAL REDUCTION OF THE Δ^4-DOUBLE BOND TO THE 5α FORM

Substrate	Product	Microorganism	Reference
Testosterone	17β-Hydroxy-5α-androstan-3-one	Putrefactive bacteria	Mamoli and Schramm (1938)
Progesterone	11α-Hydroxy-5α-pregnane-3,20-dione	*Rhizopus nigricans*	Peterson *et al.* (1952)

Table 26

MICROBIOLOGICAL OXIDATION OF THE 11β-HYDROXY FUNCTION

Substrate	Product	Microorganism	Reference
Corticosterone	14α-Hydroxy-11-dehydrocorticosterone	*Absidia regnieri*	Shirasaka (1961b)
	6β-Hydroxy-11-dehydrocorticosterone	*Sclerotium hydrophilium*	Shirasaka and Tsuruta (1961a)
	15β-Hydroxy-11-dehydrocorticosterone	*Sclerotium hydrophilium*	Shirasaka and Tsuruta (1961a)

Table 27

MICROBIOLOGICAL OXIDATION OF THE 17β-OH GROUP TO THE 17-KETONE

Substrate	Product	Microorganism	Reference
Testosterone	Androst-4-ene-3,17-dione	*Proactinomyces erythropolis*	Turfitt (1946)
		Aspergillus oryzae	Kurosawa (1957)
Androst-5-ene-3β,17β-diol	Dehydroepiandrosterone	*Pseudomonas* sp.	Talalay and Dobson (1953)
19-Nortestosterone	Estrone	*Pseudomonas testosteroni* (cell-free extract)	Levy and Talalay (1957)
		Septomyxa affinis	Meeks *et al.* (1958)

Table 28

MICROBIOLOGICAL REDUCTION OF THE 17-KETO GROUP TO 17β-HYDROXY GROUP

Substrate	Product	Microorganism	Reference
Estrone	Estradiol-17β	*Corynebacterium mediolanum*	Arnaudi (1942b); Arnaudi and Ercoli (1941)
		Yeast	Mamoli (1938a); Wettstein (1939)
		Pseudomonas sp.	Eppstein *et al.* (1956)
Androst-4-ene-3,17-dione	Testosterone	*Pseudomonas* sp.	Talalay and Dobson (1953)
		Yeast	Mamoli and Vercellone (1937a)
	17β-Hydroxy-5β-androstan-3-one 5β-androstane-3α,17β-diol	*Bacillus putrificus*	Mamoli *et al.* (1939)
Dehydroepiandrosterone	Testosterone	Yeast	Koester *et al.* (1941)
	Androst-5-ene-3β,17β-diol	*Bacillus putrificus*	Mamoli *et al.* (1939); Mamoli and Vercellone (1937b)
Dehydroepiandrosterone acetate	Androst-5-ene-3β,17β-diol-3-acetate	Yeast	Mamoli (1938a, b)
5α-Androst-1-ene-3,17-dione	17β-Hydroxy-5α-androst-1-en-3-one	Yeast	Butenandt and Dannenberg (1938)
5β-Androstane-3,17-dione	17β-Hydroxy-5β-androstan-3-one	Putrefactive bacteria	Ercoli (1938); Mamoli *et al.* (1939)
	5β-Androstane-3α,17β-diol	Putrefactive bacteria	Ercoli (1938)
3,5-Cyclo-5α-androstane-6,17-dione	17β-Hydroxy-3,5-cyclo-5α-androstan-6-one	Yeast	Butenandt and Suranyi (1942)
Adrenosterone	17β-Hydroxypregn-4-ene-3,11-dione	Yeast	Herzog *et al.* (1957)

Table 29

MICROBIOLOGICAL REDUCTION OF THE 20-KETO FUNCTION TO THE 20β FORM

Substrate	Product	Microorganism	Reference
Deoxycorticosterone	20β,21-Dihydroxy-pregn-4-en-3-one	*Streptomyces* sp.	Peterson (1955)
11-Deoxycortisol	11β,17α,20β,21-Tetrahydroxypregn-4-en-23-one	*Curvularia lunata* *Streptomyces hydrogenans*	Shull (1956) Lindner *et al.* (1958)
	17α,20β,21-Trihydroxy-pregn-4-en-3-one	*Fusarium solani*	Szpilfogel *et al.* (1956a)
	17α,20β,21-Trihydroxy-pregna-1,4-dien-3-one	*Fusarium solani* *Alcaligenes* sp. *Mycobacterium lacticola* *Pseudomonas* sp. 109	Szpilfogel *et al.* (1956b) Sutter *et al.* (1957) Sutter *et al.* (1957) Uchibayashi (1960b)
	17α,20β,21-Trihydroxy-pregn-4-en-3-one	*Pseudomonas* sp. M8 *Diplodia tubericola* *Pythium ultimum*	Uchibayashi (1960b) Asai *et al.* (1961) Shirasaka and Ozaki (1961)
16α-Hydroxy-progesterone	16α,20β-Dihydroxy-pregn-4-en-3-one	*Streptomyces lavendulae*	Fried *et al.* (1955b)
Progesterone	20β-Hydroxypregn-4-en-3-one	*Streptomyces lavendulae*	Fried *et al.* (1953)
17α,21-Dihydroxy-pregna-4,6-diene-3,11,20-trione	17α,20β,21-Trihydroxy-pregna-4,6-diene-3,11-dione	*Curvularia lunata*	Gould *et al.* (1957)
Cortisol	11β,17α,20β,21-Tetrahydroxypregn-4-en-3-one	*Streptomyces hydrogenans*	Schmidt-Thomé (1957); Lindner *et al.* (1958)
11-Epicortisone	11α,17α,20β,21-Tetrahydroxypregn-4-en-3-one	*Streptomyces hydrogenans*	Lindner *et al.* (1958)
Prednisone	17α,20β,21-Trihydroxy-pregna-1,4-diene-3,11-dione		
Prednisolone	11β,17α,20β,21-Tetra-hydroxypregna-1,4-dien-3-one		
Cortisone	17α,20β,21-Trihydroxy-pregn-4-ene-3,11-dione		

Continued on following page

Table 29 (*continued*)

MICROBIOLOGICAL REDUCTION OF THE 20-KETO FUNCTION TO THE 20β FORM

Substrate	Product	Microorganism	Reference
9α-Fluoro-prednisolone	11β,17α,20β,21-Tetra-hydroxy-9α-fluoro-pregn-4-en-3-one	*Streptomyces roseochromogenes*	Smith *et al.* (1962)
Cortisol	11β,17α,20β,21-Tetrahydroxypregn-4-en-3-one	*Streptomyces hydrogenans* (purified preparation, 100-fold)	Hübener and Lehmann (1958)
17α,21-Dihydroxy-pregna-4,9(11)-diene-3,20-dione	17α,20β,21-Trihydroxy-9β,11β-epoxidopregn-4-ene-3,20-dione	*Curvularia lunata*	Shull (1956)

Table 30

MICROBIOLOGICAL REDUCTION OF THE 20-KETO FUNCTION TO THE 20α FORM

Substrate	Product	Microorganism	Reference
11-Deoxycortisol	17α,20α,21-Trihydroxy-pregn-4-en-3-one	*Rhodotorula* *Cryptococcus* *Candida* *Sporotrichum* *Stereum*	Takahashi *et al.* (1960)
Progesterone	20α-Hydroxypregn-4-en-3-one	*Rhodotorula longissima*	Chang and Idler (1961)
11β-Hydroxy-progesterone	11β,20α-Dihydroxy-pregn-4-en-3-one		
11-Ketoproge-sterone	20α-Hydroxypregn-4-ene-3,11-dione		
17α-Hydroxy-progesterone	17α,20α-Dihydroxy-pregn-4-en-3-one		
21-Deoxycortisol	11β,17α,20α-Trihydroxy-pregn-4-en-3-one		
11-Keto-17α-hydroxyprog-esterone	17α,20α-Dihydroxy-pregn-4-ene-3,11-dione		
Cortisol	11β,17α,20α,21-Tetrahydroxypregn-4-en-3-one		
Cortisone	17α,20α,21-Trihydroxy-pregn-4-ene-3,11-dione		
11-Deoxycortisol	17α,20α,21-Trihydroxy-pregn-4-en-3-one		

Table 31

MICROBIOLOGICAL REDUCTION OF THE 21-ALDO GROUP AND THE 21-ALCOHOL

Substrate	Product	Microorganism	Reference
9α-Fluoro-11β,17α-dihydroxy-21-aldopregn-4-ene-3,20-dione	9α-Fluorocortisol	*Streptomyces roseochromogenes*	Smith *et al.* (1962)

Table 32

MICROBIOLOGICAL INTRODUCTION OF THE Δ^1-DOUBLE BOND

Substrate	Product	Microorganism	Reference
Androst-4-ene-3,17-dione 5α-Androstane-3,17-dione Dehydroepiandrosterone	Androsta-1,4-diene-3,17-dione	Fusaria	Vischer and Wettstein (1953)
Dehydroepiandrosterone	Androsta-1,4-diene-3,17-dione	*Bacillus pulvifaciens*	Iizuka *et al.* (1960b)
Testosterone	1-Dehydrotestololactone	*Cylindrocarpon radicola*	Fried *et al.* (1953)
5α-Androstane-3,11,17-trione 5β-Androstane-3,11,17-trione	5α-Androst-1-ene-3,11,17-trione	*Septomyxa affinis*	Meeks *et al.* (1958)
Pregnenolone	Androsta-1,4-diene-3,17-dione	Fusaria	Vischer and Wettstein (1953)
	Pregna-1,4-diene-3,20-dione	*Bacillus pulvifaciens*	Iizuka *et al.* (1960a)
19-Nortestosterone	Estrone	*Pseudomonas testosteroni* (cell-free extract)	Levy and Talalay (1957)
		Septomyxa affinis	Meeks *et al.* (1958)
	Estradiol-17β	*Septomyxa affinis*	Meeks *et al.* (1958)
Deoxycorticosterone acetate	21-Hydroxypregna-1,4-diene-3,20-dione	*Corynebacterium simplex*	Nobile *et al.* (1955)
		Calonectria decora	Vischer *et al.* (1955)
Deoxycorticosterone	Androsta-1,4-diene-3,17-dione	Fusaria	Vischer and Wettstein (1953)

Continued on following page

Table 32 (*continued*)

MICROBIOLOGICAL INTRODUCTION OF THE Δ^1-DOUBLE BOND

Substrate	Product	Microorganism	Reference
	21-Hydroxypregna-1,4-diene-3,20-dione	*Gliocladium roseum* *Helminthosporium turcicum* *Ophiobolus heterostropus*	Shirasaka and Tsurata (1961a)
19-Norprogesterone	17β-Acetylestra-1,3,5(10)-trien-3-ol	*Corynebacterium simplex*	Bowers *et al.* (1958)
Progesterone	1-Dehydrotestololactone	*Cylindrocarpon radicola*	Fried *et al.* (1953)
		Fusarium solani	Nishikawa *et al.* (1956)
	1-Dehydroprogesterone	*Calonectria decora*	Vischer *et al.* (1955)
		Fusarium solani	Nishikawa *et al.* (1956)
	1-Dehydrotestosterone	*Streptomyces lavendulae*	Fried *et al.* (1953)
		Fusarium solani	Nishikawa *et al.* (1956)
	Androsta-1,4-diene-3,17-dione	Fusaria	Vischer and Wettstein (1953); Nishikawa *et al.* (1956)
Corticosterone	1-Dehydrocorticosterone	*Corynebacterium simplex*	Nobile *et al.* (1955)
		Calonectria decora	Vischer *et al.* (1955)
		Gliocladium roseum *Helminthosporium turcicum* *Ophiobolus heterostropus*	Shirasaka and Tsuruta (1961a)
11-Deoxycortisol	1-Dehydro-11-deoxycortisol	*Corynebacterium simplex*	Nobile *et al.* (1955)
		Fusarium solani	Vischer *et al.* (1955)
	17α,20β,21-Trihydroxypregna-1,4-dien-3-one	*Fusarium solani*	Szpilfogel *et al.* (1956a)
	17α,21-Dihydroxypregna-1,4-diene-3,20-dione	*Pseudomonas* sp. 125	Uchibayashi (1960b)
		Pseudomonas	Iizuka *et al.* (1959)
		Gloeosporium olivarum	Kondo and Masuo (1960)

Continued on following page

Table 32 (*continued*)
MICROBIOLOGICAL INTRODUCTION OF THE Δ^1-DOUBLE BOND

Substrate	Product	Microorganism	Reference
		Helminthosporium zizania (H-4)	Kondo (1960)
		H. gramineum (H-32)	Kondo (1960)
		Corticium solani	Hasegawa and Takahashi (1958)
		Bacillus pulvifaciens	Iizuka *et al.* (1960b)
		Gliocladium roseum	Shirasaka and Tsuruta (1961a)
		Helminthosporium turcicum	
		Ophiobolus heterostropus	
	1-Dehydrotestolo-lactone	*Cylindrocarpon radicola*	Fried *et al.* (1953)
	Prednisolone	*Pseudomonas* mutant sp. 109	Uchibayashi (1960a, c)
5α-Pregnane-3,20-dione	Androst-1,4-diene-3,17-dione	Fusaria	Vischer and Wettstein (1953)
3β-Hydroxy-5α-pregnan-20-one-3-acetate			
6-Dehydrocortisol	11β,17α,21-Trihydroxy-pregna-1,4,6-triene-3,20-dione	*Bacillus sphaericus*	Gould *et al.* (1957)
6-Dehydrocortisone	17α,21-Dihydroxypregna 1,4,6-triene-3,11,20-trione		
2α-Methyl-19-nortestosterone	2-Methylestrone	*Septomyxa affinis*	Peterson (1960)
Cortisone	Prednisone	*Corynebacterium simplex*	Nobile *et al.* (1955)
		Fusarium solani	Vischer *et al.* (1955)
		Gliocladium roseum	Shirasaka and Tsuruta (1961a)
		Helminthosporium turcicum	
		Ophiobolus heterostropus	

Continued on following page

Table 32 (*continued*)

MICROBIOLOGICAL INTRODUCTION OF THE Δ^1-DOUBLE BOND

Substrate	Product	Microorganism	Reference
9α-Fluorocortisol	9α-Fluoroprednisolone	*Corynebacterium simplex*	Nobile *et al.* (1955)
Cortisol	Prednisolone	*Corynebacterium simplex*	Nobile *et al.* (1955)
		Bacillus pulvifaciens	Iizuka *et al.* (1960b)
		Flavobacterium *Micrococcus*	Isono and Abe (1959)
Androst-4-ene-3,17-dione	Androsta-1,4-diene-3,17-dione	*Nocardia restrictus* (cell-free preparation)	Sih (1961)
Cortisone	Prednisone		
Corticosterone	17α,21-Dihydroxypregna-1,4-diene-3,20-dione		
9α-Fluorocortisol	9α-Fluoroprednisolone		
9α-Fluoro-16α-hydroxycortisol	Triamcinolone		
Androst-4-ene-3,17-dione	Androsta-1,4-diene-3,17-dione	*Pseudomonas testosteroni*	Levy and Talalay (1957)
Testosterone	17α-Hydroxyandrosta-1,4-dien-3-one		
Testosterone Androst-4-ene-3,17-dione	Androsta-1,4-diene-3,17-dione	*Bacillus sphaericus*	Hayano *et al.* (1961)
5α-Androstane-3,17-dione	5α-Androst-1-ene-3,17-dione		
17β-Hydroxy-5α-androstan-3-one			
1β-Methyl-17β-hydroxy-5α-androstan-3-one	1-Methylandrost-1-ene 3,17-dione		
2α-Methyltestosterone	2-Methylandrosta-1,4-diene-3,17-dione		
2α-Hydroxytestosterone	2-Hydroxyandrosta-1,4-diene-3,17-dione		

Table 33

MICROBIOLOGICAL CONVERSION OF C_{21} TO C_{19} STEROIDS (WITH RING D LACTONE FORMATION) AND CONVERSION OF C_{19} STEROIDS TO RING D LACTONES

Substrate	Product	Microorganism	Reference
Progesterone	Testololactone	*Mucor mucedo*	Peterson *et al.* (1953a)
		Penicillium chrysogenum	Peterson *et al.* (1953a)
		Aspergilli	Fried *et al.* (1953); Peterson *et al.* (1953a)
		Penicillia	Fried *et al.* (1953); Peterson *et al.* (1953a)
		Cylindrocarpon radicola	Fried *et al.* (1953)
		Fusarium caucasicum	Eppstein *et al.* (1956)
		Pythium ultimum	Shirasaka and Tsuruta (1961a)
	1-Dehydrotestololactone	*Fusarium solani*	Nishikawa *et al.* (1956); Szpilfogel *et al.* (1956a)
Testosterone	1-Dehydrotestololactone	*Cylindrocarpon radicola*	Fried *et al.* (1953)
	Testololactone	Aspergilli	Peterson *et al.* (1953a)
		Penicillia	Peterson *et al.* (1953a)
Androst-4-ene-3,17-dione	Testololactone	Aspergilli	Peterson *et al.* (1953a)
		Penicillia	Peterson *et al.* (1953a)
		Pythium ultimum	Shirasaka and Ozaki (1961)
11-Deoxycortisol	1-Dehydrotestololactone	*Cylindrocarpon radicola*	Fried *et al.* (1953)
	Testololactone	Aspergilli	Peterson *et al.* (1953a)
		Penicillia	Peterson *et al.* (1953a)
17α-Hydroxyprogesterone	Testololactone	Aspergilli	Peterson *et al.* (1953a)
		Pythium ultimum	Shirasaka and Ozaki (1961)
		Penicillia	Peterson *et al.* (1953a)
Deoxycorticosterone	Testololactone	Aspergilli	Peterson *et al.* (1953a)
		Penicillia	Peterson *et al.* (1953a)
		Pythium ultimum	Shirasaka and Ozaki (1961)

Table 34

MICROBIOLOGICAL CONVERSION OF C_{21} TO C_{19} STEROIDS (NO LACTONE FORMATION)

Substrate	Product	Microorganism	References
Progesterone	1-Dehydrotestosterone	*Streptomyces lavendulae*	Fried *et al.* (1953)
		Fusarium solani	Nishikawa *et al.* (1956); Szpilfogel *et al.* (1956a)
	Androst-4-ene-3,17-dione	Gliocladia Aspergilli Penicillia	Peterson *et al.* (1953a)
		Pseudomonas sp.	Talalay and Dobson (1953)
		Fusarium solani	Szpilfogel *et al.* (1956a)
	6β-Hydroxyandrost-4-ene-3,17-dione	*Gliocladium catenulatum*	Peterson *et al.* (1953a)
	Androsta-1.4-diene-3,17-dione	*Streptomyces lavendulae*	Fried *et al.* (1953)
		Fusaria	Vischer and Wettstein (1953)
		Fusarium solani	Nishikawa *et al.* (1956)
14α-Hydroxy-progesterone	14α-Hydroxyandrost-4-ene-3,17-dione	*Penicillium lilacinum*	Meister *et al.* (1953c); Eppstein *et al.* (1956)
16α-Hydroxy-progesterone	16α-Hydroxytesto-sterone	*Streptomyces lavendulae*	Fried *et al.* (1955b)
Pregnenolone	Dehydroepiandrosterone	*Fusarium solani*	Vischer and Wettstein (1953)
	Androsta-1,4-diene-3,17-dione	Fusaria	Vischer and Wettstein (1953)
Deoxycorticosterone	Androst-4-ene-3,17-dione	Aspergilli Penicillia	Peterson *et al.* (1953a) Peterson *et al.* (1953a)
	Androsta-1,4-diene-3,17-dione	Fusaria	Vischer and Wettstein (1953)
11-Deoxycortisol	Androst-4-ene,17-dione	Aspergilli Penicillia	Peterson *et al.* (1953a)
5α-Pregnane-3,20-dione	5α-Androstane-3,17-dione	Fusaria	Vischer and Wettstein (1953)
3β-Hydroxy-5α-pregnan-20-one-	5α-Androstane-3,17-dione		

Continued on following page

Table 34 (*continued*)

MICROBIOLOGICAL CONVERSIONS OF C_{21} TO C_{19} STEROIDS (NO LACTONE FORMATION)

Substrate	Product	Microorganism	Reference
Progesterone	Androst-1,4-diene-3,17-dione		
11-Ketoprogesterone	11-Ketotestosterone	*Penicillium citrinum*, also *P. notatum*, *P. decumbens*	Hanc *et al.* (1957b)
11α-Hydroxyprogesterone	11α-Hydroxytestosterone		
Progesterone	Testosterone		
Progesterone	Testosterone acetate Testosterone		Fonken *et al.* (1960)

Table 35

MICROBIOLOGICAL ACETYLATION OF STEROIDS

Substrate	Product	Microorganism	Reference
9α-Fluoro-11β,21-dihydroxy-16α,17α-isopropylidenedioxypregn-4-ene-3,20-dione	21-Acetate of substrate	*Trichoderma glaucum*	Holmund *et al.* (1961)

Table 36

MICROBIOLOGICAL DEACETYLATION

Substrate	Product	Microorganism	Reference
Cortisol 11β,21-diacetate	Cortisol	*Flavobacterium dehydrogenans* var. *hydrolyticum*	Charney *et al.* (1959)
Dehydroepiandrosterone acetate	Testosterone	*Streptomyces globisporus* and *S. vividochromogenes*	Hanc *et al.* (1957a)

Table 37

MICROBIOLOGICAL EPOXIDATION OF UNSATURATED STEROIDS

Substrate	Product	Microorganism	Reference
17α,21-Dihydroxypregna-4,9(11)-diene-3,20-dione	17α,21-Dihydroxy-9β,11β-epoxidopregn-4-ene-3,20-dione	*Curvularia* sp. *Curvularia lunata*	Kurosawa *et al.* (1961a)
Pregna-4,11-diene 3,20-dione	11β,12β-Epoxidoprogesterone	*Curvularia lunata*	Kurosawa *et al.* (1961a)
17α,21-Dihydroxypregna-4,9(11)-diene-3,20-dione	17α,21-Dihydroxy-9β,11β-epoxidopregn-4-ene-3,20-dione	*Curvularia lunata*	Bloom and Shull (1955); Shull (1956)
17α,21-Dihydroxypregna-4,14-diene-3,20-dione	17α,21-Dihydroxy-14α,15α-epoxidopregn-4-ene-3,20-dione	*Curvularia lunata* *Cunninghamella blakesleeana* *Helicostylum piriforme*	

Table 38

MICROBIOLOGICAL OXIDATIVE FORMATION OF SECO COMPOUNDS

Substrate	Product	Microorganism	Reference
Progesterone	7α-Methyl-1-acetyl-perhydroindanon-(5)-[β-propionic acid-(4)]	*Mycobacterium smegmatis*	Schubert *et al.* (1961)
Dehydroepiandrosterone Androst-4-ene-3,17-dione	9,10-Seco-3-hydroxyandrosta-1,3,5(10)-triene-9,17-dione	*Mycobacterium smegmatis*	Schubert *et al.* (1960b)
Androsta-1,4-diene-3,17-dione	9,10-Seco-3,9-dihydroxyandrosta-1,3,5(10)-trien-17-one		
Androst-4-ene-3,17-dione	9,10-Seco-3-hydroxyandrosta-1,3,5(10)-trien-17-one	*Pseudomonas*	Dodson and Muir (1958)
Androst-4-ene-3,17-dione	9,10-Seco-3-hydroxyandrosta-1,3,5(10)-triene-3,17-dione	*Mycobacterium smegmatis* *M. fortuitum* *M. tuberculosis*	Schubert *et al.* (1960a)

Table 39

MISCELLANEOUS MICROBIOLOGICAL REACTIONS

Substrate	Product	Microorganism	Reference
16α,17α-Epoxido-progesterone	17β-Methyl-16α,20α-dihydroxy-18-norpregna-4,13-diene-3-one	Fermenting yeast	Camerino and Vercellone (1956); Camerino and Modelli (1956)
16α,17α-Epoxido-pregnenolone	17β-Methyl-3β,16α-20α-trihydroxy-18-norpregna-5,13-diene		

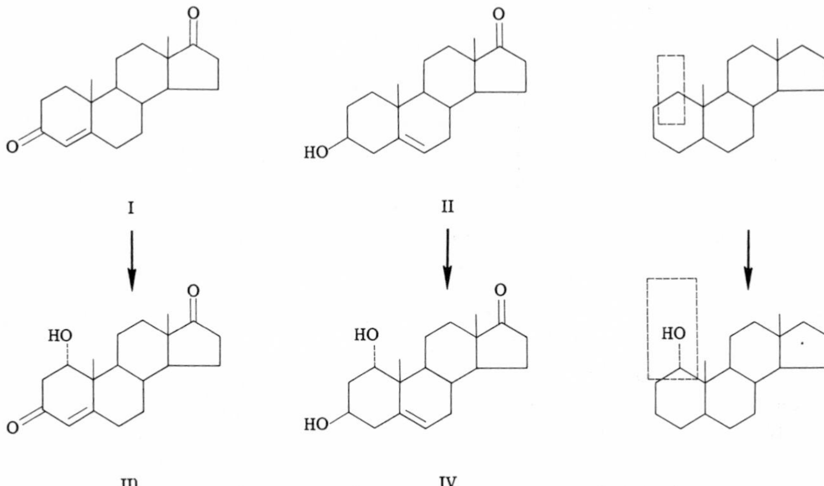

FIG. 1. Typical microbiological 1α-hydroxylation reaction.

I. Androst-4-ene-3,17-dione
II. Dehydroepiandrosterone
III. 1α-Hydroxylandrost-4-ene-3,17-dione
IV. 1α,3β-Dihydroxyandrost-5-en-17-one

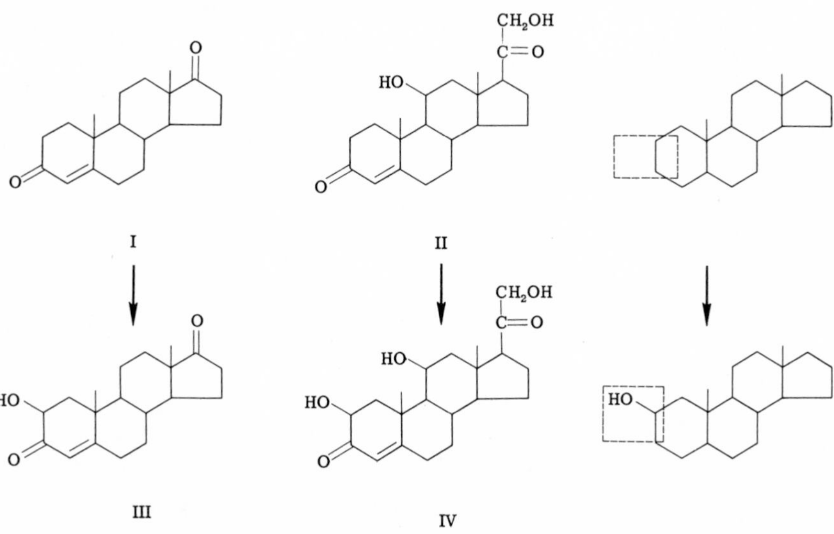

FIG. 2. Typical microbiological 2β-hydroxylation reaction.

I. Androst-4-ene-3,17-dione
II. Corticosterone
III. 2β-Hydroxyandrost-4-ene-3,17-dione
IV. 2β,11β,21-Trihydroxypregn-4-ene-3, 20-dione

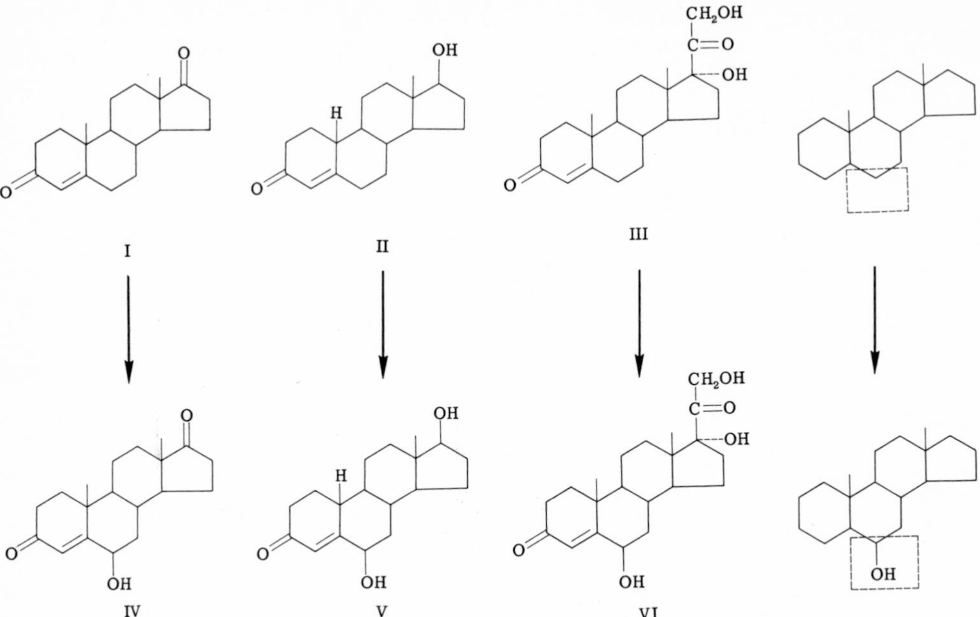

FIG. 3. Typical microbiological 6β-hydroxylation reaction.

I. Androst-4-ene-3,17-dione
II. 19-Nortestosterone
III. 11-Deoxycortisol
IV. 6β-Hydroxyandrost-4-ene-3,17-dione
V. 6β,17β-Dihydroxy-19-norandrost-4-en-3-one
VI. 6β,17α,21-Trihydroxypregn-4-ene-3,20-dione

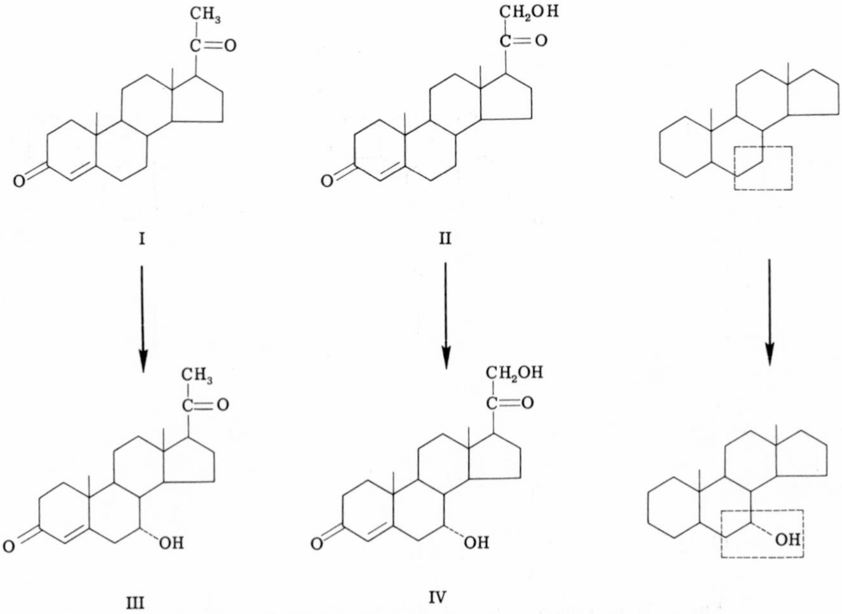

FIG. 4. Typical microbiological 7α-hydroxylation reaction.

I. Progesterone
II. Deoxycorticosterone
III. 7α-Hydroxypregn-4-ene-3,20-dione
IV. 7α,21-Dihydroxypregn-4-ene-3,20-dione

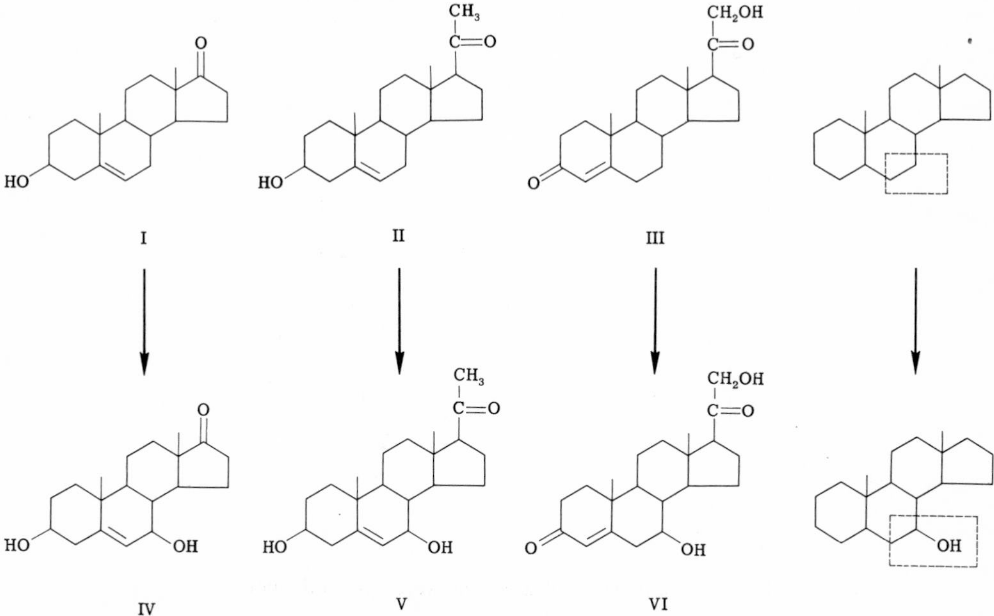

FIG. 5. Typical microbiological 7β-hydroxylation reaction.

I. Dehydroepiandrosterone
II. Pregnenolone
III. Deoxycorticosterone
IV. 3β,7β-Dihydroxyandrost-5-en-17-one
V. 3β,7β-Dihydroxypregn-5-en-20-one
VI. 7β,21-Dihydroxypregn-4-ene-3,20-dione

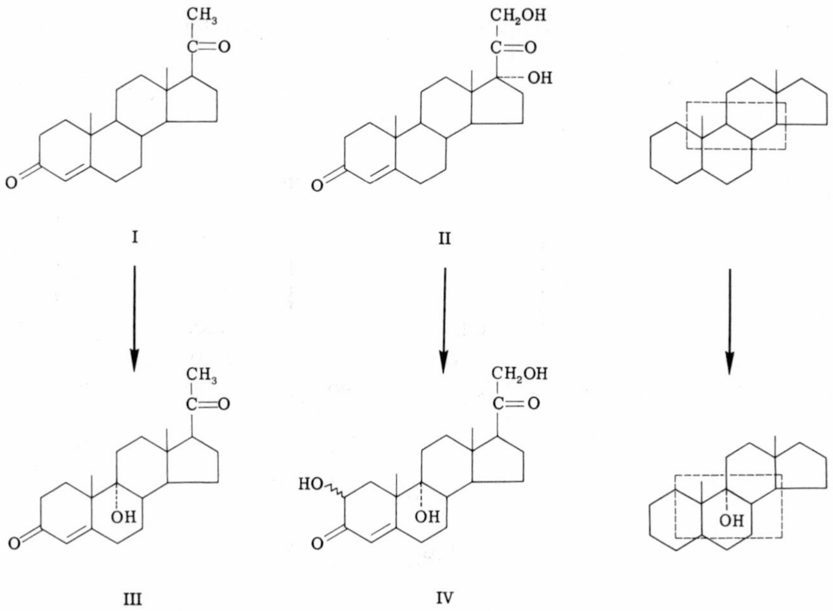

FIG. 6. Typical microbiological 9α-hydroxylation reaction.

I. Progesterone
II. 11-Deoxycortisol
III. 9α-Hydroxypregn-4-ene-3,20-dione
IV. 2ξ,9α,21-Trihydroxypregn-4-ene-3,20-dione

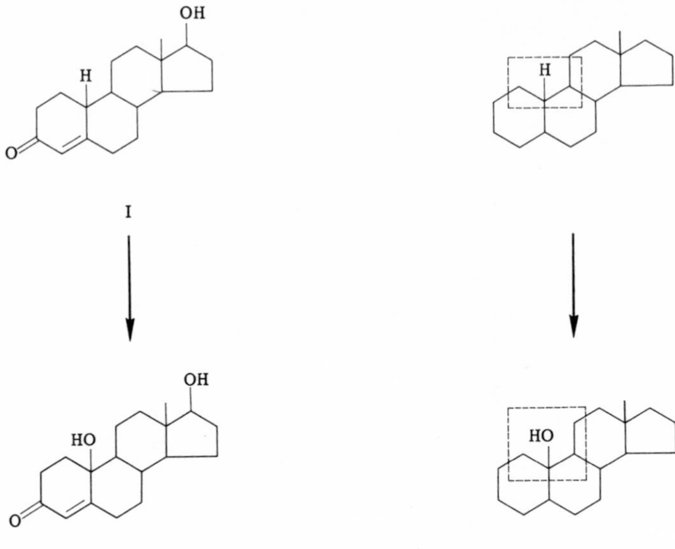

FIG. 7. Typical microbiological 10β-hydroxylation reaction.

I. 19-Nortestosterone II. 10β-17β-Dihydroxyandrost-4-en-17-one

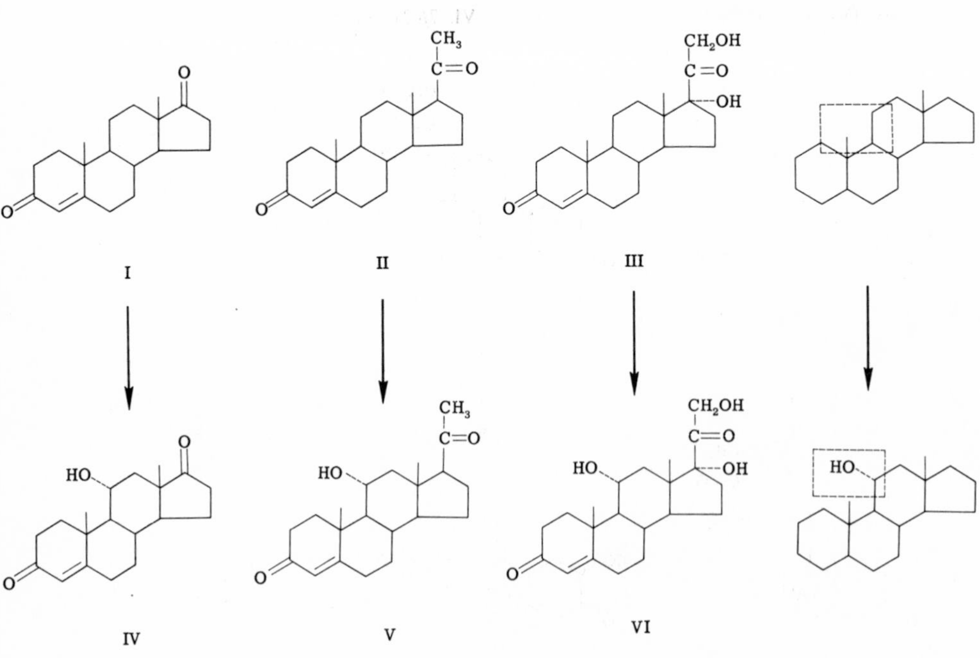

FIG. 8. Typical microbiological 11α-hydroxylation reaction.

I. Androst-4-ene-3,17-dione
II. Progesterone
III. 11-Deoxycortisol
IV. 11α-Hydroxyandrost-4-ene-3,17-dione
V. 11α-Hydroxypregn-4-ene-3,20-dione
VI. 11α,17α,21-Trihydroxypregn-4-ene-3,20-dione

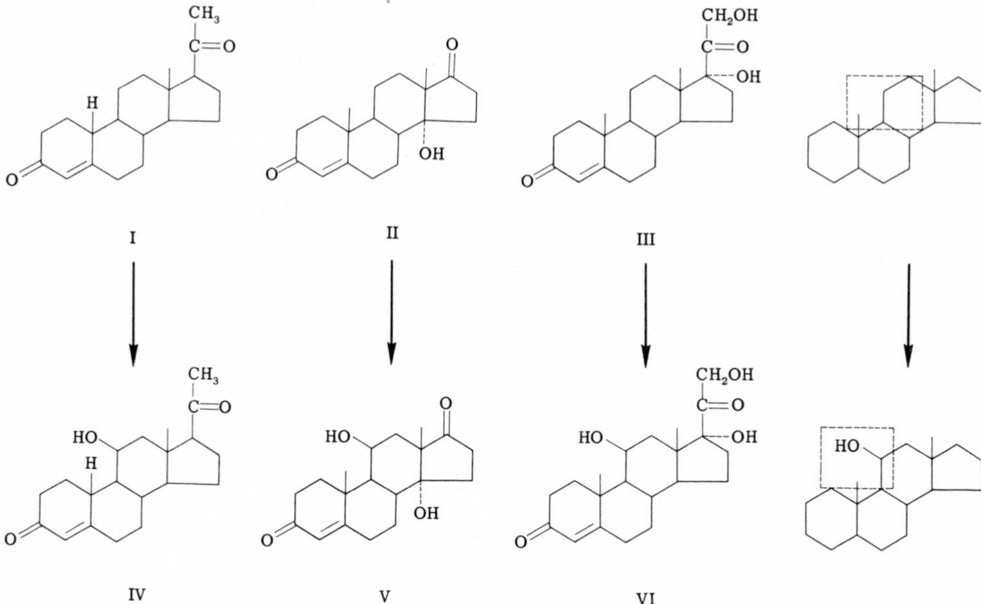

FIG. 9. Typical microbiological 11β-hydroxylation reaction.

I. 19-Norprogesterone
II. 14α-Hydroxyandrost-4-ene-3,17-dione
III. 11-Deoxycortisol
IV. 11β-Hydroxy-19-norpregn-4-ene-3,20-dione
V. 11β,14α-Dihydroxyandrost-4-ene-3,17-dione
VI. Cortisol

FIG. 10. Typical microbiological 12β-hydroxylation reaction.

I. Progesterone
II. 5β-Pregnane-3,20-dione
III. Pregnenolone
IV. 12β-Hydroxypregn-4-ene-3,20-dione
V. 12β-Hydroxy-5β-pregnane-3,20-dione
VI. 3β,12β-Dihydroxypregn-5-en-20-one

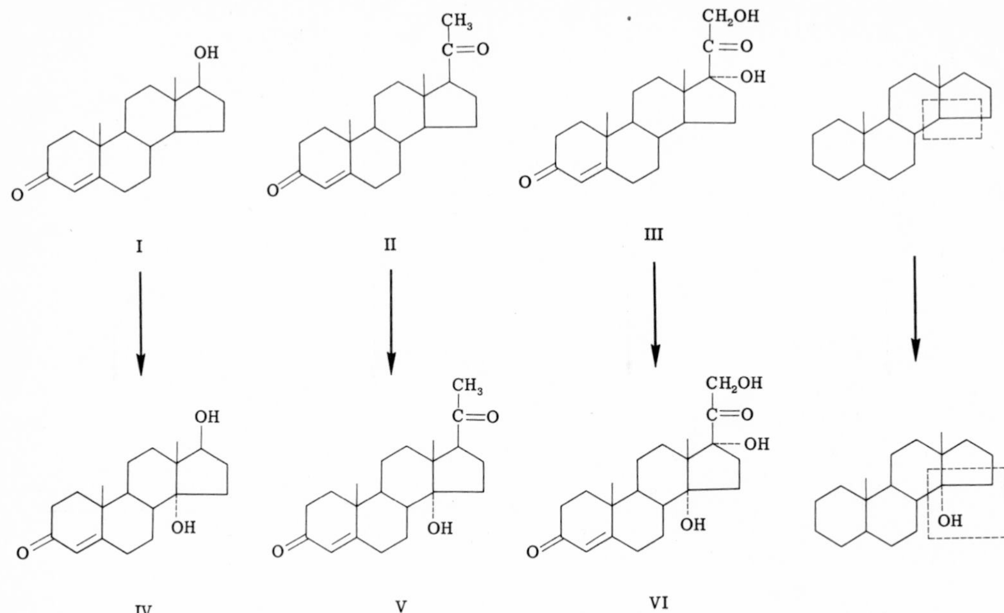

FIG. 11. Typical microbiological 14α-hydroxylation reaction.

I. Testosterone
II. Progesterone
III. 11-Deoxycortisol
IV. 14α,17β-Dihydroxyandrost-4-en-3-one
V. 14α-Hydroxypregn-4-ene-3,20-dione
VI. 14α,17α,21-Trihydroxypregn-4-ene-3,20-dione

OH CH3 C=O CH2OH C=O OH O
I II III
IV V VI

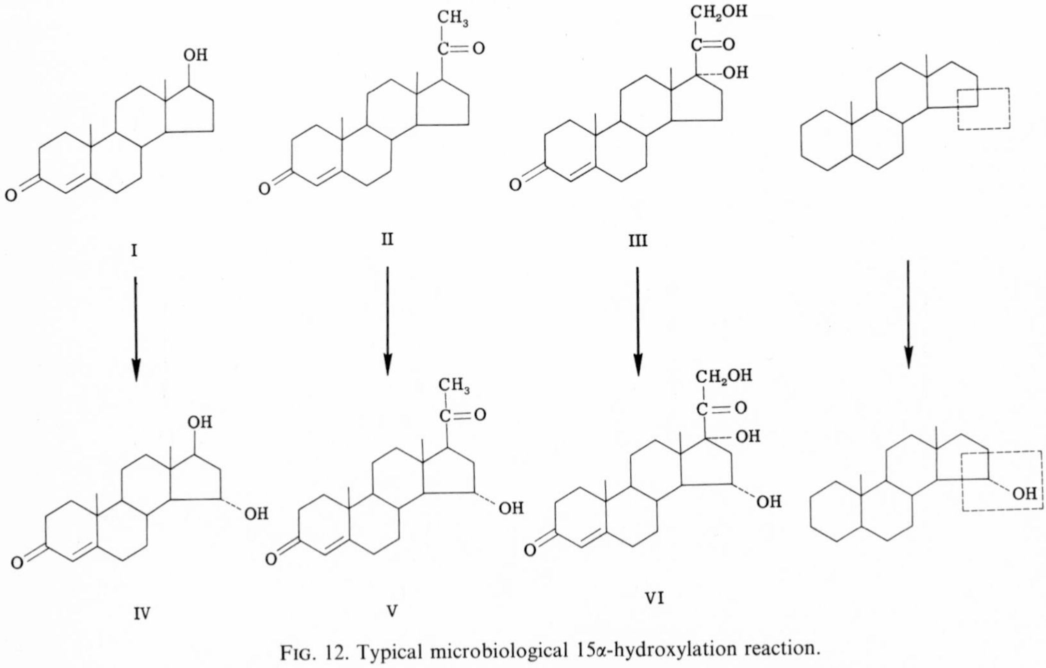

FIG. 12. Typical microbiological 15α-hydroxylation reaction.

I. Testosterone
II. Progesterone
III. 11-Deoxycortisol
IV. 15α,17β-Dihydroxyandrost-4-en-3-one
V. 15α-Hydroxypregn-4-ene-3,20-dione
VI. 15α,17α,21-Trihydroxypregn-4-ene-3,20-dione

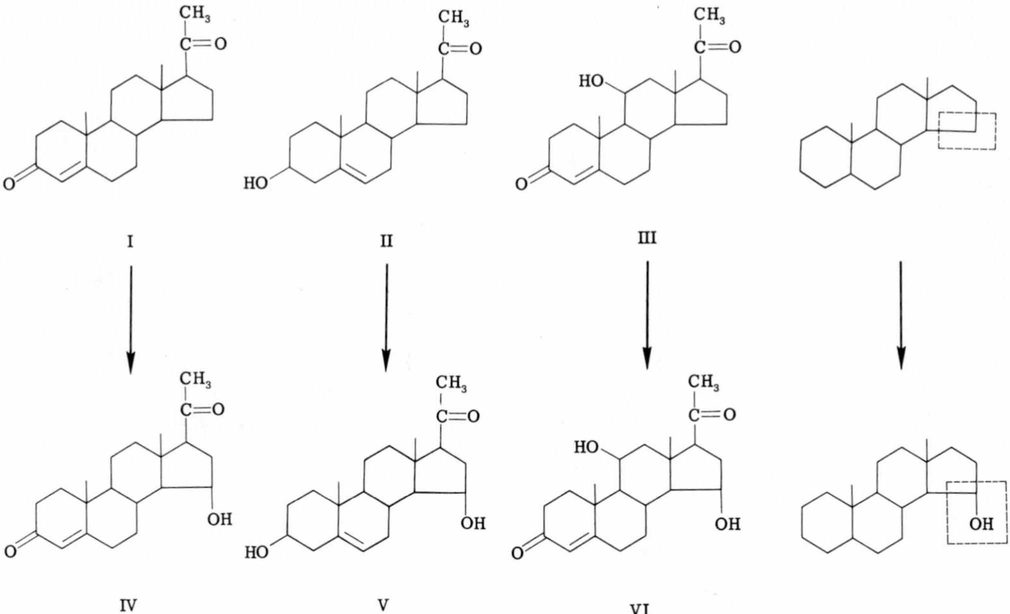

FIG. 13. Typical microbiological 15β-hydroxylation reaction.

I. Progesterone
II. Pregnenolone
III. 21-Deoxycortisol

IV. 15β-Hydroxypregn-4-ene-3,20-dione
V. 3β,15β-Dihydroxypregn-5-en-20-one
VI. 11β,15β-Dihydroxypregn-4-ene-3,20-dione

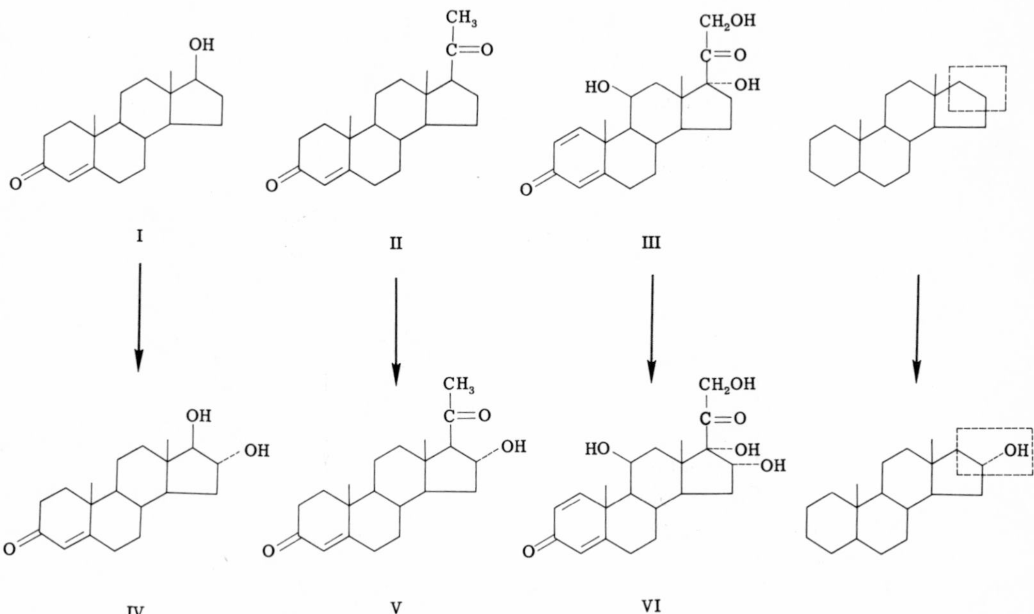

FIG. 14. Typical microbiological 16α-hydroxylation reaction.

I. Testosterone
II. Progesterone
III. Prednisolone

IV. 16α,17β-Dihydroxyandrost-4-en-3-one
V. 16α-Hydroxypregn-4-ene-3,20-dione
VI. 11β,16α,17α,21-Tetrahydroxypregna-1,4-diene-3,20-dione

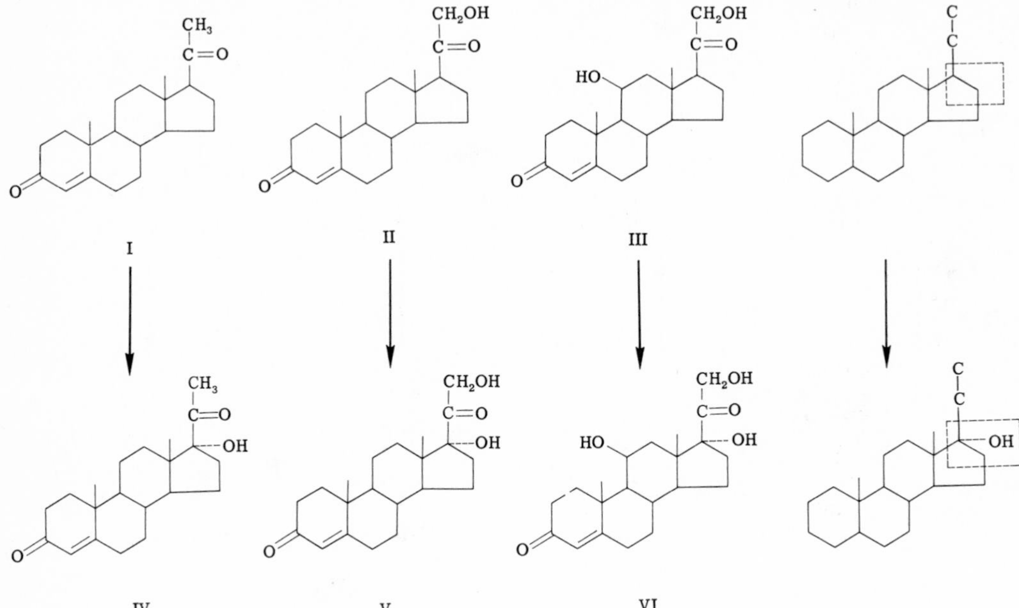

FIG. 15. Typical microbiological 17α-hydroxylation reaction.

I. Progesterone
II. Deoxycorticosterone
III. Corticosterone
IV. 17α-Hydroxyprogesterone
V. 11-Deoxycortisol
VI. Cortisol

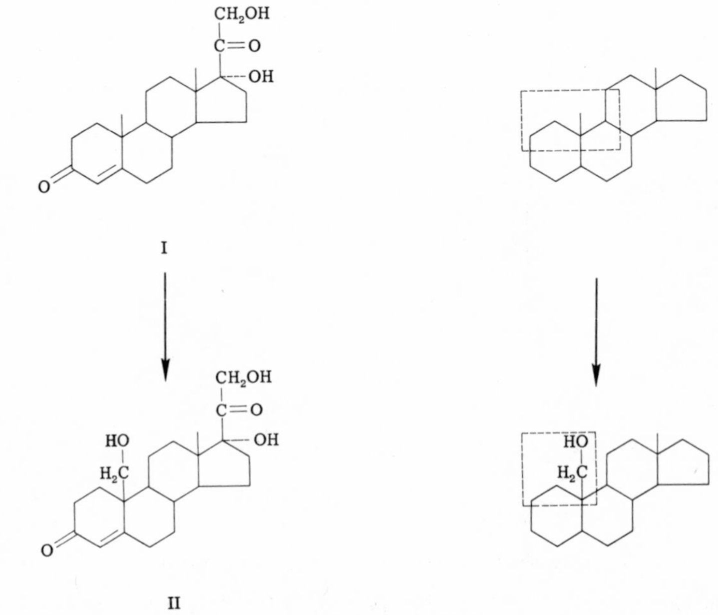

FIG. 16. Typical microbiological 19 hydroxylation reaction.

I. 11-Deoxycortisol
II. 17α,19,21-Trihydroxypregn-4-ene-3,20-dione

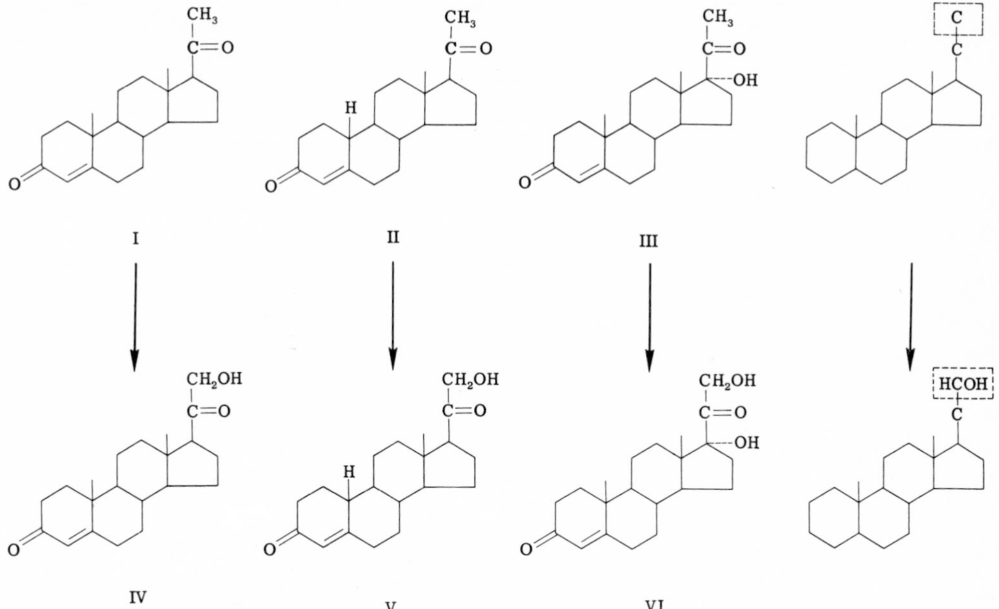

FIG. 17. Typical microbiological 21 hydroxylation reaction.

I. Progesterone
II. 19-Norprogesterone
III. 17α-Hydroxyprogesterone
IV. Deoxycortisol
V. 21-Hydroxy-19-norpregn-4-ene-3,20-dione
VI. 11-Deoxycortisol

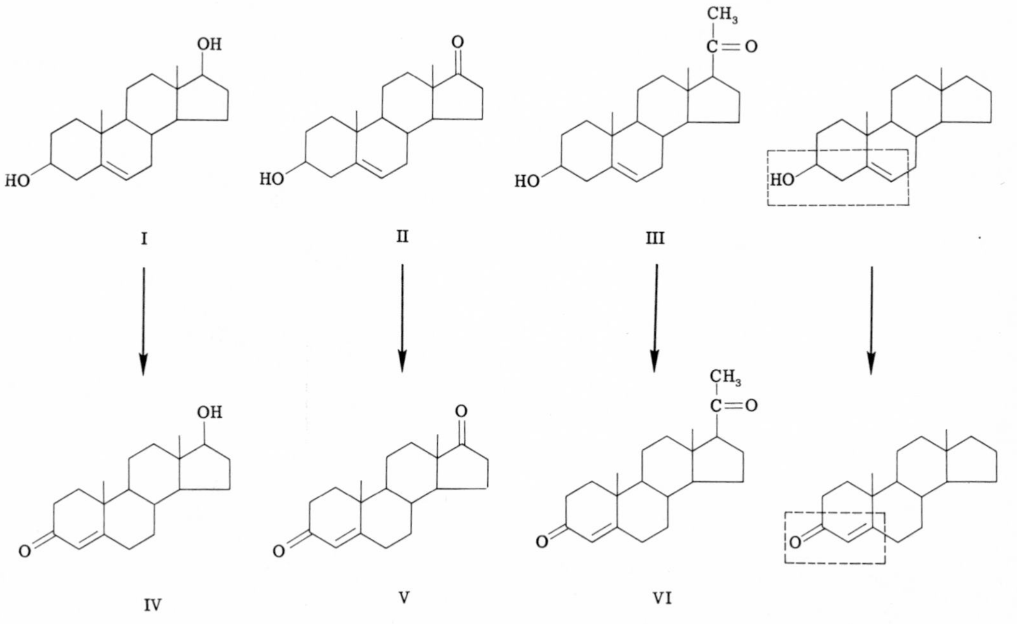

FIG. 18. Typical microbiological conversion of the Δ^5-3β-OH to the Δ^4-3-C=O group.

I. Androst-5-ene-3β,17β-diol
II. Dehydroepiandrosterone
III. Pregnenolone
IV. Testosterone
V. Androst-4-ene-3,17-dione
VI. Progesterone

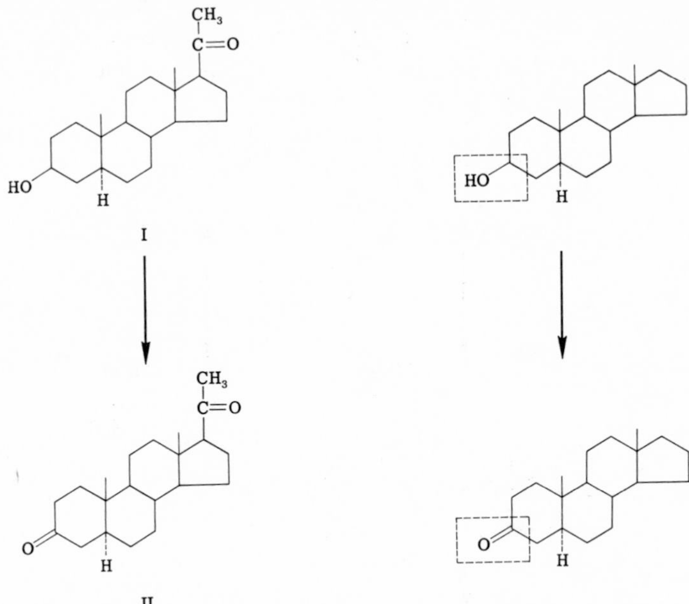

FIG. 19. Typical microbiological conversion of the 3β-OH to the 3-C=O group.

I. 3β-Hydroxy-5α-pregnan-3-one II. 5α-Pregnane-3,20-dione

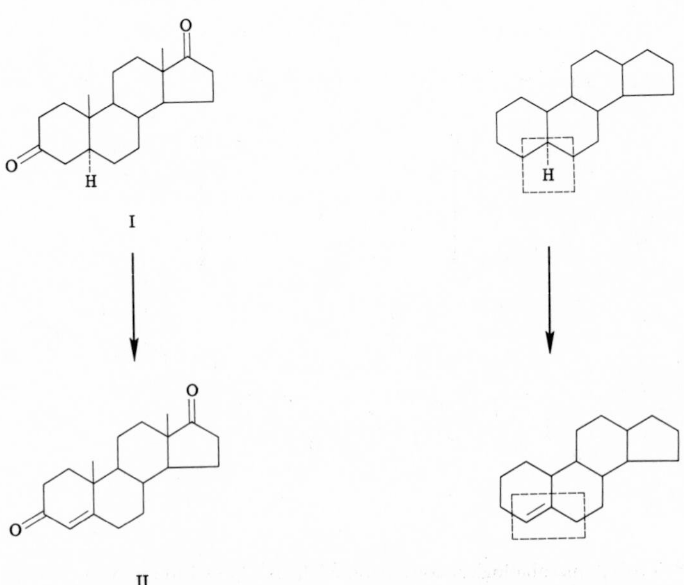

FIG. 20. Typical microbiological conversion of a 5α- to a Δ^4-steroid.

I. 5α-Androstane-3,17-dione II. Androst-4-ene-3,17-dione

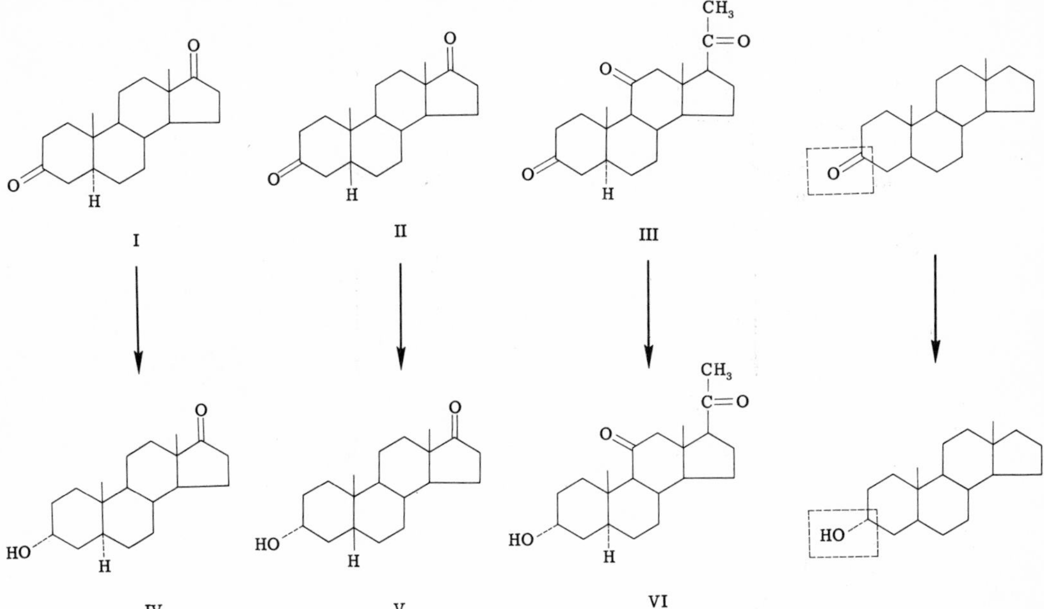

FIG. 21. Typical microbiological conversion of the 3-C=O to the 3α-OH group.

I. 5α-Androstane-3,17-dione
II. 5β-Androstane-3,17-dione
III. 5α-Pregnane-3,11,20-trione
IV. Androsterone
V. 5β-Androsterone
VI. 3α-Hydroxy-5α-pregnane-11,20-dione

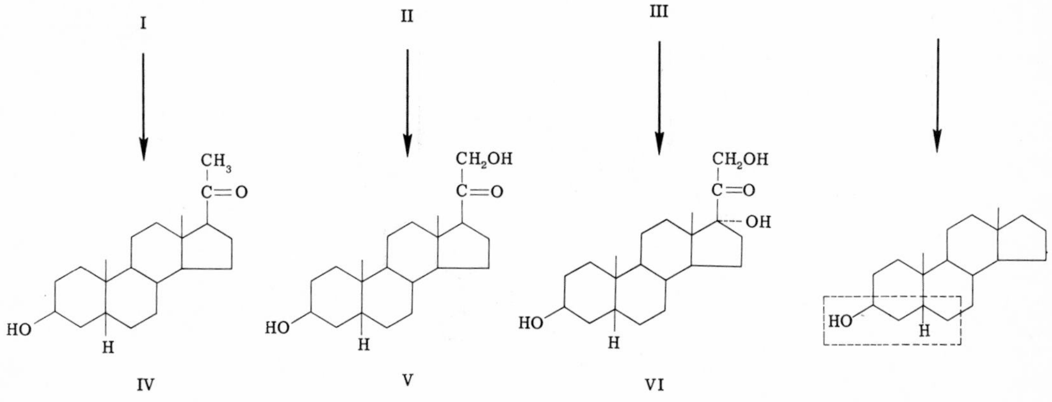

FIG. 22. Typical microbiological conversion of the 3-C=O to the 3β-OH group.

I. Progesterone
II. Deoxycorticosterone
III. 11-Deoxycortisol
IV. 3β-Hydroxy-5β-pregnan-20-one
V. 3β,21-Dihydroxy-5β-pregnan-20-one
VI. 3β,17α,21-Trihydroxy-5β-pregnan-20-one

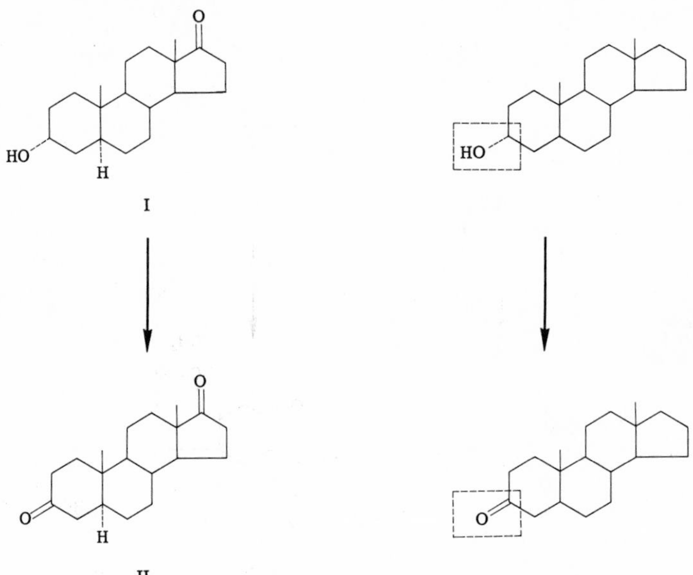

FIG. 23. Typical microbiological conversion of the 3α-OH to the 3-C=O group.

I. Androsterone II. 5α-Androstane-3,17-dione

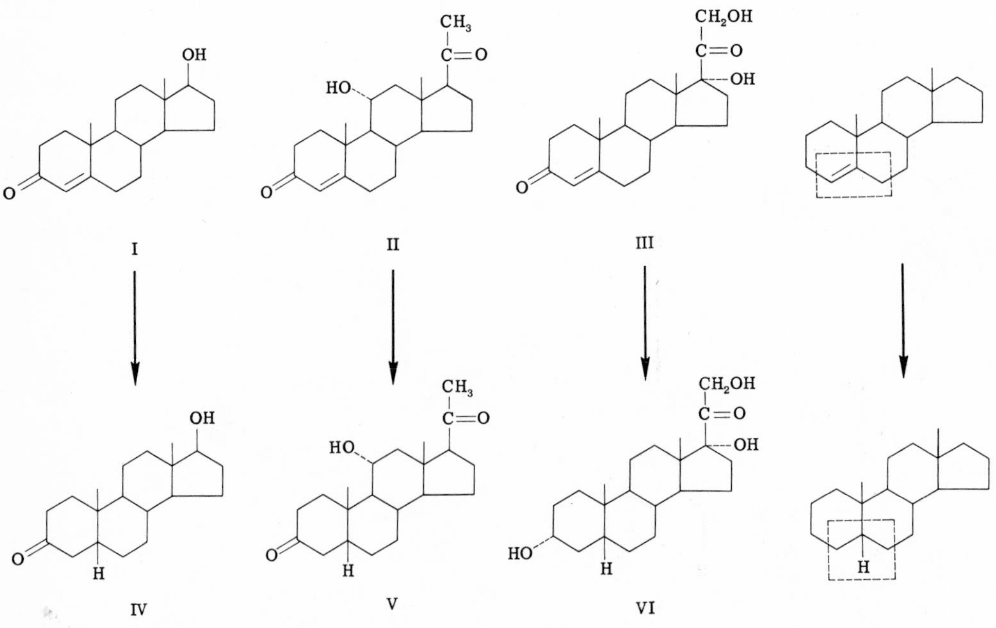

FIG. 24. Typical microbiological conversion of the Δ^4-group to the 5β group.

I. Testosterone
II. 11α-Hydroxypregn-4-ene-3,20-dione
III. 11-Deoxycortisol
IV. 17β-Hydroxy-5β-androstan-3-one
V. 11α-Hydroxy-5β-pregn-ane-3,20-dione
VI. 3α,17α,21-Trihydroxy-5β-pregnan-20-one

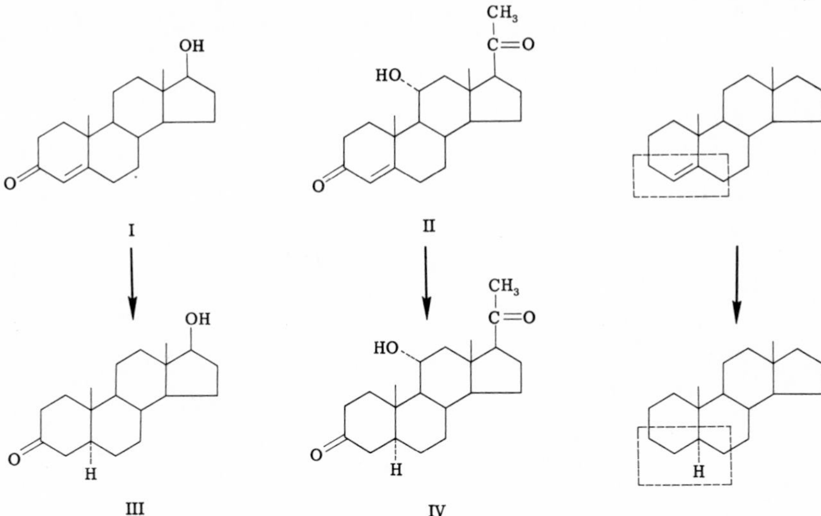

FIG. 25. Typical microbiological conversion of the Δ^4-group to the 5α group.

I. Testosterone
II. 11α-Hydroxypregn-4-ene-3,20-dione
III. 17β-Hydroxy-5α-androstan-3-one
IV. 11α-Hydroxypregnane-3,20-dione

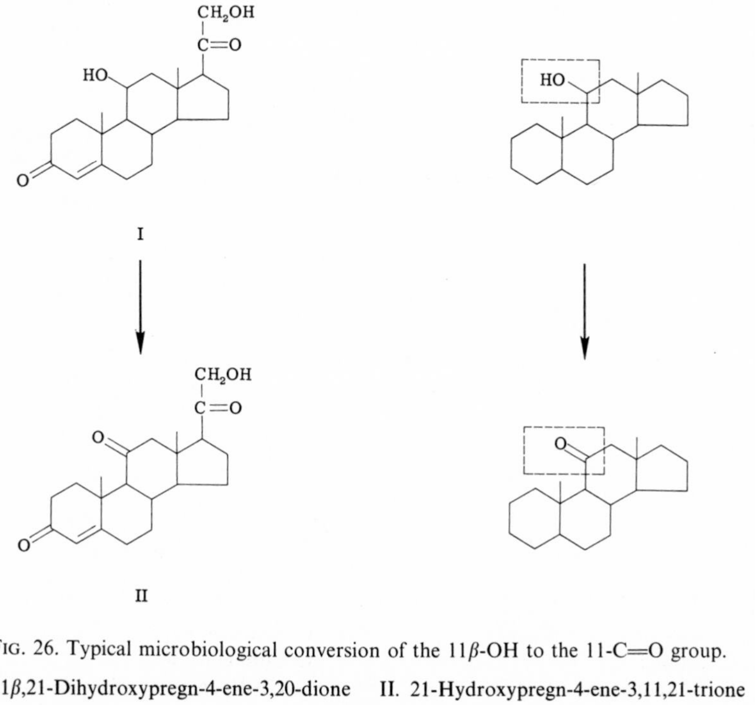

FIG. 26. Typical microbiological conversion of the 11β-OH to the 11-C=O group.

I. 11β,21-Dihydroxypregn-4-ene-3,20-dione
II. 21-Hydroxypregn-4-ene-3,11,21-trione

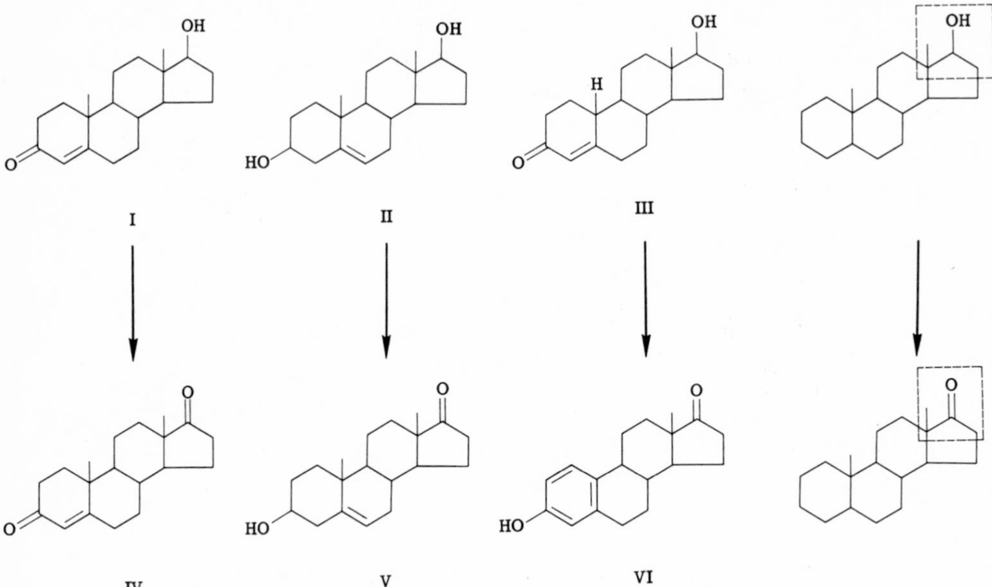

FIG. 27. Typical microbiological conversion of the 17β-OH to the 17-C=O group.

I. Testosterone
II. Androst-5-ene-3β,17β-diol
III. 19-Nortestosterone
IV. Androst-4-ene-3,17-dione
V. Dehydroepiandrosterone
VI. Estrone

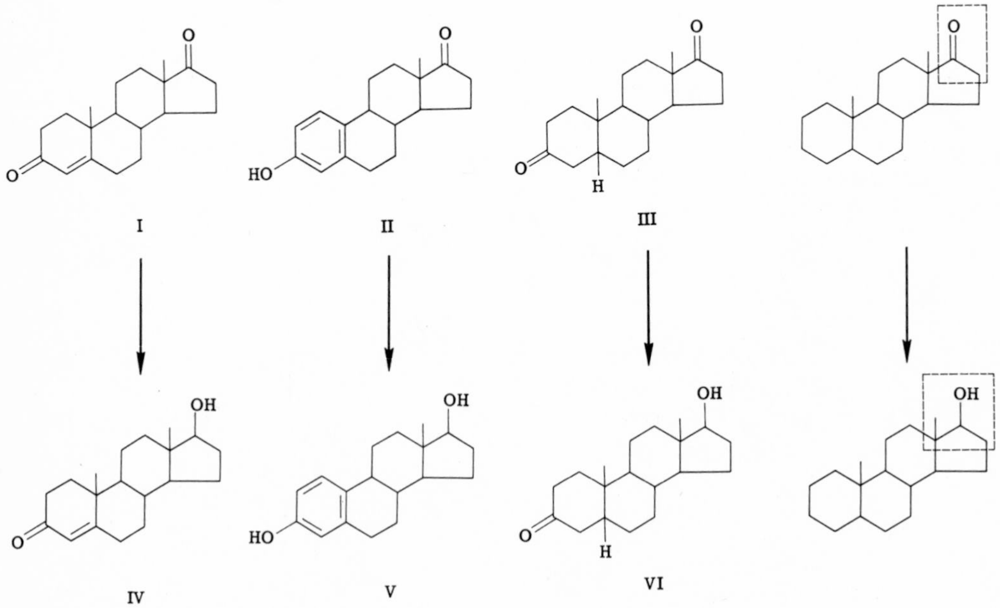

FIG. 28. Typical microbiological conversion of the 17-C=O to the 17β-OH group.

I. Androst-4-ene-3,17-dione
II. Estrone
III. 5β-Androstane-3,17-dione
IV. Testosterone
V. Estradiol-17β
VI. 17β-Hydroxy-5β-androstan-3-one

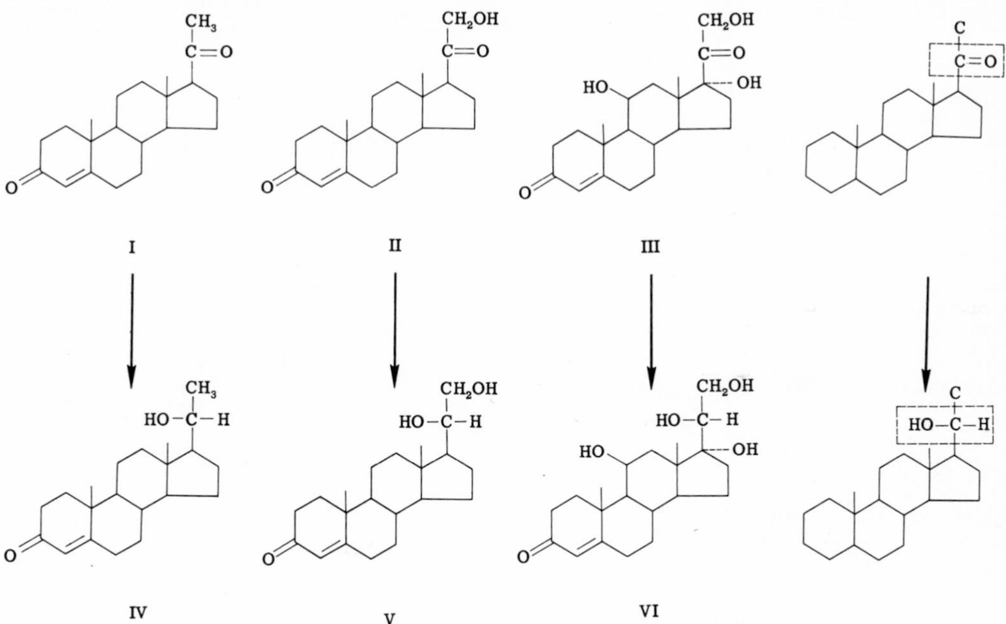

FIG. 29. Typical microbiological conversion of the 20-C=O to the 20β-OH group.

I. Progesterone
II. Deoxycorticosterone
III. Cortisol

IV. 20β-Hydroxypregn-4-en-3-one
V. 20β,21-Dihydroxypregn-4-en-3-one
VI. 11β,17α,20β,21-Tetrahydroxypregn-4-en-3-one

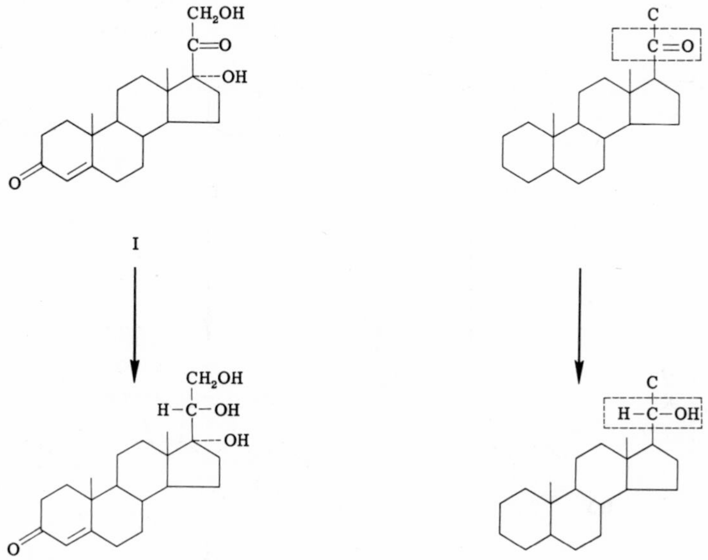

FIG. 30. Typical microbiological conversion of the 20-C=O to the 20α-OH group.

I. 11-Deoxycortisol

II. 17α,20α,21-Trihydroxypregn-4-en-3-one

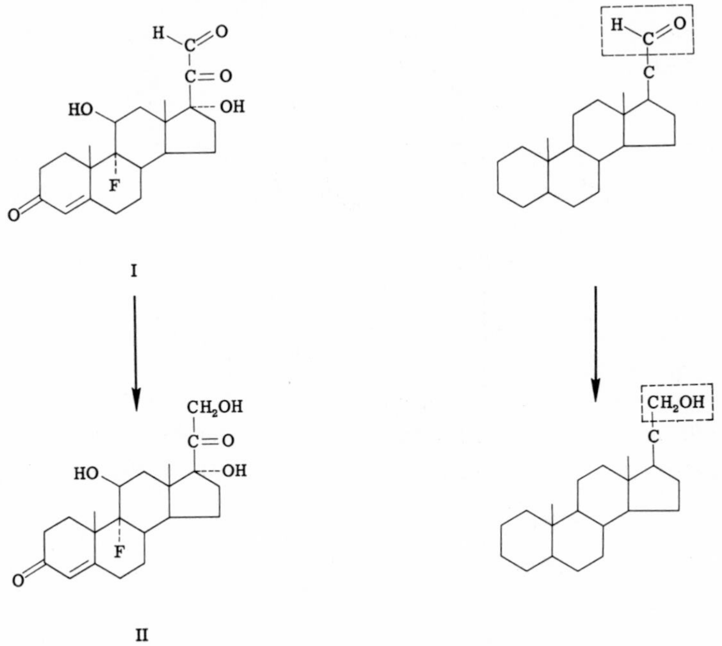

I

II

FIG. 31. Typical microbiological conversion of the 21-$\overset{\overset{\displaystyle O}{\|}}{C}$-H to the 21-OH group.

I. 9α-Fluoro-11β,17α-dihydroxy-21-aldopregn-4-ene-3,20-dione II. 9α-Fluorocortisol

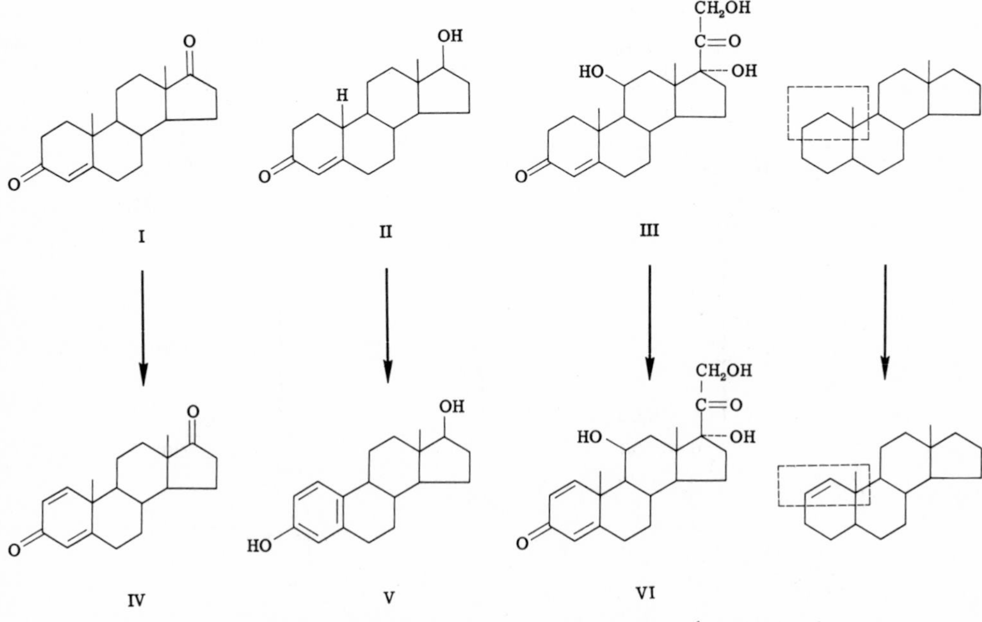

FIG. 32. Typical microbiological introduction of the Δ^1-double bond.

I. Androst-4-ene-3,17-dione
II. 19-Nortestosterone
III. Cortisol
IV. Androsta-1,4-diene-3,17-dione
V. Estradiol-17β
VI. Prednisolone

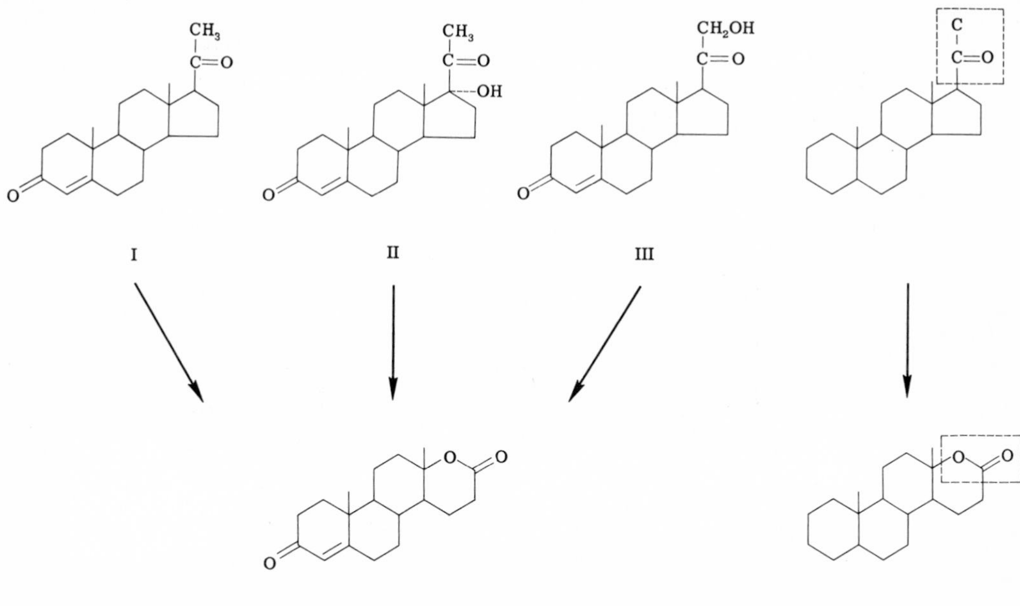

FIG. 33. Typical microbiological conversion of C_{21} to C_{19} steroids with ring D lactone formation.

I. Progesterone
II. 17α-Hydroxyprogesterone
III. Deoxycorticosterone
IV. Testololactone

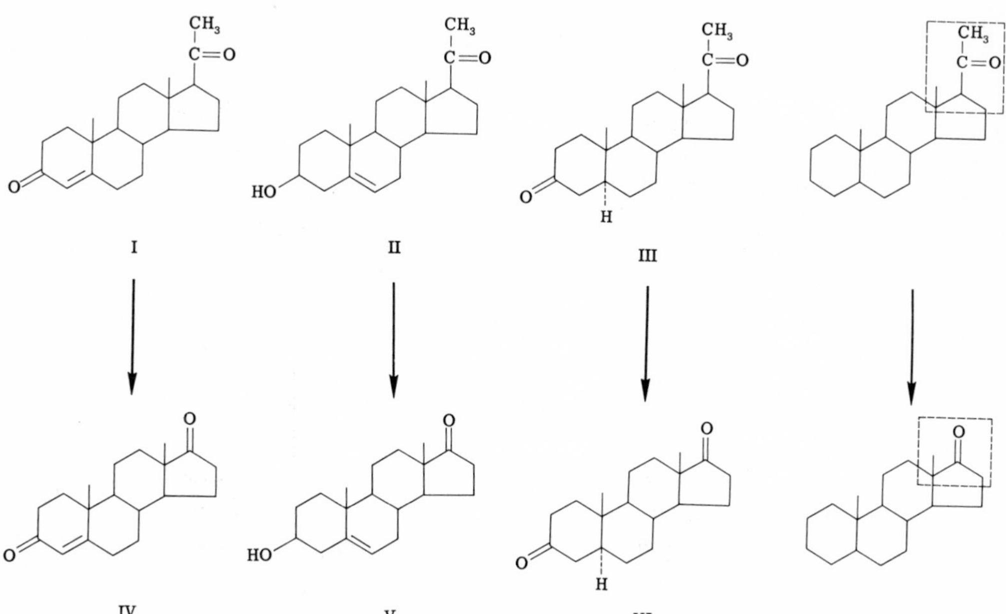

FIG. 34. Typical microbiological conversion of C_{21} to C_{19} steroids without ring D lactone formation.

I. Progesterone
II. Pregnenolone
III. 5α-Pregnane-3,20-dione
IV. Androst-4-ene-3,17-dione
V. Dehydroepiandrosterone
VI. 5α-Androstane-3,17-dione

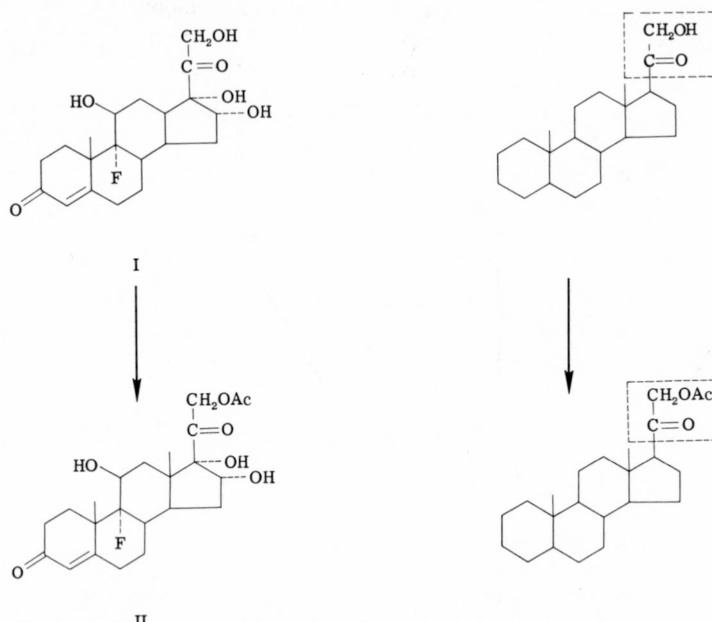

FIG. 35. Microbiological acetylation.

I. 9α-Fluoro-11β,16α,17α,21-tetrahydroxypregn-4-ene-3,20-dione
II. 9α-Fluoro-11β,16α,17α,21-tetrahydroxypregn-4-ene-3,20-dione-21-acetate

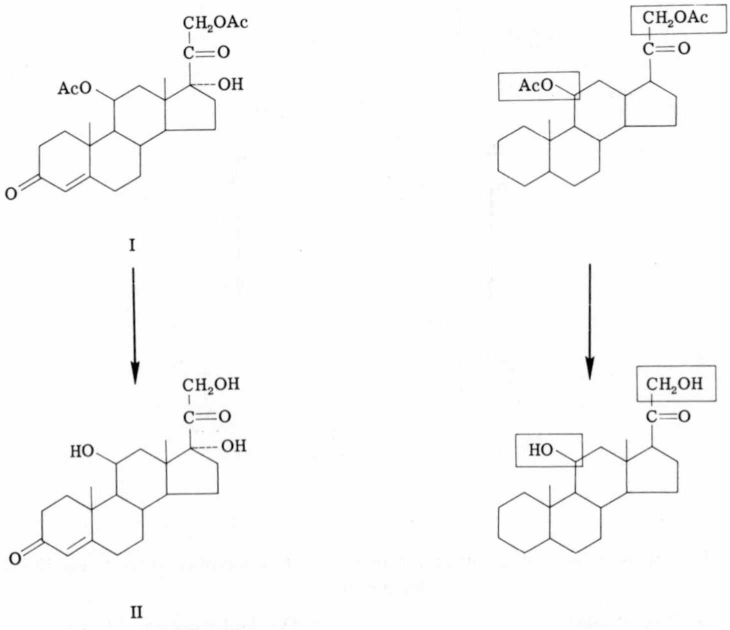

FIG. 36. Microbiological deacetylation.

I. Cortisol-11β,21-diacetate II. Cortisol

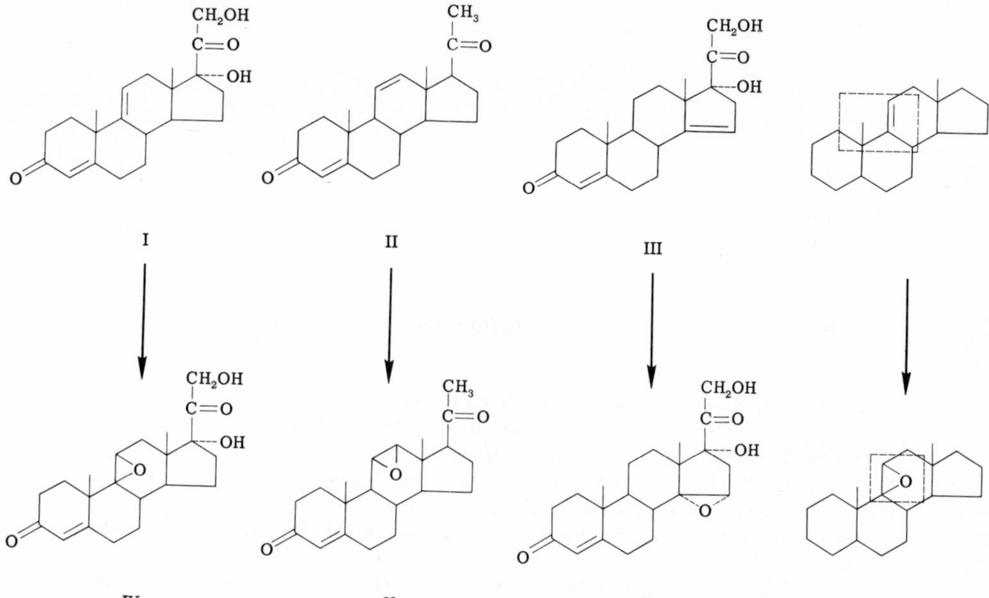

FIG. 37. Microbiological epoxidation.

I. 17α,21-Dihydroxypregna-4,9(11)-diene-3,20-dione
II. Pregna-4,11-diene-3,20-dione
III. 17α,21-Dihydroxypregna-4,14-diene-3,20-dione
IV. 9β,11β-Epoxy-17α,21-Dihydroxypregn-4-ene-3,20-dione
IV. 11β,12β-Epoxypregn-4-ene-3,20-dione
VI. 14α,15α-Epoxy-17α,21-Dihydroxypregn-4-ene-3,20-dione

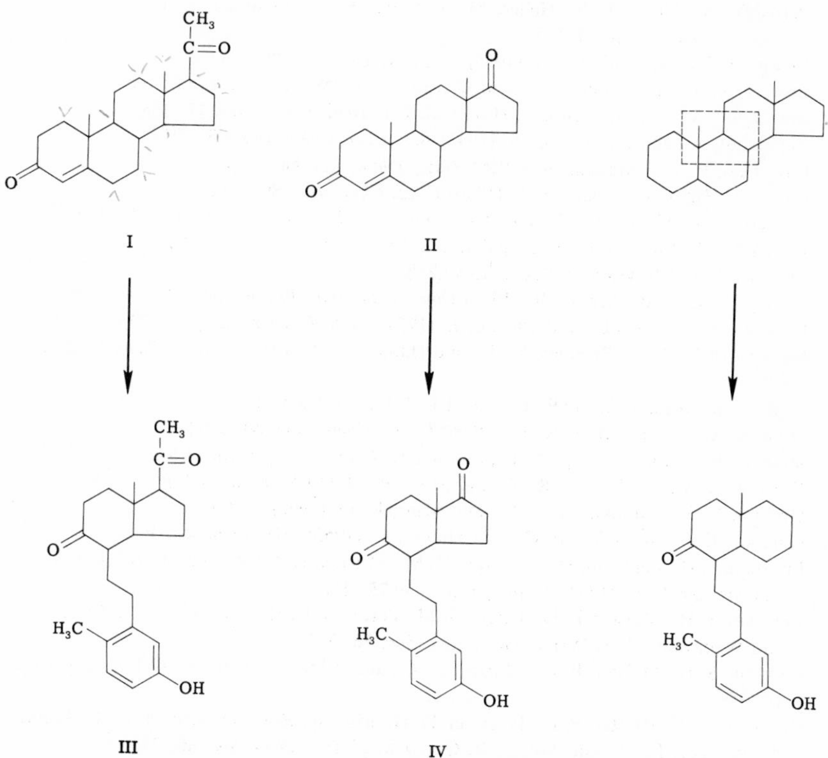

FIG. 38. Microbiological oxidative formation of seco compounds.

I. Progesterone
II. Androst-4-ene-3,17-dione
III. 9,10-Seco-pregna-1,3,5(10)-trien-3-ol-9,20-dione
IV. 9,10-Seco-androsta-1,3,5(10)-trien-3-ol-9,17-dione

References

Agnello, E. J., Bloom, B. L., and Laubach, G. D. (1955) *J. Am. Chem. Soc.* **77**: 4684.

Arnaudi, C. (1939) *Boll. Sez. Ital. Soc. Intern. Microbiol.* **11**: 208.

Arnaudi, C. (1942a) *Boll. Ist. Sieroterap. Milan.* **21**: 1.

Arnaudi, C. (1942b) *Zentr. Bakteriol. Parasitenk. Abt. II* **105**: 352.

Arnaudi, C., and Ercoli, A. (1941) *Boll. Ist. Sieroterap. Milan.* **20**: 3.

Asai, T., Aida, K., Ohki, E., Tanaka, T., and Hattori, M. (1958a) *Nippon Nogeikagaku Kaishi* **32**: 723.

Asai, T., Tsuda, K., Aida, K., Ohki, E., Tanaka, T., Hattori, M., and Machida, H. (1958b) *J. Gen. Appl. Microbiol.* **4**: 63.

Asai, T., Aida, K., Tanaka, T., Ohki, E., and Matsuhira, T. (1959) *Nippon Nogeikagaku Kaishi* **33**: 985.

Asai, T., Aida, K., Tanaka, T., and Sato, Y. (1961) *Nippon Nogeikagaku Kaishi* **35**: 122.

Barmenkov, A. S., Fedotova, M. V., Eroshin, V. K., Cusakova, E. G., and Orgareva, O. B. (1961) *Med. Prom SSSR* **15**: 39–40.

Bernstein, S., Feldman, L. I., Allen, W. S., Blank, R. H., and Linden, C. E. (1956). *Chem. Ind.* (*London*) p. 111.

Bernstein, S., Allen, W. S., Heller, M., Lenhard, R. H., Feldman, L. I., and Blank, R. H. (1959) *J. Org. Chem.* **24**: 286.

Bloom, B. L., and Shull, G. M. (1955) *J. Am. Chem. Soc.* **77**: 5767.

Bowers, A., Casas-Campillo, C., and Djerassi, C. (1958). *Tetrahedron* **2**: 165–166.

Butenandt, A., and Dannenberg, H. (1938). *Ber. Deut. Chem. Ges.* **71**: 1681.

Butenandt, A., and Suranyi, L. A. (1942) *Ber. Deut. Chem. Ges.* **75**: 591.

Camerino, B., and Modelli, R. (1956). *Gazz. Chim. Ital.* **86**: 1219.

Camerino, B., and Vercellone, A. (1956) *Gazz. Chim. Ital.* **86**: 260.

Camerino, B., Alberti, C. G., and Vercellone, A. (1953) *Helv. Chim. Acta* **36**: 1945.

Camerino, B., Modelli, R., and Spalla, C. (1956). *Gazz. Chim. Ital.* **86**: 1226.

Cervajal, F. (1960) German Patent 1,095,278.

Chang, V. M., and Idler, D. R. (1961) *Can. J. Biochem. Physiol.* **39**: 1277.

Charney, W., Weber, L., and Oliveto, E. (1959) *Arch. Biochem. Biophys.* **79**: 402.

Colingsworth, D. R., Brunner, M. P., and Haines, W. J. (1952). *J. Am. Chem. Soc.* **74**: 2381–2382.

Dodson, R. M., and Muir, R. D. (1957) U.S. Patent 2,805,231.

Dodson, R. M., and Muir, R. D. (1958) *J. Am. Chem. Soc.* **80**: 5004.

Dodson, R. M., Goldkamp, A. H., and Muir, R. D. (1957). *J. Am. Chem. Soc.* **79**: 3921.

Dodson, R. M., Nicholson, R. T., and Muir, R. D. (1959) *J. Am. Chem. Soc.* **81**: 6295.

Dodson, R. M., Goldkamp, A. H., and Muir, R. D. (1960) *J. Am. Chem. Soc.* **82**: 4026.

Dulaney, E. L., Stampley, E. O., and Hlavac, C. (1955). *Mycologia* **47**: 464.

Eppstein, S. H., Peterson, D. H., Leigh, H. M., Murray, H. C., Weintraub, A., Reineke, L. M., and Meister, P. D. (1953) *J. Am. Chem. Soc.* **75**: 421.

Eppstein, S. H., Meister, P. D., Leigh, H. M., Peterson, D. H., Murray, H. C., Reineke, L. M., and Weintraub, A. (1954) *J. Am. Chem. Soc.* **76**: 3174.

Eppstein, S. H., Meister, P. D., Murray, H. C., and Peterson, D. H. (1956) *Vitamins Hormones* **14**: 359.

Eppstein, S. H., Meister, P. D., Peterson, D. H., Murray, H. C., Osborn, H. M. L., Weintraub, A., Reineke, L. M., and Meeks, R. C. (1958) *J. Am. Chem. Soc.* **80**: 3382.

Ercoli, A. (1938) *Ber. Deut. Chem. Ges.* **71**: 650.
Ercoli, A. (1941) *Z. Physiol. Chem.* **270**: 266.
Ercoli, A., and Molina, L. (1944) *Boll. Ist. Sieroterap. Milan.* **23**: 158.
Fonken, G. S., Murray, H. C., and Reineke, L. M. (1960) *J. Am. Chem. Soc.* **82**: 5507.
Fried, J., and Sabo, E. F. (1953). *J. Am. Chem. Soc.* **75**: 2273.
Fried, J., Thoma, R. W., Gerke, J. R., Herz, J. E., Donin, M. N., and Perlman, D. (1952) *J. Am. Chem. Soc.* **74**: 3962.
Fried, J., Thoma, R. W., and Klingsberg, A. (1953) *J. Am. Chem. Soc.* **75**: 5764.
Fried, J., Thoma, R. W., Grabowicz, P., and Gerke, J. R. (1955a) *J. Am. Chem. Soc.* **77**: 3673.
Fried, J., Thoma, R. W., Perlman, D., Herz, J. E., and Borman, A. (1955b) *Recent Progr. Hormone Res.* **11**: 149.
Fried, J., Thoma, R. W., Perlman, D., and Gerke, J. R. (1956). U.S. Patent 2,753,290.
Gould, D., Ilavsky, J., Gutekunst, R., and Hershberg, E. B. (1957) *J. Org. Chem.* **22**: 829.
Greenspan, G., Schaffner, C. P., Charney, W., Herzog, H. L., and Hershberg, E. B. (1957) *J. Am. Chem. Soc.* **79**: 3922.
Gubler, A., and Tamm, C. (1958) *Helv. Chim. Acta* **41**: 301.
Hanc, O., Capek, A., and Tadra, M. (1957a). *Cesk. Farm.* **6**: 373; (1958) *Chem. Abstr.* **52**: 13865.
Hanc, O., Capek, O., Tadra, M., Macek, K., and Simek, A. (1957b) *Arzneimittel-Forsch.* **7**: 175.
Hanson, F. R., Mann, K. M., Nielson, E. D., Anderson, H. V., Brunner, M. P., Karnemaat, J. N., Colingsworth, D. R., and Haines, W. J. (1953) *J. Am. Chem. Soc.* **75**: 5369.
Hasegawa, T., and Takahashi, T. (1958) *Bull. Agr. Chem. Soc. Japan* **22**: 212.
Hayano, M., Saito, A., Stone, D., and Dorfman, R. I. (1956) *Arch. Biochem. Biophys.* **21**: 380.
Hayano, M., Gut, M., Dorfman, R. I., Schubert, A., and Silbert, R. (1959). *Biochim. Biophys. Acta* **32**: 269.
Hayano, M., Ringold, H. J., Stefanovic, V., Gut, M., and Dorfman, R. I. (1961). *Biochem. Biophys. Res. Commun.* **4**: 454.
Herzog, H. L., Gentles, M. J., Hershberg, E. B., Carvajal, F., Sutter, D., Charney, W., and Schaffner, C. P. (1957) *J. Am. Chem. Soc.* **79**: 3921.
Holmund, C. E., Feldman, L. I., Rigler, N. E., Nielsen, B. E., and Evans, R. H., Jr. (1961) *J. Am. Chem. Soc.* **83**: 2586.
Hübener, H. J., and Lehmann, C. O. (1958). Z.f.c. **313**: 124.
Iizuka, H., Naito, A., and Hattori, M. (1958) *Nippon Nogeikagaku Kaishi* **32**: 674.
Iizuka, H., Naito, A., and Sato, Y. (1959) Meeting Agr. Chem. Soc. Japan, April 9.
Iizuka, H., Naito, A., Tsuda, K., and Sato, Y. (1960a). Meeting Agr. Chem. Soc. Japan, April 7.
Iizuka, H., Naito, A., Ohki, E., Sato, Y., and Hattori, M. (1960b). *Nippon Nogeikagaku Kaishi* **34**: 472.
Isono, M., and Abe, M. (1959). Meeting Agr. Chem. Soc. Japan, April 9.
Kahnt, F. W., Meystre, C., Neher, R., Vischer, E., and Wettstein, A. (1952) *Experientia* **8**: 422.
Kita, D. A., Sardinas, J. L., and Shull, G. M. (1961) *Nature* **190**: 627.
Klüger, B., Siebert, R., and Schubert, A. (1957) *Naturwissenschaften* **44**: 40.
Koester, H., Mamoli, L., and Vercellone, A. (1941) U.S. Patent 2,236,574.
Kondo, E. (1960) *Nippon Nogeikagaku Kaishi* **34**: 762.
Kondo, E., and Masuo, E. (1960) *Nippon Nogeikagaku Kaishi* **34**: 759.
Kondo, E., and Mitsugi, T. (1961) *Nippon Nogeikagaku Kaishi* **35**: 521.
Kondo, E., Morihara, K., Nozaki, Y., and Masuo, E. (1960). *Nippon Nogeikagaku Kaishi* **34**: 844.
Kramli, A., and Horvath, J. (1948) *Nature* **162**: 619.
Kramli, A., and Horvath, J. (1949) *Nature* **163**: 219.
Kurosawa, Y. (1957) *Nippon Nogeikagaku Kaishi* **31**: 478.

Kurosawa, Y. (1958) *Nippon Nogeikagaku Kaishi* **32**: 515.

Kurosawa, Y., Hayano, M., and Bloom, B. M. (1961a) *Agr. Biol. Chem.* (*Tokyo*) **25**: 838.

Kurosawa, Y., Hayano, M., Gut, M., Dorfman, R. I., Schubert, A., and Burton, C. A. (1961b) *Agr. Biol. Chem.* (*Tokyo*) **25**: 424.

Lepetit, S. (1957) Belgian Patent 553,590.

Lerner, S. (1962) U.S. Patent 3,005,017.

Levy, H. R., and Talalay, P. (1957) *J. Am. Chem. Soc.* **79**: 2658.

Lindner, F., Junk, R., Nesemann, G., and Schmidt-Thomé, J. (1958) Z. f. c. **313**: 117.

McAleer, W. J. (1958). *Arch. Biochem. Biophys.* **73**: 127.

McAleer, W. J., and Dulaney, E. L. (1956) *Arch. Biochem. Biophys.* **62**: 109.

McAleer, W. J., Kozlowski, M. A., Stoudt, T. H., and Chemerda, J. M. (1958a) *J. Org. Chem.* **23**: 958.

McAleer, W. J., Kozlowski, M. A., Stoudt, T. H., and Chemerda, J. M. (1958b) *J. Org. Chem.* **23**: 508.

Mamoli, L. (1938a) *Ber. Deut. Chem. Ges.* **71**: 2696.

Mamoli, L. (1938b) *Ber Deut. Chem. Ges.* **71**: 2701.

Mamoli, L. (1939a) *Ber. Deut. Chem. Ges.* **72**: 1863.

Mamoli, L. (1939b) *Gazz. Chim. Ital.* **69**: 237.

Mamoli, L., and Schramm, G. (1938) *Ber. Deut. Chem. Ges.* **71**: 2698.

Mamoli, L., and Vercellone, A. (1937a) *Ber. Deut. Chem. Ges.* **70**: 470.

Mamoli, L., and Vercellone, A. (1937b) *Z. Physiol. Chem.* **245**: 93.

Mamoli, L., and Vercellone, A. (1938) *Ber. Deut. Chem. Ges.* **71**: 154.

Mamoli, L., Koch, R., and Teschen, H. (1939) *Z. Physiol. Chem.* **261**: 287.

Mancera, O., Zaffaroni, A., Rubin, B. A., Sondheimer, F., Rosenkranz, G., and Djerassi, C. (1952) *J. Am. Chem. Soc.* **74**: 3711.

Mann, K. M., Hanson, F. R., and O'Connell, P. W. (1955a) *Federation Proc.* **14**: 251.

Mann, K. M., Hanson, F. R., O'Connell, P. W., Anderson, H. V., Brunner, M. P., and Karnemaat, J. N. (1955b) *Appl. Microbiol.* **3**: 14.

Meeks, R. C., Meister, P. D., Eppstein, S. H., Rosselet, J. P., Weintraub, A., Murray, H. C., Sebek, O. K., Reineke, L. M., and Peterson, D. H. (1958) *Chem. Ind.* (*London*) p. 39.

Meister, P. D., Eppstein, S. H., Peterson, D. H., Murray, H. C., Leigh, H. M., Weintraub, A., and Reineke, L. M. (1953a) *Abstr. 123rd Meeting Am. Chem. Soc. Los Angeles, Calif.* p. 5C.

Meister, P. D., Peterson, D. H., Murray, H. C., Eppstein, S. H., Reineke, L. M., Weintraub, A., and Leigh, H. M. (1953b) *J. Am. Chem. Soc.* **75**: 55.

Meister, P. D., Peterson, D. H., Murray, H. C., Spero, G. B., Eppstein, S. H., Weintraub, A., Reineke, L. M., and Leigh, H. M. (1953c) *J. Am. Chem. Soc.* **75**: 416.

Meister, P. D., Reineke, L. M., Meeks, R. C., Murray, H. C., Eppstein, S. H. Osborn, H. M. L., Weintraub, A., and Peterson, D. H. (1954) *J. Am. Chem. Soc.* **76**: 4050.

Merck and Company, Inc. (1956) British Patent 767,360.

Meystre, C., Vischer, E., and Wettstein, A. (1954) *Helv. Chim. Acta* **37**: 1548.

Meystre, C., Vischer, E., and Wettstein, A. (1955) *Helv. Chim. Acta* **38**: 381.

Molina, L., and Ercoli, A. (1944) *Boll. Ist. Sieroterap. Milan.* **23**: 164.

Murray, H. C., and Peterson, D. H. (1952) U.S. Patent 2,602,769.

Murray, H. C., and Peterson, D. H. (1953) U.S. Patent 2,649,402.

Murray, H. C., and Peterson, D. H. (1954) U.S. Patent 2,695,260.

Murray, H. C., and Peterson, D. H. (1955a) U.S. Patent 2,702,809.

Murray, H. C., and Peterson, D. H. (1955b) U.S. Patent 2,703,326.

Murray, H. C., and Peterson, D. H. (1955c) U.S. Patent 2,703,806.

Murray, H. C. and Reineke, L. M. (1911) U.S. Patent 3,011,951.

Narita, M., Oono, S., Nakamura, M., and Koda, U. (1958) Japanese Patent 7809.

Nishikawa, M., and Hagiwara, H. (1958a) *Yakugaku Zasshi* **78**: 1256.

Nishikawa, M., and Hagiwara, H. (1958b) *Chem. Pharm. Bull.* (*Tokyo*) **6**: 226.

Nishikawa, M., Noguchi, S., Hasegawa, T., and Banno, I. (1956) *Yakugaku Zasshi* **76**: 383.

Nishikawa, M., Noguchi, S., Hasegawa, T., Takahashi, K., and Sakano, I. (1959) Japanese Patent 426.

Nobile, A., Charney, W., Perlman, P. L., Herzog, H. L., Payne, C. C., Tully, M. E., Jevnik, M. A., and Hershberg, E. B. (1955) *J. Am. Chem. Soc.* **77**: 4184.

Nussbaum, A. L., Carlon, F. E., Gould, D., Oliveto, E. P., Hershberg, E. B., Gilmore, M. L., and Charney, W. (1957) *J. Am. Chem. Soc.* **79**: 4814.

Pederson, R. L., Campbell, J. A., Babcock, J. C., Eppstein, S. H., Meister, L. M., Murray, H. C., Meeks, R. C., Weintraub, A., Reineke, L. M., and Peterson, D. H. (1956)) *J. Am. Chem. Soc.* **78**: 1512.

Perlman, D. (1952) *Science* **115**: 529.

Perlman, D., Titus, E., and Fried, J. (1952) *J. Am. Chem. Soc.* **74**: 2126.

Perlman, D., O'Brien, E., Bayan, A. P., and Greenfield, R. B., Jr. (1955) *J. Bacteriol.* **69**: 347.

Peterson, D. H. (1955) *J. Am. Chem. Soc.* **77**: 4428.

Peterson, D. H. (1958) *Proc. Intern. Congr. Biochem. 4th Vienna 1958.*

Peterson, D. H. (1960) *Chem. Ind.* (*London*) p. 1301.

Peterson, D. H., and Murray, H. C. (1952) *J. Am. Chem. Soc.* **74**: 1871.

Peterson, D. H., Murray, H. C., Eppstein, S. H., Reineke, L. M., Weintraub, A., Meister, P. D., and Leigh, H. M. (1952) *J. Am. Chem. Soc.* **74**: 5933.

Peterson, D. H., Nathan, A. H., Meister, P. D., Eppstein, S. H., Murray, H. C., Weintraub, A., Reineke, L. M., and Leigh, H. M. (1953a) *J. Am. Chem. Soc.* **75**: 419.

Peterson, D. H., Eppstein, S. H., Meister, P. D., Magerlein, B. J., Murray, H. C., Leigh, H. M., Weintraub, A., and Reineke, L. M. (1953b) *J. Am. Chem. Soc.* **75**: 412.

Peterson, D. H., Eppstein, S. H., Meister, P. D., Murray, H. C., Leigh, H. M., Weintraub, A., and Reineke, L. M. (1953c) *J. Am. Chem. Soc.* **75**: 5768.

Peterson, D. H., Meister, P. D., Weintraub, A., Reineke, L. M., Eppstein, S. H., Murray, H. C., and Osborn, H. M. L. (1955) *J. Am. Chem. Soc.* **77**: 4428.

Pfizer, Charles & Co. (1955) British Patent 740,858.

Pfizer, Charles & Co. (1957) British Patent 769,999.

Rubin, B. A., Campillo, C., Hendricks, G., Cordova, F., and Zaffaroni, A. (1956) *Bacteriol. Proc.* (*Soc. Am. Bacteriologists*) **56**: 33.

Schmidt-Thomé, J. (1957) *Agnew Chem.* **69**: 238.

Schneider, J. J., and Lewbart, M. L. (1959) *Recent Progr. Hormone Res.* **15**: 201.

Schubert, A., and Siebert, R. (1958) *Chem. Ber.* **91**: 1856.

Schubert, A., Langbein, G., and Siebert, R. (1957) *Chem. Ber.* **90**: 2576.

Schubert, A., Heller, K., Onken, D., Zetsche, K., and Klüger, B. (1960) *Z. Naturforsch.* **15b**: 269.

Schubert, K. (1959) *Proc. Intern. Congr. Biochem. 4th Vienna 1958* **4**: 150.

Schubert, K., Bohme, K. H., and Horhold, C. (1960a) *Z. Naturforsch.* **15b**: 584.

Schubert, K., Bohme, K. H., and Horhold, C. L. (1960b) *Deut. Akad. Wiss.* (*Berlin*) **2**: 308.

Schubert, K., Bohme, K. H., and Horhold, C. (1961) *Z. Physiol. Chem.* **325**: 260.

Shirasaka, M. (1961a) *Chem. Pharm. Bull.* (*Tokyo*) **9**: 54.

Shirasaka, M. (1961b) *Chem. Pharm. Bull.* (*Tokyo*) **9**: 59.

Shirasaka, M. (1961c) *Chem. Pharm. Bull.* (*Tokyo*) **9**: 152.

Shirasaka, M. (1961d) *Chem. Pharm. Bull.* (*Tokyo*) **9**: 203.

Shirasaka, M., and Ozaki, M. (1961) *Nippon Nogeikagaku Kaishi* **35**: 206.

Shirasaka, M., and Tsuruta, M. (1959) *Chem. Pharm. Bull.* (*Tokyo*) **7**: 804.

Shirasaka, M., and Tsuruta, M. (1961a) *Chem. Pharm. Bull.* (*Tokyo*) **9**: 159.

Shirasaka, M., and Tsuruta, M. (1961b) *Chem. Pharm. Bull.* (*Tokyo*) **9**: 196.

Shirasaka, M., and Tsuruta, M. (1961c) *Chem. Pharm. Bull.* (*Tokyo*) **9**: 207.

Shirasaka, M., Tsuruta, M., and Nakamura, M. (1958) *Bull. Agr. Chem. Soc. Japan* **22**: 273.

Shirasaka, M., Hayashi, R., and Tsuruta, M. (1959a) *Bull Agr. Chem. Soc. Japan* **23**: 244.

Shirasaka, M., Takasaki, R., Hayashi, R., and Tsuruta, M. (1959b) *Bull. Agr. Chem. Soc. Japan* **23**: 245.

Shull, G. M. (1956) *Trans. N.Y. Acad. Sci.* **19**(2): 147.

Shull, G. M., and Kita, D. A. (1955) *J. Am. Chem. Soc.* **77**: 763.
Shull, G. M., Sardinas, J. L., and Routien, J. B. (1954) Canadian Patent 507,009.
Shull, G. M., Kita, D. A., and Davisson, J. W. (1955a) U.S. Patent 2,702,812.
Shull, G. M., Sardinas, J. L., and Routien, J. B. (1955b) French Patent 1,091,743.
Shull, G. M., Kita, D. A., and Davisson, J. W. (1956) U.S. Patent 2,765,258.
Sih, C. J. (1961) *J. Pharm. Sci.* **50**: 712.
Smith, L. L., Mendelsohn, H., Foell, T., and Goodman, J. J. (1961) *J. Org. Chem.* **26**: 2859.
Smith, L. L., Foell, T., and Goodman, J. J. (1962) *Biochemistry* **1**: 353.
Stimmel, B. F. (1957) *Proc. Amer. Ass. Cancer Res.* **2**: 253.
Stone, D., Hayano, M., Dorfman, R. I., Hechter, O., Robinson, C. R., and Djerassi, C. (1955) *J. Am. Chem. Soc.* **77**: 3926.
Sutter, D., Charney, W., O'Neill, P. L., Carvajal, F., Herzog, H. L., and Hershberg, E. B. (1957) *J. Org. Chem.* **22**: 578.
Szpilfogel, S. A., DeWinter, M. S., and Alsche, W. J. (1956a) *Rec. trav. Chim.* **75**: 402.
Szpilfogel, S. A., Van Hemert, P. A., and DeWinter, M. S. (1956b) *Rec. Trav. Chim.* **75**: 1227.
Takahashi, K., Uchibori, Y., Kazinami, S., and Hasegawa, T. (1960) Meeting Agr. Chem. Soc. Japan, April 7, 1960.
Talalay, P. (1957) *Record Chem. Progr. Kreesge-Hooker Sci. Lib.* **18**: 31.
Talalay, P., and Dobson, M. M. (1953) *J. Biol. Chem.* **205**: 823.
Talalay, P., and Marcus, P. I. (1954) *Nature* **173**: 1189.
Tanabe, K., Hayashi, R., Takasaki, R., and Shirasaka, M. (1959) *Chem. Pharm. Bull.* (*Tokyo*) **7**: 811.
Testa, E. (1957) *Ann. Chim.* (*Rome*) **47**: 1132.
Thoma, R. W., Fried, J., Bananno, S., and Grabowicz, P. (1957) *J. Am. Chem. Soc.* **79**: 4818.
Tollman, D., Titus, E., and Fried, J. (1952) *J. Am. Chem. Soc.* **74**: 2126.
Tsuda, K., Asai, T., Sato, Y., Tanaka, T., Matsuhira, T., and Hasegawa, H. (1960) *Chem. Pharm. Bull.* (*Tokyo*) **8**: 626.
Turfitt, G. E. (1946) *Biochem. J.* **40**: 79.
Turfitt, G. E. (1948) *Biochem. J.* **42**: 376.
Uchibayashi, M. (1960a) *Chem. Pharm. Bull.* (*Tokyo*) **8**: 112.
Uchibayashi, M. (1960b) *Chem. Pharm. Bull.* (*Tokyo*) **8**: 117.
Uchibayashi, M. (1960c) *Chem. Pharm. Bull.* (*Tokyo*) **8**: 255.
Underkofler, L. A., and Hickey, R. J. (eds.) (1954) "Industrial Fermentations", Vols. I, II. Chemical Publ., New York.
Urech, J., Vischer, E., and Wettstein, A. (1960) *Helv. Chim. Acta* **43**: 1077.
Vercellone, A., and Mamoli, L. (1938) *Ber. Deut. Chem. Ges.* **71**: 152.
Vischer, E., and Wettstein, A. (1953) *Experientia* **9**: 371.
Vischer, E., and Wettstein, A. (1958) *Advan. Enzymol.* **20**: 237.
Vischer, E., Schmidlin, J., and Wettstein, A. (1954) *Helv. Chim. Acta* **37**: 321.
Vischer, E., Meystre, C., and Wettstein, A. (1955) *Helv. Chim. Acta* **38**: 835.
Vischer, E., Schmidlin, J., and Wettstein, A. (1956) *Experientia* **12**: 50.
Vondrova, O., and Hanc, O. (1960) *Folia Microbiol.* (*Prague*) **5**: 247.
Weisz, E., Wix, G., and Bodanszky, M. (1956) *Naturwissenschaften* **43**: 39.
Wettstein, A. (1939) *Helv. Chim. Acta* **22**: 250.
Wettstein, A. (1955) *Experientia* **11**: 465.
Zaffaroni, A., Ringold, H. J., Rosenkranz, G., Sondheimer, F., Thomas, G. H., and Djerassi, C. (1954) *J. Am. Chem. Soc.* **76**: 6210.
Zaffaroni, A., Campillo, C. C., Cordova, F., and Rosenkranz, G. (1955) *Experientia* **11**: 219.
Zuidweg, M. H., Van der Waard, W. F., and DeFlines, J. (1962) *Biochim. Biophys. Acta* **58**: 131.

CHAPTER V

Catabolic Reactions of the Steroids

The catabolic reactions of the neutral and phenolic steroids are presented in this chapter in a series of 60 tables and 46 accompanying figures. This illustrative material is essentially self-explanatory. The enzyme systems involved in these reactions are discussed in Chapter VI and the relationship between the secreted steroid hormones and their metabolites are the subject matter of Chapter VIII. In the latter chapter, the concept of unique catabolites is discussed, and methods for the measurement or evaluation of certain of the steroid hormones are described.

The reduction of the Δ^1-double bond has been demonstrated *in vivo* (Table 1) and *in vitro* (Table 2). A good proportion of the studies deal with the corticoids, prednisone and prednisolone, which are not naturally occurring steroids. Only one naturally occurring Δ^1-steroid has been isolated (Lieberman *et al.*, 1948). This steroid, 5α-androst-1-ene-3,17-dione, was reduced *in vivo* to both androsterone and epiandrosterone (Ungar and Dorfman, 1952a). The corresponding 17β-hydroxy steroid, 17β-hydroxy-5α-androst-1-en-3-one was shown more recently to be convertible to androsterone when administered to a human subject (Langecker and Kramer, 1962). A similar *in vivo* reduction was reported for 17β-hydroxy-1-methyl-5α-androst-1-en-3-one by these latter investigators.

Androsta-1,4-diene-3,17-dione is reduced *in vivo* to androsterone (Table 1), (Fig. 1) and to a mixture of other unidentified saturated and unsaturated 17-ketosteroids.

The *in vivo* and *in vitro* reduction of the 3-C=0 to 3α-OH grouping occurs in both C_{19} and C_{21} steroids and for steroids of the 5α and 5β configurations (Tables 3 and 4, Fig. 2). The 3-C=0 group may be reduced to the 3β form for C_{19} and C_{21} steroids of the 5α and 5β series. Examples of *in vivo* transformation are listed in Table 5, while Table 6 lists data from *in vitro* experiments. Figure 3 illustrates these reactions in the C_{21} and C_{19} series.

Tables 7–10 summarize the reported reactions demonstrating oxidation of both the 3α-hydroxy and 3β-hydroxy grouping to the 3-ketone for *in vitro* and *in vivo* experiments.

Tables 3–6 deal with reductive changes at carbon 3 in 5α- and 5β-dihydro reduced derivatives. Tables 11–16 summarize reductive changes involving various substituted steroids possessing the Δ^4-3-keto group where the conversions involve the reduction of the Δ^4-double bond only, or in combination with the 3α or 3β reductions. These catabolic changes occur in both C_{19} and C_{21} steroids.

Figures 4–10 illustrate the various oxidative changes of the 3α- or 3β-hydroxy group to the corresponding 3-ketone.

Tables 17–19 deal with peripheral modifications of the Δ^5-3β-hydroxy group to the Δ^4-3-ketone or to reductive products involving both carbon 3 and the formed Δ^4-group. Table 19 documents the change to the Δ^4-3-ketone for two related steroids, dehydroepiandrosterone and androst-5-ene-3β,17α-diol. The transformations summarized in Tables 17 and 18 appear to require the prior two-step reaction of the Δ^5-3β-ol-dehydrogenase reaction, which has been postulated in forming first the Δ^5-3-ketone then the Δ^4-double bond. The formed Δ^4-3-keto is reduced to the 3α-5α tetrahydro (Table 17) and 3α-5β derivatives (Table 18).

Figures 11–13 illustrate some metabolic modifications of the Δ^5-3β-hydroxy group. The conversion of this group to the 3α,5α compound (Fig. 11), the 3α,5β-steroid (Fig. 12), and the Δ^4-3-ketone derivatives (Fig. 13) are presented.

The *in vivo* interconversions of the 11β-hydroxy and 11-keto groupings listed in Table 20 involve various substrates, including oxidative changes in cortisol, urocortisol, 11β,17α,21-trihydroxy-5β-pregnane-3,20-dione, corticosterone, 11β-hydroxyandrost-4-ene-3,17-dione, prednisolone, and allotetrahydrocortisol; and reductive changes to the 11β-hydroxy groups for 11-dehydrocorticosterone, 3α,17α-21-trihydroxy-5α-pregnane-11,20-dione, cortisone, adrenosterone, 2α-methyladrenosterone, prednisone, urocortisone, 11-ketoandrosterone, and 11-ketoetiocholanolone.

Table 21 is similar to Table 20, but the examples of the 11β-dehydrogenase reaction listed are from *in vitro* experiments. Incubation of the C-11 ketonic steroids, cortisone and urocortisone, yielded the corresponding 11β-hydroxy steroids, while 11β-hydroxyandrost-4-ene-3,17-dione and cortisol were transformed into 11-ketosteroids. Typical interconversions at carbon 11 between the 11β-hydroxy and 11-keto derivatives are illustrated in Figs. 14 and 15.

Catabolic changes involving the 17β-hydroxy and 17-keto groupings in the neutral steroids are presented in Tables 22–24. The *in vivo* experiments recorded in Table 22 dealing with the oxidation to the 17-ketone include data obtained from a variety of animals of different species: humans, guinea pigs, chimpanzees, and monkeys. The reductive step to the 17β-hydroxy grouping from the 17-ketone is depicted in Table 23, which represents *in vivo* studies in humans and the rat.

The interconversion by *in vitro* technics of 17α-hydroxy, 17β-hydroxy, and the 17-keto group is illustrated in Table 24. Rabbit liver and bovine erythrocyte suspensions showed the presence of the neutral steroid 17α-dehydrogenase. Rabbit muscle, human liver, Earle's Cells, dog liver, and human skin contained the 17β-dehydrogenase activity.

Reduction of the 17-keto group to the 17β-hydroxy configuration is illustrated in a 5β and in a Δ^5-3β-hydroxy steroid in Fig. 16. Examples of the reverse reaction in the neutral steroid series are well known (Fig. 17). Figure 18 illustrates the oxidation of a 17α-hydroxy steroid to the 17-ketone, indicating the presence of a 17α-dehydrogenase.

The reduction of the Δ^{16} group in C_{21} steroids to the saturated 17β side chain is listed in Table 25 (Fig. 19).

A characteristic steroid reaction, of importance in biosynthetic and in catabolic reactions, involves the conversion of C_{21} steroids possessing C-17, C-20 oxygen functions to the corresponding 17-ketosteroid. The many examples of *in vivo* studies are illustrated in Table 26, while the *in vitro* experiments are presented in Table 27. Typical examples can be seen in Fig. 20. Details concerning the conversion of a C_{21}-Δ^4-3-ketosteroid to the ring A saturated C_{21} steroid are discussed in Chapter VIII, with certain generalizations for human catabolic studies. Actually, by far the greatest number of *in vivo* experiments have been done in human subjects. On the other hand, *in vitro* studies have been reported mainly for the rat, dog, and bovine species, with the use of liver, muscle, kidney, and connective tissue (Table 27).

The interconvertibility of the 20-keto group and the 20α- and 20β-hydroxyl group has been established by *in vitro* and *in vivo* experiments. The details of these changes are presented in Tables 28–31 and Figs. 21–24.

In vivo experiments dealing with the conversion of the 20-keto to the 20β-hydroxy group include the substrates cortisol, cortisone, 11-dehydrocorticosterone, urocortisone, corticosterone, and 17α-hydroxyprogesterone. These substrates have been administered to human subjects (Table 28). Rats have been used for cortisol and cortisone studies, while guinea pigs have been employed in one cortisol study (Table 28).

The *in vivo* reduction of the 20-keto group to the 20α-hydroxy form, described in Table 29, has been reported extensively in humans, rats, rabbits, chimpanzees, and guinea pigs with a variety of substrates ranging from $C_{21}O_2$ to $C_{21}O_5$ steroids. The reverse reaction involving the oxidation of the 20α-hydroxy group to the 20-ketone is illustrated by only one example, the administration of pregnanediol to humans with the isolation of pregnanolone (Table 30).

20β-Dehydrogenase is widely distributed, as is seen by the extensive list of glands and tissue in the many species that contain this enzyme (Table 31). The enzyme is present in steroid-forming tissues such as the corpus luteum, ovary, placenta, adrenal, and in peripheral tissues, including the liver, connective tissue, fibroblasts, and muscle strips.

The reduction of the 21-hydroxy group to the 21-methyl group has been demonstrated in the human, rabbit, and chimpanzee (Table 32, Fig. 25). There is some question as to what extent this is a naturally occurring reaction or whether this is due in some measure to side reactions arising from the chemical procedures employed.

Hydroxylation reactions are known to play important roles in biosynthetic reactions in steroid-forming glands. Their function in catabolism is not clear, but these reactions have been adequately demonstrated by *in vivo* and *in vitro* methods (Tables 33 and 34) and include hydroxylation at positions 6β (Fig. 26), 7α (Fig. 27), 16α (Fig. 28), and 18 (Fig. 29). Indirect evidence indicates the possibility of a peripheral 19-hydroxylase on the basis of estrogen formation from androgen precursors in the ovariectomized, adrenalectomized woman.

The formation of C_{20} acids from C_{21} steroids (Table 35, Fig. 30) is now established. These acids arise from the C-20, C-21 α-ketal by oxidation of the C-21 hydroxyl group to the acid via the aldehyde, and then decarboxylation of the C-21 carboxylic acid.

Table 36 records two reactions, the first involving the reduction of the ketone group of a Δ^4-3-ketone to the 3ξ hydroxy-Δ^4-unsaturated group (Fig. 31 and 32) and the second, formation of a 17-iso-C_{21} steroid and a Δ^{16}-C_{21} steroid. These reactions were shown by *in vivo* technics.

Various miscellaneous reactions, *in vitro*, are presented in Table 37. This table records the transformation of the 11β-hydroxy group to the 11α-hydroxy group, the 11-C=0 group to the 11-CH_2 group, and the removal of the 17-OH group. Each of these reactions requires confirmation.

Tables 38–58 give summaries of the catabolic reactions of phenolic steroids. Reactions at carbon 2 involve hydroxylation (Fig. 33), hydroxylation and methylation (Fig. 34), or methylation only (Fig. 35). Table 38 considers the reaction *in vivo*, and the *in vitro* studies are presented in Table 39. These compounds have been isolated in the human, guinea pig, and rat, and it would be expected that they and their corresponding reactions may be found in the tissues of other species. These reactions are known for estrone, estradiol-17β, and estriol.

The important 16α-hydroxylation of a ring A phenolic steroid is presented in Table 40. The main route of estradiol-17β catabolism is through a 16α-hydroxylation reaction (Fig. 36) involving estrone (Fishman *et al.*, 1960a). Table 41 deals with the transformation from estrone and estradiol-17α to a 16β-hydroxy derivative. This reaction most likely proceeds indirectly from 16α-hydroxylation to 16-keto formation to reduction to the 16β-hydroxy form.

In vitro hydroxylations of phenolic steroids involving carbon atoms 6 and 16 are presented in Table 42.

The oxidative-reductive changes involving on the one hand the 16-keto group and on the other the 16α- and 16β-hydroxy groups in the ring A phenolic series are concerned with two enzymatic systems, the 16α- and the 16β-dehydrogenases, which are categorized in Tables 43–48 and Figs. 41–43.

The introduction of the 16-keto group indicated in Table 49 most likely proceeds by way of 16α-hydroxylation and the action of a 16α-dehydrogenase.

The oxidative-reductive changes involving carbon 17 are presented in Tables 50–56 and illustrate that both ring A phenolic 17α- and 17β-dehydrogenases have been observed. The former enzyme is associated particularly with bovine tissues and rabbits. Figures 37 and 38 illustrate examples of the phenolic 17β-dehydrogenase reaction and Figures 39 and 40 deal with the corresponding 17α-dehydrogenase.

Brown (1962) demonstrated demethylation at carbon 3 of estrone, estradiol-17β, and estriol (Table 57, Fig. 44). Miscellaneous reactions of phenolic steroids are documented in Table 58.

Conjugate formation (Figs. 45 and 56), originally considered to be exclusively a catabolic reaction, has been demonstrated in steroid-forming tissue, as in placental tissue. Table 59 summarizes various *in vivo* and *in vitro* studies demonstrating these reactions.

During the past years, a considerable number of therapeutically important synthetic steroids have been studied both by *in vitro* methods in humans and by *in vitro* technics, usually involving rat liver preparations. The catabolic changes are essentially those already documented for the naturally occurring steroids. The specific studies are summarized in Table 60.

Table 1

CATABOLISM OF NEUTRAL STEROIDS, *In Vivo*: REDUCTION OF Δ^1-GROUP

Substrate	Product	Species	Reference
5α-Androst-1-ene-3,17-dione	Androsterone Epiandrosterone	Human (male hypergonad)	Ungar and Dorfman (1952a)
Androsta-1,4-diene-3,17-dione	Androsterone	Human male	Ungar and Dorfman (1952b)
Prednisolone	3α,11β,17α,21-Tetra-hydroxy-5α-pregnan-20-one 11β-Hydroxyetiocholanolone 11-Ketoetiocholanolone	Human	Caspi and Pechet (1957)
	3α,11β,17α,21-Tetra-hydroxy-5β-pregnan-20-one 11β-Hydroxyetiocholanolone 11-Ketoetiocholanolone	Human	Caspi and Pechet (1958)
	Cortisone Cortisol 17α,20β,21-Trihydroxy-pregn-4-ene-3,11-dione	Human	Lamedica *et al.* (1957)
17β-Hydroxy-1α-methyl-5α-androst-1-en-3-one	1α-Methyl-5α-andro-stane-3,17-dione	Human	Langecker and Kramer (1962)
17β-Hydroxy-5α-androst-1-en-3-one	Androsterone		

Table 2

CATABOLISM OF NEUTRAL STEROIDS, *In Vitro*: REDUCTION OF Δ^1-GROUP

Substrate	Product	Test system	Species	Reference
Prednisone	Urocortisone	Liver homogenate	Rat	Tomkins (1956a)
Prednisolone	Cortisol 11β,17α,21-Trihydroxy-5α-pregnane-3,20-dione 11β,17α,20β,21-Tetra-hydroxypregn-4-en-3-one	Liver homogenate	Rat	Vermeulen and Caspi (1958)
Testosterone	17α-Hydroxy-5α-androst-1-en-3-one (Possible bacterial contamination)	Prostate slices	Human	Ofner *et al.* (1957)

Table 3

CATABOLISM OF NEUTRAL STEROIDS, *In Vivo*: REDUCTION OF 3—C=O TO 3α—OH[a]

Substrate	Product	Species	Reference
5α-Androstane-3,17-dione	Androsterone	Human (hypogonadal male)	Dorfman and Hamilton (1940); Dorfman *et al.* (1950); Gallagher *et al.* (1951)
Epiandrosterone	Androsterone (through 3C=0)	Human	Dorfman *et al.* (1948)
5α-Pregnane-3,20-dione 5β-Pregnane-3,20-dione	5α-Pregnane-3α,20α-diol 5β-Pregnane-3α,20α-diol	Human	Ungar *et al.* (1951b)
17β-Hydroxy-5β-androstan-3-one	3α-Hydroxy-5β-androstan-17-one 5β-Androstane-3α,17β-diol	Human	Ungar *et al.* (1951a)
17α,21-Dihydroxy-5β-pregnane	3α,17α,21-Trihydroxy-5β-pregnan-20-one	Human	Ungar *et al.* (1954a)
21-Hydroxy-5β-pregnane-3,20-dione	3α,21-Dihydroxy-5β-pregnan-20-one	Human	Langecker (1959)
11β-Hydroxyandrost-4-ene-3,17-dione	11β-Hydroxyandrosterone 11β-Hydroxyetiocholanolone 11-Ketoandrosterone 11-Ketoetiocholanolone	Human	Bradlow and Gallagher (1957)
Androst-5-ene-3,17-dione	3α-Hydroxyandrost-5-en-17-one	Human	Fukushima *et al.* (1962b)
Progesterone	5α-Pregnane-3α,6α,20α-triol	Rabbit	Knights *et al.* (1962)

[a] For reduction of Δ^4—3C=0, see Tables 6–8.

Table 4

CATABOLISM OF NEUTRAL STEROIDS, *In Vitro*: REDUCTION OF 3C=O TO 3α—OH

Substrate	Product	Test system	Species	Reference
17α,21-Dihydroxy-5β-pregnane-3,20-dione	3α,17α,21-Trihydroxy-5β-pregnan-20-one	Liver homogenate	Rat	Ungar and Dorfman (1954b)
		Powder extract	Rabbit	
		Kidney homogenate	Rabbit	

Continued on following page

Table 4 (*continued*)

CATABOLISM OF NEUTRAL STEROIDS, *In Vitro*: REDUCTION OF 3C=O TO 3α—OH

Substrate	Product	Test system	Species	Reference
11β,17α,21-Trihydroxy-5β-pregnane-3,20-dione	Urocortisol	Liver homogenate	Rat	Tomkins (1956b)
17α,21-Dihydroxy-5β-pregnane-3,11,20-trione	Urocortisone			
5α-Androstane-3,17-dione	Androsterone	Liver homogenate	Rat	Rubin (1957)
	Androsterone	Liver perfusion	Rabbit	Benard *et al.* (1961)

Table 5

CATABOLISM OF NEUTRAL STEROIDS, *In Vivo*: REDUCTION OF 3C=O TO 3β—OH[a]

Substrate	Product	Species	Reference
5α-Androstane-3,17-dione	Epiandrosterone	Human	Dorfman *et al.* (1950)
5α-Androstane-3α,17α-diol	Epiandrosterone (through 3C=0)	Human	Dorfman *et al.* (1950)
Androsterone	Epiandrosterone (through 3C=0)	Guinea pig	Schiller and Dorfman (1948)
5α-Pregnane-3,20-dione	5α-Pregnane-3β,20α-diol	Human	Ungar *et al.* (1951b)
Androsterone	Epiandrosterone (through 3C=0)	Human	Schneider and Lewbart (1959)
Epiandrosterone	Androsterone (through 3C=0)	Guinea pig	Charollais *et al.* (1961)

[a] For reduction of Δ^4—3C=0, see Tables 6–8.

Table 6

CATABOLISM OF NEUTRAL STEROIDS, *In Vitro*: REDUCTION OF 3C=O TO 3β—OH

Substrate	Product	Test system	Species	Reference
17α-21-Dihydroxy-5β-pregnane-3,20-dione	3β,17α,21-Trihydroxy-5β-pregnan-20-one	Kidney homogenate	Rabbit	Ungar and Dorfman (1954b)
5α-Androstane-3,17-dione	Epiandrosterone	Liver homogenate	Rat	Rubin (1957)
21-Hydroxy-5α-pregnane-3,20-dione	3β,21-Dihydroxy-5α-pregnan-20-one	Adrenal homogenate	Bovine	Pincus (1954)

Continued on following page

Table 6 *(continued)*

CATABOLISM OF NEUTRAL STEROIDS, *In Vitro*: REDUCTION OF 3C=O TO 3β—OH

Substrate	Product	Test system	Species	Reference
Androsterone	Epiandrosterone (probably through 3C=0)	Liver slices	Rabbit	Schneider and Mason (1948b)
5α-Androstane-3α,17β-diol	Epiandrosterone (probably through 3C=0)	Liver slices	Rabbit	Kochakian and Aposhian (1952)
5α-Androstane-3,17-dione	Epiandrosterone	Liver perfusion	Rabbit	Benard *et al.* (1961)
17β-Hydroxy-5α-androstan-3-one	5α-Androstane-3β,17β-diol	Erythrocyte suspension	Rat	Portius and Repke (1960b)

Table 7

CATABOLISM OF NEUTRAL STEROIDS, *In Vivo*: OXIDATION OF 3α—OH TO 3C=O

Substrate	Product	Species	Reference
Androsterone	Epiandrosterone (through 3C=0)	Human	Schiller and Dorfman (1948)
Etiocholanolone	5β-Androstane-3,17-dione	Human	Kappas *et al.* (1958)

Table 8

CATABOLISM OF NEUTRAL STEROIDS, *In Vitro*: OXIDATION OF 3α—OH TO 3C=O

Substrate	Product	Test system	Species	Reference
Androsterone	Epiandrosterone (through 3C=0)	Liver slices	Rabbit	Schneider and Mason (1948b)
	5α-Androstane-3,17-dione	Liver slices	Rabbit	Schneider and Mason (1948a)
Etiocholanolone	5β-Androstane-3,17-dione	Liver slices	Rabbit	Schneider and Mason (1948a)
5α-Androstane-3α,17β-diol	5α-Androstane-3,17-dione	Liver slices	Rabbit	Kochakian and Aposhian (1952)
Androsterone	Androstane-3,17-dione	Liver perfusion	Rabbit	Benard *et al.* (1961)
Tetrahydrocortisone	5β-Dihydrocortisone	Placental slices Liver homogenate	Human	Meigs and Engel (1961)
Androsterone	5α-Androstane-3,17-dione	Erythrocyte suspension	Bovine	Portius and Repke (1960b)

Table 9

CATABOLISM OF NEUTRAL STEROIDS, *In Vivo*: OXIDATION OF 3β—OH TO 3C=O

Substrate	Product	Species	Reference
Epiandrosterone	Androsterone (through 3C=0)	Human Guinea pig	Dorfman *et al.* (1948) Charollais *et al.* (1961)
3β-Hydroxy-5β-androstan-17-one	5β-Androstane-3,17-dione Etiocholanolone (through 3C=0)	Human	Kappas *et al.* (1958)

Table 10

CATABOLISM OF NEUTRAL STEROIDS, *In Vitro*: OXIDATION OF 3β—OH TO 3C=O GROUP

Substrate	Product	Test system	Species	Reference
Epiandrosterone	5α-Androstane-3,17-dione 11β-Hydroxy-5α-androstane-3,17-dione	Adrenal perfusion	Bovine	Meyer *et al.* (1953)
Epiandrosterone	5α-Androstane-3,17-dione	Liver perfusion	Rabbit	Benard *et al.* (1961)
		Erythrocyte suspension	Rat Bovine	Portius and Repke (1960b)

Table 11

CATABOLISM OF NEUTRAL STEROIDS, *In Vivo*: REDUCTION OF Δ^4—3C=O TO 3C=O—5α, 3α—5α, AND 3β—5α GROUPINGS

Substrate	Product	Species	Reference
Testosterone	Androsterone	Human (hypergonadal males)	Dorfman *et al.* (1939); Callow (1939)
		Human (castrate)	Dorfman (1941)
		Human (female)	Schiller *et al.* (1945a)
		Monkey (pregnant)	Horwitt *et al.* (1944b)
		Chimpanzee (male)	Fish *et al.* (1942)
		Human (male)	Gallagher *et al.* (1951); Lotti *et al.* (1960)
	Epiandrosterone	Guinea pig (male)	Dorfman and Fish (1940)

Continued on following page

Table II (*continued*)

CATABOLISM OF NEUTRAL STEROIDS, *In Vivo*: REDUCTION OF Δ^4—3C=O TO 3C=O—5α, 3α—5α, AND 3β—5α GROUPINGS

Substrate	Product	Species	Reference
	Androsterone 5α-Androstane-3,17-dione	Rat	Pearlman and Pearlman (1961a, b)
	Androsterone Epiandrosterone	Human	Slaunwhite and Sandberg (1957)
19-Nortestosterone	19-Norandrosterone	Human	Engel *et al.* (1958a)
Androst-4-ene-3,17-dione	Androsterone	Human (hypogonadal male)	Dorfman and Hamilton (1940); Dorfman *et al.* (1950)
		Human (male)	Gallagher *et al.* (1951)
2α-Methyladrenosterone	2α-Methyl-3α-hydroxy-5α-androstane-11,17-dione	Human	Bush and Mahesh (1958a)
Progesterone	5α-Pregnane-3α,20α-diol	Human (female)	Ungar *et al.* (1951b); Marrian and Kyle (1951); Chang *et al.* (1960)
Adrenosterone	11-Ketoandrosterone 11β-Hydroxyandrosterone	Human (male)	Savard *et al.* (1953)
11β-Hydroxyandrost-4-ene-3,17-dione	11-Ketoandrosterone 11-Ketoetiocholanolone	Human	Bradlow and Gallagher (1957)
	11β-Hydroxyandrosterone	Human	Bradlow and Gallagher (1959)
Cortisol	3α,11β,17α,21-Tetrahydroxy-5α-pregnan-20-one	Human	Romanoff *et al.* (1961)
	5α-Pregnane-3β,11β,17α,20β,21-pentol	Rat	Ulrich (1958)
	3α,11β,17α,21-Tetrahydroxy-5α-pregnan-20-one Allocortol β-Allocortol Allocortolone 11β-Hydroxyandrosterone	Human	Fukishima *et al.* (1960)
11-Deoxycortisol	Etiocholanolone	Human	Pasargiklian (1959); Birke and Plantin (1953b)
Corticosterone	3α,11β,21-Trihydroxy-5α-pregnan-20-one 3α,21-Dihydroxy-5α-pregnane-11,20-dione (tentative)	Human	Touchstone *et al.* (1959)

Continued on following page

Table 11 *(continued)*

CATABOLISM OF NEUTRAL STEROIDS, *In Vivo*: REDUCTION OF Δ^4—3C=O TO 3C=O—5α, 3α—5α, AND 3β—5α GROUPINGS

Substrate	Product	Species	Reference
17α-Hydroxy-progesterone	5α-Pregnane-3α,17α,20α-triol 3α,17α-Dihydroxy-5α-pregnan-20-one Androsterone	Human	Fukushima *et al.* (1961)
	5α-Pregnane-3α,17α,20α-triol 17α-Hydroxy-5α-pregnane-3,20-dione	Human	Vermeulen *et al.* (1961)
Progesterone	5α-Pregnane-3α,6α,20α-triol	Rabbit	Knights *et al.* (1962)
Progesterone	5α-Pregnane-3α,20α-diol	Human Monkey	Knights and Thomas (1962)
17α-Hydroxy-progesterone	Androsterone	Human	Fukushima *et al.* (1962a)
Cortisol	11β-Hydroxyandrosterone 3α,11β,17α,21-Tetra-hydroxy-5α-pregnan-20-one	Human	Gallagher *et al.* (1962)
Cortisol	3α,1β,17α,21-Tetra-hydroxy-5α-pregnan-20-one	Human	Gold (1962)

Table 12

CATABOLISM OF NEUTRAL STEROIDS, *In Vitro*: REDUCTION OF Δ^4—3C=O TO 3β—5α AND 3α—5α GROUPINGS

Substrate	Product	Test system	Species	Reference
Deoxycorticosterone	3β,21-Dihydroxy-5α-pregnan-20-one	Liver slices	Rat	Schneider and Horstmann (1951)
		Liver homogenate	Rabbit	Taylor (1957)
	3α,21-Dihydroxy-5α-pregnan-20-one 3β,21-Dihydroxy-5α-pregnan-20-one	Liver disintegrated	Rabbit	Taylor (1959)
Progesterone	3β,17α-Dihydroxy-5α-pregnan-20-one	Adrenal perfusion	Bovine	Pincus (1954)
Androst-4-ene-3,17-dione	Androsterone Epiandrosterone	Liver homogenate	Rat	Rubin (1957)

Continued on following page

Table 12 (*continued*)

CATABOLISM OF NEUTRAL STEROIDS, *In Vitro*: REDUCTION OF Δ^4—3C=O TO 3β—5α AND 3α—5α GROUPINGS

Substrate	Product	Test system	Species	Reference
Aldosterone	Allotetrahydro-aldosterone (3α,5α)	Liver	Rat	Romani *et al.* (1959)
	Allotetrahydro-aldosterone (3β,5α)	Liver homogenate	Rat	Pechet *et al.* (1961a)
Cortisone	3α,17α,21-Trihydroxy-5α-pregnane-11,20-dione 3β,17α,21-Trihydroxy-5α-pregnane-11,20-dione 3α,11β,17α,21-Tetra-hydroxy-5α-pregnan-20-one 3β,11β,17α,21-Tetra-hydroxy-5α-pregnan-20-one 3β,17α,20β,21-Tetra-hydroxy-5α-pregnan-11-one	Liver perfusion	Rat	Caspi *et al.* (1953); Caspi and Hechter (1954); Caspi (1955)
	11-Ketoandrosterone 3β,17α,20β,21-Tetra-hydroxy-5α-pregnan-11-one	Liver perfusion	Rat	Caspi (1955)
	3β,17α,21-Trihydroxy-5α-pregnane-11,20-dione	Adrenal perfusion	Bovine	Pincus (1954)
	3α,17α,21-Trihydroxy-5α-pregnane-11,20-dione 3β,11β,17α,21-Tetra-hydroxy-5α-pregnan-20-one 3α,11β,17α,21-Tetra-hydroxy-5α-pregnan-20-one 17α,21-Dihydroxy-5α-pregnane-3,11,20-trione	Liver perfusion	Rat	Miller and Axelrod (1954)
Cortisol	5α-Pregnane-3β,11β,17α,20β-21-pentol 3β,11β,17α,21-Tetra-hydroxy-5α-pregnan-20-one	Liver perfusion	Rat	Caspi (1955); Caspi and Hechter (1956)

Continued on following page

Table 12 (*continued*)

CATABOLISM OF NEUTRAL STEROIDS, *In Vitro*: REDUCTION OF Δ^4—3C=O TO 3β—5α AND 3α—5α GROUPINGS

Substrate	Product	Test system	Species	Reference
11-Deoxycortisol	17α,21-Dihydroxy-5α-pregnane-3,20-dione 3α,17α,21-Trihydroxy-5α-pregnan-20-one 3β,17α,21-Trihydroxy-5α-pregnan-20-one	Liver homogenate	Rat	Forchielli (1956); Forchielli *et al.* (1955); Forchielli and Dorfman (1956)
16α-Hydroxyprogesterone Progesterone	3β,16α-Dihydroxy-5α-pregnan-20-one 3α,16α,Dihydroxy-5α-pregnan-20-one	Liver homogenate	Rat	Wettstein *et al.* (1959)
19-Hydroxycorticosterone	3α,5α-Tetrahydro-19-hydroxycorticosterone	Liver homogenate	Rat	Pechet *et al.* (1961b)
Testosterone	5α-Androstan-3α,17β-diol 5α-Androstan-3β,17β-diol	Liver homogenate	Human	Stylianou *et al.* (1961)
Androst-4-ene-3,17-dione	3β-Hydroxy-5α-androstan-17-one	Skeletal muscle strips	Rabbit	Thomas and Dorfman (1964b)

Table 13

CATABOLISM OF NEUTRAL STEROIDS, *In Vitro*: REDUCTION OF Δ^4—3C=O TO 3C=O—5α GROUPING

Substrate	Product	Test system	Species	Reference
Androst-4-ene-3,17-dione	11β-Hydroxy-5α-androstane-3,17-dione	Adrenal perfusion	Bovine	Jeanloz *et al.* (1953)
17α-Hydroxyprogesterone Progesterone 21-Deoxycortisone Cortisone	17α-Hydroxy-5α-pregnane-3,20-dione 5α-Pregnane-3,20-dione 17α-Hydroxy-5α-pregnane-3,20-dione 17α,21-Dihydroxy-5α-pregnane-3,11,20-trione 17α,21-Dihydroxy-5α-pregnane-3,11,20-trione	Adrenal perfusion	Bovine	Pincus (1954)

Continued on following page

Table 13 (*continued*)

CATABOLISM OF NEUTRAL STEROIDS, *In Vitro*: REDUCTION OF Δ^4—3C=O TO 3C=O—5α GROUPING

Substrate	Product	Test system	Species	Reference
Testosterone	17β-Hydroxy-5α-androstan-3-one	Liver homogenate	Rat	Rubin and Dorfman (1956)
Deoxycorticosterone	21-Hydroxy-5α-pregnane-3,20-dione	Adrenal perfusion	Bovine	Levy and Maloney (1962)
19-Hydroxycorticosterone	5α-Dihydro-19-hydroxycorticosterone	Liver homogenate	Rat	Pechet *et al.* (1961b)
Aldosterone	5α-Dihydroaldosterone	Liver homogenate	Rat	Pechet *et al.* (1961a)
Androst-4-ene-3,17-dione	5α-Androstane-3,17-dione	Muscle strip and homogenate	Rabbit	Thomas and Dorfman (1962)
Testosterone	17β-Hydroxy-5α-androstan-3-one			
Androst-4-ene-3,17-dione	5α-Androstane-3,17-dione	Liver homogenate supernatant	Rat	Forchielli *et al.* (1963)
Androst-4-ene-3,17-dione	5α-Androstane-3,17-dione	Skeletal muscle strips	Rabbit	Thomas and Dorfman (1964b)
Progesterone	5α-Pregnane-3,20-dione	Endometrium (human secretory)	Human	Bryson and Sweat (1963)

Table 14

CATABOLISM OF NEUTRAL STEROIDS, *In Vivo*: REDUCTION OF Δ^4—3C=O TO 3C=O—5β, 3α—5β, AND 3β—5β GROUPINGS

Substrate	Product	Species	Reference
Testosterone	Etiocholanolone	Human (hypogonadal males)	Callow (1939); Dorfman (1940)
		Human (female)	Schiller *et al.* (1945a)
		Rat	Pearlman and Pearlman (1961a)
		Human (male)	Gallagher *et al.* (1951); Lotti *et al.* (1960)
		Chimpanzee (male)	Fish *et al.* (1942)
		Human	Slaunwhite and Sandberg (1957)
19-Nortestosterone	19-Noretiocholanolone	Human	Engel *et al.* (1958a)

Continued on following page

Table 14 (*continued*)

CATABOLISM OF NEUTRAL STEROIDS, *In Vivo*: REDUCTION OF Δ^4—3C=O TO 3C=O—5β, 3α—5β, AND 3β—5β GROUPINGS

Substrate	Product	Species	Reference
Androst-4-ene-3,17-dione	Etiocholanolone	Human (male hypogonad)	Dorfman *et al.* (1950)
		Human (male)	Gallagher *et al.* (1951)
17α-Hydroxy-progesterone	Etiocholanolone	Human	Dorfman (1954a, b)
	Pregnanolone (artifact)	Human	Rosselet *et al.* (1954)
	Pregnanetriol 17α-Hydroxypregnanolone	Human	Brooks (1960)
Progesterone	Pregnanediol	Human (females and males)	Venning and Browne (1937); Buxton and Westphal (1938)
		Human (hyster-ectomized)	Müller (1940)
		Rabbit	Verly *et al.* (1950)
		Human	Pearlman (1957)
	Pregnanediol Pregnanolone	Human	Davis *et al.* (1956)
	Pregnanolone	Human (male and female)	Dorfman *et al.* (1948); Venning and Ripstein (1947)
		Rabbits (hyster-ectomized)	Heard *et al.* (1941)
	Pregnanediol Pregnanolone (in urine and bile)	Human	Chang *et al.* (1960)
11-Dehydrocorti-costerone	11-Ketopregnanediol	Human (Addison's disease)	Mason (1948)
	3α,11β,21-Trihydroxy-5α-pregnan-20-one 3α,21-Dihydroxy-5β-pregnane-11,20-dione	Human	Richardson *et al.* (1955)
	3α,21-Dihydroxy-5β-pregnane-11,20-dione	Human	Gomez-Mont and Berliner (1953)
Pregn-16-ene-3,20-dione	Pregnanediol Pregnanolone	Human	Dorfman *et al.* (1952)

Continued on following page

Table 14 *(continued)*

CATABOLISM OF NEUTRAL STEROIDS, *In Vivo*: REDUCTION OF Δ^4—3C=O TO 3C=O—5β, 3α—5β, AND 3β—5β GROUPINGS

Substrate	Product	Species	Reference
Deoxycorticosterone	Pregnanediol (may be artifact)	Human (male and female)	Horwitt *et al.* (1944a)
		Chimpanzee (ovariecto-mized)	Fish *et al.* (1943)
		Rabbit	Hoffman *et al.* (1943); Westphal (1942)
	3α,21-Dihydroxy-5β-pregnan-20-one	Human	Richardson *et al.* (1955)
Adrenosterone	11β-Hydroxyetio-cholanolone 11-Ketoetiocholanolone	Human	Savard *et al.* (1953)
11β-Hydroxyandrost-4-ene-3,17-dione	11-Ketoetiocholanolone 11β-Hydroxyetio-cholanolone	Human	Bradlow and Gallagher (1959)
	11β-Hydroxyetio-cholanolone 11β-Hydroxyandrosterone	Human	Bradlow and Gallagher (1957)
21-Deoxycortisone	11β-Hydroxyetio-cholanolone 11-Ketoetiocholanolone 21-Deoxyurocortisone	Human	Burstein *et al.* (1953b)
	11-Ketoetiocholanolone 21-Deoxyurocortisone 11-Ketopregnanolone (may be artifact)	Human	Rosselet *et al.* (1954, 1955)
	3α,17α,20α-Trihydroxy-5β-pregnan-11-one	Human	Fukushima and Gallagher (1957)
11-Deoxycortisol	Etiocholanolone	Human	Dorfman (1954a)
	3α,17α,21-Trihodroxy-5β-pregnan-20-one	Human	Richardson *et al.* (1954); Bongiovanni *et al.* (1958); Pasqualini and Jayle (1962)
11-Ketoprogesterone	11-Ketopregnanediol	Human	Dorfman (1954a)
Corticosterone	3α,11β,21-Trihydroxy-5β-pregnan-20-one 3α,21-Dihydroxy-5β-pregnane-11,20-dione	Human	Richardson *et al.* (1955)

Continued on following page

Table 14 *(continued)*

Catabolism of Neutral Steroids, *In Vivo*: Reduction of Δ^4—3C=O to 3C=O—5β, 3α—5β, and 3β—5β Groupings

Substrate	Product	Species	Reference
	5β-Pregnane-3α,11β,20-triol 3α,11β-Dihydroxy-5β-pregnan-20-one	Human	Fukushima *et al.* (1960)
	3α,11β,21-Trihydroxy-5β-pregnan-20-one	Human	Touchstone *et al.* (1959)
	3α,21-Dihydroxy-5β-pregnane-11,20-dione 3α,11β,21-Trihydroxy-5β-pregnan-20-one 3α,20α-Dihydroxy-5β-pregnan-11-one	Human	Engel *et al.* (1955)
Cortisone	11-Ketoetiocholanolone 11β-Hydroxyetiocholanolone	Human	Birke and Plantin (1953a)
	11-Ketoetiocholanolone 11β-Hydroxyetiocholanolone 21-Deoxyurocortisone Urocortisone Urocortisol	Human	Burstein *et al.* (1953c)
	11-Ketoetiocholanolone 11β-Hydroxyetiocholanolone 21-Deoxyurocortisone	Human	Dobriner and Lieberman (1952)
	Urocortisol Urocortisone	Human	Burton *et al.* (1953); Cope and Hurlock (1954); Richardson *et al.* (1955)
	Urocortisone 11β-Hydroxyetiocholanolone 11-Ketoetiocholanolone	Human	Lombardo and Hudson (1957)
	Cortolone β-Cortolone	Human	Fukushima *et al.* (1955)
	Allocortol Allocortolone	Human	Fukushima *et al.* (1960)

Continued on following page

Table 14 (*continued*)

CATABOLISM OF NEUTRAL STEROIDS, *In Vivo*: REDUCTION OF Δ^4—3C=O TO 3C=O—5β, 3α—5β, AND 3β—5β GROUPINGS

Substrate	Product	Species	Reference
Cortisol	Urocortisone Urocortisol 11β-Hydroxyetio-cholanolone	Human	Burstein *et al.* (1953a)
	Urocortisone Urocortisol	Human	Richardson *et al.* (1955)
	Urocortisone Urocortisol	Mouse	Dougherty *et al.* (1958)
	5α-Pregnane-3α,11β,17α,20β,21-pentol	Rat	Ulrich (1958)
	Urocortisone	Human	Cope and Hurlock (1954)
	Cortol β-Cortol Cortolone β-Cortolone	Human	Fukushima *et al.* (1955)
	11β,17α,20α,21-Tetra-hydroxy-5β-pregnan-3-one	Human	Peterson *et al.* (1957)
	11-Ketoetiocholanolone 11β-Hydroxyetio-cholanolone	Human	Gallagher (1957)
	Urocortisone glucuronoside Urocortisol glucuronoside	Human	Vermeulen (1956a, b)
	Urocortisone Urocortisol Cortol β-Cortol Cortolone β-Cortolone 11β-Hydroxyetio-cholanolone 11-Ketoetiocholanolone	Human	Fukushima *et al.* (1960)
11-Deoxycortisol	Androsterone (minor)	Human	Birke and Plantin (1953b)

Continued on following page

Table 14 (*continued*)

CATALOBISM OF NEUTRAL STEROIDS, *In Vivo*: REDUCTION OF Δ^4—3C=O TO 3C=O—5β, 3α—5β, ADD 3β—5β GROUPINGS

Substrate	Product	Species	Reference
17α-Hydroxy-progesterone	Pregnane-3α,17α,20α-triol Pregnane-3α,17α,20β-triol 3α,17α-Dihydroxy-5β-pregnane-20-one Etiocholanolone	Human	Fukushima *et al.* (1961); Vermeulen *et al.* (1961)
Aldosterone	3α,5β-Teterahydro-aldosterone	Human	Ulick *et al.* (1961); Cope *et al.* (1961)
	3α,21-Dihydroxy-5α-pregnan-(11β-18), (18-20) dioxide 3α-Hydroxy-5α-pregnane-(11β-18),(18-20) dioxide	Human	Kelly *et al.* (1962a)
	Tetrahydroaldosterone (3α,5β)	Human	Coppage *et al.* (1962)
Progesterone	5β-Pregnane-3α,20α-diol	Human Monkey Rabbit	Knights and Thomas (1962)
20α-Hydroxy-pregn-4-en-3-one 20β-Hydroxypregn-4-en-3-one	5β-Pregnane-3α,20α-diol	Rabbit	
17α-Hydroxy-progesterone	Pregnanetriol 3α,17α-Dihydroxy-5β-pregnan-20-one Etiocholanoline	Human	Fukushima *et al.* (1962a)
Cortisol	Urocortisol Urocortisone 11β-Hydroxyetiocholanolone 11-Ketoetiocholanolone	Human	Gallagher *et al.* (1962)
	Urocortisol Urocortisone Cortol Cortolone	Human	Gold (1962)

Table 15

CATABOLISM OF NEUTRAL STEROIDS, *In Vitro*: REDUCTION OF Δ^4—3—C=O TO 3—C=O—5β GROUPING

Substrate	Product	Test system	Species	Reference
Cortisol	11β,17α,21-Trihydroxy-5β-pregnane-3,20-dione	Connective tissue	Rat	Berliner and Dougherty (1958a, b)
Progesterone	5β-Pregnane-3,20-dione	Blood proteins	Bovine	Rongone *et al.* (1957)
Androst-4-ene-3,17-dione	5β-Androstane-3,17-dione			
Cortisone	17α,21-Dihydroxy-5β-pregnane-3,20-dione			
Androst-4-ene-3,17-dione	5β-Androstane-3,17-dione	Liver homogenate supernatant	Rat	Forchielli *et al.* (1963)
Progesterone	5β-Pregnane-3,20-dione	Endometrium (secretory)	Human	Bryson and Sweat (1963)

Table 16

CATABOLISM OF NEUTRAL STEROIDS, *In Vitro*: REDUCTION of Δ^4—3—C=O TO 3α—5β AND 3β—5β GROUPINGS

Substrate	Product	Test system	Species	Reference
Testosterone	Etiocholanolone 3β-Hydroxy-5β-androstan-17-one	Liver homogenate	Fowl	Samuels *et al.* (1950); Samuels (1949)
Deoxycorticosterone	3α,21-Dihydroxy-5β-pregnan-20-one	Liver homogenate	Rabbit	Taylor (1957)
		Liver disintegrate	Rabbit	Taylor (1959)
11-Deoxycortisol	3α,17α,21-Trihydroxy-5β-pregnan-20-one 3β,17α,21-Trihydroxy-5β-pregnan-20-one	Liver homogenate	Rat	Forchielli (1956); Forchielli and Dorfman (1956); Forchielli *et al.* (1955)
Cortisol	Cortolone Urocortisone Urocortisol	Liver perfusion	Dog	Axelrod and Miller (1956)
	Urocortisol	Liver	Rat	Tomkins (1956a, b)

Continued on following page

Table 16 *(continued)*

CATABOLISM OF NEUTRAL STEROIDS, *In Vitro*: REDUCTION OF Δ^4—3—C═O TO 3α—5β AND 3β—5β GROUPINGS

Substrate	Product	Test system	Species	Reference
	β-Cortol	Liver homogenate	Rat	Hübener (1956); Hübener *et al.* (1956)
Progesterone	Pregnanediol 3α-Hydroxy-5β-pregnan-20-one	Liver homogenate Liver perfusion	Rabbit	Ishizuka *et al.* (1957)
Testosterone	5β-Androstane-3α-,17β-diol	Liver homogenate	Human	Stylianou *et al.* (1961)
Aldosterone	Tetrahydroaldosterone (3α,5β)	Liver	Human	Romani *et al.* (1959)
16α-Hydroxy-progesterone Progesterone	3α,16α,Dihydroxy-5β-pregnan-20-one	Liver homogenate	Rat	Wettstein *et al.* (1959)
19-Hydroxy-corticosterone	3α,5β-Tetrahydro-19-hydroxycorticosterone	Liver homogenate	Rat	Pechet *et al.* (1961b)
Cortisone	5β-Dihydrocortisone Urocortisone	Liver homogenate	Human	Meigs and Engel (1961)
Cortisol	Urocortisol Urocortisone	Liver slice	Human	Lipman *et al.* (1962)
	Urocortisol and Urocortisone (these products decreased in presence of estrone)			

Table 17

CATABOLISM OF NEUTRAL STEROIDS, *In Vivo*: CONVERSION OF Δ^5—3β—OH TO THE 3α—5α GROUPING

Substrate	Product	Species	Reference
Dehydroepiandrosterone	Androsterone	Human	Mason and Kepler (1945a, b); Miller *et al.* (1950)
Androst-5-ene-3β,17β-diol	Androsterone	Human	Ungar *et al.* (1954b)

Table 18

CATABOLISM OF NEUTRAL STEROIDS, *In Vivo*: CONVERSION OF Δ^5—3β—OH TO THE 3α—5β GROUPING

Substrate	Product	Species	Reference
Dehydroepiandrosterone	Etiocholanolone	Human	Mason and Kepler (1945a, b); Miller *et al.* (1950)
Androst-5-ene-3β,17β-diol	Etiocholanolone	Human	Ungar *et al.* (1954b)
Pregnenolone	Pregnanediol	Rabbit	Pearlman and Pincus (1946);
		Human	Ungar *et al.* (1951b)

Table 19

CATABOLISM OF NEUTRAL STEROIDS, *In Vitro* AND *In Vivo*: OXIDATION OF Δ^5—3β—OH GROUPING TO Δ^4—3—C=O

Substrate	Product	Test system	Species	Reference
Dehydroepiandrosterone	Androst-4-ene-3,17-dione	Liver perfusion	Rat	Ungar *et al.* (1954b)
	Testosterone Androst-4-ene-3,17-dione	Liver perfusion	Dog	Klempien *et al.* (1961)
Androst-5-ene-3β,17β-diol	Androst-4-ene-3,17-dione	Erythrocyte preparation	Rat	Portius and Repke (1960b)
Androst-5-ene-3β,17α-diol	17α-Hydroxyandrost-4-en-3-one			
Dehydroepiandrosterone	Androst-4-ene-3,17-dione			
Dehydroepiandrosterone	Testosterone Androst-4-ene-3,17-dione	*In vivo*	Human	Mahesh and Greenblatt (1962)

Table 20

CATABOLISM OF NEUTRAL STEROIDS, *In Vivo*: INTERCONVERSION OF 11β—OH AND 11—C=O GROUPINGS

Substrate	Product	Species	Reference
Cortisol	Urocortisone 11-Ketoetiocholanolone	Human	Burstein *et al.* (1953a)
	Urocortisone	Human	Richardson *et al.* (1955); Cope and Hurlock (1954)

Continued on following page

Table 20 *(continued)*

Catabolism of Neutral Steroids, *In Vivo*: Interconversion of 11β—OH and 11—C=O Groupings

Substrate	Product	Species	Reference
	Cortolone β-Cortolone	Human	Fukushima *et al.* (1955)
	Urocortisone	Human	Vermeulen (1956a, b)
	11-Ketoandrosterone 11-Ketoetiocholanolone	Human	Gallagher (1957)
Urocortisol	Urocortisone 11-Ketoetiocholanolone	Human	Savard and Goldfaden (1954)
11β,17α,21-Trihydroxy-5β-pregnane-3,20-dione	Urocortisone 11-Ketoetiocholanolone	Human	
Corticosterone	3α,21-Dihydroxy-5β-pregnane-11,20-dione	Human	Richardson *et al.* (1955)
	11β,20β,21-Trihydroxypregn-4-en-3-one 11β,20α-21-Trihydroxypregn-4-en-3-one	Human	Bulaschenko *et al.* (1960)
	3α,21-Dihydroxy-5β-pregnane-11,20-dione 3α,20α-Dihydroxy-5β-pregnan-11-one	Human	Engel *et al.* (1955)
	21-Hydroxypregn-4-ene-3,11,20-trione	Human	Touchstone *et al.* (1959)
11-Dehydrocorticosterone	11β,20β,21-Trihydroxypregn-4-en-3-one	Human	Richardson *et al.* (1958a, b)
3α,17α,21-Trihydroxy-5α-pregnane-11,20-dione	3α,11β,17α,21-Tetrahydroxy-5α-pregnan-20-one	Human	Bush and Mahesh (1958a)
Cortisone	Cortisol 11β-Hydroxyetiocholanolone	Human	Lombardo and Hudson (1957)
	Cortisol Urocortisol	Human	Cope and Hurlock (1954)
	Cortisol	Human	Richardson *et al.* (1955)
	Cortisol 11β,17α,20β,21-Tetrahydroxypregn-4-en-3-one	Rat	Caspi and Bergen (1955)
	Cortisol 11β-Hydroxyetiocholanolone Urocortisol	Human	Burstein *et al.* (1953c)

Continued on following page

Table 20 *(continued)*

Catabolism of Neutral Steroids, *In Vivo*: Interconversion of 11β—OH and 11—C=O Groupings

Substrate	Product	Species	Reference
	11β-Hydroxyetio-cholanolone	Human	Birke and Plantin (1953a); Dobriner and Lieberman (1952)
	Cortisol Urocortisol	Human	Burton *et al.* (1953)
Adrenosterone	11β-Hydroxyetio-cholanolone 11β-Hydroxyandrosterone	Human	Savard *et al.* (1953)
2α-Methyladreno-sterone	2α-Methyl-11β-hydroxy-androst-4-ene-3,17-dione 2α-Methyl-11β,17β-dihydroxyandrost-4-en-3-one	Human	Bush and Mahesh (1958a)
11β-Hydroxyandrost-4-ene-3,17-dione	11-Ketoandrosterone 11-Ketoetiocholanolone	Human	Bradlow and Gallagher (1957)
	11-Ketoetiocholanolone	Human (congenital adrenal hyperplasia)	Bradlow and Gallagher (1959)
Prednisolone	Androsta-1,4-diene-3,11,17-trione	Human	Vermeulen (1957)
	11-Ketoetiocholanolone	Human	Caspi and Pechet (1957)
	Prednisone	Human	Johnson *et al.* (1957)
	Prednisone 17α,20α,21-Trihydroxy-pregna-1,4-diene-3,11-dione	Human	Gray *et al.* (1956)
	17α,21-Dihydroxy-5β-pregn-1-ene-3,11,20-trione 11-Ketoetiocholanolone		Caspi and Pechet (1958)
Prednisone	Prednisolone (presumptive)	Human	Gray *et al.* (1955); Vermeulen (1956a)
	Prednisolone	Human	Johnson *et al.* (1957); Gray *et al.* (1956); Bush and Mahesh (1958a)
	Cortisol	Human	Lamedica *et al.* (1957)
Urocortisone	Urocortisol	Human	Bush and Mahesh (1958a)
11β-Hydroxy-androsterone	No 11-Ketoandrosterone	Human	Bush and Mahesh (1959a)
11β-Hydroxyetio-cholanolone	No 11 Ketoetiocholanolone		

Continued on following page

Table 20 *(continued)*

CATABOLISM OF NEUTRAL STEROIDS, *In Vivo*: INTERCONVERSION OF 11β—OH AND 11—C=O GROUPINGS

Substrate	Product	Species	Reference
Allotetrahydrocortisol	Allotetrahydrocortisone		
Tetrahydrocortisone	Tetrahydrocortisol		
11-Ketoandrosterone	11β-Hydroxyandrosterone		
11-Ketoetiocholanolone	11β-Hydroxyetiocholanolone		
Cortisol	Cortisone	Sockeye salmon	Idler and Truscott (1963)
Urocortisol	Urocortisone Cortolone 11β-Hydroxyetiocholanolone	Human	Rappaport and Migeon (1962)

Table 21

CATABOLISM OF NEUTRAL STEROIDS, *In Vitro*: Interconversion of 11β—OH and 11—C=O GROUPINGS

Substrate	Product	Test system	Species	Reference
Cortisone	3α,11β,17α,21-Tetrahydroxy-5α-pregnane-20-one 3β,11β,17α,21-Tetrahydroxy-5α-pregnan-20-one Cortisol	Liver perfusion	Rat	Caspi *et al.* (1953)
	Cortisol	Liver homogenate	Rat Bovine Porcine	Fish *et al.* (1953); Eisenstein (1952)
	11β,17α,20β,21-Tetrahydroxypregn-4-en-3-one Cortisol 3α,11β,17α,21-Tetrahydroxy-5α-pregnan-20-one	Liver perfusion	Rat	Caspi and Hechter (1954); Caspi (1955)
	Cortisol	Liver homogenate	Rat Porcine	Amelung *et al.* (1953a, b)
			Rat	Hübener *et al.* (1956); Hübener (1956)

Continued on following page

Table 21 (*continued*)

CATABOLISM OF NEUTRAL STEROIDS, *In Vitro*: Interconversion of 11β—OH AND 11—C=O GROUPINGS

Substrate	Product	Test system	Species	Reference
	Cortisol 3β,11β,17α,21-Tetrahydroxy-5α-pregnan-20-one 3α,11β,17α,21-Tetrahydroxy-5α-pregnan-20-one	Liver perfusion	Rat	Miller and Axelrod (1954)
11β-Hydroxyandrost-4-ene-3,17-dione	Adrenosterone	Adrenal homogenate	Bovine	Meyer *et al.* (1955)
Cortisol	Cortisone	Connective tissue	Rat	Berliner and Dougherty (1958a)
	Cortisone Cortolone Urocortisone	Liver perfusion	Dog	Axelrod and Miller (1956)
	17α,20β,21-Trihydroxypregn-4-ene-3,11-dione	Liver perfusion	Rat	Caspi (1955); Caspi and Hechter (1956)
	Cortisone	Kidney mince	Bovine	Ganis *et al.* (1956)
		Liver homogenate Placental slices	Human	Meigs and Engel (1961)
Cortisone	Cortisol	Liver homogenate	Human	Meigs and Engel (1961)
Tetrahydrocortisone	Cortol	Placental slices		
Cortisol	Urocortisone	Liver slices	Human	Lipman *et al.* (1962)
Cortisol	Cortisone	Placental slices	Human Rat	Venning and Sybulski (1962)
Cortisol	Cortisone	Cerebral cortical homogenates or minces	Rats	Grosser and Bliss (1963)
11β-Hydroxyandrost-4-ene-3,17-dione	Adrenosterone			
Corticosterone	21-Hydroxypregn-4-ene-3,11,20-trione			

Table 22

CATABOLISM OF NEUTRAL STEROIDS, *In Vivo*: OXIDATION OF 17β—OH TO THE 17—C=O GROUPINGS

Substrate	Product	Test system	Species	Reference
Testosterone	Androsterone Etiocholanolone Epiandrosterone		Human (hypogonadal male)	Dorfman *et al.* (1939); Callow (1939); Dorfman (1954a)
	Androsterone Etiocholanolone		Human (female)	Schiller *et al.* (1945b)
	Androsterone Etiocholanolone		Human (male)	Gallagher *et al.* (1951)
	Epiandrosterone		Guinea pig (male)	Dorfman and Fish (1940)
	Androsterone		Chimpanzee (male)	Fish *et al.* (1942)
	Androsterone		Monkey (pregnant)	Horwitt *et al.* (1944b)
19-Nortestosterone	19-Norandrosterone 19-Noretiocholanolone		Human	Engel *et al.* (1958a)
5α-Androstane-3α,17β-diol	Androsterone Epiandrosterone		Human	Dorfman *et al.* (1950)
5α-Androstane-3β,17β-diol	Epiandrosterone Androsterone		Human	Ungar *et al.* (1951a); Dorfman *et al.* (1952)
Testosterone	Etiocholanolone 3β-Hydroxy-5β-androstan-17-one	Liver homogenate	Fowl	Samuels *et al.* (1950); Samuels (1949)
	Androst-4-ene-3,17-dione	Liver brei	Rabbit	Clark and Kochakian (1947)
	Androst-4-ene-3,17-dione	Liver	Rat	Sweat *et al.* (1950)
	Androst-4-ene-3,17-dione	Slices of: mammary cancer prostatic cancer hypertrophied prostate thyroid adenoma bronchial adenoma	Human	Breuer *et al.* (1959e)

Continued on following page

Table 22 (*continued*)

CATABOLISM OF NEUTRAL STEROIDS, *In Vivo*: OXIDATION OF 17β—OH TO THE 17—C=O GROUPINGS

Substrate	Product	Test system	Species	Reference
5α-Androstane-3α,17β-diol	Androsterone	Liver and kidney	Guinea pig Rabbit	Kochakian and Aposhian (1952)
	Epiandrosterone	Liver	Rabbit	
5α-Androstane-3α,17β-diol	Androsterone	Erythrocyte suspension	Rat	Portuis and Repke (1960b)
Testosterone	Androst-4-ene-3,17-dione			
Androst-5-ene-3β,17β-diol	Dehydroepiandrosterone Androst-4-ene-3,17-dione			
17β-Hydroxy-5α-androstan-3-one	5α-Androstane-3,17-dione			
Androst-5-ene-3β,17β-diol	Dehydroepiandrosterone Androsterone Etiocholanolone		Human	Ungar *et al.* (1951a, 1954b); Dorfman *et al.* (1952)
	Dehydroepiandrosterone		Guinea pig	Miller and Dorfman (1945)

Table 23

CATABOLISM OF NEUTRAL STEROIDS, *In Vivo*: REDUCTION OF 17—C=O TO THE 17β—OH GROUPING

Substrate	Product	Species	Reference
Dehydroepiandrosterone	5β-Androstane-3α,17β-diol Androst-5-ene-3β,17β-diol	Human	Mason and Kepler (1945a, b); Miller *et al.* (1950)
	Androst-5-ene-3β,16α,17β-triol	Human	Mason and Kepler (1945b, 1947)
Etiocholanolone	5β-Androstane-3α,17β-diol	Human	Gallagher *et al.* (1951); Kappas *et al.* (1958)
Androst-4-ene-3,17-dione	Testosterone	Rat	Pearlman and Pearlman (1961b)
Dehydroepiandrosterone	Testosterone	Human	Mahesh and Greenblatt (1962)
Androst-4-ene-3,17-dione	Testosterone		

Table 24

CATABOLISM OF NEUTRAL STEROIDS, *In Vitro*: INTERCONVERSION OF 17α—OH, 17β—OH, AND 17—C=O GROUPINGS

Substrate	Product	Test system	Species	Reference
Androst-4-ene-3,17-dione	Epitestosterone	Liver slices	Rabbit	Clark and Kochakian (1947)
Epitestosterone	Androst-4-ene-3,17-dione	Liver slices	Rabbit	Kochakian *et al.* (1952)
Etiocholanolone	5β-Androstane-3α,17α-diol	Liver slices	Rabbit	Schneider and Mason (1948a)
17α-Hydroxyandrost-4-en-3-one	Androst-4-ene-3,17-dione	Erythrocyte suspension	Bovine	Portuis and Repke (1960b)
Testosterone	Androst-4-ene-3,17-dione	Liver homogenate	Human	Stylianou *et al.* (1961)
		Skin slices	Human	Wotiz *et al.* (1956)
Androst-4-ene-3,17-dione	Testosterone	Muscle strip and homogenate	Rabbit	Thomas and Dorfman (1962)
Androsterone Etiocholanolone	5α-Androstane-3α,17β-diol	Liver slices	Rabbit	Schneider and Mason (1948a, b)
Dehydroepiandrosterone	Androst-5-ene-3β,17β-diol	Liver	Rabbit	Rosenkrantz and Dorfman (1962)
			Rat	Ungar *et al.* (1954b)
	Androst-5-ene-3β,16α,17β-triol	Liver	Rabbit	Schneider and Mason (1948b)
Androst-4-ene-3,17-dione	Testosterone	Liver brei	Rabbit	Clark *et al.* (1947)
Dehydroepiandrosterone	Androst-5-ene-3β,17β-diol Testosterone	Liver perfusion	Dog	Klempien *et al.* (1961)
Testosterone	Androst-4-ene-3,17-dione	Earle's cells WCTC 929		Perlman *et al.* (1960)
Androst-4-ene-3,17-dione	Testosterone	Skeletal muscle homogenate	Rabbit	Thomas and Dorfman (1963a)
Androst-4-ene-3,17-dione	Testosterone	Skeletal muscle strips	Rabbit	Thomas and Dorfman (1963b)

Table 25

CATABOLISM OF NEUTRAL STEROIDS, *In Vivo*: REDUCTION OF Δ^{16}-GROUPING

Substrate	Product	Species	Reference
Pregna-4,16-diene-3,20-dione	Pregnanediol	Human	Dorfman *et al.* (1952)
3β-Hydroxypregna-5,16-dien-20-one	Pregnanolone Pregnanediol	Human	Dorfman *et al.* (1952)

Table 26

CATABOLISM OF NEUTRAL STEROIDS, *In Vivo*: CONVERSION OF C_{21} TO C_{19} STEROIDS

Substrate	Product	Species	Reference
17α,21-Dihydroxy-5β-pregnane-3,20-dione	Etiocholanolone	Human	Ungar *et al.* (1954a)
11β,17α,21-Trihydroxy-5β-pregnane-3,20-dione and urocortisol	11β-Hydroxyetiocholanolone 11-Ketoetiocholanolone	Human	Savard and Goldfaden (1954)
21-Deoxycortisone	11β-Hydroxyetiocholanolone 11-Ketoetiocholanolone	Human	Burstein *et al.* (1953b, 1954)
21-Deoxycortisol	Etiocholanolone Androsterone	Human	Dorfman (1954a)
3α,17α,21-Trihydroxy-5α-pregnan-20-one	11β-Hydroxyandrosterone	Human	Bush and Mahesh (1958a)
Cortisone	11β-Hydroxyetiocholanolone 11-Ketoetiocholanolone	Human	Dobriner and Lieberman (1952); Burstein *et al.* (1953c); Birke and Plantin (1953a); Lombardo and Hudson (1957)
Cortisol	11β-Hydroxyetiocholanolone 11-Ketoetiocholanolone	Human	Burstein *et al.* (1953a)
	11β-Hydroxyandrosterone 11-Ketoandrosterone 11β-Hydroxyetiocholanolone 11-Ketoetiocholanolone	Human	Gallagher (1957); Fukushima *et al.* (1960)
	11β-Hydroxyepiandrosterone	Human	Kemp *et al.* (1954)

Continued on following page

Table 26 (*continued*)

CATABOLISM OF NEUTRAL STEROIDS, *In Vivo*: CONVERSION OF C_{21} TO C_{19} STEROIDS

Substrate	Product	Species	Reference
17α-Hydroxyprogesterone	Androsterone Etiocholanolone	Human	Dorfman (1954a)
	Etiocholanolone	Human	Brooks (1960)
Prednisolone	Androsta-1,4-diene-3,11,17-trione 11β-Hydroxyandrosta-1,4-diene-3,17-dione	Human	Vermeulen (1957)
	11β-Hydroxyetiocholanolone 11-Ketoetiocholanolone	Human	Caspi and Pechet (1957, 1958)
11-Deoxycortisol	Etiocholanolone	Human	Pasargiklian (1959)
	Etiocholanolone (major) Androsterone (minor)	Human	Birke and Plantin (1953b)
3α,17α-Dihydroxy-5β-pregnane-11,20-dione	11-Ketoetiocholanolone	Human	Ungar *et al.* (1960)
Cortisone	11-Ketoandrosterone 11-Ketoetiocholanolone 11β-Hydroxyandrosterone 11β-Hydroxyetiocholanolone	Guinea pig	Charollais *et al.* (1961)
17α-Hydroxyprogesterone	Androsterone Etiocholanolone	Human	Fukushima *et al.* (1961)
	Etiocholanolone	Human	Vermeulen *et al.* (1961)
Allotetrahydrocortisol (3α,5α) Urocortisone	11β-Hydroxyandrosterone 11-Ketoetiocholanolone	Human	Bush and Mahesh (1959b)
17α-Hydroxyprogesterone	11-Ketotestosterone Testosterone	Sockeye salmon (*Oncorhynchus*)	Idler and Truscott (1963)
Urocortisol	11β-Hydroxyetiochollanolone 11-Ketoetiocholanolone	Human	Rappaport and Migeon (1962)
17α-Hydroxyprogesterone	Androsterone Etiocholanolone	Human	Fukushima *et al.* (1962a)

Table 27

CATABOLISM OF NEUTRAL STEROIDS, *In Vitro*: CONVERSION OF C_{21} TO C_{19} STEROIDS

Substrate	Product	Test system	Species	Reference
Cortisone	Adrenosterone	Liver perfusion	Rat	Caspi *et al.* (1953)
	3α-Hydroxy-5α-androstane-11,17-dione Adrenosterone	Liver perfusion	Rat	Caspi and Hechter (1954); Caspi (1955)
17α-Hydroxy-pregnenolone	Dehydroepiandrosterone	Hind limb perfusion	Dog	Oertel and Eik-Nes (1959)
Cortisol	11β-Hydroxyandrost-4-ene-3,17-dione	Connective tissue (mast cells)	Rat	Berliner and Dougherty (1958a, b)
	11β-Hydroxyandrost-4-ene-3,17-dione Adrenosterone	Kidney mince	Bovine	Ganis *et al.* (1956)
	11β-Hydroxyandrost-4-ene-3,17-dione	Liver perfusion	Dog	Axelrod and Miller (1956)
	11β-Hydroxyandrost-4-ene-3,17-dione 11β-Hydroxyepiandrosterone	Liver perfusion	Rat	Caspi (1955); Caspi and Hechter (1956)
11-Deoxycortisol	Androsterone 5α-Androstane-3,17-dione Androst-4-ene-3,17-dione Etiocholanolone	Liver	Rat	Forchielli *et al.* (1955); Forchielli and Dorfman (1956)

Table 28

CATABOLISM OF NEUTRAL STEROIDS, *In Vivo*: REDUCTION OF 20—C=O TO 20β—OH GROUPING

Substrate	Product	Species	Reference
Cortisol	11β,17α,20β,21-Tetrahydroxypregn-4-en-3-one	Guinea pig	Burstein and Dorfman (1955)
	β-Cortol β-Cortolone	Human	Fukushima *et al.* (1955)

Continued on following page

Table 28 (*continued*)

CATABOLISM OF NEUTRAL STEROIDS, *In Vivo*: REDUCTION OF 20—C=O TO 20β—OH GROUPING

Substrate	Product	Species	Reference
	β-Cortol β-Allocortol β-Cortolone	Human	Fukushima *et al.* (1960)
	11β,17α,20β,21-Tetra-hydroxypregn-4-en-3-one	Rat	Abelson *et al.* (1955)
	β-Allocortol 5β-Pregnane-3β,11β,17α,20β,21-pentol	Rat	Ulrich (1958)
Cortisone	17α,20β,21-Trihydroxy-pregn-4-ene-3,11-dione	Human	Lombardo and Hudson (1957)
	11β,17α,20β,21-Tetra-hydroxypregn-4-en-3-one	Rat	Caspi and Bergen (1955)
		Human	Fukushima *et al.* (1955)
11-Dehydrocorti-costerone	11β,20β,21-Trihydroxy-pregn-4-en-3-one	Human	Richardson *et al.* (1958a); Bulaschenko *et al.* (1960)
Urocortisone	β-Cortolone	Human	Schneider *et al.* (1955)
Corticosterone	20β,21-Dihydroxypregn-4-ene-3,11-dione 11β,20β,21-Trihydroxy-pregn-4-en-3-one 11β,20α,21-Trihydroxy-pregn-4-en-3-one	Human	Bulaschenko *et al.* (1960)
17α-Hydroxy-progesterone	5β-Pregnane-3α,17α,20β-triol	Human	Fukushima *et al.* (1961); Vermeulen *et al.* (1961)
Corticosterone	11β,20β,21-Trihydroxy-pregn-4-en-3-one	Mouse	Krehbiel *et al.* (1962)

Table 29

CATABOLISM OF NEUTRAL STEROIDS, *In Vivo*: REDUCTION OF 20—C=O TO 20α—OH GROUPING

Substrate	Product	Species	Reference
Pregnanolone	Pregnanediol	Human and rabbit	Pearlman and Pincus (1946)
Pregnenolone	Pregnanediol Pregn-5-ene-3β,20α-diol	Human (male)	Ungar *et al.* (1951b)

Continued on following page

Table 29 (*continued*)

CATABOLISM OF NEUTRAL STEROIDS, *In Vivo*: REDUCTION OF 20—C=O TO 20α—OH GROUPING

Substrate	Product	Species	Reference
Pregna-4,16-diene-3,20-dione	Pregnanediol	Human	Dorfman *et al.* (1952)
3β-Hydroxypregna-5,16-dien-20-one	Pregnanediol Pregnanolone	Human	Dorfman *et al.* (1952)
Progesterone	Pregnanediol	Human (male and female)	Buxton and Westphal (1938); Venning and Browne (1937); Müller (1940); Pearlman (1957); Davis *et al.* (1956)
	Pregnanediol	Rabbit	Heard *et al.* (1941); Verly *et al.* (1950)
	20α-Hydroxypregn-4-en-3-one	Rat (eviscerated)	Wiest (1956)
	Pregnanediol Allopregnanediol	Human	Chang *et al.* (1960)
Deoxycorticosterone	Pregnanediol	Human (male and female)	Horwitt *et al.* (1944a)
		Chimpanzee (ovariectomized)	Fish *et al.* (1943)
		Rabbit	Hoffman *et al.* (1943); Westphal (1942)
11-Dehydrocorticosterone	11-Ketopregnanediol	Human	Mason (1948)
17α,21-Dihydroxy-5β-pregnane-3,20-dione	Pregnanetriol	Human	Ungar *et al.* (1954a)
Cortisol	Cortol Cortolone	Human	Fukushima *et al.* (1955)
	11β,17α,20α,21-Tetrahydroxypregn-4-en-3-one	Guinea pig	Burstein and Dorfman (1955)
	11β,17α,20α,21-Tetrahydroxy-5β-pregnan-3-one	Human	Peterson *et al.* (1957)
	Cortol Allocortol Cortolone Allocortolone	Human	Fukushima *et al.* (1960)
Cortisone	3α,17α,20α-Trihydroxy-5β-pregnan-11-one	Human	Burstein *et al.* (1953c); Dobriner and Lieberman (1952)

Continued on following page

Table 29 (*continued*)

CATABOLISM OF NEUTRAL STEROIDS, *In Vivo*: REDUCTION OF 20—C=O TO 20α—OH GROUPING

Substrate	Product	Species	Reference
	Cortolone	Human	Lombardo and Hudson (1957)
Cortisone	Allocortol Allocortolone	Human	Fukushima *et al.* (1960)
21-Deoxycortisone	3α,17α,20α-Trihydroxy-5β-pregnan-11-one	Human	Fukushima and Gallagher (1957)
Corticosterone	3α,20α-Dihydroxy-5β-pregnan-11-one	Human	Engel *et al.* (1955)
	11β,20α,21-Trihydroxy-pregn-4-en-3-one	Human	Southcott *et al.* (1958)
Prednisolone	17α,20α,21-Trihydroxy-pregna-1,4-diene-3,11-dione	Human	Gray *et al.* (1956)
3α,17α-Dihydroxy-5β-pregnane-11,20-dione	3α,17α,20α-Trihydroxy-5β-pregnan-11-one	Human	Ungar *et al.* (1960)
17α-Hydroxy-progesterone	Pregnanetriol	Human	Brooks (1960)
	Pregnanetriol 5α-Pregnane-3α,17α,20α-triol	Human	Fukushima *et al.* (1961); Vermeulen *et al.* (1961)
Progesterone	5α-Pregnane-3α,6α,20α-triol	Rabbit	Knights *et al.* (1962)
Corticosterone	11β,20α,21-Trihydroxy-pregn-4-en-3-one	Mouse	Krehbiel *et al.* (1962)
Progesterone	20α-Hydroxypregn-4-en-3-one	Rat (pregnant)	Lawson and Pearlman (1963)
Urocortisol	Cortol Cortolone	Human	Rappaport and Migeon (1962)
Progesterone	5α-Pregnane-3α,20α-diol 5β-Pregnane-3α,20α-diol	Human Monkey	Knights and Thomas (1962)
Cortisol	Cortol Cortolone	Human	Gold (1962)

Table 30

CATABOLISM OF NEUTRAL STEROIDS, *In Vivo*: OXIDATION OF 20α—OH TO 20—C=O GROUPING

Substrate	Product	Species	Reference
Pregnenediol	Pregnanolone	Human	Ungar and Dorfman (1954c)

Table 31

CATABOLISM OF NEUTRAL STEROIDS, *In Vitro*: INTERCONVERSION OF 20C=O WITH THE 20α—OH AND 20β—OH GROUPINGS

Substrate	Product	Test system	Species	Reference
Progesterone	20β-Hydroxypregn-4-en-3-one	Corpus luteum homogenate	Bovine	Hayano *et al.* (1954)
		Earle's L cells (WCTC929)		Perlman *et al.* (1960)
	20α-Hydroxypregn-4-en-3-one	Ovarian homogenate supernatant	Rat	Wiest (1959)
	20β-Hydroxypregn-4-en-3-one 20α-Hydroxypregn-4-en-3-one (presumptive)	Adrenal cells (tissue culture)	Line 3G29 (Gey)	Perlman *et al.* (1961)
	20α-Hydroxypregn-4-en-3-one	Placental liver mole	Human	Little *et al.* (1959)
		Placenta	Cow	
	Pregnanediol	Liver homogenate perfusion	Rabbit	Ishizuka *et al.* (1957)
Cortisone	17α,20β,21-Trihydroxy-pregn-4-ene-3,11-dione 3β,17α,20β,21-Tetra-hydroxy-5α-pregnan-11-one	Liver perfusion	Rat	Caspi *et al.* (1953); Caspi and Hechter (1954); Caspi (1955)
Pregnanediol	Pregnanolone	Liver homogenate	Rat Rabbit	Grant (1952) Taylor (1956)
Urocortisone	β-Cortolone	Liver homogenate	Rat	De Courcy and Schneider (1956)
	Cortolone	Liver	Rat	Hübener (1956); Hübener *et al.* (1956)
Deoxycorti-costerone	20α,21-Dihydroxy-pregn-4-en-3-one	Liver brei	Porcine	Caspi *et al.* (1956)
	20β,21-Dihydroxy-pregn-4-en-3-one	Corpus luteum homogenate	Bovine	Hayano *et al.* (1954)
	20α,21-Dihydroxy-pregn-4-en-3-one 20β,21-Dihydroxy-pregn-4-en-3-one	Liver dis-integrated	Rabbit	Taylor (1959)

Continued on following page

Table 31 (*continued*)

CATABOLISM OF NEUTRAL STEROIDS, *In Vitro*: INTERCONVERSION OF 20C=O with the 20α—OH AND 20β—OH GROUPINGS

Substrate	Product	Test system	Species	Reference
Urocortisol	β-Cortol	Liver homogenate	Rat	Hübener (1956); Hübener *et al.* (1956)
Cortisol	11β,17α,20β,21-Tetrahydroxypregn-4-en-3-one	Kidney mince	Bovine	Ganis *et al.* (1956)
	Cortolone	Liver perfusion	Dog	Axelrod and Miller (1956)
	17α,20β,21-Trihydroxypregn-4-ene-3,11-dione 5α-Pregnane-3β,11β,17α,20β,21-pentol	Liver perfusion	Rat	Caspi (1955); Caspi and Hechter (1956)
	β-Cortol	Liver homogenate	Rat	Hübener *et al.* (1956); Hübener (1956)
	11β,17α,20α,21-Tetrahydroxypregn-4-en-3-one	Connective tissue	Rat	Berliner and Dougherty (1958a)
11-Deoxycortisol	17α,20α,21-Trihydroxypregn-4-en-3-one	Liver brei	Porcine	Caspi *et al.* (1956)
	17α,20α,21-Trihydroxypregn-4-en-3-one	Liver homogenate	Rat	Hübener *et al.* (1956); Hübener (1956)
	5α-Pregnane-3β,17α,20β,21-tetrol 17α,20β,21-Trihydroxypregn-4-en-3-one 17α,20α,21-Trihydroxypregn-4-en-3-one	Liver homogenate	Rat	Forchielli *et al.* (1955); Forchielli (1956); Forchielli and Dorfman (1956)
Corticosterone	11β,20β,21-Trihydroxypregn-4-en-3-one	Fibroblasts	Rat	Berliner (1960)
11α-Hydroxyprogesterone	11α,20β-Dihydroxypregn-4-en-3-one	Adrenal cells (tissue culture)	Line 3G29 (Gey)	Perlman *et al.* (1961)
Urocortisone	Cortolone	Liver homogenate	Human	Meigs and Engel (1961)
Cortisone	17α,20α,21-Trihydroxypregn-4-ene-3,11-dione	Liver homogenate	Human	Meigs and Engel (1961)
Progesterone	20α-Hydroxypregn-4-en-3-one	Placental homogenate	Human	Little *et al.* (1959)

Continued on following page

Table 31 *(continued)*

CATABOLISM OF NEUTRAL STEROIDS, *In Vitro*: INTERCONVERSION OF 20C=O WITH THE 20α—OH AND 20β—OH GROUPINGS

Substrate	Product	Test system	Species	Reference
Progesterone	20β-Hydroxypregn-4-en-3-one 20α-Hydroxypregn-4-en-3-one	Liver slices	Chicken	Nakao *et al.* (1959)
17α-Hydroxy-pregnenolone	Pregn-5-ene-3β,17α,20α-triol Pregn-5-ene-3β,17α,20β-triol	Muscle strips	Rabbit	Thomas *et al.* (1960)
Progesterone	20α-Hydroxypregn-4-en-3-one 20α-Hydroxy-5β-pregnan-3-one	Endometrium (secretory)	Human	Bryson and Sweat (1963)

Table 32

CATABOLISM OF NEUTRAL STEROIDS, *In Vivo*: REDUCTION OF 21—C—OH TO 21—C—H GROUPING

Substrate	Product	Species	Reference
Deoxycorticosterone	Pregnanediol	Human (male and female)	Horwitt *et al.* (1944a)
	Pregnanediol	Chimpanzee (ovariecto-mized)	Fish *et al.* (1943)
	Pregnanediol	Rabbit	Hoffman *et al.* (1943); Westphal (1942)
11-Dehydrocorti-costerone	11-Ketopregnanediol	Human	Mason (1948)
17α,21-Dihydroxy-5β-pregnane-3,20-dione	Pregnanetriol	Human	Ungar *et al.* (1954a)
Cortisone	3α,17α-Dihydroxy-5β-pregnane-11,20-dione	Human	Lieberman *et al.* (1951)
Corticosterone	3α,20β-Dihydroxy-5β-pregnan-11-one	Human	Engel *et al.* (1955)

Table 33

CATABOLISM OF NEUTRAL STEROIDS, *In Vivo*: HYDROXYLATION REACTIONS

Substrate	Product	Species	Reference
Cortisol	6β-Hydroxycortisol	Human Guinea pig	Burstein *et al.* (1954) Burstein and Dorfman (1955)
Dehydroepiandrosterone	7α-Hydroxydehydroepiandrosterone	Human	Schneider and Lewbart (1959); Stárka *et al.* (1962)
	Androst-5-ene-3β,16α, 17β-triol	Human	Mason and Kepler (1945b, 1947); Schneider and Lewbart (1959)
	3β,16α-Dihydroxyandrost-5-en-17-one	Human	Fotherby *et al.* (1957)
Testosterone	18-Hydroxyetiocholanolone	Human	Fukushima and Bradlow (1962)
	11-Ketotestosterone (probably through 11β-hydroxy derivative)	Sockeye salmon	Idler and Truscott (1963)
Progesterone	5α-Pregnane-3α,6α,20α-triol	Rabbit	Knights *et al.* (1962)
Cortisol	6β-Hydroxycortisol	Human	Gold (1962)

Table 34

CATABOLISM OF NEUTRAL STEROIDS, *In Vitro*: HYDROXYLATIONS (OTHER THAN TESTIS, PLACENTA, OVARY, AND ADRENAL)

Substrate	Product	Test system	Species	Reference
Dehydroepiandrosterone	Androst-5-ene-3β,16α,17β-triol	Liver	Rabbit	Schneider and Mason (1948b)
		Liver slice	Rat	Colas (1962)
Androst-4-ene-3,17-dione	6β-Hydroxyandrost-4-ene-3,17-dione	Liver perfusion	Rat	Axelrod and Miller (1954)
Deoxycorticosterone	6β,21-Dihydroxyprogesterone	Liver	Dog	Axelrod and Miller (1954)
11-Deoxycortisol	6β,17α,21-Trihydroxyprogesterone	Liver homogenate	Rat	Forchielli *et al.* (1955); Forchielli and Dorfman (1956)
Progesterone	3β,16α-Dihydroxy-5α-pregnan-20-one 3α,16α-Dihydroxy-5β-pregnan-20-one	Liver homogenate	Rat	Wettstein *et al.* (1959)

Continued on following page

Table 34 (*continued*)

CATABOLISM OF NEUTRAL STEROIDS, *In Vitro*: HYDROXYLATIONS (OTHER THAN TESTIS, PLACENTA, OVARY, AND ADRENAL)

Substrate	Product	Test system	Species	Reference
	3α,16α-Dihydroxy-5α-pregnan-20-one			
Cortisol	6β-Hydroxycortisol	Liver Kidney Skeletal muscle (slices)	Human	Lipman *et al.* (1962)
	6β-Hydroxycortisol (Increased 6β-hydroxylation in presence of estrone)	Liver slice		
Dehydroepi-androsterone	Androst-5-ene-3β,7α,17β-triol 3β,7α-Dihydroxy-androst-5-en-17-one	Liver homogenate	Rat	Stárka *et al.* (1962)
Dehydroepi-androsterone	3β-Hydroxyandrost-5-ene-7,17-dione 3β,7α-Dihydroxy-androst-5-en-17-one Androst-5-ene-3β,7α,17β-triol	Liver homogenate	Rat	Stárka and Kutová (1962)
Progesterone	6β-Hydroxy-progesterone	Endometrium (secretory)	Human	Bryson and Sweat (1963)
Deoxycorti-costerone	7α,21-Dihydroxypregn-4-ene-3,20-dione	Liver	Rodents (but not rats)	Schneider (1962a)
Dehydroepi-androsterone	3β,16α-Dihydroxy-androst-5-en-17-one	Liver slices	Rat (male)	Colas (1962)
Testosterone	7α-Hydroxytesto-sterone 6β-Hydroxytestosterone 16α-Hydroxytestosterone 2β-Hydroxytestosterone	Liver microsomes	Rat	Conney and Klutch (1963)
Androst-4-ene-3,17-dione	7α-Hydroxyandrost-4-ene-3,17-dione 6β-Hydroxyandrost-4-ene-3,17-dione			

Table 35

CATABOLISM OF NEUTRAL STEROIDS: FORMATION OF ACID METABOLITES

Substrate	Product	Test system	Species	Reference
Deoxycorticosterone	3-Keto-4-etienic acid	Adrenal perfusion Liver perfusion Placental perfusion (isolated product from control with substrate)	Bovine Rat Human	Levy and Maloney (1962) Picha *et al.* (1952) Romanoff (1959)
	18-Hydroxy-3-keto-4-etien-20-oic acid 20,18-lactone	Adrenal	Bovine	Pappo (1959)
	3-Keto-4-etienic acid 3,20-Diketopregn-4-en-21-oic acid 20α-Hydroxy-3-keto-pregn-4-en-21-oic acid 20β-Hydroxy-3-keto-pregn-4-en-21-oic acid	Liver slices	Guinea pig	Schneider (1962a)

Table 36

CATABOLISM OF NEUTRAL STEROIDS *In Vivo*: MISCELLANEOUS REACTIONS

Substrate	Product	Species	Reference
11β-Hydroxyandrost-4-ene-3,17-dione	3ξ,11β-Dihydroxy-androst-4-en-17-one	Human	Neeman *et al.* (1960)
Testosterone Etiocholanolone	18-Hydroxyetiocho-lanolone	Human	Fukushima and Bradlow (1962)
16α-Hydroxy-progesterone	3α-Hydroxy-5β-pregn-16-en-20-one 3α-Hydroxy-5β-17-isopregnan-20-one	Human	Calvin and Lieberman (1962)
Testosterone 19-Nortestosterone Androsta-1,4-diene-3,17-dione	Estrone and/or estradiol-17β	Human	Breuer (1962)

Continued on following page

Table 36 (*continued*)

CATABOLISM OF NEUTRAL STEROIDS, *In Vivo*: MISCELLANEOUS REACTIONS

Substrate	Product	Species	Reference
Androst-5-ene-3,17-dione	3α-Hydroxyandrost-5-en-17-one	Human	Fukushima *et al.* (1962b)
Cortisone acetate	11β-Hydroxyestrone 11β-Hydroxyestradiol-17β	Human	Chang and Dao (1962)
Testosterone	Estradiol-17β	Human	Braun-Cantilo *et al.* (1962)

Table 37

CATABOLISM OF NEUTRAL STEROIDS, *In Vitro*: MISCELLANEOUS REACTIONS

Reaction	Substrate	Product	Test system (species)	Reference
Reduction of 21-OH group	Deoxycorticosterone	Progesterone	Kidney homogenate (rabbit)	Ishizuka *et al.* (1957, 1958)
Reduction of 17-OH group	Cortisol	Corticosterone	Connective tissue (rat)	Berliner and Dougherty (1958a, b)
	Cortisone	6β,21-Dihydroxyprogesterone	Cirrhotic liver perfusion (rat)	Axelrod and Miller (1954)
Inversion of 11β-OH to 11α-OH	Cortisol	Epicortisol (presumptive evidence)	Liver perfusion (dog)	Axelrod and Miller (1956)
Reduction of 11-C=0 group	Cortisone	6β,21-Dihydroxyprogesterone	Cirrhotic liver perfusion (rat)	Axelrod and Miller (1954)
Δ^4-3β(3α)-ol to Δ^4-3-ketone	Androst-4-ene-3β,17β-diol	Testosterone		Ungar and Bloom (1957)
	3α-Hydroxypregn-4-en-20-one	Progesterone		
	3β-Hydroxypregn-4-en-20-one			
Dehydration at carbon 16,17	Testosterone	Androsta-4,16-dien-3-one	Liver homogenate (human)	Stylianou *et al.* (1961)

Continued on following page

Table 37 *(continued)*

CATABOLISM OF NEUTRAL STEROIDS, *In Vitro*: MISCELLANEOUS REACTIONS

Reaction	Substrate	Product	Test system (species)	Reference
Reduction of Δ^4-3-keto group to 3β-hydroxy-Δ^4 group	Androst-4-ene-3,17-dione	3β-Hydroxy-androst-4-en-17-one	Skeletal muscle supernatant (rabbit)	Thomas and Dorfman (1964a)

Table 38

CATABOLISM OF PHENOLIC STEROIDS, *In Vivo*: INTRODUCTION OF 2-METHOXY OR 2-HYDROXY GROUPS

Substrate	Product	Species	Reference
Estradiol-17β	2-Methoxyestrone	Human	Engel *et al.* (1957); Fishman *et al.* (1960a, 1962); Kraychy and Gallagher (1957a, b)
	2-Methoxyestriol	Human	Fishman and Gallagher (1958)
	2-Hydroxyestrone	Human	Fishman *et al.* (1960b)
	2-Methoxyestrone	Human	Engel *et al.* (1961)

Table 39

CATABOLISM OF PHENOLIC STEROIDS, *In Vitro*: INTRODUCTION OF 2—OH, 2—CH_3O, AND 2-METHYLATION

Substrate	Product	Test system	Species	Reference
2-Hydroxy-estradiol-17β	2-Methoxy-estradiol-17β	Brei Kidney Spleen Uterus Muscle plus Methionine	Guinea pig	Axelrod (1960)
		Liver slices	Human	Breuer and Knuppen (1960b)
	2-Methoxyestradiol-17β and/or 2-methoxyestrone	Fetus (whole mince) Or mince of following: Kidney, brain, muscle, lung, spleen, liver and pancreas	Human	Axelrod and Goldzieher (1961b)

Continued on following page

Table 39 (*continued*)

Catabolism of Phenolic Steroids, *In Vitro*: Introduction of 2—OH, 2—CH_3O, and 2-Methylation

Substrate	Product	Test system	Species	Reference
	No product	Liver adrenal (minced)	Human	Axelrod and Goldzieher (1961b)
	2-Methoxy-estradiol-17β	Liver (mince and slice)	Human	Breuer *et al.* (1961)
		Liver slices, kidney, spleen, uterus	Rat	Knuppen *et al.* (1961)
		Liver, spleen, kidney, placenta		
Estradiol-17β	2-Methoxyestrone	Placenta (perfusion with or without HCG)	Human	Troen (1961)
Estriol	2-Hydroxyestriol 2-Methoxyestriol	Liver plus methionine	Rat	King (1960)
	2-Methoxyestriol	Liver slices	Rat	Breuer *et al.* (1960c)
	2-Hydroxyestriol 2-Methoxyestriol	Liver homogenate	Rat	King (1961b)
Estradiol-17β	2-Methoxy-estradiol-17β	Liver homogenate	Rat	King (1961b)
Estriol	2-Methoxyestriol 2-Hydroxyestriol	Liver slices	Rat and rabbit	King (1961a)

Table 40

Catabolism of Phenolic Steroids, *In Vivo*: 16α-Hydroxylation

Substrate	Product	Species	Reference
Estrone	Estriol	Human (male)	Pearlman and Pincus (1942)
	Estriol	Human	Beer and Gallagher (1955); Pearlman *et al.* (1953)
	16-Ketoestrone (probably through 16α-OH)	Human	Slaunwhite and Sandberg (1956)
Estradiol-17β	Estriol	Dog	Mayer (1952)
		Human	Engel *et al.* (1957); Gallagher *et al.* (1958); Fishman *et al.* (1962)

Continued on following page

Table 40 *(continued)*

Catabolism of Phenolic Steroids, *In Vivo*: 16α-Hydroxylation

Substrate	Product	Species	Reference
		Hen	MacRae *et al.* (1959)
	16-Ketoestradiol-17β (probably through 16α-OH)	Human	Levitz *et al.* (1956)
	2-Methoxyestriol	Human	Levitz *et al.* (1956)
	Estriol	Human	Engel *et al.* (1961)
Estrone	Estriol	Human	Fishman *et al.* (1960a)

Table 41

Catabolism of Phenolic Steroids, *In Vivo*: 16β-Hydroxylation[a]

Substrate	Product	Species	Reference
Estradiol-17β	16β-Hydroxyestrone	Human	Gallagher *et al.* (1958)
	16-Epiestriol	Hen	MacRae *et al.* (1959)
		Human	Engel *et al.* (1961)
Estrone	16-Epiestriol	Human (male)	Migeon *et al.* (1959); Fishman *et al.* (1960a)

[a] This hydroxylation may not occur but rather result from reduction of the 16-keto group.

Table 42

Catabolism of Phenolic Steroids, *In Vitro*: Hydroxylation Reactions

Substrate	Product	Test system	Species	Reference
Estradiol-17β	6α-Hydroxyestradiol-17β	Liver microsomes	Mouse and rat	Rumney (1956); Mueller and Rumney (1957)
	6-Ketoestradiol-17β			
	Estriol	Liver	Rat	Hagopian (1955)
	6ξ-Hydroxyestradiol-17β	Liver slices	Rat	Breuer and Knuppen (1960a)
	Estriol	Liver and ovary	Human	Dowben and Rabinowitz (1956)
	Estriol	Liver slices	Avian	Mitchell and Hobkirk (1959)

Continued on following page

Table 42 (*continued*)

Catabolism of Phenolic Steroids, *In Vitro*: Hydroxylation Reactions

Substrate	Product	Test system	Species	Reference
	Estriol	Liver slices (fetal)	Human	Engel *et al.* (1958b)
16-Ketoestrone	Estriol	Placental homogenate supernatant	Human	Ryan (1960)
Estradiol-17β Estrone Estradiol-17β	Estriol 6-Hydroxyestrone 6-Hydroxyestradiol-17β	Liver slices	Rat	Breuer *et al.* (1960d)
Estradiol-17β	6ξ-Hydroxyestradiol-17β Estriol	Liver slices	Human (fetal) Human	Breuer *et al.* (1960a)
Estrone	6ξ-Hydroxyestradiol-17β Estriol 6ξ-Hydroxyestrone	Liver slices	Rat (male)	Breuer *et al.* (1959d)
Estradiol-17β	6ξ-Hydroxyestradiol-17β Estriol 6ξ-Hydroxyestrone			
Estriol 6ξ-Hydroxy-estradiol-17β	6ξ-Hydroxyestriol	Liver slices	Rat	Breuer *et al.* (1960c)
Estradiol-17β 2-Methoxy-estradiol-17β	6ξ-Hydroxyestradiol-17β 2-Methoxyestriol			
Estradiol-17β	6β-Hydroxyestradiol-17β 6β-Hydroxyestrone	Liver slices	Rat	Breuer *et al.* (1958a)
	Estriol 16-Epiestriol	Placental perfusion with HCG	Human	Troen (1961)

Table 43

Catabolism of Phenolic Steroids, *In Vivo*: Reduction of 16C=O to 16α—OH Grouping

Substrate	Product	Species	Reference
16-Ketoestrone 16-Ketoestradiol-17β	Estriol (presumptive evidence)	Human (male)	Stimmel *et al.* (1950)
16-Ketoestrone	Estriol Estriol 17-Epiestriol	Human Human	Stimmel (1958) Nocke *et al.* (1961)
16-Ketoestradiol-17β	Estriol	Human (female)	Levitz *et al.* (1960a)

Table 44

Catabolism of Phenolic Steroids, *In Vivo*: Reduction of 16C=O to 16β—OH Grouping

Substrate	Product	Species	Reference
16-Ketoestrone	16-Epiestriol	Human	Stimmel (1958); Nocke *et al.* (1961)
Estriol	16-Epiestriol (probably through 16-ketoestradiol-17β which was also isolated)	Hen	MacRae *et al.* (1959)
16-Ketoestradiol-17β	16-Epiestriol	Human (female)	Levitz *et al.* (1960a)

Table 45

Catabolism of Phenolic Steroids, *In Vitro*: Reduction of 16—C=O to 16α—OH or 16β—OH Groupings

Substrate	Product	Test system	Species	Reference
16-Ketoestrone	Estriol 16-Epiestriol	Liver slices	Human	Breuer *et al.* (1958b)
	Estriol 16-Epiestriol	Liver slices	Rat Guinea pig	Breuer *et al.* (1959c)
	16α-Hydroxyestrone Estriol	Placenta	Human	Ryan (1960)
	16-Epiestriol 16β-Hydroxyestrone 16α-Hydroxyestrone Estriol	Liver ovary slices	Human	Breuer *et al.* (1959b)
	16β-Hydroxyestrone Estriol	Liver slices	Human	Breuer and Knuppen (1958)

Continued on following page

Table 45 (*continued*)

CATABOLISM OF PHENOLIC STEROIDS, *In Vitro*: REDUCTION OF 16—C=O TO 16α—OH OR 16β—OH GROUPINGS

Substrate	Product	Test system	Species	Reference
	Epiestriol 17-Epiestriol 16α-Hydroxyestrone			
16-Ketoestra-diol-17β	Estriol 16-Epiestriol	Liver slices	Rat Guinea pig	Breuer *et al.* (1959c)
	17-Epiestriol 16,17-Epiestriol	Liver slices	Human	Breuer and Nocke (1959)
16-Ketoestrone	16-Epiestriol	Erythrocyte suspension	Rat Human	Portuis and Repke (1960b)
16-Ketoestra-diol-17β	16-Epiestriol	Erythrocyte preparations	Rat Human Bovine	

Table 46

CATABOLISM OF PHENOLIC STEROIDS, *In Vivo*: OXIDATION OF 16β—OH TO 16—C=O GROUPING

Substrate	Product	Species	Reference
16β-Hydroxyestrone	Estriol (probably through 16—C=O)	Human (male)	Nocke *et al.* (1961)

Table 47

CATABOLISM OF PHENOLIC STEROIDS: OXIDATION OF 16α—OH TO 16—C=O GROUPING

Substrate	Product	Species	Reference
Estradiol-17β	16-Ketoestradiol-17β (probably through 16α—OH)	Human	Levitz *et al.* (1956)
Estrone	16-Ketoestrone (probably through 16α—OH)	Human	Slaunwhite and Sandberg (1956)
Estriol	16-Ketoestradiol-17β	Hen	MacRae *et al.* (1959)
16α-Hydroxyestrone	16-Epiestriol (probably through 16C=0)	Human (male)	Nocke *et al.* (1961)
Estriol	16-Epiestriol (through 16C=O) 16-Ketoestradiol-17β 16-Ketoestrone	Human	Levitz *et al.* (1958)

Table 48

CATABOLISM OF PHENOLIC STEROIDS, *In Vitro*: CONVERSION OF 16α—OH OR 16β—OH

Substrate	Product	Test system	Species	Reference
Estriol	16-Ketoestradiol-17β	Liver homogenate	Rat	King (1961b)
Estriol	16-Epiestriol	Liver	Rat	Balestreri and Correale (1962)

Table 49

CATABOLISM OF PHENOLIC STEROIDS: INTRODUCTION OF 16—C=O GROUPING

Substrate	Product	Test system	Species	Reference
Estrone	16-Ketoestrone 16-Ketoestradiol-17β	*In vivo*	Human (male)	Migeon *et al.* (1959)

Table 50

CATABOLISM OF PHENOLIC STEROIDS, *In Vivo*: OXIDATION OF 17β—OH TO 17—C=O GROUP

Substrate	Product	Test system	Species	Reference
Estradiol-17β	Estrone		Rabbit (ovariectomized-hysterectomized)	Fish and Dorfman (1942)
			Guinea pig (males and ovariectomized females)	Fish and Dorfman (1940a, b, 1941)
			Rabbit (female)	Heard *et al.* (1941)
			Human (male)	Heard *et al.* (1941)
			Human	Engel *et al.* (1957); Beer and Gallagher (1955); Fishman *et al.* (1962)
			Monkey	Dorfman *et al.* (1945)
			Dog	Mayer (1952); Siegel *et al.* (1962) Stimmel (1955)

Continued on following page

Table 50 (*continued*)

CATABOLISM OF PHENOLIC STEROIDS, *In Vivo*: OXIDATION OF 17β—OH TO 17—C=O GROUP

Substrate	Product	Test system	Species	Reference
	16β-Hydroxyestrone		Human	Gallagher *et al.* (1958)
	Estrone 2-Methoxyestrone		Human	Fishman *et al.*(1960a) Engel *et al.* (1961)
Estriol	16α-Hydroxyestrone 16-Ketoestrone		Human	Levitz *et al.* (1958)
Dihydroequilenin	Equilenin		Pregnant mare	Savard *et al.* (1961)
16-Ketoestradiol-17β	16-Ketoestrone	Uterine fibroids (minced)	Human	Lucis and Hobkirk (1963)
6α-Hydroxyestradiol-17β 6β-Hydroxyestradiol-17β 16-Oxoestradiol-17β	6α-Hydroxyestrone 6β-Hydroxyestrone 6-Oxoestrone	Liver microsomes	Rat	Breuer *et al.* (1962)

Table 51

CATABOLISM OF PHENOLIC STEROIDS, *In Vitro*: OXIDATION OF 17β—OH TO 17—C=O

Substrate	Product	Test system	Species	Reference
Estradiol-17β	Estrone	Liver	Rat	Pearlman and DeMeio (1949); Ryan and Engel (1953a)
		Placenta, liver, and other tissues	Human	Ryan and Engel (1953a)
		Liver slices	Rabbit	Breuer and Pangels (1960)
		Testes Kidney	Human	Dowben and Rabinowitz (1956)
		Liver slices	Human (fetal)	Breuer *et al.* (1960c)

Continued on following page

Table 51 (*continued*)

CATABOLISM OF PHENOLIC STEROIDS, *In Vitro*: OXIDATION OF 17β—OH TO 17—C=O

Substrate	Product	Test system	Species	Reference
		Blood	Bovine	Axelrod and Werthessen (1959)
			Human Rat	Brown *et al.* (1961)
		Ethryrocytes	Rat	Portius and Repke (1960a)
		Testis endometrium amnion (tissue culture)	Bovine	Erichsen and Velle (1960)
	Estrone 2-Methoxyestrone	Placental perfusion with or without HCG	Human	Troen (1961)
	Estrone	Blood cells or plasma	Human Rat	Brown *et al.* (1961)
	6ξ-Hydroxyestrone Estrone	Liver slices	Rat (male)	Breuer *et al.* (1959d)
6ξ-Hydroxy-estradiol-17β	6ξ-Hydroxyestrone	Liver slices	Rat (male)	Breuer *et al.* (1959d)
6-Ketoestra-diol-17β	6ξ-Hydroxyestrone 6-Ketoestrone			
	16-Ketoestrone	Erythrocyte suspension	Rat	Portius and Repke (1960b)

Table 52

CATABOLISM OF PHENOLIC STEROIDS, *In Vivo*: OXIDATION OF 17α—OH TO 17—C=O GROUPING

Substrate	Product	Species	Reference
Estradiol-17α	Estrone	Bovine (calf)	Velle (1958c)

Table 53

CATABOLISM OF PHENOLIC STEROIDS, *In Vitro*: OXIDATION OF 17α—OH TO 17—C=O

Substrate	Product	Test system	Species	Reference
Estradiol-17α	Estrone	Liver slices	Rabbit	Breuer and Pangels (1960)

Table 54

CATABOLISM OF PHENOLIC STEROIDS, *In Vivo*: REDUCTION OF 17C=O TO 17β—OH GROUPING

Substrate	Product	Species	Reference
Estrone	Estriol	Human	Pearlman and Pincus (1942)
	Estriol Estradiol-17β	Human	Pearlman *et al.* (1953)
	Estradiol-17β 16-Epiestriol 16-Ketoestradiol-17β	Human (male)	Migeon *et al.* (1959)
16-Ketoestrone	Estriol (presumptive evidence)	Human (male)	Stimmel *et al.* (1950)
	16-Ketoestradiol-17β Estriol Epiestriol	Human (male)	Stimmel (1958)
16α-Hydroxyestrone	Estriol	Human	Brown and Marrian (1957)
	Estriol 16-Epiestriol 17-Epiestriol	Human (male)	Nocke *et al.* (1961)
Estrone	Estradiol-17β Estriol Epiestriol	Human	Fishman *et al.* (1960a)
16β-Hydroxyestrone	Estriol 16-Epiestriol 16,17-Epiestriol	Human	Nocke *et al.* (1961)

Table 55

CATABOLISM OF PHENOLIC STEROIDS, *In Vivo*: REDUCTION OF 17C=O TO 17α—OH GROUPING

Substrate	Product	Species	Reference
Estradiol-17β	Estradiol-17α (through 17—C=O)	Rabbit (ovariectomized and hysterectomized)	Fish and Dorfman (1942)
	Estradiol-17α	Rabbit (female) Rabbit Dog Bovine (calf)	Heard *et al.* (1941) Stroud (1939) Pearlman *et al.* (1948) Velle (1958b)
Estrone	Estradiol-17α	Bovine (calf)	Velle (1958c)
16α-Hydroxyestrone	17-Epiestriol	Human (male)	Nocke *et al.* (1961)
16β-Hydroxyestrone	16,17-Epiestriol		
Estradiol-17β	Estradiol-17α (through estrone)	Dog	Siegel *et al.* (1962)

Table 56

CATABOLISM OF PHENOLIC STEROIDS, *In Vitro*: REDUCTION OF 17C=O TO 17α AND 17β—OH GROUPINGS

Substrate	Product	Test system	Species	Reference
Estrone	Estradiol-17β	Liver	Rat	Ryan and Engel (1953a)
		Various tissues	Human	Ryan and Engel (1953b)
		Amnion endometrium testis (tissue culture)	Bovine	Erichsen and Velle (1960)
		Red blood cells	Rabbit Human	Gray and Bischoff (1955)
			Human, rat	Brown *et al.* (1961)
			Rat	Portius and Repke (1960a)
		Liver slices	Rabbit	Breuer and Pangels (1960)
	Estradiol-17β sulfate	Placenta	Guinea pig	Levitz *et al.* (1960b)
16α-Hydroxyestrone	Estriol	Liver slices	Rat Guinea pig	Breuer *et al.* (1959c)
	Estriol 16α-Hydroxy-estradiol-17α	Liver slices	Human	Breuer *et al.* (1958b)
16-Ketoestrone	Estriol 16-Ketoestradiol-17β	Placental homogenate supernatant	Human	Ryan (1960)
	Estriol 16-Epiestriol 16-Ketoestradiol-17β	Liver, ovary slices	Human	Breuer *et al.* (1959b)
	Estriol 17-Epiestriol 16-Ketoestradiol-17β Epiestriol	Liver slices	Human	Breuer and Knuppen (1958)
16β-Hydroxyestrone	16-Epiestriol 16-Ketoestradiol-17β	Liver slices	Rat and human	Breuer *et al.* (1959a)
	16-Epiestriol	Liver slices	Human	Breuer and Nocke (1959)
16-Ketoestrone	16-Ketoestradiol-17β	Erythrocyte preparation	Rat	Portius and Repke (1960b)
Estrone	Estradiol-17α	Blood	Bovine	Axelrod and Werthessen (1960)

Continued on following page

Table 56 (*continued*)

CATABOLISM OF PHENOLIC STEROIDS, *In Vitro*: REDUCTION OF 17C=O TO 17α AND 17β—OH GROUPINGS

Substrate	Product	Test system	Species	Reference
		Liver slices	Rabbit	Breuer and Pangels (1960)
16-Ketoestrone	17-Epiestriol	Liver Ovary slices	Human	Breuer *et al.* (1959b)
16β-Hydroxyestrone	16,17-Epiestriol	Liver slices	Human	Breuer and Nocke (1959)
Estrone	Estradiol-17β	Blood cells or plasma	Human or rat	Brown *et al.* (1961)
6α-Hydroxyestrone	6α-Hydroxy-estradiol-17β	Liver micro-somes	Rat	Breuer *et al.* (1962)
6β-Hydroxyestrone	6β-Hydroxy-estradiol-17β			
6-Ketoestrone	6-Ketoestradiol-17β			

Table 57

CATABOLISM OF PHENOLIC STEROIDS: REACTIONS OF DEMETHYLATION

Substrate	Product	Test system	Species	Reference
Estrone methyl ether	Estrone	*In vivo*	Human	Brown (1962)
Estradiol-17β-3-methyl ether	Estradiol-17β			
Estriol-3-methyl ether	Estriol-3-methyl ether			

Table 58

CATABOLISM OF PHENOLIC STEROIDS: MISCELLANEOUS REACTIONS

Substrate	Product	Test system	Species	Reference
2-Hydroxy-estradiol-17β	2-Methoxy-estradiol-17β	Kidney (cancer) *In vitro*	Human	Axelrod and Goldzieher (1961b)
	2-Methyestrone	*In vivo*	Human	Axelrod *et al.* (1960)
6ξ-Hydroxy-estradiol-17β	6-Ketoestradiol-17β	Liver slices	Human	Breuer *et al.* (1960a)

Continued on following page

Table 58 (*continued*)

Catabolism of Phenolic Steroids: Miscellaneous Reactions

Substrate	Product	Test system	Species	Reference
6ξ-Hydroxyestrone	6-Ketoestrone	Liver slices	Human	Breuer *et al.* (1960a)
6-Hydroxy-estradiol-17β	6-Ketoestradiol-17β	Liver slices	Rat (male)	Breuer *et al.* (1959d)
6-Ketoestradiol-17β	6ξ-Hydroxy-estradiol-17β 6ξ-Hydroxyestrone			
6-Ketoestrone	6ξ-Hydroxyestradiol-17β 6ξ-Hydroxyestrone			
16β-Hydroxy-estrone	16-Ketoestradiol-17β	Liver slices	Rat and man	Breuer *et al.* (1959a)
Estra-1,3,5(10), 16-tetren-3-ol	16α,17α-Epoxyestra-1,3,5(10)-trien-3-ol 16,17-Epiestriol	Liver slices	Rat	Breuer and Knuppen (1961)
Estradiol-17β	17β-Hydroxy-estra-*p*-quinol-(10β)	Liver micro-somes	Rat	Hecker and Zayed (1961)
Estra-1,3,5(10),16-tetren-3-ol	16,17-Epiestriol 16α,17α-Epoxyestra-1,3,5(10)-trien-3-ol	*In vivo*	Human	Knuppen and Breuer (1962)
16β,17β-Epoxyestra-1,3,5(10)-trien-3-ol	Estriol 16,17-Epiestriol			
Estradiol-17β	6α-Hydroxy-estradiol-17β 6β-Hydroxy-estradiol-17β	Liver micro-somes	Rat	Breuer *et al.* (1962)
6α-Hydroxy-estradiol-17β 6β-Hydroxy-estradiol-17β	6-Ketoestradiol-17β 6α-Hydroxyestrone 6β-Hydroxyestrone			
6α-Hydroxyestrone 6β-Hydroxyestrone	6-Ketoestrone 6α-Hydroxyestradiol-17β 6β-Hydroxyestradiol-17β			
16-Ketoestradiol-17β	6-Ketoestrone 6α-Hydroxyestradiol-17β 6β-Hydroxyestradiol-17β			
6-Ketoestrone	6-Ketoestradiol-17β 6α-Hydroxyestrone 6β-Hydroxyestrone			

Table 59

FORMATION OF CONJUGATES

Substrate	Product	Test system	Species	Reference
Dehydroepiandrosterone	Dehydroepiandrosterone sulfate	Liver homogenate	Rat and bovine	DeMeio and Lewycka (1955); DeMeio *et al.* (1956)
			Rabbit	Schneider and Lewbart (1956)
Urocortisone	Urocortisone glucuronoside	Liver microsomes	Rat	Isselbacher and Axelrod (1955)
Urocortisol	Urocortisol glucuronoside	Liver microsomes	Rat and guinea pig	Isselbacher and Axelrod (1955); Isselbacher (1956)
Etiocholanolone	Etiocholanolone sulfate	*In vivo*	Human (infant)	Baulieu (1960)
Estrone	Estrone sulfate Estradiol-17β sulfate	Placental tissue	Guinea pig	Levitz *et al.* (1960b)
Deoxycorticosterone	3α,21-Dihydroxy-5β-pregnan-20-one glucuronoside	*In vivo*	Man	Pasqualini and Jayle (1962)
Dehydroepiandrosterone	Dehydroepiandrosterone sulfate	Liver perfusion	Dog	Klempien *et al.* (1961)
Dehydroepiandrosterone Testosterone Estrone Estradiol-17β	Dehydroepiandrosterone sulfate Testosterone sulfate Estrone sulfate Estradiol-17β sulfate	Liver homogenate	Rat	DeMeio *et al.* (1958)
Testosterone	Testosterone glucuronoside	Liver homogenate	Rat, mouse, rabbit, guinea pig, dog, hamster	Fishman and Sie (1956); Wotiz *et al.* (1958)
Dehydroepiandrosterone	Dehydroepiandrosterone sulfate	Purified homogenate	Rat	Roy (1956)
Estradiol-17β Estriol	Estradiol-3-sulfate Estrone-3-sulfate Estriol-3-sulfate	*In vivo*	Human	Diczfalusy *et al.* (1961)
Adrenosterone	11β-Hydroxy-17-keto-androsta-3,5-dien-3-yl-β-*D*-glucopyranosiduronic acid	*In vivo*	Rat	Wotiz and Fishman (1963)

Continued on following page

Table 59 (*continued*)

FORMATION OF CONJUGATES

Substrate	Product	Test system	Species	Reference
Dehydroapiandrosterone	Dehydroepiandrosterone sulfate	Adrenal tumor homogenate supernatant	Human	Migeon (1963)

Table 60

CATABOLISM OF SYNTHETIC (NON-NATURALLY OCCURRING) STEROIDS

Substrate	Product	Test system	Species	Reference
17α-Hydroxyprogesterone caproate	3β,17α-Dihydroxy-5α-pregnan-20-one-17α-caproate 3β,17α-Dihydroxy-5β-pregnan-20-one-17α-caproate	Liver homogenate	Rat	Wiener *et al.* (1961)
19-Nortestosterone	3β-Hydroxy-19-nor-5α-androstan-17-one 19-Nor-5α-androstane-3α,17β-diol 19-Nor-5α-androstane-3β,17β-diol 3α-Hydroxy-19-nor-5α-androstan-17-one	Liver homogenate	Rat	Kupfer *et al.* (1960)
	19-Norandrosterone	*In vivo*	Human	Engel *et al.* (1958a)
2α-Methyladrenosterone	2α-Methyl-3α-hydroxy-5α-androstane-11,17-dione	*In vivo*	Human	Bush and Mahesh (1958a)
Estra-1,3,5(10),16-tetraen-3-ol	16β-Hydroxyestradiol-17α	*In vivo*	Human	Stimmel and Notchev (1961)
17α-Methyltestosterone	17α-Methyl-5β-androstane-3α,17β-diol (10 parts) 17α-Methyl-5α-androstane-3α,17β-diol (1 part)	*In vivo*	Human	Rongone and Segaloff (1961, 1962)
Prednisolone	Prednisone 11β,17α,20β,21-Tetrahydroxypregna-1,4-dien-3-one	*In vivo*	Human	Vermeulen (1959)

Continued on following page

Table 60 (*continued*)

CATABOLISM OF SYNTHETIC (NON-NATURALLY OCCURRING) STEROIDS

Substrate	Product	Test system	Species	Reference
	17α,20β,21-Trihydroxy-pregna-1,4-diene-3,11-dione 3α,11β,17α,21-Tetra-hydroxy-5β-pregnan-20-one 3α,17α,21-Trihydroxy-5β-pregnane-11,20-dione			
17α-Ethynyl-19-nortestosterone	Ethynylestradiol-17β	*In vivo*	Human	Langecker (1961)
Triamcinolone	6β-Hydroxytriamcino-lone	*In vivo*	Dog Human	Florini *et al.* (1961)
9α-Fluorocortisone or 9α-fluoro-cortisol	9α-Fluorocortisol 9α-Fluoro-11β,17α,20(?),21-tetrahydroxypregn-4-en-3-one 9α-Fluoro-3α,11β,17α,21-tetrahydroxy-5β-pregnan-20-one 9α-Fluoro-3α,11β,17α,21-tetrahydroxy-5α-pregnan-20-one 9α-Fluoro-11β-hydroxy-etiocholanolone 9α-Fluoro-11β-hydroxy-androsterone 9α-Fluoro-11-keto-etiocholanolone (this metabolite only after 9α-fluorocortisone)	*In vivo*	Human	Bush and Mahesh (1958b)
4-Chlorotesto-sterone	4-Chloro-3α-hydroxy-androst-4-en-17-one	*In vivo*	Human	Castegnaro and Sala (1961)
Stilbestrol	*O*-Methoxystilbestrol	Liver homo-genate	Rat	King (1961b)
17α-Ethynyl-estradiol-17β	*O*-Methoxy-17α-ethynyl-estradiol-17β			
2α-Methylcortisone	6β,11β,17α,20ξ,21-Penta-hydroxy-2α-methyl-pregn-4-en-3-one 6β,17α,20ξ,21-Tetra-hydroxy-2α-methyl-pregn-4-ene-3,11-dione	*In vivo*	Human	Bush and Mahesh (1959b)

Continued on following page

Table 60 (*continued*)

CATABOLISM OF SYNTHETIC (NON-NATURALLY OCCURRING) STEROIDS

Substrate	Product	Test system	Species	Reference
	11β,17α,20ξ,21-Tetrahydroxy-2α-methylpregn-4-en-3-one			
	17α,20ξ,21-Trihydroxy-2α-methylpregn-4-ene-3,11-dione			
	11β,17α,21-Trihydroxy-2α-methylpregn-4-ene-3,20-dione(2-methylcortisol)			
	17α,21-Dihydroxy-2α-methylpregn-4-ene-3,11,20-trione(2α-methylcortisone)			
	3α,17α,20ξ,21-Tetrahydroxy-2α-methyl-5α-pregnan-11-one			
	6β,11β-Dihydroxy-2α-methylandrost-4-ene-3,17-dione			
	6β-Hydroxy-2α-methylandrost-4-ene-3,11,17-trione			
	11β-Hydroxy-2α-methylandrost-4-ene-3,6,17-trione			
	2α-Methylandrost-4-ene-3,6,11,17-tetraone			
	11β-Hydroxy-2α-methylandrost-4-ene-3,17-dione			
	2α-Methylandrost-4-ene-3,11,17-trione			
2α-Methylcortisol	6β,11β,17α,20ξ,21-Pentahydroxy-2α-methylpregn-4-en-3-one	*In vivo*	Human	Bush and Mahesh (1959b)
	6β,17α,20ξ,21-Tetrahydroxy-2α-methylpregn-4-ene-3,11-dione			
	11β,17α,20ξ,21-Tetrahydroxy-2α-methylpregn-4-en-3-one			
	17α,20ξ,21-Trihydroxy-2α-methylpregn-4-ene-3,11-dione			

Continued on following page

Table 60 (*continued*)

CATABOLISM OF SYNTHETIC (NON-NATURALLY OCCURRING) STEROIDS

Substrate	Product	Test system	Species	Reference
	11β,17α,21-Trihydroxy-2α-methylpregn-4-ene-3,20-dione(2α-methylcortisol)			
	17α,21-Dihydroxy-2α-methylpregn-4-ene-3,11,20-trione(2α-methylcortisone)			
	3α,17α,20ξ,21-Tetrahydroxy-2α-methyl-5α-pregnan-11-one			
	11β-Hydroxy-2α-methylandrost-4-ene-3,17-dione			
	2α-Methylandrost-4-ene-3,11,17-trione			
2α-Methyladrenosterone	6β,11,17ξ-Trihydroxy-2α-methylandrost-4-en-3-one	*In vivo*	Human	Bush and Mahesh (1959b)
	6β,17ξ-Dihydroxy-2α-methylandrost-4-ene-3,11-dione			
	11β-Hydroxy-2α-methylandrost-4-ene-3,17-dione			
	2α-Methylandrost-4-ene-3,11,17-trione (2α-methyladrenosterone)			
	11β,17ξ-Dihydroxy-2α-methylandrost-4-en-3-one			
	17ξ-Hydroxy-2α-methylandrost-4-ene-3,11-dione			
	3α,17ξ-Dihydroxy-2α-methyl-5α-androstan-11-one			
	3α-Hydroxy-2α-methyl-5α-androstane-11,17-dione			
17β-Hydroxy-1α-methyl-5α-androst-1-en-3-one	1α-Methyl-5α-androst-1-ene-3,17-dione	*In vivo*	Human	Langecker and Kramer (1962)
	1α-Methylandrostane-3,17-dione			Langecker (1962)
17β-Hydroxy-5α-androst-1-en-3-one	Androsterone			

Continued on following page

Table 60 *(continued)*

CATABOLISM OF SYNTHETIC (NON-NATURALLY OCCURRING) STEROIDS

Substrate	Product	Test system	Species	Reference
6α-Methyl-17-acetoxyprogesterone	6α-Methyl-6β,17α,21-trihydroxypregn-4-ene-3,20-dione-17-acetate	*In vivo*	Human	Helmreich and Huseby (1962)
19-Norprogesterone	20α-Hydroxy-19-norpregn-4-en-3-one	*In vivo*	Rabbit	Thomas (1962)
Stilbestrol	Glucuronide (presumptive)	*In vivo*	Chicken	Hopwood and Gassner (1962)
Blood				
Bile				
6α-Methyl-17-acetoxyprogesterone	6α-Methyl-6β,17α,21-trihydroxypregn-4-ene-3,20-dione-21-acetate	*In vivo*	Human	Castegnaro and Sala (1962)
17α-Methyl-17β-hydroxyandrosta-1,4-dien-3-one	17β-Methyl-6β,17β-dihydroxyandrosta-1,4-dien-3-one	*In vivo*	Human	Rongone and Segaloff (1963)
D-Homotestosterone	*D*-Homo-5β-androstane-3α,17β-diol	*In vivo*	Human	Rongone *et al.* (1963)
Δ^1-Dehydrotestololactone	3α-hydroxy-13,17-seco-5β-androst-1-en-17-oic acid lactone	*In vivo*	Human	Rongone *et al.* (1961)
3β,17β-Diacetoxy-17α-ethynyl-19-norandrost-4-ene	17α-Ethynylestradiol-17β	*In vivo*	Human	Besch *et al.* (1963)

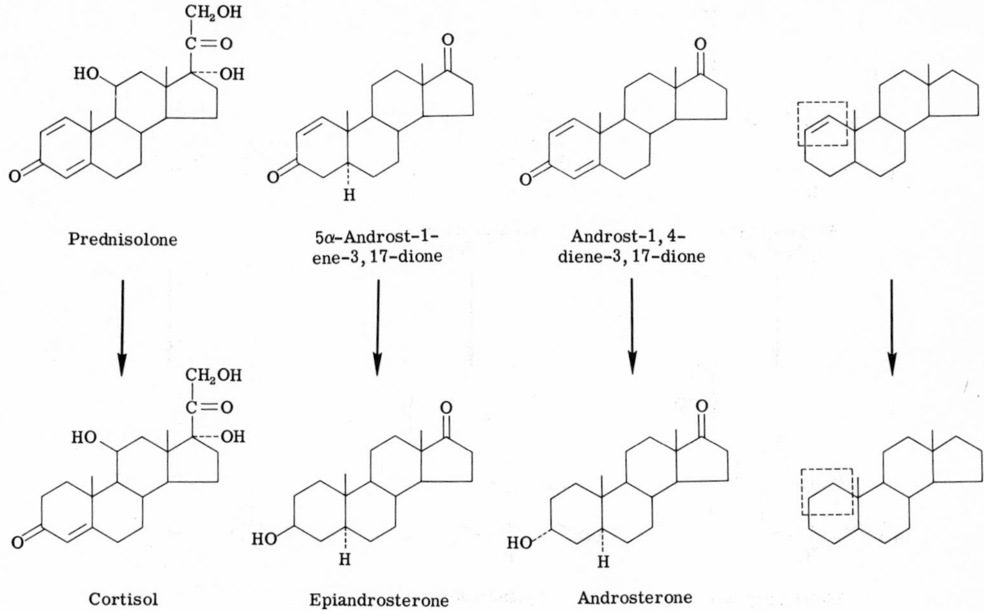

FIG. 1. Neutral steroids: typical example of reduction of Δ^1 group.

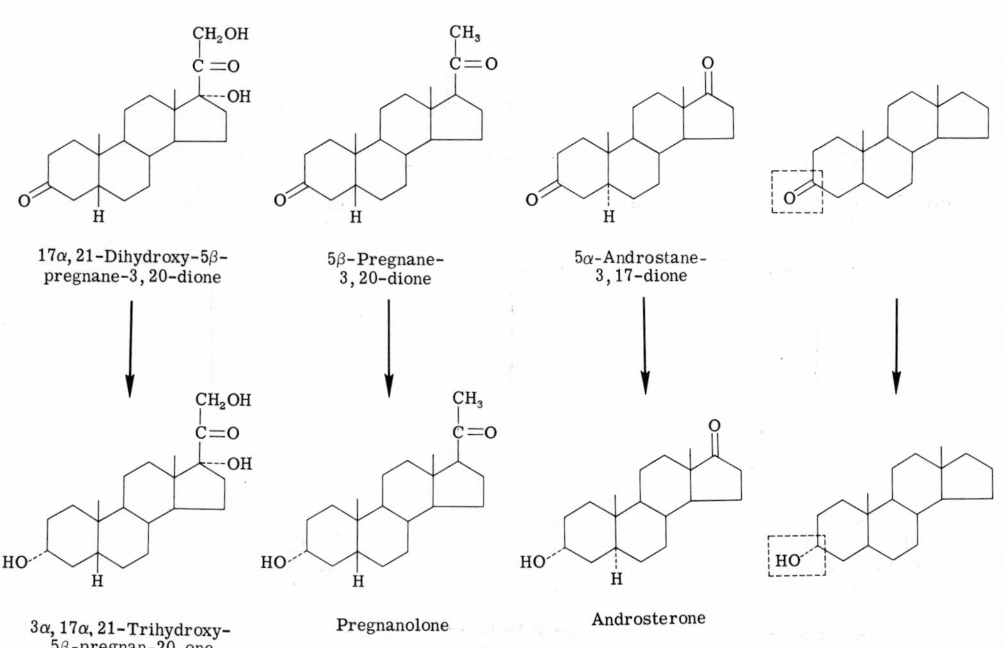

FIG. 2. Neutral steroids: typical example of reduction of 3C=O to 3α—OH group.

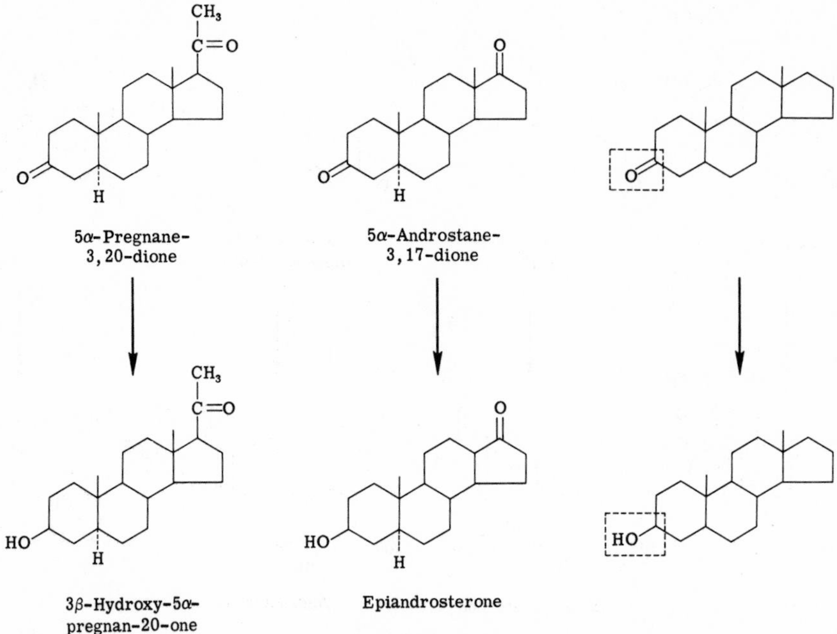

FIG. 3. Neutral steroids: typical example of reduction of 3C=O to 3β—OH group.

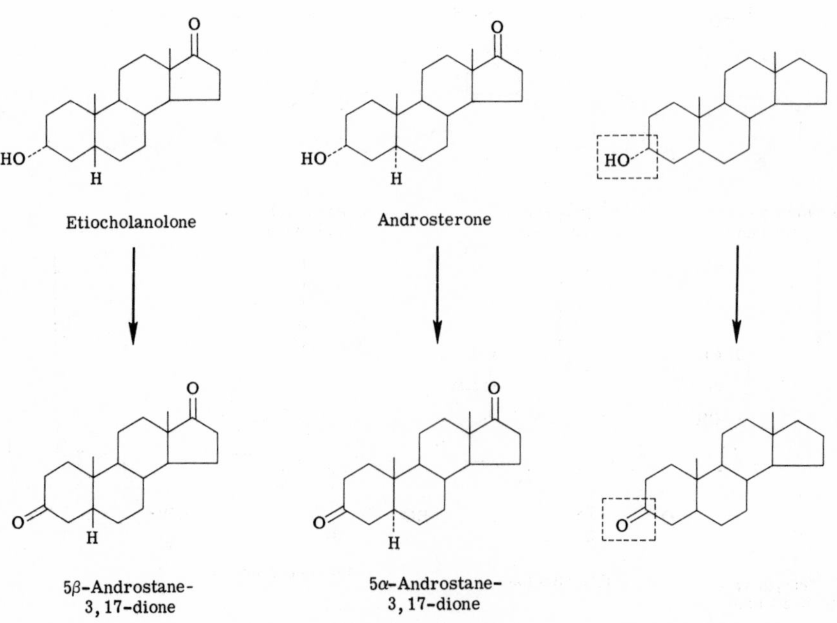

FIG. 4. Neutral steroids: typical example of oxidation of 3α—OH to 3C=O group.

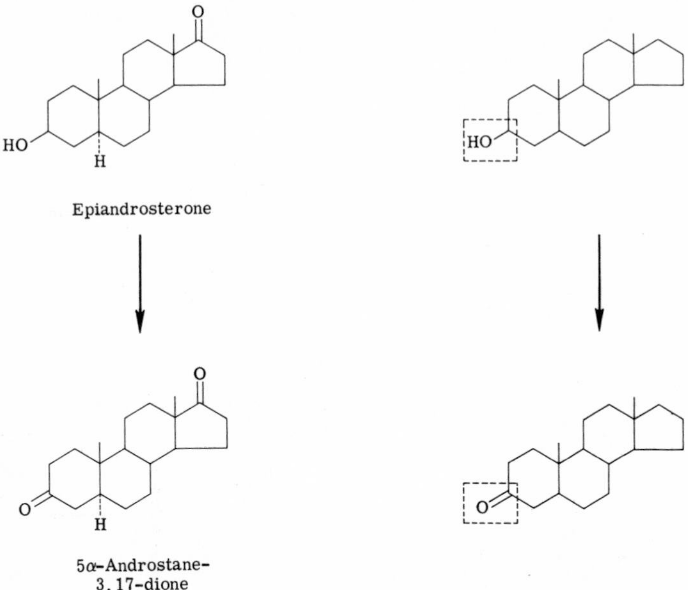

FIG. 5. Neutral steroids: typical example of oxidation of 3β—OH to 3C=O group.

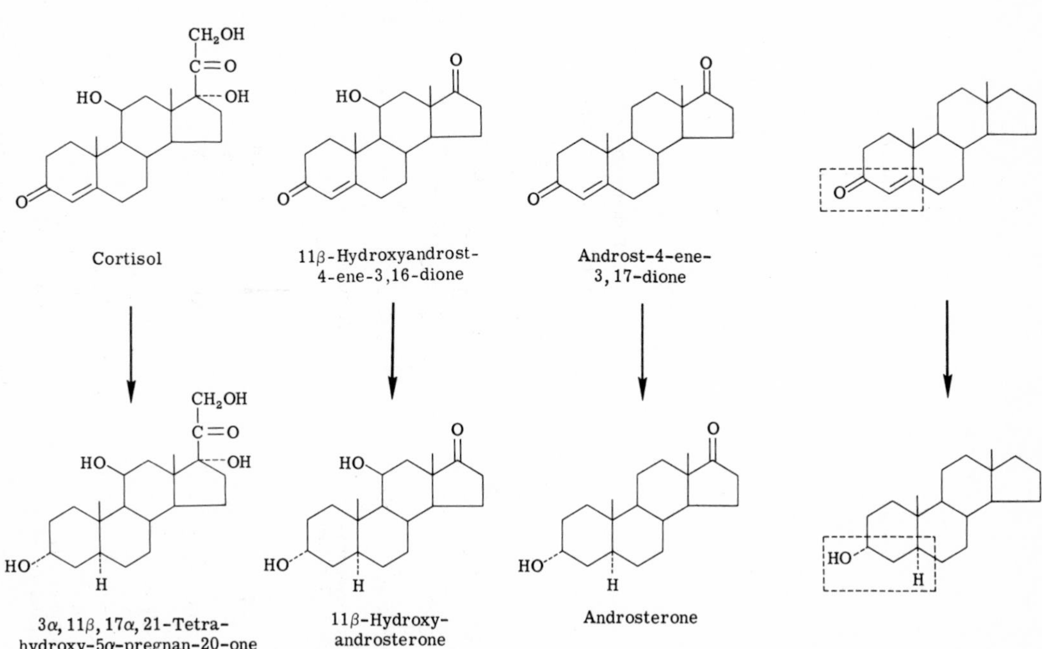

FIG. 6. Neutral steroids: typical example of reduction of Δ^4—3—C=O to 3α—5α grouping.

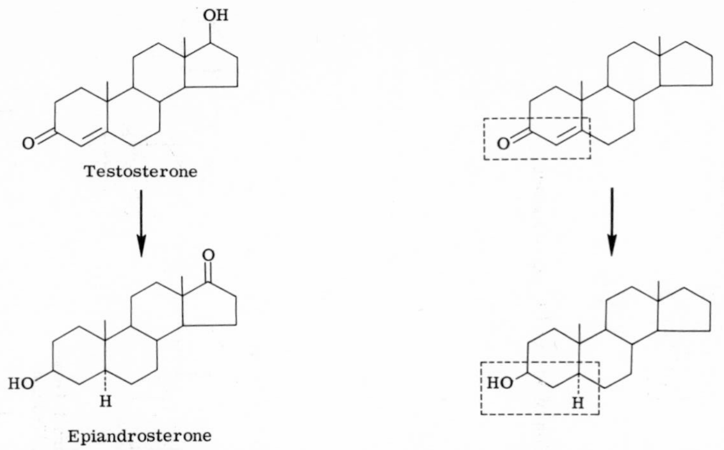

Testosterone

Epiandrosterone

FIG. 7. Neutral steroids: typical example of reduction of Δ^4—3—C=O to 3β—5α grouping.

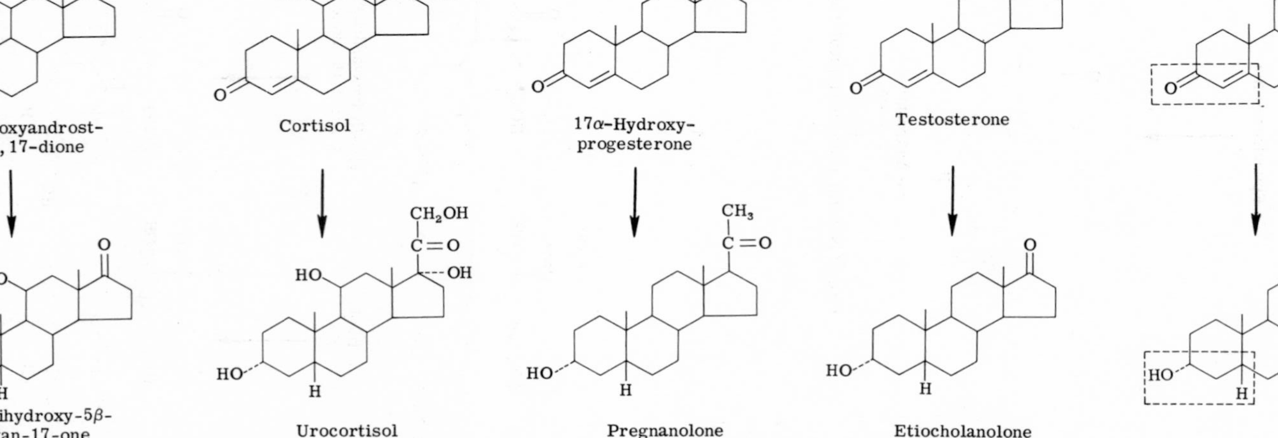

FIG. 8. Neutral steroids: typical example of reduction of Δ^4—3—C=O to 3α—5β grouping.

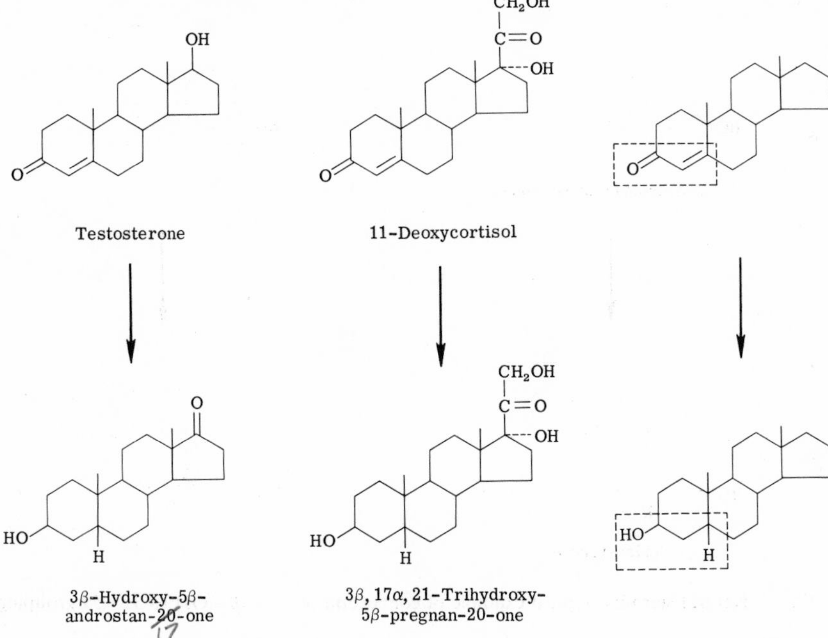

FIG. 9. Neutral steroids: typical example of reduction of Δ^4—3—C=O to 3β—5β grouping.

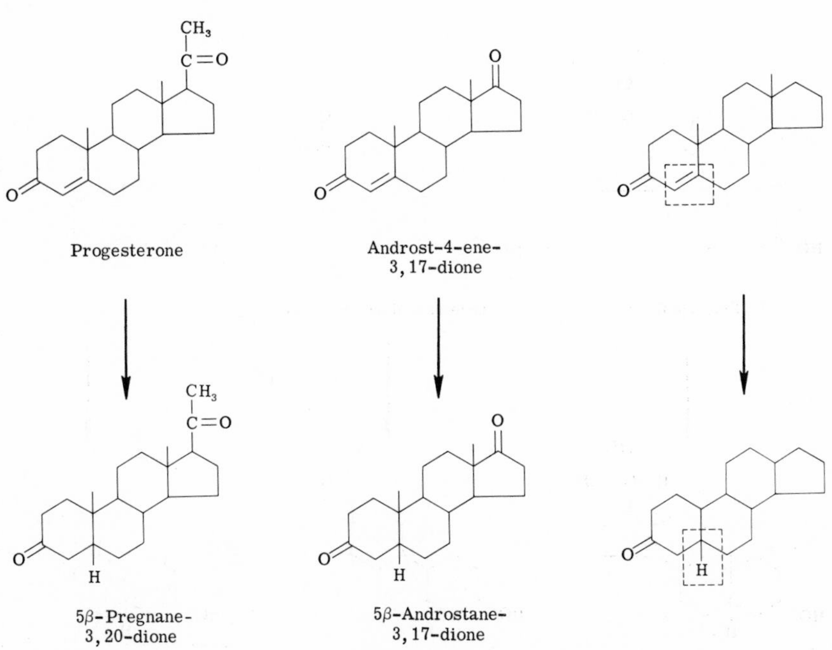

FIG. 10. Neutral steroids: typical example of reduction of Δ^4—3—C=O to 3—C=O—5β grouping.

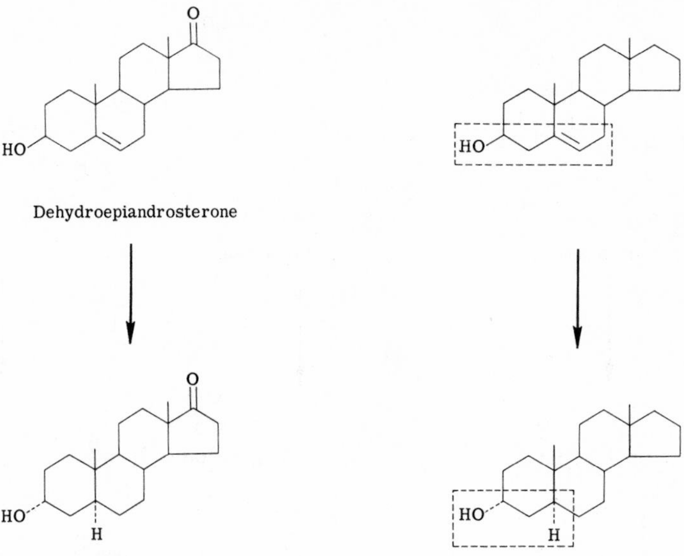

FG. 11. Neutral steroids: typical example of conversion of Δ^5—3β—OH to 3α—5α grouping.

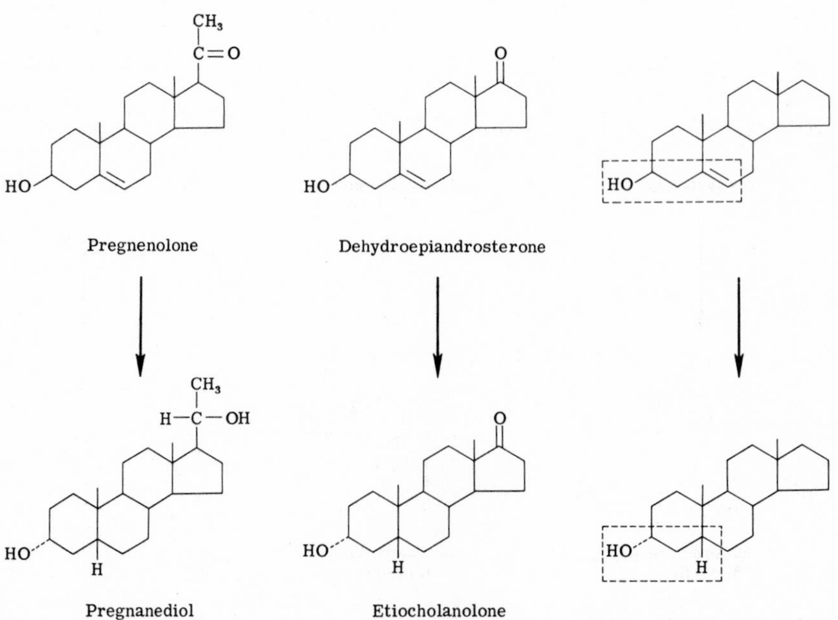

FIG. 12. Neutral steroids: typical example of conversion of Δ^5—3β—OH to 3α—5β grouping.

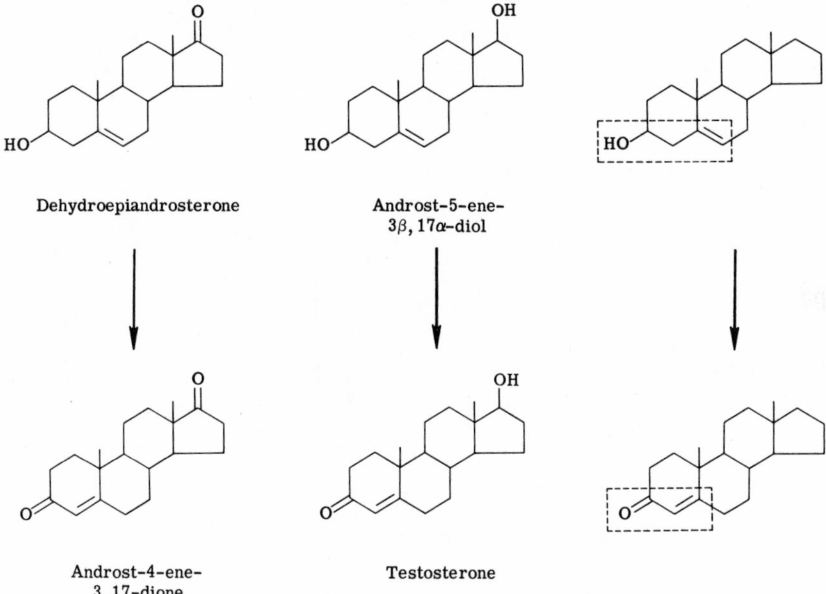

FIG. 13. Neutral steroids: typical example of oxidation of Δ^5—3β—OH to the Δ^4—3—C=O grouping.

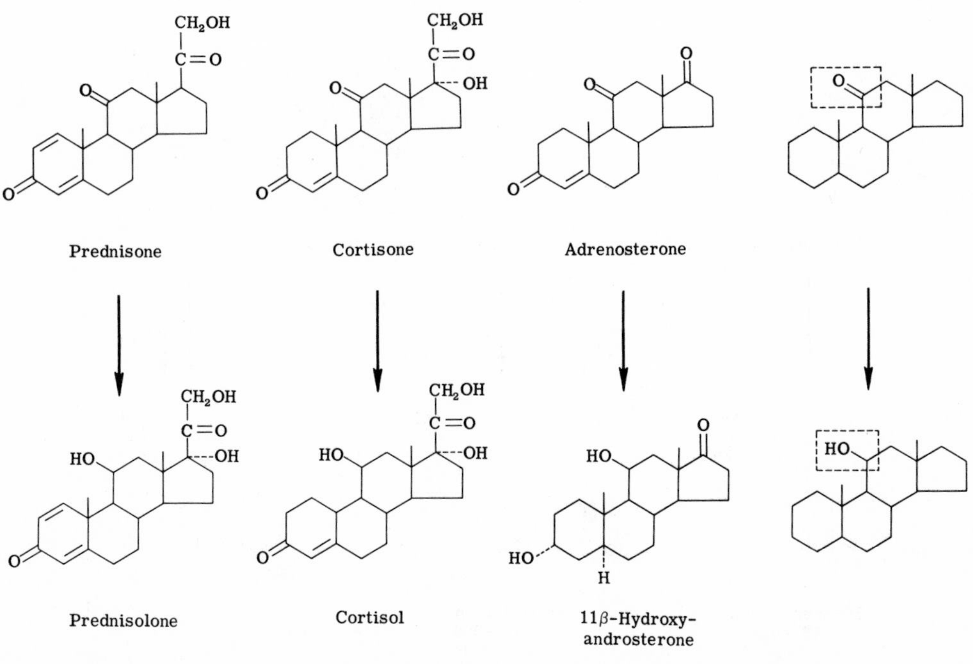

FIG. 14. Neutral steroids: typical example of reduction of 11C=O to 11β—OH group.

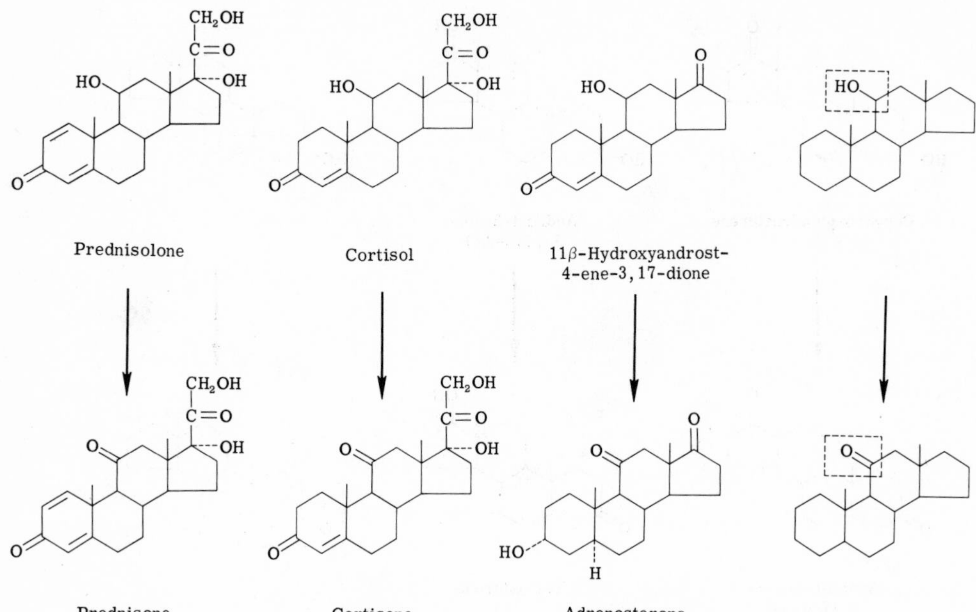

FIG. 15. Neutral steroids: typical example of oxidation of 11β—OH to 11C=O group.

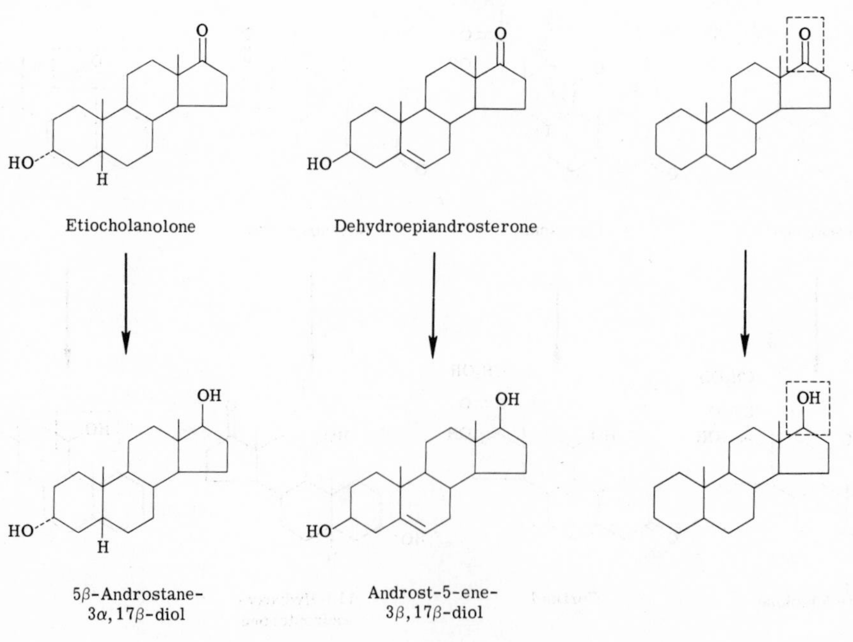

FIG. 16. Neutral steroids: typical example of reduction of 17C=O to 17β—OH group.

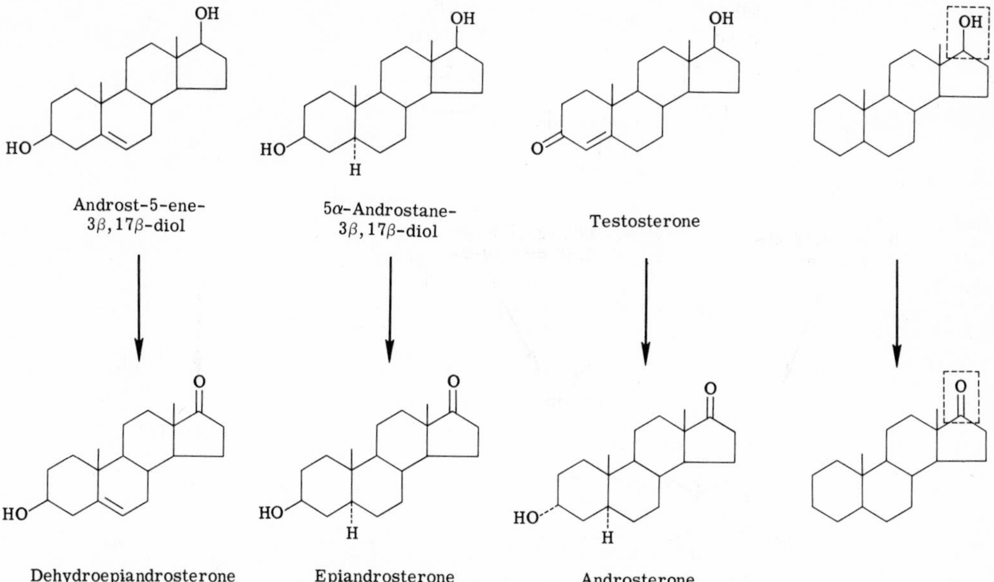

FIG. 17. Neutral steroids: typical example of oxidation of 17β—OH to 17C=O group.

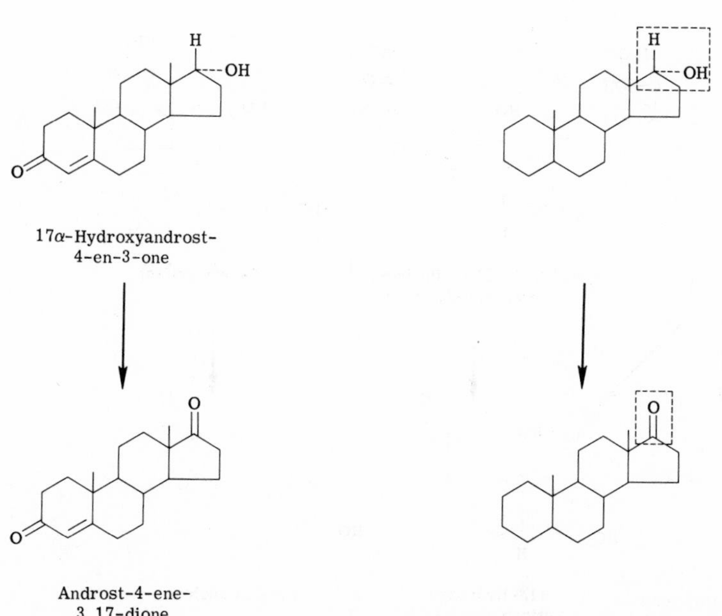

FIG. 18. Neutral steroids: typical example of oxidation of 17α—OH to 17C=O group.

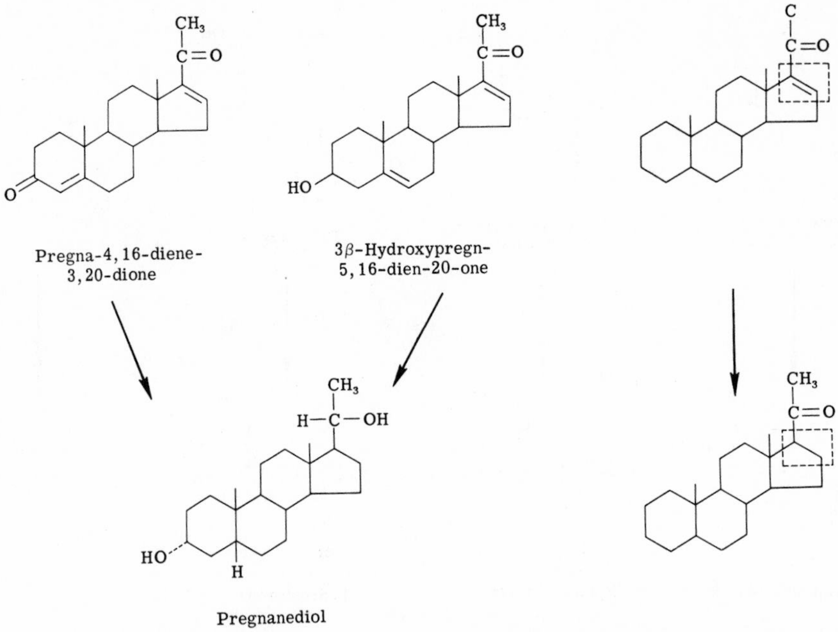

Pregna-4, 16-diene-3, 20-dione
3β-Hydroxypregn-5, 16-dien-20-one
Pregnanediol

FIG. 19. Neutral steroids: typical example of Δ^{16}-reduction.

Cortisol
11β, 17α, 21-Trihydroxy-5β-pregnane-3, 20-dione
21-Deoxycortisol
11-Ketoetiocholanolone
11β-Hydroxy-etiocholanolone
Etiocholanolone

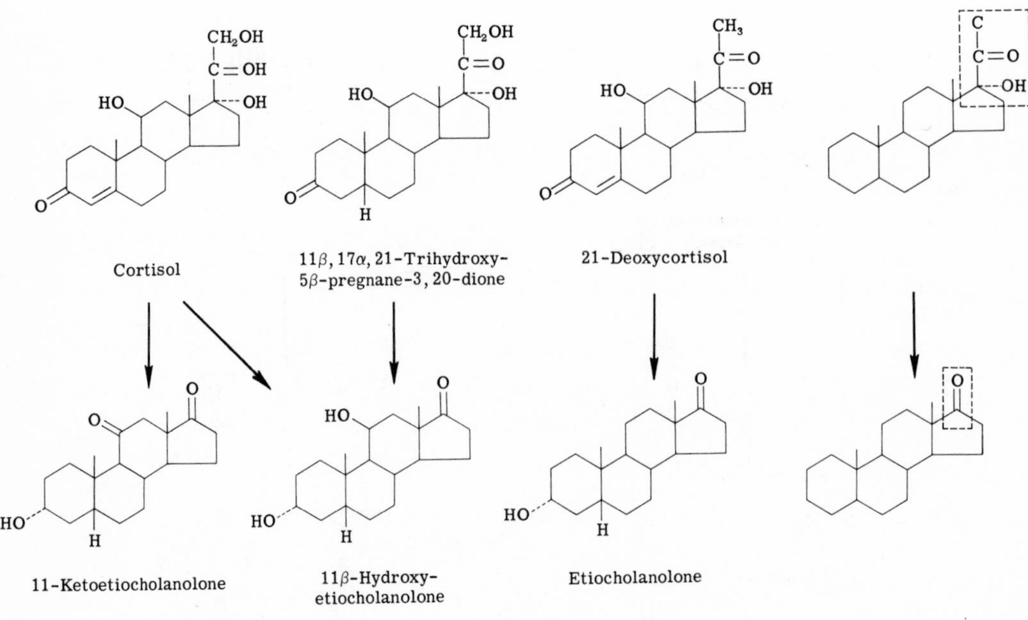

FIG. 20. Neutral steroids: typical example of conversion of C_{21} to C_{19} steroids.

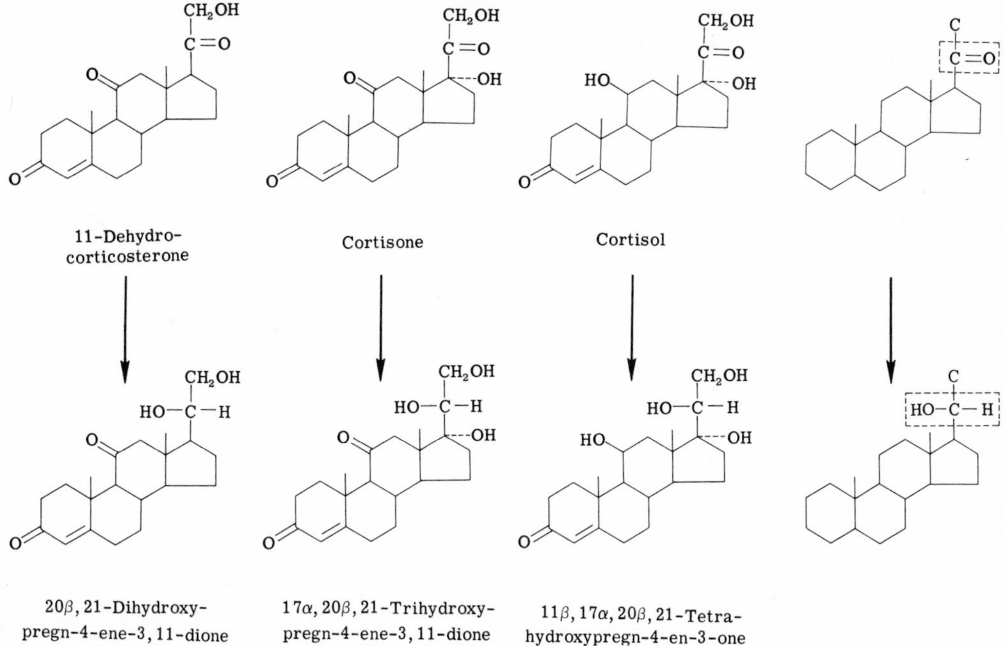

FIG. 21. Neutral steroids: typical example of reduction of 20C=O to 20β—OH grouping.

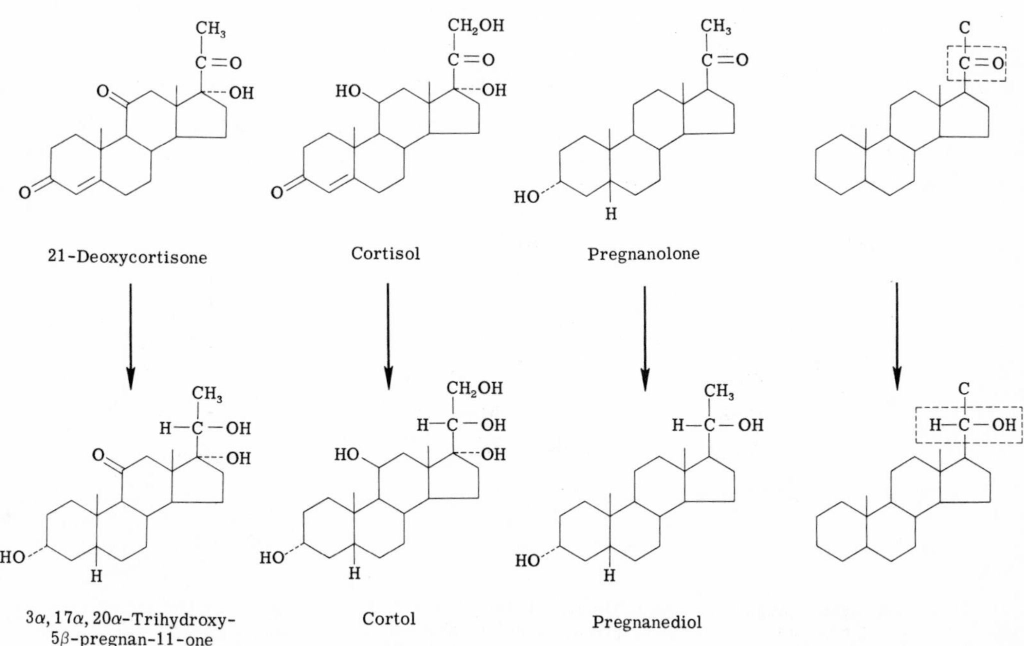

FIG. 22. Neutral steroids: typical example of reduction of 20C=O to 20α—OH grouping.

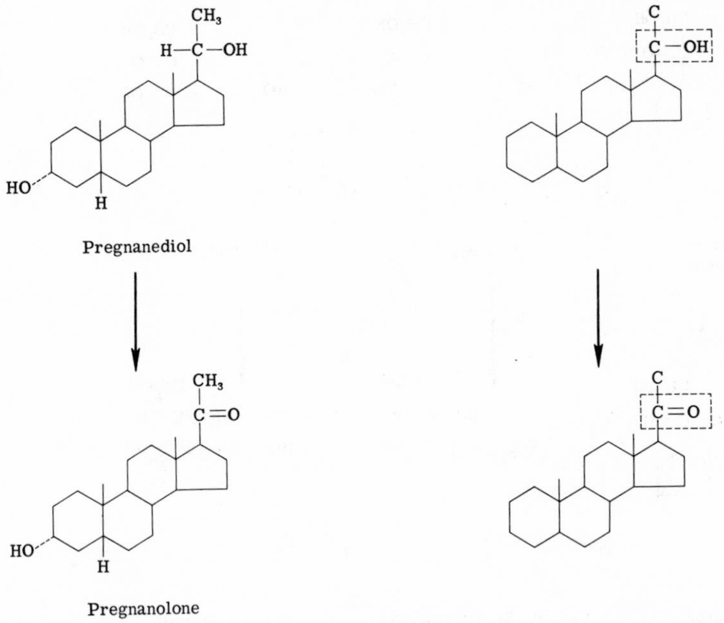

Pregnanediol

Pregnanolone

FIG. 23. Neutral steroids: typical example of oxidation of 20α—OH to 20C=O grouping.

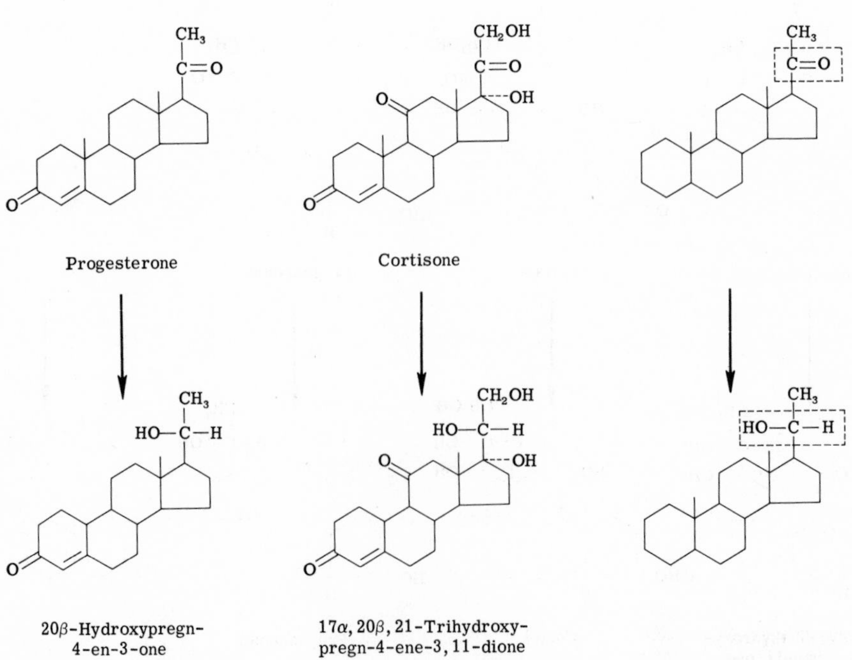

FIG. 24. Neutral steroids: typical example of reduction of 20C=O to 20β—OH grouping.

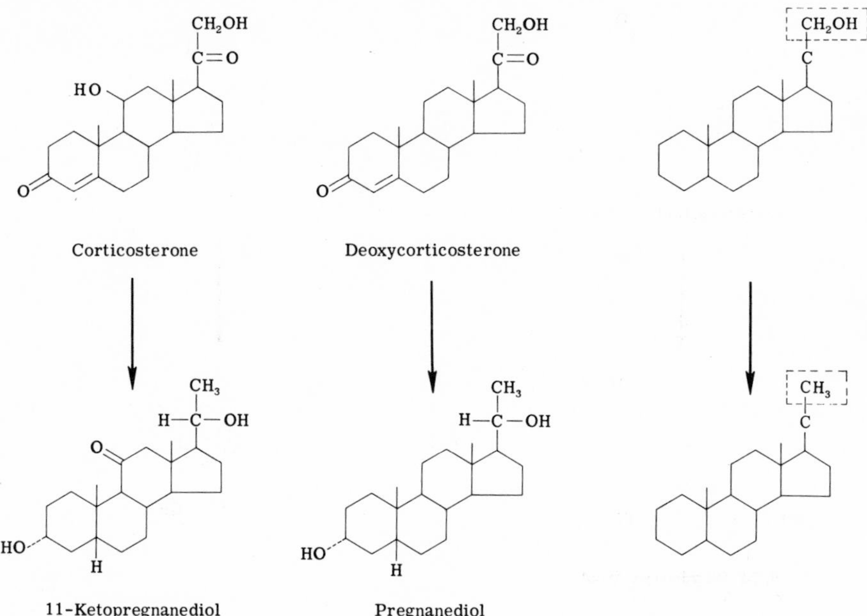

FIG. 25. Neutral steroids: typical example of reduction of 21C—OH to 21—CH group.

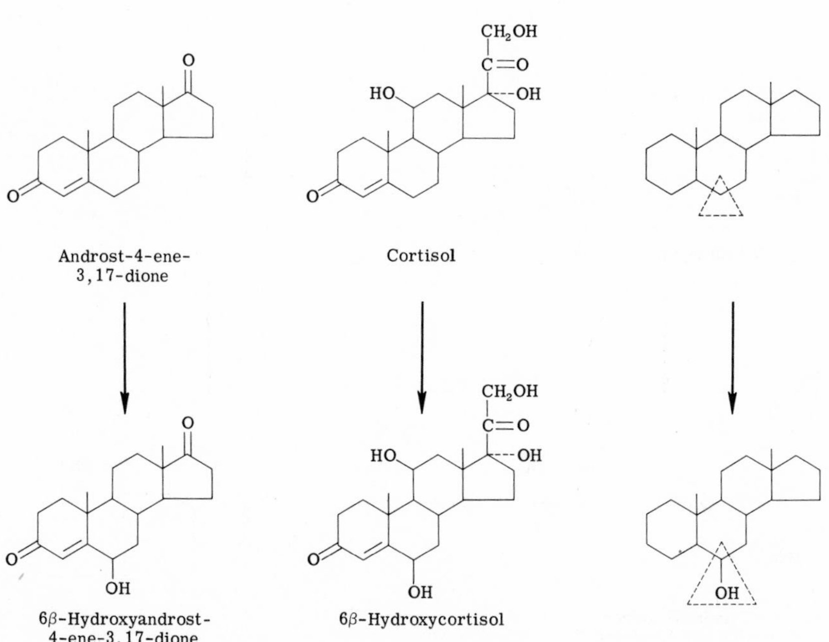

FIG. 26. Neutral steroids: typical example of 6β-hydroxylation.

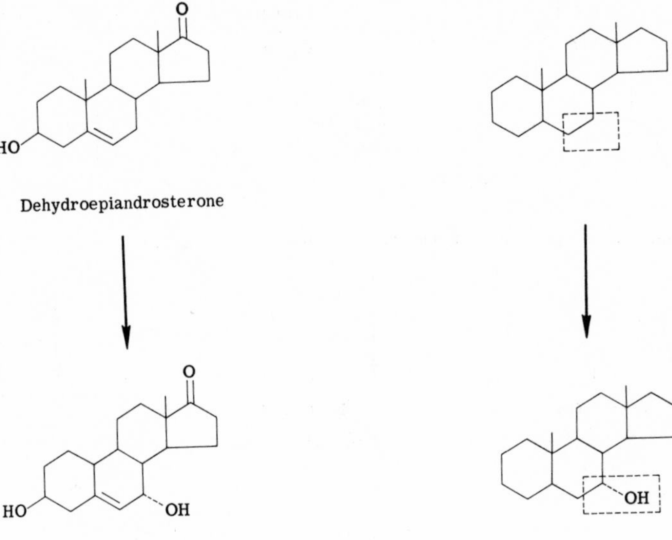

FIG. 27. Neutral steroids: typical example of 7α-hydroxylation.

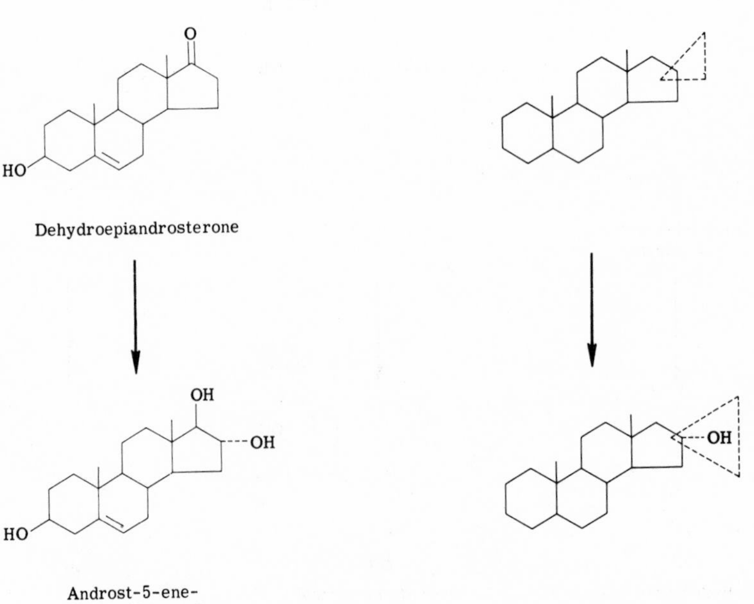

FIG. 28. Neutral steroids: typical example of 16α-hydroxylation.

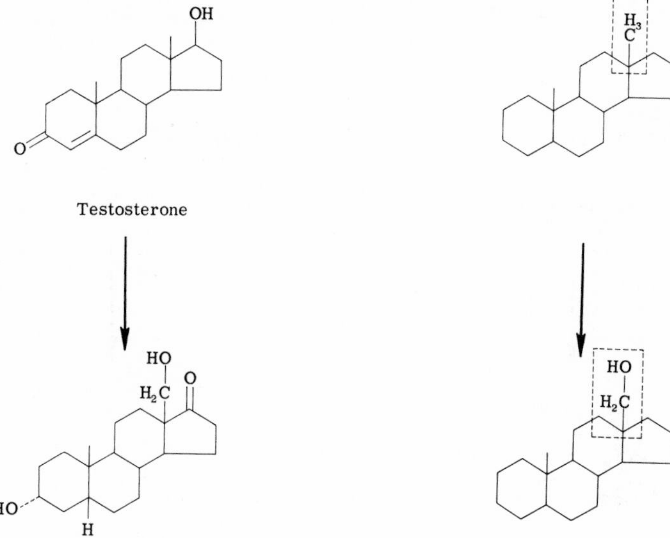

FIG. 29. Neutral steroids: typical example of 18-hydroxylation.

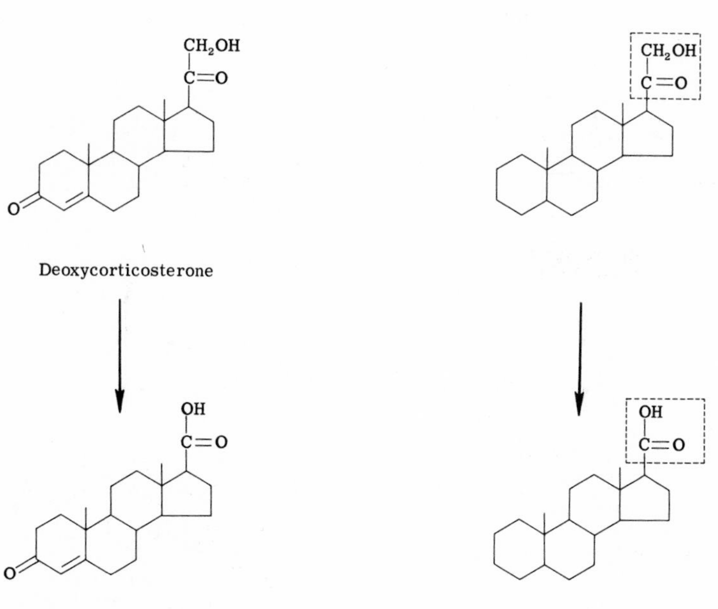

FIG. 30. Neutral steroids: typical example of conversion of C_{21} to C_{20} acid.

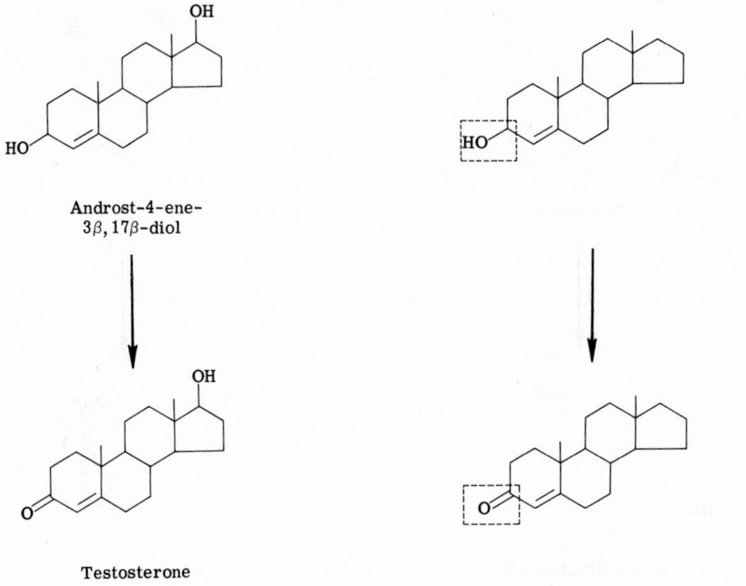

OH

HO

Androst-4-ene-
3β, 17β-diol

OH

O

Testosterone

FIG. 31. Neutral steroids: typical example of conversion of the Δ^4—3β—ol to Δ^4—3—C=O grouping.

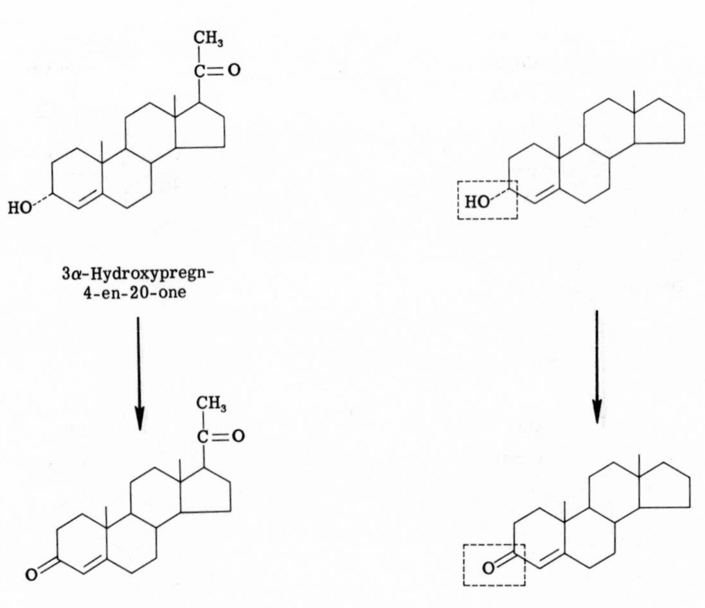

FIG. 32. Neutral steroids: typical example of conversion of the Δ^4—3α—ol to Δ^4—3—C=O grouping.

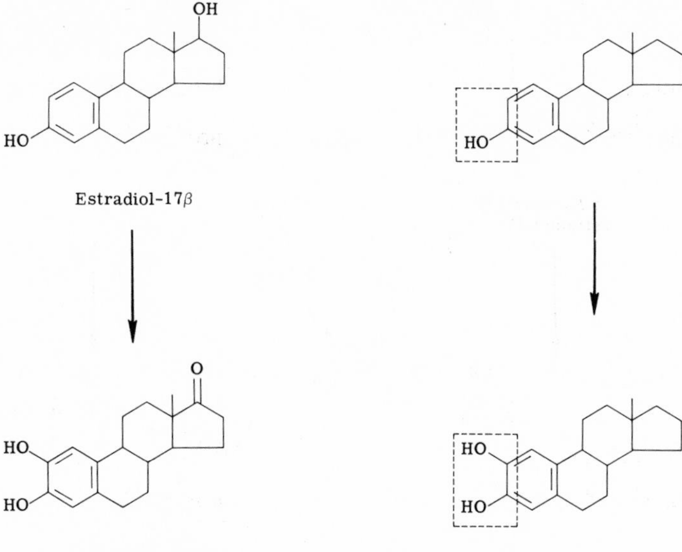

FIG. 33. Phenolic steroids: typical example of 2-hydroxylation.

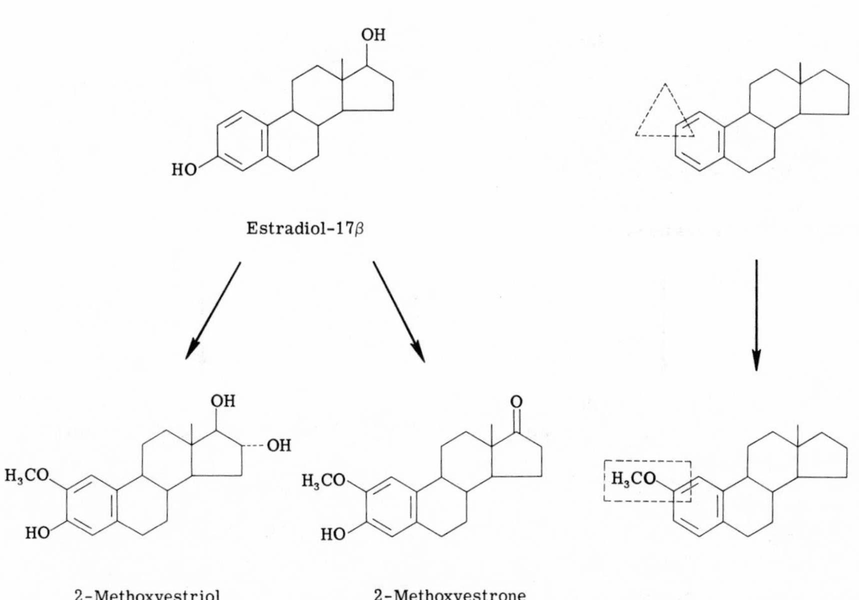

FIG. 34. Phenolic steroids: typical example of 2-methoxylation.

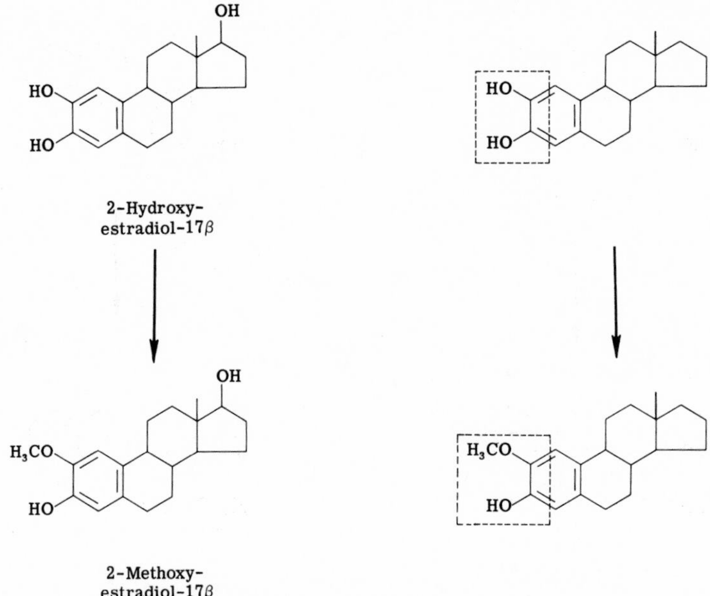

FIG. 35. Phenolic steroids: typical example of 2-methoxylation of a 2—OH steroid.

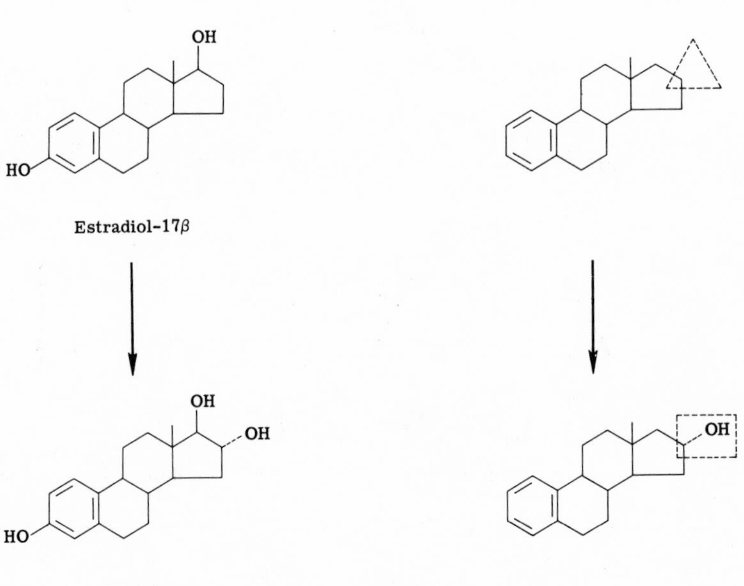

FIG. 36. Phenolic steroids: typical example of 16α-hydroxylation.

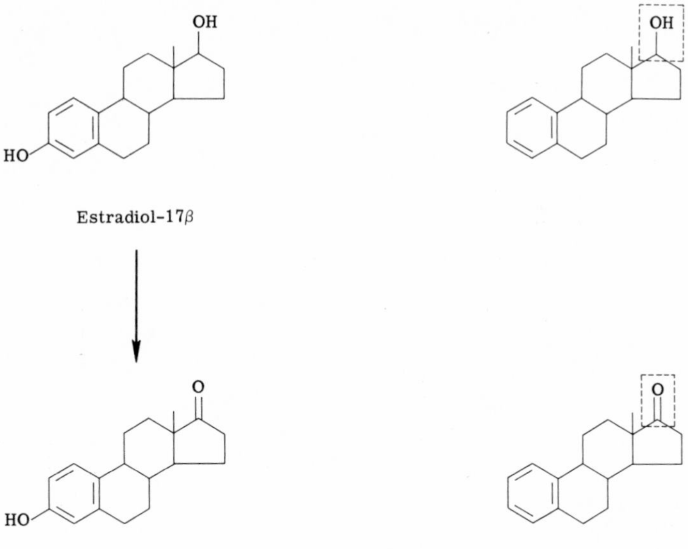

FIG. 37. Phenolic steroids: typical example of oxidation of 17β—OH to 17C=O group.

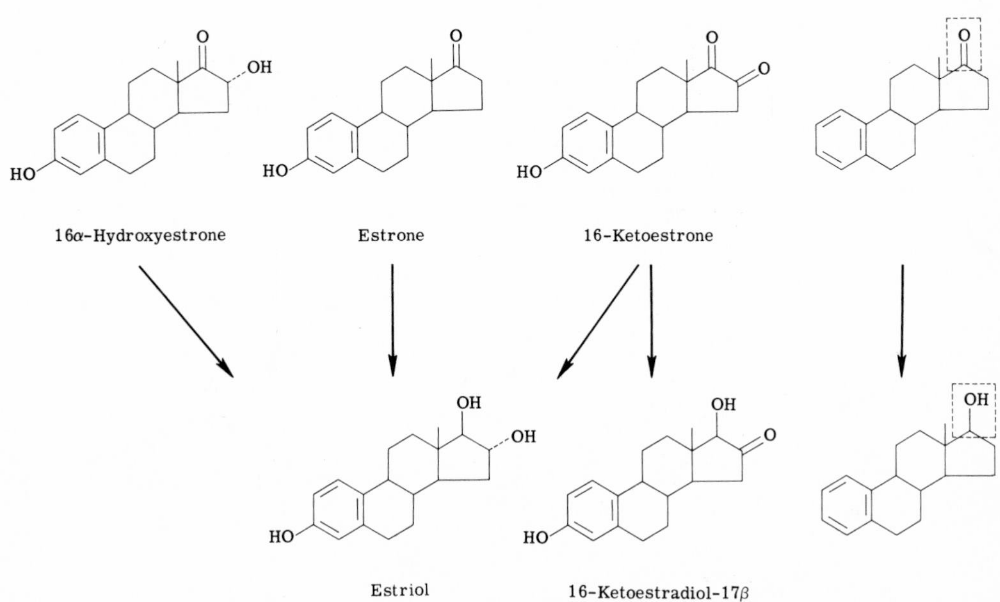

FIG. 38. Phenolic steroids: typical example of reduction of 17C=O to 17β—OH group.

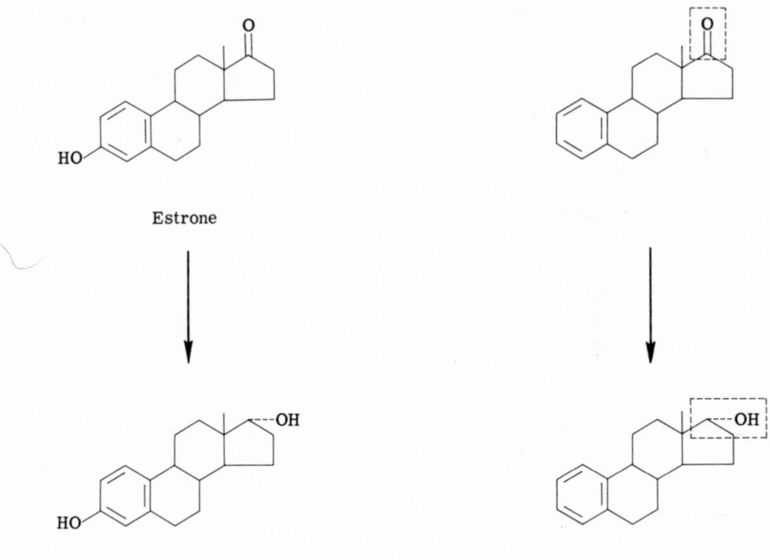

FIG. 39. Phenolic steroids: typical example of reduction of 17C=O to the 17α—OH group.

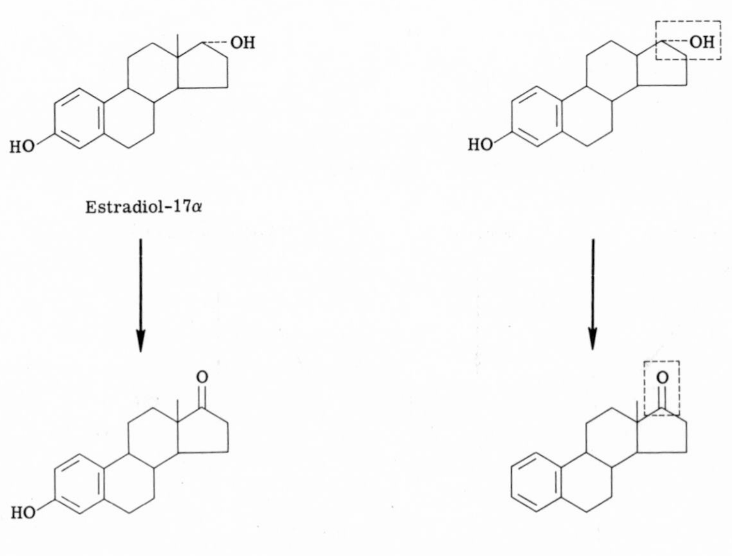

FIG. 40. Phenolic steroids: typical example of oxidation of 17α—OH to 17C=O group.

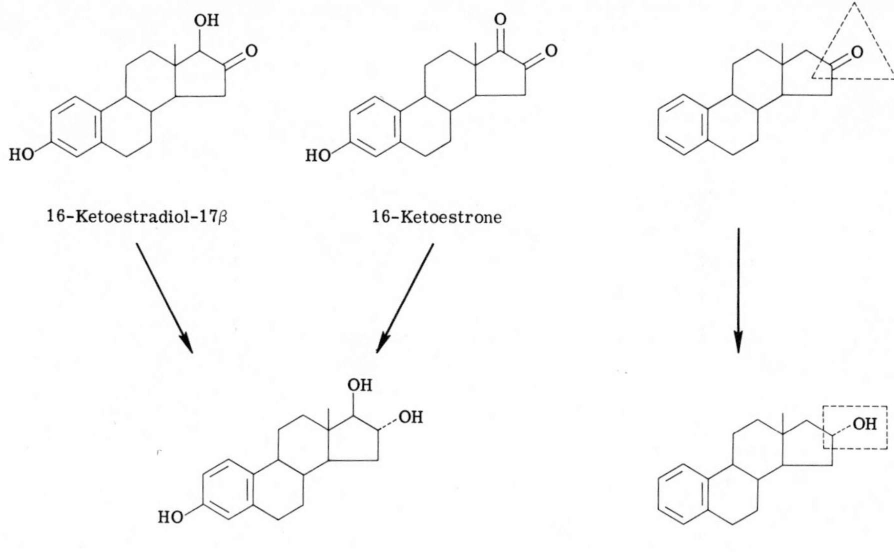

FIG. 41. Phenolic steroids: typical example of reduction of 16C═O to 16α—OH group.

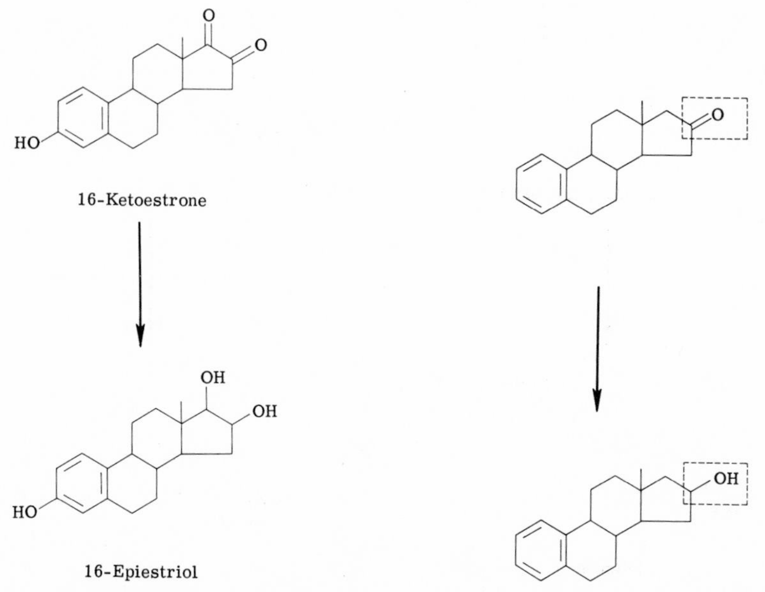

FIG. 42. Phenolic steroids: typical example of reduction of 16C═O to 16β—OH group.

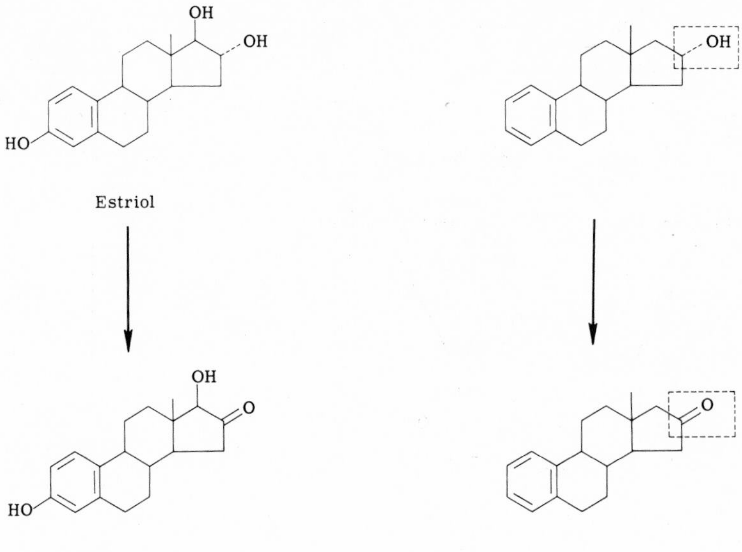

FIG. 43. Phenolic steroids: typical example of oxidation of 16α—OH to 16C=O group.

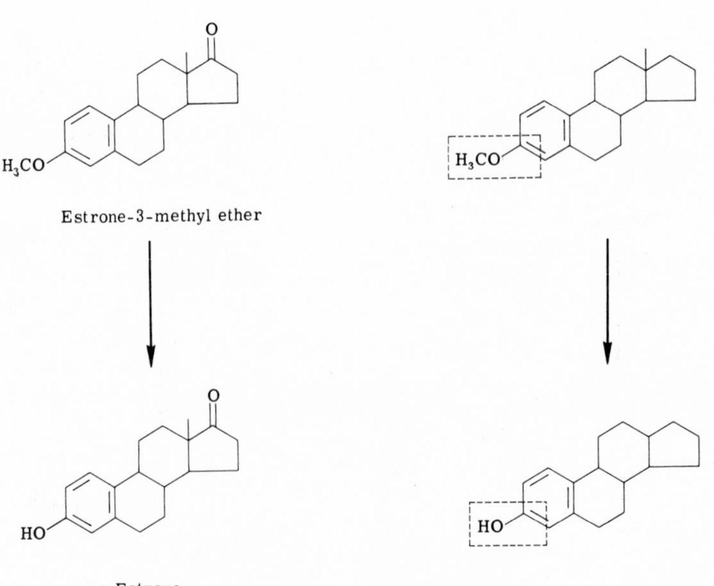

FIG. 44. Phenolic steroids: typical example of demethylation reaction.

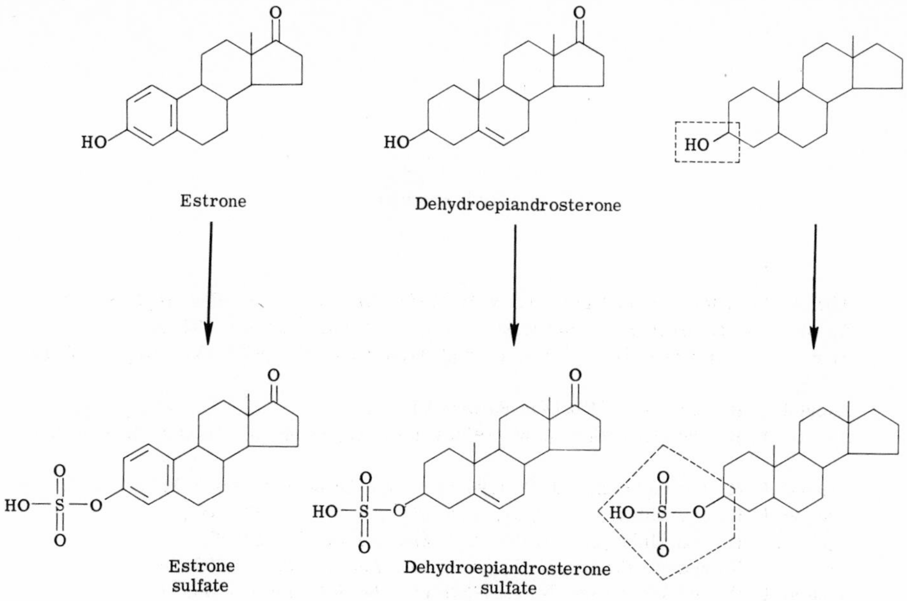

Estrone

Dehydroepiandrosterone

HO

Estrone sulfate

Dehydroepiandrosterone sulfate

HO—S—O

FIG. 45. Formation of sulfates.

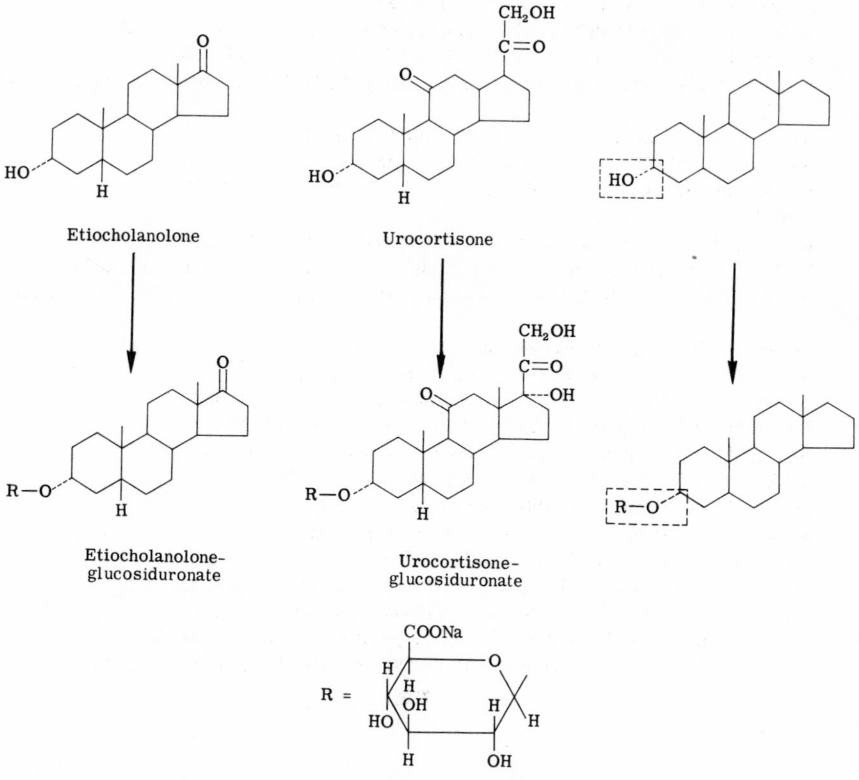

Etiocholanolone

Urocortisone

Etiocholanolone-glucosiduronate

Urocortisone-glucosiduronate

R = (COONa, H, OH, HO, H, OH, H, O, H, H)

FIG. 46. Formation of glucosiduronates.

References

Abelson, D., Ulrich, F., and Long, C. N. H. (1955) *Proc. Soc. Exptl. Biol. Med.* **89**: 386.

Amelung, D., Hübener, H. J., and Roka, L. (1953a) *Z. Physiol. Chem.* **294**: 36.

Amelung, D., Hübener, H. J., Roka, L., and Meyerheim, G. (1953b) *Klin. Wochschr.* **15**: 386.

Axelrod, L. R. (1960) *Arch. Biochem. Biophys.* **91**: 152.

Axelrod, L. R., and Goldzieher, J. W. (1961a) *Abstr. Endocrine Soc. 3rd Ann. Meeting N.Y.* p. 24.

Axelrod, L. R., and Goldzieher, J. W. (1961b) *J. Clin. Endocrinol. Metab.* **21**: 211.

Axelrod, L. R., and Miller, L. L. (1954) *Arch. Biochem. Biophys.* **49**: 248.

Axelrod, L. R., and Miller, L. L. (1956) *Arch. Biochem. Biophys.* **60**: 373.

Axelrod, L. R., and Werthessen, N. T. (1959) *Arch. Biochem. Biophys.* **83**: 567.

Axelrod, L. R., and Werthessen, N. T. (1960) *Arch. Biochem. Biophys.* **86**: 53.

Axelrod, L. R., Rao, P. N., and Goldzieher, J. W. (1960) *Arch. Biochem. Biophys.* **87**: 152.

Balestreri, R., and Correale, L. (1962) *Arch. "E. Maragliano" Pathol. Clin.* **18**: 465.

Baulieu, E. E. (1960) *Compt. Rend.* **250**: 4219.

Beer, C. T., and Gallagher, T. F. (1955) *J. Biol. Chem.* **214**: 335.

Benard, H., Cruz-Horn, A., and David, H. (1961) *Compt. Rend. Soc. Biol.* **105**: 235.

Berliner, D. L. (1960) *Biochim. Biophys. Acta* **38**: 184.

Berliner, D. L., and Dougherty, T. F. (1958a) *Proc. Soc. Exptl. Biol. Med.* **98**: 3.

Berliner, D. L., and Dougherty, T. F. (1958b) *Federation Proc.* **17**: 189.

Besch, P. K., Watson, D. J., Vorys, N., and Barry, R. D. (1963) *Biochim. Biophys. Acta* **69**: 417.

Birke, G., and Plantin, L. O. (1953a) *Acta Med. Scand.* **146**: 184.

Birke, G., and Plantin, L. O. (1953b) *Science* **118**: 751.

Bongiovanni, A. M., Eberlein, W. R., Caddell, J. L., and Eden, W. (1958) *J. Clin. Invest.* **37**: 1087.

Bradlow, H. L., and Gallagher, T. F. (1957) *J. Biol. Chem.* **299**: 505.

Bradlow, H. L., and Gallagher, T. F. (1959) *J. Clin. Endocrinol. Metab.* **19**: 1575.

Braun-Cantilo, J. A., Roche, G. L., Wovitsky, M., and Lawrence, J. H. (1962) *Acta Isotopica* **1**: 351.

Breuer, H. (1962) *Acta Endocrinol.* **40**: 111.

Breuer, H., and Knuppen, R. (1958) *Nature* **182**: 1512.

Breuer, H., and Knuppen, R. (1960a) *Biochim. Biophys. Acta* **39**: 408.

Breuer, H., and Knuppen, R. (1960b) *Naturwissenschaften* **47**: 280.

Breuer, H., and Knuppen, R. (1961) *Biochim. Biophys. Acta* **49**: 620.

Breuer, H., and Nocke, L. (1959) *Biochim. Biophys. Acta* **36**: 271.

Breuer, H., and Pangels, G. (1960) *Acta Endocrinol.* **33**: 532.

Breuer, H., and Pangels, G. (1961) *Z. Physiol. Chem.* **322**: 177.

Breuer, H., Nocke, L., and Knuppen, R. (1958a) *Naturwissenschaften* **45**: 397.

Breuer, H., Nocke, L., and Knuppen, R. (1958b) *Z. Physiol. Chem.* **311**: 275.

Breuer, H., Knuppen, R., and Nocke, L. (1959a) *Biochem. J.* **71**: 26P.

Breuer, H., Knuppen, R., and Pangels, G. (1959b) *Acta Endocrinol.* **30**: 247.

Breuer, H., Nocke, L., and Knuppen, R. (1959c) *Biochim. Biophys. Acta* **33**: 254.

Breuer, H., Nocke, L., and Knuppen, R. (1959d) *Z. Physiol. Chem.* **315**: 72.
Breuer, H., Nocke, L., and Pechthold, I. (1959e) *Z. Vitamin-Hormon-Fermentforsch.* **10**: 106.
Breuer, H., Knuppen, R., and Pangels, G. (1960a) *Z. Physiol. Chem.* **321**: 57.
Breuer, H., Knuppen, R., Ortlepp, R., Pangels, G., and Puck, A. (1960b) *Biochim. Biophys. Acta* **40**: 560.
Breuer, H., Knuppen, R., and Schriefers, H. (1960c) *Z. Physiol. Chem.* **319**: 136.
Breuer, H., Nocke, L., and Pangels, G. (1960d) *Acta Endocrinol.* **34**: 359.
Breuer, H., Pangels, G., and Knuppen, R. (1961) *J. Clin. Endocrinol. Metab.* **21**: 1331.
Breuer, H., Knuppen, R., and Pangels, G. (1962) *Biochim. Biophys. Acta* **65**: 1.
Brooks, R. V. (1960) *J. Endocrinol.* **21**: 277.
Brown, B. T., Golder, W. S., and Wright, S. E. (1961) *Australian J. Exptl. Biol. Med. Sci.* **39**: 345.
Brown, J. B. (1962) *J. Endocrinol.* **24**: 251.
Brown, J. B., and Marrian, G. F. (1957) *J. Endocrinol.* **15**: 307.
Bryson, M. J., and Sweat, M. L. (1963) *Federation Proc.* **22**: 469.
Bulaschenko, H., Richardson, E. M., and Dohan, F. C. (1960) *Arch. Biochem. Biophys.* **87**: 81.
Burstein, S., and Dorfman, R. I. (1955) *J. Biol. Chem.* **213**: 581.
Burstein, S., Savard, K., and Dorfman, R. I. (1953a) *Endocrinology* **53**: 88.
Burstein, S., Savard, K., and Dorfman, R. I. (1953b) *Endocrinology* **53**: 267.
Burstein, S., Savard, K., and Dorfman, R. I. (1953c) *Endocrinology* **52**: 448.
Burstein, S., Dorfman, R. I., and Nadel, E. M. (1954) *Arch. Biochem. Biophys.* **53**: 307.
Burton, R. B., Keutmann, E. H., and Waterhouse, C. (1953) *J. Clin. Endocrinol. Metab.* **13**: 48.
Bush, I. E., and Mahesh, V. B. (1958a) *Biochem. J.* **69**: 21P.
Bush, I. E., and Mahesh, V. B. (1958b) *Biochem. J.* **69**: 9P.
Bush, I. E., and Mahesh, V. B. (1959a) *Biochem. J.* **71**: 705.
Bush, I. E., and Mahesh, V. B. (1959b) *Biochem. J.* **71**: 718.
Buxton, C. L., and Westphal, U. (1938) *Proc. Soc. Exptl. Biol. Med.* **41**: 1284.
Callow, R. K. (1939) *Biochem. J.* **33**: 559.
Calvin, H. I., and Lieberman, S. (1962) *Biochemistry* **1**: 639.
Caspi, E. (1955) Ph.D. Thesis, Clark Univ., Worcester, Massachusetts.
Caspi, E., and Bergen, J. R. (1955) *Arch. Biochem. Biophys.* **59**: 207.
Caspi, E., and Hechter, O. (1954) *Arch. Biochem. Biophys.* **52**: 478.
Caspi, E., and Hechter, O. (1956) *Arch. Biochem. Biophys.* **61**: 299.
Caspi, E., and Pechet, M. M. (1957) *Arch. Biochem. Biophys.* **68**: 236.
Caspi, E., and Pechet, M. M. (1958) *J. Biol. Chem.* **230**: 843.
Caspi, E., Levy, H., and Hechter, O. (1953) *Arch. Biochem. Biophys.* **45**: 169.
Caspi, E., Lindberg, M. C., Hayano, M., Cohen, J. L., Matsuba, M., Rosenkrantz, H., and Dorfman, R. I. (1956) *Arch. Biochem. Biophys.* **61**: 267.
Castegnaro, E., and Sala, G. (1961) *Folia Endocrinol.* **14**: 581.
Castegnaro, E., and Sala, G. (1962) *J. Endocrinol.* **24**: 445.
Chang, E., and Dao, T. L. (1962) *Biochim. Biophys. Acta* **57**: 609.
Chang, E., Slaunwhite, W. R., Jr., and Sandberg, A. A. (1960) *J. Clin. Endocrinol. Metab.* **20**: 1568.
Charollais, E. J., Ponse, K., and Jayle, M. F. (1961) *Compt. Rend. Soc. Biol.* **155**: 689.
Clark, L. C., Jr., and Kochakian, C. D. (1947) *J. Biol. Chem.* **170**: 23.
Clark, L. C., Jr., Kochakian, C. D., and Lobotsky, J. (1947) *J. Biol. Chem.* **171**: 493.
Colás, A. (1962) *Biochem. J.* **82**: 390.
Conney, A. H., and Klutch, A. (1963) *J. Biol. Chem.* **238**: 1611.
Cope, C. L., and Hurlock, B. (1954) *Clin. Sci.* **13**: 69.
Cope, C. L., Nicolis, G., and Frazer, B. (1961) *Clin. Sci.* **21**: 367.
Coppage, W. S., Jr., Island, D. P., Cooner, A. E., and Liddle, G. W. (1962) *J. Clin. Invest.* **41**: 1672.

Davis, M. E., Plotz, E. J., LeRoy, G. V., Gould, R. G., and Werbin, H. (1956) *Am. J. Obstet. Gynecol.* **72**: 740.
DeCourcey, E., and Schneider, J. J. (1956) *Chem. Ind.* (*London*) p. 315.
DeMeio, R. H., and Lewycka, C. (1955) *Endocrinology* **56**: 489.
DeMeio, R. H., Lewycka, C., and Wizerkaniuk, M. (1956) *Federation Proc.* **15**: 241.
DeMeio, R. H., Lewycka, C. M., Wizerkaniuk, M., and Salciunas, O. (1958) *Biochem. J.* **68**: 1.
Diczfalusy, E., Cassmer, O., Alonso, C., and deMiguel, M. (1961) *Acta Endocrinol.* **38**: 31.
Dobriner, K., and Lieberman, S. (1952) *Ciba Found. Colloq. Endocrinol.* **2**: 381.
Dorfman, R. I. (1940) *Proc. Soc. Exptl. Biol. Med.* **45**: 739.
Dorfman, R. I. (1941) *Proc. Soc. Exptl. Biol. Med.* **46**: 351.
Dorfman, R. I. (1954a) *Recent Progr. Hormone Res.* **9**: 5.
Dorfman, R. I. (1954b) *J. Clin. Endocrinol. Metab.* **14**: 318.
Dorfman, R. I., and Fish, W. R. (1940) *J. Biol. Chem.* **135**: 349.
Dorfman, R. I., and Hamilton, J. B. (1940) *J. Biol. Chem.* **133**: 753.
Dorfman, R. I., Cook, J. W., and Hamilton, J. B. (1939) *J. Biol. Chem.* **130**: 285.
Dorfman, R. I., Wise, J. E., and Van Wagenen, G. (1945) *Endocrinology* **36**: 347.
Dorfman, R. I., Wise, J. E., and Shipley, R. A. (1948) *Endocrinology* **42**: 81.
Dorfman, R. I., Wise, J. E., and Shipley, R. A. (1950) *Endocrinology* **46**: 127.
Dorfman, R. I., Ungar, F., Vignos, P. Jr., Stecher, R. M., and Shumway, N. (1952) *Ciba Found. Colloq. Endocrinol.* **2**, 347.
Dougherty, T. F., Brown, H. E., and Berliner, D. L. (1958) *Endocrinology* **62**: 455.
Dowben, R. M., and Rabinowitz, J. L. (1956) *Nature* **178**: 696.
Eisenstein, A. B. (1952) *Science* **116**: 520.
Engel, L. L., Carter, P., and Fielding, L. L. (1955) *J. Biol. Chem.* **213**: 99.
Engel, L. L., Baggett, B., and Carter, P. (1957) *Endocrinology* **61**: 113.
Engel, L. L., Alexander, J., and Wheeler, M. (1958a) *J. Biol. Chem.* **231**: 159.
Engel, L. L., Baggett, B. and Halla, M. (1958b) *Biochim. Biophys. Acta* **30**: 209.
Engel, L. L., Cameron, C. B., Stoffyn, A., Alexander, J. A., Klein, O., and Trofimow, N. D. (1961) *Anal. Biochem.* **2**: 114.
Erichsen, S., and Velle, W. (1960) *Acta Endocrinol.* **34**: 27.
Fish, C. A., Hayano, M., and Pincus, G. (1953) *Arch. Biochem. Biophys.* **42**: 480.
Fish, W. R., and Dorfman, R. I. (1940a) *Science* **91**: 388.
Fish, W. R., and Dorfman, R. I. (1940b) *J. Biol. Chem.* **135**: 349.
Fish, W. R., and Dorfman, R. I. (1941) *J. Biol. Chem.* **140**: 83.
Fish, W. R., and Dorfman, R. I. (1942) *J. Biol. Chem.* **143**: 15.
Fish, W. R., Dorfman, R. I., and Young, W. C. (1942) *J. Biol. Chem.* **143**: 715.
Fish, W. R., Horwitt, B. N., and Dorfman, R. I. (1943) *Science* **97**: 227.
Fishman, J., and Gallagher, T. F. (1958) *Arch. Biochem. Biophys.* **77**: 511.
Fishman, J., Bradlow, H. L., and Gallagher, T. F. (1960a) *J. Biol. Chem.* **235**: 3104.
Fishman, J., Cox, R. I. and Gallagher, T. F. (1960b) *Arch. Biochem. Biophys.* **90**: 318.
Fishman, J., Hellman, L., Zumoff, B., and Gallagher, T. F. (1962) *J. Clin. Endocrinol. Metab.* **22**: 389.
Fishman, W. H., and Sie, H.-G. (1956) *J. Biol. Chem.* **218**: 335.
Florini, J. R., Smith, L. L., and Buyske, D. A. (1961) *J. Biol. Chem.* **236**: 1038.
Forchielli, E. (1956) Ph.D. Thesis, Boston Univ., Boston, Massachusetts.
Forchielli, E., and Dorfman, R. I. (1956) *J. Biol. Chem.* **223**: 443.
Forchielli, E., Rosenkrantz, H., and Dorfman, R. I. (1955) *J. Biol. Chem.* **215**: 713.
Forchielli, E., Ramachandran, S., and Ringold, H. J. (1963) *Steroids* **1**: 157.
Fotherby, K., Colás, A., Atherden, S. M., and Marrian, G. F. (1957) *Biochem. J.* **66**: 664.
Fukushima, D. K., and Bradlow, H. L. (1962) *J. Biol. Chem.* **237**: PC975.
Fukushima, D. K., and Gallagher, T. F. (1957) *J. Biol. Chem.* **226**: 725.
Fukushima, D. K., Leeds, N. S., Bradlow, H. L., Kritchevsky, T. H., Stokem, M. B., and Gallagher, T. F. (1955) *J. Biol. Chem.* **212**: 449.

Fukushima, D. K., Bradlow, H. L., Hellman, L., Zumoff, B., and Gallagher, T. F. (1960) *J. Biol. Chem.* **235**: 2246.

Fukushima, D. K., Bradlow, H. L., Hellman, L., Zumoff, B., and Gallagher, T. F. (1961) *J. Clin. Endocrinol. Metab.* **21**: 765.

Fukushima, D. K., Bradlow, H. L., Hellman, L., and Gallagher, T. F. (1962a) *J. Clin. Endocrinol. Metab.* **22**: 765.

Fukushima, D. K., Williams, K. I. H., Zumoff, B., and Gallagher, T. F. (1962b) *Acta Endocrinol.* **41**: 391.

Gallagher, T. F. (1957) *Cancer Res.* **17**: 520.

Gallagher, T. F., Fukushima, D. K., Barry, M. C., and Dobriner, K. (1951) *Recent Progr. Hormone Res.* **6**: 131.

Gallagher, T. F., Kraychy, S., Fishman, J., Brown, J. B., and Marrian, G. F. (1958) *J. Biol. Chem.* **233**: 1093.

Gallagher, T. F., Bradlow, H. L., Miller, D. G., Zumoff, B., and Hellman, L. (1962) *J. Clin. Endocrinol. Metab.* **22**: 1049.

Ganis, F. M., Axelrod, L. R., and Miller, L. L. (1956) *J. Biol. Chem.* **218**: 841.

Gold, N. I. (1962) *J. Clin. Invest.* **41**: 1871.

Gomez-Mont, F., and Berliner, D. L. (1953) *Gac. Med. Mex.* **83**: 413.

Grant, J. K. (1952) *Biochem. J.* **51**: 358.

Gray, C. H., Green, M. A. S., Holness, N. J., and Lunnon, J. B. (1955) *Lancet* **ii**: 1067.

Gray, C. H., Green, M. A. S., Holness, N. J., and Lunnon, J. B. (1956) *J. Endocrinol.* **14**: 146.

Gray, C. L., and Bischoff, F. (1955) *Am. J. Physiol.* **180**: 279.

Grosser, B. I., and Bliss, E. L. (1963) *Federation Proc.* **22**: 271.

Hagopian, M. (1955) M.S. Thesis, Clark Univ., Worcester, Massachusetts.

Hayano, M., Lindberg, M. C., Wiener, M., Rosenkrantz, H., and Dorfman, R. I. (1954) *Endocrinology* **55**: 326.

Heard, R. D. H., Bauld, W. S., and Hoffman, M. M. (1941) *J. Biol. Chem.* **141**: 709.

Hecker, E., and Zayed, S. M. A. D. (1961) *Biochim. Biophys. Acta* **50**: 607.

Helmreich, M. L., and Huseby, R. A. (1962) *J. Clin. Endocrinol. Metab.* **22**: 1018.

Hoffman, M. M., Kazmin, V. E., and Browne, J. S. L. (1943) *J. Biol. Chem.* **147**: 259.

Hopwood, M. L., and Gassner, F. X. (1962) *Endocrinology* **70**: 886.

Horwitt, B. N., Dorfman, R. I., Shipley, R. A., and Fish, W. R. (1944a) *J. Biol. Chem.* **155**: 213.

Horwitt, B. N., Dorfman, R. I., and Van Wagenen, G. (1944b) *Endocrinology* **34**: 352.

Hübener, H. J. (1956) *Recent Progr. Hormone Res.* **12**: 146.

Hübener, H. J., Fukushima, D. K., and Gallagher, T. F. (1956) *J. Biol. Chem.* **220**: 499.

Idler, D. R., and Truscott, B. (1963) *Can. J. Biochem. Physiol.* **41**: 875.

Ishizuka, N., Maeyama, M., Ide, T., and Kawata, M. (1957) *Med. J. Osaka Univ.* **7**: 953.

Ishizuka, N., Maeyama, M., Ide, T., and Kawata, M. (1958) *Chem. Abstr.* **52**: 2116.

Isselbacher, K. J. (1956) *Recent Progr. Hormone Res.* **12**: 134.

Isselbacher, K. J., and Axelrod, J. (1955) *J. Am. Chem. Soc.* **77**: 1070.

Jeanloz, R. W., Levy, H., Jacobsen, R. P., Hechter, O., Schenker, V., and Pincus, G. (1953) *J. Biol. Chem.* **203**: 453.

Johnson, D. F., Heftmann, E., and Bunim, J. J. (1957) *Proc. Soc. Exptl. Biol. Med.* **94**: 291.

Kappas, A., Hellman, L., Fukushima, D. F., and Gallagher, T. F. (1958) *J. Clin. Endocrinol. Metab.* **18**: 1043.

Kelly, W. G., Bandi, L., Shoolery, J. N., and Lieberman, S. (1962a) *Biochemistry* **1**: 172.

Kelly, W. G., Bandi, L., and Lieberman, S. (1962b) *Biochemistry* **1**: 792.

Kemp, A. D., Kappas, A., Salamon, I. I., Herling, F., and Gallagher, T. F. (1954) *J. Biol. Chem.* **210**: 123.

King, R. J. B. (1960) *Biochem. J.* **74**: 22P.

King, R. J. B. (1961a) *Biochem. J.* **79**: 355.

King, R. J. B. (1961b) *Biochem. J.* **79**: 361.

Klempien, E. J., Voigt, K. D., and Tamm, J. (1961) *Acta Endocrinol.* **36**: 498.
Knights, B. A., and Thomas, G. H. (1962) *J. Endocrinol.* **24**: III-IV.
Knights, B. A., Rogers, A. W., and Thomas, G. H. (1962) *Biochem. Biophys. Res. Commun.* **8**: 253.
Knuppen, R., and Breuer, H. (1962) *Z. Physiol. Chem.* **328**: 226.
Knuppen, R., Breuer, H., and Pangels, G. (1961) *Z. Physiol. Chem.* **324**: 108.
Kochakian, C. D., and Aposhian, H. V. (1952) *Arch. Biochem. Biophys.* **37**: 442.
Kochakian, C. D., Nall, D. M., and Parente, N. (1952) *Federation Proc.* **11**: 442.
Kraychy, S., and Gallagher, T. F. (1957a) *J. Am. Chem. Soc.* **79**: 754.
Kraychy, S., and Gallagher, T. F. (1957b) *J. Biol. Chem.* **229**: 519.
Krehbiel, R. E., Burton, A. F., and Darrach, M. (1962) *Can. J. Biochem. Physiol.* **40**: 1797.
Kupfer, D., Forchielli, E., and Dorfman, R. I. (1960) *J. Biol. Chem.* **235**: 1968.
Lamedica, G., Correale, L., and Bonanni, R. (1957) *Arch. Studio Fisiopatol. Clin. Ricambio* **21**: 41.
Langecker, H. (1959) *Acta Endocrinol.* **30**: 369.
Langecker, H. (1961) *Acta Endocrinol.* **37**: 14.
Langecker, H. (1962) *Arzneimittel-Forsch.* **12**: 23.
Langecker, H., and Kramer, M. (1962) *Excerpta Med. Intern. Congr. Ser.* **51**: 210.
Lawson, D. E. M., and Pearlman, W. H. (1963) *Federation Proc.* **22**: 469.
Levitz, M., Spitzer, J. R., and Twombly, G. H. (1956) *J. Biol. Chem.* **222**: 981.
Levitz, M., Spitzer, J. R., and Twombley, G. H. (1958) *J. Biol. Chem.* **231**: 787.
Levitz, M., Rosen, M. F., and Twombley, G. H. (1960a) *Arch. Biochem. Biophys.* **88**: 212.
Levitz, M., Condon, G. P., Money, W. L., and Dancis, J. (1960b) *J. Biol. Chem.* **235**: 973.
Levy, H., and Maloney, P. J. (1962) *Biochim. Biophys. Acta* **57**: 149.
Lieberman, S., Dobriner, K., Hill, B. R., Fieser, L. F., and Rhoads, C. P. (1948) *J. Biol. Chem.* **172**: 263.
Lieberman, S., Haiton, L. B., Stoken, M. B., Studer, P. E., and Dobriner, K. (1951) *Federation Proc.* **10**: 216.
Lipman, M. M., Katz, F. H., and Jailer, J. W. (1962) *J. Clin. Endocrinol. Metab.* **22**: 268.
Little, B., DiMartinis, J., and Nyholm, B. (1959) *Acta Endocrinol.* **30**: 530.
Lombardo, M., and Hudson, P. B. (1957) *J. Biol. Chem.* **229**: 181.
Lotti, P., Capone, M., Forchielli, E., and Dorfman, R. I. (1960) *Folia Endocrinol.* **8**: 814.
Lucis, O. J., and Hobkirk, R. (1963) *Steroids* **1**: 678.
MacRae, H. F., Layne, D. S., and Common, R. H. (1959) *Poultry Sci.* **38**: 684.
Mahesh, V. B., and Greenblatt, R. B. (1962) *Acta Endocrinol.* **41**: 400.
Marrian, G. F., and Kyle, T. I. (1951) *Biochem. J.* **49**: 80.
Mason, H. L. (1948) *J. Biol. Chem.* **172**: 783.
Mason, H. L., and Kepler, E. J. (1945a) *J. Biol. Chem.* **161**: 235.
Mason, H. L., and Kepler, E. J. (1945b) *J. Biol. Chem.* **160**: 255.
Mason, H. L., and Kepler, E. J. (1947) *J. Biol. Chem.* **167**: 73.
Mayer, C. (1952) *Ann. Endocrinol.* (*Paris*) **13**: 675.
Meigs, R. A., and Engel, L. L. (1961) *Endocrinology* **69**: 152.
Meyer, A. S., Rodgers, O. G., and Pincus, G. (1953) *Endocrinology* **53**: 245.
Meyer, A. S., Hayano, M., Lindberg, M. C., Gut, M., and Rodgers, O. G. (1955) *Acta Endocrinol.* **18**: 148.
Migeon, C. J. (1963) *Federation Proc.* **22**: 468.
Migeon, C. J., Wall, P. E., and Bertrand, J. (1959) *J. Clin. Invest.* **38**: 619.
Miller, A. M., and Dorfman, R. I. (1945) *Endocrinology* **37**: 217.
Miller, A. M., Dorfman, R. I., and Miller, M. (1950) *Endocrinology* **46**: 105.
Miller, L. L., and Axelrod, L. R. (1954) *Metab. Clin. Exptl.* **3**: 438.
Mitchell, J. E., and Hobkirk, R. (1959) *Biochem. Biophys. Res. Commun.* **1**: 72.
Mueller, G. C., and Rumney, G. (1957) *J. Am. Chem. Soc.* **79**: 1004.
Müller, H. A. (1940) *Klin. Wochschr.* **19**: 318.

Nakao, T., Omori, Y., and Morisugi, M. (1959) *Jikeikai Med. J.* **6**: 61.

Neeman, M., Slaunwhite, W. R., Jr., Neely, L. M., Colson, J. G., and Sandberg, A. A. (1960) *J. Biol. Chem.* **235**: PC58.

Nocke, W., Breuer, H., and Knuppen, R. (1961) *Acta Endocrinol.* **36**: 393.

Oertel, G. W., and Eik-Nes, K. B. (1959) *Endocrinology* **65**: 766.

Ofner, P., Smakula, E. E., Wotiz, H. H., Lemon, H. M., and Mescon, H. (1957) *Biochem. J.* **66**: 53P.

Pappo, R. (1959) *J. Am. Chem. Soc.* **81**: 1010.

Pasargiklian, E. (1959) *Studi Sassaresi* **37**: 79.

Pasqualini, J. R., and Jayle, M. F. (1961) *Biochem. J.* **81**: 147.

Pasqualini, J. R., and Jayle, M. F. (1962) *J. Clin. Invest.* **41**: 981.

Pearlman, W. H. (1957) *Biochem. J.* **67**: 1.

Pearlman, W. H., and DeMeio, R. H. (1949) *J. Biol. Chem.* **179**: 1141.

Pearlman, W. H., and Pearlman, M. R. J. (1961a) *J. Biol. Chem.* **236**: 1321.

Pearlman, W. H., and Pearlman, M. R. J. (1961b) *Federation Proc.* **20**: 197.

Pearlman, W. H., and Pincus, G. (1942) *J. Biol. Chem.* **144**: 569.

Pearlman, W. H., and Pincus, G. (1946) *Federation Proc.* **5**: 79.

Pearlman, W. H., Rakoff, A. E., Paschkis, K. E., Cantarow, A., and Walkling, A. A. (1948) *J. Biol. Chem.* **173**: 175.

Pearlman, W. H., Pearlman, M. R. J., and Rakoff, A. E. (1953) *Am. J. Obstet. Gynecol.* **66**: 370.

Pechet, M. M., Hesse, R. H., and Kohler, H. (1961a) *J. Am. Chem. Soc.* **82**: 5251.

Pechet, M. M., Kohler, H., Yates, K., and Wan, J. (1961b) *J. Biol. Chem.* **236**: PC68.

Perlman, D., Jackson, P. W., and Giuffre, N. (1960) *Can. J. Biochem. Physiol.* **38**: 393.

Perlman, D., Giuffre, N., and Pan, S. C. (1961) *Federation Proc.* **20**: 148.

Peterson, R. E., Pierce, C. E., and Kliman, B. (1957) *Arch. Biochem. Biophys.* **70**: 614.

Picha, G. M., Saunders, F. J., and Green, D. M. (1952) *Science* **115**: 704.

Pincus, G. (1954) *Progr. Allergy* **4**: 199.

Portius, J., and Repke, K. (1960a) *Arch. Exptl. Pathol. Pharmakol.* **239**: 144.

Portius, J., and Repke, K. (1960b) *Arch. Exptl. Pathol. Pharmakol.* **239**: 299.

Rappaport, R., and Migeon, C. J. (1962) *J. Clin. Endocrinol. Metab.* **22**: 1065.

Richardson, E. M., Touchstone, J. C., and Dohan, F. C. (1954) *Federation Proc.* **13**: 118.

Richardson, E. M., Touchstone, J. C., and Dohan, F. C. (1955) *J. Clin. Invest.* **34**: 285.

Richardson, E. M., Bulaschenko, H., and Dohan, F. C. (1958a) *J. Clin. Endocrinol. Metab.* **18**: 666.

Richardson, E. M., Bulaschenko, H., and Dohan, F. C. (1958b) *Federation Proc.* **17**: 132.

Romani, J. D., Bessard, C., Sosa-Castellanos, J., and Keller, A. (1959) *Ann. Endocrinol. (Paris)* **20**: 299.

Romanoff, E. B. (1959) *Recent Progr. Endocrinol. Reprod. Conf. Syracuse 1958* p. 283.

Romanoff, L. P., Morris, C. W., Welch, P., Rodriguez, R. M., and Pincus, G. (1961) *J. Clin. Endocrinol. Metab.* **21**: 1413.

Rongone, E. L., and Segaloff, A. (1961) *Abstr. Endocrine Soc. 43rd Ann. Meeting N.Y.* p. 96.

Rongone, E. L., and Segaloff, A. (1962) *J. Biol. Chem.* **237**: 1066.

Rongone, E. L., and Segaloff, A. (1963) *Steroids* **1**: 179.

Rongone, E. L., Strength, D. R., Bocklage, B. C., and Doisy, E. A. (1957) *J. Biol. Chem.* **225**: 959.

Rongone, E. L., Segaloff, A., Fried, J., and Sabo, E. F. (1961) *J. Biol. Chem.* **236**: 2624.

Rongone, E. L., Segaloff, A., Gabbard, R. B., Carter, A. C., and Feldman, E. B. (1963) *Steroids* **1**: 664.

Rosenkrantz, H., and Dorfman, R. I. (1962) Unpublished data.

Rosselet, J. P., Furman, M., Lieberman, S., and Jailer, J. W. (1954) *Science* **120**: 788 (abstr.).

Rosselet, J. P., Jailer, J. W., and Lieberman, S. (1955) *Federation Proc.* **14**: 272.

Roy, A. B. (1956) *Biochem. J.* **63**: 294.

Rubin, B. L. (1957) *J. Biol. Chem.* **227**: 917.

Rubin, B. L., and Dorfman, R. I. (1956) *Proc. Soc. Exptl. Biol. Med.* **91**: 585.
Rumney, G. (1956) *Federation Proc.* **15**: 343.
Ryan, K. J. (1960) *Endocrinology* **66**: 491.
Ryan, K. J., and Engel, L. L. (1953a) *Endocrinology* **52**: 277.
Ryan, K. J., and Engel, L. L. (1953b) *Endocrinology* **52**: 287.
Savard, K., and Goldfaden, S. H. (1954) *Federation Proc.* **13**: 288.
Savard, K., Burstein, S., Rosenkrantz, H., and Dorfman, R. I. (1953) *J. Biol. Chem.* **202**: 717.
Savard, K., Mason, N. R., Ingram, J. T., and Gassner, F. X. (1961) *Endocrinology* **69**: 324.
Samuels, L. T. (1949) *Recent Progr. Hormone Res.* **4**: 65.
Samuels, L. T., Sweat, M. L., Levedahl, B. H., Pottner, M. N., and Helmreich, M. L. (1950) *J. Biol. Chem.* **183**: 231.
Schiller, S., and Dorfman, R. I. (1948) *Endocrinology* **42**: 476.
Schiller, S., Dorfman, R. I., and Miller, M. (1945a) *Endocrinology* **36**: 355.
Schiller, S., Miller, A. M., Dorfman, R. I., Sevringhaus, E. H., and McCullough, E. P. (1945b) *Endocrinology* **27**: 262.
Schneider, J. J. (1962a) *Excerpta Med. Intern. Congr. Ser.* **51**: 16.
Schneider, J. J. (1962b) *Arch. Biochem. Biophys.* **98**: 249.
Schneider, J. J., and Horstmann, P. M. (1951) *J. Biol. Chem.* **191**: 327.
Schneider, J. J., and Lewbart, M. L. (1959) *Recent Progr. Hormone Res.* **15**: 201.
Schneider, J. J., and Mason, H. L. (1948a) *J. Biol. Chem.* **175**: 231.
Schneider, J. J., and Mason, H. L. (1948b) *J. Biol. Chem.* **172**: 771.
Schneider, J. J., Lewbart, M., Levitan, D., and Lieberman, S. (1955) *J. Am. Chem. Soc.* **77**: 4184.
Siegel, E. T., Dorfman, R. I., Brodey, R. S., and Friedman, M. H. F. (1962) *Proc. Soc. Exptl. Biol. Med.* **111**: 533.
Slaunwhite, W. R., Jr., and Sandberg, A. A. (1956) *Arch. Biochem. Biophys.* **63**: 478.
Slaunwhite, W. R., Jr., and Sandberg, A. A. (1957) *J. Biol. Chem.* **225**: 427.
Southcott, C. M., Sproule, V. A., McIntosh, H., and Darrach, M. (1958) *Can. J. Biochem. Physiol.* **36**: 819.
Stárka, L., and Kutová, J. (1962) *Biochim. Biophys. Acta* **56**: 76.
Stárka, L., Šulcova, J., and Šilink. K. (1962) *Excerpta Med. Intern. Congr. Ser.* **51**: 171.
Stimmel, B. F. (1955) *Federation Proc.* **14**: 930.
Stimmel, B. F. (1958) *Federation Proc.* **17**: 317.
Stimmel, B. F., and Notchev, V. D. (1961) *Federation Proc.* **20**: 200.
Stimmel, B. F., Grollman, A., and Huffman, M. N. (1950) *J. Biol. Chem.* **184**: 677.
Stroud, S. W. (1939) *J. Endocrinol.* **1**: 201.
Stylianou, M., Forchielli, E., Tummillo, M., and Dorfman, R. I. (1961) *J. Biol. Chem.* **236**: 692.
Sweat, M. L., Samuels, L. T., and Lumry, R. (1950) *J. Biol. Chem.* **185**: 75.
Taylor, W. (1956) *Biochem. J.* **62**: 332.
Taylor, W. (1957) *Biochem. J.* **66**: 58P.
Taylor, W. (1959) *Biochem. J.* **72**: 442.
Thomas, G. H. (1962) *Biochem. J.* **83**: 450.
Thomas, P. Z., and Dorfman, R. I. (1962) *Excerpta Med. Intern. Congr. Ser.* **51**: 138.
Thomas, P. Z., and Dorfman, R. I. (1964a) *J. Biol. Chem.* **239**: 766.
Thomas, P. Z., and Dorfman, R. I. (1964b) *J. Biol. Chem.* **239**: 762.
Thomas, P. Z., Forchielli, E., and Dorfman, R. I. (1960) *J. Biol. Chem.* **235**: 2797.
Tomkins, G. M. (1956a) *Recent Progr. Hormone Res.* **12**: 125.
Tomkins, G. M. (1956b) *J. Biol. Chem.* **218**: 437.
Touchstone, J. C., Bulaschenko, H., Richardson, E. M., and Dohan, F. C. (1959) *Arch. Biochem. Biophys.* **81**: 5.
Troen, P. (1961) *J. Clin. Endocrinol. Metab.* **21**: 895.
Ulick, S., Kusch, K., and August, J. T. (1961) *J. Am. Chem. Soc.* **83**: 4482.
Ulrich, F. (1958) *Biochem. J.* **68**: 361.

Ungar, F., and Bloom, B. R. (1957) *Biochim. Biophys. Acta* **24**: 431.
Ungar, F., and Dorfman, R. I. (1952a) *Science* **115**: 115.
Ungar, F., and Dorfman, R. I. (1952b) *Ciba Found. Collog. Endocrinol.* **11**: 244.
Ungar, F., and Dorfman, R. I. (1954a) *J. Biol. Chem.* **207**: 375.
Ungar, F., and Dorfman, R. I. (1954b) *J. Am. Chem. Soc.* **76**: 1197.
Ungar, F., and Dorfman, R. I. (1954c). Unpublished data.
Ungar, F., Dorfman, R. I., and Prins, D. A. (1951a) *J. Biol. Chem.* **189**: 11.
Ungar, F., Dorfman, R. I., Stecher, R. M., and Vignos, P. J., Jr. (1951b) *Endocrinology* **49**: 440.
Ungar, F., Davis, J. W., Rosenkrantz, H., and Dorfman, R. I. (1954a) *J. Biol. Chem.* **207**: 375.
Ungar, F., Miller, A. M., and Dorfman, R. I. (1954b) *J. Biol. Chem.* **206**: 597.
Ungar, F., Bloom, B. R., and Dorfman, R. I. (1960) *J. Clin. Endocrinol. Metab.* **20**: 1191.
Velle, W. (1958a) *Acta Endocrinol.* **28**: 255.
Velle, W. (1958b) *Acta Endocrinol.* **28**: 186.
Velle, W. (1958c) *Acta Endocrinol.* **29**: 109.
Venning, E. H., and Browne, J. S. L. (1937) *Endocrinology* **21**: 711.
Venning, E. H., and Ripstein. (1957) *Proc. Can. Phys. Soc.* p. 43.
Venning, E. H., and Sybulski, S. (1962) *Excerpta Med. Intern. Congr. Ser.* **51**: 267.
Verly, W. G., Sommerville, I. F., and Marrian, G. F. (1950) *Biochem.* J. **46**: 186.
Vermeulen, A. (1956a) *Acta Endocrinol.* **23**: 113.
Vermeulen, A. (1956b) *J. Clin. Endocrinol. Metab.* **16**: 163.
Vermeulen, A. (1957) *Lancet* **ii**: 79.
Vermeulen, A. (1959) *J. Endocrinol.* **18**: 278.
Vermeulen, A., and Caspi, E. (1958) *J. Biol. Chem.* **233**: 54.
Vermeulen, A., Slaunwhite, W. R., Jr., and Sandberg, A. A. (1961) *J. Clin. Endocrinol. Metab.* **21**: 1534.
Westphal, U. (1942) *Z. Physiol. Chem.* **273**: 13.
Wettstein, A., Neher, R., and Urech, H. J. (1959) *Helv. Chim. Acta* **42**: 956.
Wiener, M., Lupin, C. I., and Plotz, E. J. (1961) *Acta Endocrinol.* **36**: 511.
Wiest, W. G. (1956) *J. Biol. Chem.* **221**: 461.
Wiest, W. G. (1959) *J. Biol. Chem.* **234**: 3115.
Wotiz, H. H., and Fishman, W. H. (1963) *Steroids* **1**: 211.
Wotiz, H. H., Mescon, H., Doppel, H., and Lemon, H. M. (1956) *J. Invest. Dermatol.* **26**: 113.
Wotiz, H. H., Sie, H.-G., and Fishman, W. H. (1958) *J. Biol. Chem.* **232**: 723.

CHAPTER VI

Enzymes and Mechanisms of Reactions

The enzymes concerned with the biosynthesis of cholesterol have been adequately reviewed and discussed in detail elsewhere (Popjak and Cornforth, 1960) and will not be considered here. The enzymes discussed in this chapter are involved in the biosynthetic pathways leading to the formation of the various steroid hormones and the many reactions involved in their catabolism. For the purpose of convenience of discussion, the enzymes may be classified as follows:

A. Hydroxylases
B. Dehydrogenases
C. Reductases
D. Desmolases (Synthetases)
E. Lactonizing Enzyme
F. Enzymes Concerned with Conjugation
  1. Formation of Sulfates
  2. Formation of Glucuronides
G. Enzymes Concerned with Deconjugations
  1. Glucuronidase
  2. Aryl Sulfatase
  3. Aliphatic Sulfatase
  4. Steroid Esterase
H. Miscellaneous
  1. Carboxylase
  2. Transmethylase
  3. Isomerase
  4. 21-OH → 21-H Enzymatic Removal of the Hydroxy Group

Hydroxylases

Mammalian hydroxylation reactions pertaining to steroid metabolism have been noted at carbons 20α and 22x in cholesterol and at carbons 2α, 2(aromatic), 6α, 6β, 7α, 11β, 15α, 16α, 16β (possible but not certain), 17α, 18, 19, and 21. Microbiological hydroxylations have been proven to occur at 1α, 1, 2β, 6α, 6β, 7α, 7β, 8β, 8, 9α, 10β, 11α, 11β, 12β, 14α, 15α, 15β, 16α, 17α, 19, and 21. With the suitable deoxy steroid substrate it is likely that hydroxylation could be shown to occur at any position on the steroid molecule.

20α- and 22x-Hydroxylase

In the initial report by Solomon *et al.* (1956), the incubation of cow adrenal homogenate with cholesterol-4-C^{14} led to the formation of 20α-hydroxycholesterol. Attempts at this time to demonstrate the presence of 22α, 22β, 22-keto, 24-hydroxy, and the 24-keto derivatives of cholesterol failed. Subsequent studies have shown that hydroxylation of cholesterol occurs to give a 20α,22*x*-dihydroxycholesterol. This last derivative is subjected to a desmolase reaction and the products pregnenolone and isocaproic aldehyde are formed (Shimizu *et al.*, 1960, 1961, 1962; Chaudhuri *et al.*, 1962; Constantopoulos and Tchen, 1961; Constantopoulos *et al.*, 1962; Halkerston *et al.*, 1959, 1960).

A mechanism for the carbon-carbon rupture of the cholesterol side chain has been described (Hayano, 1962). The mobilizing influence would be the initial enzymatic removal of a hydride ion from the C-20α hydroxyl group. A double shift of electrons follows, with the expulsion of a proton from the C-22 hydroxyl function. Alternatively, initial attack could occur at the C-22 hydroxyl function with the ejection of a proton from the C-20 hydroxyl group. The entire process probably occurs in a concerted action with concomitant breakage of the 20,22 carbon-to-carbon bond yielding a ketone and an aldehyde as products. The C-20,22α-ketol structure need only be hydrated at C-22 prior to the process. A ketone and carboxylic acid would be the products from this scission. The elements of coenzyme A (CoA) may be as easily added to the carbonyl function, in which case the C_6 moiety would be eliminated as isocaproyl CoA.

The enzymology of the biosynthetic steps, cholesterol to pregnenolone, have been studied by Halkerston *et al.* (1959, 1961). Reduced nicotinamide-adenine dinucleotide phosphate ($NADPH_2$) and aerobic conditions are essential requirements for cholesterol side chain cleavage by subcellular preparations of bovine adrenal cortex, the enzymatic activity being concentrated in the mitochondrial fraction. The $NADPH_2$ concentration was maintained during the metabolism of certain tricarboxylic acid intermediates, or by the extramitochondrial reaction of glucose-6-phosphate and its dehydrogenase with exogenous nicotinamide-adenine dinucleotide phosphate (NADP).

Mitochondrial NADP appears to be firmly associated with the mitochondrial enzymes, and although it can apparently be brought to its reduced state during the metabolism of fumarate, succinate, or α-ketoglutarate, neither isocitrate nor glucose-6-phosphate can react with the bound cofactor. Acetone drying and solubilization in phosphate only partially overcome the barrier to the reduction of mitochondrial NADP by glucose-6-phosphate metabolism.

20α-Hydroxycholesterol conversion to pregnenolone has been demonstrated in rat testes, bovine ovaries, and human term placenta, but not in liver (Shimizu *et al.*, 1961; Tamaoki and Pincus, 1961).

β-Sitosterol-H^3 was converted to cortisol in the guinea pig in an *in vivo* experiment by Werbin *et al.* (1960). The cholesterol-H^3 isolated in this experiment had a specific activity, as compared with that of cortisol-H^3, which permitted the conclusion that cholesterol was not an intermediate. If true, the additional ethyl group in the side chain of β-sitosterol does not appear to hinder the action of the C-20 and C-22 hydroxylases and the subsequent action of the desmolase. Only fragmentary information is available on the enzyme systems involved in the cleavage of the sterol side chain. Bryson (1962) has reported that the desmolase resides in that fraction precipitated between 25 and 70% saturated ammonium sulfate, in contrast to the 11β-hydroxylating enzymes which are precipitated more sharply between 25–40 and 70–80%. The products of cholesterol incubation included progesterone, deoxycorticosterone, and 20α,21-dihydroxypregn-4-en-3-one. Pregnenolone was a minor product.

17α-Hydroxylase

The 17α-hydroxylase system has been studied in the testis (Hofmann, 1960; Lynn and Brown, 1958a), in the adrenal, and in the ovary (Sweat *et al.*, 1960). The activity is associated with the microsomal fraction and with $NADPH_2$ and O_2 as obligatory requirements.

17α-Hydroxylase of adrenals could not be separated from the 21-hydroxylase. When 0.01 *M* progesterone was incubated, some 8% of the 17α,21-dihydroxylated product 11-deoxycortisol was obtained in 1.5–2 hours of incubation time. Deoxycorticosterone was not 17α-hydroxylated by the adrenal preparation, and pregnenolone was transformed to deoxycortisol but 3β-hydroxy-16,17-epoxypregn-5-en-20-one and 3β-hydroxypregna-5,16-dien-20-one were not attacked by the enzyme.

Testis homogenates contain a 17α-hydroxylase system and at least two other enzyme systems related to androgen biosynthesis. Lynn and Brown (1958a) were able to achieve a separation of enzymes, 17α-hydroxylase, a C-17,20-desmolase, and 17-dehydrogenase. The enzymes were concentrated by adsorbtion on hydroxy apatite columns and resolved by elution with phosphate buffers of increasing molarities. The authors reported that these enzymes were activated by adsorbtion on testis microsomes, a phenomenon suggested to be a regulatory mechanism in the living cell. Lynn and Brown (1958b) noted that amphenone B, an inhibitor of steroidogenesis, was strongly adsorbed on the microsomal surface and interfered with the steroid-enzyme complex formation.

The pH optimum of the testis 17α-hydroxylase is about 8.5. The specificity for $NADPH_2$ and a need for oxygen were demonstrated for both the 17α-hydroxylase and the C-17,20-desmolase. Catalase did not inhibit the 17α-hydroxylase enzyme, nor did an external source of H_2O_2 replace $NADPH_2$, indicating the generation of a bound form of activated oxygen. The enzyme was inhibited by *p*-chloromercuribenzoate but not by iodoacetate. 17α-Hydroxylase was not influenced by ethylene-diamine tetraacetic acid (EDTA).

A measure of the oxygen and $NADPH_2$ utilized in the course of the 17α-hydroxylase reaction disclosed the requirement of one mole of oxygen.

19-Hydroxylase

19-Hydroxylation appears to be an obligatory step in the biosynthesis of estrogens from androgens. The enzyme was first discovered in bovine adrenal tissue which is capable of forming 17-hydroxylated C_{19}- and C_{21}-steroids (Meyer, 1955; Hayano *et al.*, 1956). 19-Hydroxyandrost-4-ene-3, 17-dione was isolated after the incubation of androst-4-ene-3,17-dione with human placenta during the biosynthesis of estrone (Longchampt *et al.*, 1960). The enzyme system appears to be present in all steroid-producing tissues. Since testosterone may be converted to estrogens in the adrenalectomized-ovariectomized subject (West *et al.*, 1958), it has been suggested that a 19-hydroxylase is present in non-steroid-producing tissue, perhaps in the liver.

11β-Hydroxylase

The 11β-hydroxylase is the most thoroughly studied mammalian enzyme involved in steroid metabolism. The enzyme located in the mitochondria fraction of adrenals has been prepared in various stages of purification (Hayano and Dorfman, 1962), the most active being an acetone powder preparation. Tomkins (1960) obtained three separate protein fractions from an acetone powder by extraction with successive portions of deionized water, 0.1 *M* KC1, and 0.5% digitonin. The combination of all three fractions plus $NADPH_2$ and a boiled extract of adrenal or liver, all incubated at pH 7.4 in air, gave the best yields. Kinetic data indicated that $NADPH_2$ reacted with either the KCl- or digitonin-precipitated protein fractions. The factor in the boiled extract was not identified. It was destroyed by ashing, and was not adsorbed by charcoal at an acid pH. It was not tetrahydrofolic acid, nor the natural cofactor of the phenylalanine hydroxylase system, H_2O_2, peroxidase, ascorbic acid, or dihydroxyfumaric acid.

Sharma *et al.* (1962), on the basis of mathematical consideration of the kinetic data, have suggested that deoxycorticosterone and 11-deoxycortisol are hydroxylated at the 11β position by the same reactive sites on the enzyme. The ratio of the rates of hydroxylation of the two substrates was found to be proportional to the ratio of their concentrations; in other words, 11-deoxycortisol and deoxycorticosterone were in competition for the same reactive sites (Foster and Niemann, 1951). If different enzymes or different active sites of the same enzyme were involved in the 11β-hydroxylation of the two substrates, there would not have been any interference of one substrate with the other, since they would have reacted independently. The respective products, namely, corticosterone and cortisol, were found not to inhibit the hydroxylation of the two substrates, 11-deoxycortisol and deoxycorticosterone.

It has also been demonstrated by Sharma *et al.* (1962) that the 11β-hydroxylating enzyme obtained from bovine adrenal mitochondria can be completely solubilized and separated from cell particulates by ultrasonic treatment of fresh or lyophylized mitochondria. Once solubilized, the enzyme system remains stable for at least 3 months in the freeze-dried state. The procedure offers a better yield of enzyme activity than does the KCl extraction used by Grant (1956). The latter method may result in the recovery of only about 10% of the 11β-hydroxylating activity present in the intact mitochondria.

The Mg^{++} requirement for the 11β-hydroxylating system was found by Sharma *et al.* (1962), confirming the observation of others (Hayano and Dorfman, 1953; Sweat and Lipscomb, 1955). In the absence of added Mg^{++}, only minimal activity was observed which could be attributed to the presence of endogenous ion. Both Cu^{++} and Zn^{++} markedly inhibited the rate of 11β-hydroxylation. This was probably a typical heavy metal effect; however, the inhibitory effect of Fe^{++} was significantly less than that observed with Cu^{++} and Zn^{++}. On the other hand, Co^{++} had no inhibitory action on the enzyme activity.

The effect of Su-4885 (metapyrapone) on 11β-hydroxylation is of interest. At a concentration of $2 \times 10^{-6}M$, the compound inhibited 11β-hydroxylation about 50% and the suppression was not relieved by increased additions of substrate, $NADPH_2$ or boiled extracts of tissues. This drug is used clinically in the suppression of hyperadrenocortical activity, and because of its effect on 11β-hydroxylase, in particular, as an agent in assessing pituitary function.

Sweat (1962) separated two 11β-hydroxylase fractions, F-40 and F-80, by ammonium sulfate precipitation from soluble extracts of acetone-dried adrenal mitochondria. The 11β-hydroxylase system included $NADPH_2$ and O_2 in addition to the two protein fractions, as well as manganese, which markedly enhanced the reaction. Ammonium sulfate preparations of F-80 were 20*x* as active, on a protein basis, as the mitochondrial extract. Chromatography on an anion exchange resin increased the activity to 140 times that of the mitochondrial extract. The extracted principle was non-dialyzable and was inactivated at 80°C for 1 minute (pH 7.3).

Substrate specificity for 11β-hydroxylase has been reported by Hayano and Dorfman (1962). Deoxycorticosterone and 11-deoxycortisol were converted efficiently by the enzyme to their respective products, corticosterone and cortisol. Reduction of the ring A 4,5-double bond to either the 5α or 5β configuration decreased the turnover rate to about one-half. The 21-deoxy structure, or one whose C-3 or C-20 keto group had been reduced to an alcohol, were hydroxylated at very low rates. Androst-4-ene-3,17-dione was transformed about one-third as efficiently as deoxycorticosterone. A substituent at C-6β almost totally inhibited 11β-hydroxylation, whereas one at C-6α had little effect (Meyer *et al.*, 1955).

Sharma *et al.* (1963a) demonstrated that androst-4-ene-3,17-dione, dehydroepiandrosterone, dehydroepiandrosterone sulfate, and testosterone are competitive inhibitors of 11β-hydroxylation in the conversion of deoxycorticosterone to corticosterone. 11β-Hydroxyandrost-4-ene-3,17-dione, progesterone, and 17α-hydroxyprogesterone were ineffective.

16α-Hydroxylase

The concentration of rat liver 16α-hydroxylase was higher in male tissue than in female tissue when the substrate was dehydroepiandrosterone. Castration decreased the effective concentration of this hydroxylase which was reported to be stimulated by reduced nicotinamide-adenine dinucleotide ($NADH_2$) (Colás, 1962).

Pangels and Breuer (1962) reported that the microsomal fraction of rat liver homogenates can hydroxylate estradiol-17β at position 16 in the presence of nicotinamide-adenine dinucleotide (NAD) and oxygen at pH 7.4.

18-Hydroxylase

Detailed studies of the enzyme 18-hydroxylase have not been reported. 18-Hydroxylation has been of primary interest in the biosynthesis of aldosterone and in the formation of 18-hydroxycorticosterone. Investigations of precursors and biosynthetic pathways leading to aldosterone are documented in Chapter III. Corticosterone appears to be transformed more directly than deoxycorticosterone or progesterone. 18-Hydroxydeoxycorticosterone has been isolated from incubation of rat adrenal sections in the presence of $NADPH_2$ and oxygen (Peron, 1961). Its further conversion (11β-hydroxylation) to aldosterone, however, has not been reported.

Estrone incubated with bovine adrenal resulted in a modest yield of 18-hydroxyestrone (Loke and Marrian, 1958).

21-Hydroxylase

Ryan and Engel (1957) demonstrated that 21-hydroxylase was associated with the adrenal microsomes. The pH optimum was between 6.5 and 7.0, and $NADPH_2$ and oxygen appeared to be required. Progesterone and 17α-hydroxyprogesterone were converted with equal facility to deoxycorticosterone and 11-deoxycortisol, respectively. 21-Deoxycortisol and 11β-hydroxyprogesterone could also be hydroxylated at C-21.

The effect of various inhibitors on 21-hydroxylase was investigated. Cytochrome c, mersalyl, cupric sulfate, and carbon monoxide inhibited 21-hydroxylation, whereas the following were not inhibitory: iodoacetate, *o*-iodosobenzoate, dipyridyl, cyanide, amide, SKF 525 A (diethylaminoethyl-diphenylpropylacetic acid) at $10^{-3}M$; ascorbate, glutathione, EDTA at $10^{-2}M$; antimycin A, catalase, and ribonuclease. The response in enzyme activity to agents employed to demonstrate the presence of a metal at the active enzymatic site varies among the different steroid hydroxylases. For 21-hydroxylase, there does not appear to be a specific metal cofactor and it was suggested that cytochrome m, which is present in large quantities in microsomes, could substitute in this capacity.

Hydroxylation at C-21 is dependent upon O_2, and by the use of $O_2{}^{18}$, it was shown that 82% of the theoretical abundance was incorporated into this position, proving that the hydroxylation in the side chain proceeds via a mechanism similar to that for the ring position of the steroid molecule (Hayano *et al.*, 1956).

Cooper *et al.* (1963) measured the stoichiometry of the C-21 hydroxylation of 17-hydroxyprogesterone by bovine adrenal microsomes. The oxygen uptake was measured polarographically, and oxidation of $NADPH_2$ was measured fluorimetrically. The relationship of one mole of oxygen, one mole of $NADPH_2$ consumed, and one mole of steroid hydroxylated was established.

Miscellaneous Hydroxylases

A number of hydroxylases have been indicated on the basis of products isolated, but detailed enzyme studies are lacking.

Neher and Wettstein (1960a, b) have isolated 15α-hydroxytestosterone from the testis of the young bull. The existence of a 2(aromatic)-hydroxylase is assumed from the isolation of 2-hydroxyestrone (Fishman *et al.*, 1960). The former steroid could arise from the biological aromatization of either a 2α- or 2β-hydroxy androgen, in addition to the possibility of the direct introduction of the 2-phenol group in the aromatic steroid (See Chapter III).

The existence in guinea pigs of a 2α-hydroxylase is based on the isolation of 2α-hydroxycortisol from urine (Burstein, 1956; Peron and Dorfman, 1956).

6α-Hydroxylation has been reported for a C_{19} substrate (Meyer, 1955). A 6β-hydroxylase has been found in many tissues and appears to act on C_{19} and C_{21} steroid substrates.

Mueller and Rumney (1957) have shown that $NADPH_2$ and oxygen are necessary requirements for the microsomal 6"β"-hydroxylase of estrogens. Wintersteiner and Moore (1959) investigated the two epimeric 6-hydroxylated estradiols in three syntheses from the 6-keto analog; the comparison of mobility behavior in alumina chromatography and other physical data cast some doubt on the Mueller and Rumney assignment of configuration at C-6. Breuer *et al.* (1961a, b) have demonstrated conclusively that rat liver contains both 6α- and 6β-hydroxylases which can act on phenolic substrates.

Treatment of rats with phenobarbital or chlorcyclizine for as little as 4 days increases several-fold the following hydroxylase activities of the liver microsome fraction: 7α-, 6β-, 6α-, and 2β-hydroxylases for testosterone, and the 7α- and 6β-hydroxylases for androst-4-ene-3,17-dione (Conney and Klutch, 1963).

Hydroxylases of Microbiological Origin

The field of microbiological steroid reactions has been highly developed for synthetic purposes. Fungi, molds, and bacteria have served as "reagents" for these transformations. The detailed summaries of these reactions are presented in Chapter IV, and only a few additional comments will be made here with regard to the previously indicated hydroxylations at positions 1α, 2β, 6α, 6β, 7α, 7β, 8, 9α, 10β, 11α, 11β, 12β, 14α, 15α, 15β, 16α, 17α, 19, and 21.

Hydroxylation in the microbiological series, as in the animal series, involves the direct utilization of molecular oxygen. The initial demonstration of this requirement was made with an atmosphere of O^{18} in incubations of 11-deoxycorticosterone with bovine adrenal homogenates. In a similar manner, hydroxylations using microorganisms at positions 6β, 11α, 11β, 12β, 15α, 17α, and 21 were examined (Hayano *et al.*, 1956; Kurasawa *et al.*, 1961) with the use of pure strains of fungi and O_2^{18}. In every instance, a maximal percentage (83–96%) of O_2^{18} was incorporated; thus establishing the existence of very similar, if not identical, oxygenating mechanisms in all steroid hydroxylases.

Three different laboratories have defined the stereospecific aspects of the hydroxylase reaction in a series of similar experiments with consistent results. 5β-Pregnane-3,20-dione-11α,12α-H^3 fermented with *Rhizopus nigricans* yielded the 11α-hydroxylated derivative with the loss of all the radioactivity originally at 11α (Hayano *et al.*, 1958); progesterone-11α,12α-H^3 fermented with *Calonectria decora* yielded the 12β,15α-dihydroxy derivative with retention of all the original radioactivity (Hayano *et al.*, 1959); progesterone-11α,12α-H^3 perfused through bovine adrenal glands yielded corticosterone (11β-hydroxylation) and cortisol (11β-hydroxylation) with no loss of the original tritium content (Hayano *et al.*, 1958). Cholesterol-4-C^{14},7α-H^3 administered to rats yielded cholic acid (7α,12α-dihydroxylation) with essentially all the tritium removed (Bergstrom *et al.*, 1958). 5β-Pregnane-3,20-dione-11β-*d* fermented with *Rhizopus nigricans* yielded 11α-hydroxy-5β-pregnane-3,20-dione with essentially all the deuterium intact (Corey *et al.*, 1958). 5β-Pregnane-3,20-dione-9α,11α,12α-D fermented with the same organism yielded the 11α-hydroxy derivative, retaining deuterium only at carbons 9α and 12α (Corey *et al.*, 1958). In each instance the incoming hydroxyl group stereospecifically displaced the hydrogen of the position hydroxylated.

Formation of epoxidation was demonstrated for the first time by Bloom and Shull (1955). Microorganisms which converted 11-deoxycortisol to cortisol also converted 17α,21-dihydroxypregna-4,9(11)-diene-3,20-dione to the corresponding 9β,11β-epoxide compound; microorganisms containing a 14α-hydroxylase carried out epoxidation to the 14α,15α-epoxide derivative. These two epoxidations could not be effected by unrelated microorganisms possessing 11α- and 6β-hydroxylases.

A bovine adrenal 11β-hydroxylase system formed 9β,11β-epoxide in low yields from 17α-21-dihydroxypregna-4,9(11)-diene-3,20-dione (Kurasawa *et al.*, 1961). When this steroid was incubated with a *Curvularia* species capable of 9α-hydroxylation, some 9α,11α-epoxide was produced. Incubation of pregna-4,11-diene-3,20-dione with *Rhizopus nigricans* (11α-hydroxylase) and *Curvularia lunata* (11β-hydroxylase) were carried out, and the 11β,12β-epoxidoprogesterone was isolated as expected.

Steroid Hydroxylation Mechanisms

Hydroxylation and epoxidation experiments may be summarized as follows: an enzyme system capable of forming an axial hydroxyl function at a specific carbon of a saturated steroid could also cause the formation of an epoxide in the unsaturated substrate. Equatorial hydroxylases did not effect a similar conversion. From this interesting correlation, a hypothesis encompassing the gross mechanistic features of oxidative attack on steroidal substrates has been proposed by Bloom (1962). Epoxidation of olefinic steroids may occur because of the spatial resemblance of double bond π-electron distribution in a given unsaturated substrate to the area of maximal electron density in the related axial carbon-hydroxy bond of the corresponding saturated compound. That is, in the appropriate enzyme-substrate complexes, the spatial relationship required for reaction between an "axial" hydroxylase and an axial carbon-hydrogen bond in the case of a saturated steroid is adequately approximated by the "axial" hydroxylase-π-electron relationship in the unsaturated analog. It follows that a reasonable degree of structural specificity in the oxidizing enzyme system would preclude occurrence of the epoxidation phenomenon with "equatorial" hydroxylase, since equatorial bonds extend outward more in the plane of the cyclohexane ring to which they are attached, while in the corresponding cyclohexane system maximal π-electron density would occur directly above and below the plane of the trigonal carbons and their substituents, with minimal electron density in the plane.

Inherent in this hypothesis is the assumption that hydroxylations proceed by direct electrophilic attack. Evidence compatible with the hypothesis is provided by the demonstrations of enzymatic hydroxylations at 7α (Bergstrom *et al.*, 1958), at 11α (Corey *et al.*, 1958), and at 11β (Hayano *et al.*, 1958) of C_{21} steroids where the incoming hydroxyl groups directly replaced the hydrogens at those positions hydroxylated, with retention of configuration. In chemical systems electrophilic displacement at saturated carbon atoms has been found to occur in this way (Corey and Gregoriou, 1959).

Steroid hydroxylations involve the direct incorporation of molecular oxygen. Although reduced nicotinamide-adenine dinucleotides have been shown to be an absolute requirement for many hydroxylations, and probably are for all, the exact nature of the role that reduced nicotinamide-adenine dinucleotide plays in the hydroxylation process is unclear. The participation of metal ions is assumed in the activation of oxygen. Some aspects of the internal mechanism of the catalysis have been discussed by Talalay (1957b) and Tomkins (1960). Analysis of the hydroxylation reaction reveals discrete steps involving (1) oxygen activation, (2) substrate activation, if any, and oxygen transfer, and (3) regeneration of coenzymes. Except for the regeneration of $NADPH_2$, the entire sequence may occur in a single concerted process. Hayano (1962) suggested that in the case of the oxygen in 11β-hydroxylation, the substrate and $NADPH_2$ are brought together to a single active site on the enzyme surface. In the proximity of a suitably oriented steroid substrate, the oxygen is activated probably by fixation to a metal followed by $NADPH_2$ reduction. Momentary "stretching" of the hydrogen of the position under attack may occur, although on the basis of chemical analogy this would not be necessary, and finally the species OH^+ displaces the original H to complete the formation of the hydroxylated steroid. The unutilized atom of oxygen can accept the hydrogen taken from the substrate and, together with a proton, is liberated as water. The metal throughout the process need not undergo a change in cationic state. Regeneration of $NADPH_2$ would occur as a final step and as a prelude to the next cycle.

The question of substrate activation has been discussed by Hayano (1962), particularly with respect to positions adjacent to or vinylogous to carbonyl functions. The suggestion has been made that in reactions at carbons 2, 6, 10, 16, 17, and 21 the substrate may undergo reaction while in an enol state. Enolization of the substrate hydrogens on methyl or methylene groups adjacent to keto oxygens occurs on the enzyme surface producing a high electron density at the positions under attack, thus aiding the incoming positively charged hydroxylating species depicted here as OH^+. Maximal overlap of π-electrons is expected to occur with axial attack and, thus, in the plane favorable for the 2β-, 6β-, 10β-, and 17α-configurations. In chemical systems, hydroxylations at these sites predictably predominate as compared with those at 2α, 6α, 10α, and 17β. In biological systems where enzyme specificity is the controlling factor, a valid comparison cannot be made. However, in the literature the documentation of hydroxylations effected by both microorganisms and animal tissues at these sites shows that some parallelism exists.

Consider the 17α- and 21-hydroxylation of progesterone to 17α-hydroxyprogesterone and deoxycorticosterone. This action has been analyzed by Hayano (1962) as follows: "The enolization of 17α-hydroxyprogesterone at carbons 20, 21 with enzymatic hydroxylation at C-21 is straight forward. In the case of progesterone, enolization is possible in two directions, between carbons 17, 20 (A) and between 20, 21 (B). Both are favored states: A, kinetically and B, thermodynamically. Thus, at specific enzyme loci 17α- and 21-hydroxylations of appropriate enol forms may proceed. With deoxycorticosterone on the other hand, the 20, 21 enol is the form both thermodynamically and kinetically favored, allowing only a very low contribution of the 17, 20 form. Thus, theoretically 17α-

hydroxylation of this structure is essentially impossible. This is indeed observed in incubations with this substance, where no more than trace quantities of 11-deoxycortisol have ever been noted."

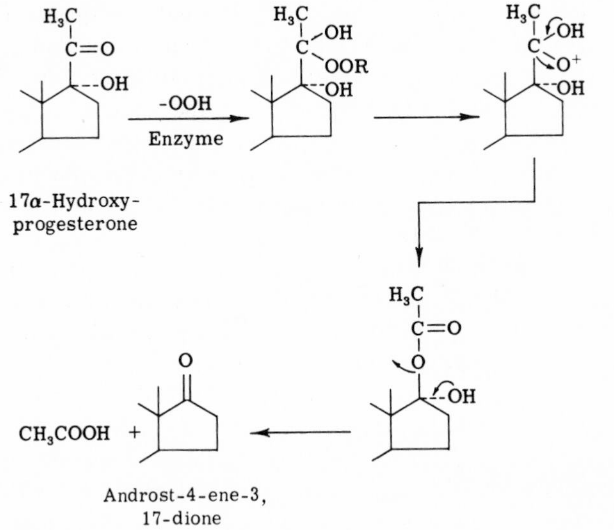

-OOH

Enzyme

17α-Hydroxy-progesterone

CH_3COOH +

Androst-4-ene-3,17-dione

FIG. 1. A mechanism for the conversion of 17α-hydroxyprogesterone to androst-4-ene-3,17-dione. (From Hayano, 1962.)

Androst-4-ene-3,17-dione-6α,7-H^3 was synthesized and incubated with the mold *Rhizopus arrhizus* (ATCC 11145) to study the hydroxylating reaction at an enolizable position (Baba *et al.*, 1963). After incubation, 6β-hydroxyandrost-4-ene-3,17-dione, 11α-hydroxyandrost-4-ene-3,17-dione, and androst-4-ene-3,6,17-trione were isolated. There was no loss in radioactivity in either the 6β-hydroxy or 11α-hydroxy derivatives. The 6-keto derivative lost 60% of the tritium, which was the identical result obtained if the 6β-hydroxy steroid was oxidized to the 6-keto compound with chromic acid. If the 6-keto compound obtained chemically from 6β-hydroxyandrostene-3,17-dione or from the incubation mixture was directly treated with base, all tritium was lost, showing that the remaining tritium was at C-7. On this basis, it was apparent that hydroxylation at 6β or at 11α did not disturb the tritium located at positions 6α and 7 in the substrate.

Three possible pathways of reaction are outlined in Fig. 2. The substrate androstenedione is represented with tritium (*T*) in the 6α position. Pathway A represents a direct replacement of the 6β proton by OH^+ (symbol used to represent an activated oxygen) through a mechanism that would be operating also at the non-enolizable position, C-11α, in the same compound. This pathway indicates that the tritium label is retained and agrees with the results obtained.

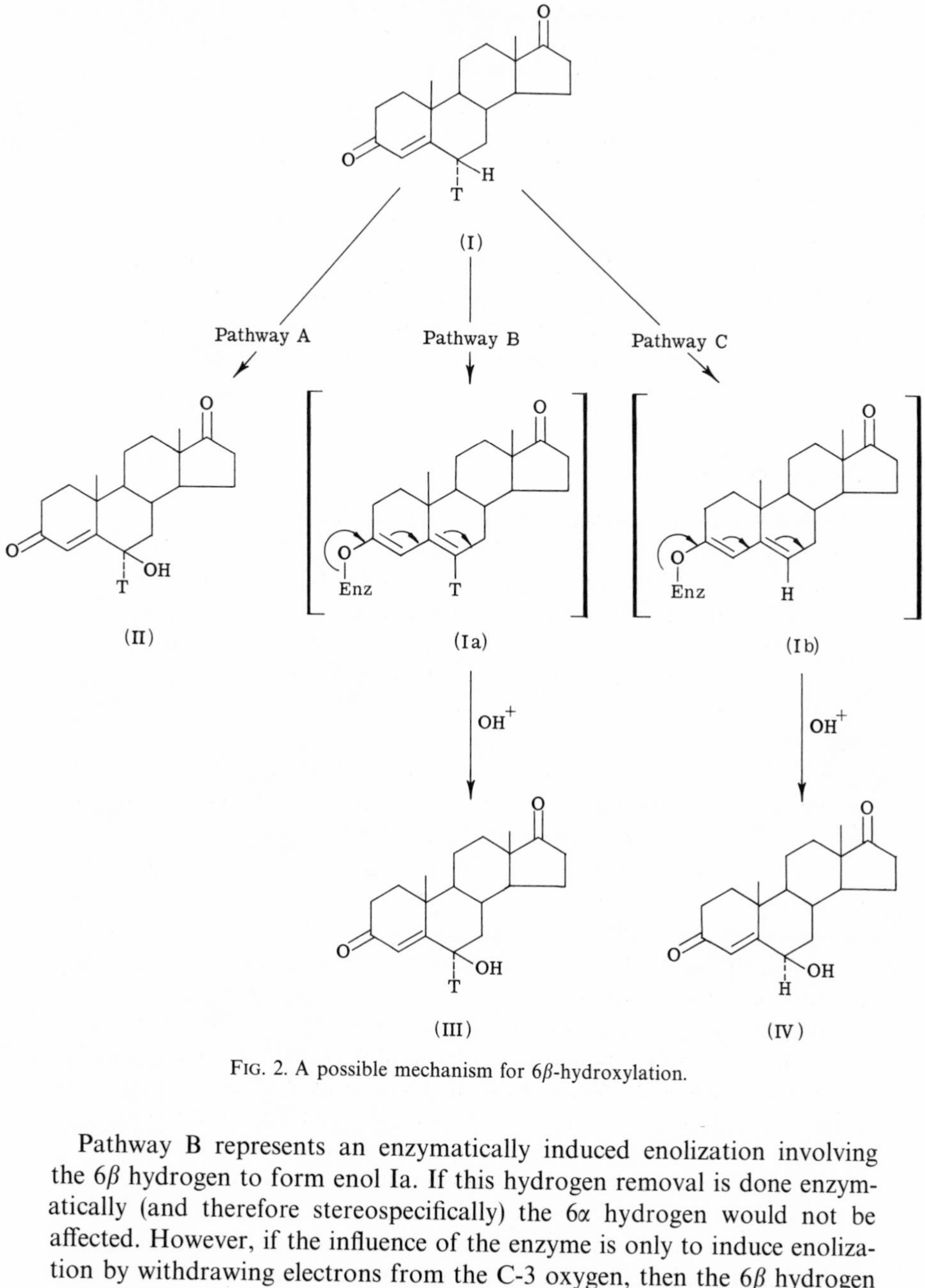

FIG. 2. A possible mechanism for 6β-hydroxylation.

Pathway B represents an enzymatically induced enolization involving the 6β hydrogen to form enol Ia. If this hydrogen removal is done enzymatically (and therefore stereospecifically) the 6α hydrogen would not be affected. However, if the influence of the enzyme is only to induce enolization by withdrawing electrons from the C-3 oxygen, then the 6β hydrogen would be only preferentially removed (because it is axial) and there should be participation by the 6α hydrogen. If the enol, once formed, goes on to product III, then no loss of the 6α tritium would be observed. However, if there was repeated binding to enzyme (with enol formation) and release of substrate prior to hydroxylation, then it is likely that such equilibration would result in some loss of tritium being observed in the product.

Pathway C represents an enolization involving the 6α hydrogen (tritium) to form Ib. From the argument thus developed, this could only occur by active enzymatic participation in preferential removal of the α proton. Ia would then be hydroxylated to form product III in which tritium would be lost.

The results obtained show that pathway C can be eliminated as a possible mechanism. The results are in agreement with pathway A and conditionally in agreement with pathway B, provided that there is no extensive keto-enol equilibration before hydroxylation. It is expected that if moderate equilibration is occurring, then a 6β-labeled substrate will be useful in detecting it.

Dehydrogenases

A number of microorganisms introduce a double bond into the C-1,2 position of various steroids (see Table 32, Chapter IV). Among these, the enzyme system of *Bacillus sphaericus* (ATCC 7055) has been studied in some detail and recently a reaction mechanism has been suggested (Stoudt *et al.*, 1955; Stefanovic *et al.*, 1963; Gale *et al.*, 1962; Ringold *et al.*, 1963). Intact and disrupted cell-free preparations carry out the reaction if an electron acceptor such as menadione, phenazine methosulfate, and 2,6-dichlorophenol indophenol or the naturally occurring Q_9 (Stefanovic *et al.*, 1963) or Vitamin K_2 (Gale *et al.*, 1962) is present.

The studies of Ringold *et al.* (1963) indicate that whole-cell or cell-free preparations of *Bacillus sphaericus* involve preferentially the *trans* diaxial loss of the 1α-2β-hydrogens. Incubations in the presence of tritiated water led to the introduction of isomers at the C-1α and C-2 positions. A mechanism of enolization followed by hydride abstraction has been proposed for the bacterial dehydrogenases and to account for the incorporation or loss of tritium.

The preparations of steroid dehydrogenases obtained from mammalian tissues are relatively crude, many consisting of little more than separation of tissue homogenates into subcellular fractions by homogenization.

Dehydrogenases active at carbon 3 of the steroid nucleus have been obtained from bacterial sources, mammalian liver, and other tissues. An attempt has been made in the following discussion to name the enzymes according to the substrate specificity that has been determined. Since most of the mammalian enzyme preparations have not been adequately purified and studied, the number of enzymes involved and their identity with respect to different tissues or even different subcellular fractions as well as their relation to those of bacterial origin remain in doubt. The "Report of the Commission on Enzymes, of the International Union of Biochemistry" (1961) lists three dehydrogenases active at C-3; a 3α-

hydroxy steroid NAD(P) oxidoreductase (1.1.1.50); a 3(or 17)β-hydroxy steroid NAD(P) oxidoreductase (1.1.1.51); and a 3α-hydroxycholanate oxidoreductase (1.1.1.52). Based on substrate specificity and source, the following list of dehydrogenases active at carbon 3 of the neutral steroids can be differentiated. Subsequent studies may increase or decrease the number which has to be separately classified.

Δ^5-3β-Hydroxy Steroid Dehydrogenase. The Δ^5-notation is added to the less specific name, 3β-ol-dehydrogenase, which has been generally used, and refers to the enzyme system present in all steroid hormone-producing tissue which converts the Δ^5-3β-hydroxyl group to the Δ^4-3-ketone. The reaction is irreversible and should be differentiated from the reversible oxidation of 3β-hydroxyl groups associated with 5α- and 5β-steroids.

3(or 17)β-Hydroxy Steroid Dehydrogenase (1.1.1.51). This enzyme was isolated by Talalay from *Pseudomonas testosteroni* and has activity for 3β, 17β (neutral steroids), 17β (phenolic steroids), 16β, and Δ^5-3β-hydroxy groups. The 3β mammalian enzymes appear to have more rigid specificity requirements.

3β-Hydroxy Steroid Dehydrogenase. The enzyme activity obtained from mammalian liver is present in microsomal and supernatant fractions. Attempts to purify this enzyme have been only partially successful, and some activity for 3α-hydroxy steroids remains. There is evidence that this enzyme is not active for Δ^5-3β-hydroxyl, 17β, or 11β-hydroxyl groups.

3α-Hydroxy Steroid Dehydrogenase (1.1.1.50). This enzyme, obtained from bacterial and mammalian sources, appears to be specific for the 3α-hydroxyl group of 5α- and 5β-steroids. Hydroxyl groups at 3β, 17β, 17α, 11α, 16α, and 20α are not attacked by the enzyme. The purified enzymes from mammalian sources still contain 3β-activity as a contaminant.

Δ^4-3β-Hydroxy Steroid Dehydrogenase and Δ^4-3α-Hydroxy Steroid Dehydrogenase. These enzymes, which have been found in liver and testis tissue and probably occurring in many other tissues, convert Δ^4-3-hydroxy steroids to the Δ^4-3-ketone. The activity is present in the same fractions which contain the 3α- or 3β-hydroxy steroid dehydrogenases, and they may in fact be the result of the action of these same enzymes.

Δ^5-3β-Hydroxy Steroid Dehydrogenase

Ovarian, testicular, adrenal, and placental tissues contain an enzyme system which catalyzes the oxidation of the Δ^5-3β-hydroxy group of both C_{19} and C_{21} steroids to form the Δ^4-3-keto group (Samuels *et al.*, 1951). It is proposed that the symbol "Δ^5-" be used in naming this enzyme, Δ^5-3β-hydroxy steroid dehydrogenase, to emphasize the fact that the C-5, C-6 double bond is involved in the reaction leading to the Δ^4-3-ketone, and to differentiate this irreversible activity from that of the 3β-hydroxy steroid dehydrogenase, obtained from mammalian sources, which is involved in the reversible oxidation of a 3β-hydroxyl group to a 3-ketone in 5α- and 5β-steroids. The enzyme, Δ^5-3β-hydroxy steroid dehydrogenase, whose cofactor is NAD, is particularly abundant in the adrenal and is associated with the microsomal fraction (Beyer and Samuels, 1956).

The pituitary influence on Δ^5-3β-hydroxy steroid dehydrogenase content of the testis was studied by Samuels and Helmreich (1956). Hypophysectomy produced a temporary increase, followed by a significant drop. Treatment with human chorionic gonadotropin produced a doubling in effective enzyme concentration.

The Δ^5-3β-hydroxy steroid dehydrogenase system has been postulated by Talalay (1957b) to consist of two enzymatic steps. The first would involve the oxidation of the Δ^5-3β-hydroxy function to the 3-ketone, to give a Δ^5-3-keto group. The second reaction would involve the shift of the C-5, C-6 double bond to the C-4, C-5 double bond and the Δ^4-3-keto grouping. In such a system, an isomerase would be required and has been isolated from the microorganism *Pseudomonas testosteroni* and in mammalian steroid-forming tissues. Adrenal, testis, ovary, and liver of rats are rich sources of this enzyme. The steroid isomerase can convert the 3 keto-Δ^5 and the 3-keto-Δ^5(10) group to the 3 keto-Δ^4-group in both C_{19} and C_{21} steroids. The characteristics of this enzyme are discussed further in another section of this chapter.

Koritz (1962) has reported the inhibition of corticoid production in rat adrenal homogenates by increased levels of $NADH_2$ which could act on Δ^5-3β-hydroxy steroid dehydrogenases. The inhibition may be reversed by pyruvate, oxaloacetate, and ascorbate, all of which are capable of oxidizing the $NADH_2$ to NAD. The inhibition is not due to a transhydrogenase-mediated depletion of $NADPH_2$ by NAD.

The role of ascorbic acid in the metabolism of the adrenal cortex has been debated for some time without reaching a real decision as to its function. Koritz (1962) suggests a function for ascorbic acid in the adrenal cortex in terms of the properties of the ascorbic acid-dependent $NADH_2$ oxidase. This possible role would be to release a $NADH_2$ inhibition of the transformation of pregnenolone to progesterone by the oxidation of the $NADH_2$ by the ascorbic acid-dependent $NADH_2$ oxidase. Ascorbic acid acts in catalytic amounts in the oxidase system. Thus, experimental results where ACTH does not cause a drop in ascorbic acid or acts in the presence of lowered levels of adrenal ascorbic acid are explicable. With respect to the initial drop in adrenal ascorbic acid after ACTH administration as seen in the rat, it can be postulated that this is a consequence of a mechanism, native to this species, needed to establish adequate concentration of monodehydroascorbic acid. Once this state is achieved, the catalytic function of ascorbic acid may be established. It has been shown that 20–40% of the adrenal ascorbic acid lost from rat adrenals after ACTH administration is apparently dehydroascorbic acid and/or diketogulonic acid (Salomon, 1951).

Rubin *et al.* (1961) developed a rapid and sensitive method for the measurement of Δ^5-3β-hydroxy steroid dehydrogenase by determining the amount of 240 mμ-absorbing material formed from dehydroepiandrosterone or pregnenolone. The method described is easily performed and is sensitive enough to assay the steroid Δ^5-3β-hydroxy steroid dehydrogenase activity in a single rat adrenal. The enzymatic activities of the two adrenals are equal, so that one gland may be used for the biochemical assay and the other for histochemical analysis. Human adrenals obtained from a 12-week-old fetus contained Δ^5-3β-hydroxy steroid dehydrogenase (Bloch *et al.*, 1962).

The activities in the adrenals of various species measured by this new procedure cannot be compared with those reported previously (Samuels *et al.*, 1951; Samuels and Helmreich, 1956; Rubin and Dorfman, 1957), since the conditions of assay used in these earlier studies were not optimal with regard to duration of incubation and perhaps not optimal for all tissues with regard to tissue concentration. Rubin *et al.* (1961) point out that their assay procedure cannot as yet be used for quantitative measure of the enzyme activity in other steroid-hormone-reducing tissues since the requirements for optimal activity with testis, ovary, and placenta have not been defined.

Levy *et al.* (1959) have demonstrated that all adrenocortical cells contain activity for the oxidation of the Δ^5-3β-hydroxyl group, whereas only the Leydig cells of the testis are active, and much of the stroma and the follicular epithelium in the ovary appear to be inactive. Only a small portion of the rat placental trophoblast is active according to Deane *et al.* (1960).

3α-Hydroxy Steroid Dehydrogenase

A 3α-dehydrogenase which was associated with cell-free homogenate supernatant was reported in rabbit liver and kidney by Ungar and Dorfman (1954). The activity was maintained in an extract of an acetone powder of rat liver. Tomkins (1956b) and Tomkins and Isselbacher (1954) have made detailed studies of this enzyme obtained from the soluble fraction of rat liver. The suggestion was made that a single enzyme catalyzes the oxidation-reduction at carbon 3, regardless of whether the steroid substrate is a C_{19} or C_{21} compound. Thus, reactions were observed with the following compounds in the relative rates noted in parenthesis: 17α,21-dihydroxy-5β-pregnane-3,11,20-trione (100); 11β,17α,21-trihydroxy-5β-pregnane-3,20-dione (36); 5β-androstane-3,17-dione (110); 5α-androstane-3,17-dione (22); and 17β-hydroxy-5α-androstan-3-one (38). The specificity for steroid substrates was inferred from the fact that no reaction was observed with cyclohexanone and acetone. The 3β-hydroxysteroid, 3β-hydroxy-5α-androstan-17-one, was not oxidized by this enzyme system nor could cholestan-3-one, coprostan-3-one, cortisone, or 5α-androst-1-ene-3,17-dione serve as substrates. Both NAD and NADP could act as hydrogen acceptors for the reaction. The enzyme activity in the rat was detected in liver, kidney, and testis, but not in lung, spleen, muscle, or brain.

It has not been possible to separate completely mammalian 3α- from 3β-dehydrogenases. Even after extensive purification of 3α-dehydrogenase from the 105,000 *g* supernatant of a 0.25 *M* sucrose homogenate prepared from rat liver, some 3β-dehydrogenase was still present (Hurlock and Talalay, 1958).

Kochakian and his co-workers have reported that male guinea pig livers contain 3α- and 3β-dehydrogenases. The greatest activity was found in the supernatant fraction (Hamm *et al.*, 1956). When *Pseudomonas testosteroni* was grown on a medium containing testosterone as the sole source of carbon, both a 3α- and a 3β-dehydrogenase were induced. The 3α-hydroxy steroid dehydrogenase was purified 50- to 150-fold and was shown to be linked to NAD as a cofactor (Talalay *et al.*, 1952).

Talalay and Marcus (1956) demonstrated that the induced *Pseudomonas* enzyme can oxidize the following substrates: androsterone, 5α-androstane-3α,17β-diol, etiocholanolone, 11β-hydroxyetiocholanolone, urocortisone, and 5α-androstan-3α-ol. Deoxycholic acid was similarly oxidized (Marcus and Talalay, 1956).

3β-Hydroxy Steroid Dehydrogenase

Rat liver contains enzymes present in the particulate and soluble fractions which reduce the 3-ketone of 5α- and 5β-steroids to the 3β-hydroxyl group (Ungar and Dorfman, 1954; Rubin, 1957; Ungar, 1960a,b). Attempts to separate the 3β-dehydrogenase activity from the 3α-dehydrogenase activity have not been completely successful (Rubin and Strecker, 1961). In the mouse, the 3α-dehydrogenase activity is mainly inactivated by heating liver homogenate at 56°C for 20 minutes (Goldstein and Ungar, 1963). Further purification by ammonium sulfate precipitation and calcium phosphate gel gives a preparation containing only a trace of 3α activity. The specificity of this preparation for the 3β-hydroxyl groups has been shown. Steroids containing the 3α- or Δ^4-3α-hydroxyl, 17β, 11β, and Δ^5-3β hydroxyl groups were not oxidized to the ketone.

The commercial preparation of horse liver alcohol dehydrogenase (ADH) is obtained from the same fraction of liver which contains steroid dehydrogenase activity. The liver ADH preparation contains only 3β-hydroxy steroid dehydrogenase activity, which has the same specificity as the mouse 3β-hydroxy steroid dehydrogenase activity (Ungar, 1960b). 3β-Hydroxy and Δ^4-3β-hydroxy steroids are oxidized while Δ^5-3β, 17β, 11β, 3α, and 17α hydroxyl groups do not react. A dialyzed alcohol dehydrogenase preparation oxides 3β-steroid substrates at a rate only 10^{-4} that of ethanol used as substrate.

Rubin (1957) described a sex difference in the reduction of the 3-keto group of androstane-3,17-dione and androst-4-ene-3,17-dione. Incubation of these steroids with male rat liver homogenate gave ratios of the 3β-hydroxy compound (epiandrosterone) to the 3α-hydroxy steroid (androsterone) varying from 2.3 to 3.5. However, in similar experiments using female rat liver preparations, the ratios were decreased to 0.12 to 0.16. The total amount of product, counted as the sum of the 3α- and 3β-products, was the same whether livers from males or females were employed. Castration resulted in a lowered ratio which approached that of the female, [illegible] treatment of females did cause an increase in ratio. This [illegible] rabbits, mice, and hamsters but not with gu[illegible]

Rubin a[illegible] ct that 3β-dehydrogenase activity in [illegible] ats was greater than that found for [illegible] this difference in fractions obtained [illegible] etone-dried preparations. Both par[illegible] r contained 3β-dehydrogenase a[illegible] with the enzyme in the particul[illegible] ction could be increased by *in vi*[illegible] te.

At le[illegible] 3α-dehydrogenase and 3β-deh[illegible] ween male and female rat liv[illegible] y in livers of male rats than i[illegible] ly procedure based on the r[illegible] ndrostane-3,17-dione.

Ru[illegible] ed 3β-dehydrogenase activ[illegible] particulate fraction. Live[illegible] al activities of the cor[illegible] hanisms by which test[illegible] rogenase activity we[illegible] me synthesis as pa[illegible] nsfer of enzyme be[illegible] or, removal of a[illegible], or an indirect r[illegible]

[illegible] of the Δ^4-3-keto [illegible] the 4,5-dihydro-[illegible] to the saturated [illegible] genases. An alter-[illegible] the Δ^4-3-ol series [illegible] shown recently by [illegible] bit skeletal muscle [illegible] 3β-hydroxyandrost-[illegible],17α-dihydroxypregn-

4-en-20-one after the perfusion of 17α-hydroxyprogesterone through bovine adrenals and ovaries.

The oxidation of Δ^4-3-ols to Δ^4-3-ketones had been previously demonstrated by Ungar *et al.* (1957) using rat liver tissues. In an *in vivo* study in man, Neeman *et al.* (1960) found that 11β-hydroxyandrost-4-ene-3,17-dione is converted in part to a Δ^4-3-hydroxy steroid.

Ringold *et al.* (1962) reported that the non-naturally occurring 6β-fluorotestosterone was reduced to two allyl alcohols, 6β-fluoroandrost-4-ene-3β,17β-diol and 6β-fluoroandrost-4-ene-3α,17β-diol, as the only metabolites in the presence of a rat liver supernatant fraction at pH 5.8 in the presence of a $NADPH_2$ generating system. In a second publication, Ringold *et al.* (1963) investigated the products resulting from the incubation of 6α-fluorotestosterone, 2α-fluorotestosterone, 4-chlorotestosterone, and 6β-fluoro-16α-methyl-17α,21-dihydroxypregn-4-ene-3,20-dione with the same rat liver system and showed that the reduction rate and total yield was increased to Δ^4-3-ol formation. This reduction proceeds with either $NADPH_2$ or $NADH_2$. The authors (Ringold *et al.*, 1963) rationalize this pathway on the basis of electronic destabilization of the Δ^4-3-keto group by electronegative substituents (halogen) with stabilization of the proposed transition state for reduction.

When 2α,4-, 6α-, and 6β-methyltestosterone derivatives were subjected to the same rat liver incubation system, severe retardation of reduction resulted. This is explained in part on electronic factors and in some cases on steric grounds.

3(or 17)β-Hydroxy Steroid Dehydrogenase

A 3(or 17)β-hydroxy steroid dehydrogenase has been prepared from *Pseudomonas testosteroni* grown on testosterone as the only source of organic carbon, which catalyzes the oxidation of 3β, 16β-, 17β-hydroxy steroids including ring A-aromatic compounds containing a 17β-hydroxyl group (Talalay and Marcus, 1956). The strength of interaction between steroid substrates and the enzyme is reported to be sensitive to minor changes in substrate structure. Estradiol-17β is very firmly bound, as are testosterone, 17β-hydroxy-5α-androstan-3-one, 3β-hydroxy-5α-androstan-17-one, 6β-hydroxytestosterone, and 19-nortestosterone. Stilbestrol is an efficient competitive inhibitor of the oxidation of several substrates. Talalay (1957b) summarized the principal structural features that influence steroid-enzyme affinity for this bacterial enzyme. Oxygen at 3 and 17 favors the binding process. Additional hydroxy substituents at 11α, 11β, 14α, and 15β but not at 6β, prevent binding. Steroids with rings A/B *cis* (5β) result in poor binding, but steroids with rings A/B *trans* (5α), or with Δ^4 or Δ^5 double bonds, or an aromatic ring A, favor binding. A C_{19} methyl group does not influence the binding process.

Δ^4-3β-Hydroxy Steroid and Δ^4-3α-Hydroxy Steroid Dehydrogenases

Both rat and chick liver contain enzyme activity for the oxidation of Δ^4-3α- and Δ^4-3β-hydroxyl groups to the Δ^4-3-ketone. These dehydrogenases are present in the soluble fraction of liver following centrifugation at 78,000 *g*. The activity can be precipitated with ammonium sulfate between 0.40 and 0.55 saturation. Both NAD and NADP are equally effective hydrogen acceptors. This enzyme preparation is equally effective on C_{21} steroids with the same configuration in ring A (Ungar *et al.*, 1957; Ungar and Bloom, 1957). The reaction has also been demonstrated in mouse testis tissue (Grosso and Ungar, 1964).

11β-Dehydrogenases

The presence of an 11β-dehydrogenase in liver tissue has been demonstrated by various investigators. The reduction of the 11-keto group is dependent upon the presence of a Δ^4-3-ketone group in ring A (Hübener *et al.*, 1956). Better than 50% of cortisone and 17α,20β-21-trihydroxypregn-4-ene-3,11-dione was reduced to the corresponding 11β-hydroxy compounds by rat liver preparations, whereas the ring A-reduced steroids, urocortisone, cortolone, β-cortolone, and 11-ketoetiocholanolone, were unaltered. No requirement of the enzyme could be shown for NADP, NAD, or cytochrome c (Amelung *et al.*, 1953a,b).

The *in vitro* reduction of the 11-ketone groups of cortisone to cortisol has been studied with porcine, bovine, and rat tissues (Fish *et al.*, 1953). The reaction could be demonstrated by preparations consisting of whole liver homogenates, a supernatant fraction after centrifugation at 5000 *g*, and an acetone powder of whole homogenate supplemented with NAD.

Mahesh and Ulrich (1959) observed that the oxidation of cortisol to cortisone occurred in the particulate fraction from a rat kidney homogenate centrifuged at 104,000 *g* for 1 hour. When the whole homogenate was separated into nuclear particles, mitochondria, microsomes, and supernatant fractions, the activity was found mainly in the nuclear particles and microsomes. Mitochondria contained very little activity. In the oxidation of cortisol to cortisone by rat kidney tissue, the addition of $5 \times 10^{-4} M$ NADP increased the yield 13-fold. Yields of cortisone from 100 μg of cortisol were 38.8 μg when incubated with the nuclear fraction, 8 μg with mitochondria, and 20.5 μg with microsomes. Further analysis of cell components by the Dounce (1955) procedure indicated that 11β-dehydrogenase is linked with the cell membrane and is partly destroyed by destruction of the cell structure. When kidney tissue was used, the reduction of the 11-ketone to the 11β-hydroxyl in the presence of $NADPH_2$ proceeded to only 10%, whereas in the presence of NADP the 11β-hydroxy group of cortisol was oxidized to the extent of 60%, suggesting that the enzyme system was not freely reversible. This effect was not observed for liver by Hurlock and Talalay (1959).

The microsomal 11β-dehydrogenase of liver from rats, guinea pigs, or bovine reversibly carries out the reaction with the NAD or NADP (Hurlock and Talalay, 1959). The activity in human placental tissue appears to have low substrate specificity, and NAD and NADP could function as cofactors (Osinski, 1960).

11-Ketosteroids with a *cis* A/B ring fusion are not reduced to the 11β-hydroxy form, but 11-ketosteroids with the *trans* A/B ring fusion are efficiently reduced (Bush and Mahesh, 1959a). Hübener and Amelung (1953) reported that the reduction of the 11-keto group of cortisone was greater by homogenates of liver from male rats than from the liver prepared from females.

The 2α-methyl-11-oxygenated steroids are poorly oxidized or reduced at C-11 (Bush and Mahesh, 1959b). This has been interpreted as meaning that the 11β-dehydrogenase interaction takes place on the α face of the steroid molecule.

17α-N-Hydroxy Steroid Dehydrogenase. The designation 17α-N- refers to the 17α-hydroxyl group in the neutral C_{19} steroids. No enzyme studies have been done specifically for this system, and its presence is assumed on the basis of isolated products containing the 17α-hydroxy group.

17β-N-Hydroxy Steroid Dehydrogenase. Guinea pig liver and kidney contain two 17β-dehydrogenases. One is present in the soluble fraction and requires NADP, whereas the second is in the mitochondrial fraction and requires NAD (Endahl *et al.*, 1960; Endahl and Kochakian, 1962).

Engel *et al.* (1963) used a combination of ammonium sulfate precipitation, DEAE-Cellulose, and hydroxyl-apatite chromatography to achieve a 200–300-fold purification of the soluble NADP-specific 17β-N-hydroxy steroid dehydrogenase from guinea pig liver. The enzyme required free sulfhydryl groups and had a pH optimum of 10.3. Reactivity was demonstrated toward C_{19}-3β-hydroxy steroid of the 5α series and saturated C_{19}-17β-hydroxy steroids in addition to testosterone. There was some correlation between planarity or rigidity of the substrate molecule and relative reaction velocity.

Sharma *et al.* (1962) showed that this enzyme in rat tissues is not "freely reversible," that there are different pH optima when going from one direction or the other. Of interest and importance is the observation that the "effective" concentration of the 17-keto reducing system for androst-4-ene-3,17-dione in mature rat tissues is particularly high when compared with that of immature testes.

17α-A-Hydroxy Steroid Dehydrogenase. The designation 17α-*A*- refers the 17α-hydroxyl group in ring A aromatic compounds. This enzyme has been detected in cow blood by the conversion of estrone primarily to estradiol-17α. Enzymatic studies are not available.

17β-A-Hydroxy Steroid Dehydrogenase. A placental 17β-*A*-dehydrogenase has been studied by Langer *et al.* (1959), Adams *et al.* (1962), and Jarabak *et al.* (1962, 1963) which reacts with the 17β-hydroxy group of estradiol-17β and other phenolic steroids, and apparently of non-phenolic steroids as well. It is this enzyme which has been suggested by Talalay and co-workers (Talalay, 1957b) to be identical to the estradiol-17β-mediated transhydrogenase in placental tissue, an observation with great implications, but one which has been vigorously disputed (Villee *et al.*, 1960).

Jarabak *et al.* (1963) reported the preparation of a highly purified 17β-*A*-hydroxy steroid dehydrogenase of human placenta which reacts with NAD and NADP and catalyzes estrogen-dependent hydrogen transfer between pyridine nucleotides. If the enzyme activity is measured in the presence of high glycerol concentrations or after storage at high phosphate concentrations, the ratios of its dehydrogenase activities and its transhydrogenase activity can be altered markedly. The authors attribute alterations to configurational changes in the protein.

A 17β-*A* dehydrogenase activity has been reported to be present in rat blood and in erythrocytes of a number of mammalian and avian species (Lunaas and Velle, 1960; Particus and Repke, 1960).

20α- and 20β-Dehydrogenases

Rat liver supernatant from a 17,500 *g* centrifugate contained both the 20α- and 20β-enzymes. Urocortisol and cortisol were reduced primarily to 20β-hydroxy derivatives, while urocortisone and 11-deoxycortisol were reduced to 20α-hydroxy derivatives (Hübener *et al.*, 1956). In another study, 11-deoxycortisol incubated with rat liver homogenates yielded both 20α- and 20β-hydroxy derivatives (Forchielli and Dorfman, 1956; Forchielli *et al.*, 1955). Both 20α and 20β reduction was observed in still another study when liver microsomes plus supernatant were used (DeCourcy and Schneider, 1956).

A sex difference in the reduction of the C-20 keto group of cortisone (stereoisomer not specified) is indicated from the work of Troop (1958, 1959). The homogenates of male rat livers produced from three to six times the 20-keto reduction found for similar preparations from female rats. This sex difference was not found in rats less than 25 days old. Androgens were associated with increased amounts of the C-20 keto reducing enzyme, while estrogens tended to produce decreased conversion.

The 20α- and 20β-dehydrogenases have been demonstrated in muscle, liver, and kidney (Thomas *et al.*, 1960; DeCourcy, 1957; Mahesh and Ulrich, 1959, 1960; Sweat *et al.*, 1958).

Castration decreases the reducing activity of rat liver homogenates, and testosterone may prevent this change if treatment is started immediately after operation. Estradiol-17β treatment decreases the rate of reduction and ovariectomy increases the activity slightly. Cortisone treatment reduces activity in both sexes (Hagen and Troop, 1960; Troop, 1959). Rat liver homogenate prepared from males produces a more rapid reducing effect than that from females (Hagen and Troop, 1960; Troop, 1959; Leybodd and Staudinger, 1959).

Wiest and Wilcox (1961) have partially purified the rat ovarian 20α-dehydrogenase and under these conditions there is a specific requirement for NADP. It did not function as NADP–NAD transhydrogenase, a fact explained on the basis of its lack of dual nucleotide specificity at pH 7.0. With equal concentrations of NADP and $NADPH_2$ the equilibrium ratio of the 20α-reduced derivative of progesterone to progesterone was 1.7. The enzyme showed an absolute specificity for the 20α-hydroxy configuration.

Hübener *et al.* (1959), employing an ultrasonic disintegration technic, solubilized a 20β-dehydrogenase and prepared the enzyme in crystalline form.

Schmidt-Thomé *et al.* (1962) studied the relative ease of 20β-reduction and enzyme inductive capacity (progesterone = 1) of a variety of steroids, but were unable to establish a relationship between the two parameters. The enzyme source was *Streptomyces hydrogenans*. Typical values for the two parameters, reduction and induction respectively, follow: progesterone 1,1; 16α,17α-oxidoprogesterone 6.4, 0.72; 11-oxoprogesterone 4.0,—; 21-deoxycortisone 2.7, 1.03; 11-oxo-16α,17α-oxidoprogesterone 2.0,—; 17α-hydroxyprogesterone 1.5,—; cortisone 1.2, 0.22; prednisone 1.1,—; 11-dehydrocorticosterone 0.85,—; 11-deoxycortisol 0.7, 1.39; 5β-pregnane-3,20-dione 0.7,—; 16α,17α-oxido-3β-hydroxypregn-5-en-20-one 0.65, 0.46; 5α-pregnane-3,20-dione 0.64,—; 11α-hydroxyprogesterone 0.51, 0.37; 17α-hydroxy-3β-hydroxy-5α-pregnan-20-one 0.5;—; pregn-5-ene-3,20-dione 0.44,—; deoxycorticosterone 0.4,—; 3β-hydroxy-5α-pregnan-20-one 0.32, —; 3β-hydroxypregn-5-en-20-one 0.32,—; 11-epicortisol 0.3, 0.2; urocortisone 0.27,—; 6α-methylcortisol 0.16, 0.16; cortisol 0.15, 1.36; prednisolone 0.14,—; 6α-methylprednisolone 0.14,—; 3β,21-dihydroxypregn-5-en-20-one 0.13,—; 11α-hydroxy-16α,17α-oxidoprogesterone 0.12,—; 21-hydroxy-5β-pregnane-3,20-dione 0.11,—; 11-epicorticosterone 0.11,—; pregna-4,16-diene-3,20-dione 0.05, 0.8; urocortisol 0.05,—; corticosterone 0.03, —; 3β-hydroxypregna-4,16-dien-20-one 0.02, 0.74.

Nesemann *et al.* (1962) have shown that deoxycorticosterone, progesterone, and 11β,21-dihydroxypregna-4,17(20)-dien-3-one caused a high maximum of 20β-hydroxy steroid dehydrogenase at concentrations of 20–100 μg/ml, using *Streptomyces hydrogenans* as the source of enzyme, but when these concentrations were increased, there followed a rapid decrease in amount of enzyme induced. Testosterone gave an increasing effect up to 200 μg, and estrone was without effect at the same concentrations.

Bryson (1962) reported that a C-20 reducing enzyme (stereospecificity not designated) could be precipitated by 50–70% ammonium sulfate.

21-Dehydrogenase

Reduction of the aldehyde group of 11β,17α-dihydroxy-21-oxopregn-4-ene-3,20-dione to the corresponding alcohol function was demonstrated with an acetone powder preparation of liver (Schneider, 1953). The corresponding 11-ketosteroid was similarly reduced. The cofactor requirement for this system was reduced NAD or NADP. Similarly, enzyme systems are indicated for the oxidation and reduction of carbon atoms 18 and 19. In addition, the isolation of C-18 carboxylic acid derivatives indicates the presence of an enzyme system in the adrenal gland which oxidizes an 18-oxo group to the corresponding acid function.

The 21-dehydrogenase system has now been studied in some detail by Monder and White (1961) in rat and beef liver tissue. It has been partially purified by ammonium sulfate precipitation followed by purification on calcium phosphate gel. The enzyme was stable at 65°C for 10 minutes but was destroyed at higher temperatures. Ethylene-diamine tetraacetate increased the activity and inhibition was found with heavy metal ions, β-mercaptoethanol, and cystein. The pH optimum was 6.9. The 21-aldehydes of cortisone, cortisol, corticosterone, deoxycortisol, deoxycorticosterone, and prednisolone were reduced.

Talalay (1957a) has suggested that some of the dehydrogenases and other related enzymes may be involved in steroid transport. This suggestion is particularly interesting in view of the report of Mahesh and Ulrich (1959), who found the 11β-dehydrogenase linked with the cell membrane.

On the basis of isolated transformation products and metabolism experiments, 6α, 6β, and 7α-dehydrogenases are indicated but no definitive reports on these enzymes are available.

Reductases

Δ^1-*Reductase*

Ungar and Dorfman (1952a) demonstrated the reduction of the Δ^1-double bond in C_{19} steroids *in vivo* in humans. *In vitro* experiments have been reported by Tomkins (1956b) and by Vermeulen and Caspi (1958).

Tomkins' enzyme preparation reduced the Δ^1-group of both C_{19} (androsta-1,4-diene-3,17-dione) and C_{21} (prednisone) steroids. In the presence of $NADPH_2$, both the Δ^1- and Δ^4-groups were reduced. This investigator suggested that the initial reduction occurs at the Δ^1-group in compounds having both Δ^1- and Δ^4-unsaturation and that separate enzyme systems exist for each reduction. The last suggestion is contrary, however, to the findings of Caspi and Pechet (1957), who reported the isolation of 3α,11β,17α,21-tetrahydroxy-5β-pregn-1-en-20-one after the administration of prednisolone, a situation where the Δ^4-double bond had been reduced without saturation of the Δ^1-nuclear double bond. In addition, the urinary metabolites of androsta-1,4-diene-3,17-dione given orally to humans included a number of unsaturated (Δ^1, presumably) steroids, not further identified (Ungar and Dorfman, 1952b).

Δ^4-5β- and Δ^4-5α-Reductases (Hydrogenases)

The Δ^4-5β-reductase has been isolated from the soluble fraction of rat liver. The enzyme has been purified by ammonium sulfate precipitation and by elution from a calcium phosphate gel (Tomkins and Isselbacher, 1954; Tomkins, 1956a,b). $NADPH_2$ was the specific cofactor involved; $NADH_2$ was not active. A crude liver preparation showed about the same order of activity for the reduction of the C_4,C_5 double bond for a wide variety of substrates ranging from cholestenone to 9α-fluorocortisol. Upon purification, however, there was a disproportionate loss of correlation of the activities of the enzyme preparation with respect to the three steroid substrates employed: cortisone, cortisol, and adrenosterone. The data were interpreted to mean that three different enzymes were actually present. Sulfhydryl groups appear to be involved, since addition of *p*-chloromercuribenzoate inhibited the reduction of cortisone. A Δ^4-5β-reductase enzyme preparation for 11-deoxycortisol from rat liver was obtained in the 78,000 *g* supernatant. Tomkins (1957) has suggested that a group of Δ^4-5β-hydrogenases (reductases) are present in the fraction of liver homogenates which are specific for each given steroid substrate.

It was originally reported (Forchielli *et al.*, 1958; Yates *et al.*, 1958) that female rat liver possessed only one steroid Δ^4-reductase which was characterized as the microsomal Δ^4-5α-hydrogenase. This was in contrast to the results obtained with male rat liver, from which two distinct and separable reductases were characterized; namely, the Δ^4-5α-reductase (5α-enzyme) associated with the liver microsomes and the Δ^4-5β-reductase (5β-enzyme associated with the soluble tissue fraction) (Forchielli and Dorfman, 1956). Under the experimental conditions originally employed the female rat liver appeared to be unique in lacking a soluble 5β-reductase, since Δ^4-reductase activity was detectable in the microsomal and soluble fractions obtained from the livers of both sexes of several other mammalian species studied (Brown-Grant *et al.*, 1962).

Under somewhat modified conditions, the presence of Δ^4-5β-reductase activity in the soluble fraction of female rat liver could be demonstrated (Forchielli *et al.*, 1963). Relatively large-scale incubation experiments were carried out in order to isolate and characterize the product and determine the steric nature of the reduction of the Δ^4-double bond. To establish the identity of the major products further, 100 μg of 4-C^{14}-androst-4-ene-3, 17-dione (10^6 cpm) were incubated and the products oxidized to the 5α- and 5β-diones. The 5α-androstane-3,17-dione zone contained 1.49×10^5 cpm and the 5β-androstane-3,17-dione zone 2.23×10^5 cpm. The eluted diones were then diluted with 40 mg of their respective carriers and crystallized to constant specific activity.

These results, contrary to earlier observations, establish the fact that the soluble fraction from female rat liver does contain steroid Δ^4-5β-reductase activity. The activity of this enzyme is much lower than that of the microsomal 5α-enzyme, and the pH optimum for the 5β-enzyme is on the acid side (about pH 5.6). These factors would contribute significantly to the previous failure to observe 5β-reductase activity. 5α-Reduced steroids are formed almost exclusively by the perfusion of corticoids through isolated livers or the incubation of these substrates with slices or whole homogenates. The lack of 5β-reduced products in these studies cannot be entirely explained by the observations stated in the preceding paragraph, since the 5β-reducing enzyme appears to be present.

The guinea pig is an unusual species with regard to steroid metabolism. The steroids excreted in the urine contain a large proportion of Δ^4-3-ketosteroids along with the usual types of ring A-reduced steroids. Brown-Grant *et al.* (1960) subsequently found a far greater activity for Δ^4-reductases in the adrenal as compared with the liver in this species.

The influence of the 11-oxygen function on the rate of ring A reduction *in vitro* was studied in detail by Brown-Grant *et al.* (1962). In both sexes of the species studied (rats, mice, hamsters, rabbits, and guinea pigs), with the exception of the female rat, Δ^4-reductase activity was found in both the microsomal and 105,000 *g* supernatant fractions. The substrates included 11-deoxy steroids, deoxycorticosterone, 11-deoxycortisol, progesterone, and androst-4-ene-3,17-dione together with their 11-keto and 11β-hydroxy derivatives. In general, the enzyme preparations, both microsomal and soluble, from the guinea pig, mouse, and rabbit livers reduced the 11β-hydroxy compounds to a lesser extent than did either the 11-deoxy or 11-keto analogs. A similar pattern of reactivity was exhibited by the soluble enzyme preparations of livers from the male rat and hamster. But, the microsomal preparations of these two species, in contrast to the other preparations studied, reduced the 11β-hydroxy compounds almost as readily as the 11-keto and 11-deoxy compounds.

The differences in the rate of Δ^4-reduction between 11-keto, 11-deoxy, and 11β-hydroxy compounds suggested either some degree of substrate specificity or, alternatively, that the rate of ring A reduction of the 11β-hydroxy compounds was dependent on prior oxidation of the 11β-hydroxyl to an 11-keto group function. The latter explanation proved to be unlikely, since tissue fractions which readily reduced the Δ^4-function of the 11β-hydroxy steroids did not show significant oxidation of the 11β-hydroxyl group under the experimental conditions employed. The more likely conclusion would seem to be that the various Δ^4-reductases have a relative preference for either 11-keto or 11β-hydroxy compounds. The preferential reduction of 11-keto over 11β-hydroxy compounds by many of these enzymes may perhaps account for the preponderance, in general, of 11-keto over 11β-hydroxy products among the known urinary steroids.

The marked difference in the extent of reduction by guinea pig liver and adrenal enzymes *in vitro* of 11β-hydroxy compounds on the one hand and the 11-keto and 11-deoxy compounds on the other is of particular interest, since this is the only species where both this particular aspect of metabolism *in vitro* and the pattern of urinary steroid excretion have been examined in any detail (Brown-Grant *et al.*, 1960; Peron and Dorfman, 1958). The major proportion of C_{21} ring A unreduced metabolites in urine are 11β-hydroxy compounds, and the C_{19} ring A reduced metabolites are mainly 11-deoxy or 11-keto compounds. Since *in vitro* the guinea pig liver enzymes are present in such low concentrations, it is difficult to assess the contribution of the liver Δ^4-reductases of this species to ring A reduced metabolites. However, the presence of a highly active soluble 5β-enzyme in guinea pig adrenal glands (Brown-Grant *et al.*, 1960) and the preponderance of reduced urinary steroids of the etiocholane type (5β) suggest that the ring A reduced products in guinea pig urine may be the result of adrenal Δ^4-reductase action.

Factors Influencing Δ^4-5α- and Δ^4-5β-Reductase

Female rat liver microsomes contain more Δ^4-5α-reductase activity than do those of male rats (Forchielli *et al.*, 1958; Yates *et al.*, 1958; Leybold and Staudinger, 1959). Ovariectomy or estrogen treatment has no particular influence on the concentration of Δ^4-reductases (Forchielli *et al.*, 1958; Yates *et al.*, 1958; Hagen and Troop, 1960). Testosterone treatment causes the Δ^4-5α-reductase activity to decrease, and castration causes an increase in the reductase (Hagen and Troop, 1960; Yates *et al.*, 1958). Cortisone decreases the reductase activity in males (Urquhart *et al.*, 1959; Hagen and Troop, 1960). Hypophysectomy decreases the Δ^4-5α-reductase activity (Forchielli *et al.*, 1958).

Various factors influencing reduction of Δ^4-3-ketosteroids by rat liver have been studied in detail by Yates *et al.* (1958). Increased effective concentration of Δ^4-reductases in female livers as compared with male livers was found for each of the following substrates: deoxycorticosterone, cortisone, cortisol, aldosterone, corticosterone, testosterone, and progesterone. There were 3- to 10-fold increases in the female liver (Forchielli *et al.*, 1958). During the period of approximately 35–60 days of age, gondal influences predominate, with estrogens increasing the Δ^4-reductase content of liver, whereas androgens produce the opposite effect. The estrogen effect becomes insignificant at about 75 days of age in the female, whereas androgen influence continues to be an important factor in the older males. Beyond 60 days of age, a non-gondal process maintains the high enzyme titer in female liver. Adrenocortical secretions do not seem to account for this non-gonadal control.

There are two effects of thyroxine on the rate of cortisone reduction: an early increase in available reduced NADP; and, following prolonged treatment, an increase in the activity of a microsomal enzyme catalyzing the reduction of the 4–5 double bond of ring A. This enhanced microsomal activity results in an increase in the production of the 5α-isomer. Since the soluble enzyme producing the 5β-dihydrosteroid is not affected by this treatment, there would result an increase in the ratio of the 5α and 5β

isomers. This is consistent with the findings of Bradlow *et al.* (1956), who reported a shift in urinary metabolites of C^{14}-testosterone from the 5β to the 5α series following the administration of triiodothyronine to humans. Evidence that Δ^4-3-ketosteroid reduction may be accelerated in the thyrotoxicosis in man has been presented (Levin and Daughaday, 1955; Peterson, 1958).

McGuire and Tomkins (1960) have presented evidence which suggests that there are at least five Δ^4-5α-reductases, one for each of the following substrates examined: cortisone, cortisol, deoxycorticosterone, and 11-deoxycortisol. The argument rests on four points. First, when rats are treated with thyroxine, the reductase activity for each steroid increases, but the increment is different for each of five steroid substrates. Second, various procedures diminish the reductase activities, but to different degrees for each steroid employed. 5α-Androstane-3,17-dione, a saturated 3-ketosteroid, interferes with the metabolism of only some of the substrates, and those which are inhibited are again affected differently. Finally, the relative reductase activities for five steroids vary substantially from animal to animal. It seems unlikely that a single protein with the ability to catalyze the reduction of a number of substrates would respond in a manner consistent with the foregoing observations. Conclusive proof that there are multiple steroid reductases must await solubilization and separation of the enzymes from one another. This latter has been accomplished for one of the cytoplasmic 5β-steroid reductases. A cortisone reductase (5β) has been separated from other activities which catalyze the reduction of closely related steroids (Tomkins, 1957). The soluble enzyme isolated was unable to reduce any other steroid but cortisone.

Recently, Peterson *et al.* (1955) have studied the rates of steroid reduction in humans with hepatic cirrhosis. They noted that the rate of reduction of hydrocortisone was diminished in these patients, but that cortisone reduction proceeded at a normal rate. Peterson has since tested a number of other 4–5 unsaturated steroids (Peterson, 1958) and found that the reduction of none of them was affected. It would, therefore, appear that in human liver, as measured *in vivo*, the steroid reductases function independently.

The reduction of a physiologically active 4–5 unsaturated 3-ketosteroid to either its 5α- or 5β-reduced product usually results in loss of its *characteristic* biological activity, although both 5α- and 5β-reduced steroids have pharmacological, and perhaps physiological, actions distinct from those of the unsaturated parent compounds. From the present work, it appears that for each steroid there are two reducing enzymes in the liver, one associated with the microsomal fraction of the cell which produces the 5α isomer, and a soluble enzyme which produces the 5β form. The apparent function of these ensymes to inactivate steroid hormones does not explain the necessity for specific reductases for different steroids, or for a particulate 5α- and soluble 5β-reductase for each individual substrate.

Δ^{16}-*Reductase*

The saturation of the Δ^{16}-double bond has been demonstrated *in vivo*; however, no specific studies related to this enzyme activity have been reported.

Lactonizing Enzyme System

Some microorganisms have enzyme systems which convert testosterone and androst-4-ene-3,17-dione to testololactone. Prairie and Talalay (1963) have studied the enzymology of the reaction and have shown that a lactonizing enzyme system from *Penicillium lilacinum* converts androst-4-ene-3,17-dione to testololactone and that the reaction has an absolute requirement for $NADPH_2$ and molecular oxygen. Tracer molecular oxygen was incorporated in the ethereal position and not in the carbonyl group linked to C-17.

20α,22-C_{27}-Desmolase (Pregnenolone Synthetase)

The enzyme system responsible for the splitting of the side chain of cholesterol to form pregnenolone has not been separated from the 20α,22-hydroxylase discussed earlier in this chapter. Halkerston *et al.* (1959, 1960) obtained a soluble enzyme from the acetone powder preparation of mitochondria which formed progesterone from cholesterol. Pregnenolone did not accumulate in the system (Halkerston *et al.*, 1960) but its presence was related to the level of NAD available for the conversion of the Δ^5-3β-hydroxyl to the Δ^4-3-ketone.

Other synthetases can be postulated on theoretical grounds or on the basis of the occurrence of specific compounds. The formation of dehydroepiandrosterone from cholesterol directly would be possible if a 17α,20α-C_{27}-desmolase were present to split the side chain between carbons 17 and 20. Evidence for such a reaction is being actively investigated (Dorfman *et al.*, 1963).

17α,20-C_{21}-Desmolase

A suggested mechanism of 17α-hydroxyprogesterone conversion to a C_{19} steroid is considered in Fig. 1. One may consider that a peroxy or peracid attack on the C-20 carbonyl group leads to an intermediate that would undergo rearrangement to androst-4-ene-3,17-dione as the primary reaction product. Enzymatic reduction to testosterone could then follow. Barring peroxidative attack, simple oxidative scission of the 17α-hydroxyprogesterone side chain should lead to acetaldehyde as a product. When Lynn and Brown (1958a) in their enzymatic studies found only acetic acid as the oxidative product of progesterone-21-C^{14} degradation, they suggested the possibility of the addition of hydrogen peroxide to the C-20 carbonyl group (after 17α-hydroxylation), a suggestion in line with their stoichiometric measurements of the reaction. Extension of Lynn and Brown's suggestion by the inclusion of a Beyer–Villiger type of mechanism as outlined above for progesterone and leaving the question of the exact nature of the peroxidative species open would allow one single enzyme system to degrade progesterone and 17-hydroxyprogesterone by an identical mechanism. It should be possible to substantiate such a concept by experimental means.

Lynn and Brown (1958a) indicated that the 17α,20-C_{21}-desmolase requires $NADPH_2$ and O_2, and is inhibited by *p*-choromercuribenzoate, EDTA, and other metal chelating agents.

17H,20-C_{21}-Desmolase

Kase *et al.* (1962) reported that progesterone is converted by human ovaries to both testosterone and androst-4-ene-3,17-dione by a pathway in which 17α-hydroxyprogesterone is not an obligatory intermediate. Testosterone acetate has been suggested as the intermediate in this case, and attempts to identify the compound are in progress. On chemical grounds, only the peracid-type mechanism would appear to account for a progesterone side chain degradation by-passing 17α-hydroxyprogesterone; thus, the metabolic pathway operating in microorganisms may be present in mammalian testes as well. The nature of the peroxidative species is open to question, since enzymatically generated peracid or hydroperoxide could function in the proposed mechanism.

10,19-Desmolase (Estrogen Synthetase)

Some pertinent observations have been made of the enzyme 10,19-desmolase, which is involved in estrogen biosynthesis. It has been shown that 19-hydroxyandrost-4-ene-3,17-dione and 19-aldoandrost-4-ene-3,17-dione are converted in good yield to estrogens by a human placental microsome preparation and are considered to be important intermediates on the pathway from androst-4-ene-3,17-dione to estrogen (Morato *et al.*, 1961). It has also been found that the 19-hydroxy compound forms both formaldehyde and formic acid in its conversion to estrogen, whereas the 19-oxo structure yields mostly formic acid (Dorfman *et al.*, 1962). In attempting to fit these facts into a mechanism for estrogen formation, information concerning the stereochemistry of the hydrogen eliminated at C-1 was necessary and has recently been elucidated. The data support the concept that the 1β hydrogen is eliminated preferentially in the aromatization process (See Chapter III).

Conjugation Enzymes

Formation of Sulfates

Schneider and Lewbart (1956) demonstrated steroid sulfate-synthesizing enzymes in a microsome-free supernatant fluid prepared from rabbit liver homogenate to which were added adenosine triphosphate (ATP), Mg^+, and sulphate. It is likely that the sulfate donor is 3′-phosphoadenosine-5′-

phosphosulfate (PAPS) (Robbins and Lipmann, 1956). According to Gregory and Nose (1957), there are at least two separate active systems present in the soluble fraction of rabbit liver extracts. One system is active for estrogens and the other with 3β-hydroxy steroids. The 3α-hydroxy steroids do not form sulfates in this system.

The presence of sulfate-forming systems in adrenal tumors is strongly indicated by the presence in this gland of dehydroepiandrosterone sulfate as well as by the secretion of this conjugate into the adrenal venous blood (Baulieu, 1959).

Nose and Lipmann (1958) made some progress toward separating different steroid sulfokinases from rabbit and lamb liver and observed different substrate specificities. Their system included phosphate buffer, magnesium sulfate, cysteine, and ATP. The relative rates of formation of sulfates for various steroid substrates were as follows: dehydroepiandrosterone, 46; epiandrosterone, 36; pregnenolone, 27; testosterone, 11; deoxycorticosterone, 6; androsterone, 4; etiocholanolone, 3; and 3β-hydroxy-5β-androstan-17-one, 2.

Wengle and Bostrom (1962) showed that a homogenate supernatant fraction of female rat livers, free from microsomes, formed a monosulfate of androst-5-ene-3β,17β-diol, which was convertible in turn to the steroid disulfate.

Formation of Glucuronosides

Isselbacher (1956) has demonstrated that the steroid glucuronide is formed through the active glucuronide donor, uridine diphosphoglucuronic acid (UDPGA). The formation of the conjugate is catalyzed by a glucuronosyl transferase present in liver microsomes. The reaction involves the transfer of UDPGA to the steroid alcohol, and uridine diphosphate is liberated. A preparation of guinea pig liver microsomes was used to form the β-glucuronide of urocortisol (Isselbacher and Axelrod, 1955). Dutton (1956) has formed the glucuronosides of androsterone, 5α-pregnane-3β,20β-diol, and stilbestrol with UDPGA and a mouse liver microsome preparation.

β-Glucuronidase

(See discussion in next paragraph.)

Deconjugation Enzymes

β-Glucuronidase

The enzyme β-glucuronidase has had a relatively long history and has been extensively studied. The reader is referred to one of the reviews by W. H. Fishman (1961) on its distribution, activity, and properties. The status of this enzyme in endocrinology, nonetheless, is puzzling. In recent years, it has been considered *not* to be involved in the synthesis of the steroid glucuronide conjugates. The physiological significance of a hydrolytic role has been surmised but never determined experimentally. Its presence in the cells lining the gastrointestinal tract suggests a function in terms of the enterohepatic circulation of estrogens and progesterone metabolites. However, glucuronide formation has been demonstrated in the transfer of testosterone and androst-4-ene-3,17-dione (Kreek *et al.*, 1962) and of estradiol-17β (Smith *et al.*, 1963) in the inverted gut sac preparation.

Aryl Sulfatases (Phenol Sulfatases)

Cohen and Bates (1949) studied the conditions of hydrolysis of estrogen sulfates by the use of the aryl sulfatase, mylase P. This enzyme was reported to have a temperature optimum of 50°C and pH optimum of 6.0–6.4 (Abbot, 1947). Katzman *et al.* (1954) used for optimum conditions pH 6.0–6.5, a 10% mylase P preparation, a few drops of chloroform, and a 24-hour incubation at 37°C.

The digestive juice of the snail *Helix pomatia* contains an aryl sulfatase to the extent of 2.5×10^5 *p*-nitrophenolsulfate units per milliliter. This material released an additional 75–100% Kober chromogenic material associated with estrone, estradiol-17β, and estriol following a prior hydrolysis for 60 minutes with hydrochloric acid and heat (Bloch and Gibree, 1959).

Aliphatic Sulfatases

An important source for an aliphatic sulfatase preparation capable of hydrolyzing some neutral steroid sulfates has been the snail *Helix pomatia*. Intestinal extracts contain about 5×10^4 units per milliliter (dehydroepiandrosterone sulfate). The extract was highly efficient for other 3β-sulfates (Bloch and Gibree, 1959).

Mammalian steroid sulfatase which splits dehydroepiandrosterone sulfate (DHS) and other 3β-hydroxy-5α-steroid sulfates was first discovered by Gibian and Bratfisch (1956) in ox and rat liver and was confirmed by Roy (1957). The occurrence and intracellular distribution of the enzyme has been further studied by Roy (1958) and by Ney and Ammon (1959). However, this microsomal enzyme has been resistant to all attempts at solubilization, and therefore purification and separation from the many other enzymes present in the microsomal particle has not been possible. Thus, demonstration of the presence and properties of steroid sulfatases in endocrine tissues has been difficult because of the concomitant conversion of the released dehydroepiandrosterone as a result of the activity of the enzymes, Δ^5-3β-ol dehydrogenase and 17β-hydrogenase. A method for the determination of steroid sulfatase has been described that uses 7α-H^3-DHS as substrate (Burstein and Dorfman, 1962). The rate of enzyme activity was determined by measuring tritium in the toluene-extractable material.

Data has been obtained with a steroid sulfatase from mammalian liver, testis, adrenal, and ovarian tissue (Burstein and Dorfman, 1963). Table 1 deals with the distribution of mammalian steroid sulfatase from various sources. The pH optimum of rat liver sulfatase preparations is 6.6–7.5.

Table I

DISTRIBUTION OF MAMMALIAN STEROID SULFATASE FROM VARIOUS SOURCES[a]

Tissue preparation[b]	Sulfatase activity[c]
Rat liver (m.)	23,000
Rat testis (m.)	1,650
Rat adrenal (w.h.)	13,200
Guinea pig liver (w.h.)	600
Guinea pig testis (m.)	12,600
Guinea pig adrenal (w.h.)	4,800
Bull testis (w.h.)	800
Ram testis (w.h.)	800
Boar testis (w.h.)	100
Human testis (w.h.)	1,200
Human adrenal (w.h.)	1,200
Human ovary[d] (w.h.)	1,000

[a] Incubations were done in 0.1 *M* Tris-acetate buffer (pH 7.2) at 37°C. DHS concentration was approximately 10^{-4} *M*. (From Burstein and Dorfman, 1963.)

[b] Microsomes (m.) or whole homogenate (w.h.).

[c] Measured as Toluene-extractable H^3 (cpm) formed during 10 min of incubation per gm wet weight of tissue.

[d] From a Stein–Leventhal syndrome patient.

The major enzyme activity is in the microsomal fraction. At a microsome concentration equivalent to 12.5% of liver, an apparent K_m value of 1.0×10^{-5} *M* was determined; however, there was a nonlinear relationship between enzyme concentration and enzyme velocity, suggesting the presence of an endogenous inhibitor of the competitive type.

The pH optimum for rat testis homogenates was 6.8–7.7. The progress of DHS hydrolysis with rat testis microsomes is presented in Fig. 3 as a typical [S]/v vs. [S] plot for which $K_m = 1.2 \times 10^{-5}$ *M*. Phosphate ions were inhibitory and, in the presence of 0.1—0.2 *M* phosphate buffer, apparent K_m values of 7.10^{-5} *M* to 1.0×10^{-4} *M* were obtained. In Tris buffer, apparent K_m values ranging from $0.85–2.5 \times 10^{-5}$ *M* were obtained. Guinea pig testis microsomes exhibited a K_m value of 1.6×10^{-5} *M* in Tris buffer (pH 7.2, 37°C) and at a tissue concentration of 25%.

The presence of a sulfatase which has been demonstrated in human testicular tissue (Burstein and Dorfman, 1963) suggests the possibility of the utilization of the large blood pool of dehydroepiandrosterone sulfate in the testis gland of man for testosterone biosynthesis. The liberated dehydroepiandrosterone could be readily converted to testosterone via

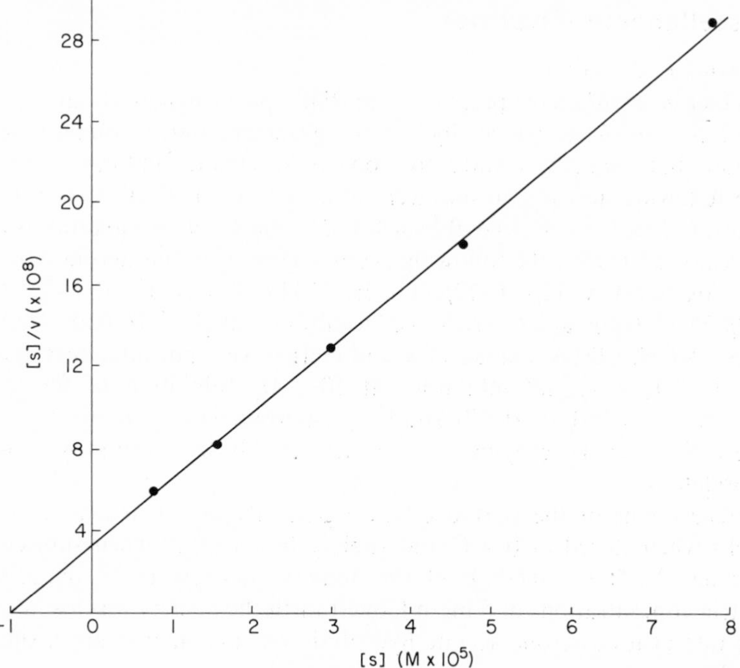

FIG. 3. Effect of substrate concentration ([S]) on initial rate (v) of toluene-extractable H^3 formation catalyzed by rat liver microsomes. Incubations were done in 10 ml of 0.1 *M* Tris-acetate buffer (pH 7.2) at 37°C. Tissue concentration was 11% of rat whole liver. The rate was expressed as the H^3 cpm released during a 10-minute incubation. Aliquots of 1 ml each were taken for each determination. (From Burstein and Dorfman, 1963.)

the Δ^5-3β-ol dehydrogenase, Δ^4–Δ^5-steroid isomerase and 17β-ol dehydrogenase enzyme systems known to be active in this tissue.

More precise and detailed *in vivo* experiments will be necessary to establish the relative importance of this suggested pathway.

The distribution of the sulfatase enzyme varied from one species to the other in a rather remarkable manner. Thus, whereas rat liver was a rich source of the enzyme and contained roughly 10–15 times as much sulfatase per unit weight as rat testis, guinea pig liver contained only 1/380 of the activity of rat liver and guinea pig testis contained roughly 50% of the enzyme concentration of rat liver.

Human placental tissue contains sulfatase capable of hydrolyzing dehydroepiandrosterone sulfate (Warren and Timberlake, 1962). In view of the fact that the free compound may be converted to estrogens (Ryan, 1959), as well as the conjugated steroid (Siiteri and MacDonald, 1963), it is possible that there may be several routes to placental estrogens.

Miscellaneous Enzymes

Steroid Esterase

Sih *et al.* (1963) have prepared a partially purified steroid esterase from *Nocardia restrictus* which hydrolyzes primary and secondary steroid acetates but is inactive toward propionates, succinates, and benzoate esters. The following acetoxy groups were attacked: C-21, C-20, C-17α, C-17β, C-16α, C-15α, C-6α, C-3 (A/B *trans*), C-2β, and C-19. No hydrolysis could be demonstrated for the following acetoxy groups on the steroid molecule: C-17 (tertiary), C-15β, C-12β, C-12α, C-11α, C-11β, C-7α, C-7β, C-6β, C-3β-5β, C-3α-5β, and C-1α. At a concentration of 10^{-3} *M*, NaF, $NaAsO_4$, NaN_3, KCN, EDTA, iodoacetate, and eserine were not inhibitory. $ZnSO_4$ and $CuSO_4$ were not inhibitory at 10^{-4} *M*. Inhibition of the steroid esterase was found for $HgCl_2$ and for *p*-chloromercuribenzoate at 10^{-3} *M*. The activity of the enzyme was lost irreversibly by diisopropylphosphofluoridate.

Preparations of the steroid esterase generally lost their activity in 2–3 weeks when stored at 0–4°C and rapidly lost activity when subjected to freezing. At 56°C, one-half of the activity was lost in 10 minutes. At protein concentrations of 5 mg/ml, one-fourth the activity was lost at 25°C. The rate of testosterone acetate hydrolysis was maximal at approximately pH 8.0.

19-Carboxylase

The decarboxylation of 19-carboxyandrost-4-ene-3,17-dione has been demonstated in ovarian tissue. The enzyme is only known by the fact that 19-norandrost-4-ene-3,17-dione, the product of the corresponding 19-carboxy compound, has been isolated.

Transmethylation

An *S*-adenosylmethionine catechol *O*-methyl transferase was purified some 25- to 30-fold from rat liver by Breuer *et al.* (1962). This enzyme, when incubated with 2-hydroxyestradiol-17β and *S*-adenosylmethionine $MgCl_2$ at pH 7.8 formed 2-methoxyestradiol-17β. The pH optimum was 7.8 and no methylation occurred with estrone, estradiol-17β, or estriol.

Steroid Isomerase

A steroid isomerase has been isolated which converts β,γ unsaturated 3-ketones (Δ^5 or $\Delta^{5(10)}$) of either the C_{19} or C_{21} series to α,β-unsaturated ketones (Δ^4-3-ketone). Talalay and Wang (1955) found this enzyme as one of those induced by growing *Pseudomonas testosteroni* with testosterone as the sole carbon source. The purified enzyme has a turnover number of 150,000 at 25°C and pH 7.0. No metal requirement has been found, and the enzyme is not inhibited by sulfhydryl reagents. The enzyme was subsequently detected in adrenal, testis, ovary, and liver tissue of rats. On the basis of D_2O and T_2O experiments, it appears that the reaction proceeds by direct hydrogen transfer from C-4 to C-6, and the reaction is essentially irreversible.

Kawahara and Talalay (1960) prepared the isomerase enzyme in crystalline form by a series of precipitation steps and obtained a yield of 25% following a 3000-fold purification. The enzyme is the most highly purified of those involved in steroid reactions.

The isomerase has now been crystallized and characterized by Kawahara *et al.* (1962). On the basis of ultracentrifuge data, a molecular weight of 40,800 ± 5% has been assigned. The sedimentation coefficient is 3.3S and the frictional ratio (f/f_0) is approximately 1.3. An empirical formula indicating 389 residues and a calculated molecular weight of 41,682 was His_9, Tyr_{10}, Met_{10}, $Ileu_{11}$, Lip_{13}, Pro_{15}, Ser_{16}, Arg_{22}, Thr_{23}, Phe_{25}, Leu_{25}, Gly_{28}, Glu_{37}, Asp_{39}, Val_{40}, and Ala_{66}.

The Michaelis constant (K_m) for androst-5-ene-3,17-dione with the crystalline enzyme was found to vary from 3.1–3.3 × 10^{-4} *M*. Assuming a molecular weight of 40,800, the turnover number at maximal velocity (molecular activity) is 1.73 × 10^{-7} min^{-1} at 25°C and pH 7.0. For 17β-hydroxyestr-5(10)-en-3-one the molecular activity was 4.25 × 10^{-3} min^{-1}. The relative velocities for various substrates, with androst-5-ene-3,17-dione listed as 100, were as follows: pregn-5-ene-3,20-dione, 150; cholest-5-en-3-one, 0.001; 17β-hydroxyestr-5(10)-en-3-one, 0.25; estr-5(10)-ene-3,17-dione, 0.27; 17α-methyl-17β-hydroxyestr-5(10)-en-3-one, 0.55; 17α-ethyl-17β-hydroxyestr-5(10)-en-3-one, 0.73; and 17α-ethynyl-17β-hydroxyestr-5(10)-en-3-one, 0.65. These measurements were made at a steroid concentration of 5.8 × 10^{-5} *M* except for pregn-5-ene-3,20-dione which was at a concentration of 2.4 × 10^{-5} *M*. A final volume of 3.0 ml containing 100 μmoles of sodium-potassium phosphate buffer at pH 7.0 and 25°C was employed (Kawahara *et al.*, 1962).

Estradiol-17β was a competitive inhibitor with androst-5-ene-3,17-dione as the substrate, and the enzyme was inhibited noncompetitively by urea.

21-Hydroxy Reductase

The extent and significance of the reduction of the 21-hydroxyl to the 21-methyl group *in vivo* is uncertain and requires further study. Specific enzyme studies have not been reported.

Δ^1-Oxidase

A study to determine the stereochemical source of steroid 1,2-dehydrogenation by *Bacillus sphaericus*, one of the numerous microorganisms known to effect this transformation, has been reported (Hayano and Dorfman, 1962). 5α-Androstane-3,17-dione-H^3-1α and androst-4-ene-3,17-dione-H^3-1α were prepared for this purpose. It soon became apparent from fermentations with these compounds that steroids thus labeled could not be used to ascertain the point in question. Following each experiment, the analysis of recovered starting material consistently showed a loss of tritium from the molecule. These results indicated the existence of the equilibrium reaction, 5α-androstane-3,17-dione = androst-4-ene-3,17-dione, or androst-4-ene-3,17-dione = androsta-1,4-dione-3,17-dione, despite the fact that no reduction of the Δ^1-structures could be demonstrated under conditions used for the forward reaction. An exploration of this phenomenon with whole-cell and cell-free preparations of *B. sphaericus* was then made with labeled and non-labeled steroids added to incubation media containing tritium oxide. A separation of two phases of the 1,2-dehydrogenation reaction was obtained in the cell-free system: first, a reversible step, in which a rapid exchange of the hydrogens of C-1α and C-2 of the steroid occurs with the hydrogen of the medium, followed by a second step, the essentially irreversible formation of the Δ^1-bond. The second phase could be minimized in whole-cell fermentation by limiting aeration, and the two steps separated in cell-free extracts through sonic disruption of cytoplasmic particulates. The protein component(s) necessary for the formation of the Δ^1-product was not sedimented at 105,000 *g*, as this supernatant was fully capable of the dehydrogenation in the presence of an added electron acceptor. Particulates sedimented at this force contained parts which catalyzed the substrate-media hydrogen exchange. Proof of the involvement of the C-1α hydrogen of the steroid substrate was obtained through known stereospecific chemical reactions. The point of equilibrium of the second step of the reaction, the formation of the Δ^1-bond, was far to the right since there was a lack of observable quantities of reduced product after incubations of Δ^1-steroid substrates. To establish the reversibility of this step, it was necessary to carry out a large-scale incubation with pure 1,4-androstadiene-dione in the presence of $H^3{}_2O$. Androst-4-ene-3,17-dione-H^3 with very high specific activity was isolated in a yield of about 1.5%.

A large number of compounds have been shown to be transformed by *B. sphaericus* (Stoudt *et al.*, 1955; Hayano *et al.*, 1961), including: 5α-androstane-3,17-dione, deoxycorticosterone acetate (product, Δ^1-deoxycorticosterone), epicorticosterone, 19-nortestosterone (product, estrone), and 19-nor-(10β)-5α-androstane-3,17-dione. Some compounds (including 5β-androstane-3,17-dione, 19-nor-(10α)-5α-androstane-3,17-dione, and 10-hydroxymethyl-octal-(9)-en-2-one), on the other hand, can be recovered unchanged after fermentation. The steroid Δ^1-dehydrogenases have been studied from cell-free extracts of *Pseudomonas testosteroni* (Levy and Talalay, 1959) and *Nocardia restrictus* (Sih and Bennett, 1962), as well as in *Bacillus sphaericus*.

It is evident that the Δ^1-oxidase system consists of the Δ^1-dehydrogenase and an electron transport system. The individual member(s) of the transport system have not been completely elucidated. It could be shown that quinone-type structures were efficient electron acceptors and small amounts of natural quinones with characteristics of Q_9 were found. Further studies of this and other members of the Δ^1-dehydrogenase electron acceptor system in microorganisms should prove to be most illuminating. The exchange of substrate hydrogen with that of the medium has been observed previously and appears to be mediated through flavin coenzymes (Drysdale, 1959; Weber *et al.*, 1957). Evidence has been presented that a flavin prosthetic group is a part of the Δ^1-dehydrogenase system (Levy and Talalay, 1959; Sih and Bennett, 1962).

References

Abbot, L. D. (1947) *Arch. Biochem.* **15**: 205.

Adams, J. A., Jarabak, J., and Talalay, P. (1962) *J. Biol. Chem.* **237**: 3069.

Amelung, D., Hübener, H. J., and Roka, L. (1953a) *Z. Physiol. Chem.* **294**: 36.

Amelung, D., Hübener, H. J., Roka, L., and Meyerheim, G. (1953b) *Klin. Wochschr.* **31**: 386.

Baba, S., Brodie, H. J., Hayano, M., Peterson, D. H., and Sebek, O. K. (1963) *Steroids* **1**: 151.

Baulieu, E. E. (1959) *Compt. Rend.* **248**: 1441.

Bergstrom, S., Goransson, A., and Samuelson, B. (1958) *Acta Chem. Scand.* **13**: 1761.

Beyer, K. F., and Samuels, L. T. (1956) *J. Biol. Chem.* **219**: 69.

Bloch, E., and Gibree, N. B. (1959) *Arch. Biochem. Biophys.* **79**: 307.

Bloch, E., Tissenbaum, B., Rubin, B. L., and Deane, H. W. (1962) *Endocrinology* **71**: 629.

Bloom, B. M. (1962) Quoted by Hayano, M. (1962) *In* "Oxygenases" (O. Hayaishi, ed.), p. 181. Academic Press, New York.

Bloom, B. M., and Shull, G. M. (1955) *J. Am. Chem. Soc.* **77**: 5767.

Bradlow, H. L., Hellman, L., Zumoff, B., and Gallagher, T. F. (1956) *Science* **124**: 1206.

Breuer, H., Knuppen, R., and Pangels, G. (1961a) *Biochem. J.* **79**: 32P.

Breuer, H., Knuppen, R., and Pangels, G. (1961b) *Nature* **190**: 720.

Breuer, H., Vogel, W., and Knuppen, R. (1962) *Z. Physiol. Chem.* **327**: 217.

Brown-Grant, K., Forchielli, E., and Dorfman, R. I. (1960) *J. Biol. Chem.* **235**: 1317.

Brown-Grant, K., Forchielli, E., and Dorfman, R. I. (1962) *J. Endocrinol.* **24**: 517.

Bryson, M. J. (1962) *Federation Proc.* **21**: 186.

Burstein, S. (1956) *J. Am. Chem. Soc.* **78**: 1769.

Burstein, S., and Dorfman, R. I. (1962) *Federation Proc.* **21**: 248.

Burstein, S., and Dorfman, R. I. (1963) In press.

Bush, I. E., and Mahesh, V. B. (1959a) *Biochem. J.* **71**: 705.

Bush, I. E., and Mahesh, V. B. (1959b) *Biochem. J.* **71**: 718.

Caspi, E., and Pechet, M. M. (1957) *Arch. Biochem. Biophys.* **63**: 236.

Chaudhuri, A. C., Harada, Y., Shimizu, K., Gut, M., and Dorfman, R. I. (1962) *J. Biol. Chem.* **237**: 703.

Cohen, H., and Bates, R. W. (1949) *Endocrinology* **44**: 317.

Colás, A. (1962) *Biochem. J.* **82**: 390.

Conney, A. H., and Klutch, A. (1963) *J. Biol. Chem.* **238**: 1611.

Cooper, D. Y., Estabrook, R. W., and Rosenthal, O. (1963) *J. Biol. Chem.* **238**: 1320.

Constantopoulos, G., and Tchen, T. T. (1961) *J. Biol. Chem.* **236**: 65.

Constantopoulos, G., Satch, P. S., and Tchen, T. T. (1962) *Biochem. Biophys. Res. Commun.* **8**: 50.

Corey, E. J., and Gregoriou, G. A. (1959) *J. Am. Chem. Soc.* **81**: 3127.

Corey, E. J., Gregoriou, G. A., and Peterson, D. H. (1958) *J. Am. Chem. Soc.* **80**: 2338.

Deane, H. W., Lobel, B. L., and Driks, E. C. (1960) *Proc. 1st Intern. Congr. Histol. Cytol.* p. 111.

DeCourcey, C. (1957) *J. Biol. Chem.* **229**: 935.

DeCourcey, C., and Schneider, J. J. (1956) *Chem. Ind.* (*London*) **3**: 15.

Dorfman, R. I., Gual, C., Morato, T., Hayano, M., and Gut, M. (1962) *Abstr. Intern. Congr. Hormonal Steroids Milan* p. 270.

Dorfman, R. I., Forchielli, E., and Gut, M. (1963) Unpublished data.

Dounce, A. L. (1955) *In* "Nucleic Acids" (E. Chargaff and J. N. Davidson, eds.), Vol. II, p. 93. Academic Press, New York.
Drysdale, G. P. (1959) *J. Biol. Chem.* **234**: 2399.
Dutton, G. J. (1956) *Biochem. J.* **64**: 693.
Endahl, G. L., and Kochakian, C. D. (1962) *Biochim. Biophys. Acta* **62**: 245.
Endahl, G. L., Kochakian, C. D., and Hamm, D. I. (1960) *J. Biol. Chem.* **235**: 2792.
Engel, L. L., Joshi, S. G., and Duncan, E. L. (1963) *Federation Proc.* **22**: 468.
Fish, C., Hayano, M., and Pincus, G. (1953) *Arch. Biochem. Biophys.* **42**: 480.
Fishman, J., Cox, R. I., and Gallagher, T. F. (1960) *Arch. Biochem. Biophys.* **90**: 318.
Fishman, W. H. (1961) *In* "Chemistry of Drug Metabolism," C. C. Thomas, Springfield, Illinois.
Forchielli, E., and Dorfman, R. I. (1956) *J. Biol. Chem.* **223**: 443.
Forchielli, E., Rosenkrantz, H., and Dorfman, R. I. (1955) *J. Biol. Chem.* **215**: 713.
Forchielli, E., Brown-Grant, K., and Dorfman, R. I. (1958) *Proc. Soc. Exptl. Biol. Med.* **99**: 594.
Forchielli, E., Ramachandran, S., and Ringold, H. J. (1963) *Steroids* **1**: 157.
Foster, R. J., and Niemann, C. (1951) *J. Am. Chem. Soc.* **73**: 1553.
Gale, P. H., Page, A. C., Jr., Stoudt, T. H., and Folkers, K. (1962) *Biochemistry* **1**: 788.
Gibian, H., and Bratfisch, G. (1956) *Z. Physiol. Chem.* **305**: 265.
Goldstein, M., and Ungar, F. (1963) Unpublished data.
Grant, J. K. (1956) *Biochem. J.* **64**: 559.
Gregory, J. D., and Nose, Y. (1957) *Federation Proc.* **16**: 189.
Grosso, L. L., and Ungar, F. (1964) *Steroids* **3**: 67.
Hagen, A. A., and Troop, R. C. (1960) *Endocrinology* **67**: 194.
Halkerston, I. D. K., Eichhorn, J., and Hechter, O. (1959) *Arch. Biochem. Biophys.* **85**: 287.
Halkerston, I. D. K., Eichhorn, J., and Hechter, O. (1960) *Federation Proc.* **19**: 160.
Hamm, D. I., Kochakian, C. D., and Carroll, B. R. (1956) *Proc. Soc. Exptl. Biol. Med.* **93**: 493.
Hayano, M. (1962) *In* "Oxygenases" (O. Hayaishi, ed.), p. 181, Academic Press, New York.
Hayano, M., and Dorfman, R. I. (1953) *J. Biol. Chem.* **201**: 175.
Hayano, M., and Dorfman, R. I. (1962) *In* "Methods in Enzymology" (S. P. Colowick and N. O. Kaplan, eds.) Vol. 5, p. 503, Academic Press, New York.
Hayano, M., Saito, A., Stone, D., and Dorfman, R. I. (1956) *Biochim. Biophys. Acta* **21**: 380.
Hayano, M., Gut, M., Dorfman, R. I., Sebek, O. K., and Peterson, D. H. (1958) *J. Am. Chem. Soc.* **80**: 2336.
Hayano, M., Gut, M., Dorfman, R. I., Schubert, A., and Siebert, R. (1959) *Biochim. Biophys. Acta* **32**: 269.
Hayano, M., Ringold, H. J., Stefanovic, V., Gut, M., and Dorfman, R. I. (1961) *Biochem. Biophys. Res. Commun.* **4**: 454.
Hofmann, F. G. (1960) *Biochim. Biophys. Acta* **37**: 566.
Hübener, H. J., and Amelung, D. (1953) *Z. Physiol. Chem.* **293**: 137.
Hübener, H. J., Fukushima, D., and Gallagher, T. F. (1956) *J. Biol. Chem.* **220**: 499.
Hübener, H. J., Sahrholz, F. G., Schmidt-Thomé, J., Nesemann, G., and Junk, R. (1959) *Biochim. Biophys. Acta* **35**: 270.
Hurlock, B., and Talalay, P. (1958) *J. Biol. Chem.* **2333**: 886.
Hurlock, B., and Talalay, P. (1959) *Arch. Biochem. Biophys.* **80**: 468.
Isselbacher, K. (1956) *Recent Progr. Hormone Res.* **12**: 134.
Isselbacher, K., and Axelrod, J. (1955) *J. Am. Chem. Soc.* **77**: 1070.
Jarabak, J., Adams, J. A., Williams-Ashman, H. G., and Talalay, P. (1962) *J. Biol. Chem.* **237**: 345.
Jarabak, J., Adams, J. A., and Talalay, P. (1963) *Federation Proc.* **22**: 468.
Kase, N., Forchielli, E., and Dorfman, R. I. (1962) Unpublished data.

Katzman, P. A., Straw, R. F., Buehler, J. J., and Doisy, E. A. (1954) *Recent Progr. Hormone Res.* **9**: 45.

Kawahara, F. S., and Talalay, P. (1960) *J. Biol. Chem.* **235**: PC1.

Kawahara, F. S., Wang, S.-F., and Talalay, P. (1962) *J. Biol. Chem.* **237**: 1500.

Koritz, S. B. (1962) *Biochim. Biophys. Acta* **59**: 326.

Kreek, M. J., Ross, J. E., and Tapley, D. F. (1962) *Proc. 44th Endocrine Soc. Meeting, Chicago* p. 8.

Kurasawa, Y., Hayano, M., Gut, M., Dorfman, R. I., Schubert, A., and Burton, C. A. (1961) *Agr. Biol. Chem.* (*Tokyo*) **25**: 424.

Langer, L. J., Alexander, J. A., and Engel, L. L. (1959) *J. Biol. Chem.* **234**: 2609.

Levin, M. E., and Daughaday, W. H. (1955) *J. Clin. Endocrinol Metab.* **15**: 1499.

Levy, H., Saito, T., Takeyama, S., Merrill, A. P., and Schepis, J. P. (1963) *Biochim. Biophys. Acta* **69**: 198.

Levy, H., Deane, H. W., and Rubin, B. L. (1959) *Endocrinology* **65**: 932.

Levy, H. R., and Talalay, P. (1959) *J. Biol. Chem.* **234**: 2014.

Leybold, M., and Staudinger, H. (1959) *Biochem. Z.* **331**: 389.

Loke, K. H., and Marrian, G. F. (1958) *Biochim. Biophys. Acta* **27**: 213.

Longchampt, J. E., Gual, C., Ehrenstein, M., and Dorfman, R. I. (1960) *Endocrinology* **66**: 416.

Lunaas, T., and Velle, W. M. (1960) *Acta Physiol. Scand.* **50** (Suppl. 175): 95.

Lynn, W. S., Jr., and Brown, R. H. (1958a) *J. Biol. Chem.* **232**: 1015.

Lynn, W. S., Jr., and Brown, R. H. (1958b) *J. Biol. Chem.* **232**: 1005.

McGuire, J. S., Jr., and Tomkins, G. M. (1960) *J. Biol. Chem.* **235**: 1634.

Mahesh, V. B., and Ulrich, F. (1959) *Nature* **184**: 1147.

Mahesh, V. B., and Ulrich, F. (1960) *J. Biol. Chem.* **235**: 356.

Marcus, P. I., and Talalay, P. (1956) *J. Biol. Chem.* **218**: 661.

Meyer, A. S. (1955) *Biochim. Biophys. Acta* **24**: 1435.

Meyer, A. S., Hayano, M., Lindberg, M. C., Gut, M., and Rogers, C. G. (1955) *Acta Endocrinol.* **18**: 148.

Monder, C., and White, A. (1961) *Proc. Intern. Congr. Biochem. 5th Moscow* p. 262.

Morato, T., Hayano, M., Dorfman, R. I., and Axelrod, L. R. (1961) *Biochim. Biophys. Acta* **6**: 334.

Mueller, G. C., and Rumney, G. (1957) *J. Am. Chem. Soc.* **79**: 1004.

Neeman, M. Slaunwhite, W. R., Jr., Neely, L. M., Colson, J. G., and Sandberg, A. A. (1960). *J. Biol. Chem.* **235**: PC58.

Neher, R., and Wettstein, A. (1960a) *Helv. Chim. Acta* **43**: 1171.

Neher, R., and Wettstein, A. (1960b) *Helv. Chim. Acta* **43**: 1628.

Nesemann, G., Hübener, H. J., and Schmidt-Thomé, J. (1962) *Biochem. Z.* **336**: 329.

Ney, K. H., and Ammon, R. (1959) *Z. Physiol. Chem.* **315**: 145.

Nose, Y., and Lipmann, F. (1958) *J. Biol. Chem.* **233**: 1348.

Osinski, P. A. (1960) *Nature* **187**: 777.

Pangels, G., and Breuer, H. (1962) *Naturwissenschaften* **49**: 106.

Particus, N. J., and Repke, K. (1960) *Naturwissenschaften* **47**: 43.

Peron, F. G. (1961) *Endocrinology* **70**: 386.

Peron, F. G., and Dorfman, R. I. (1956) *J. Biol. Chem.* **223**: 877.

Peron, F. G., and Dorfman, R. I. (1958) *Endocrinology* **62**: 1.

Peterson, R. E. (1958) *J. Clin. Invest.* **37**: 736.

Peterson, R. E., Wyngaarden, J. B., Guerra, S. L., Brodie, B. B., and Bunim, J. J. (1955) *J. Clin. Invest.* **34**: 1779.

Popjak, G., and Cornforth, J. W. (1960) *Advan. Enzymol.* **22**: 281.

Prairie, R. L., and Talalay, P. (1963) *Biochemistry* **2**: 203.

"Report of the Commission on Enzymes, of the International Union of Biochemistry" (1961) Pergamon Press, New York.

Ringold, H. J., Ramachandren, S., and Forchielli, E. (1962) *J. Biol. Chem.* **237**: PC261.

Ringold, H. J., Hayano, M., and Stefanovic, V. (1963) In press.

Robbins, P. W., and Lipmann, F. (1956) *J. Am. Chem. Soc.* **78**: 2652.

Roy, A. B. (1957) *Biochem. J.* **66**: 700.

Roy, A. B. (1958) *Biochem. J.* **68**: 519.

Rubin, B. L. (1957) *J. Biol. Chem.* **227**: 917.

Rubin, B. L., and Dorfman, R. I. (1957) *Endocrinology* **61**: 601.

Rubin, B. L., and Strecker, H. J. (1960) *Acta Endocrinol. Suppl.* **51**: 725.

Rubin, B. L., and Strecker, H. J. (1961) *Endocrinology* **69**: 257.

Rubin, B. L., Leipsner, G., and Deane, H. W. (1961) *Endocrinology* **69**: 619.

Ryan, K. (1959) *J. Biol. Chem.* **234**: 268.

Ryan, K., and Engel, L. L. (1957) *J. Biol. Chem.* **225**: 103.

Salomon, L. L. (1951) *Texas Rept. Biol. Med.* **15**: 925.

Samuels, L. T., and Helmreich, M. L. (1956) *Endocrinology* **58**: 435.

Samuels, L. T., Helmreich, M. L., Lasater, M. B., and Reich, M. (1951) *Science* **113**: 490.

Schmidt-Thomé, J., Nesemann, G., Hübener, H. J., and Alester, I. (1962) *Biochem. Z.* **336**: 322.

Schneider, J. J. (1953) *J. Am. Chem. Soc.* **75**: 2024.

Schneider, J. J., and Lewbart, M. L. (1956) *J. Biol. Chem.* **222**: 787.

Sharma, D. C., Forchielli, E., and Dorfman, R. I. (1962) *J. Biol. Chem.* **237**: 1495.

Sharma, D. C., Forchielli, E., and Dorfman, R. I. (1963a) *J. Biol. Chem.* In press.

Sharma, D., Forchielli, E., and Dorfman, R. I. (1963b) Unpublished data.

Shimizu, K., Dorfman, R. I., and Gut, M. (1960) *J. Biol. Chem.* **235**: PC25.

Shimizu, K., Gut, M., and Dorfman, R. I. (1961) *J. Biol. Chem.* **236**: 695.

Shimizu, K., Gut, M., and Dorfman, R. I. (1962) *J. Biol. Chem.* **237**: 699.

Sih, C. J., and Bennett, R. E. (1962) *Biochim. Biophys. Acta* **6**: 584.

Sih, C. J., Laval, J., and Rahim, M. A. (1963) *J. Biol. Chem.* **238**: 566.

Siiteri, P. K., and MacDonald, P. C. (1963) *Steroids* **2**: 713.

Smith, F. R., Tapley, D. F., and Ross, J. E. (1963) *Biochim. Biophys. Acta* **69**: 68.

Solomon, S., Levitan, P., and Lieberman, S. (1956) *Rev. Can. Biol.* **15**: 282.

Stefanovic, V., Hayano, M., and Dorfman, R. I. (1963). *Biochim. Biophys. Acta* In press.

Stoudt, T. H., McAleer, W. J., Chemerda, J. M., Kozlowski, M. A., Hirschmann, R. F., Marlatt, V., and Miller, R. (1955) *Arch. Biochem. Biophys.* **59**: 304.

Sweat, M. L. (1962) *Federation Proc.* **21**: 189.

Sweat, M. L., and Lipscomb, M. D. (1955) *J. Am. Chem. Soc.* **77**: 5185.

Sweat, M. L., Grosser, B. I., Berliner, D. L., Swim, H. E., Nabors, C., Jr., and Dougherty, T. F. (1958) *Biochim. Biophys. Acta* **28**: 591.

Sweat, M. L., Berliner, D. L., Bryson, M. J., Nabors, C., Jr., Haskell, J., and Holmstrome, E. G. (1960) *Biochim. Biophys. Acta* **40**: 289.

Talalay, P. (1957a) *Cancer* **10**: 738.

Talalay, P. (1957b) *Physiol. Rev.* **37**: 362.

Talalay, P., and Marcus, P. I. (1956) *J. Biol. Chem.* **218**: 675.

Talalay, P., and Wang, V. S. (1955) *Biochim. Biophys. Acta* **18**: 300.

Talalay, P., Dobson, M. M., and Tapley, D. F. (1952) *Nature* **170**: 620.

Tamaoki, B. I., and Pincus, G. (1961) *Endocrinology* **69**: 527.

Thomas, P. Z., and Dorfman, R. I. (1964) *J. Biol. Chem.* **239**: 766.

Thomas, P. Z., Forchielli, E., and Dorfman, R. I. (1960) *J. Biol. Chem.* **235**: 2797.

Tomkins, G. M. (1956a) *Recent Progr. Hormone Res.* **12**: 125.

Tomkins, G. M. (1956b) *J. Biol. Chem.* **218**: 437.

Tomkins, G. M. (1957) *J. Biol. Chem.* **225**: 13.

Tomkins, G. M. (1960) *Proc. Intern. Congr. Biochem. 4th Vienna 1958* **13**: 153.

Tomkins, G. M., and Isselbacher, K. J. (1954) *J. Am. Chem. Soc.* **76**: 3100.

Troop, R. C. (1958) *Federation Proc.* **17**: 415.

Troop, R. C. (1959) *Endocrinology* **64**: 671.

Ungar, F. (1960a) *Acta Endocrinol. Suppl.* **51**: 727; *Proc. 1st Intern. Congr. Endocrinol. Copenhagen.*
Ungar, F. (1960b). *Univ. Minn. Med. Bull.* **31**: 326.
Ungar, F., and Bloom, B. R. (1957) *Biochim. Biophys. Acta* **24**: 431.
Ungar, F., and Dorfman, R. I. (1952a) *Science* **115**: 115.
Ungar, F., and Dorfman, R. I. (1952b) *Ciba Found. Colloq. Endocrinol.* **11**: 244.
Ungar, F., and Dorfman, R. I. (1954) *J. Am. Chem. Soc.* **76**: 1197.
Ungar, F., Gut, M., and Dorfman, R. I. (1957) *J. Biol. Chem.* **224**: 191.
Urquhart, J., Yates, F. E., and Herbst, A. L. (1959) *Endocrinology* **64**: 816.
Vermeulen, A., and Caspi, E. (1958) *J. Biol. Chem.* **233**: 54.
Villee, C. A., Hoagerman, D. D., and Joel, P. B. (1960) *Recent Progr. Hormone Res.* **16**: 49.
Warren, J. C., and Timberlake, C. E. (1962) *J. Clin. Endocrinol. Metab.* **22**: 1148.
Weber, M. M., Kaplan, N. O., San Pietri, A., and Stolzenbach, F. E. (1957) *J. Biol. Chem.* **227**: 27.
Wengle, B., and Bostrom, H. (1962) *Acta Chem. Scand.* **16**: 502.
Werbin, H., Chaikoff, I. L., and Jones, E. E. (1960) *J. Biol. Chem.* **235**: 1629.
West, C. D., Damast, B., and Pearson, O. H. (1958) *J. Clin. Invest.* **37**: 341.
Wiest, W. G., and Wilcox, R. B. (1961) *J. Biol. Chem.* **236**: 2425.
Wintersteiner, O., and Moore, M. (1959) *J. Am. Chem. Soc.* **81**: 442.
Yates, F. E., Herbst, A. L., and Urquhart, J. (1958) *Endocrinology* **63**: 887.

CHAPTER VII

A System of Steroid Metabolism

The structure and biological source, actual or potential, of over 200 steroids are known (Chapters II, III, and V). Metabolism studies, *in vivo* or *in vitro*, have been reported with about 30 steroids that are hormones, precursors of hormones, or metabolites of hormones. This chapter presents a survey and a possible system for correlating the present knowledge of steroid metabolism for both neutral and phenolic steroids.

Neutral Steroids

Definitions

Androst-4-ene-3,17-dione (C_{19}-1-1) and progesterone (C_{21}-1-1) are considered arbitrarily to be the "basic compounds" in the C_{19} and C_{21} series, respectively (Fig. 1). These compounds contain the Δ^4-3-ketone grouping in ring A and an additional ketone group at position 17 or 20. All compounds (including androst-4-ene-3,17-dione and progesterone) possessing these attributes (the Δ^4-3-ketone and the 17 or 20 ketone) are considered to be "key compounds." Although the system limits the basic neutral compounds to two, a large number of key compounds are possible. A key compound is a derivative of androst-4-ene-3,17-dione or progesterone, which contains the Δ^4-3-ketone and 17 or 20 ketone group. Modifications may involve an oxygen function such as at carbons 6, 11, or 16 in the nucleus or at carbon 21 in the side chain. Obviously, the number of theoretical possibilities for key compounds would be exceedingly great. This chapter will deal only with those key compounds that have been demonstrated to occur naturally or whose presence in tissues has been indicated by the demonstration of a compound related to the special group.

In the C_{19} steroid series, many modifications of the basic androst-4-ene-3,17-dione have been discovered (Fig. 2). Unsaturation of positions 1,2; 5,6; and 16,17 has been found in naturally occurring C_{19} steroids in addition to that of positions 4,5. In addition to the oxygen at carbons 3 and 16, as in androst-4-ene-3,17-dione, oxygen has been found in C_{19} compounds at carbons 6, 7, 11, 15 and 16. Thirty-four modifications of structure have been observed in the C_{21} series (Fig. 3), two in the C_{18} neutral series, three in the C_{20} series, and eleven in the C_{18} ring A phenolic steroid series.

Key compounds undergo reduction at two ketone groups (C_3 and C_{17} or C_{20}), at the double bond (Δ^4), or at both. Such changes are considered to be changes within a "steroid group." A key compound and the theoretical reduction products involving the two ketones and the double bond constitute a "steroid group."

Figures 4–54 illustrate the 51 steroid groups which contain the C_{19} and C_{21} neutral steroid hormones and their metabolites isolated from either urine or tissue sources. It is to be noted that most of these figures extend over two pages and that compounds 16 and 17 are listed on both pages. The figures concerned with these groups illustrate the theoretically possible substances as well as those actually isolated.

In referring to Fig. 4, which represents those steroids that may arise from androst-4-ene-3,17-dione, it may be seen that some 33 theoretical metabolities are possible. The system used in this figure, as in the succeeding 50 figures, consists of illustrations of the 33 possible metabolites that arise from the key compounds. Each of these compounds are numbered. Thus, in each group we find 34 individual compounds, including the key compound. Each group is designated by a number that indicates first the number of carbon atoms and then the number of the specific group. The individual compound is designated by the number of the steroid group and a dash followed by its number within the group. For example, for the androst-4-ene-3,17-dione group, the number is C_{19}-1 and the key compound of this group, androst-4-ene-3,17-dione, receives the number C_{19}-1-1. Testosterone, also a member of this steroid group, has the number C_{19}-1-2.

In these figures, compounds designated by the letter S are those steroids which have been isolated from natural sources, either tissues or urine. Metabolic interrelationships are designated by arrows.

A certain interrelationship exists among groups, owing to the fact that the state of oxidation, reduction, and configuration from group to group in the C_{19} series is so arranged that compound C_{19}-1-4 (Fig. 4), which is dehydroepiandrosterone, has its counterpart in the other steroid groups. In other words, if we look at Fig. 5 we find that compound C_{19}-2-4 is the Δ^1-dehydro derivative of dehydroepiandrosterone. The interrelationships among the various groups are considered in Chapters III, V, and VIII, under biosynthesis and catabolism.

Neutral C_{18} and C_{20} Steroids

In addition to the 51 groups of C_{19} and C_{21} neutral steroids, there is evidence for two groups of C_{18} (designated C_{18N}) and three groups of C_{20} neutral steroids. These are represented in Figs. 55–59.

Phenolic Steroids

The key compounds in the phenolic steroid series (designated C_{18P}) are represented in Fig. 60. These compounds have a ring A aromatic and a 17-ketone group. Figure 60 lists eleven phenolic key compounds. Subsequent figures indicate the possible compounds of the various phenolic groups, together with the compounds found in natural sources. Figures 61–67 inclusive deal with key phenolic compounds having only one ketone group located at position 17, so that 17α-OH and 17β-OH derivatives are possible. Figures 68–71 have two ketone groups, and the nine possible derivatives involving reduction of the ketone forms to both α and β are listed. In these figures, the letter S designates that the compound has been isolated from a natural source, and the letter R indicates that the steroid was obtained from a reaction involving a naturally occurring substrate which had been modified by an enzyme preparation or which arose as the result of an *in vivo* metabolism experiment.

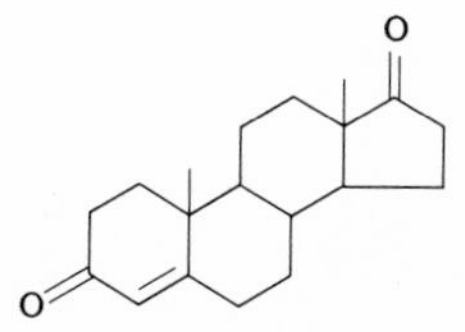

I

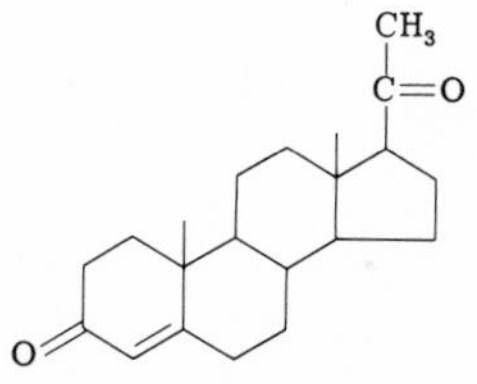

II

FIG. 1. Basic neutral steroids. I, Androst-4-ene-3,17-dione. II, Progesterone.

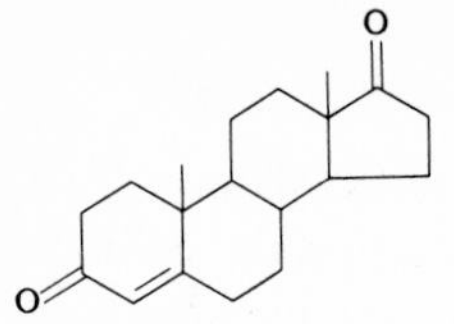

C_{19}-1-1 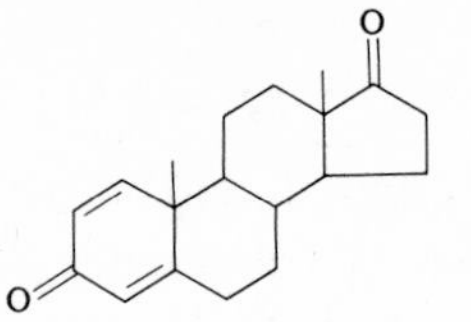 C_{19}-2-1 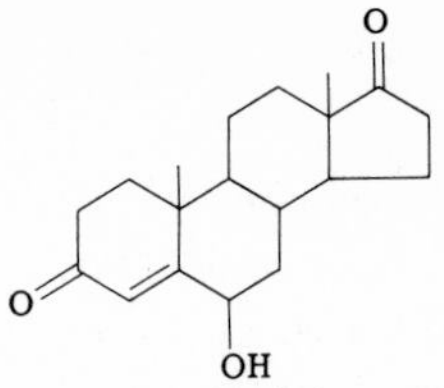 C_{19}-3-1

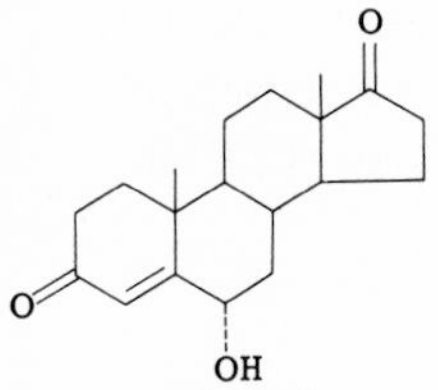

C_{19}-4-1 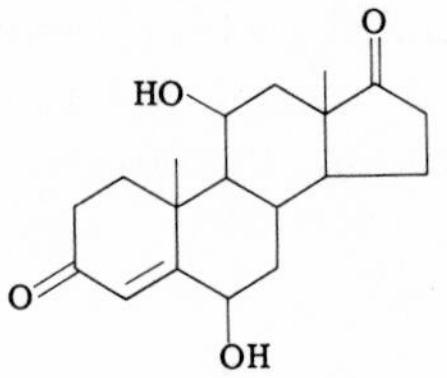 C_{19}-5-1 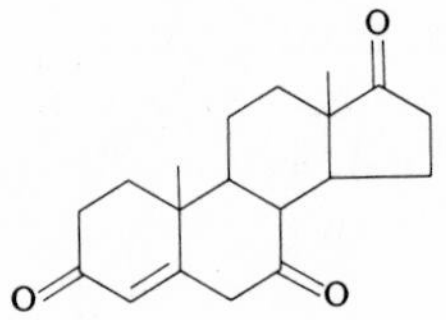 C_{19}-6-1

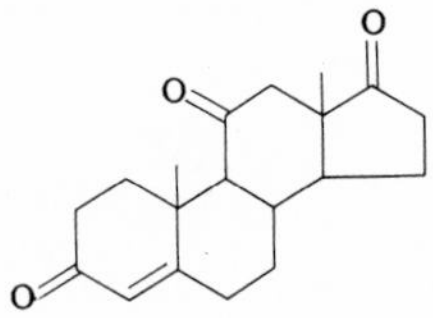

C_{19}-7-1 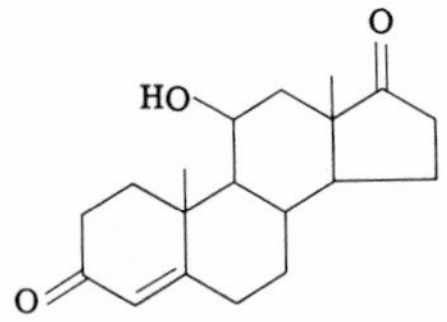 C_{19}-8-1 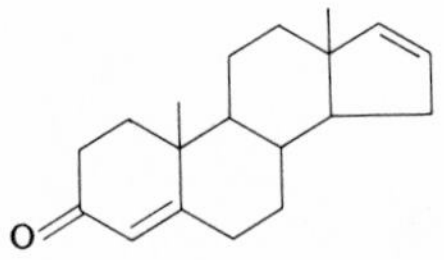 C_{19}-9-1

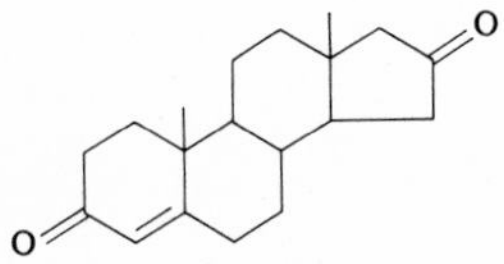

C_{19}-10-1 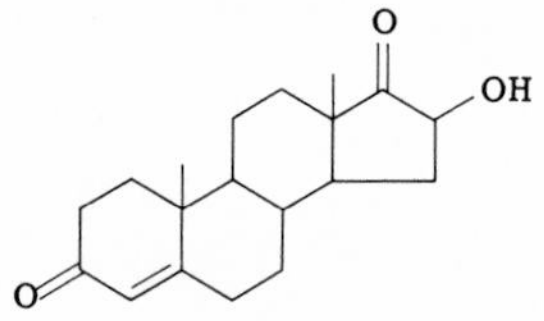 C_{19}-11-1 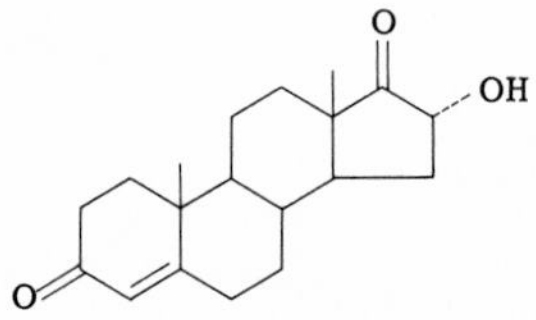 C_{19}-12-1

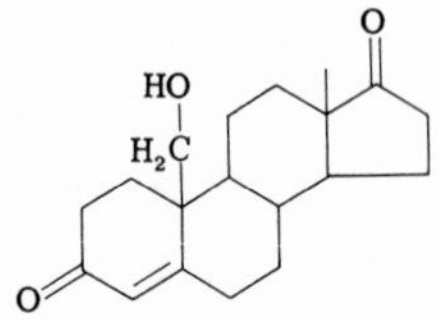

C_{19}-13-1 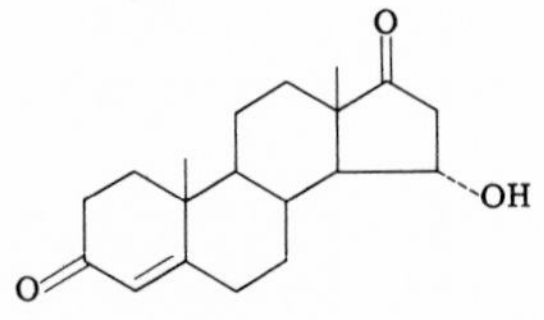 C_{19}-14-1 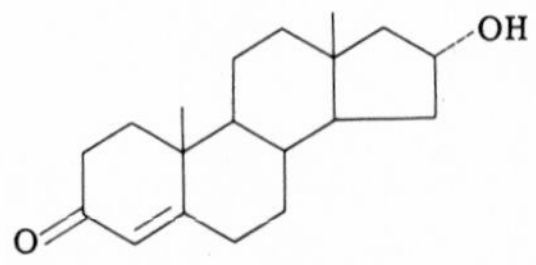 C_{19}-15-1

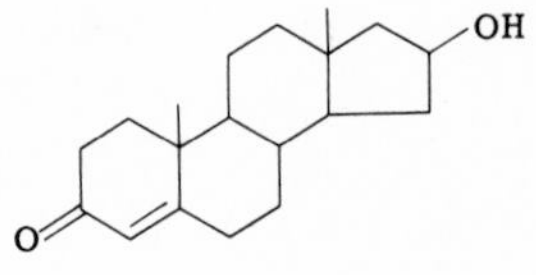

C_{19}-16-1 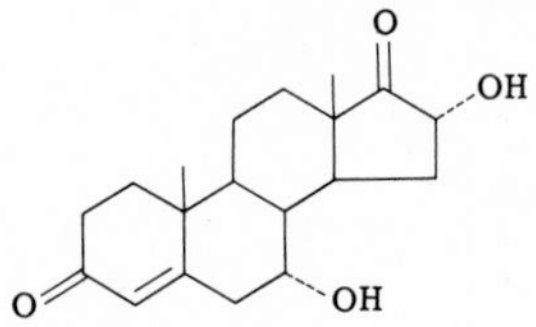 C_{19}-17-1

FIG. 2. Key C_{19} steroids.

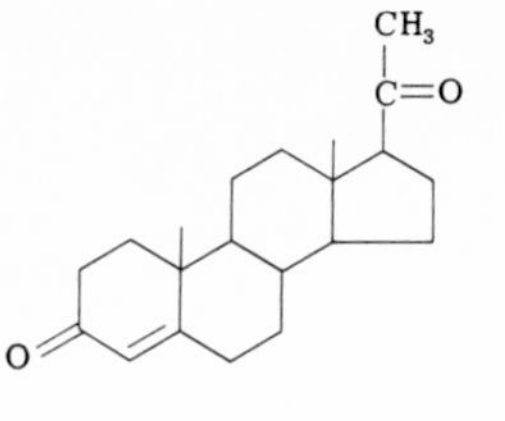

C_{21}-1-1

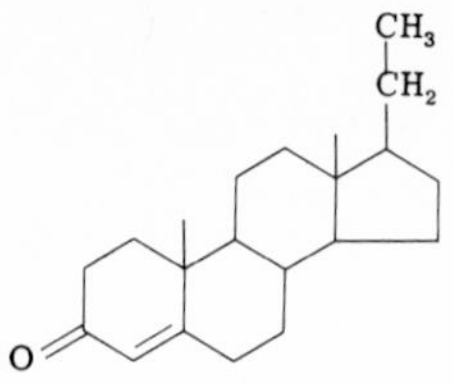

C_{21}-2-1

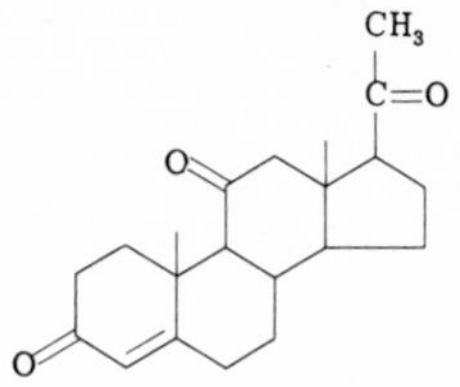

C_{21}-3-1

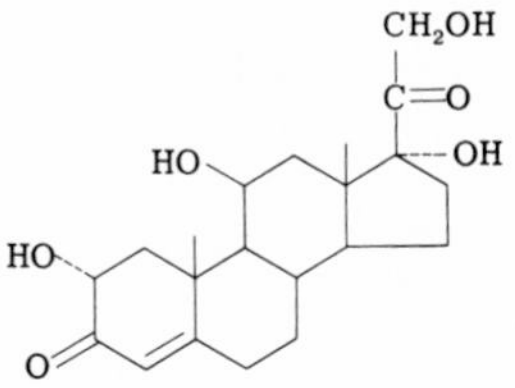

C_{21}-4-1

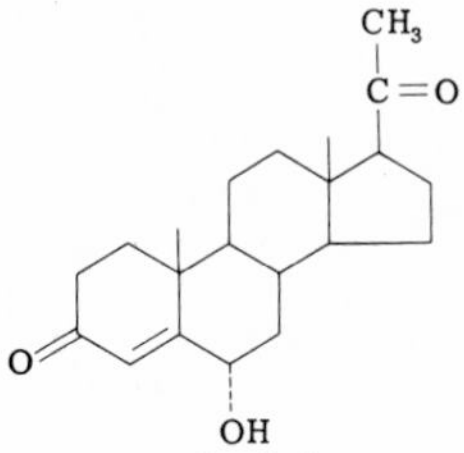

C_{21}-5-1

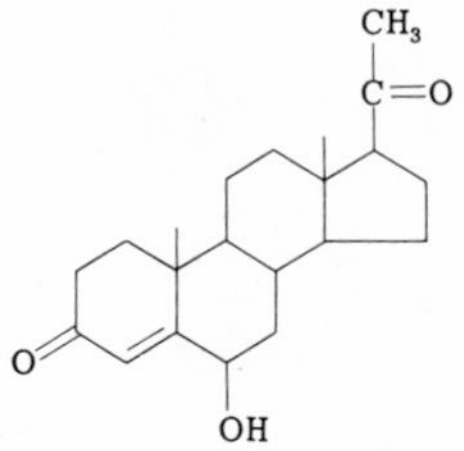

C_{21}-6-1

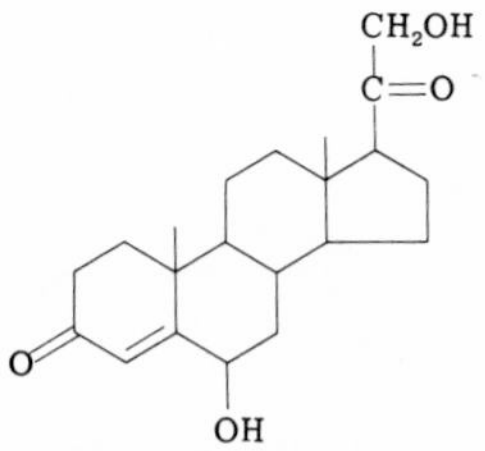

C_{21}-7-1

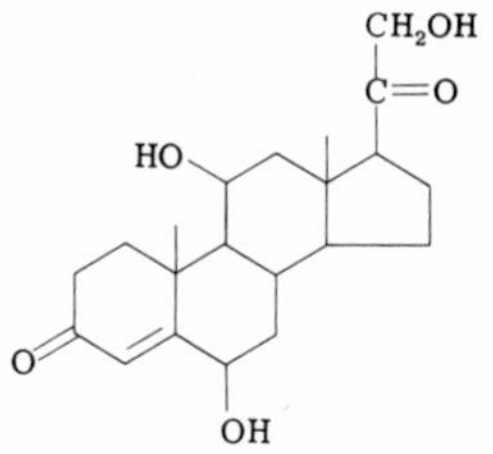

C_{21}-8-1

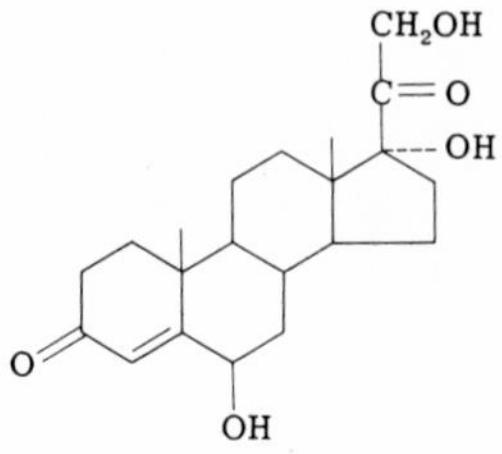

C_{21}-9-1

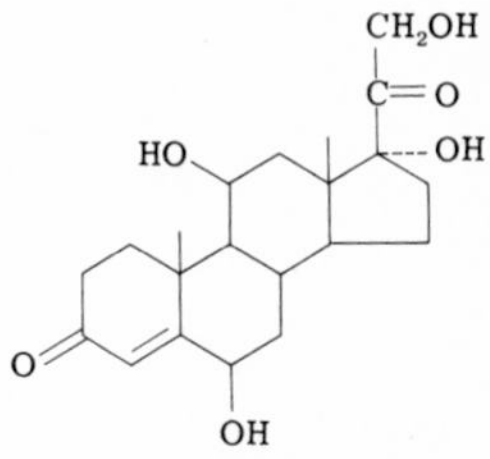

C_{21}-10-1

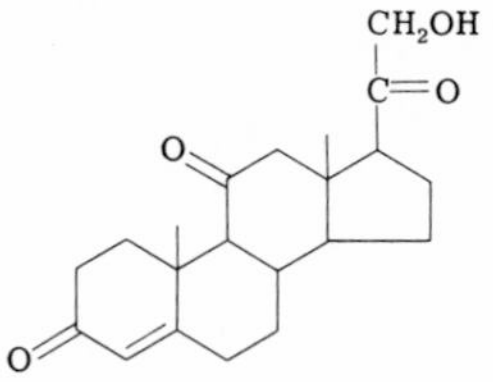

C_{21}-11-1

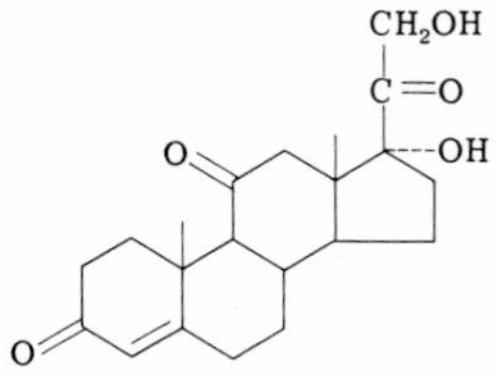

C_{21}-12-1

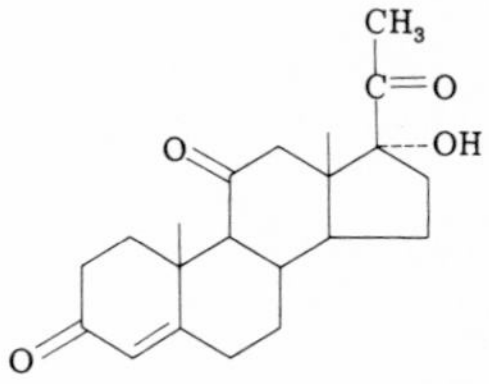

C_{21}-13-1

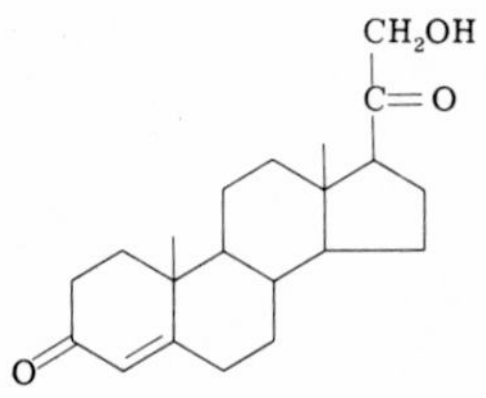

C_{21}-14-1

FIG. 3. Key C_{21} steroids.

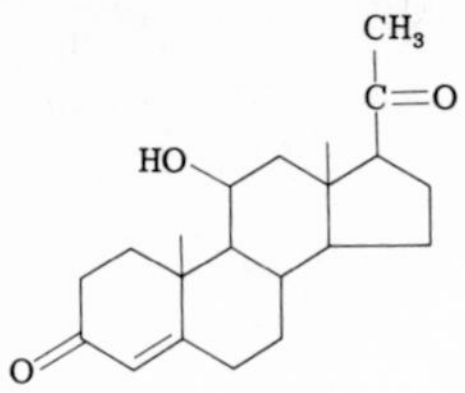

C_{21}-15-1

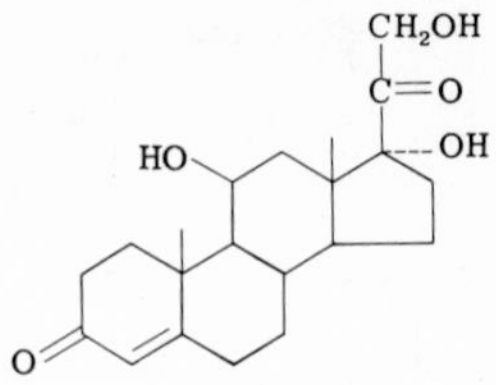

C_{21}-16-1

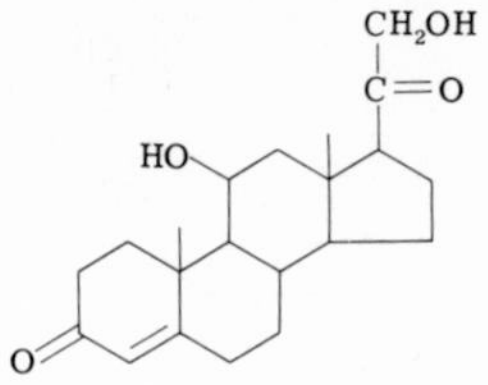

C_{21}-17-1

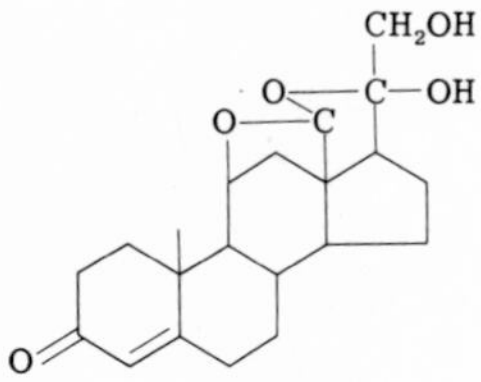

C_{21}-18-1

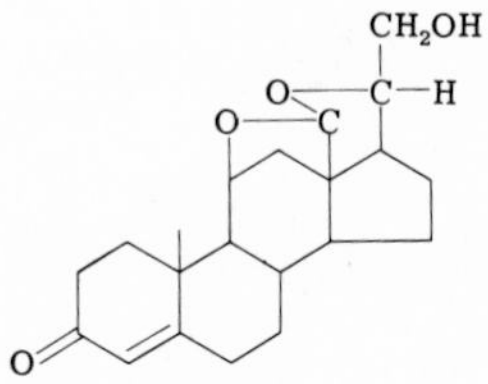

C_{21}-19-1

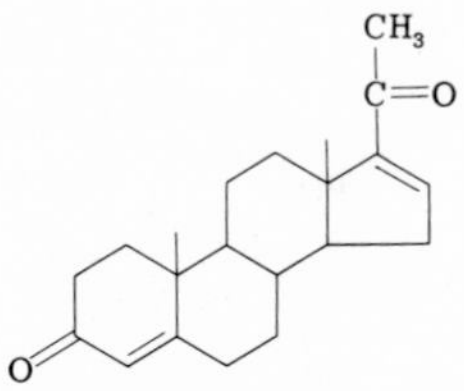

C_{21}-20-1

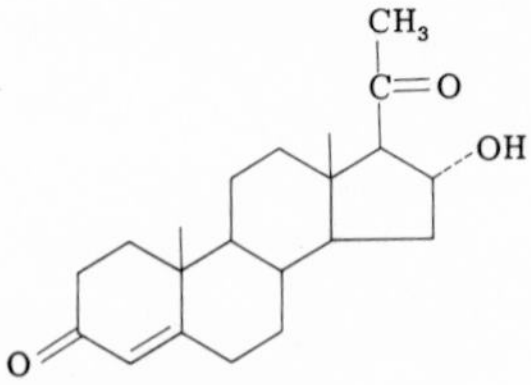

C_{21}-21-1

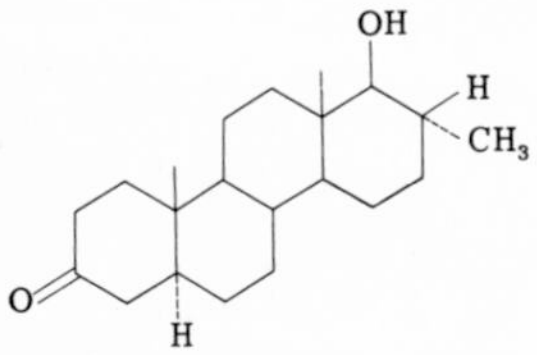

C_{21}-22-1

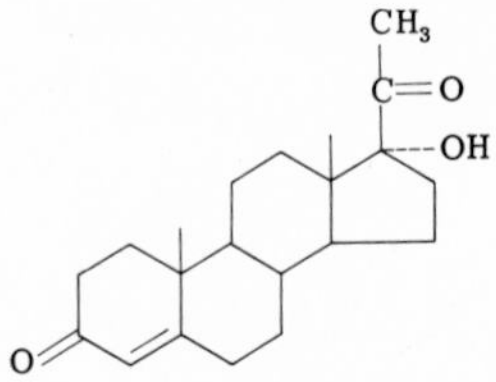

C_{21}-23-1

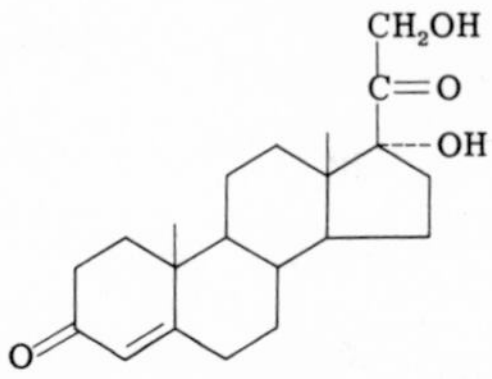

C_{21}-24-1

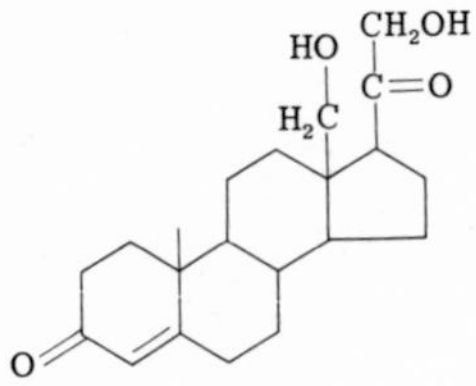

C_{21}-25-1

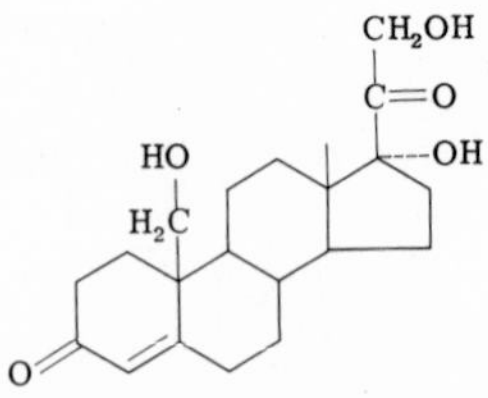

C_{21}-26-1

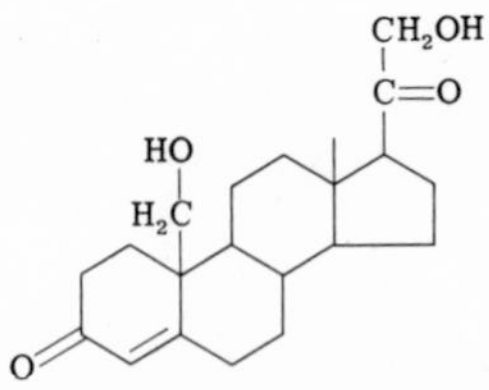

C_{21}-27-1

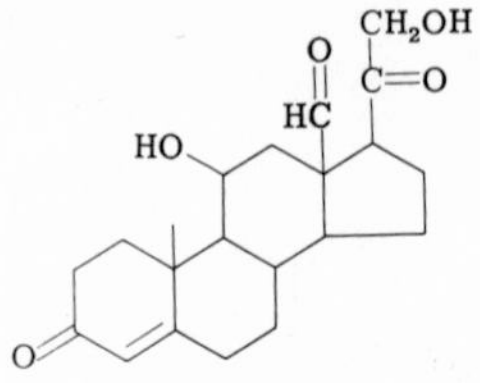

C_{21}-28-1

FIG. 3. Continued.

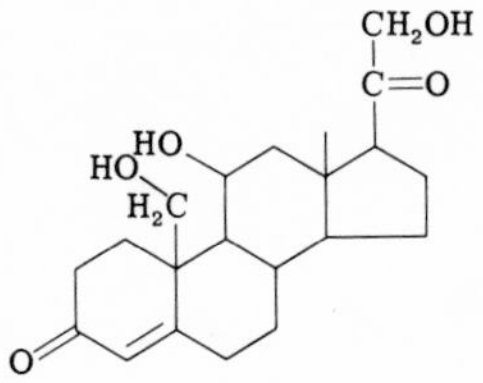

C_{21}-29-1

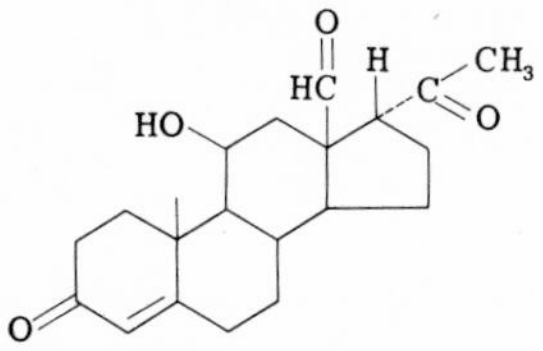

C_{21}-30-1

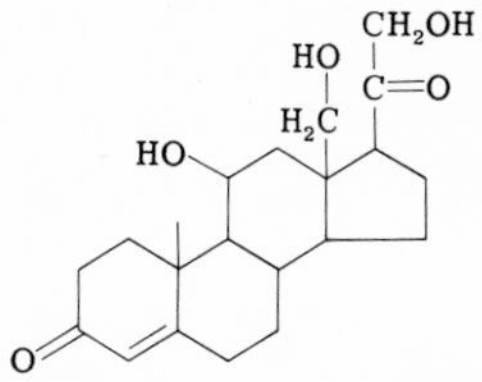

C_{21}-31-1

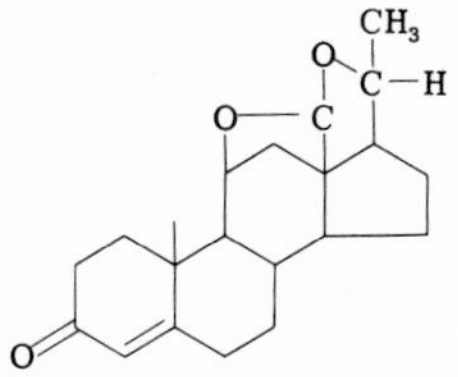

C_{21}-32-1

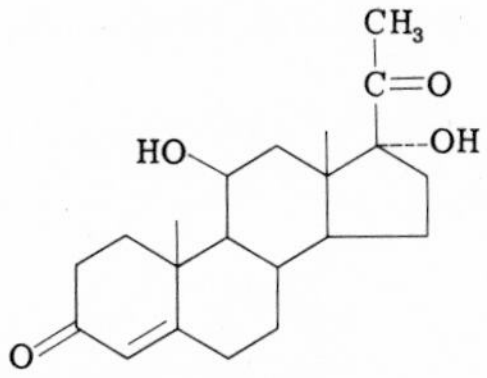

C_{21}-33-1

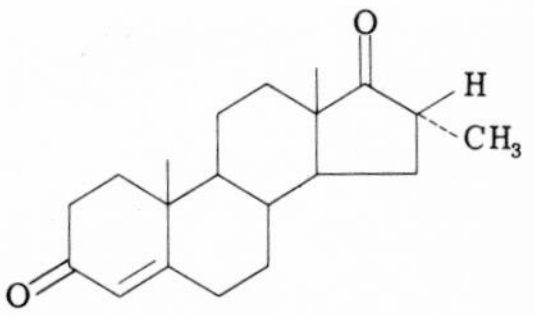

C_{21}-34-1

FIG. 3. Continued.

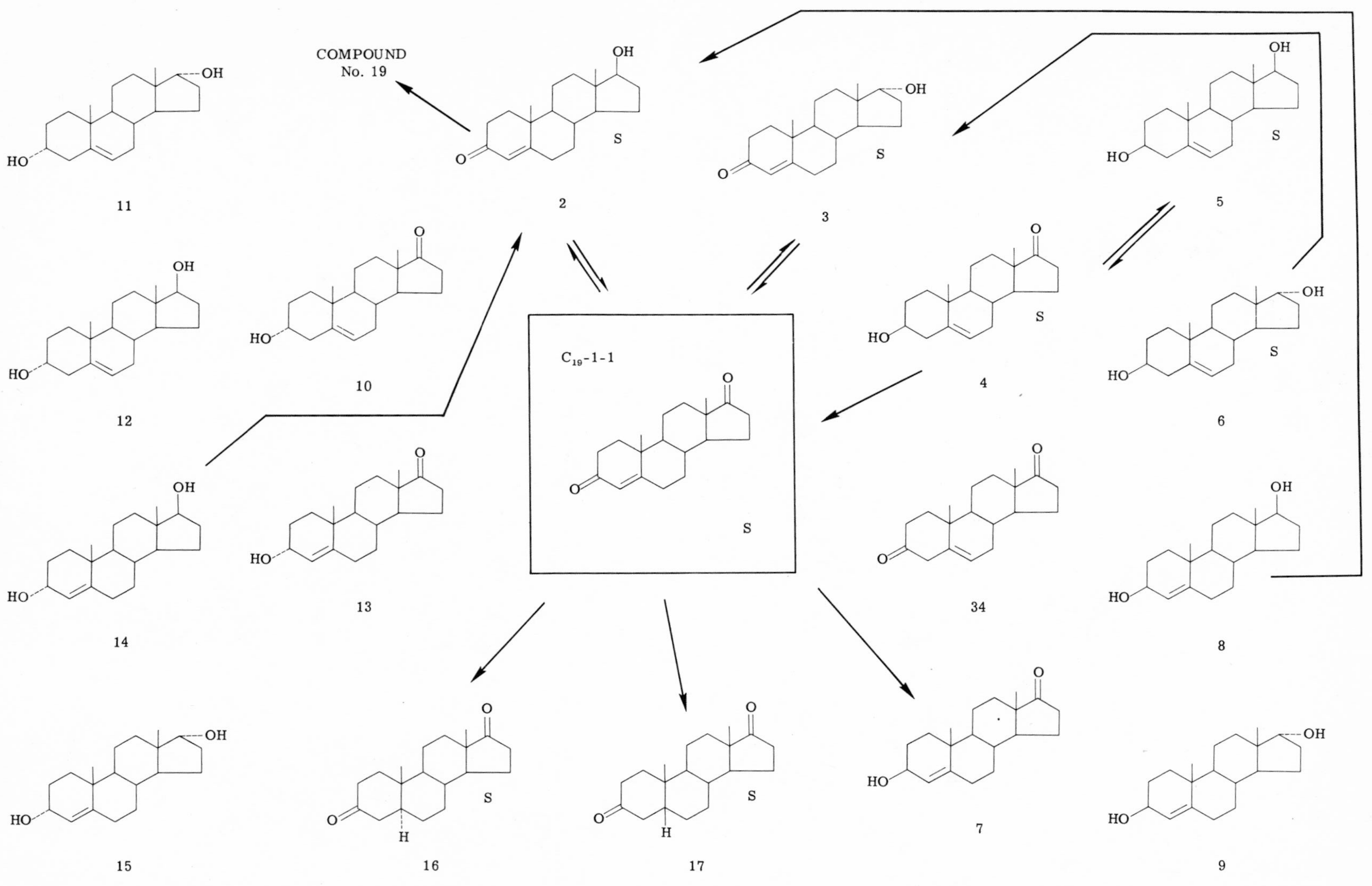
COMPOUND
No. 19
C$_{19}$-1-1
11
2
3
5
12
10
4
6
14
13
34
8
15
16
17
7
9

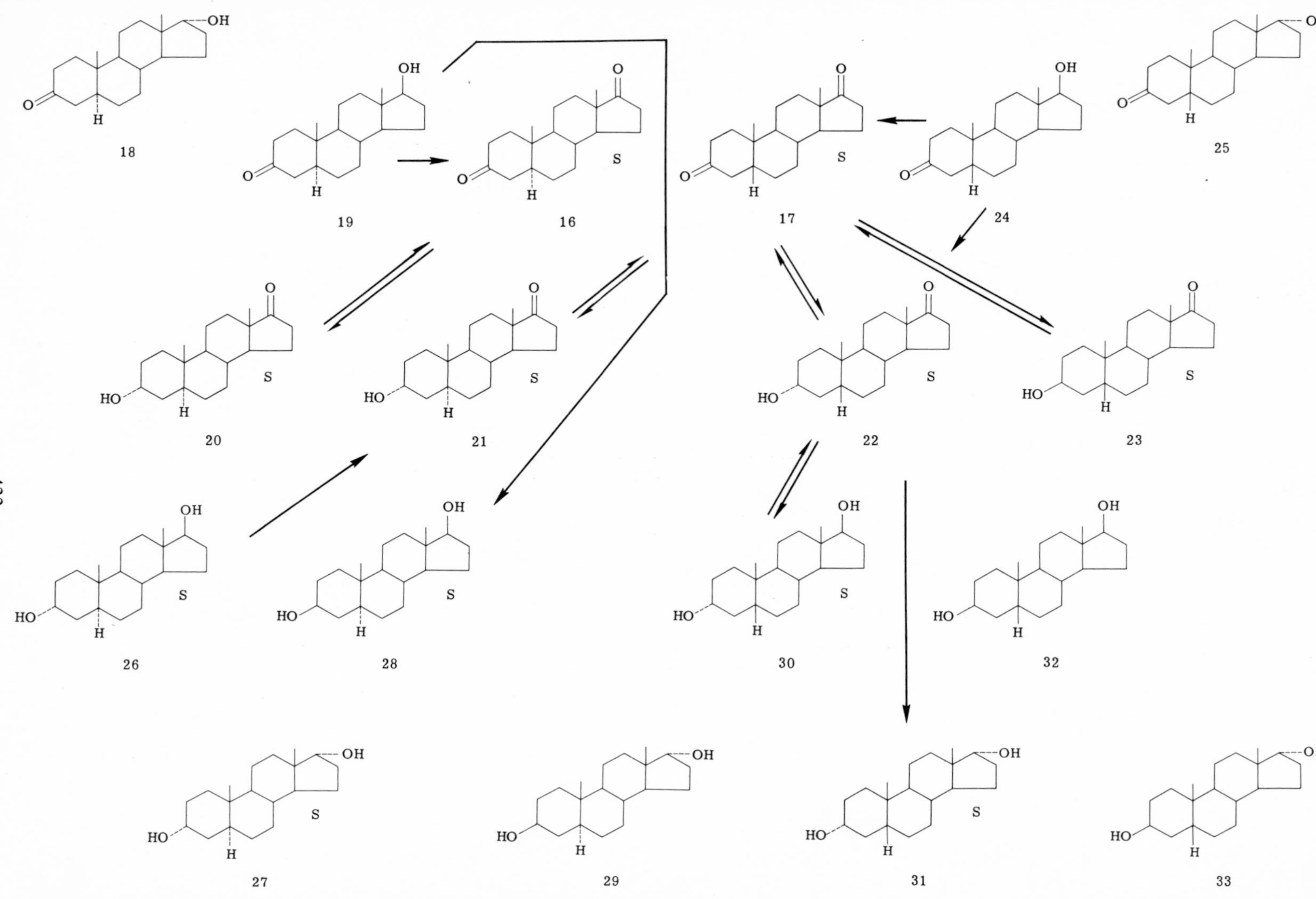

FIG. 4. C_{19}-1-1: Androst-4-ene-3,17-dione and related metabolites.

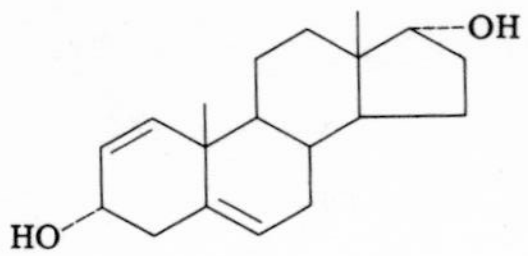

C_{19}-2-1

11 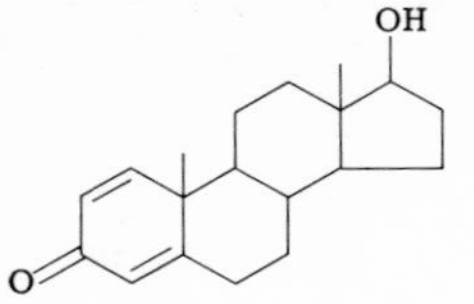 2 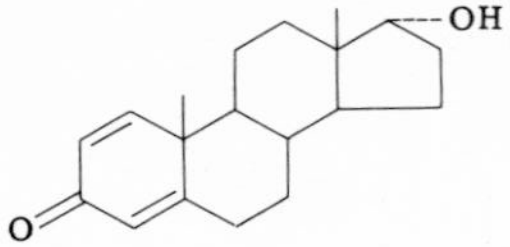 3 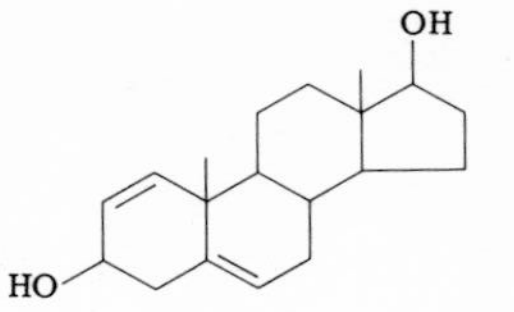 5

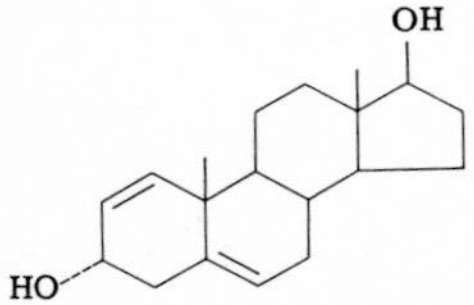

12 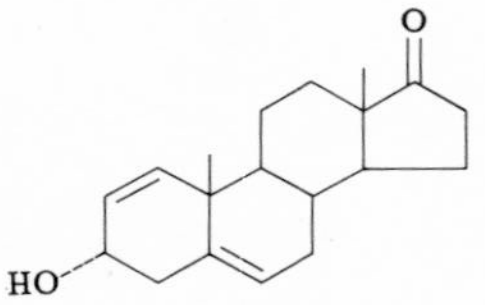 10 4 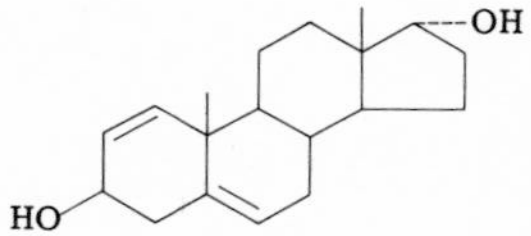 6

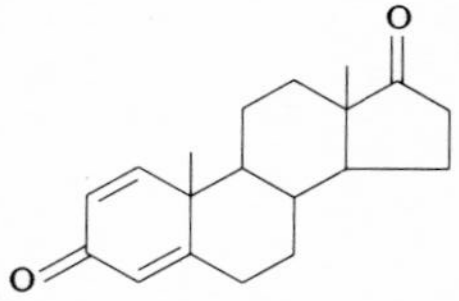

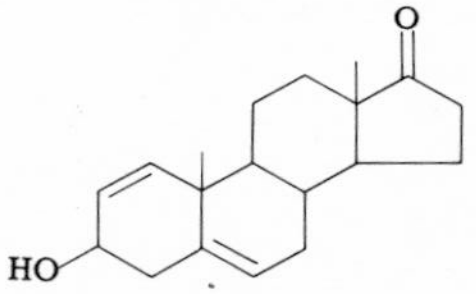

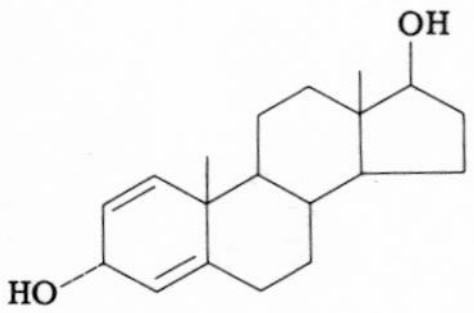

14 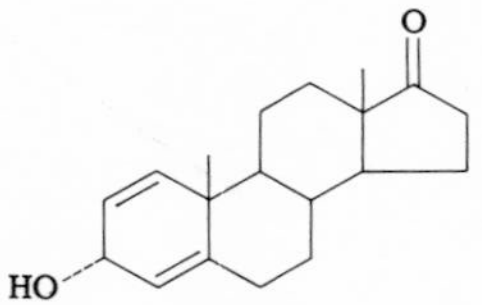 13 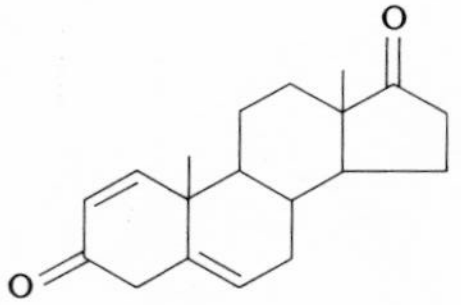 34 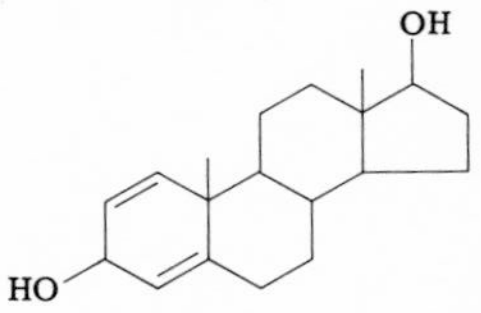 8

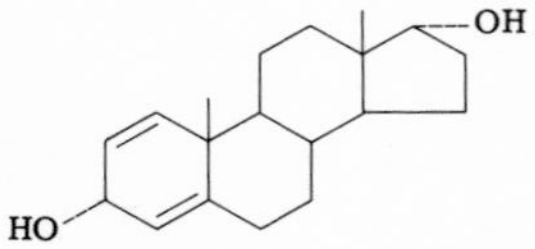

15 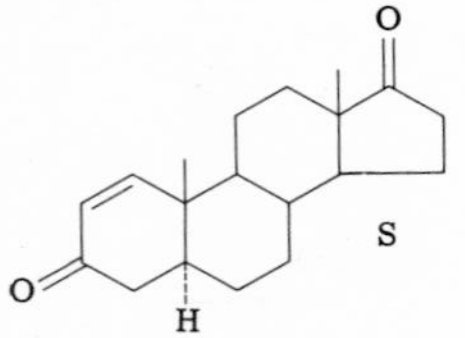 16 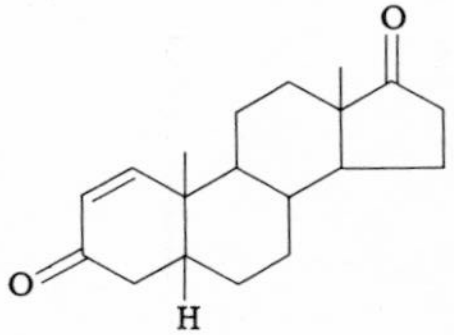 17 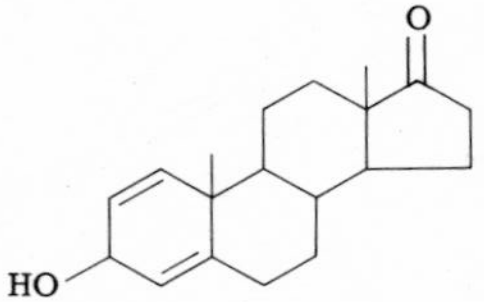 7 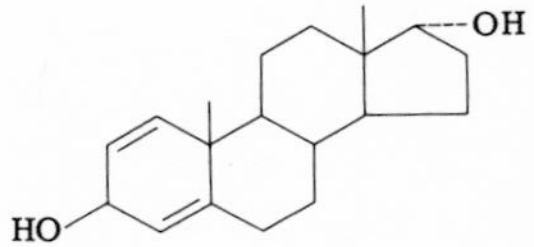 9

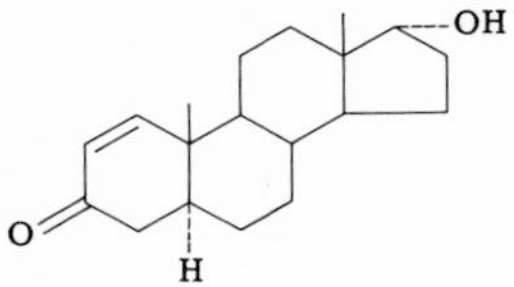

18 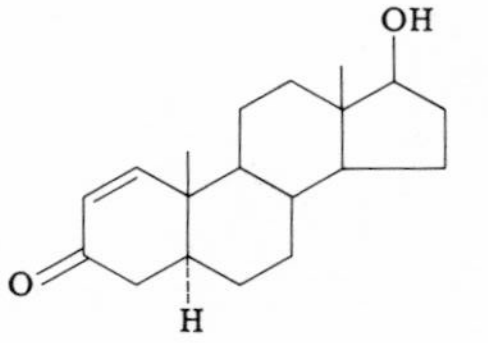 19 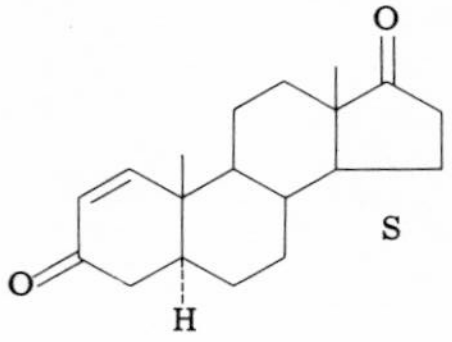 16 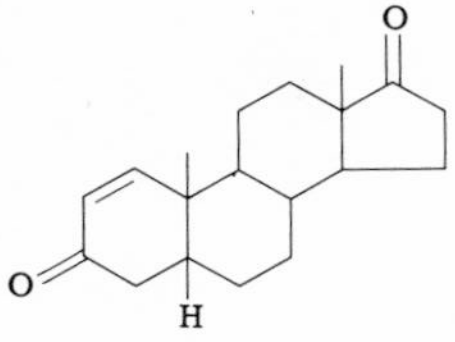 17 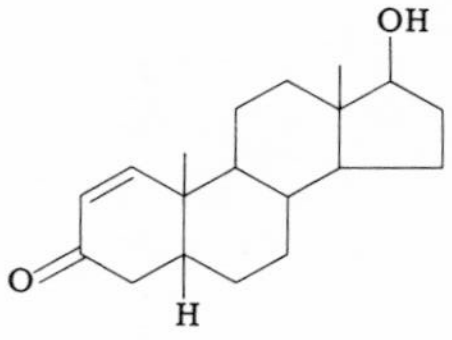 24 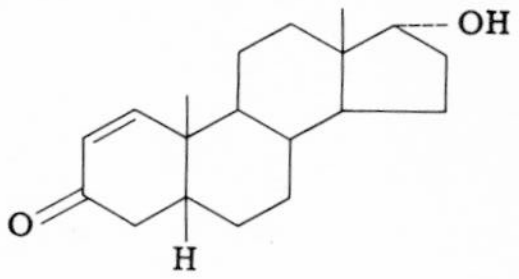 25

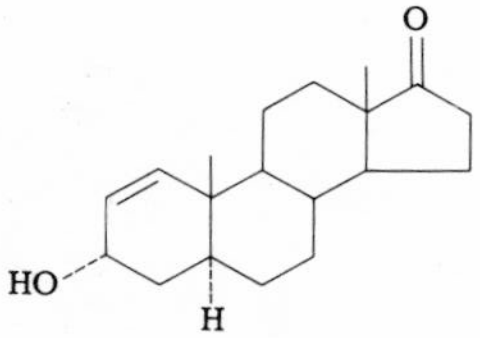

20 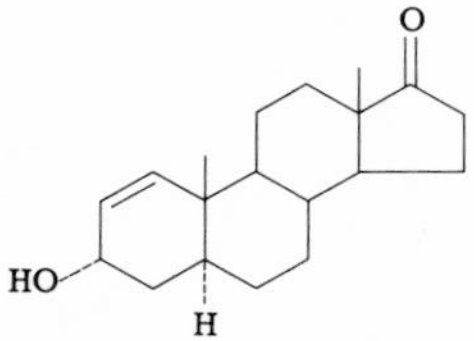 21 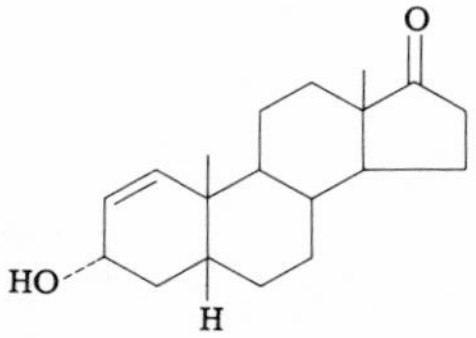 22 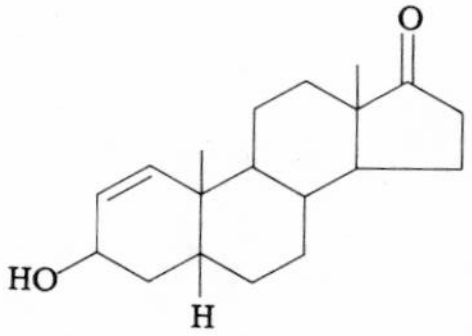 23

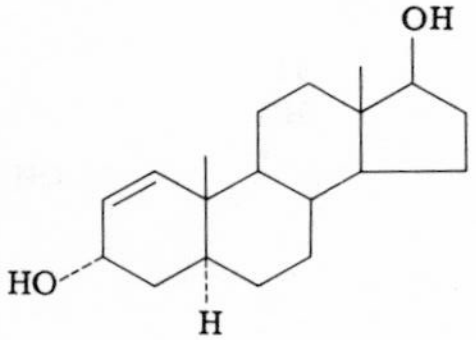

26 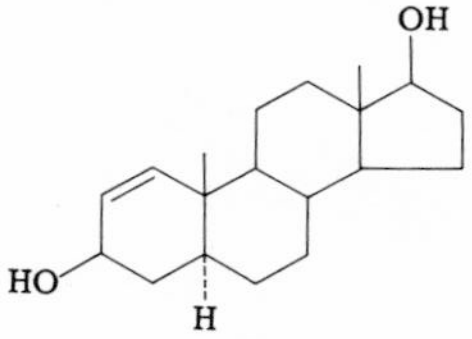 28 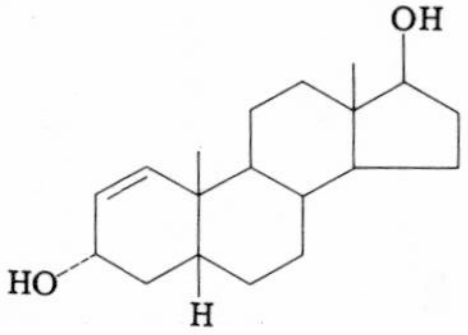 30 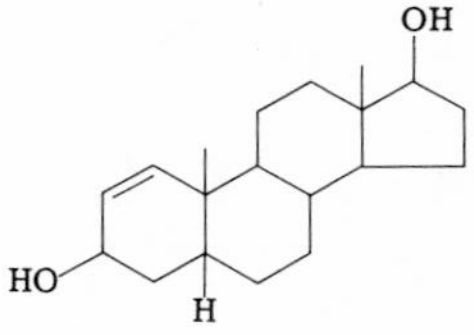 32

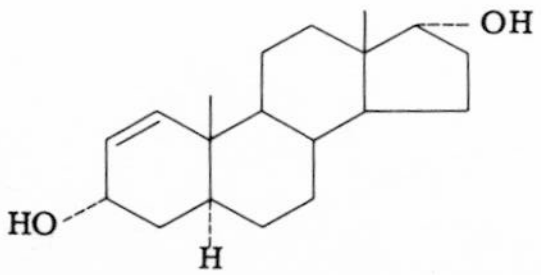

27 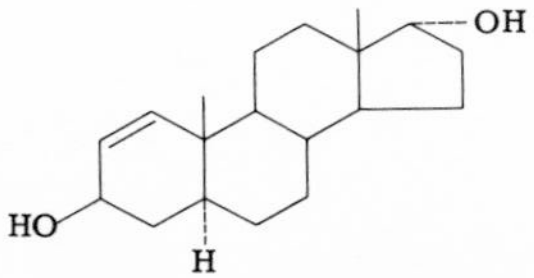 29 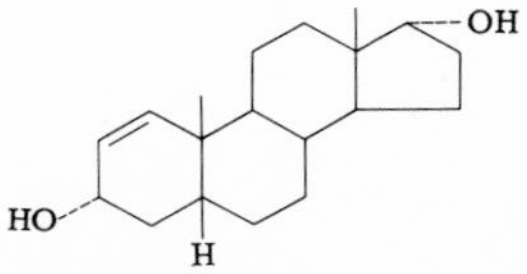 31 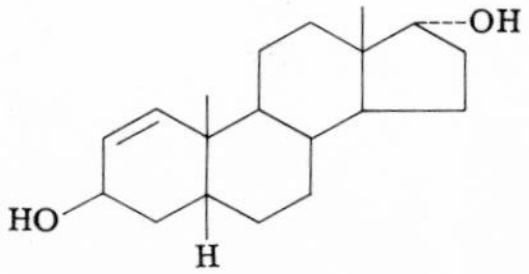 33

FIG. 5. C_{19}-2-1: Androsta-1,4-diene-3,17-dione and related metabolites.

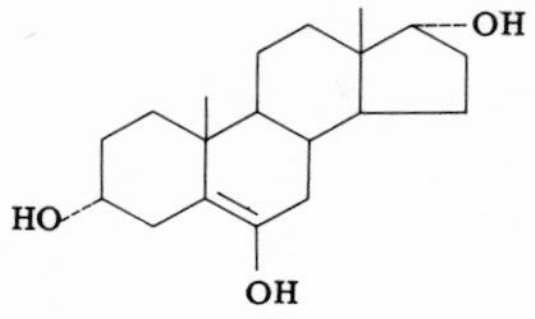

C_{19}-3-1

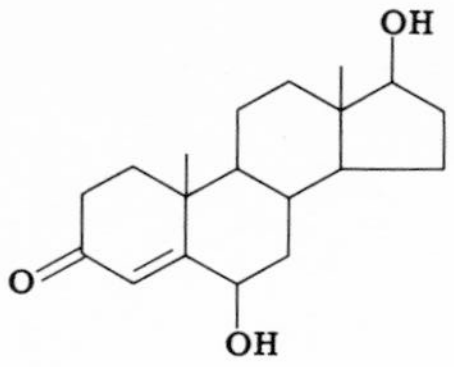

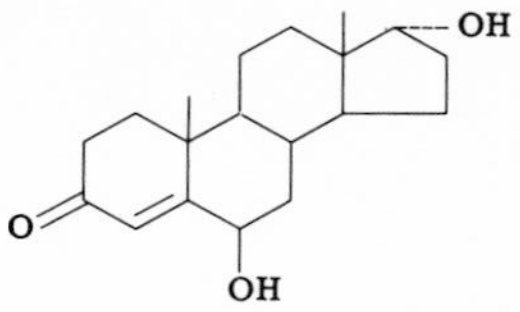

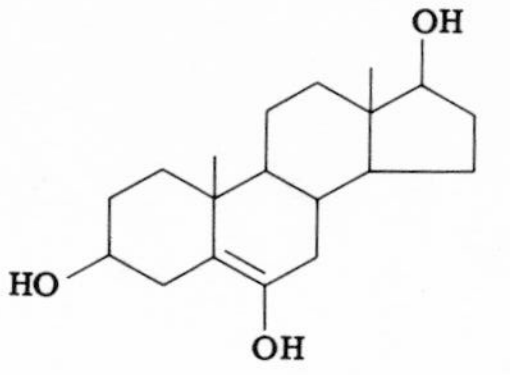

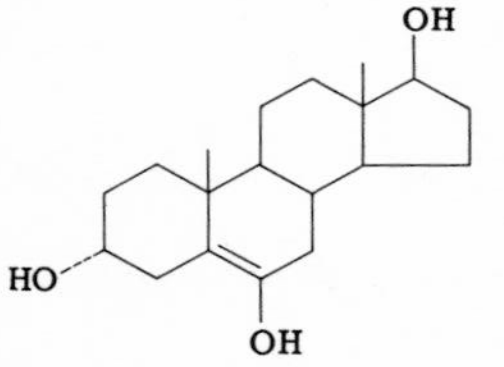

S

2 3 4 5 6 7 8 9 10 11 12 13 14 15 16 17 34

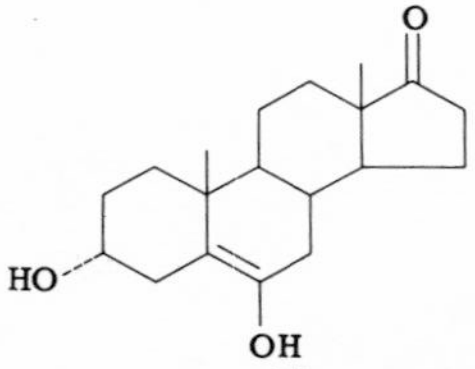

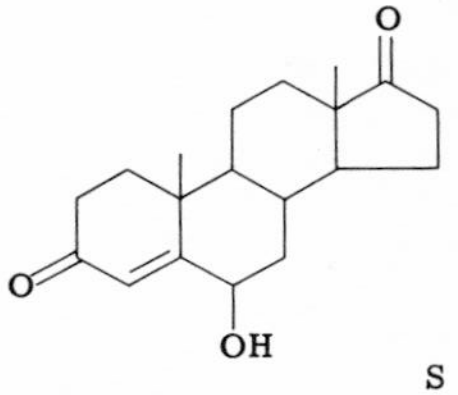

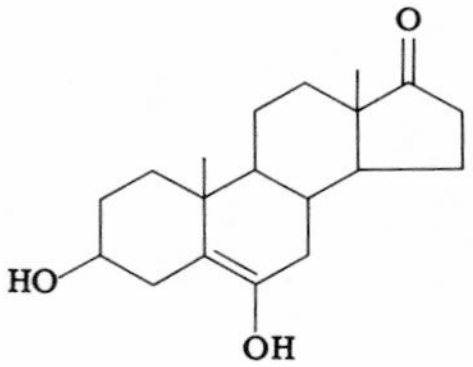

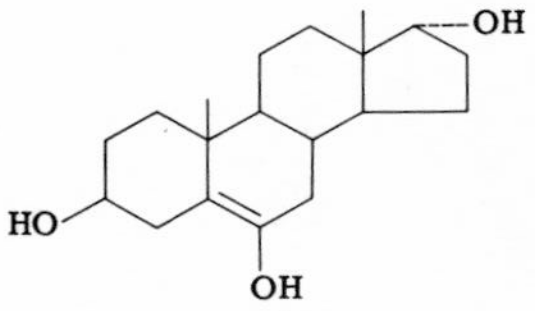

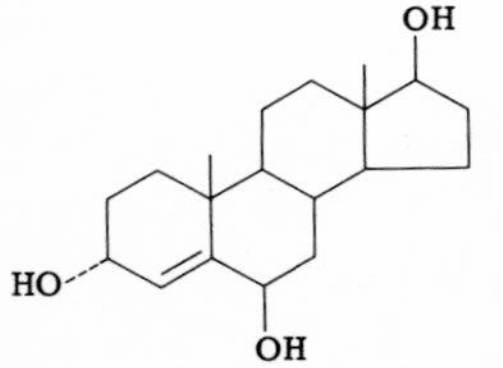

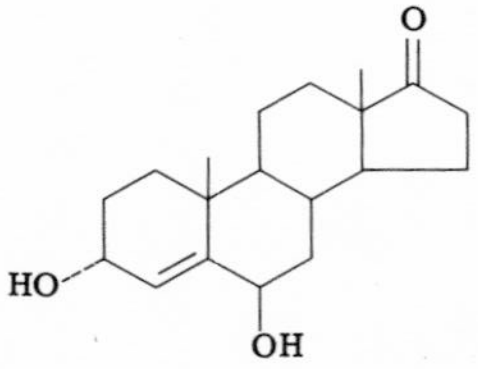

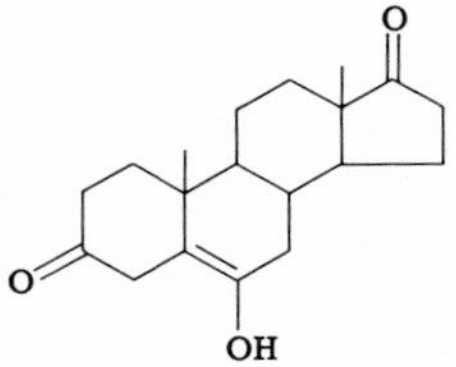

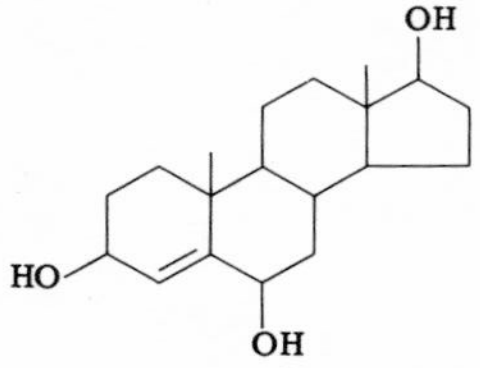

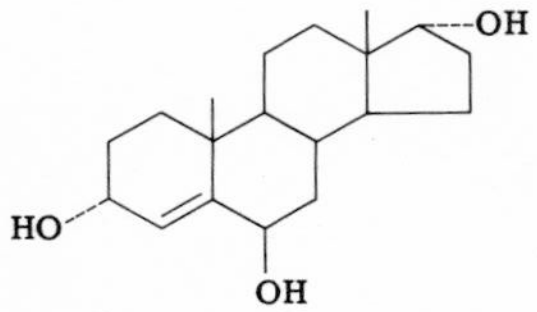

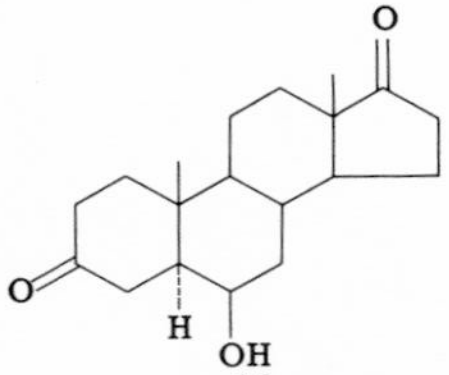

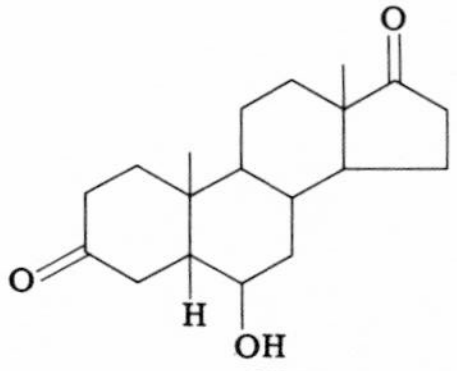

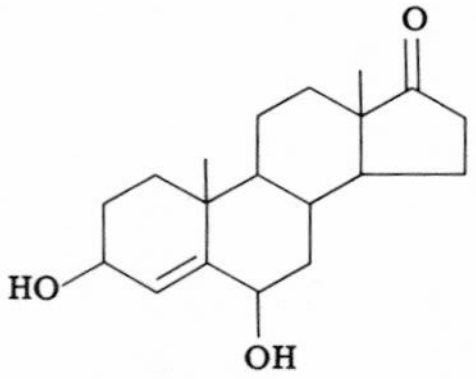

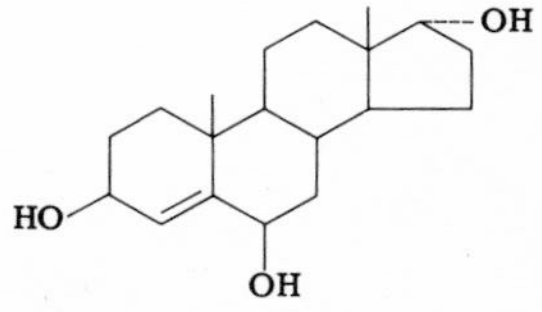

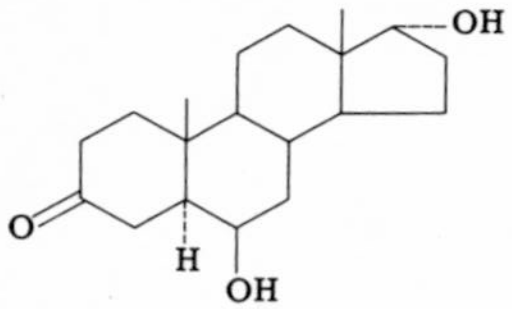

FIG. 6. C_{19}-3-1 : 6β-Hydroxyandrost-4-ene-3,17-dione and related metabolites.

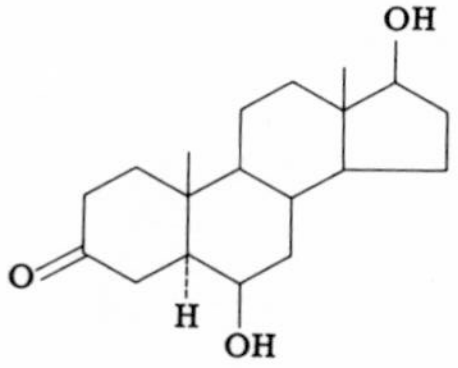

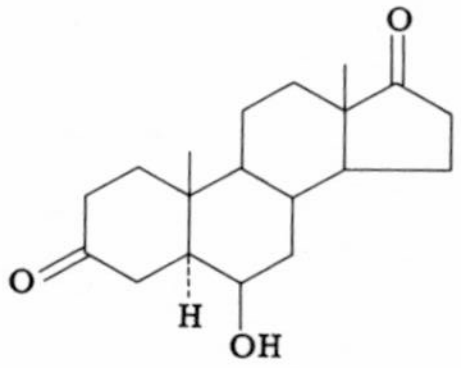

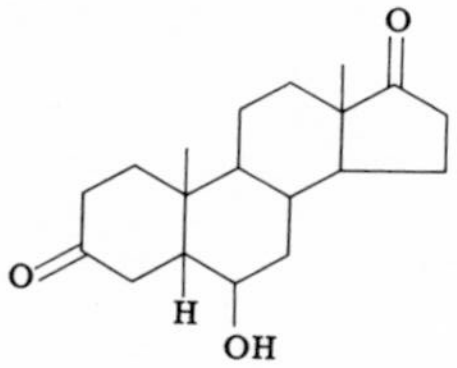

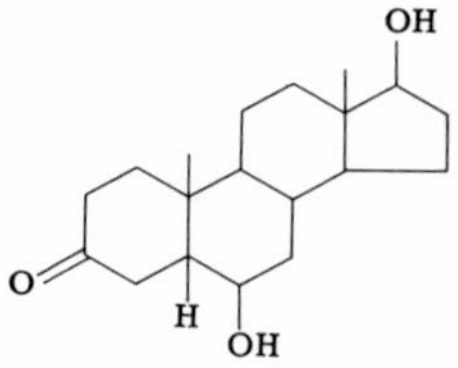

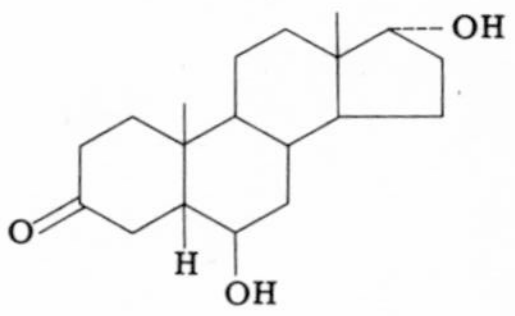

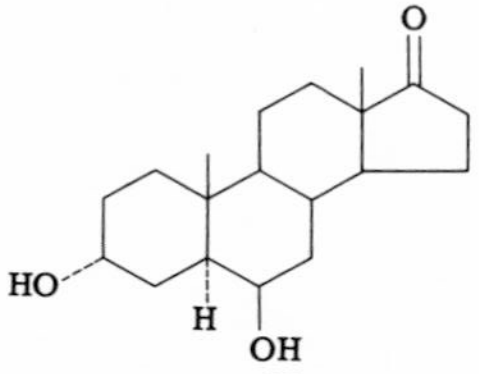

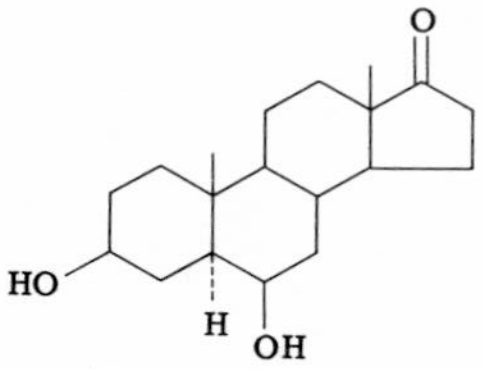

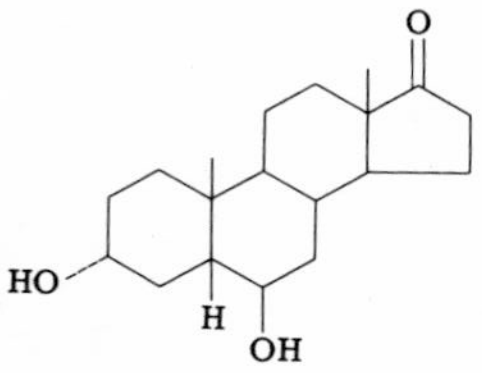

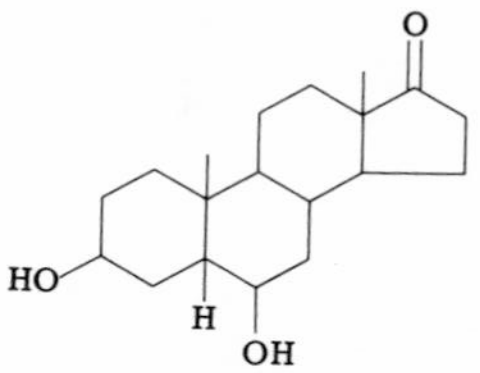

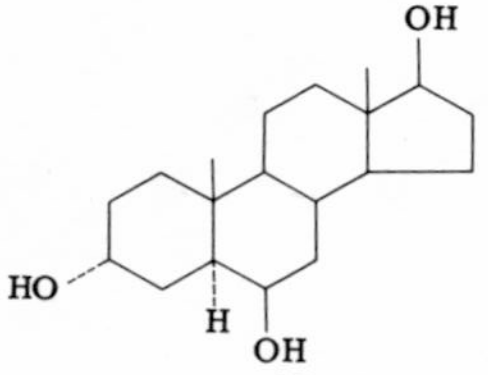

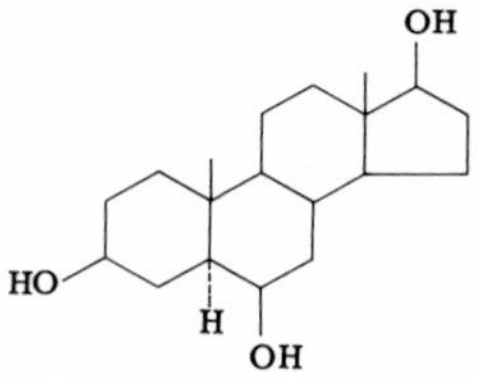

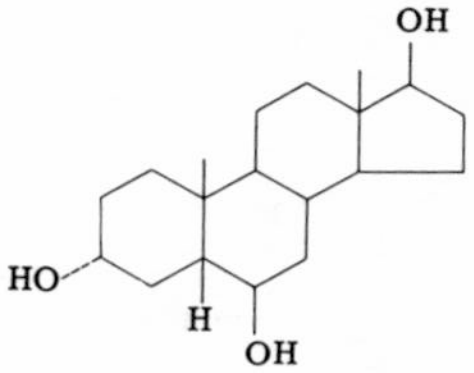

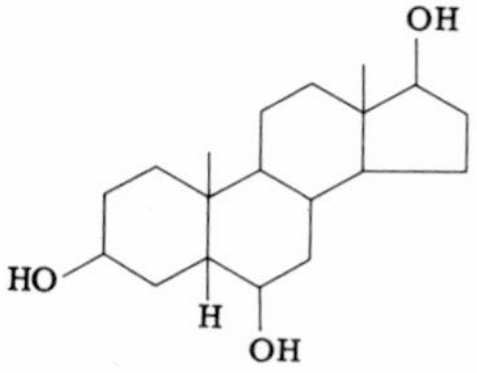

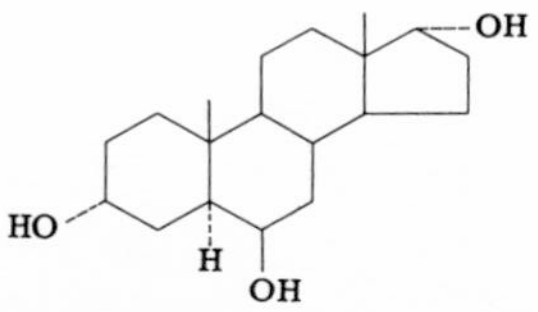

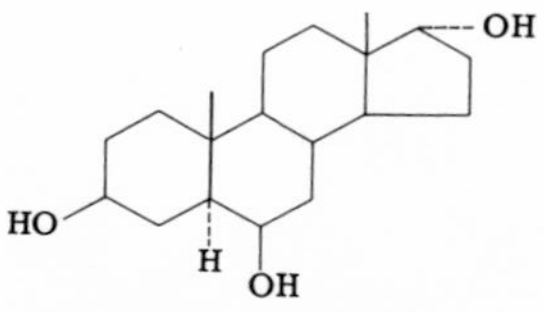

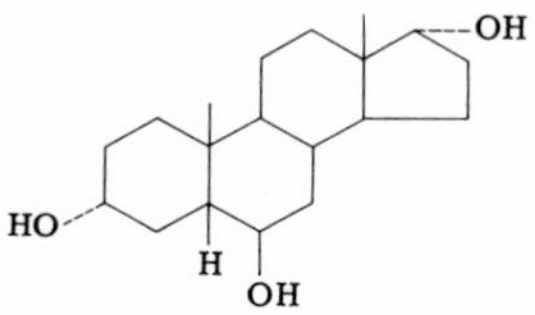

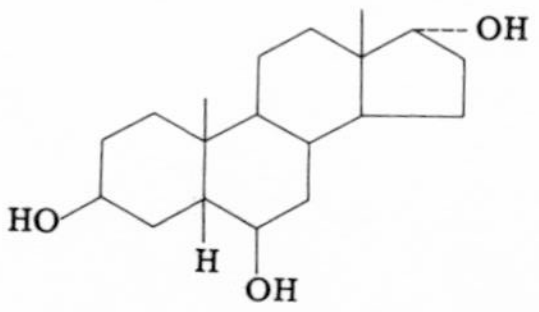

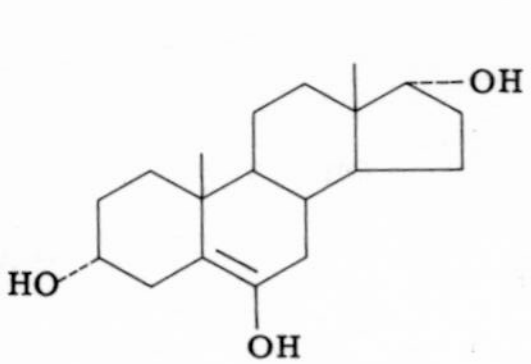

C_{19}-4-1

S

11 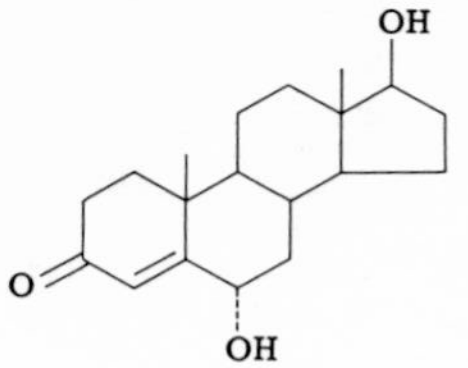 2 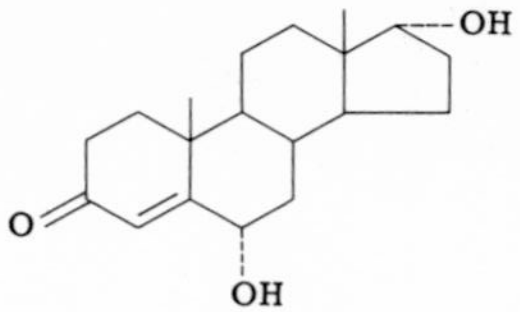 3 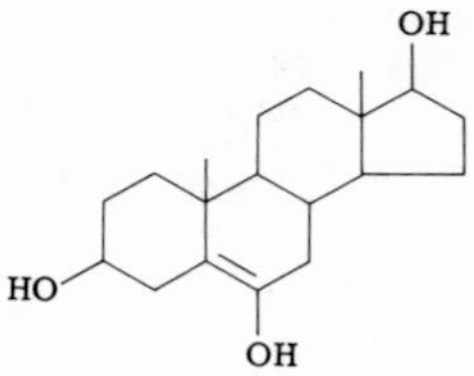 5

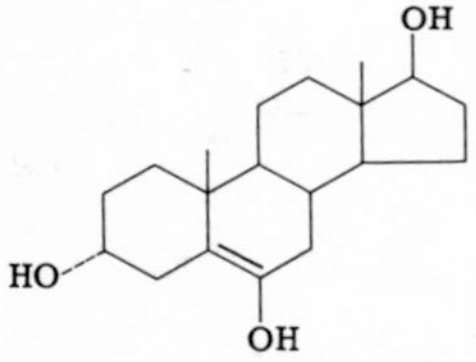

12 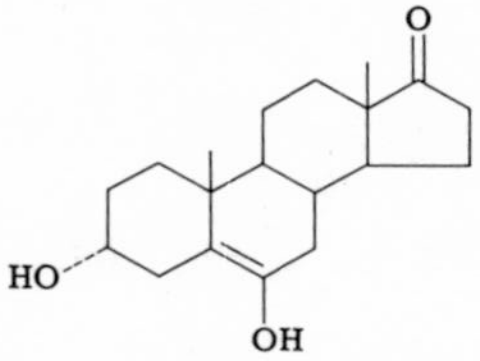 10 4 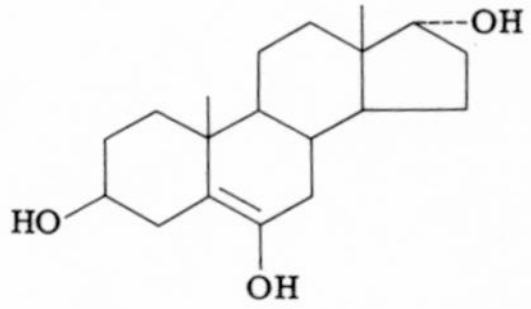 6

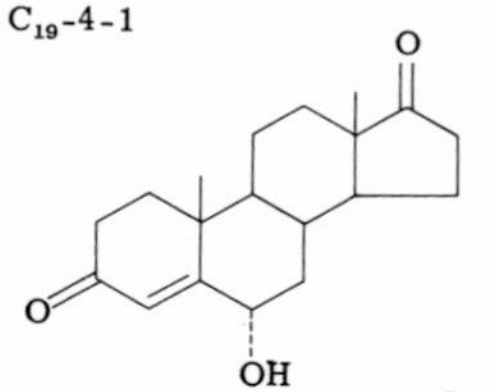

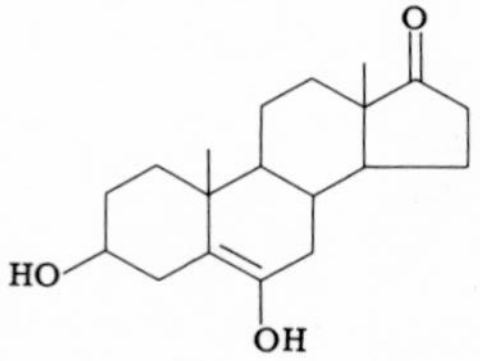

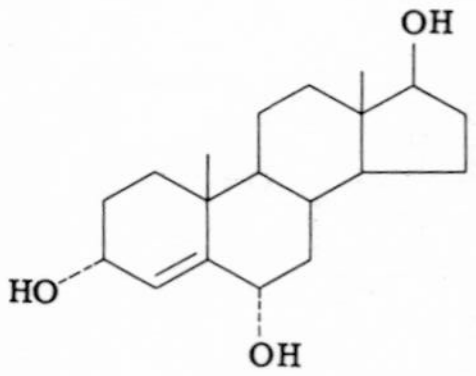

14 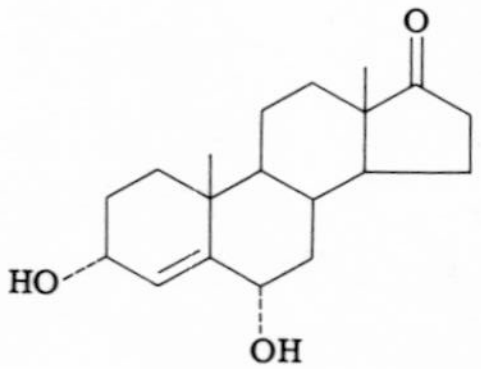 13 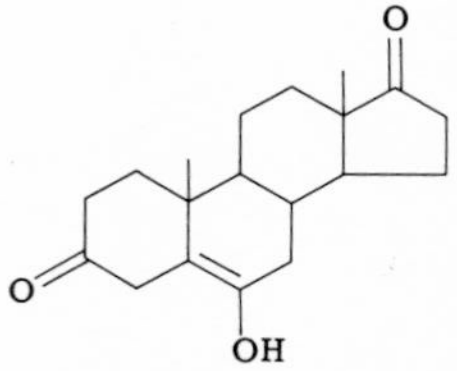 34 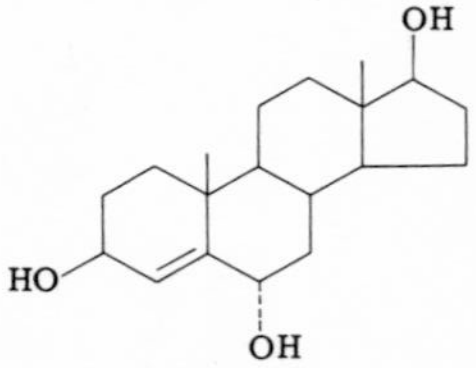 8

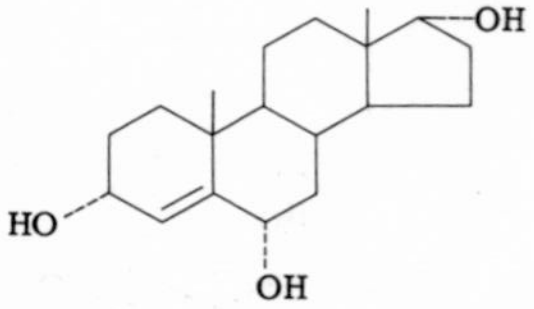

15 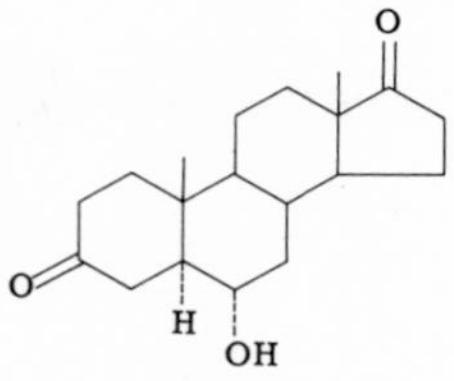 16 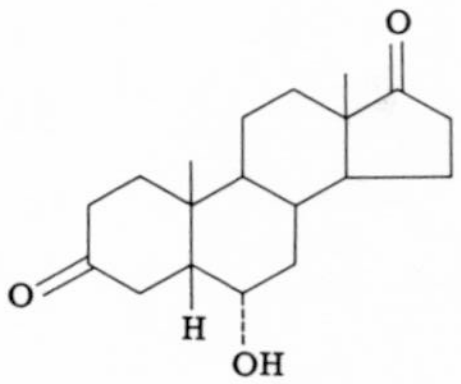 17 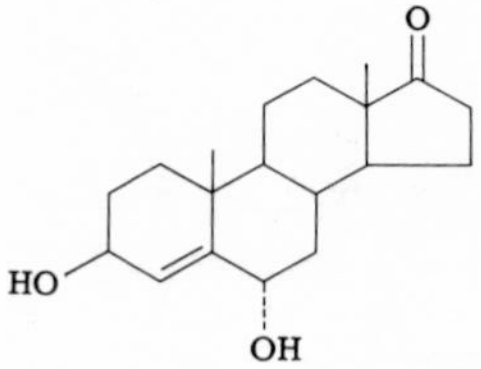 7 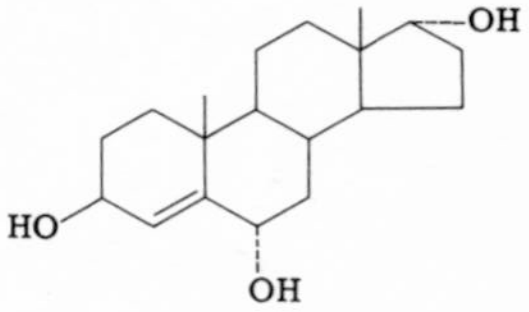 9

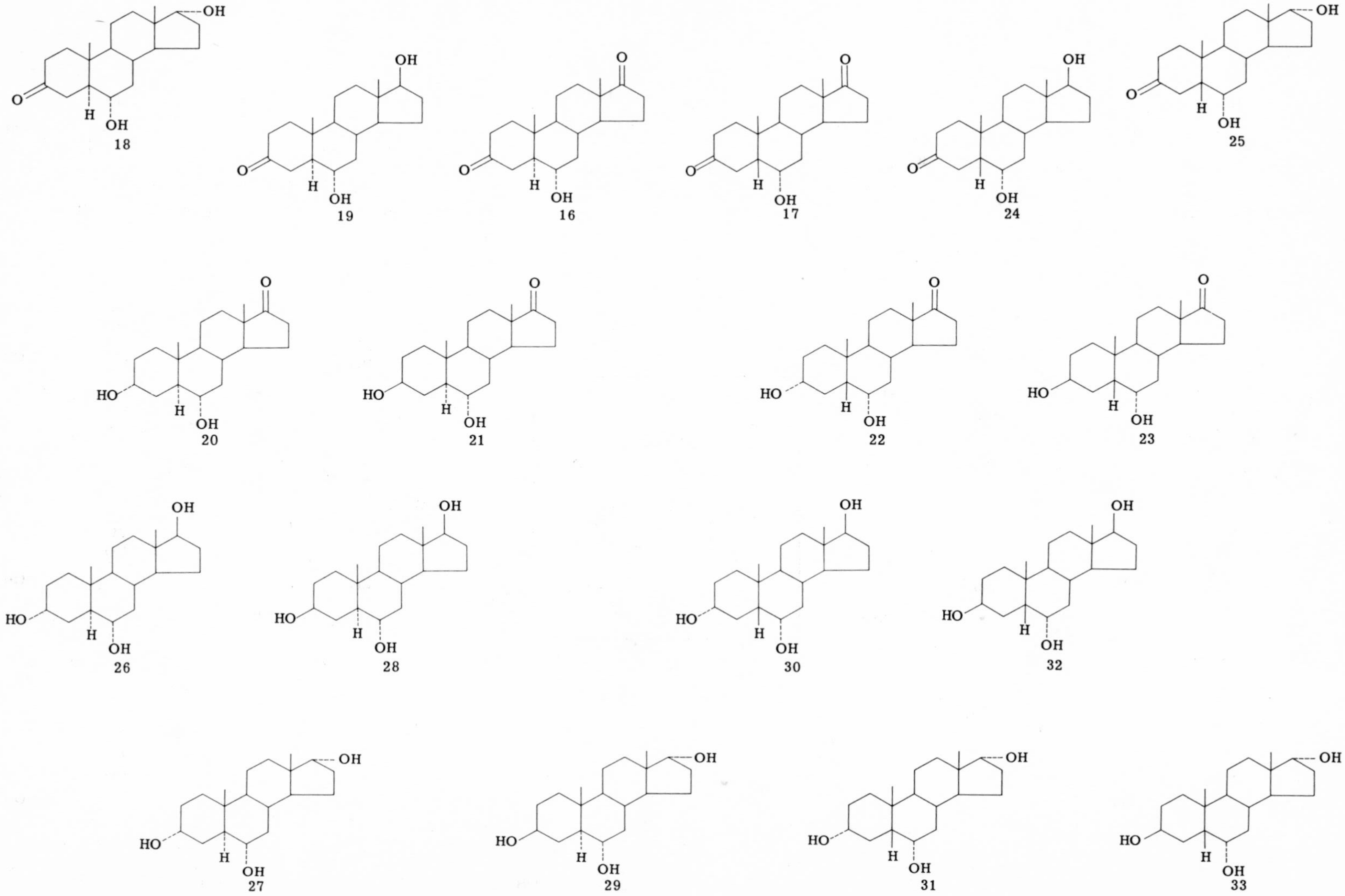

FIG. 7. C_{19}-4-1: 6α-Hydroxyandrost-4-ene-3,17-dione and related metabolites.

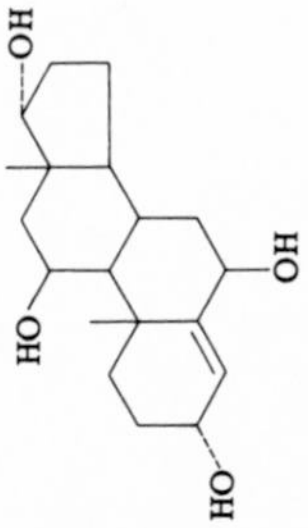

C_{19}-5-1

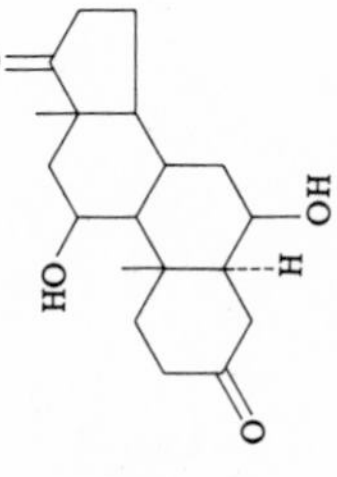

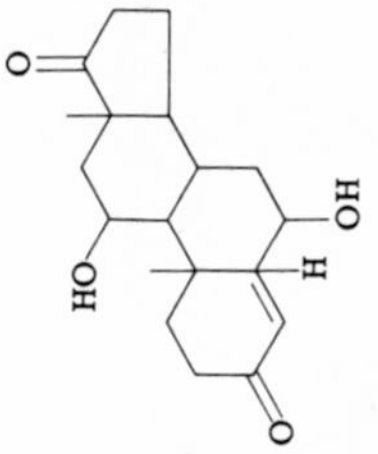

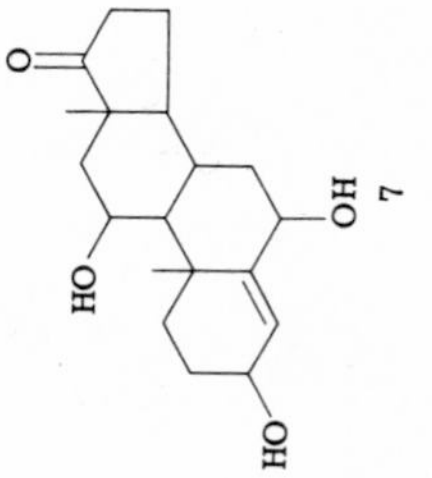

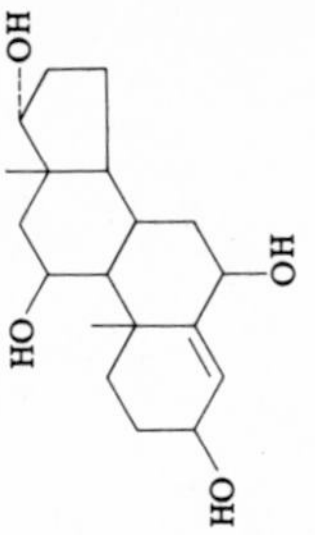

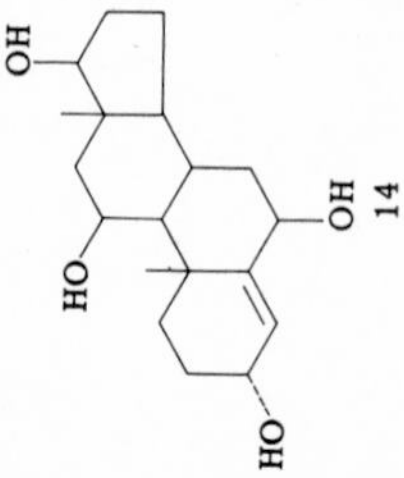

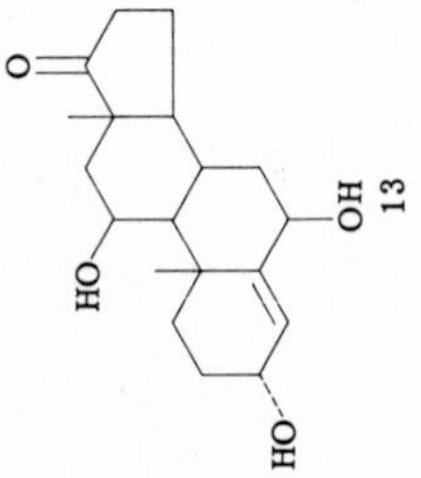

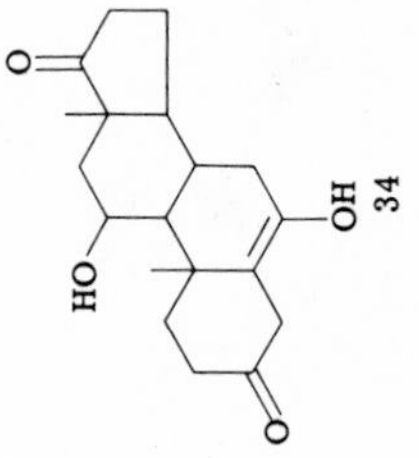

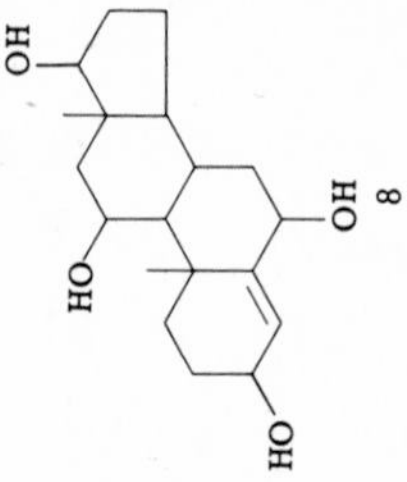

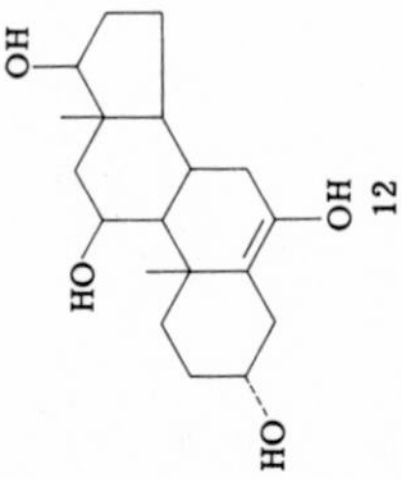

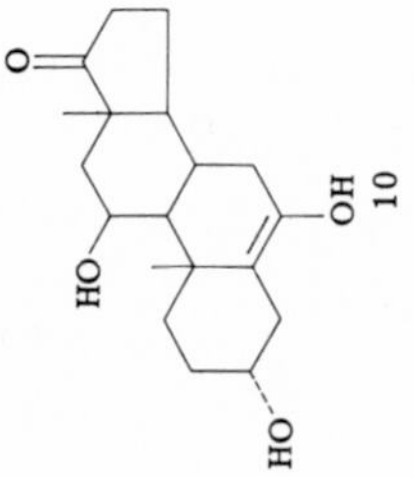

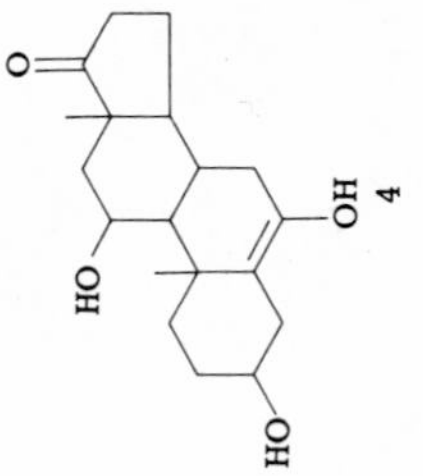

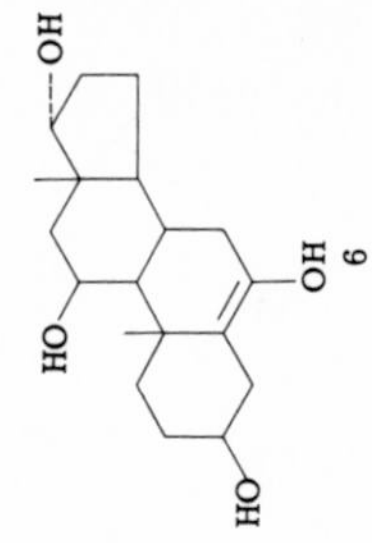

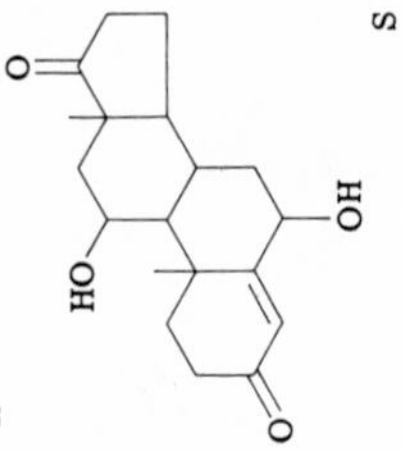

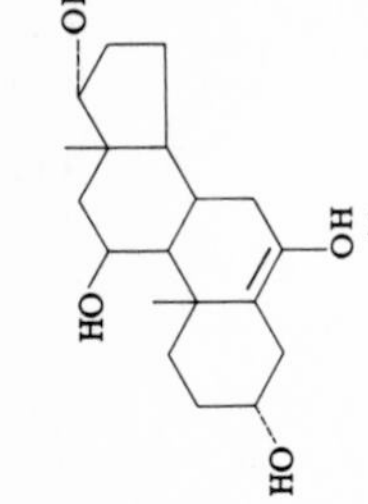

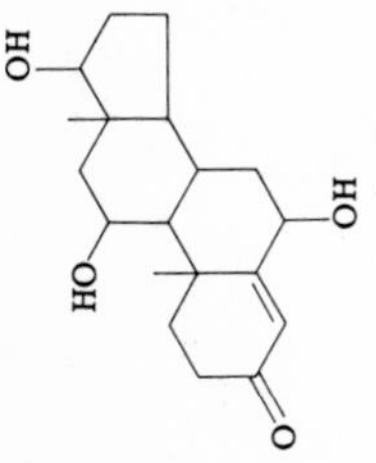

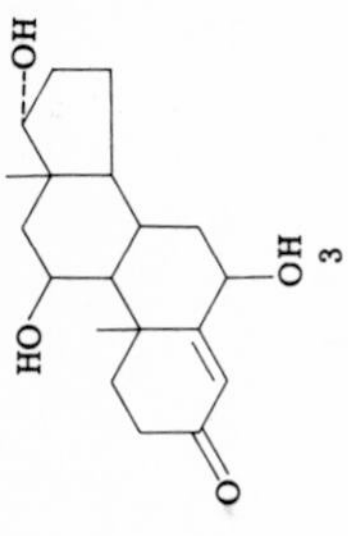

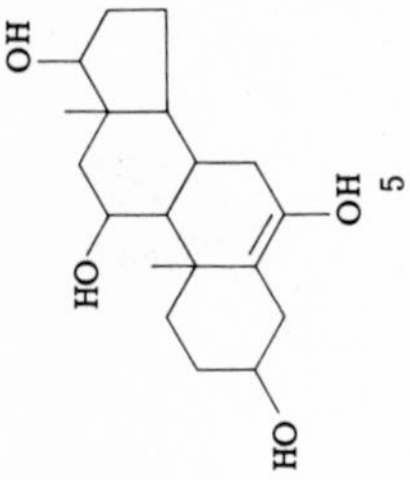

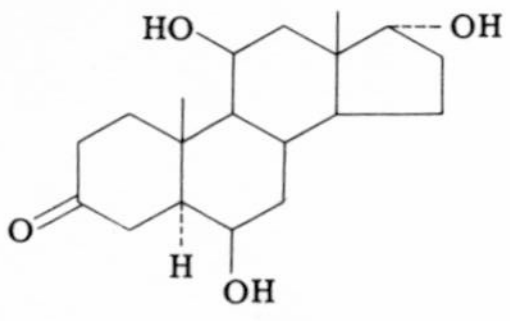

18 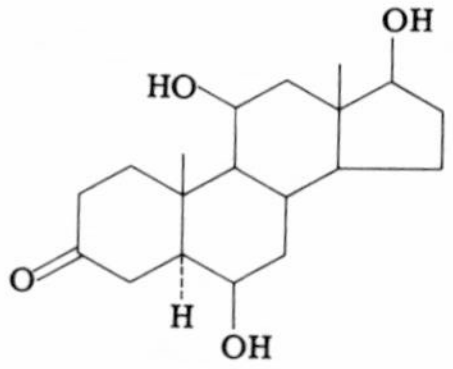 19 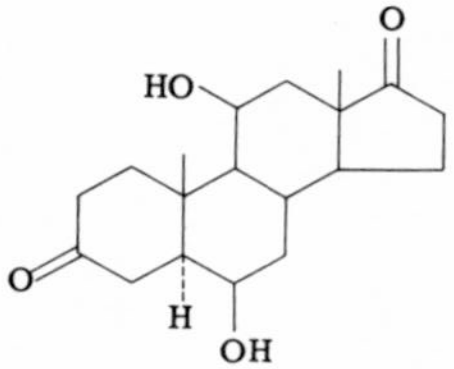 16 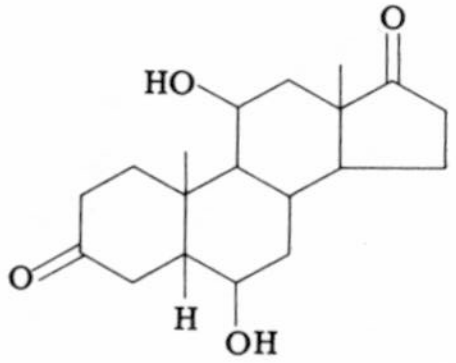 17 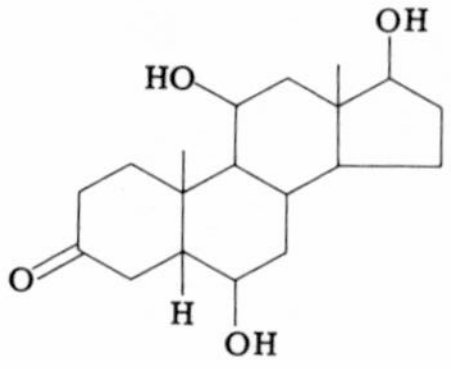 24 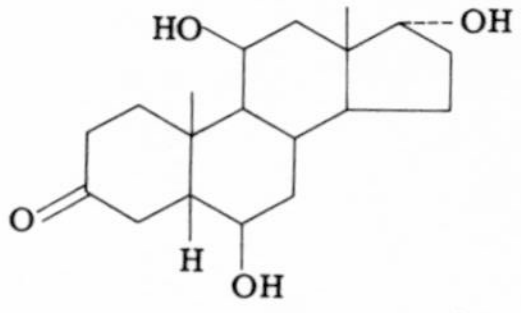 25

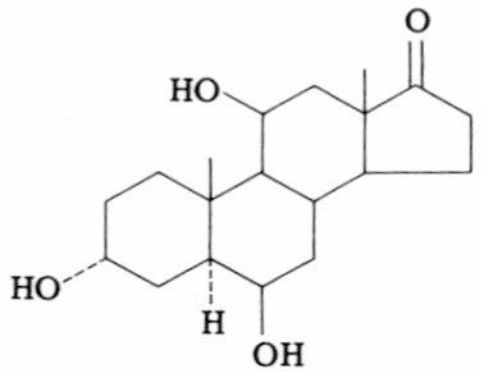

20 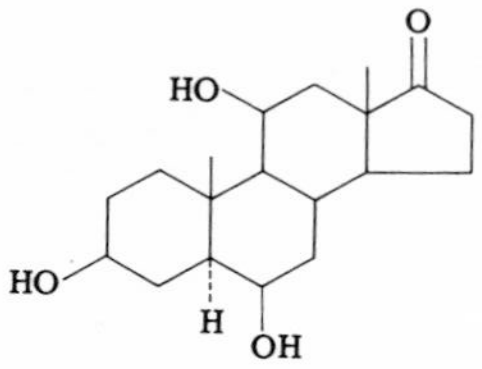 21 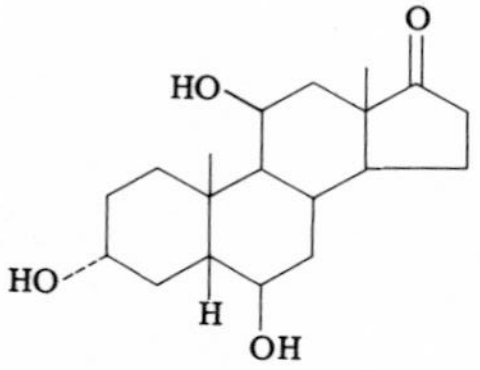 22 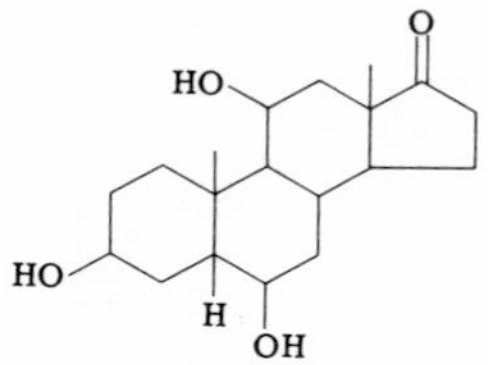 23

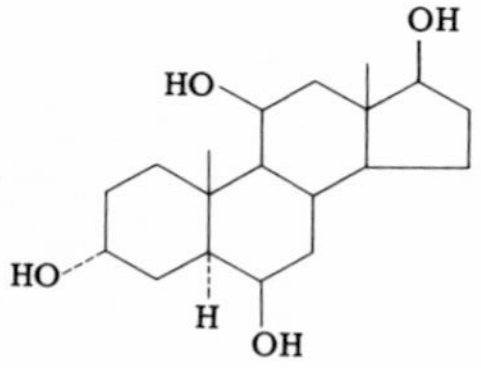

26 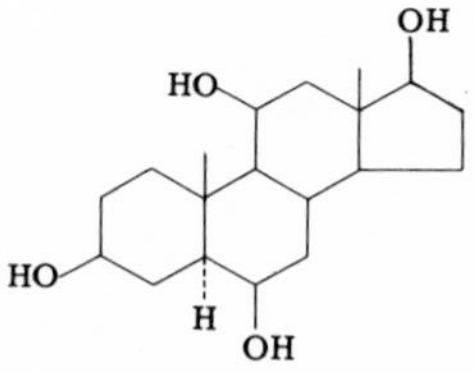 28 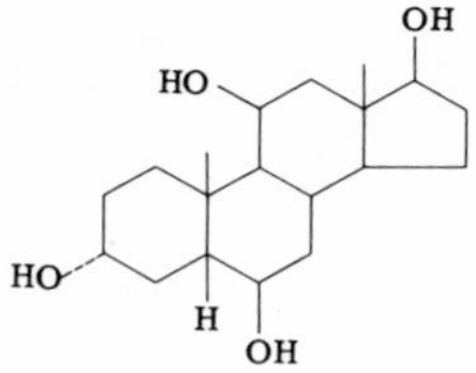 30 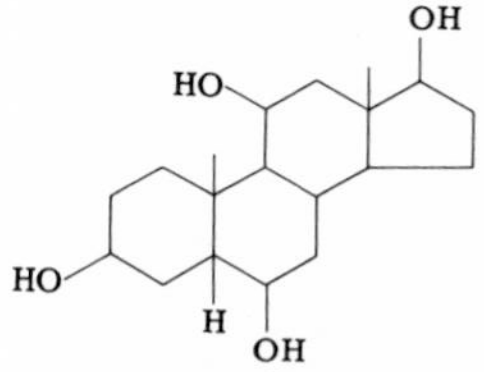 32

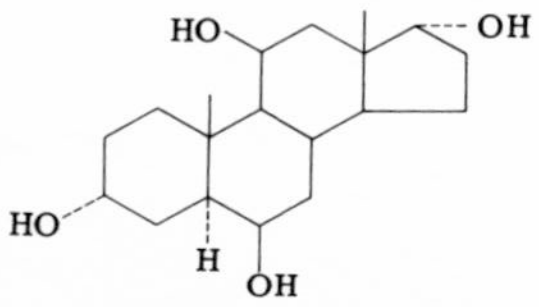

27 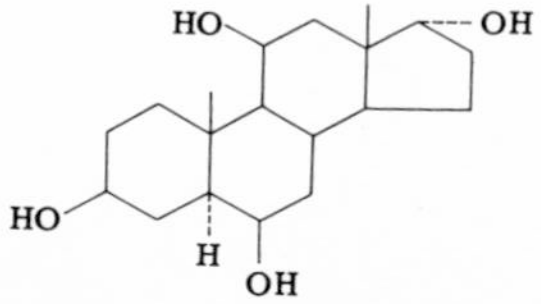 29 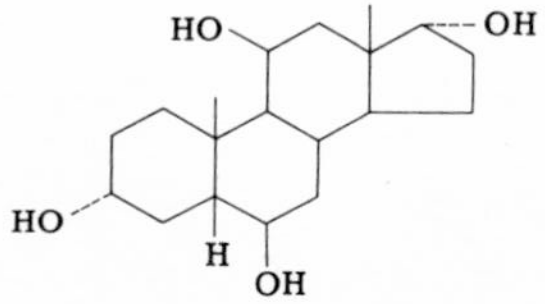 31 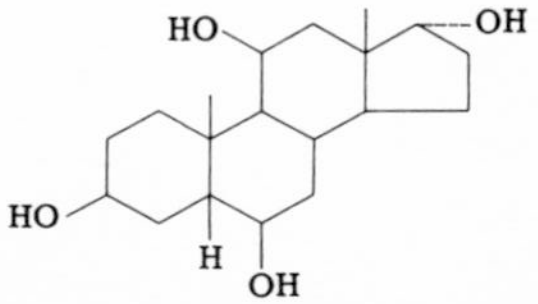 33

FIG. 8. C_{19}-5-1: 6β,11β-Dihydroxyandrost-4-ene-3,17-dione and related metabolites.

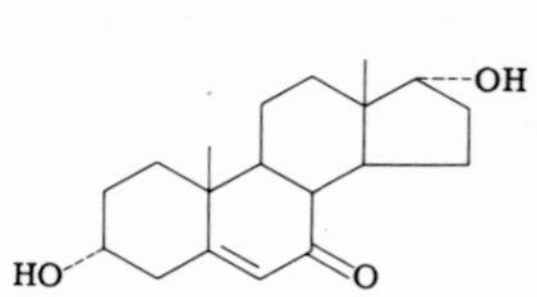

C_{19}-6-1

11 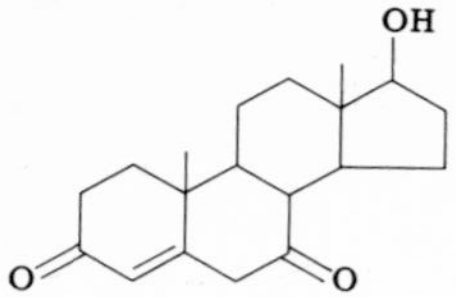 2 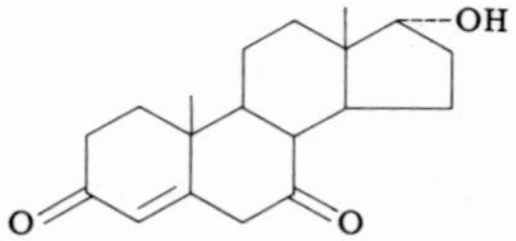 3 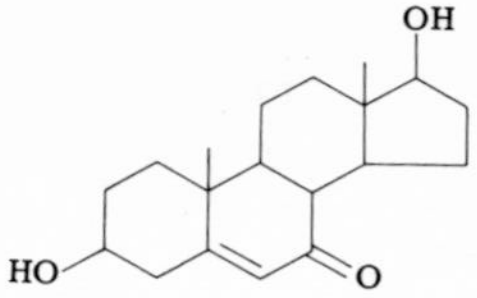 5

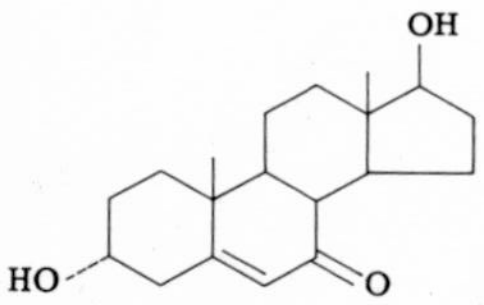

12 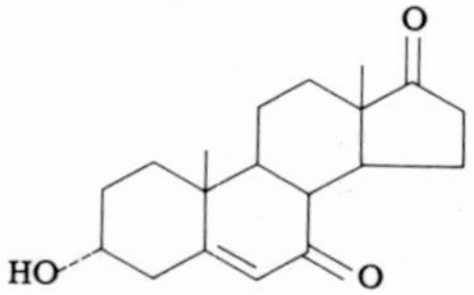 10 4 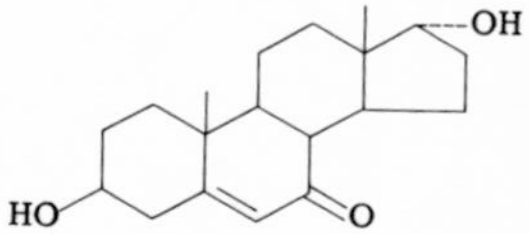 6

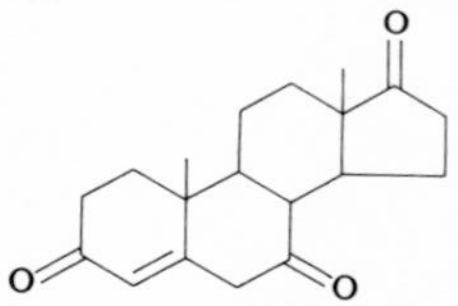

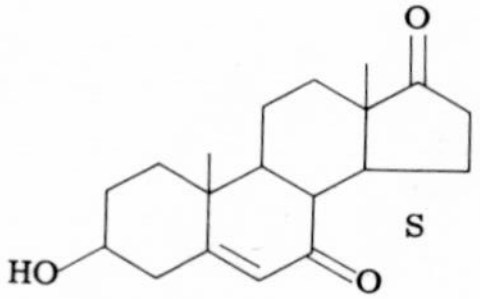

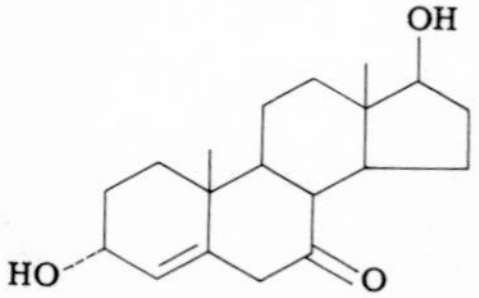

14 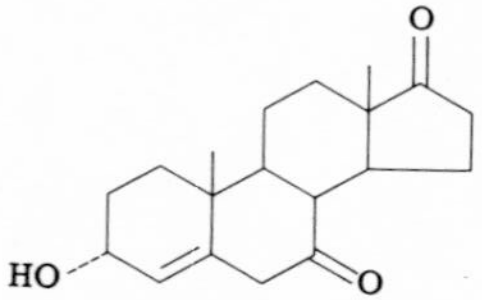 13 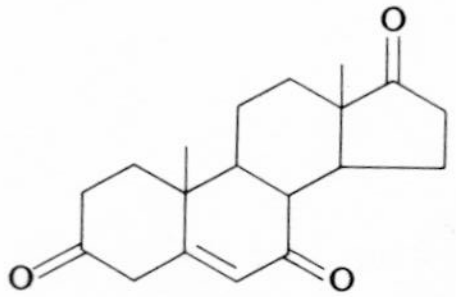 34 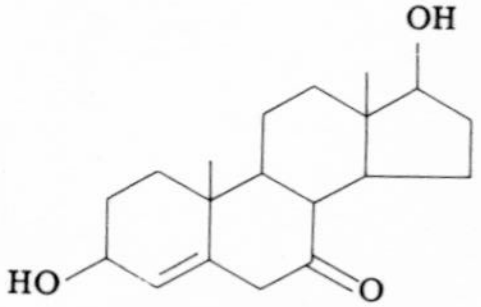 8

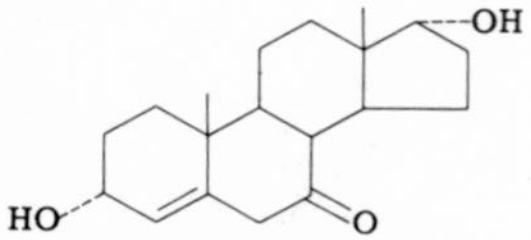

15 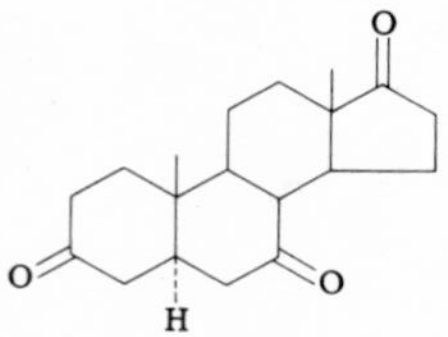 16 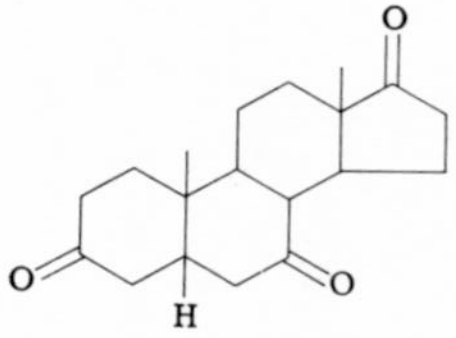 17 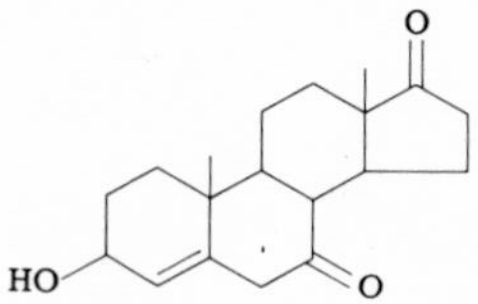 7 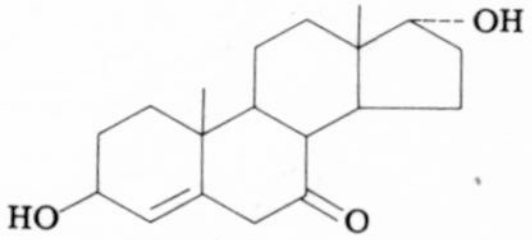 9

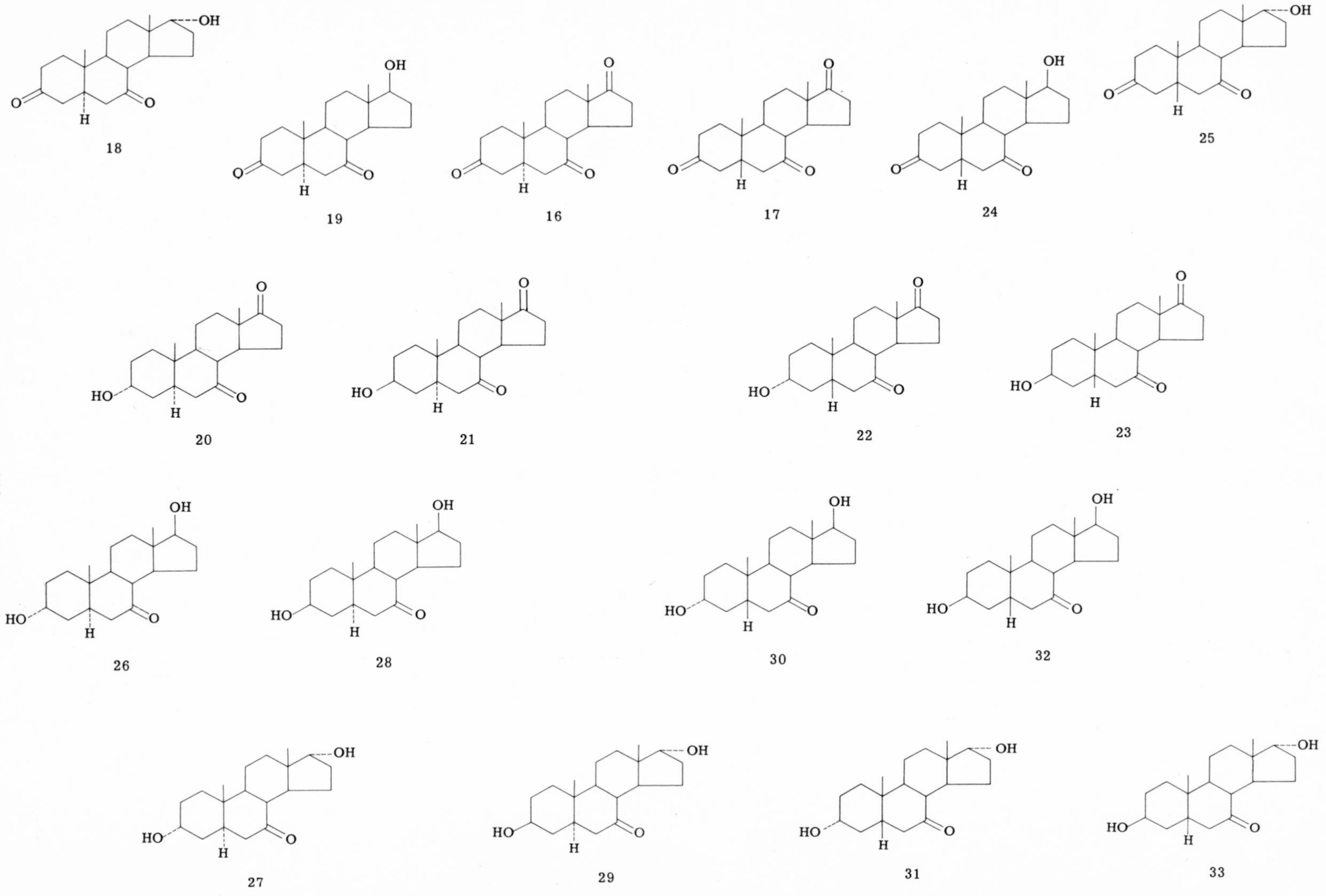

18 19 16 17 24 25

20 21 22 23

26 28 30 32

27 29 31 33

FIG. 9. C_{19}-6-1: Androst-4-ene-3, 6,17-trione and related metabolites.

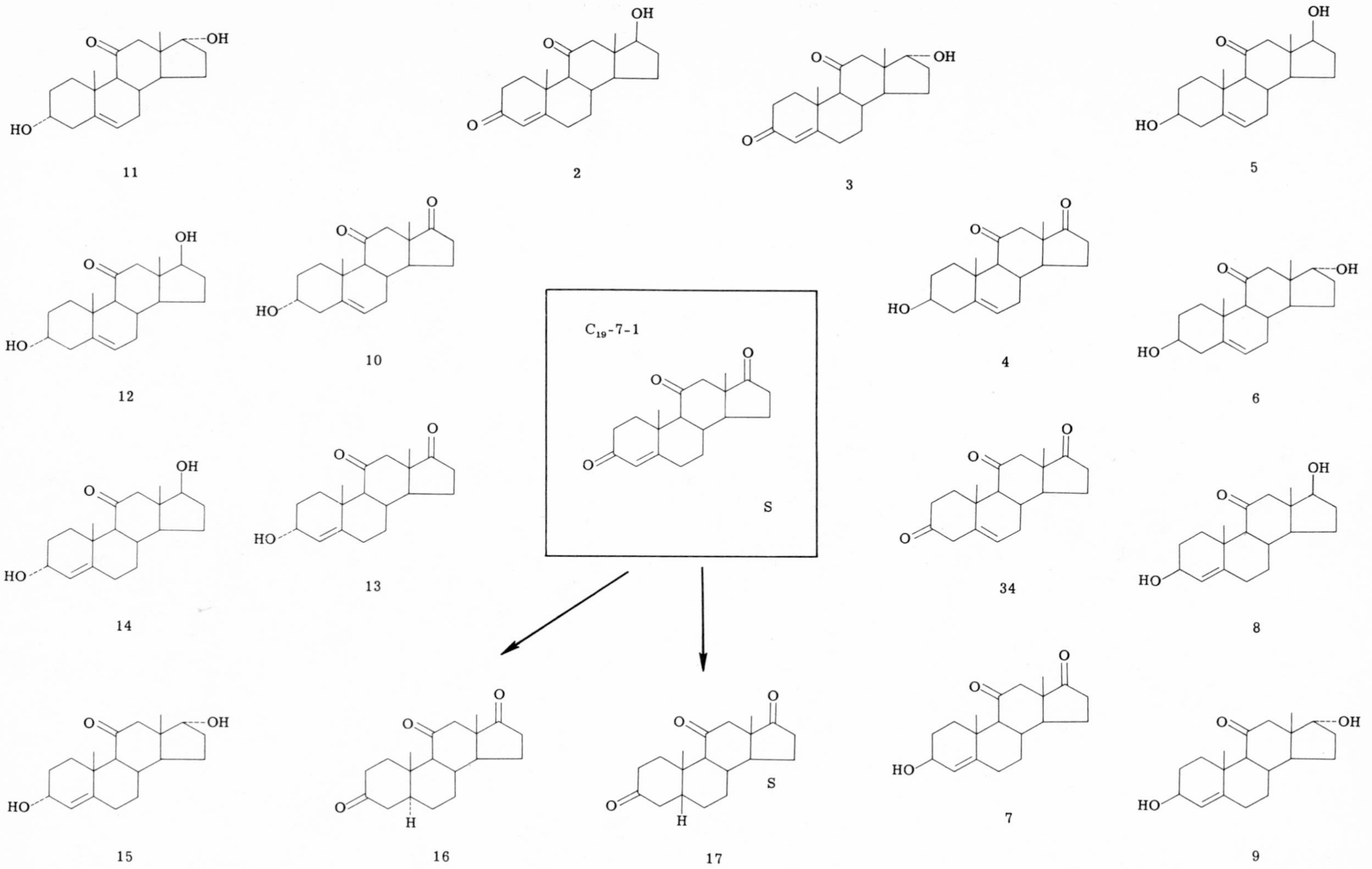

C_{19}-7-1 S

2 3 4 5 6 7 8 9 10 11 12 13 14 15 16 17 S 34

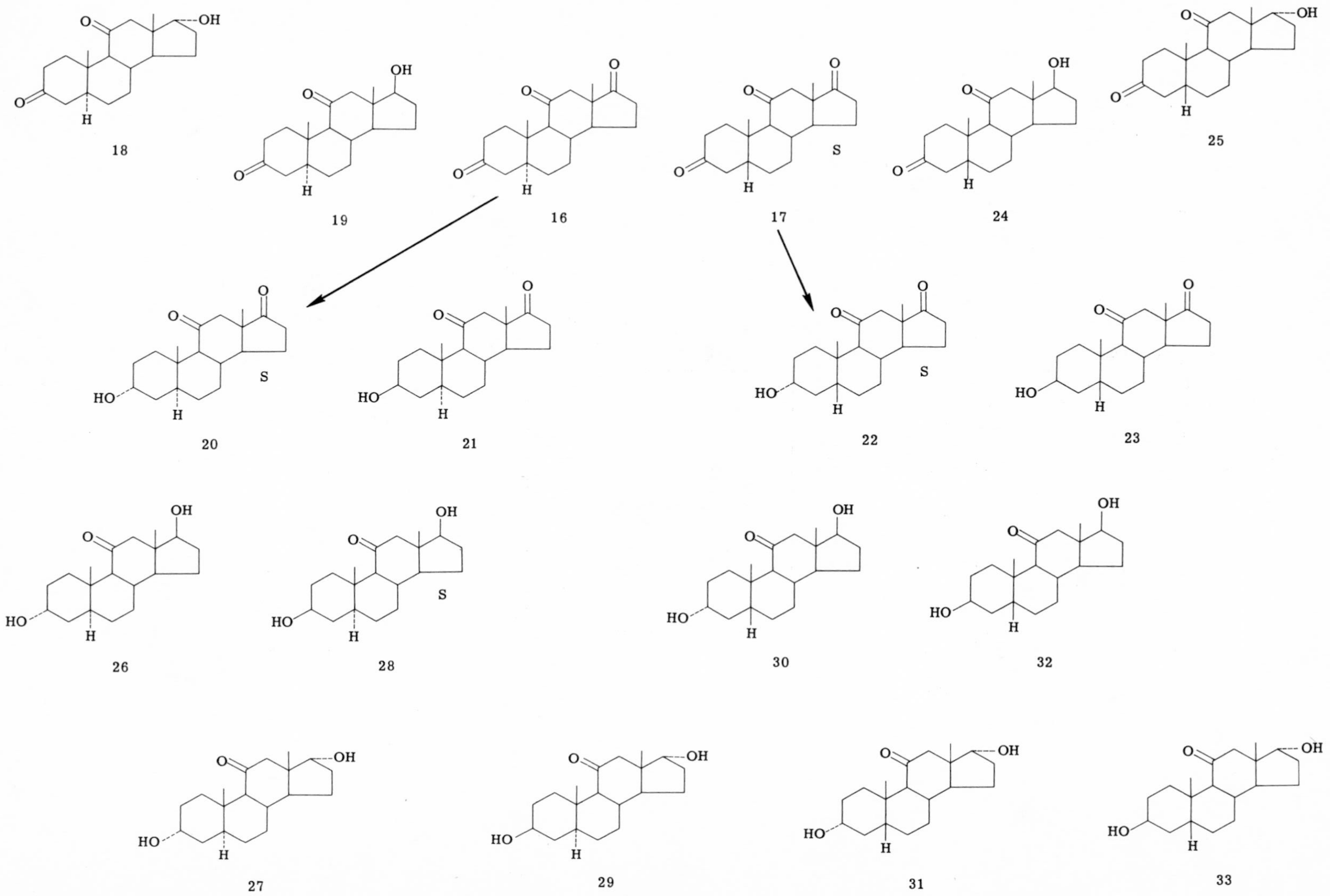

FIG. 10. C_{19}-7-1: Androst-4-ene-3,11,17-trione and related metabolites.

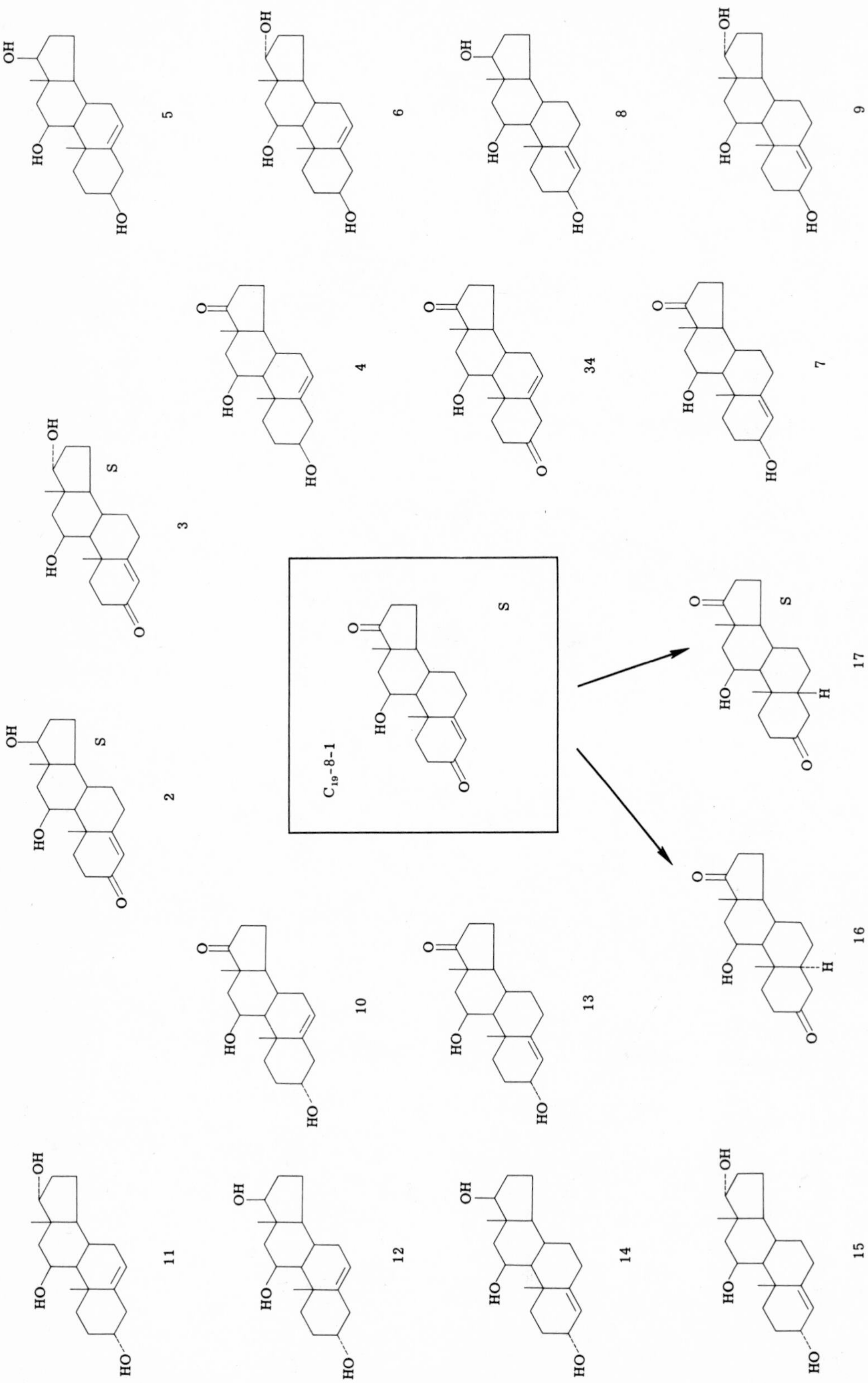

C_{19}-8-1

S

11 2 3 5

12 10 4 6

14 13 34 8

15 16 17 7 9

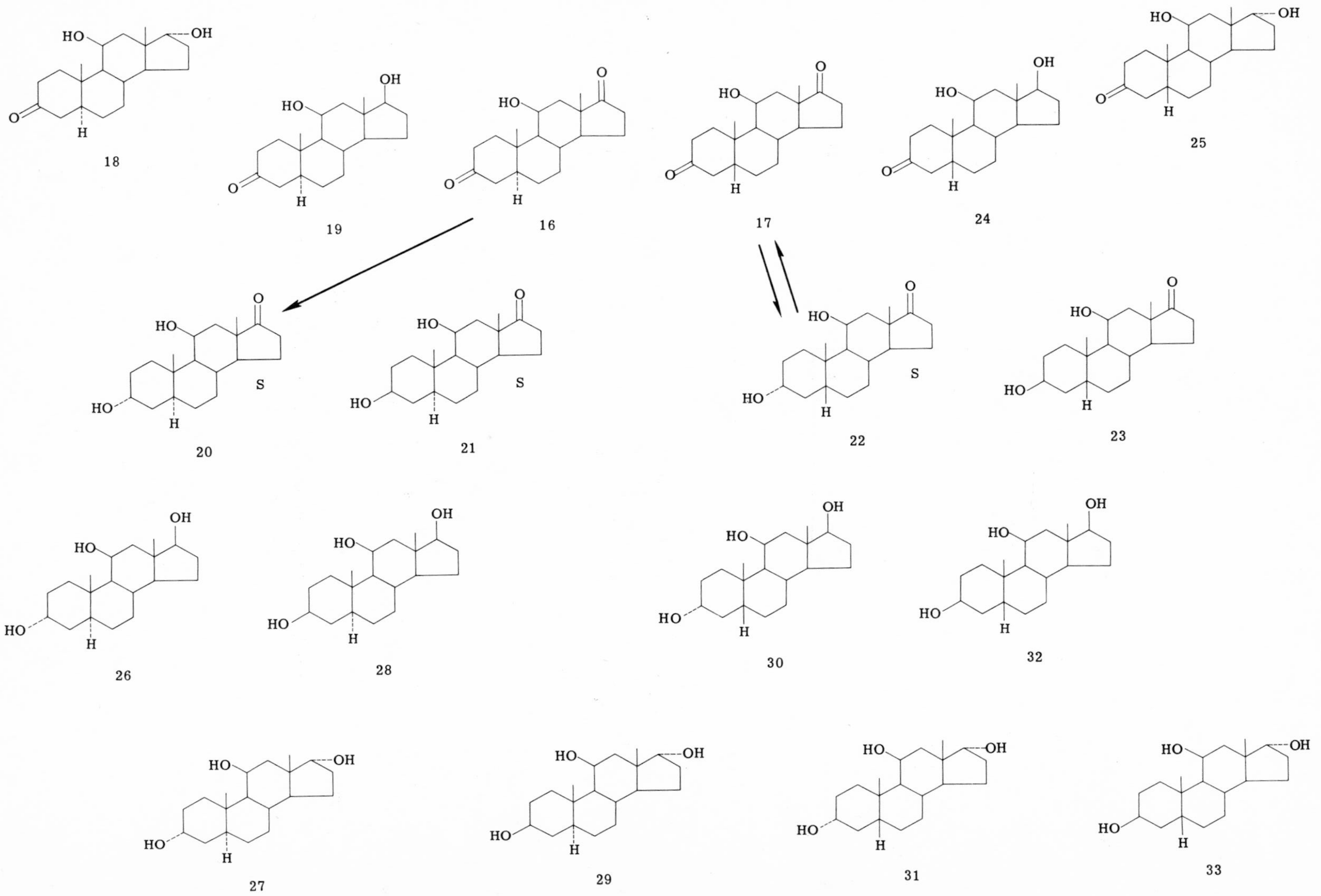

18 19 16 17 24 25

20 S 21 S 22 S 23

26 28 30 32

27 29 31 33

FIG. 11. C_{19}-8-1: 11β-Hydroxyandrost-4-ene-3,17-dione and related metabolites.

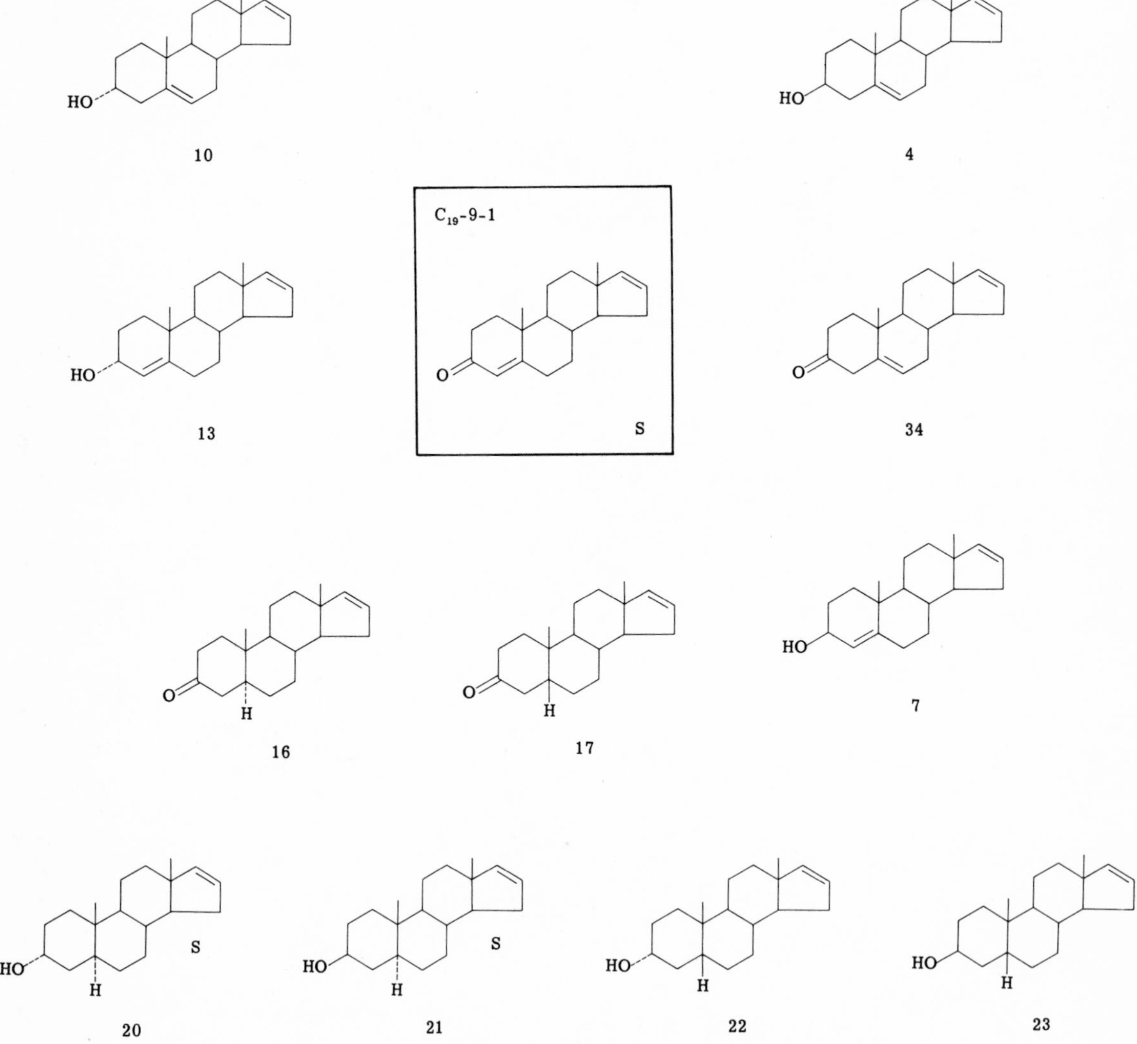

FIG. 12. C_{19}-9-1: Androsta-4,16-dien-3-one and related metabolites.

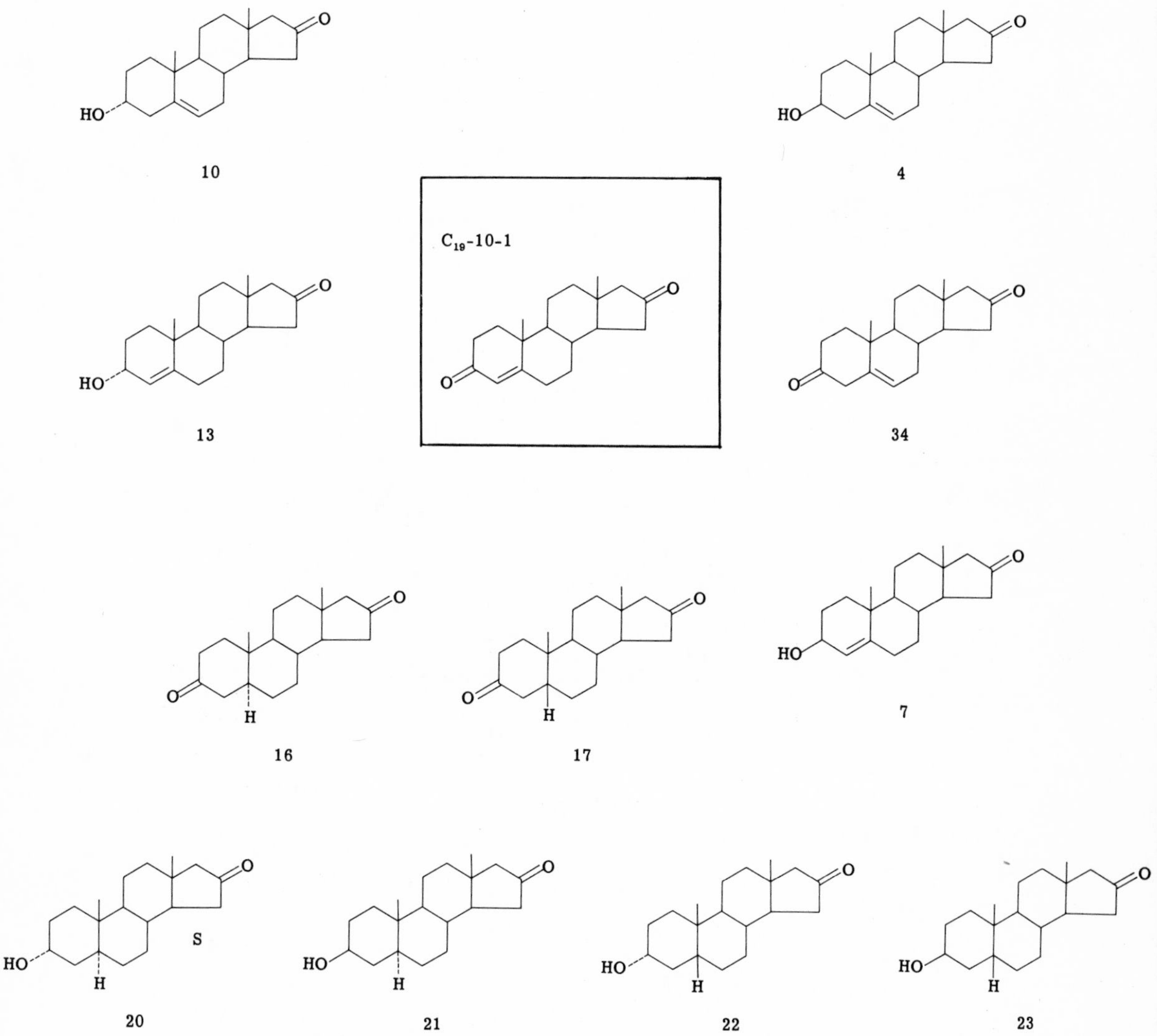

10

4

C_{19}-10-1

13

34

16

17

7

20

21

22

23

FIG. 13. C_{19}-10-1: Androst-4-ene-3,16-dione and related metabolites.

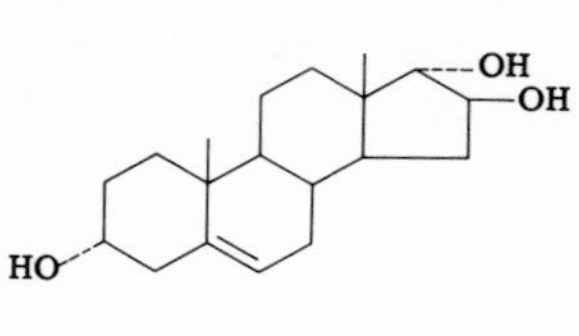

C_{19}-11-1

11 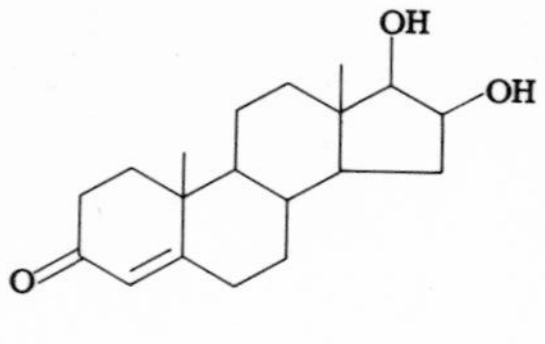 2 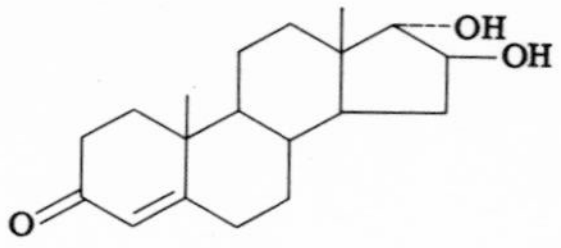 3 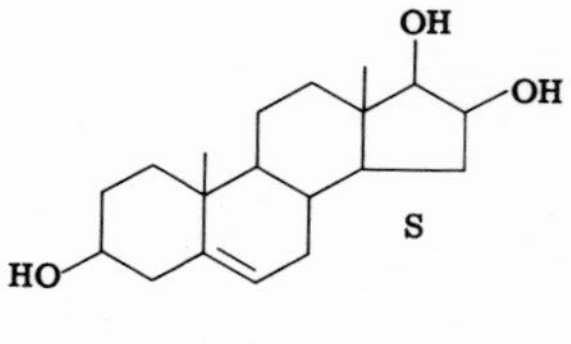 5

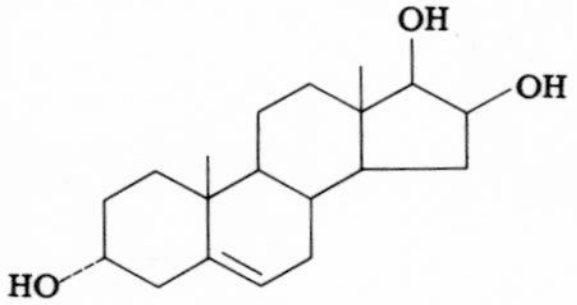

12 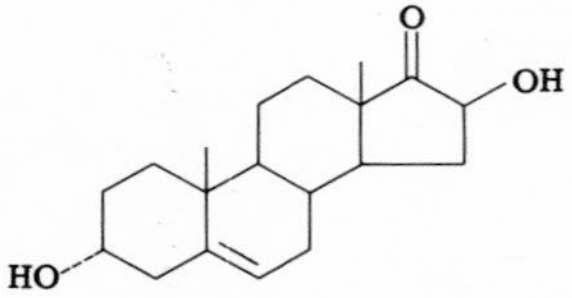 10 4 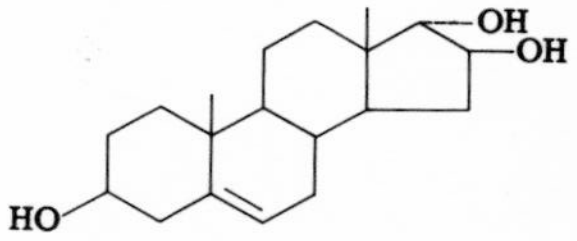 6

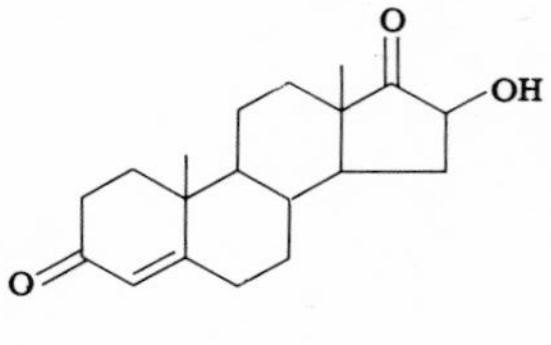

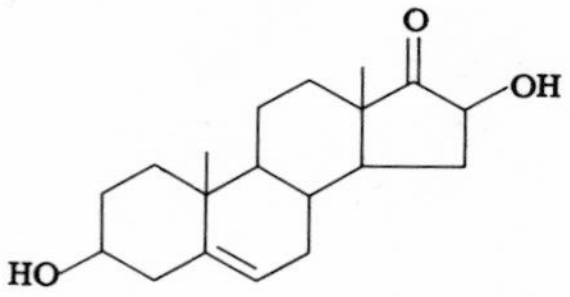

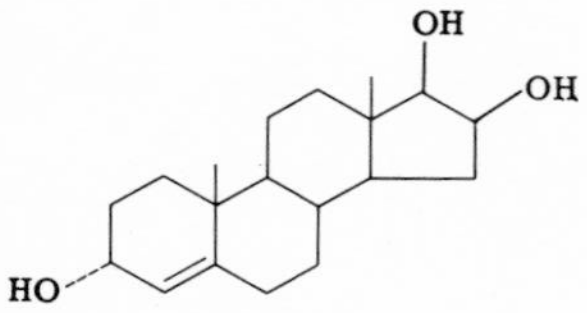

14 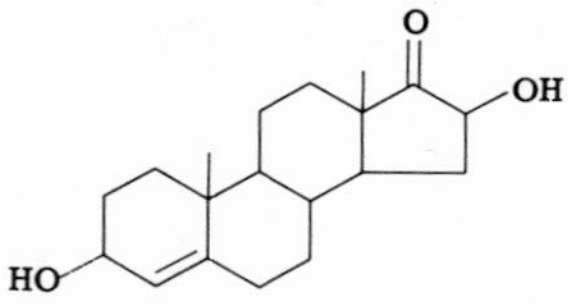 13 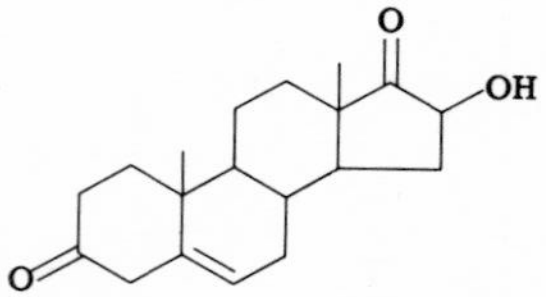 34 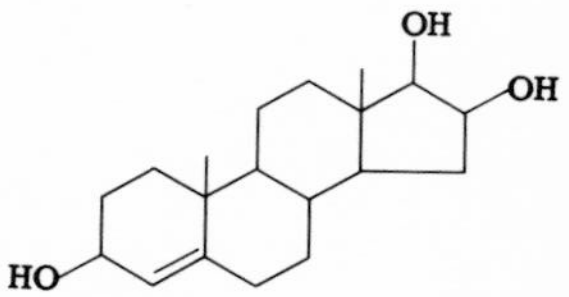 8

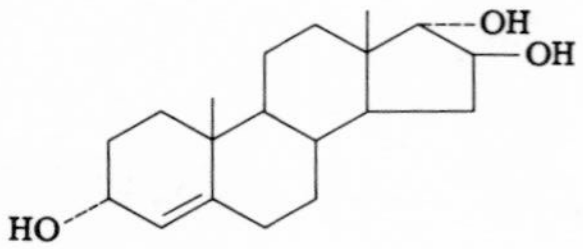

15 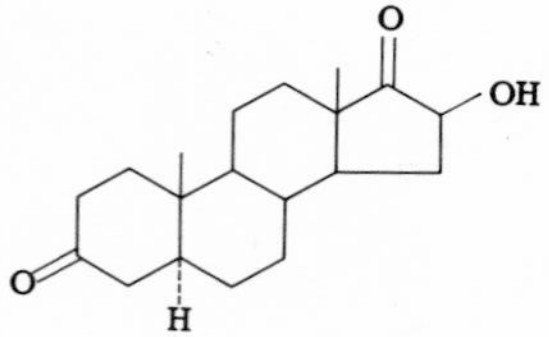 16 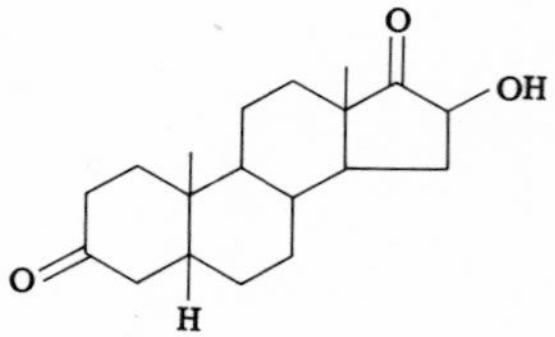 17 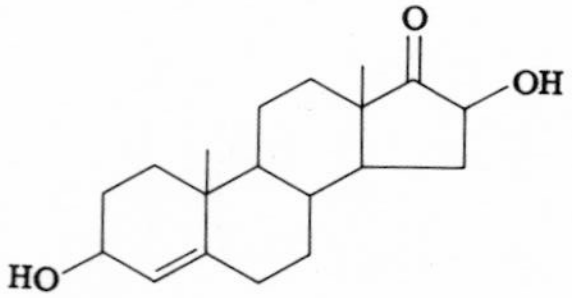 7 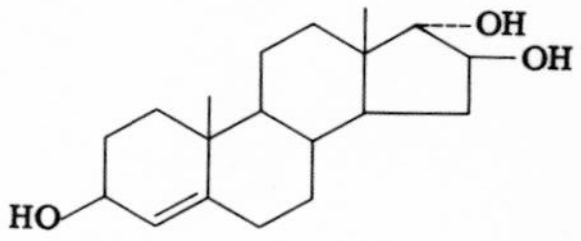 9

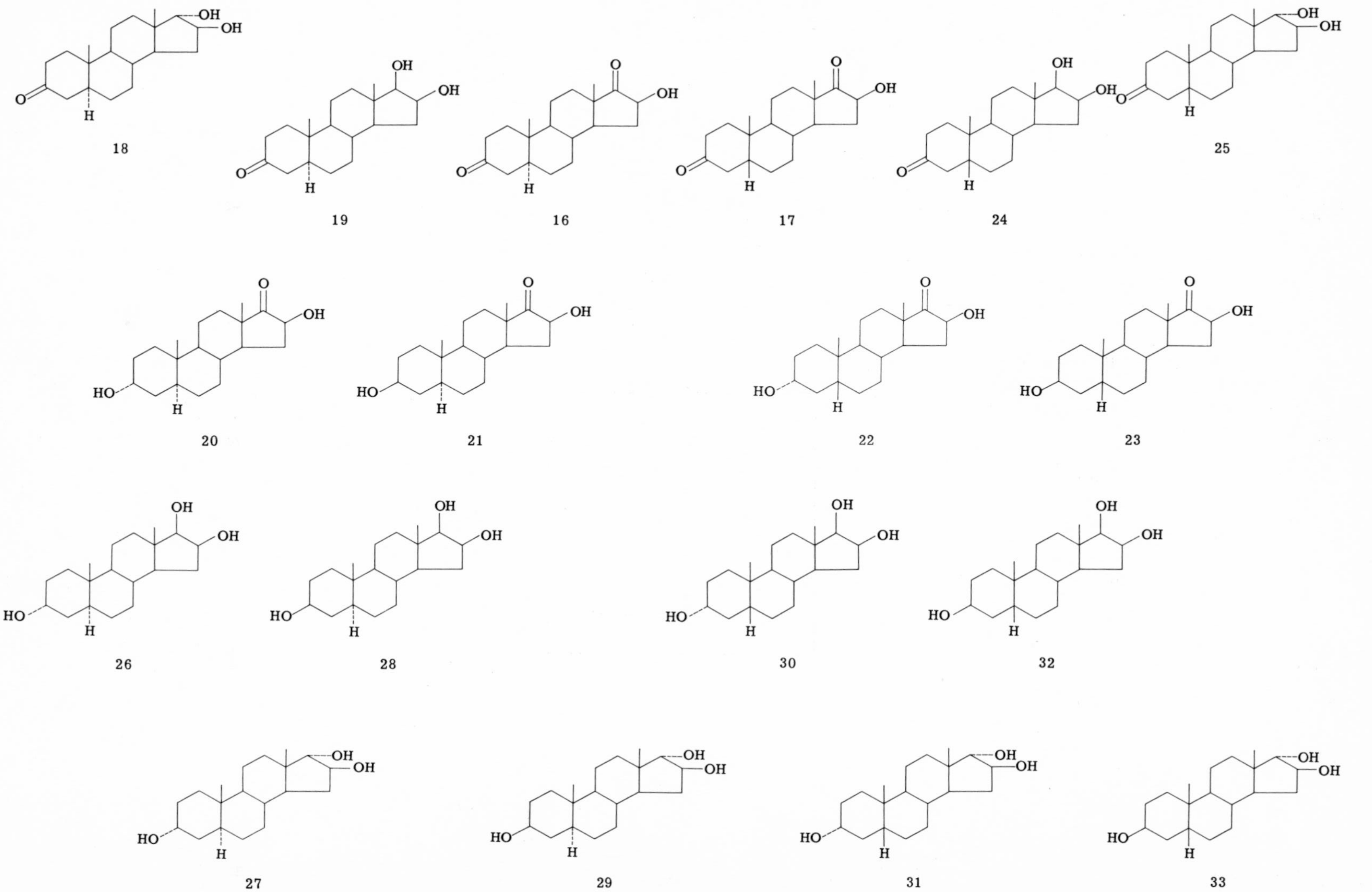

FIG. 14. C_{19}-11-1: 16β-Hydroxyandrost-4-ene-3,17-dione and related metabolites.

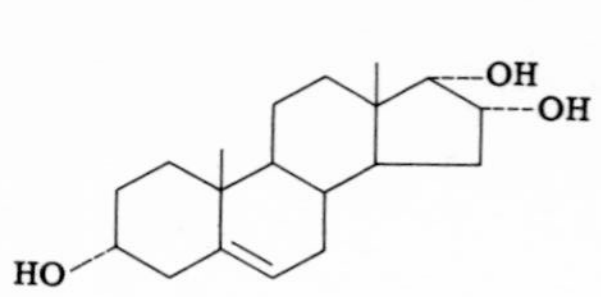

15

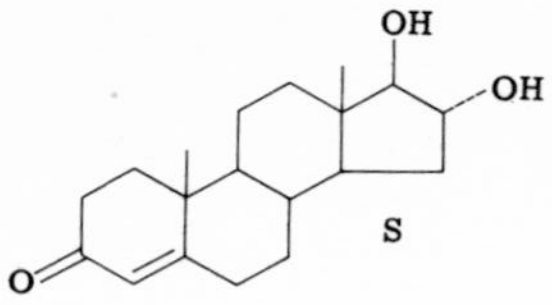

14

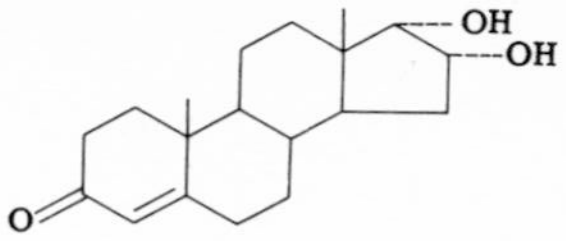

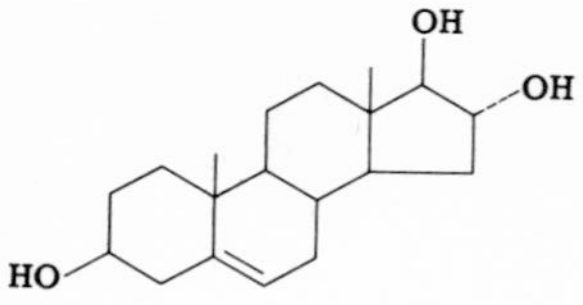

12

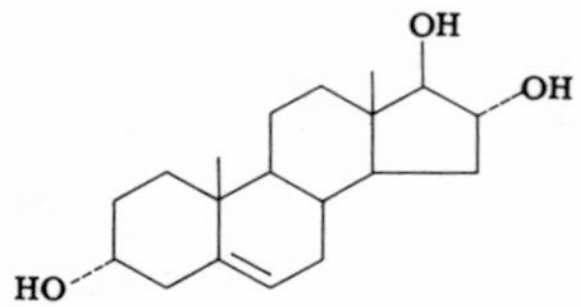

11

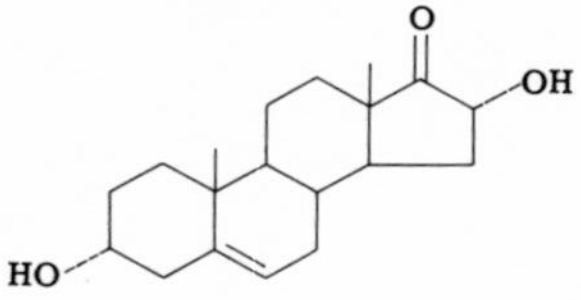

16

13

10

2

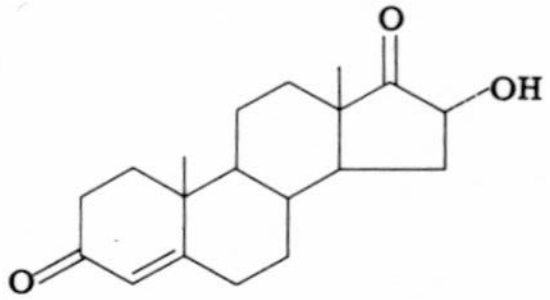

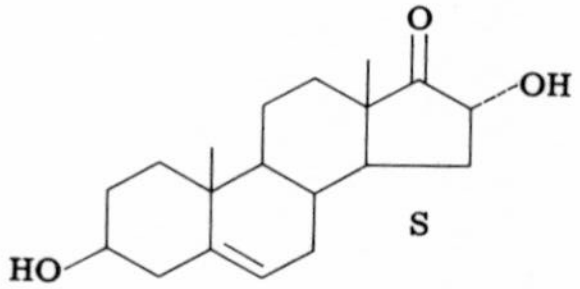

17

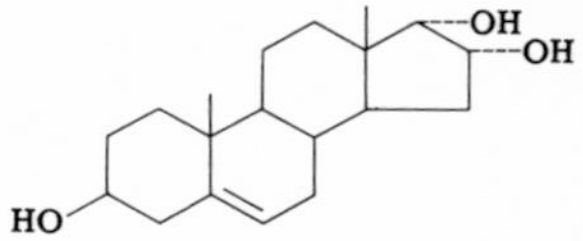

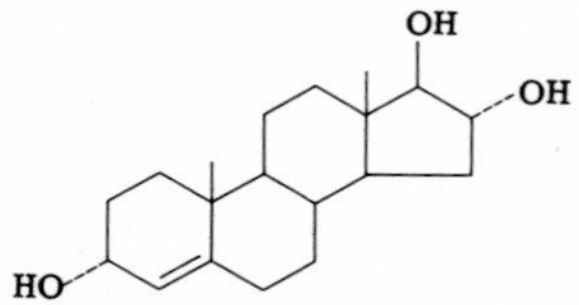

C_{19}-12-1

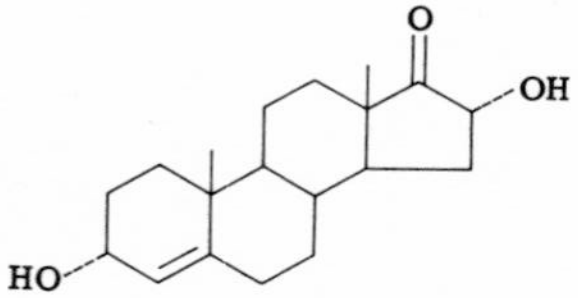

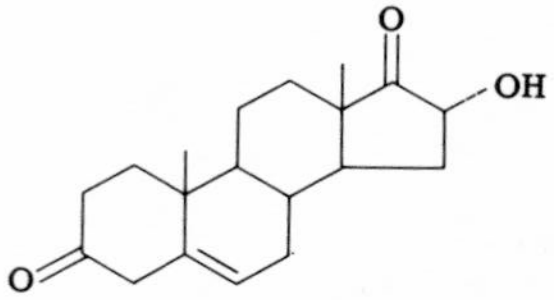

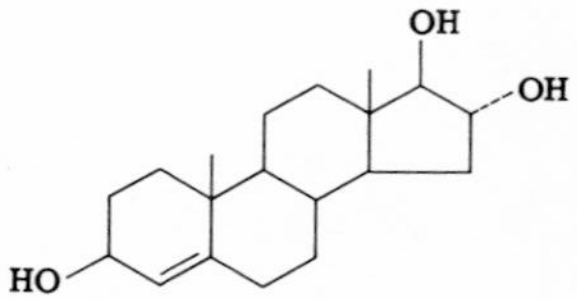

3

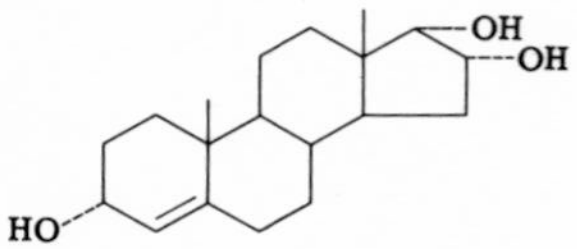

7

34

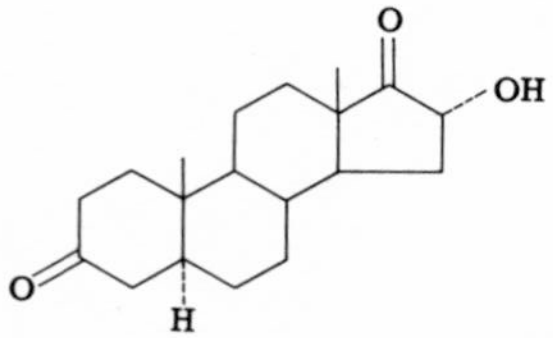

4

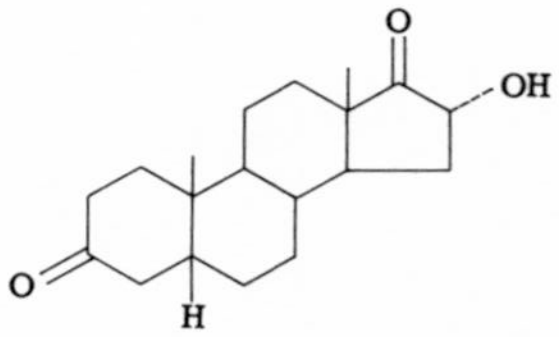

9

8

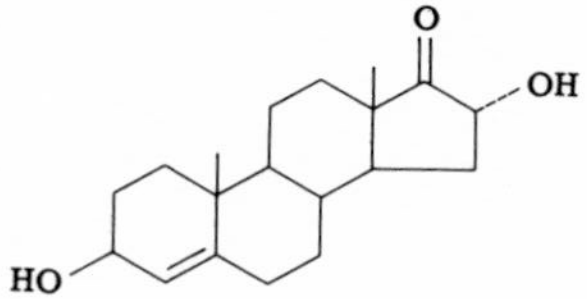

6

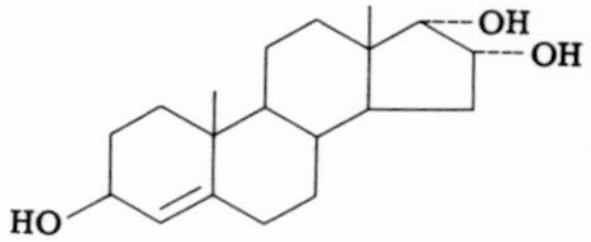

5

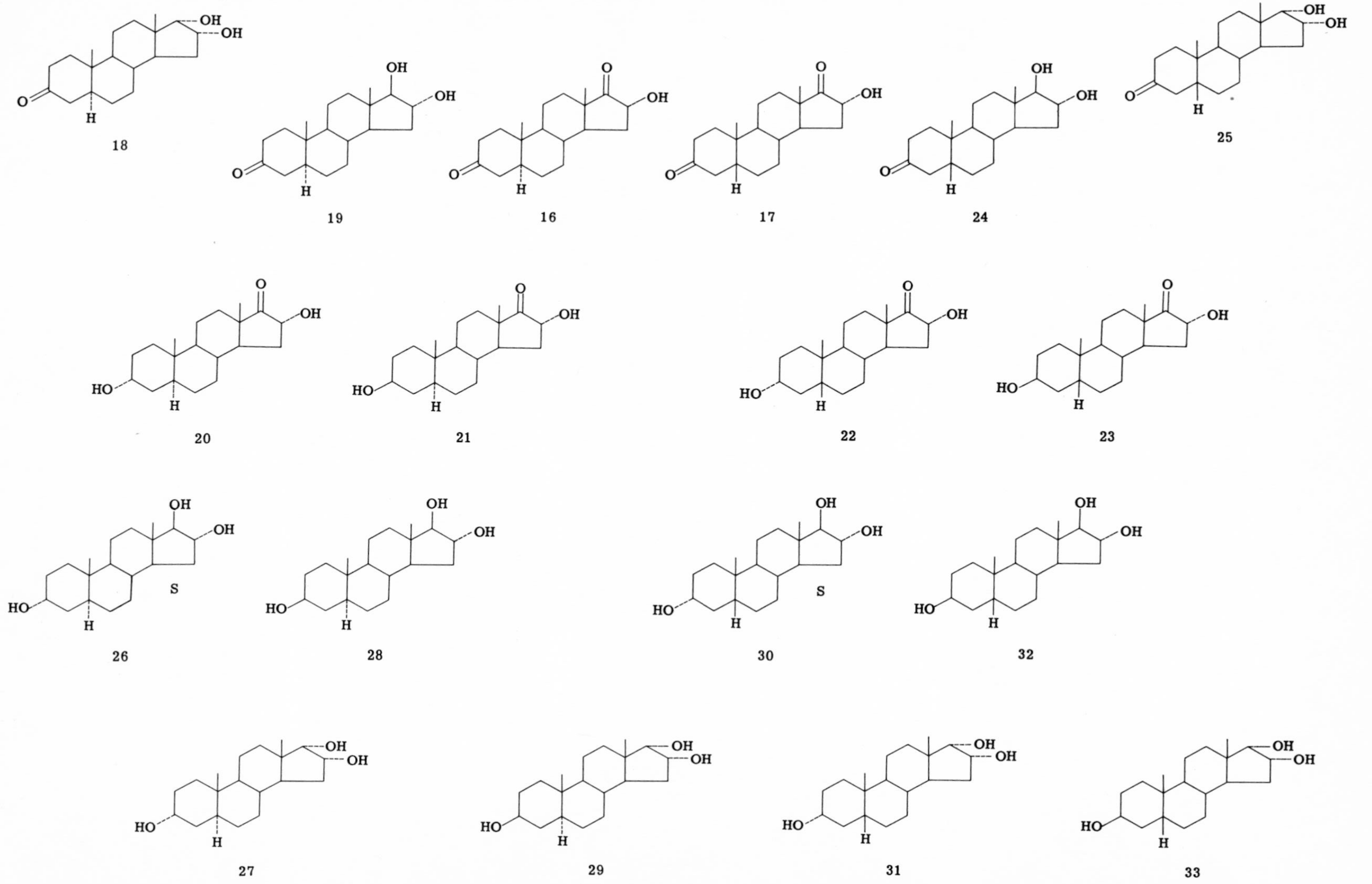

18 19 16 17 24 25

20 21 22 23

26 28 30 32

27 29 31 33

FIG. 15. C_{19}-12-1: 16α-Hydroxyandrost-4-ene-3,17-dione and related metabolites.

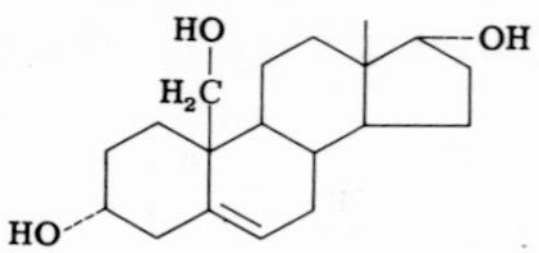

11 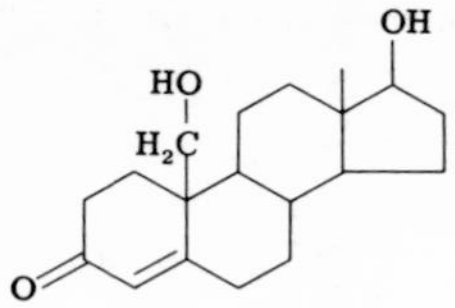 2 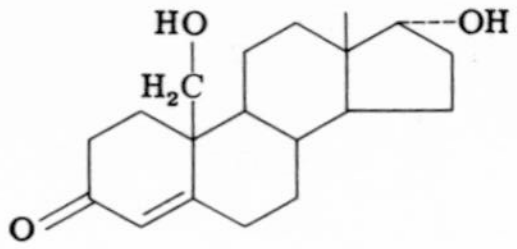 3 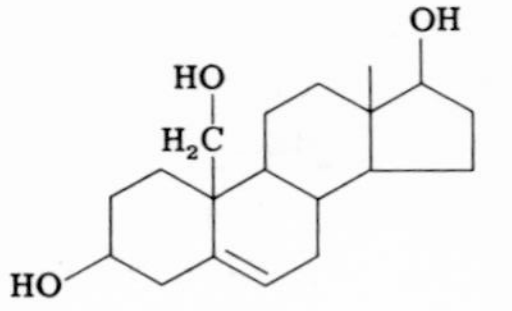 5

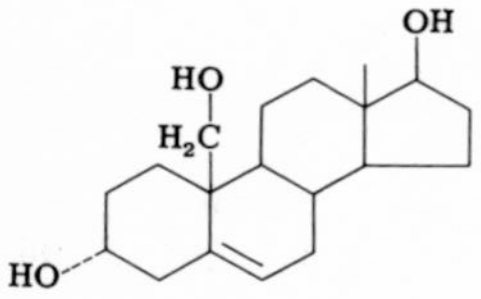

12 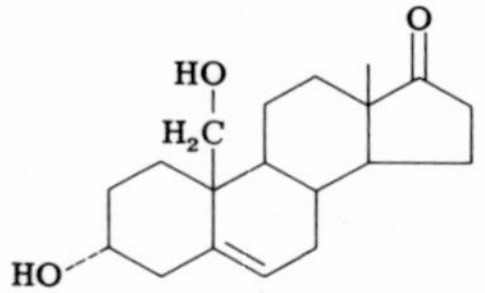 10 4 6

C_{19}-13-1

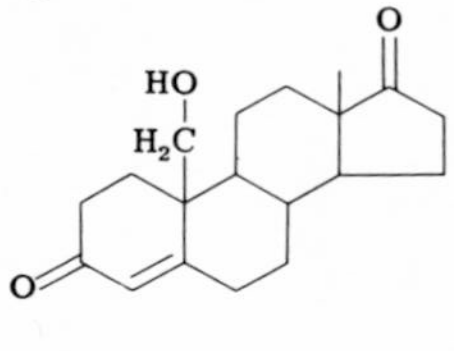

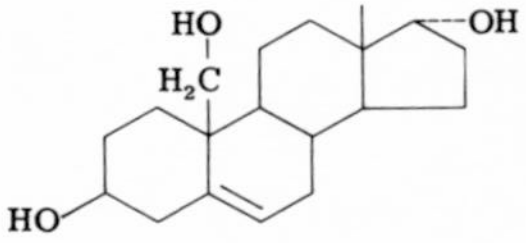

S

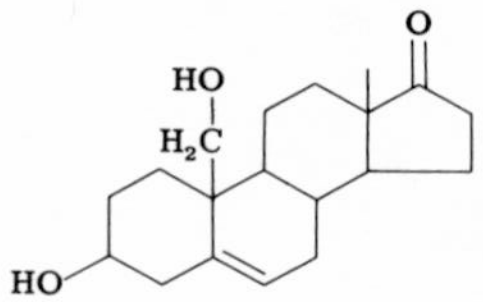

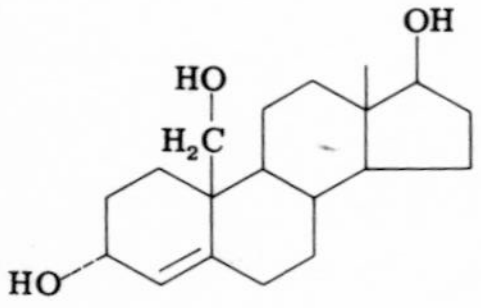

14 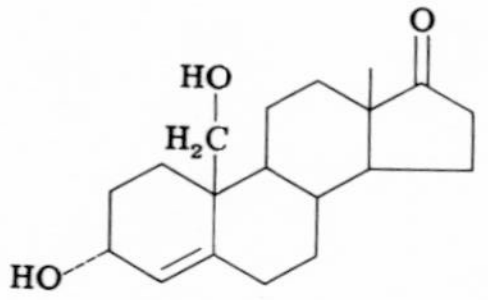 13 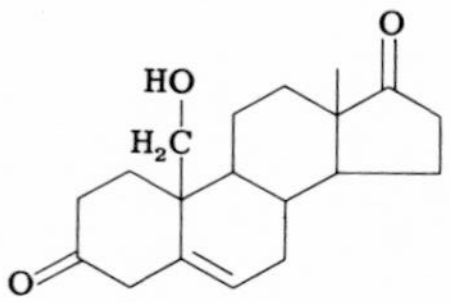 34 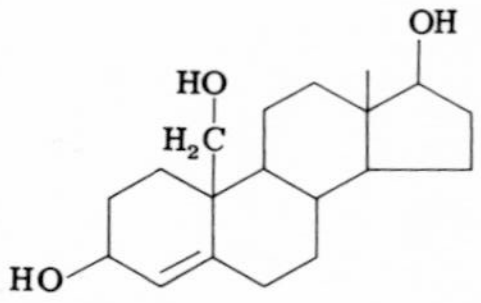 8

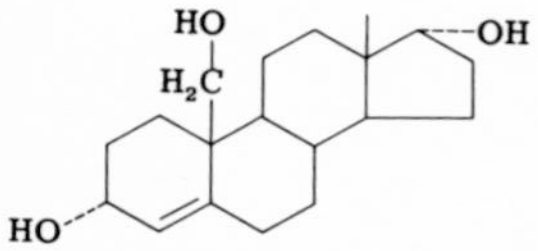

15 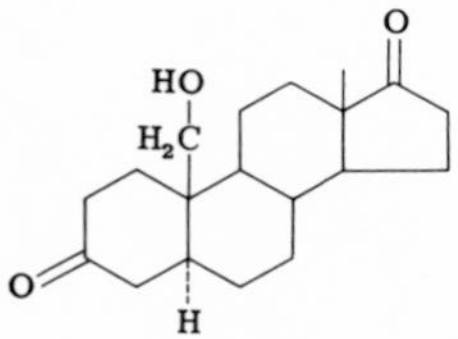 16 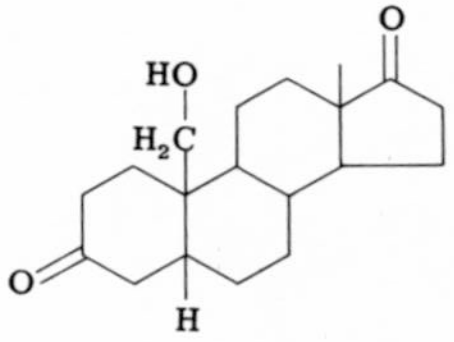 17 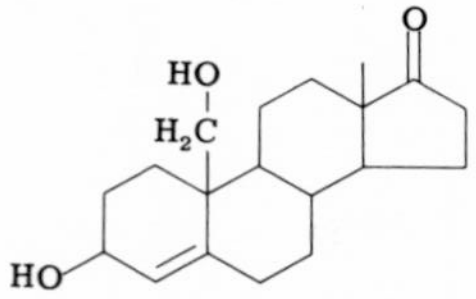 7 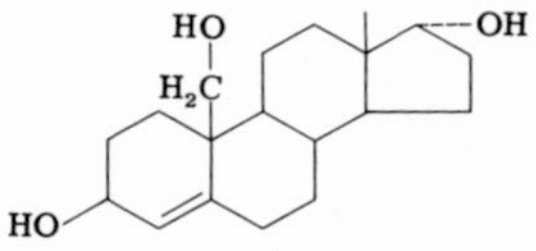 9

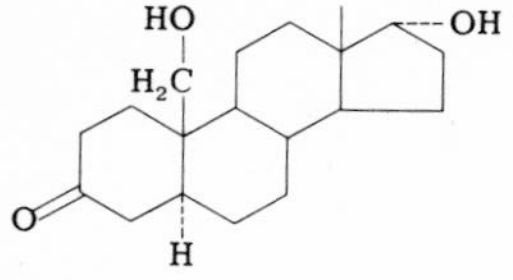

18 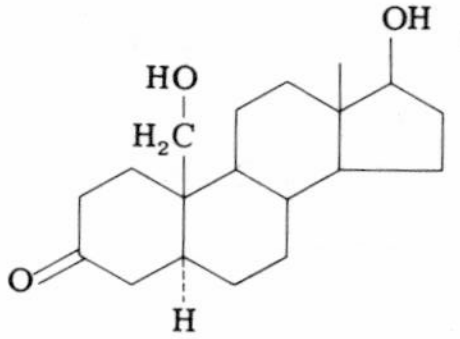 19 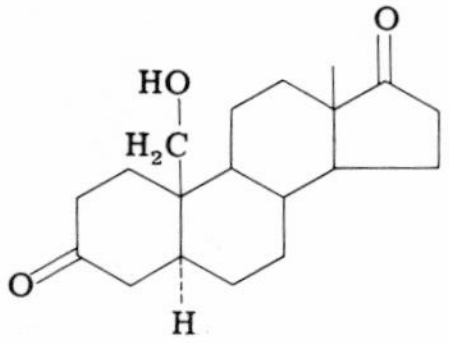 16 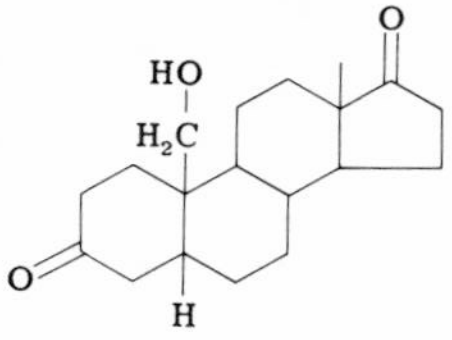 17 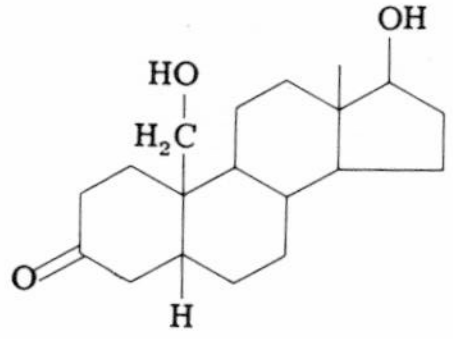 24 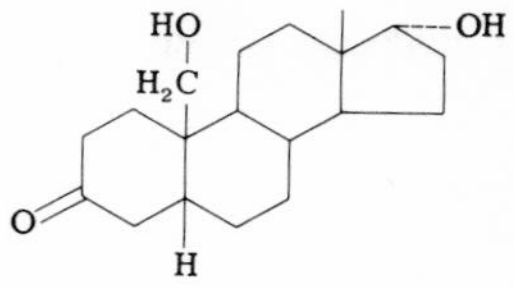 25

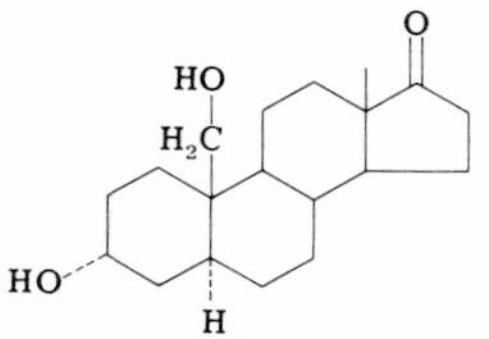

20 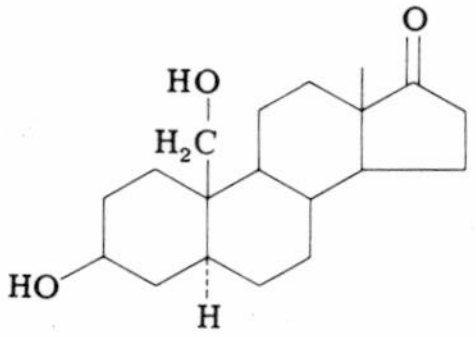 21 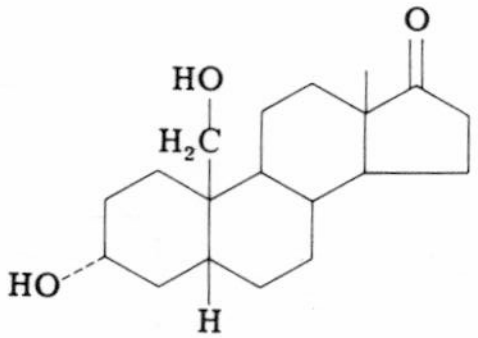 22 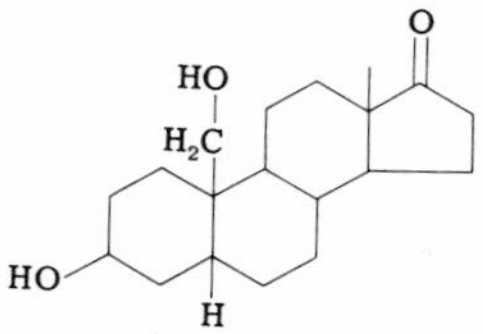 23

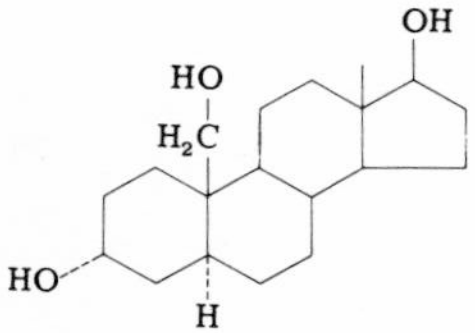

26 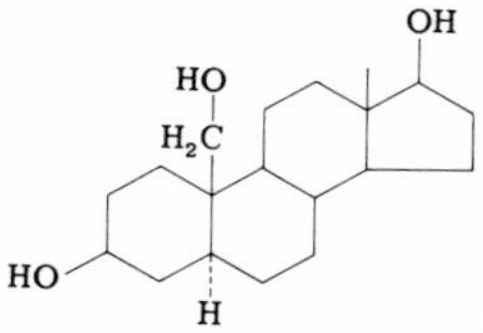 28 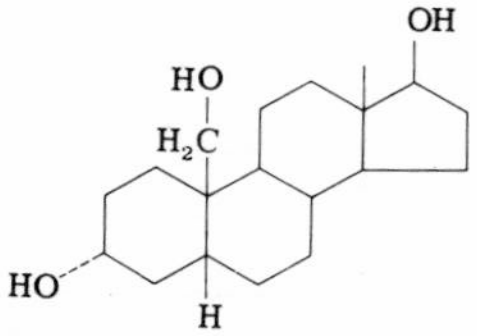 30 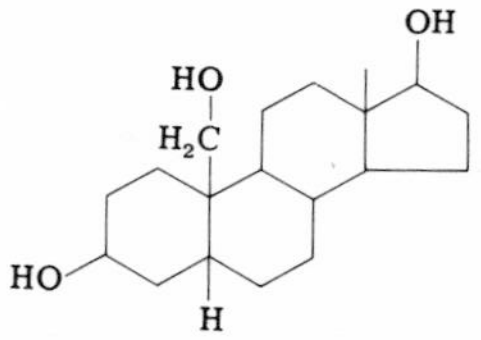 32

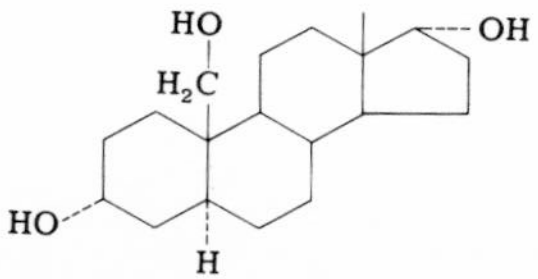

27 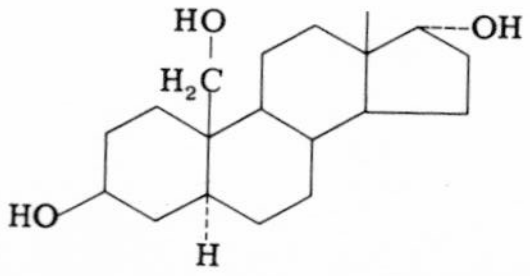 29 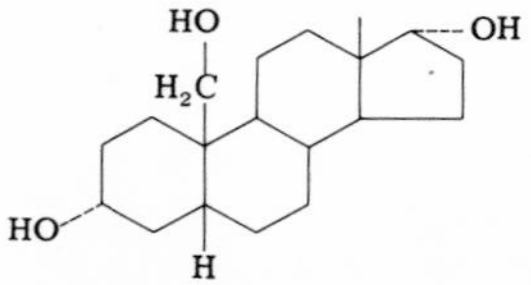 31 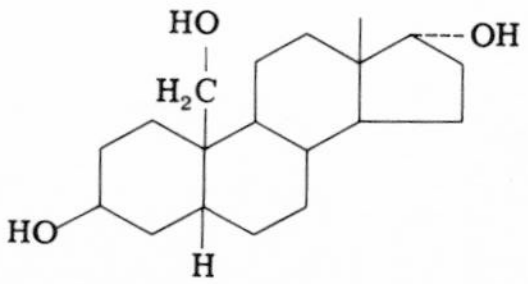 33

FIG. 16. C_{19}-13-1: 19-Hydroxyandrost-4-ene-3,17-dione and related metabolites.

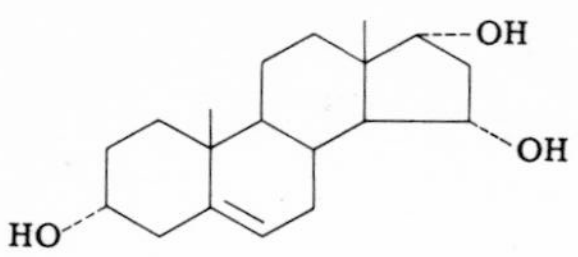

C$_{19}$-14-1

S

11

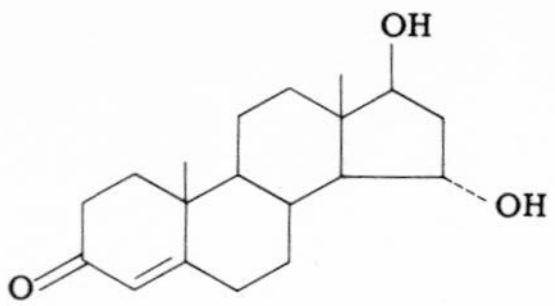

2

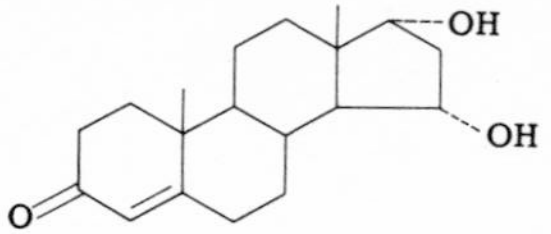

3

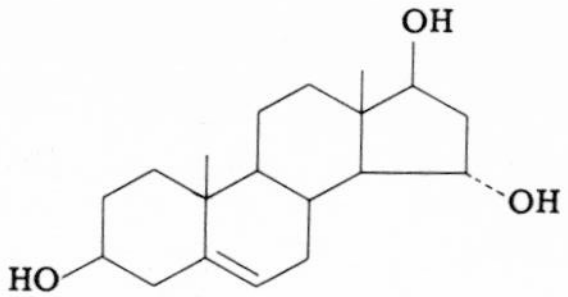

5

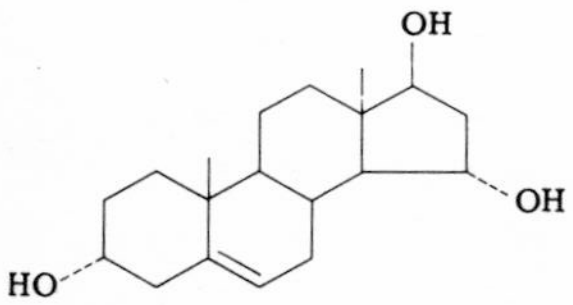

12

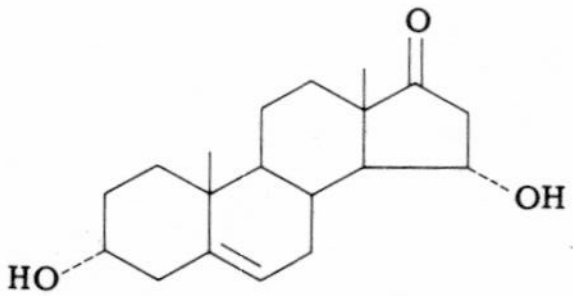

10

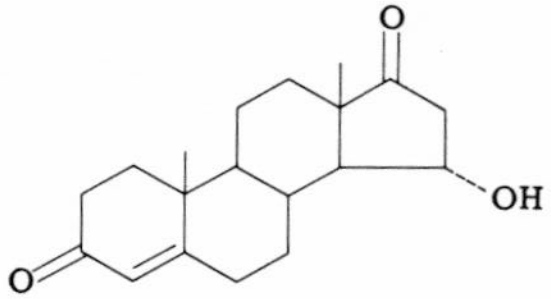

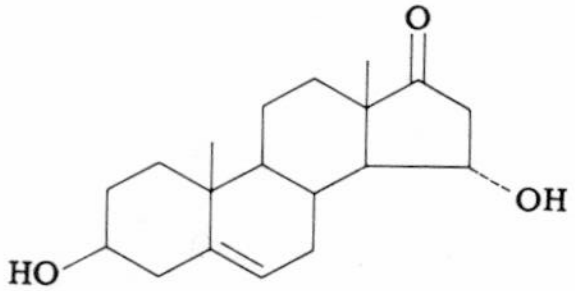

4

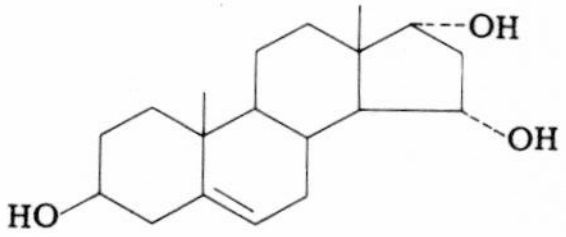

6

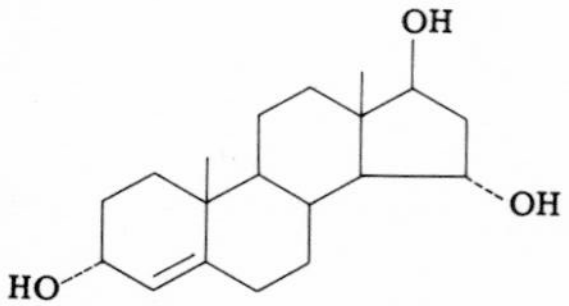

14

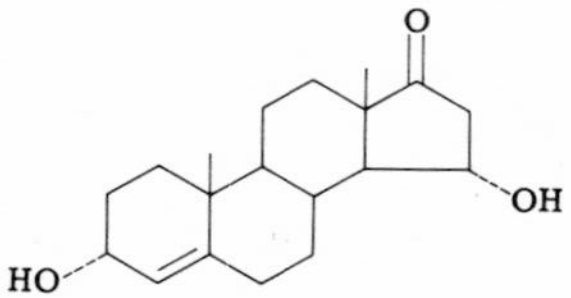

13

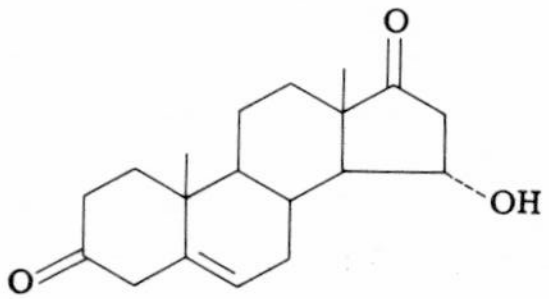

34

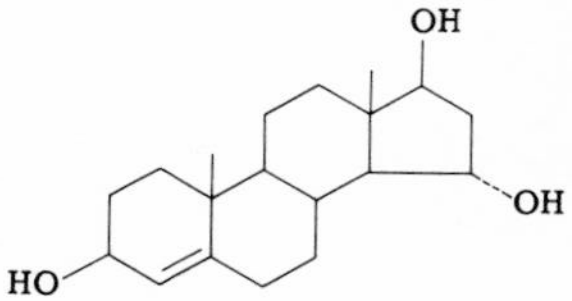

8

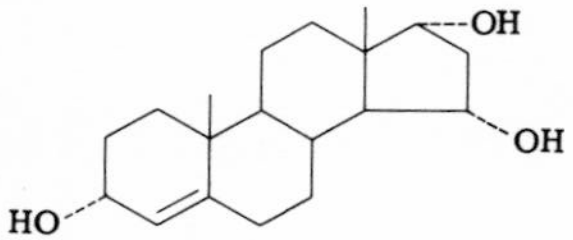

15

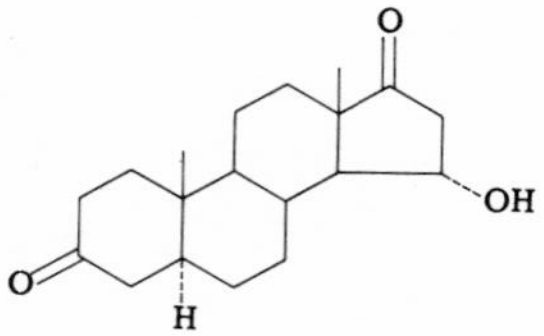

16

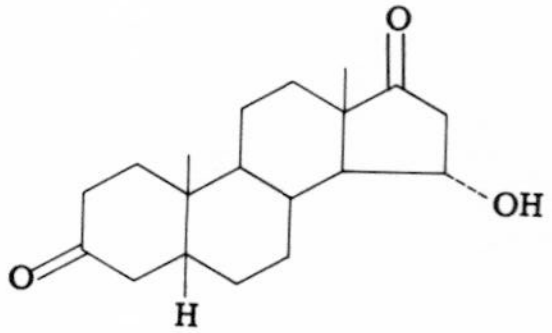

17

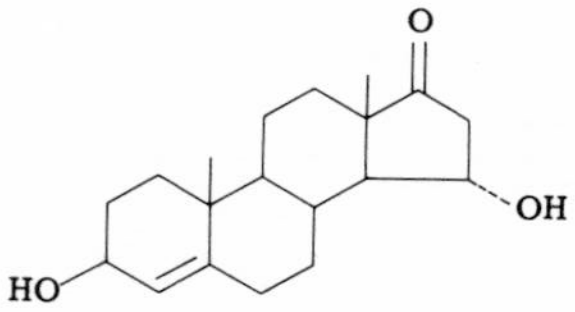

7

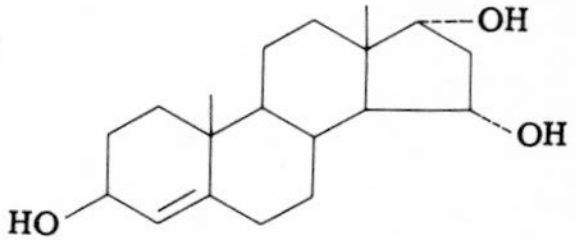

9

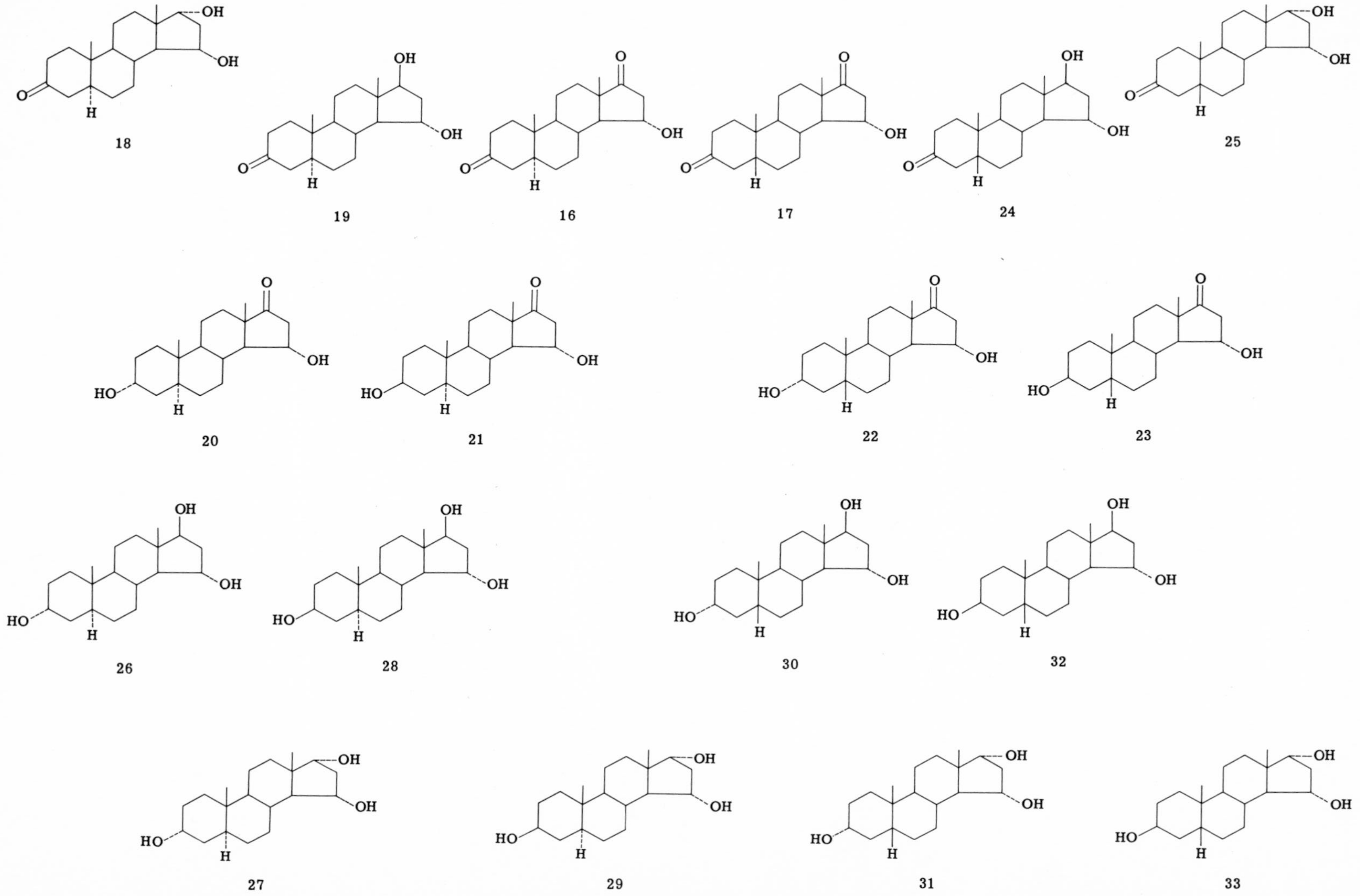

FIG. 17. C_{19}-14-1: 15α-Hydroxyandrost-4-ene-3,17-dione and related metabolites.

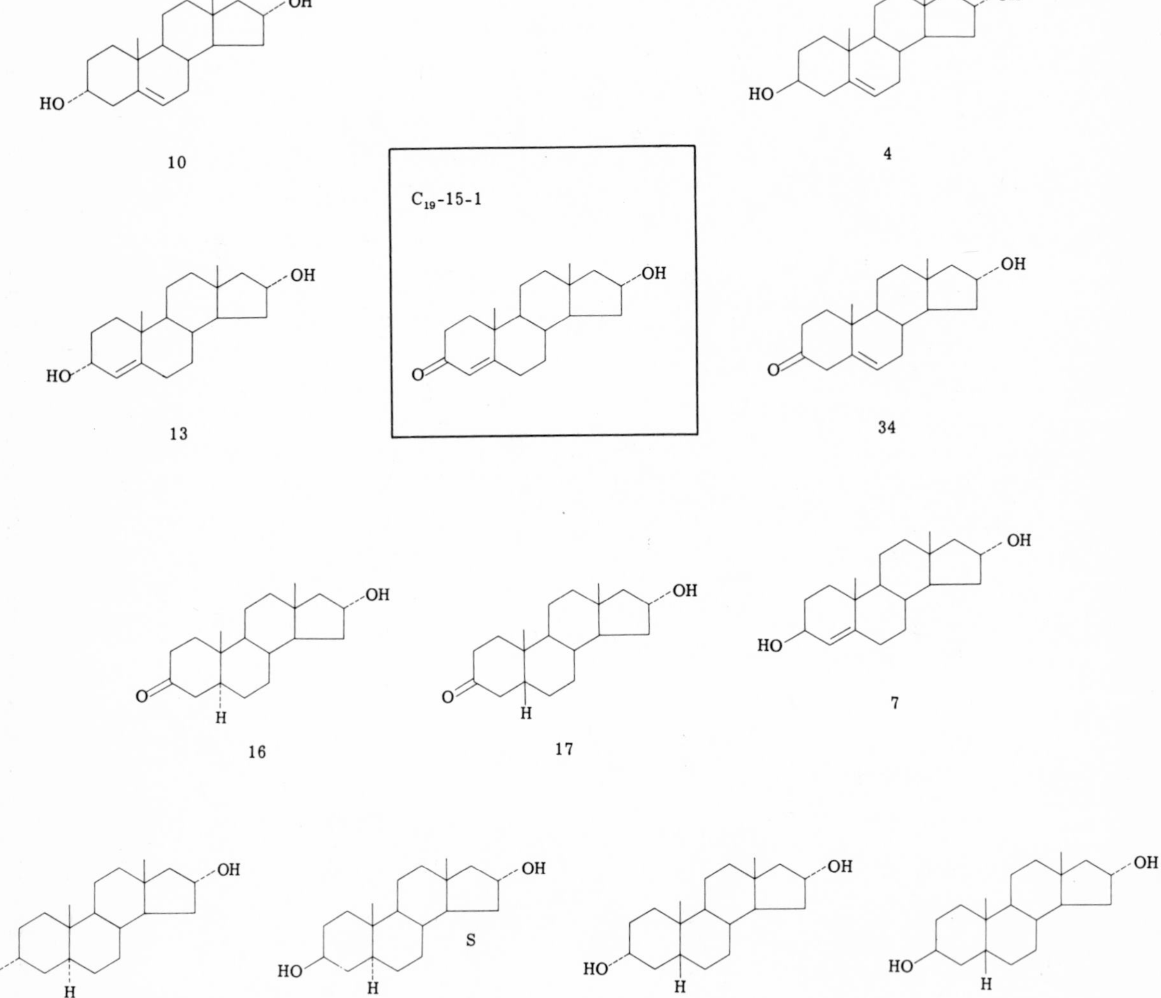

FIG. 18. C_{19}-15-1: 16α-Hydroxyandrost-4-en-3-one and related metabolites.

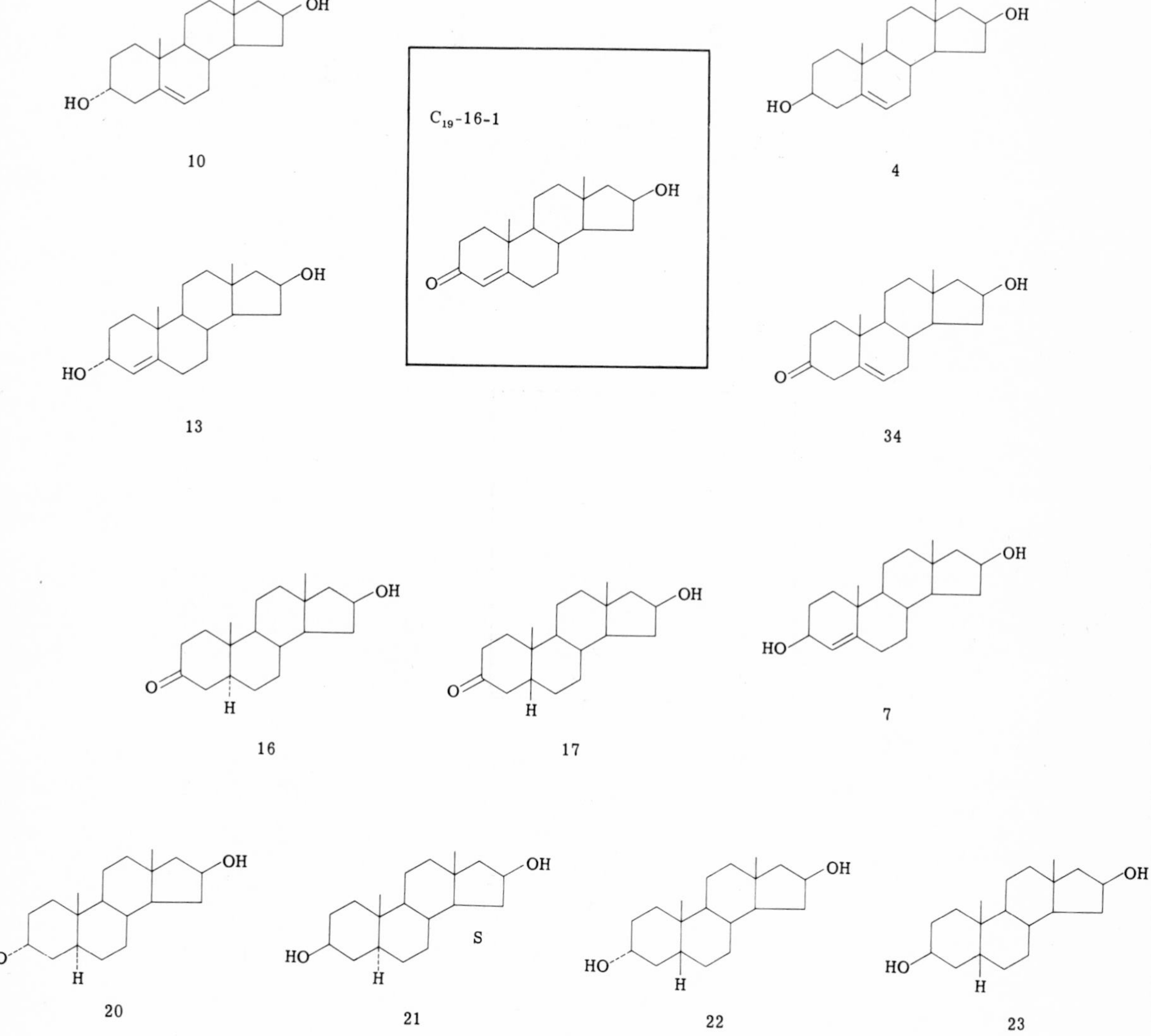

FIG. 19. C_{19}-16-1: 16β-Hydroxyandrost-4-en-3-one and related metabolites.

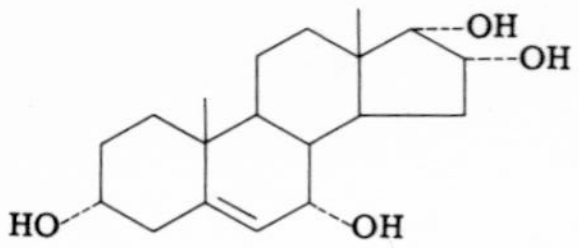

C_{19}-17-1

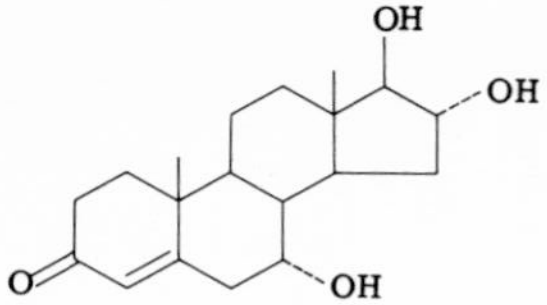

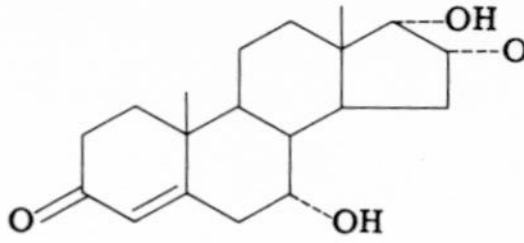

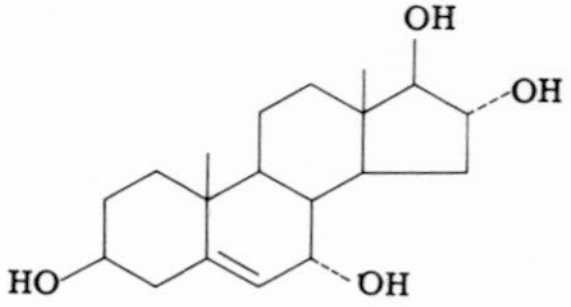

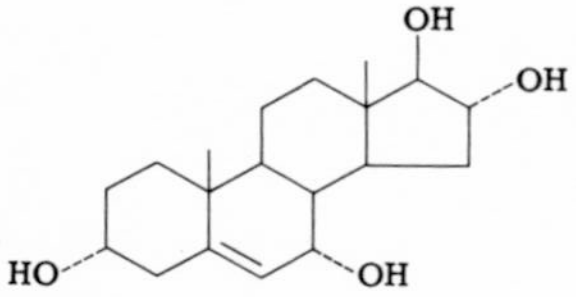

5 6 8 9

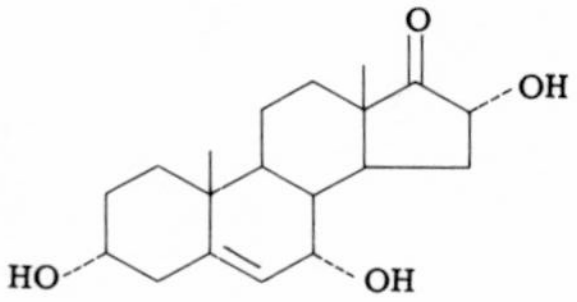

3 4 34 7

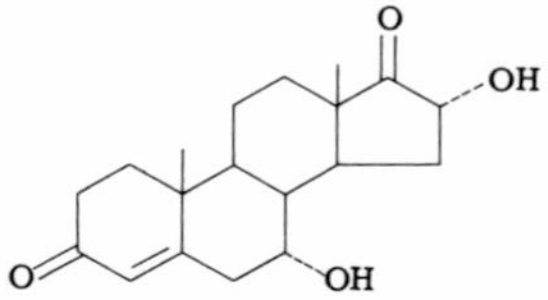

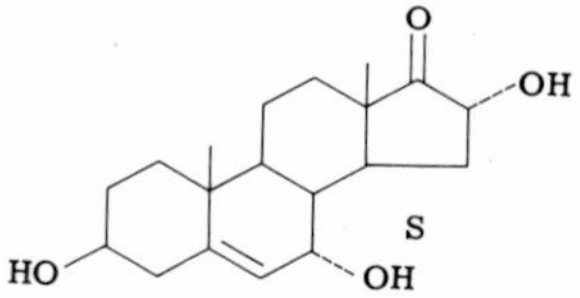

2 17

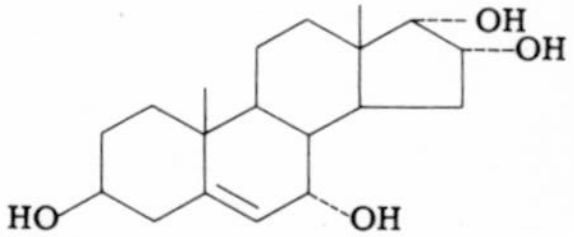

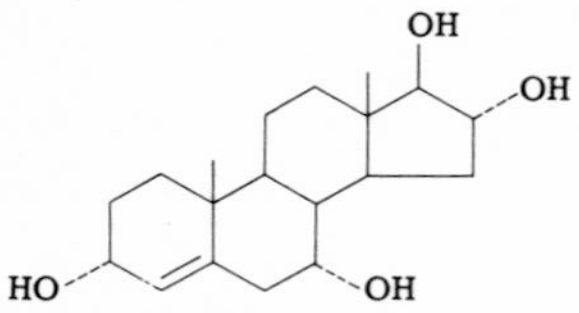

10 13 16

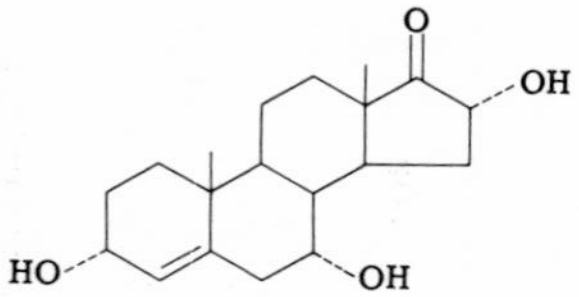

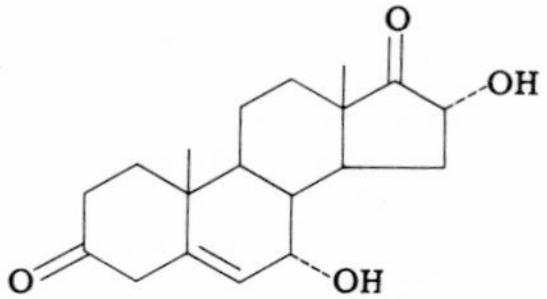

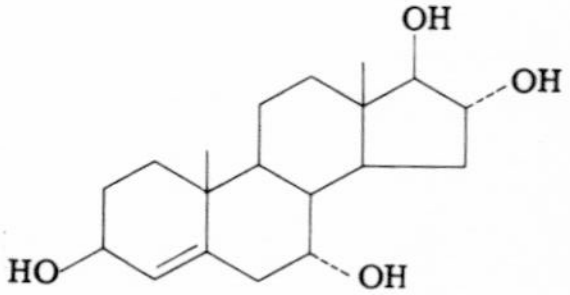

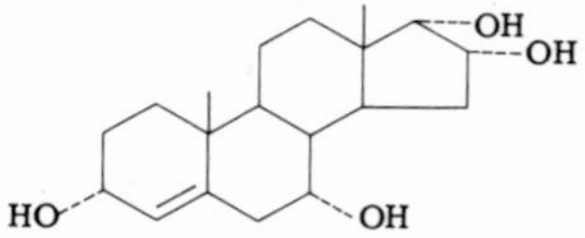

11 12 14 15

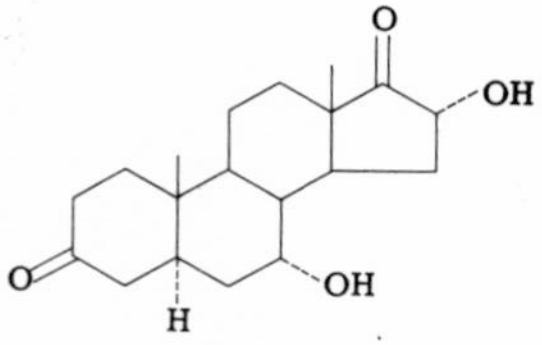

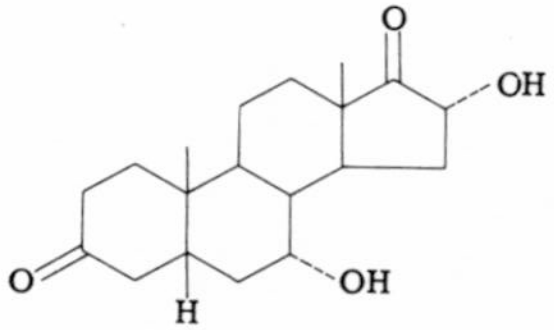

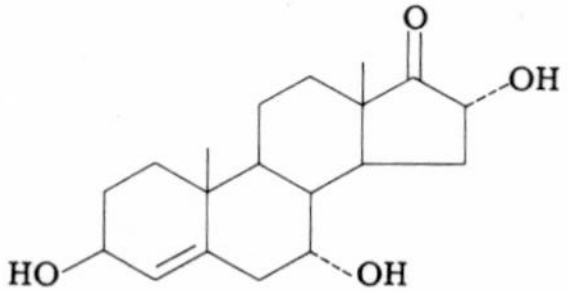

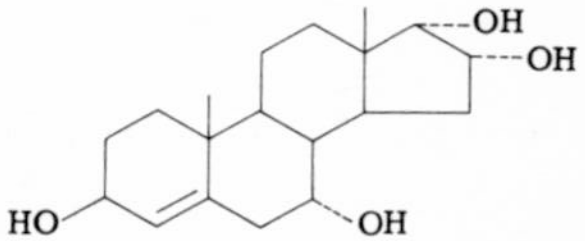

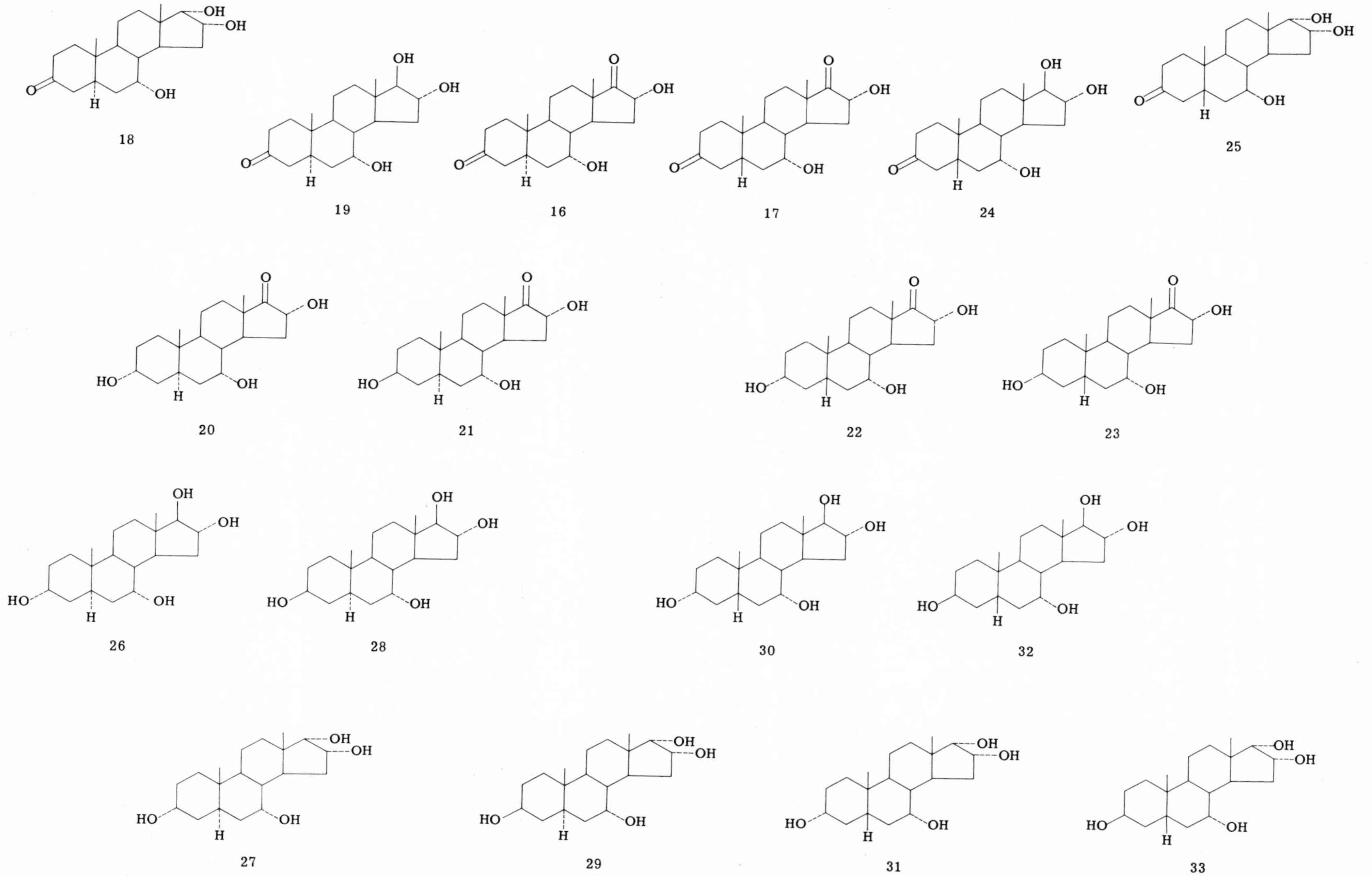

18 19 16 17 24 25

20 21 22 23

26 28 30 32

27 29 31 33

FIG. 20. C_{19}-17-1: 7α,16α-Dihydroxyandrost-4-ene-3,17-dione and related metabolites.

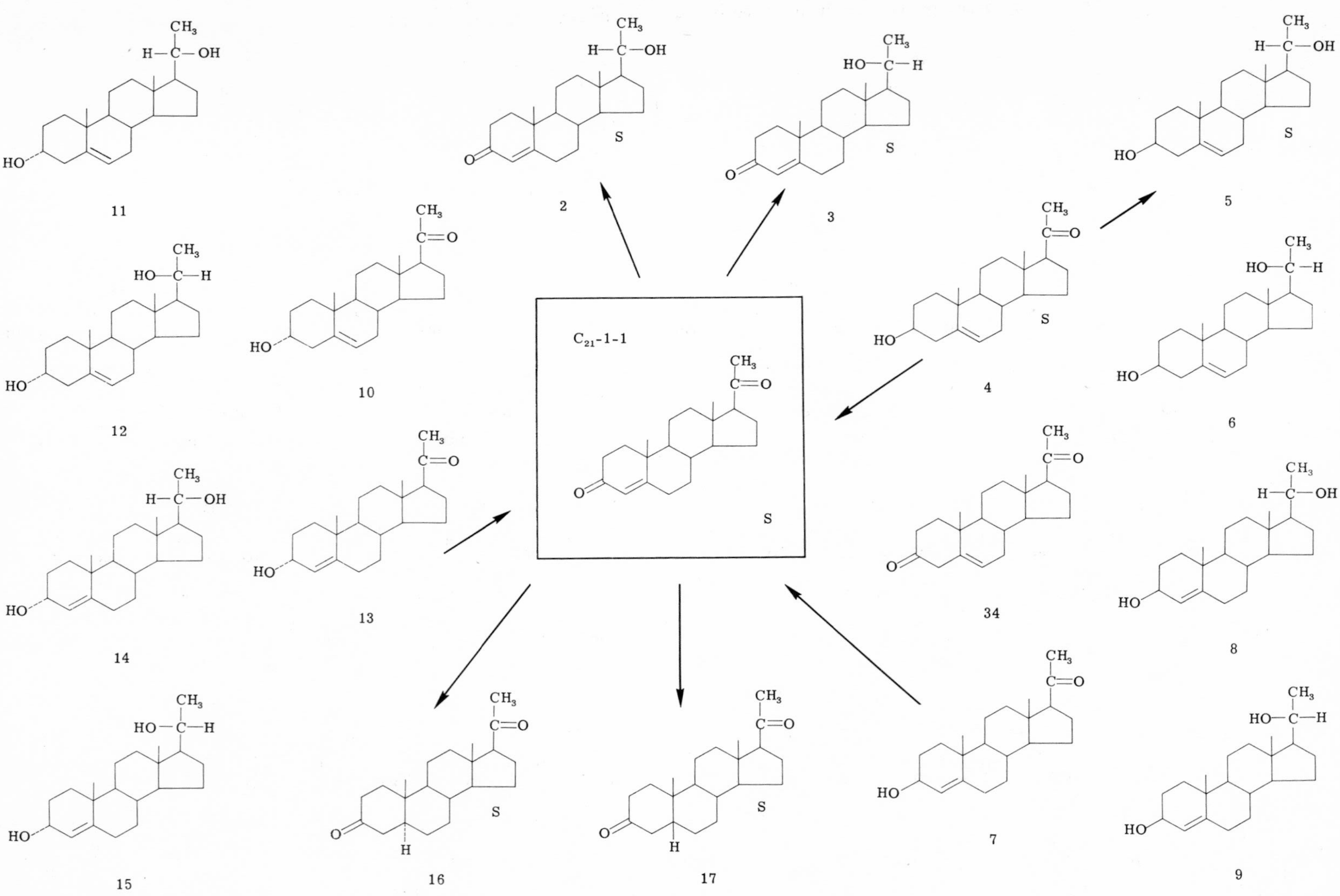
C_{21}-1-1
11
2
3
5
12
10
4
6
14
13
34
8
15
16
17
7
9

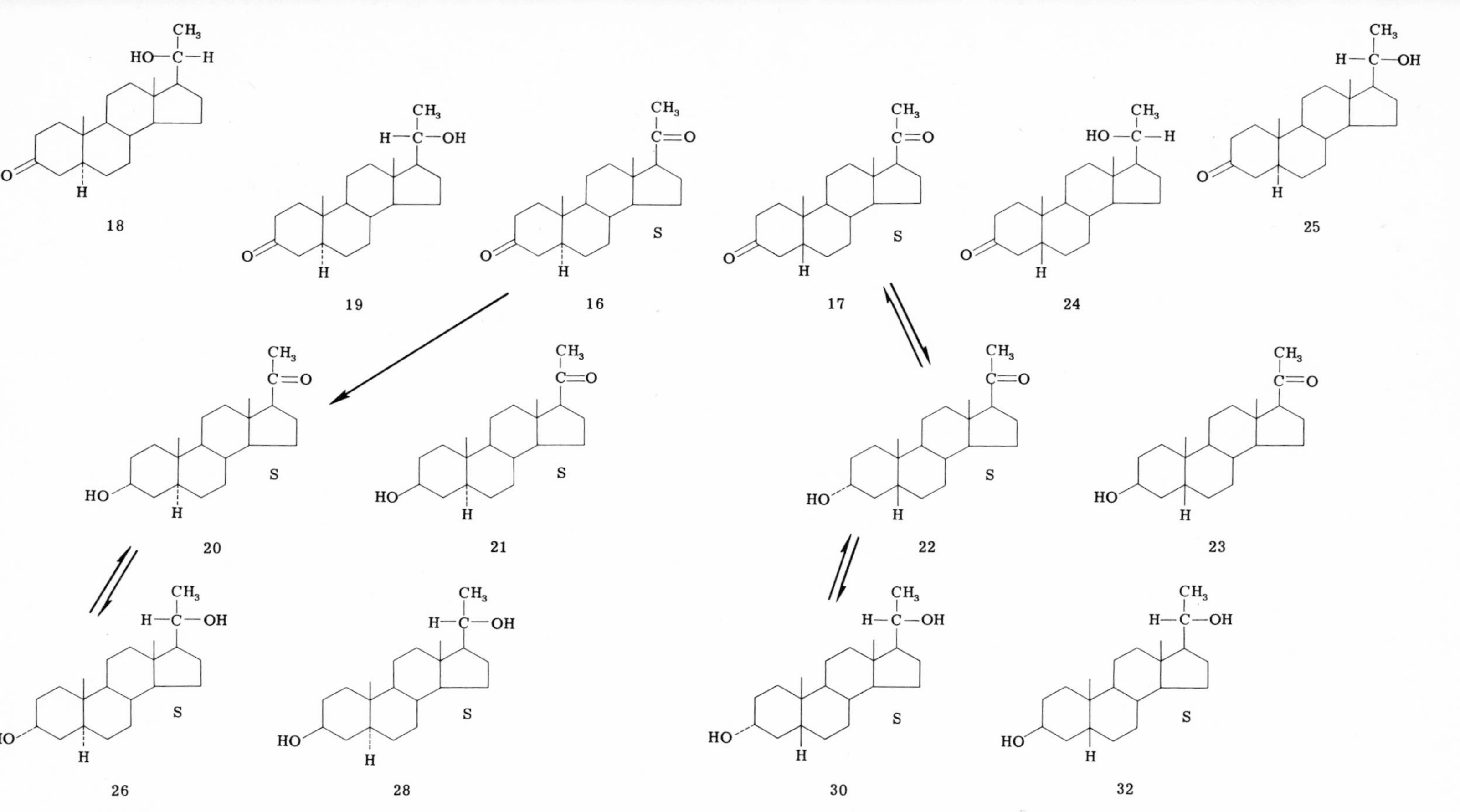

FIG. 21. C_{21}-1-1: Progesterone and related metabolites.

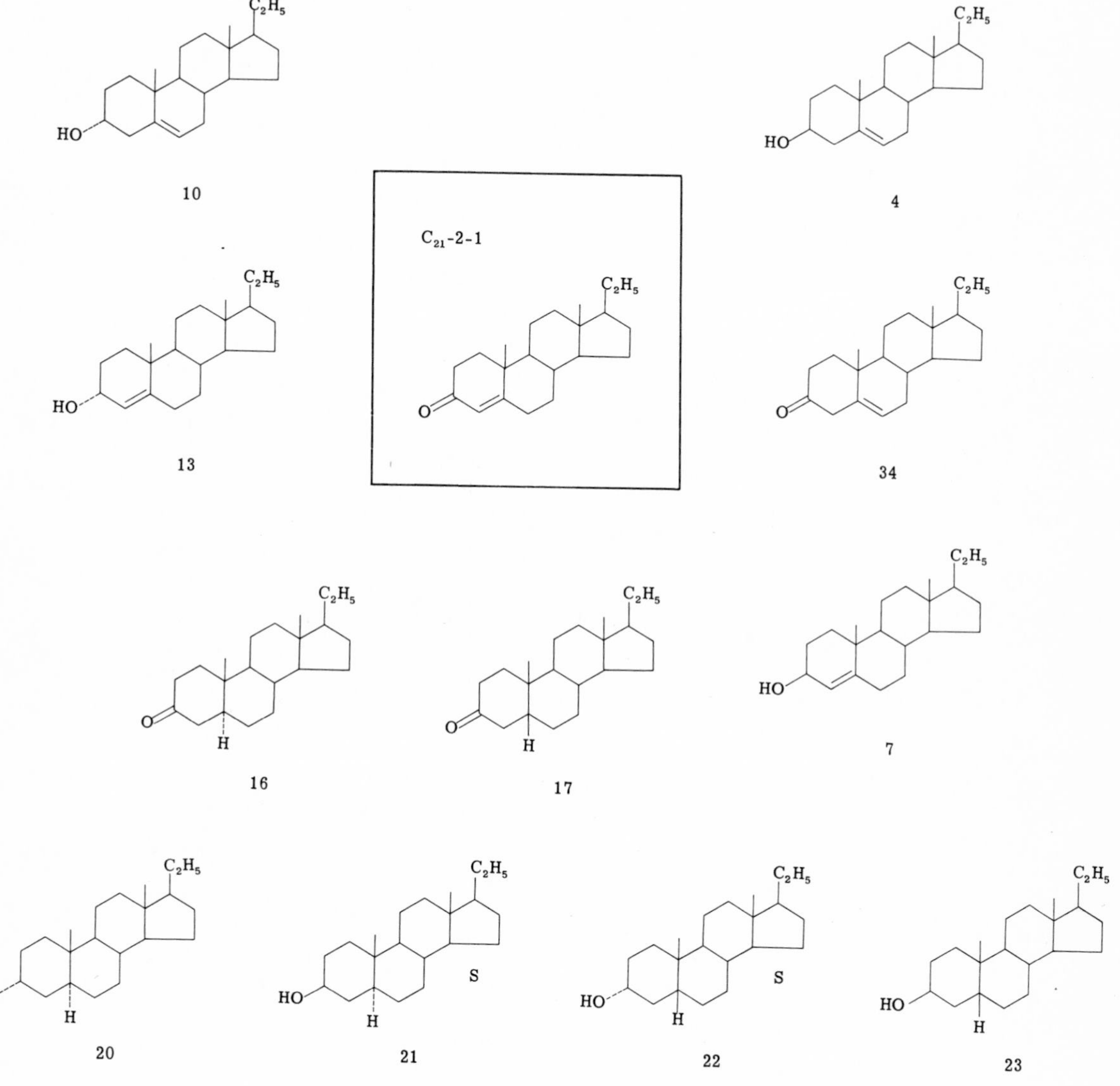

FIG. 22. C_{21}-2-1: Pregn-4-en-3-one and related metabolites.

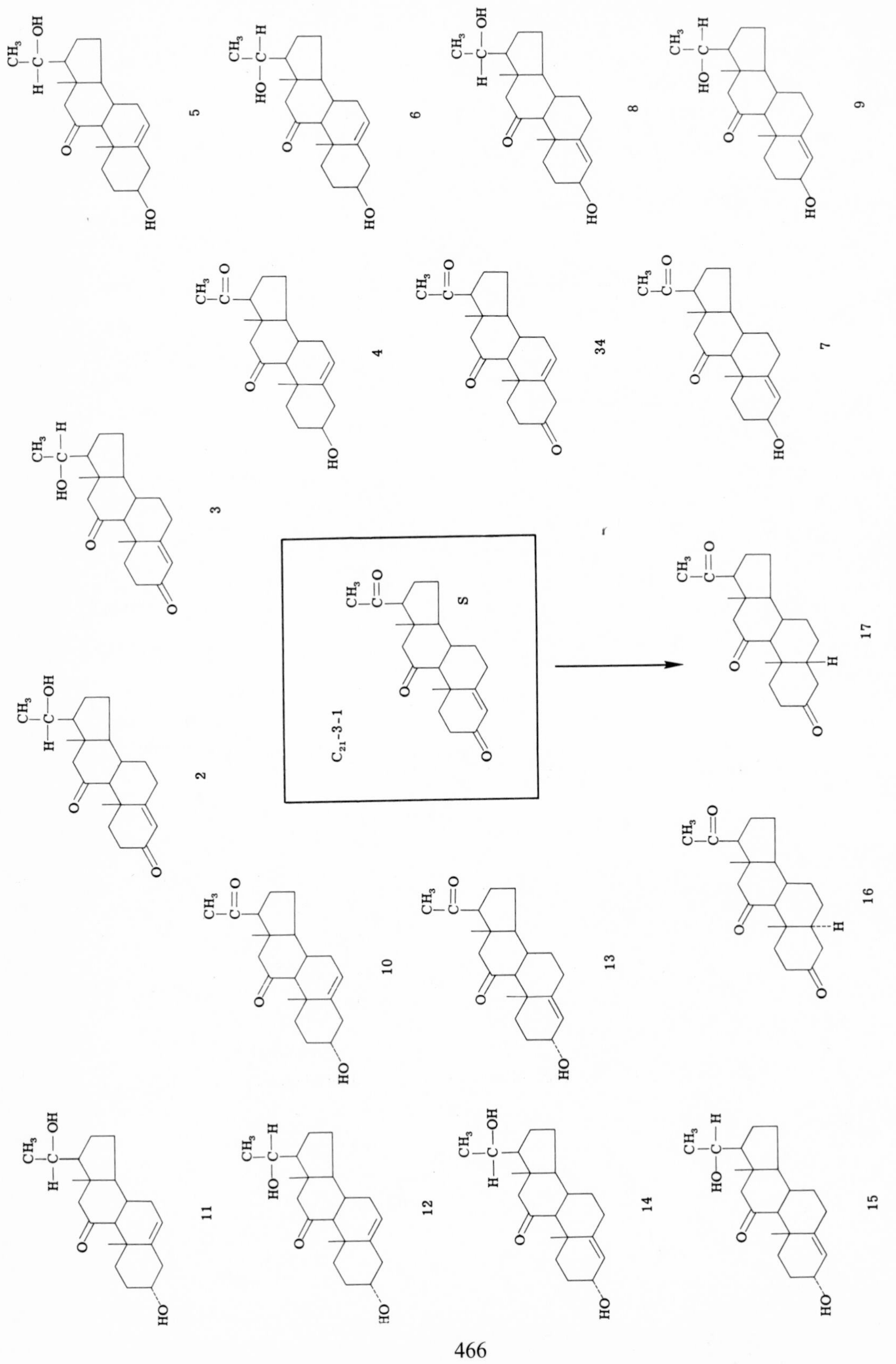

C_{21}-3-1

S

11 2 3 5

12 10 4 6

14 13 34 8

15 16 17 7 9

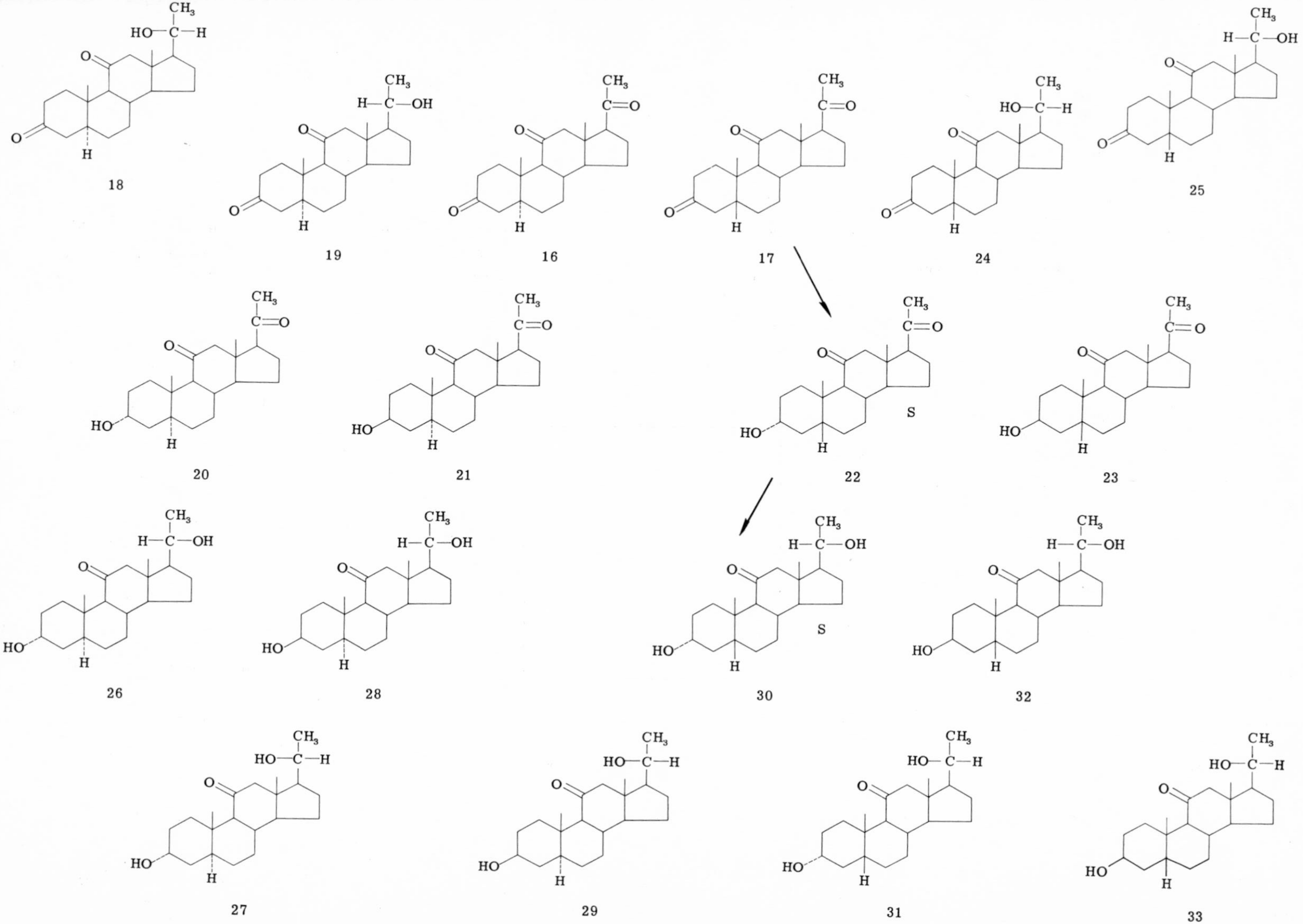

18 19 16 17 24 25

20 21 22 23

26 28 30 32

27 29 31 33

FIG. 23. C_{21}-3-1: 11-Ketoprogesterone and related metabolites.

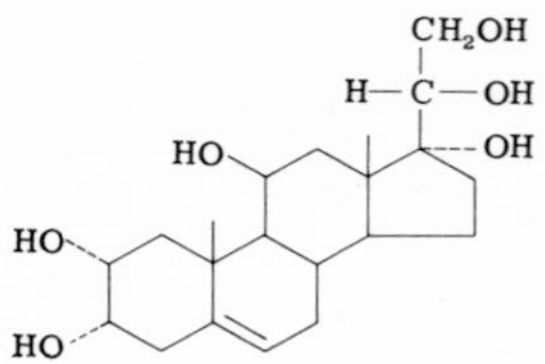

C_{21}-4-1

S

11

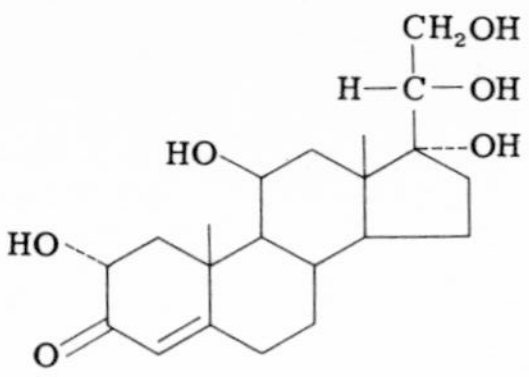

2

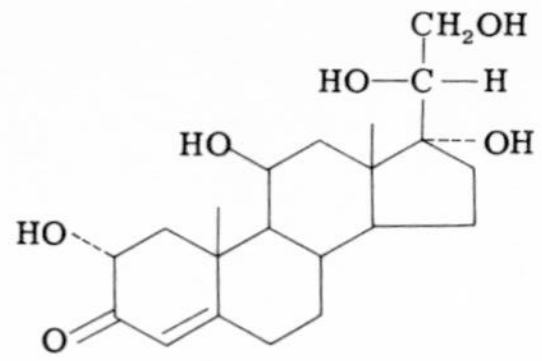

3

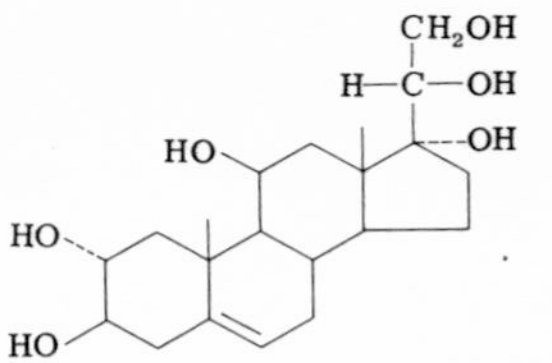

5

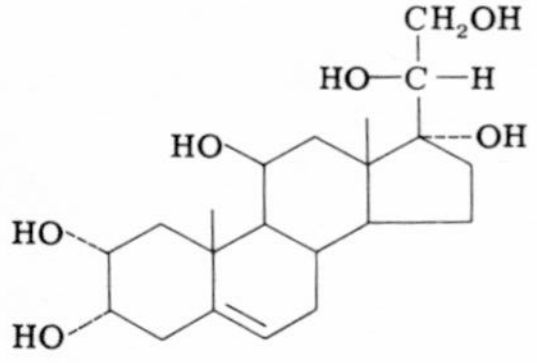

12

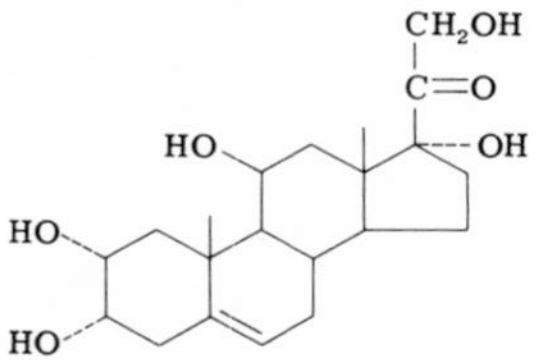

10

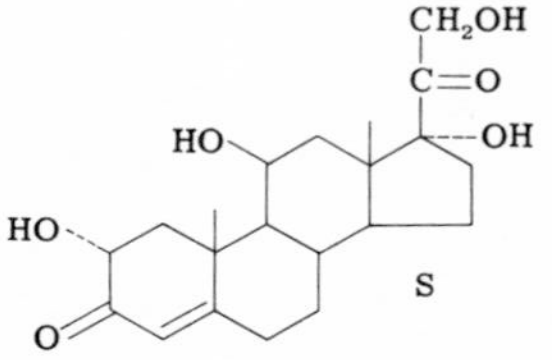

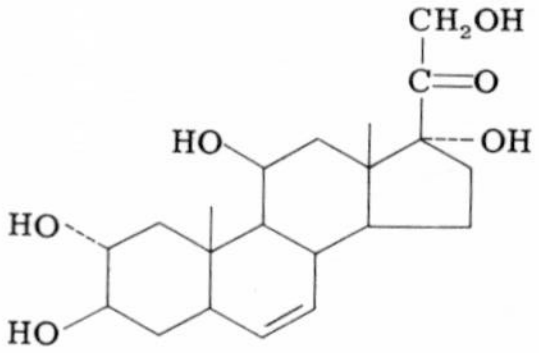

4

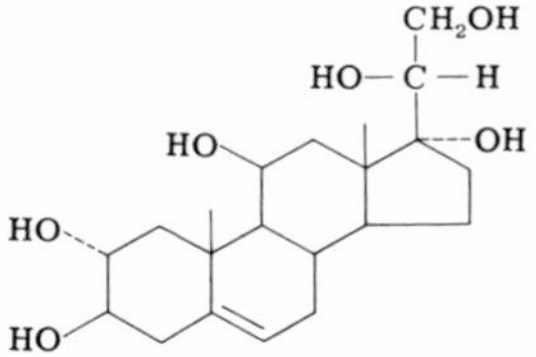

6

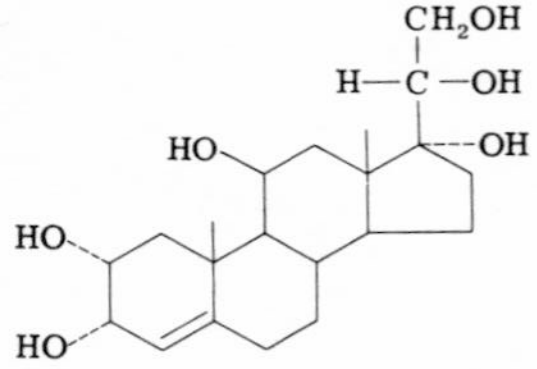

14

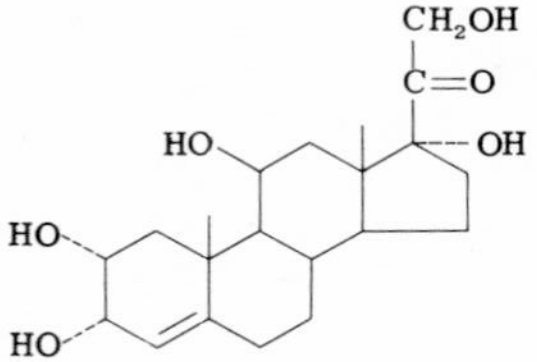

13

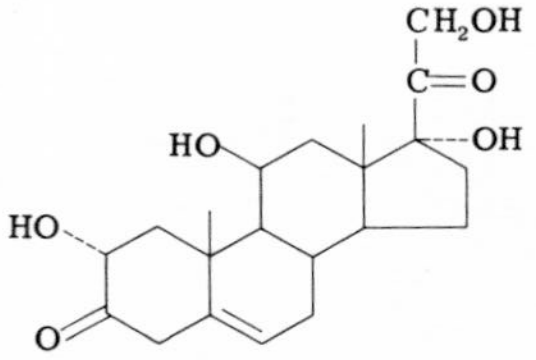

34

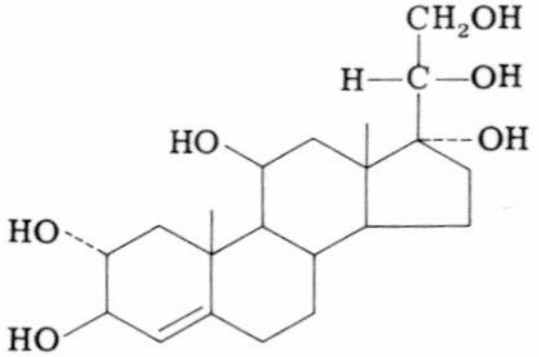

8

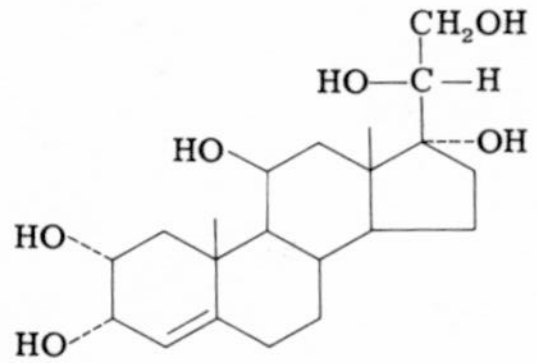

15

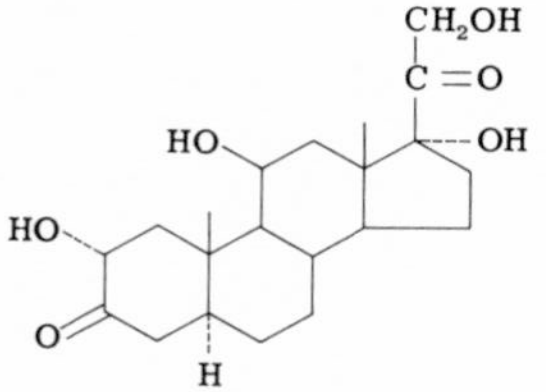

16

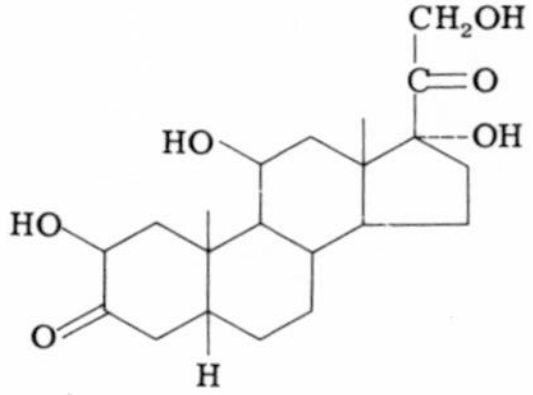

17

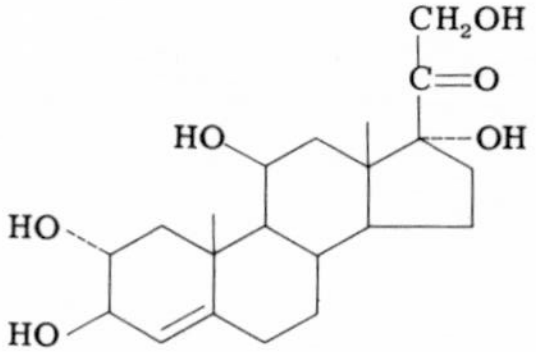

7

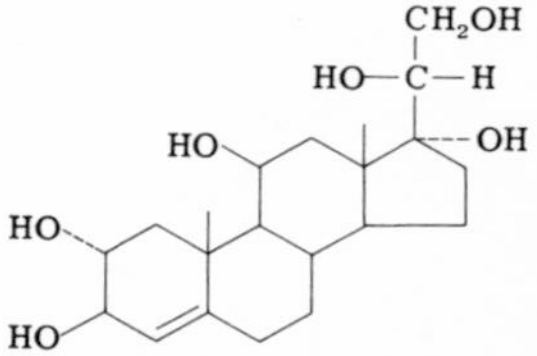

9

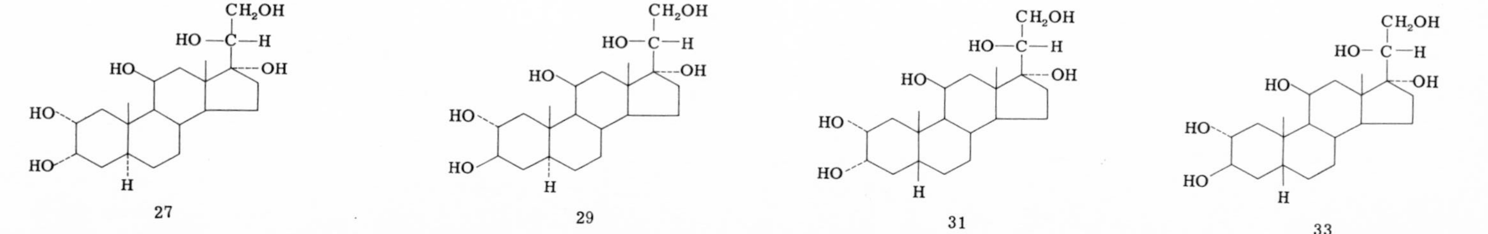

FIG. 24. C_{21}-4-1: 2α-Hydroxycortisol and related metabolites.

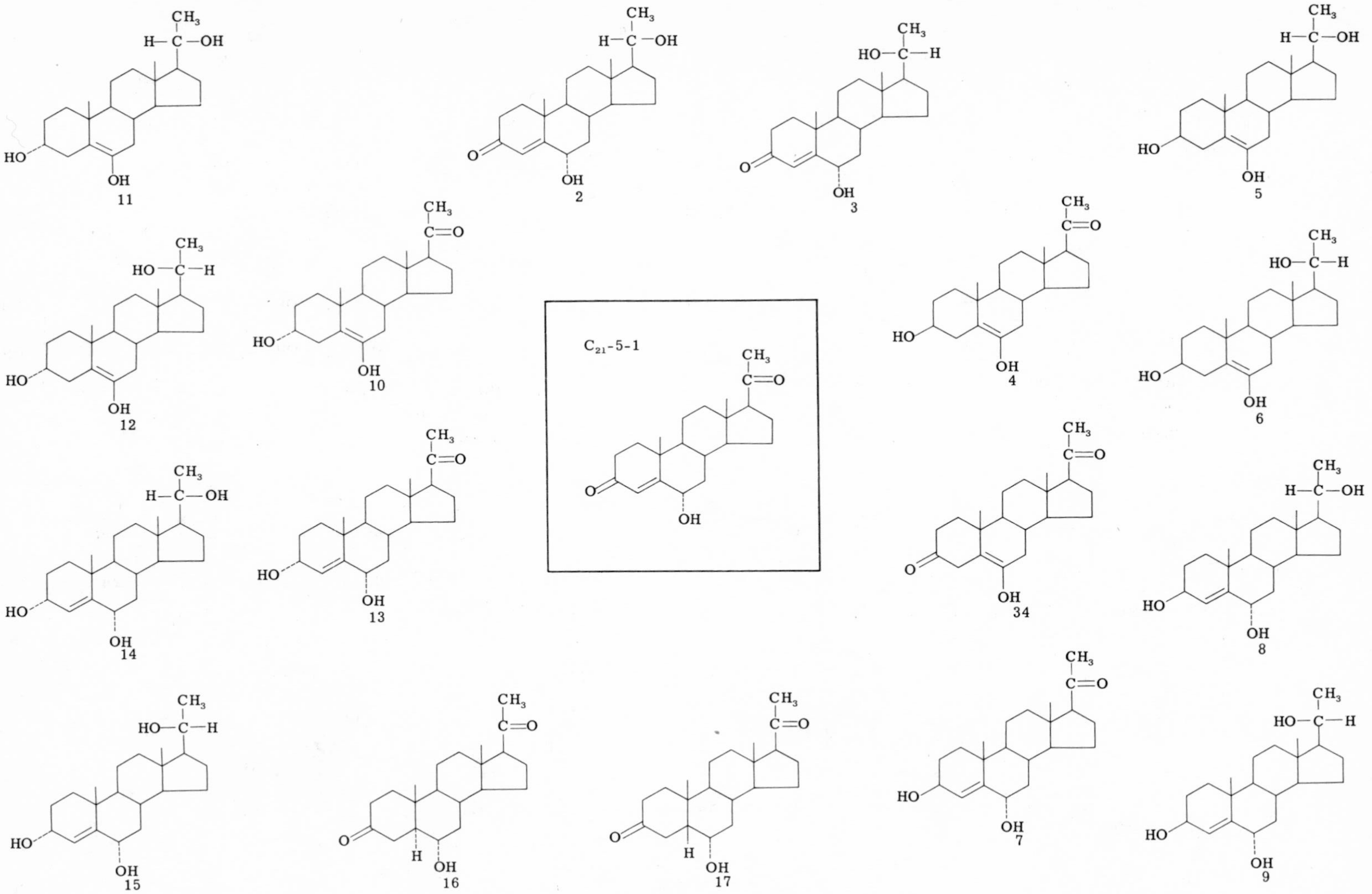

C_{21}-5-1

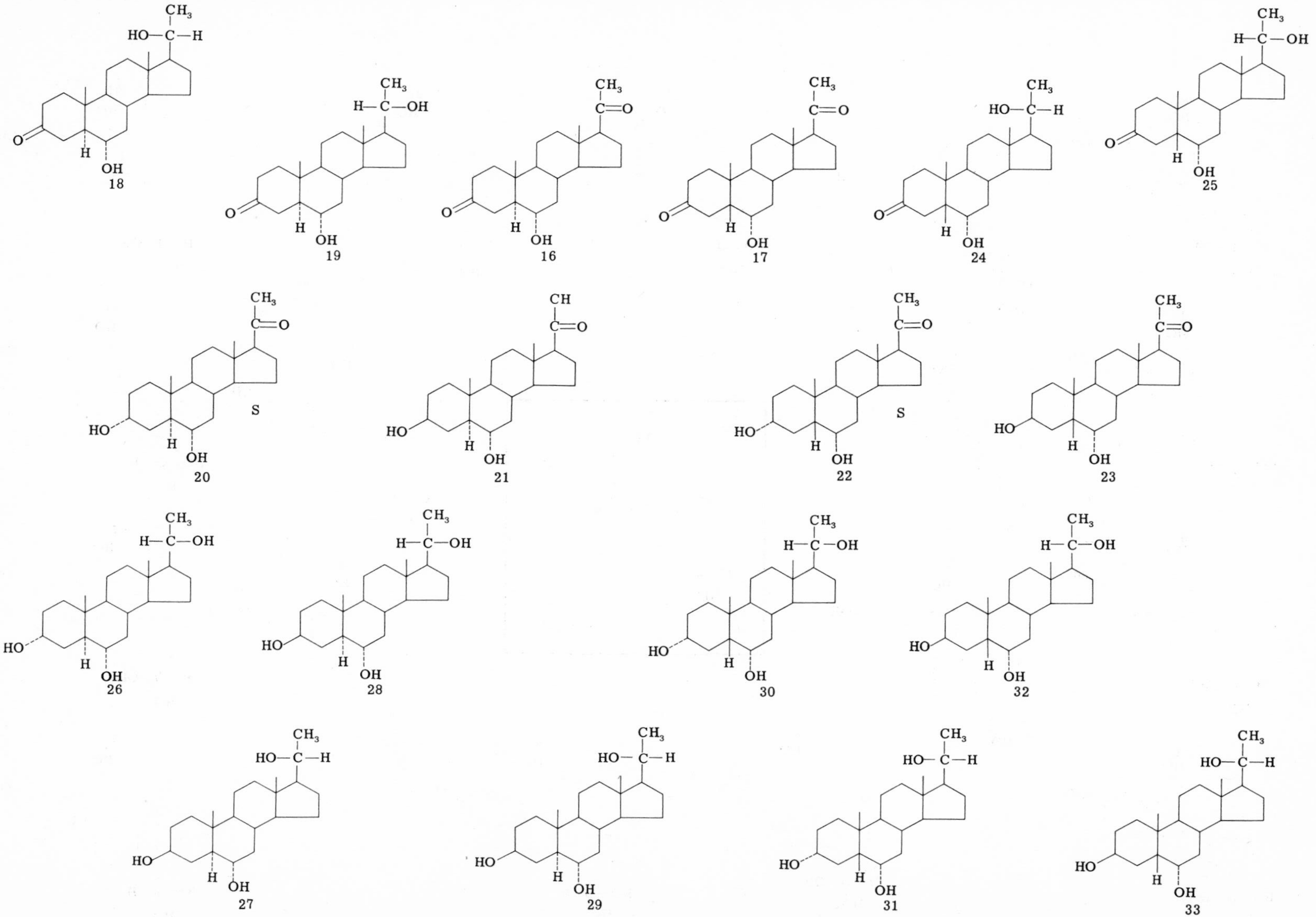

FIG. 25. C_{21}-5-1: 6α-Hydroxyprogesterone and related metabolites.

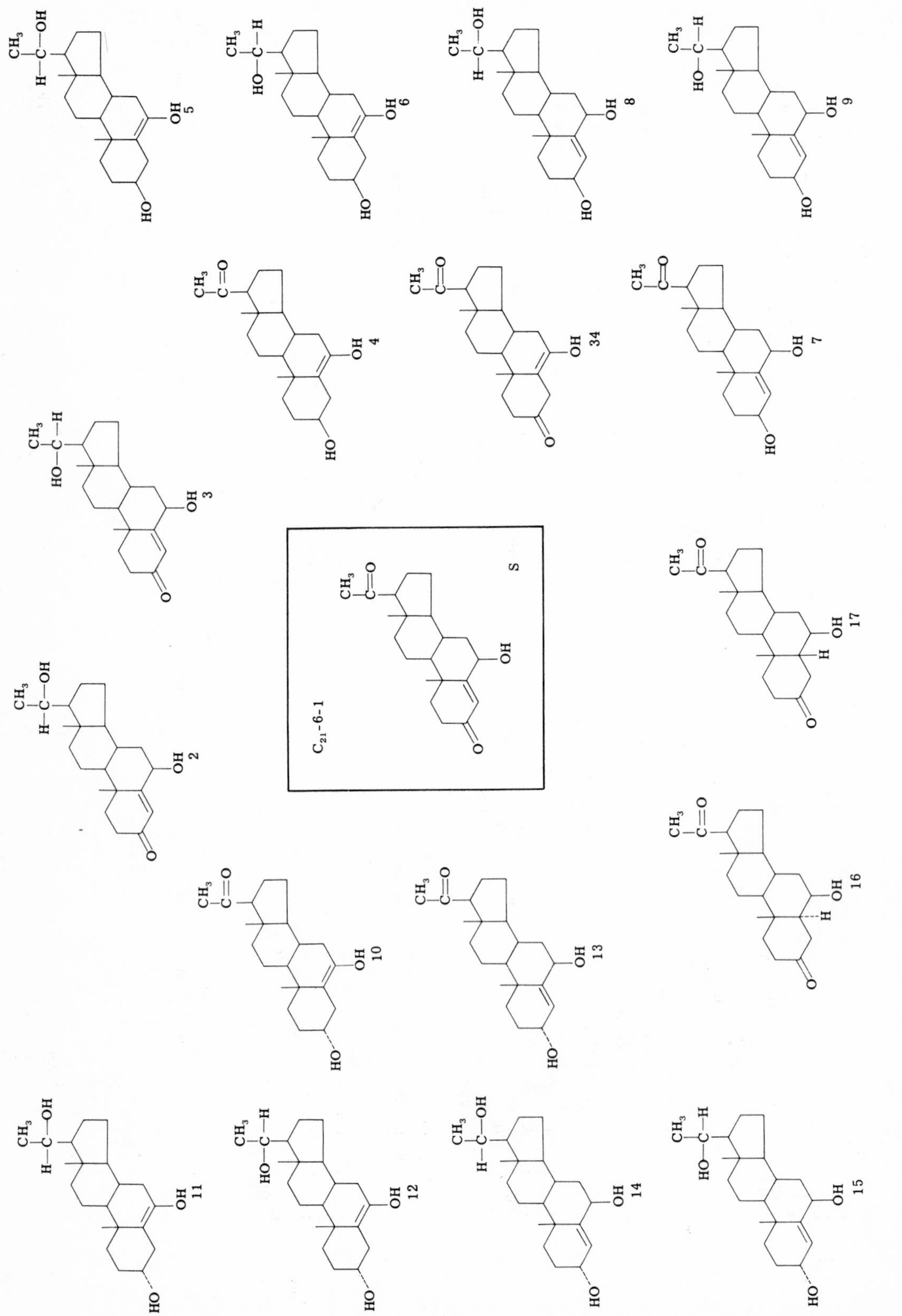

C_{21}-6-1

S

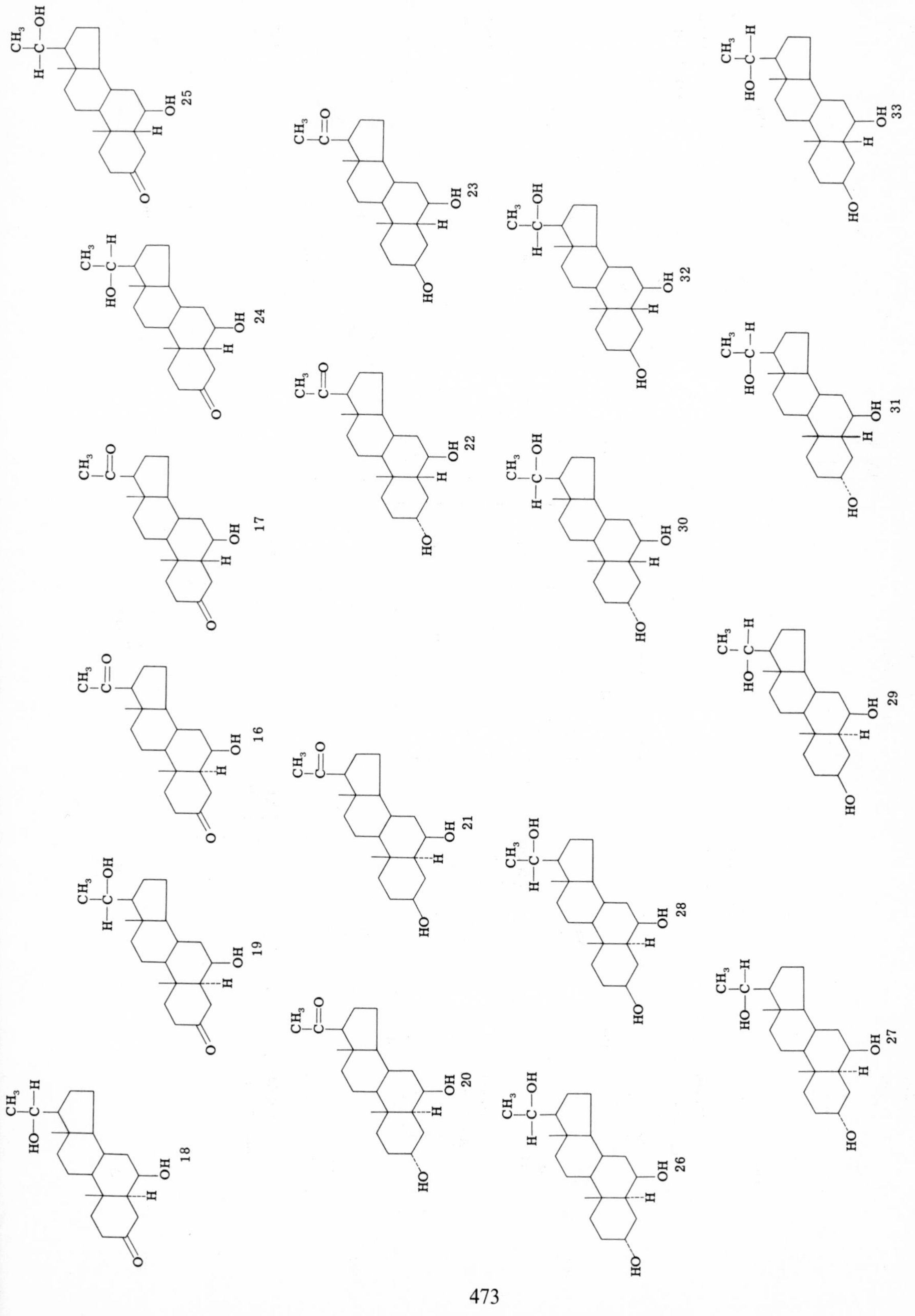

FIG. 26. C_{21}-6-1 : 6β-Hydroxyprogesterone and related metabolites.

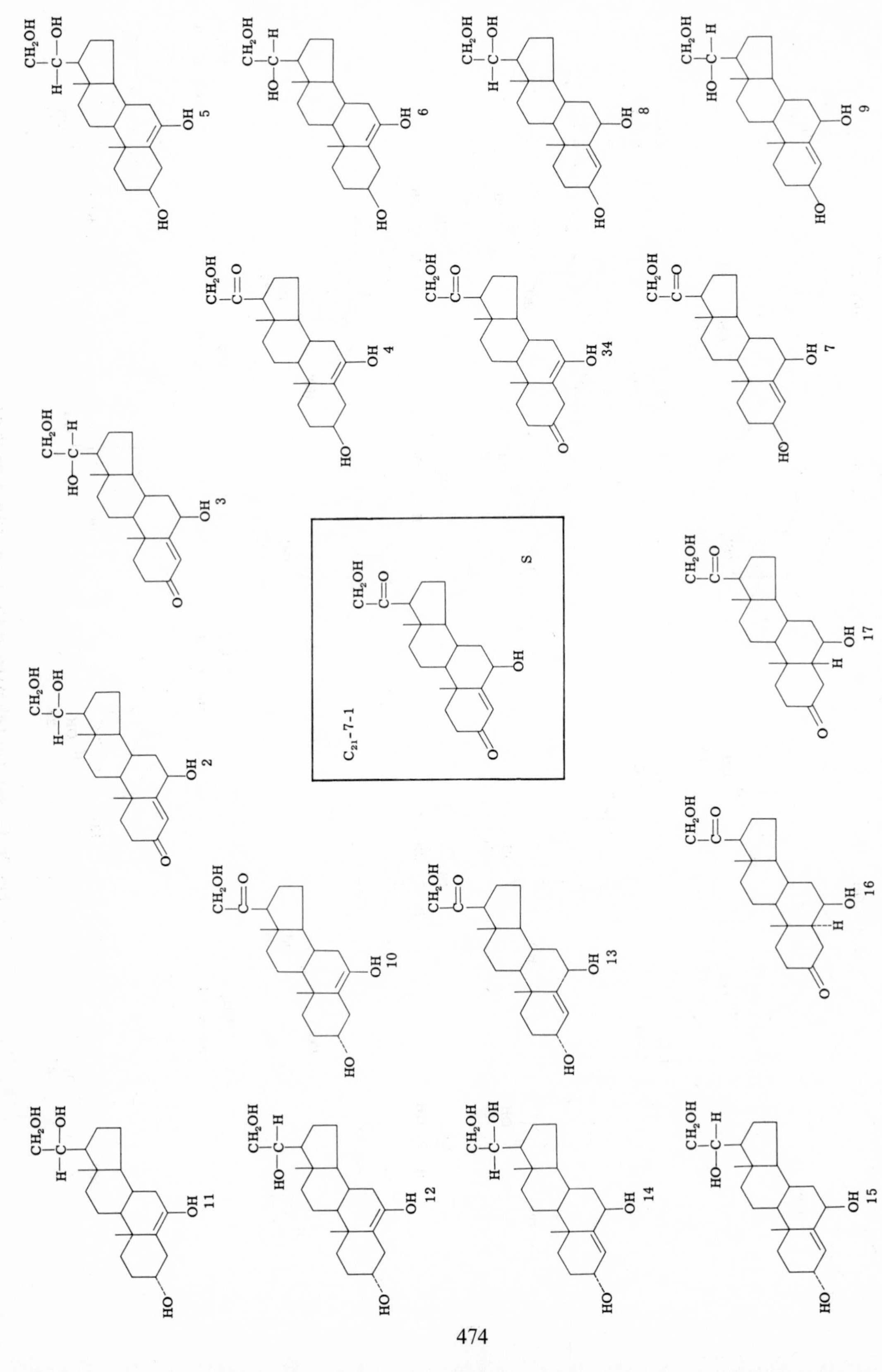
C21-7-1
S
2
3
4
5
6
7
8
9
10
11
12
13
14
15
16
17
34

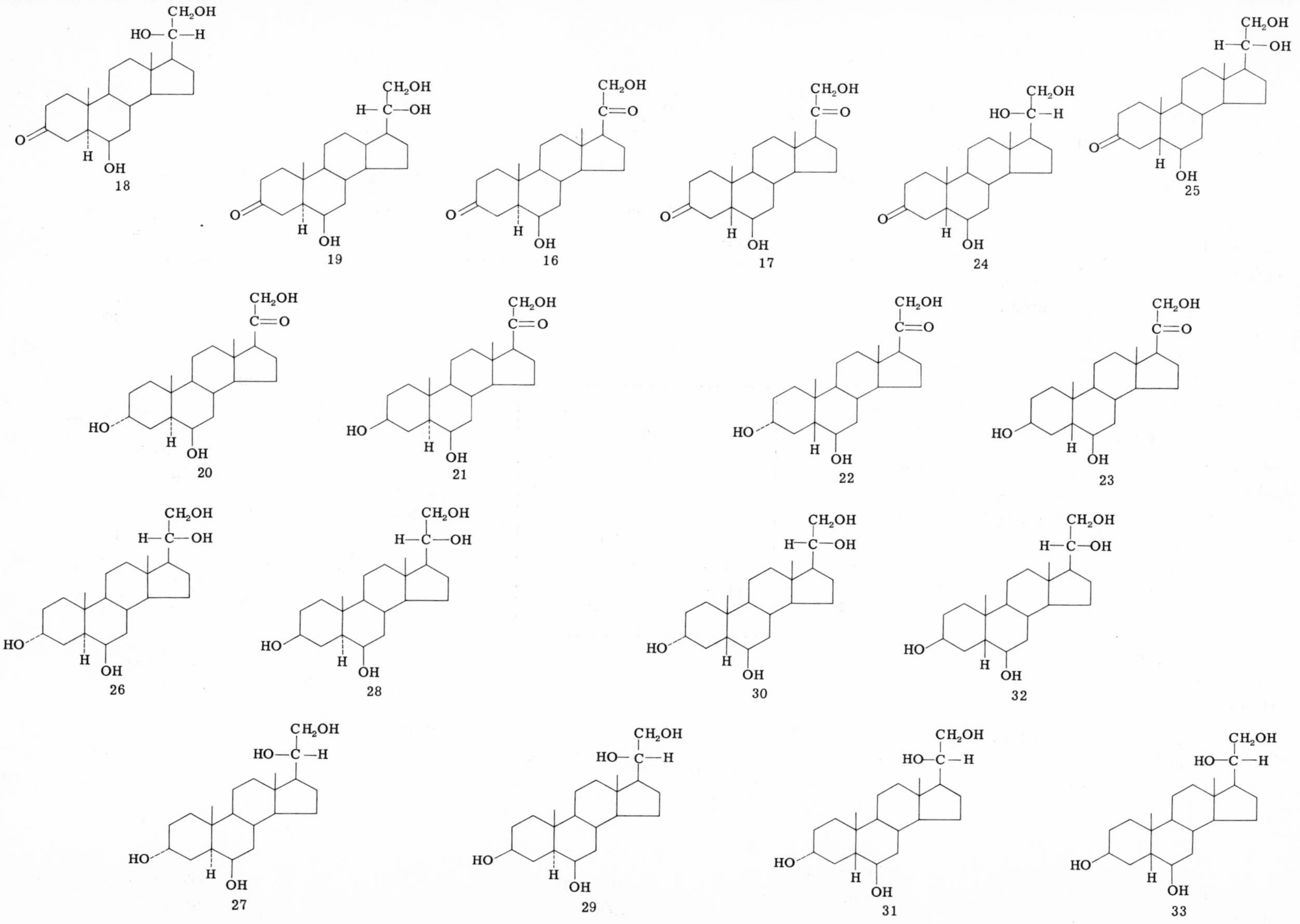

FIG. 27. C_{21}-7-1: 6β,21-Dihydroxyprogesterone and related metabolites.

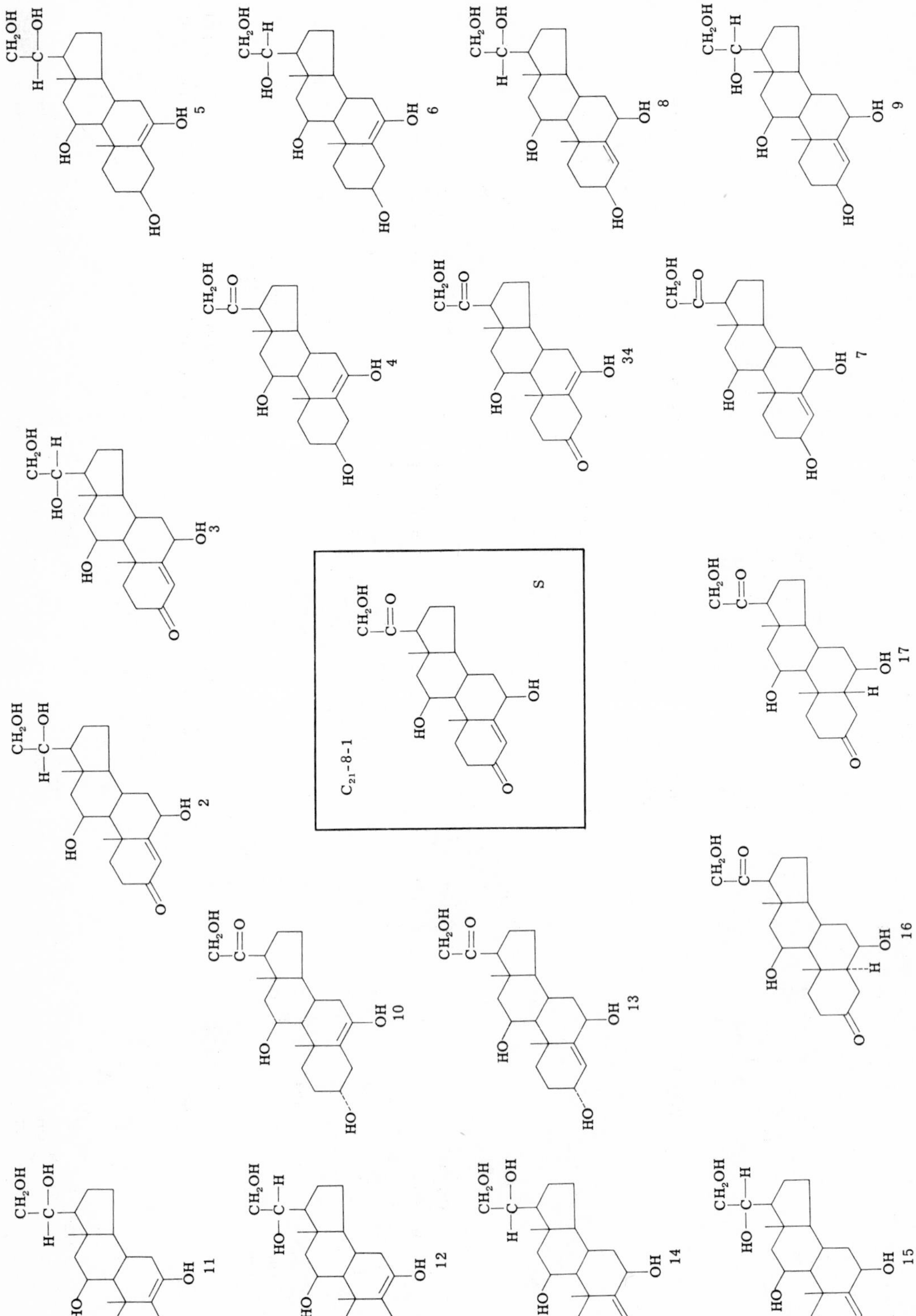

C_{21}-8-1

S

11 2 3 5

12 10 4 6

14 13 34 8

15 16 17 7 9

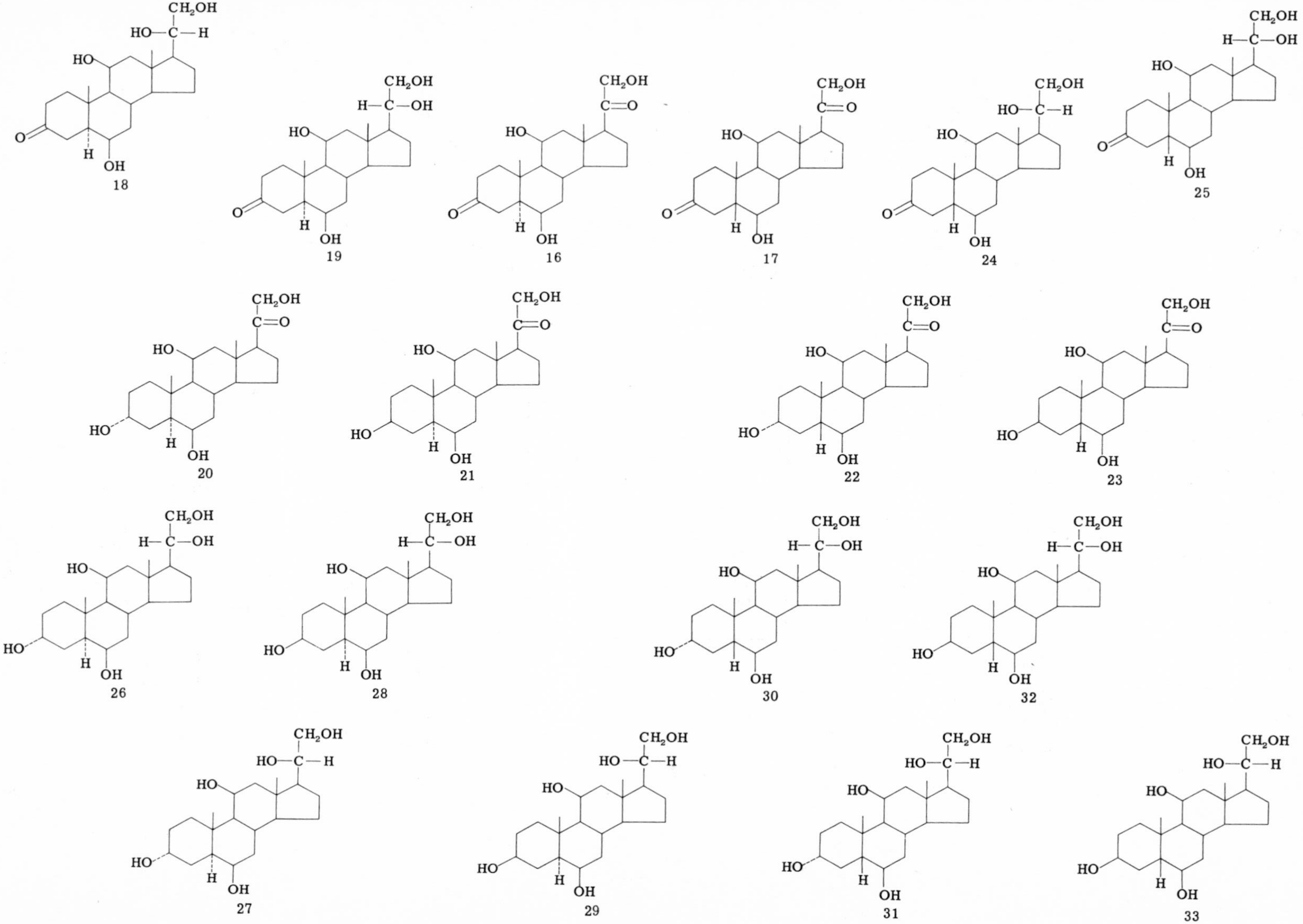

FIG. 28. C_{21}-8-1: 6β-Hydroxycorticosterone and related metabolites.

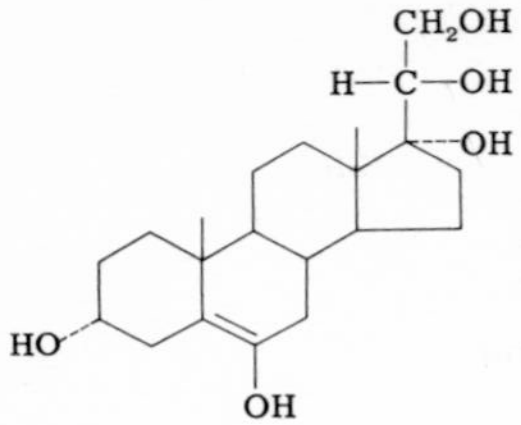

C_{21}-9-1

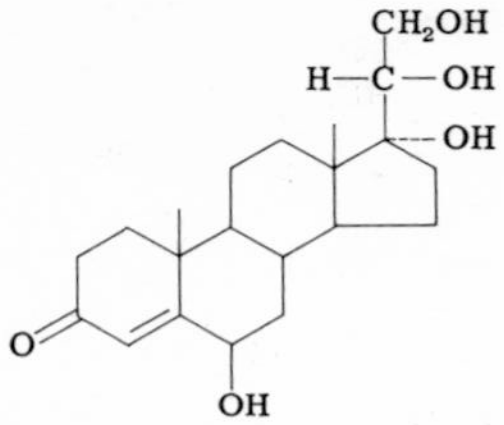

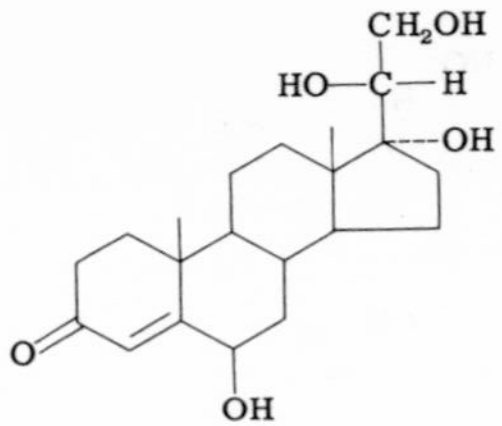

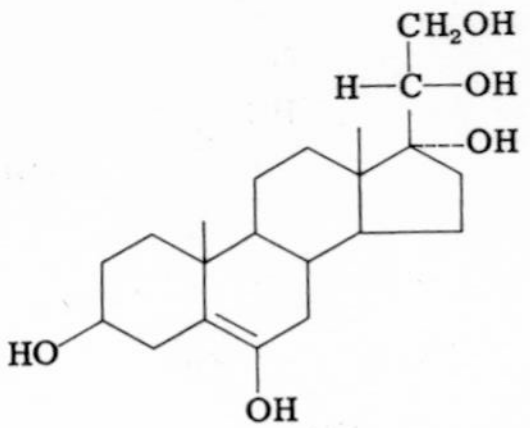

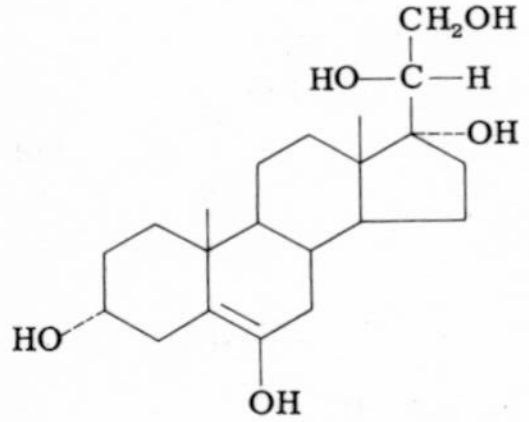

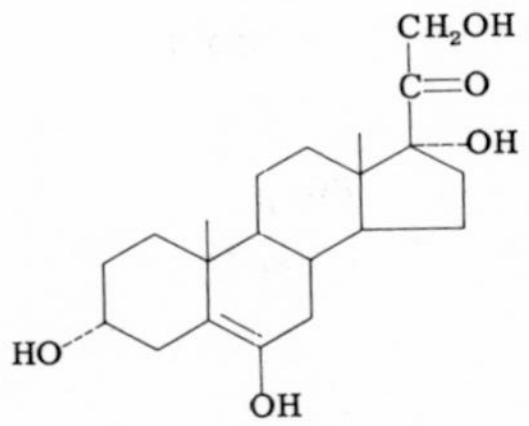

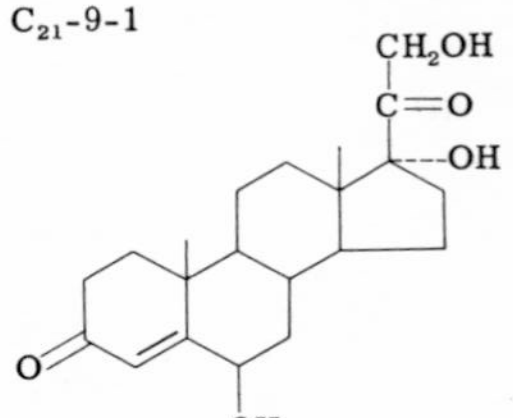

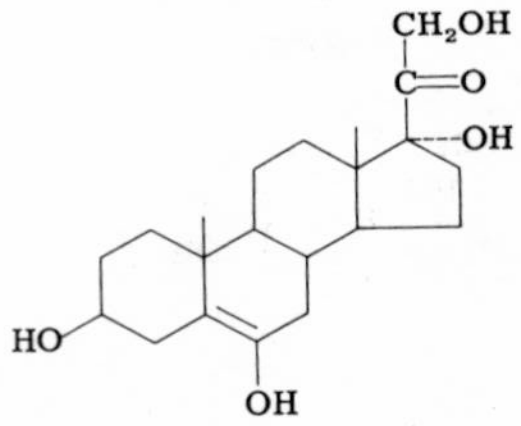

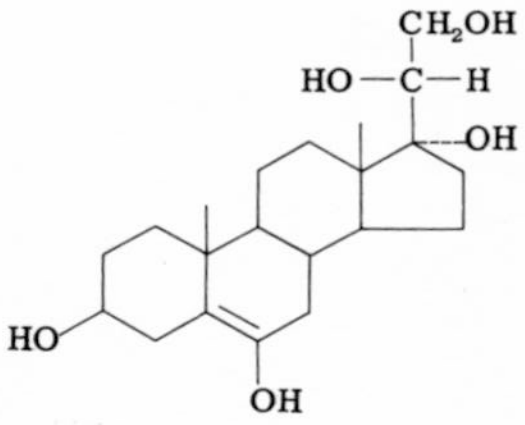

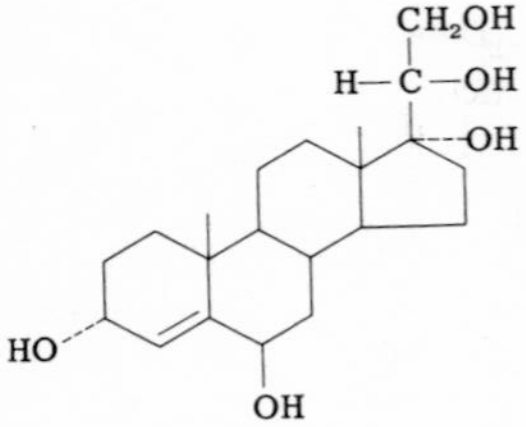

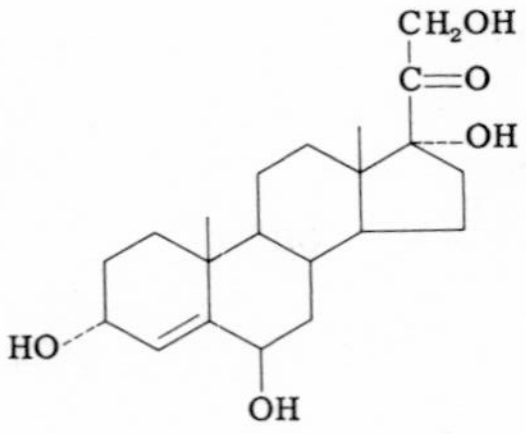

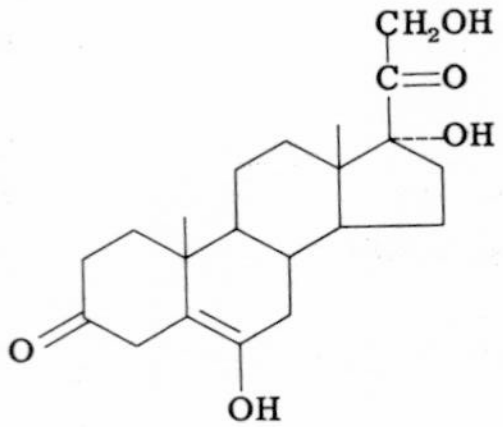

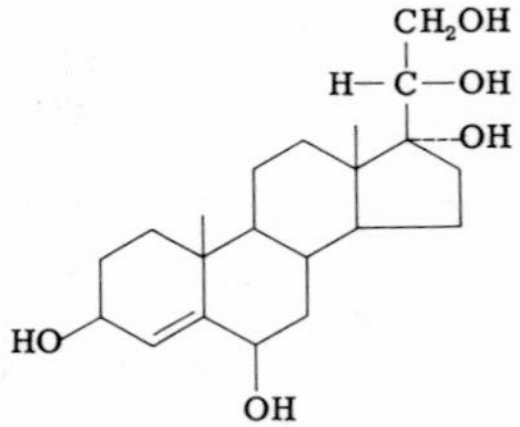

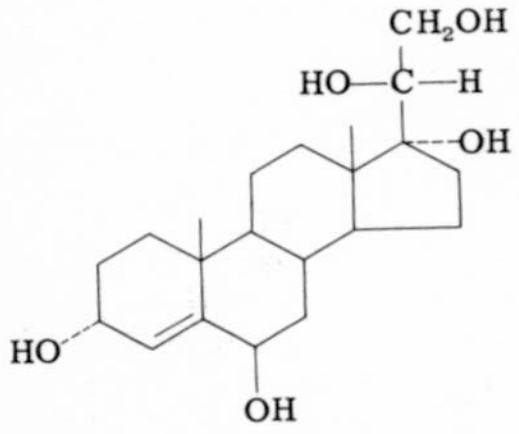

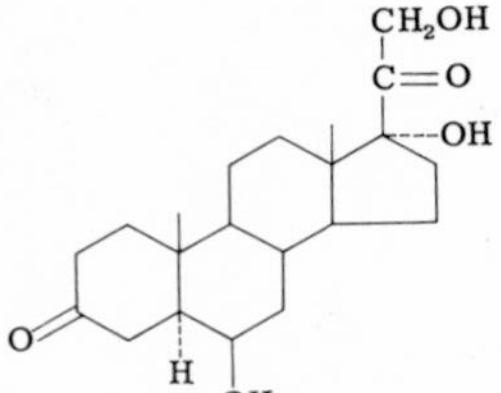

S

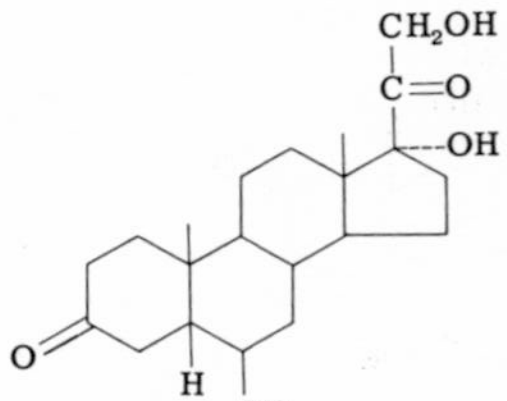

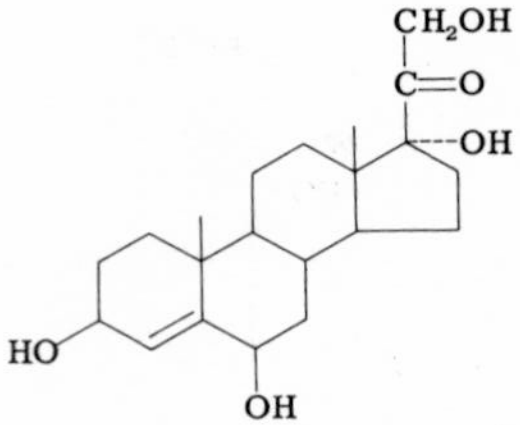

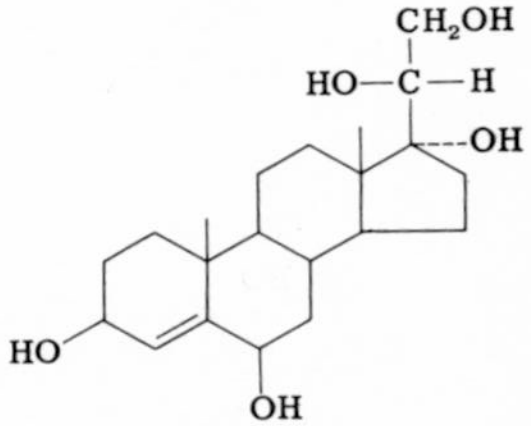

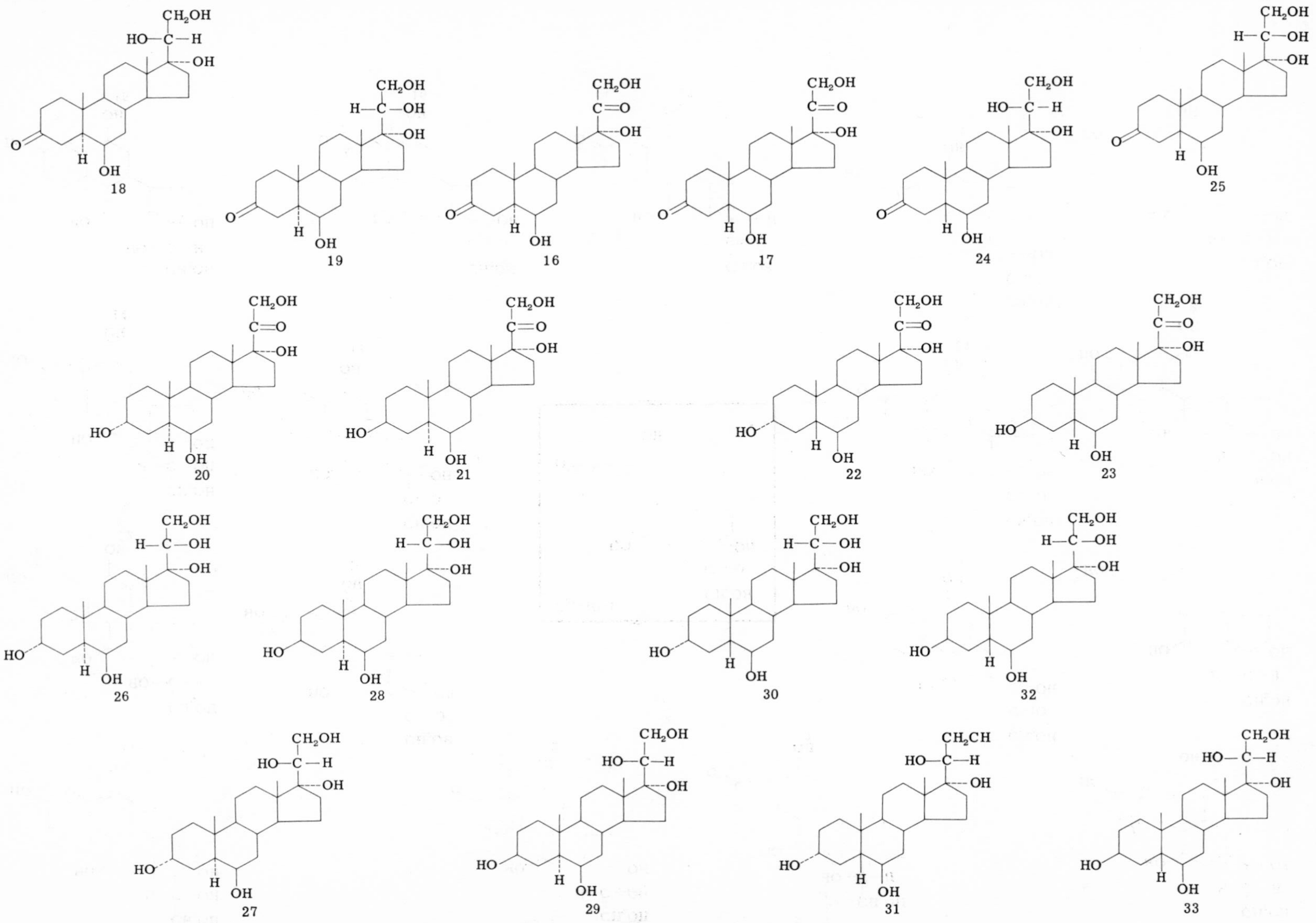

FIG. 29. C_{21}-9-1: 6β,17α,21-Trihydroxyprogesterone and related metabolites.

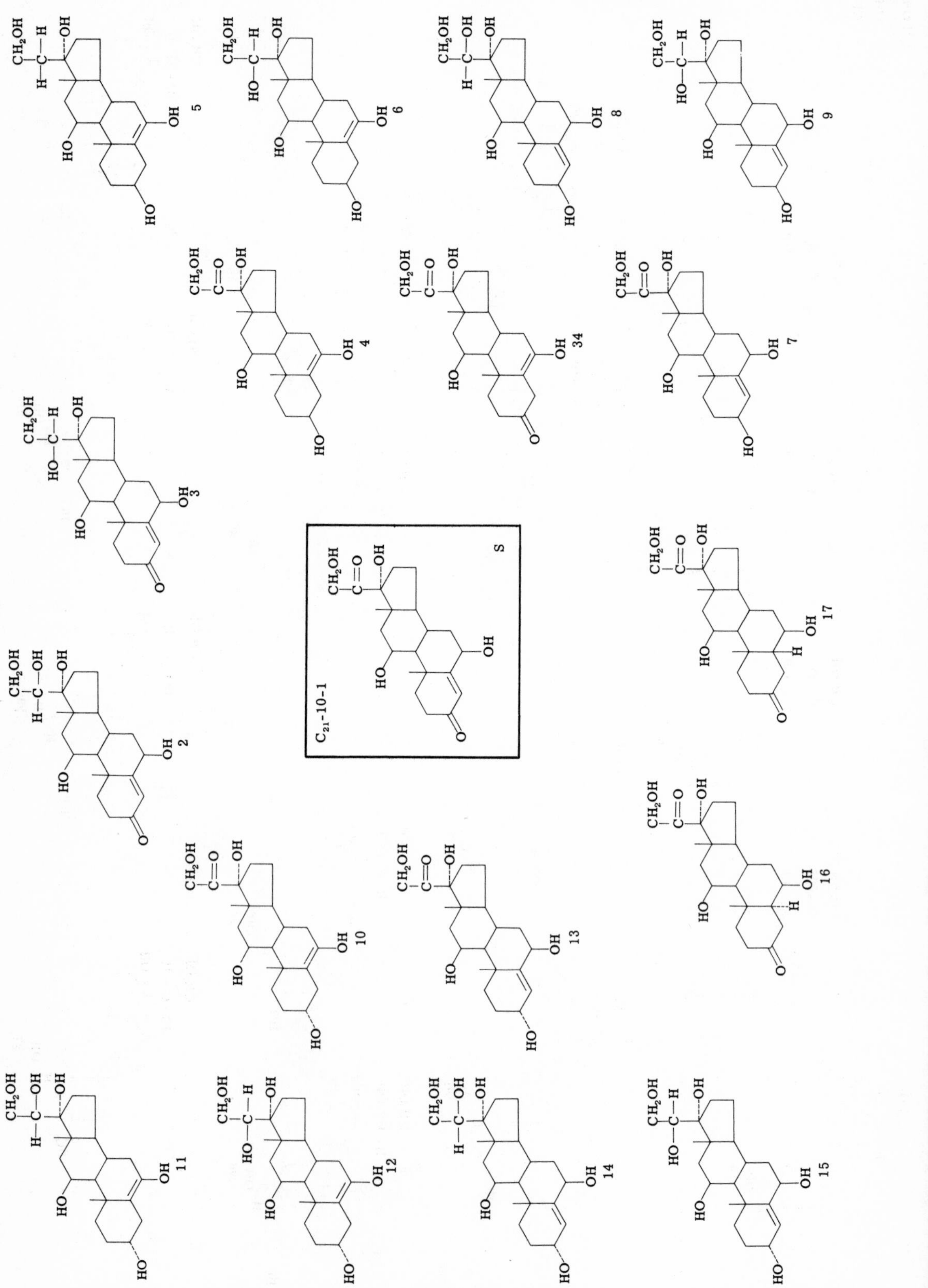

C_{21}-10-1 S

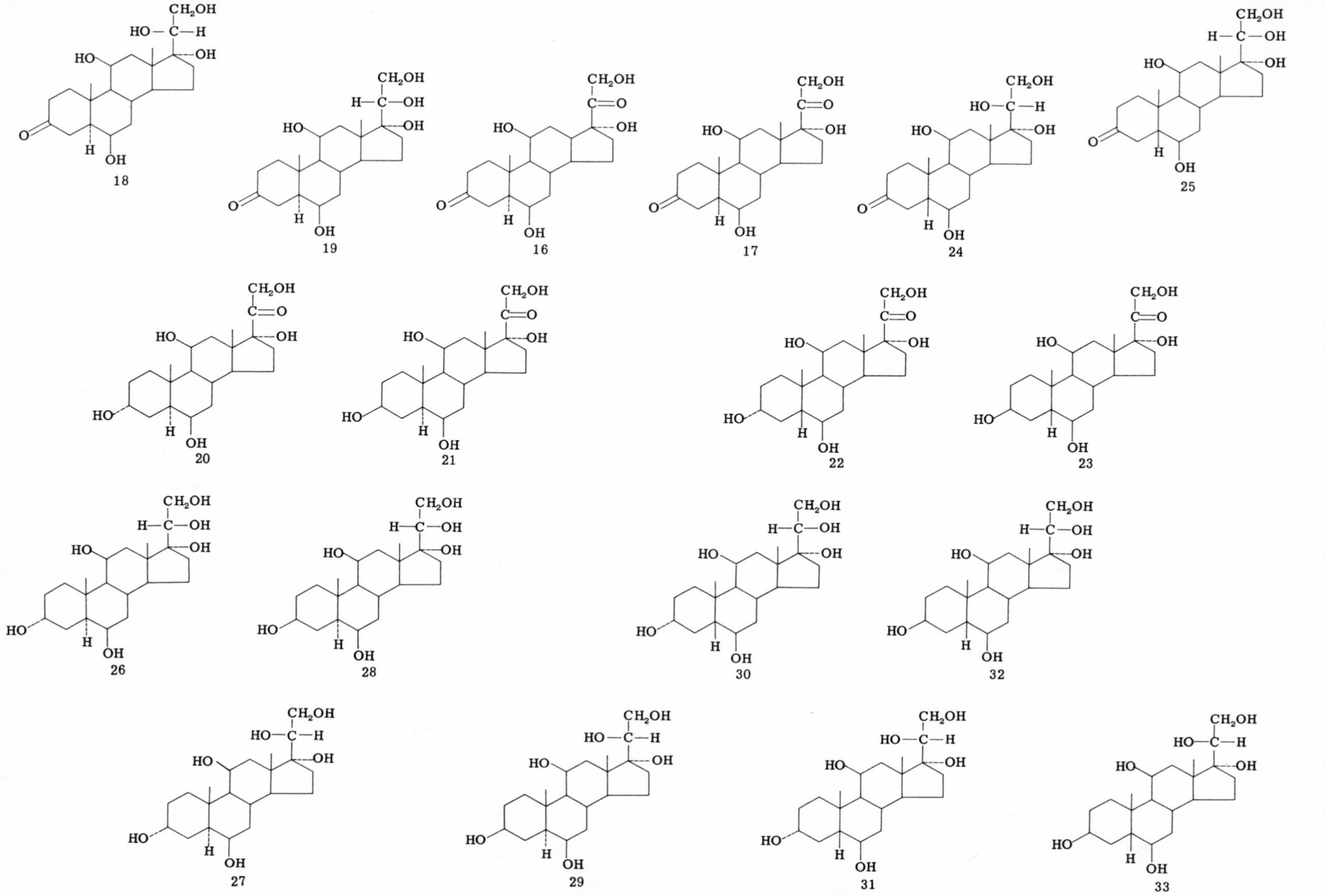

18 19 16 17 24 25

20 21 22 23

26 28 30 32

27 29 31 33

FIG. 30. C_{21}-10-1: 6β-Hydroxycortisol and related metabolites.

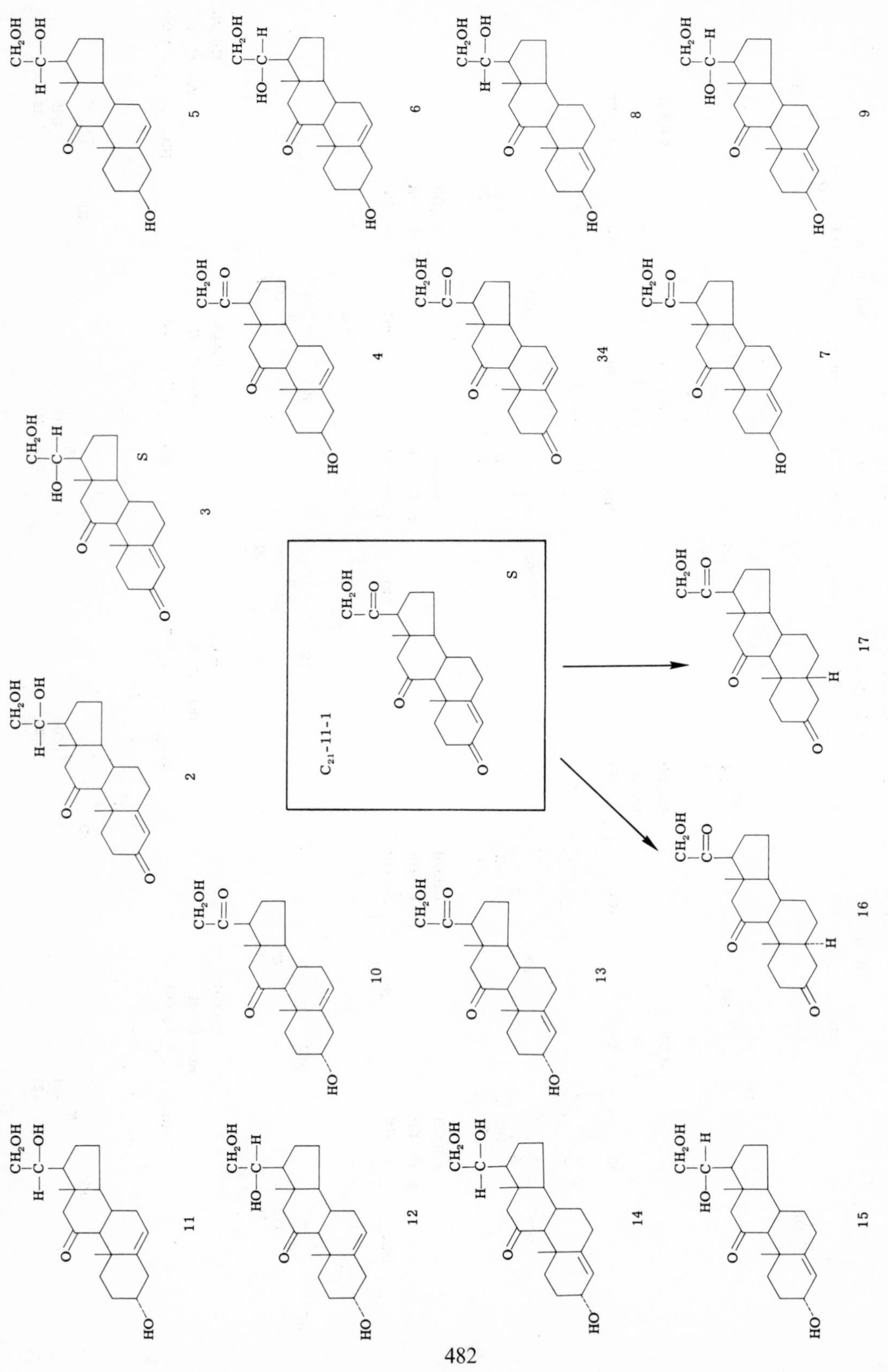

11

2

3

5

12

10

C_{21}-11-1

S

4

6

14

13

34

8

15

16

17

7

9

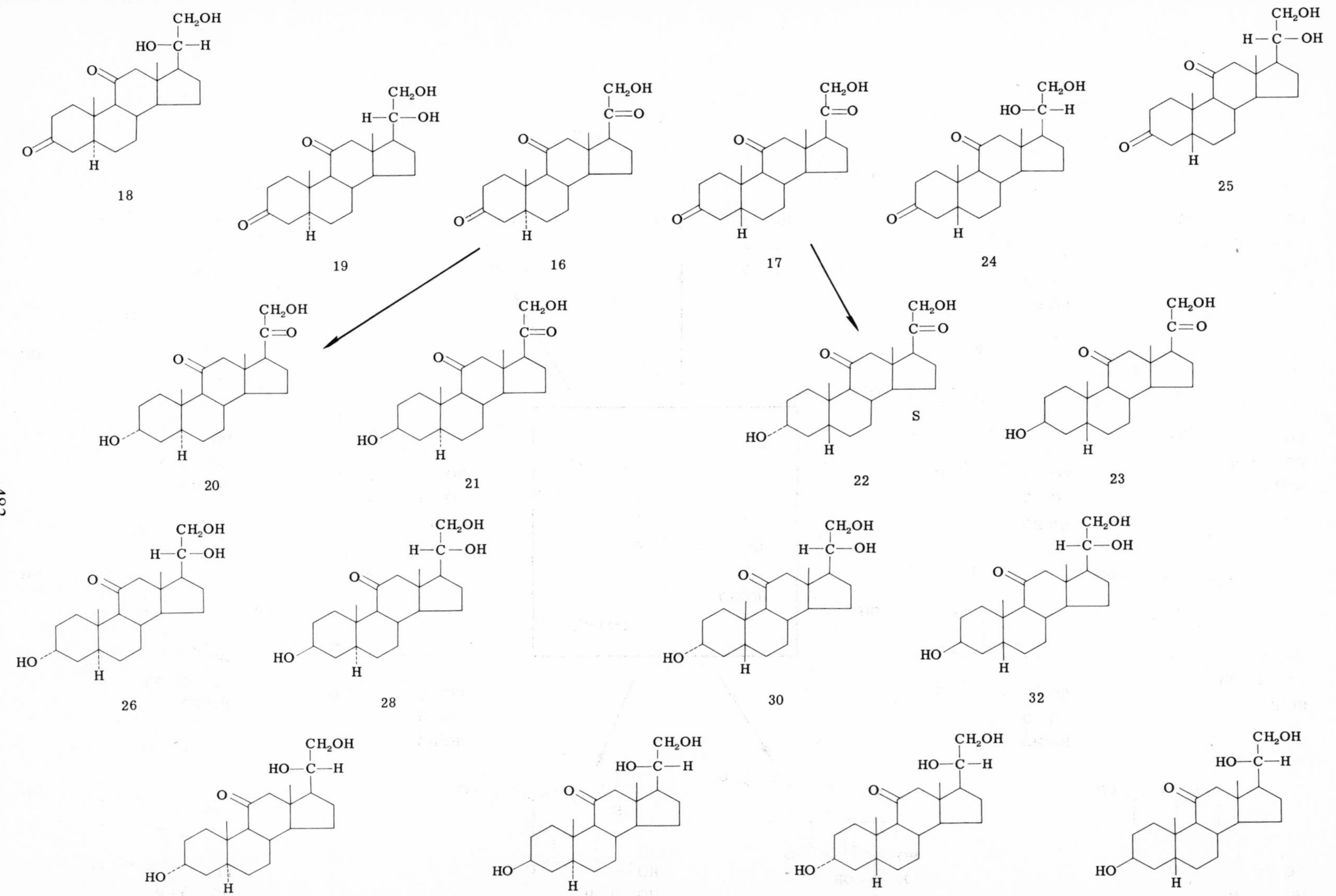

FIG. 31. C_{21}-11-1: Dehydrocorticosterone and related metabolites.

C_{21}-12-1

11 2 3 5

10 4

12 6

13 34

14 8

15 16 17 7 9

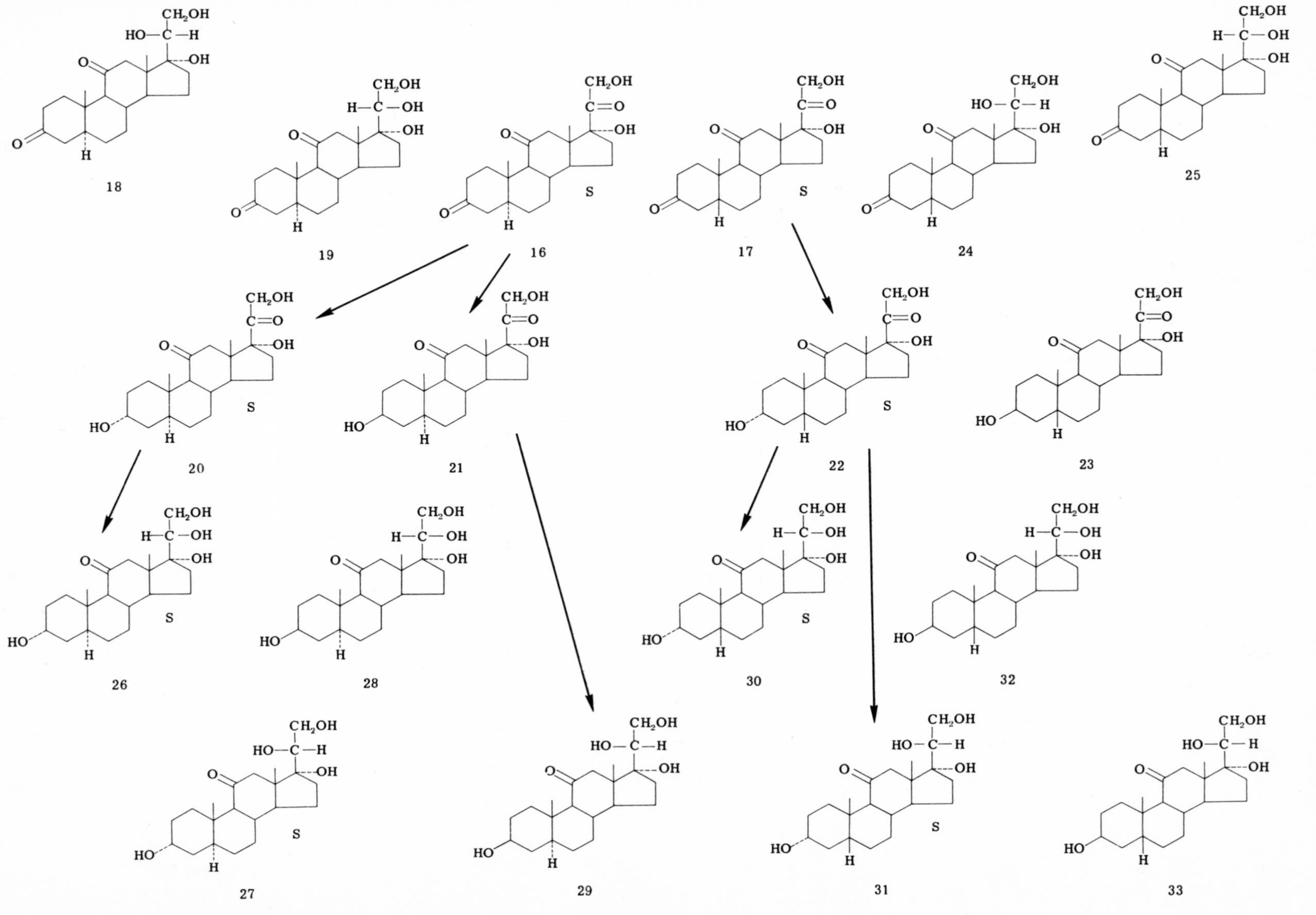

FIG. 32. C_{21}-12-1: Cortisone and related metabolites.

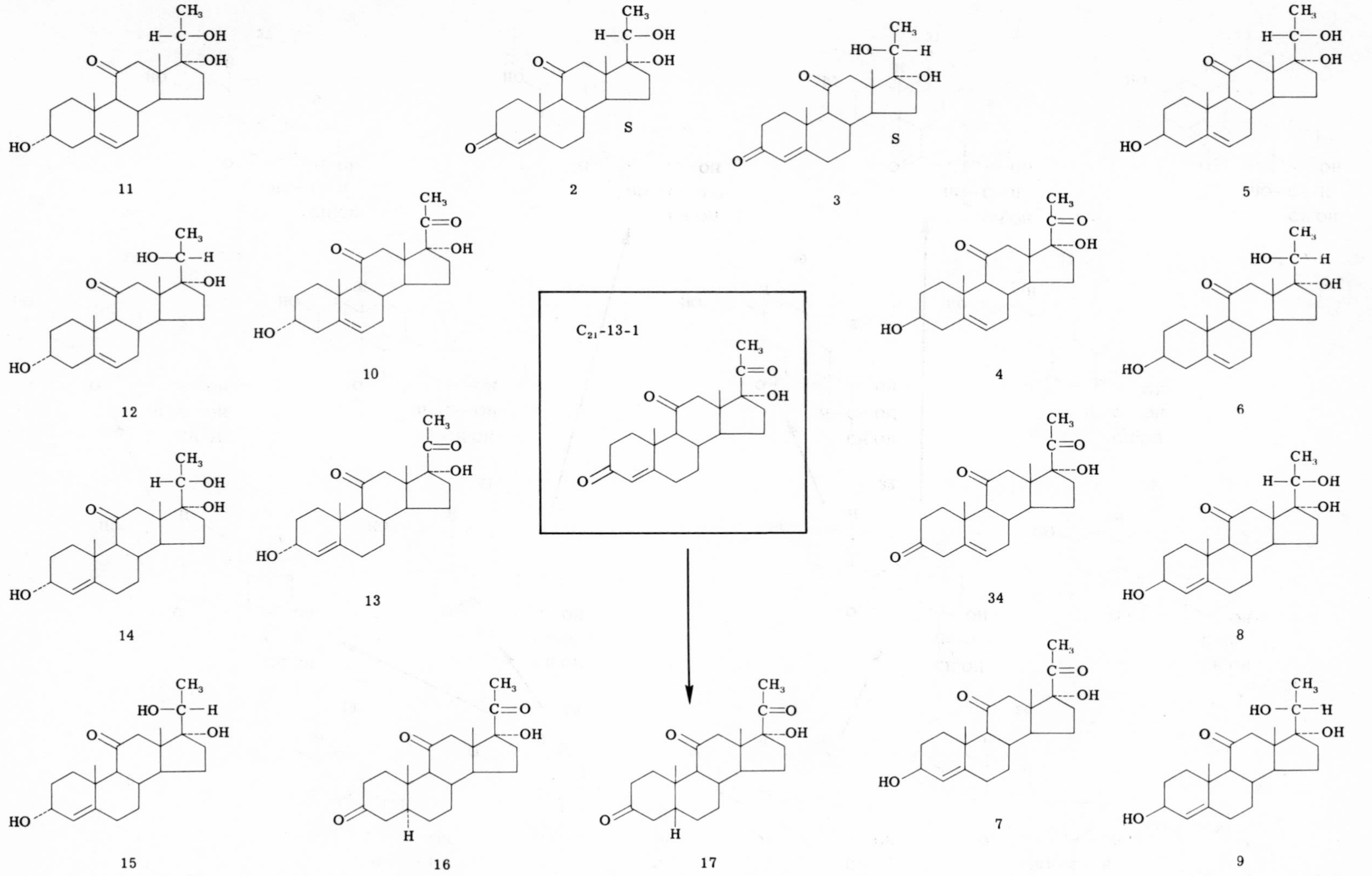

C_{21}-13-1

2 3 4 5 6 7 8 9 10 11 12 13 14 15 16 17 34

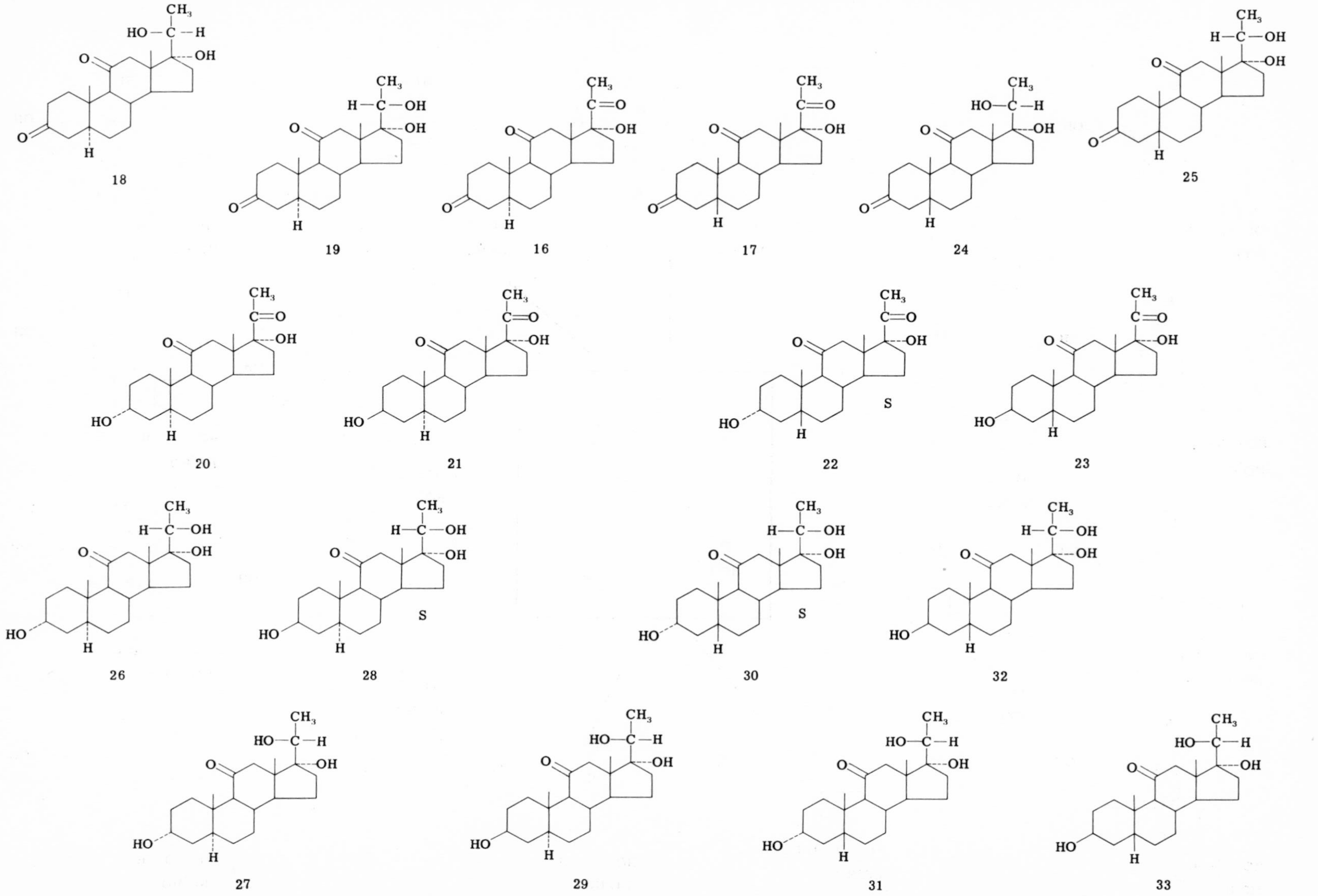

18 19 16 17 24 25

20 21 22 23

26 28 30 32

27 29 31 33

FIG. 33. C_{21}-13-1: 21-Deoxycortisone and related metabolites.

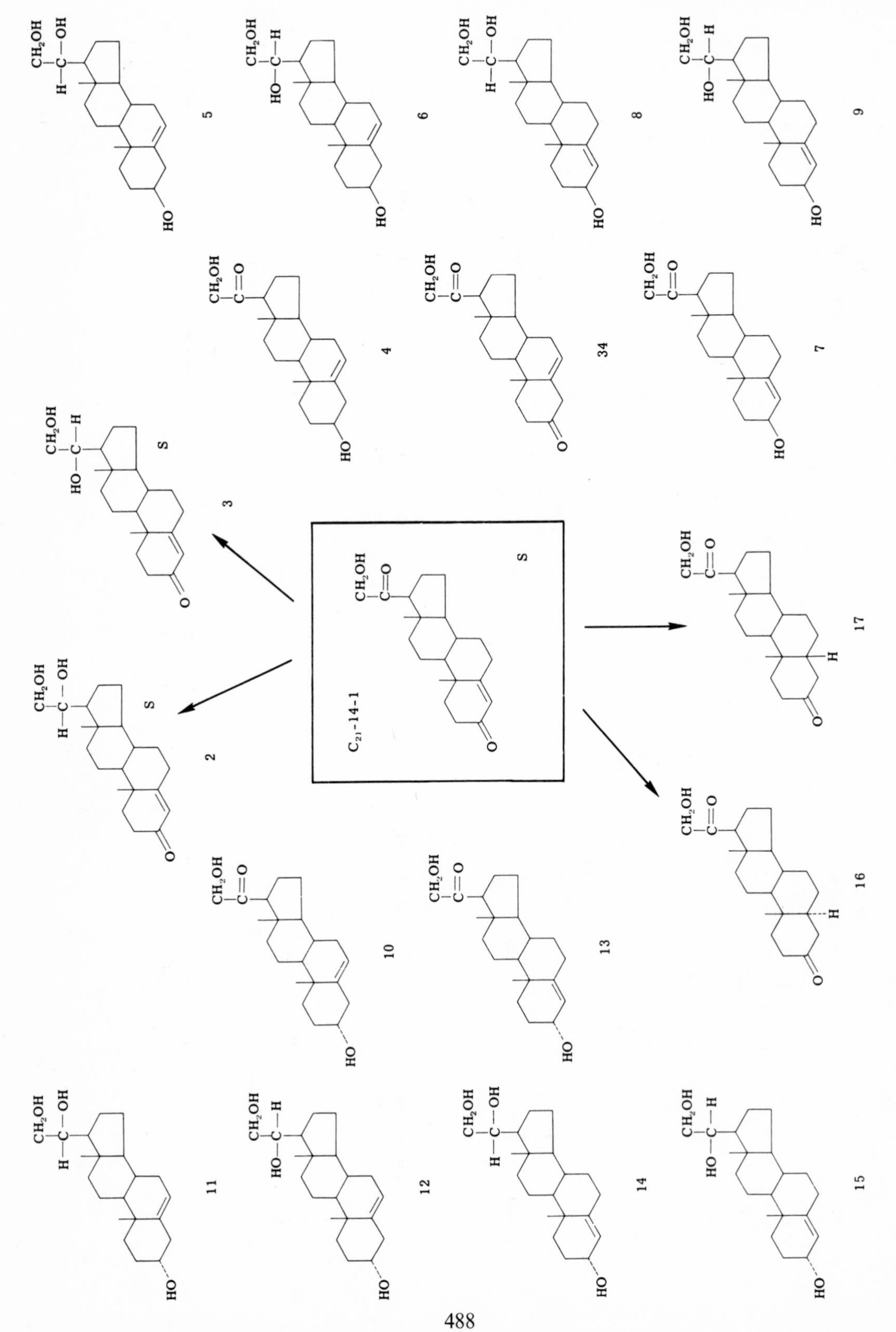

C_{21}-14-1

S

2 S

3 S

4

34

7

5

6

8

9

10

13

11

12

14

15

16

17

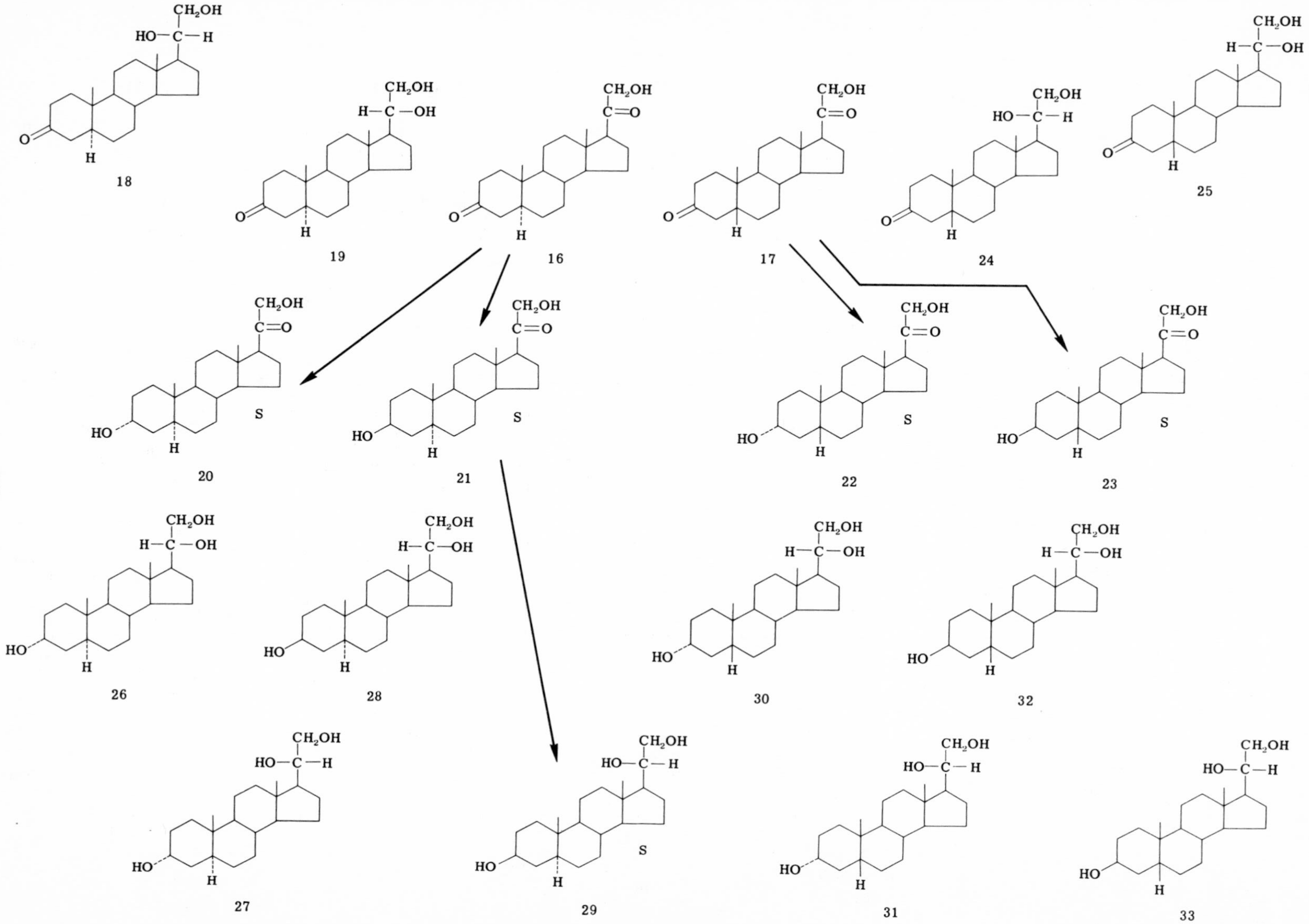

FIG. 34. C_{21}-14-1: Deoxycorticosterone and related metabolites.

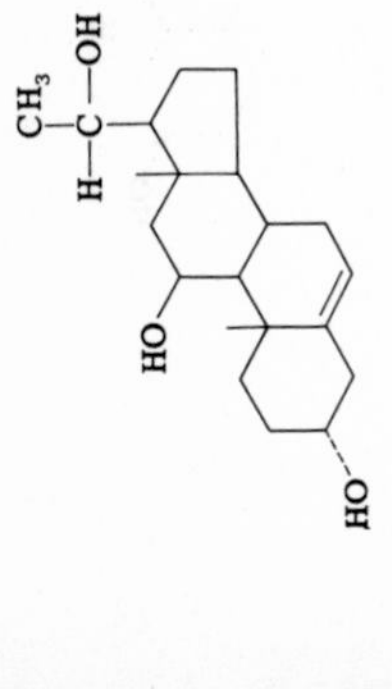

C_{21}-15-1

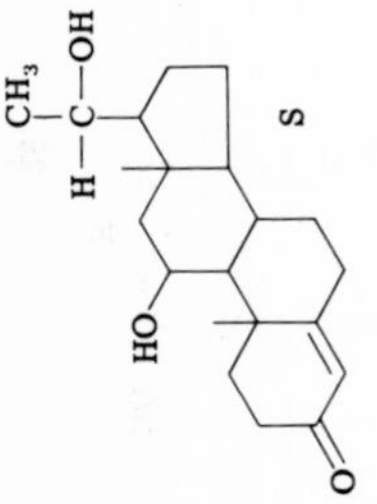

S

11

2

S

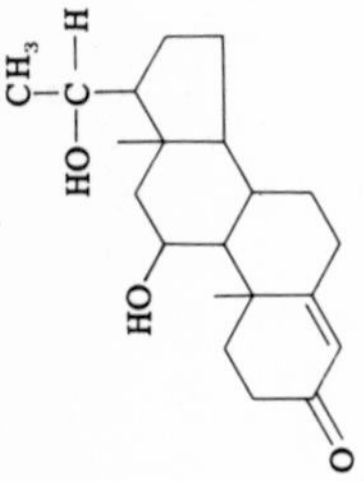

3

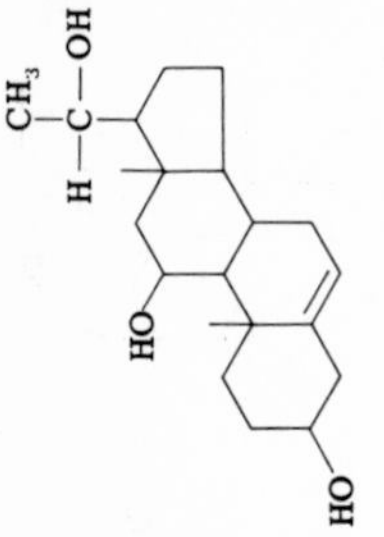

5

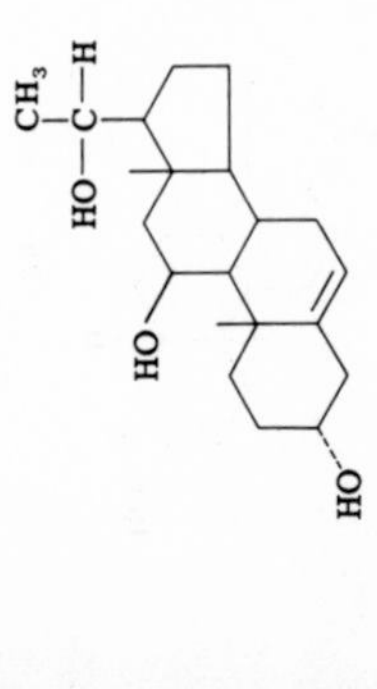

12

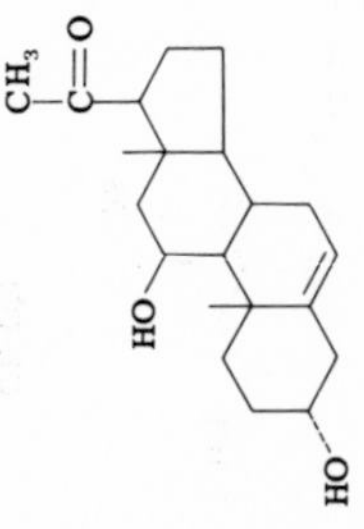

10

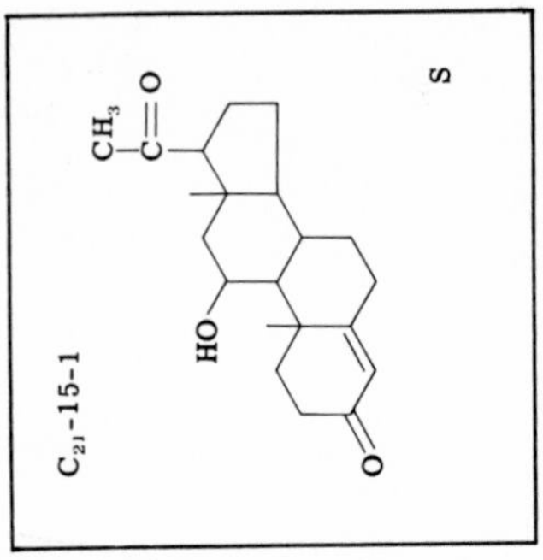

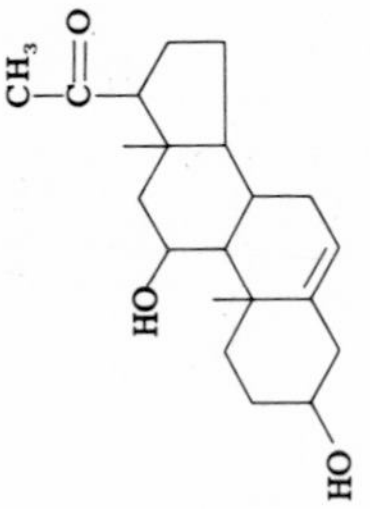

4

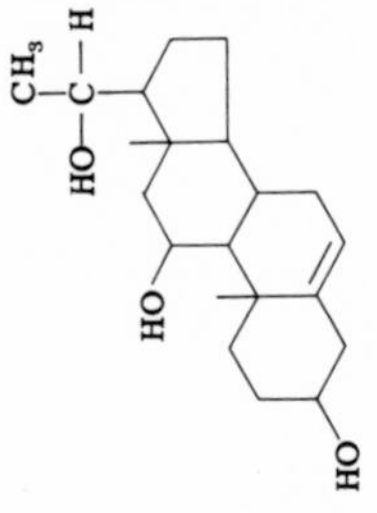

6

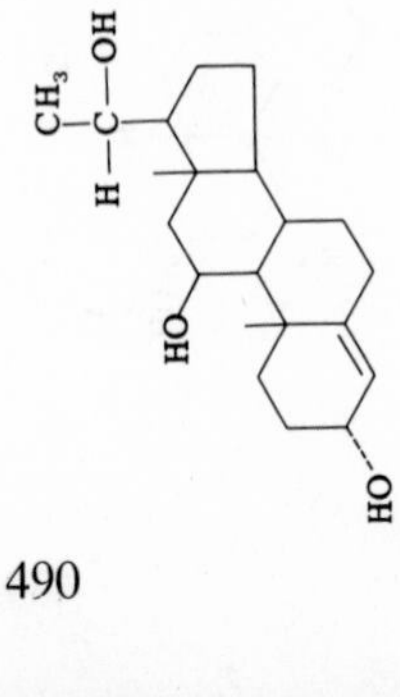

14

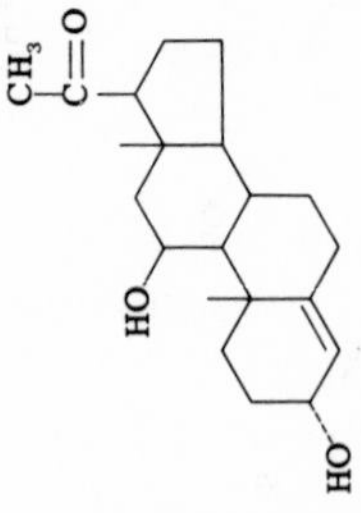

13

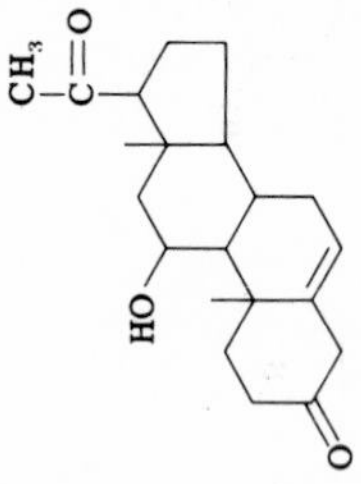

34

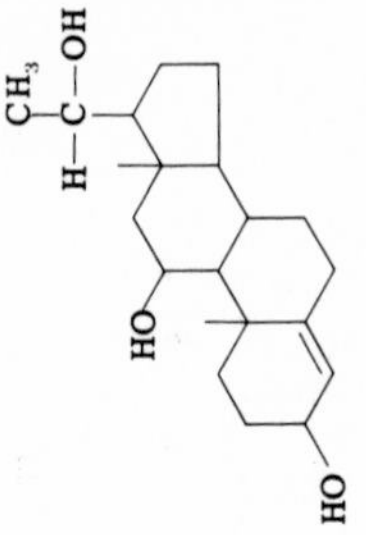

8

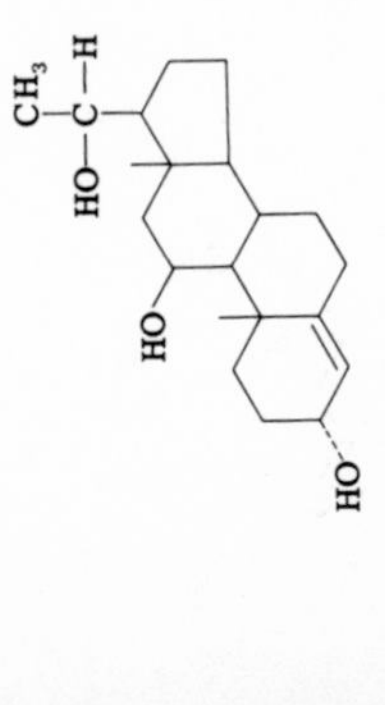

15

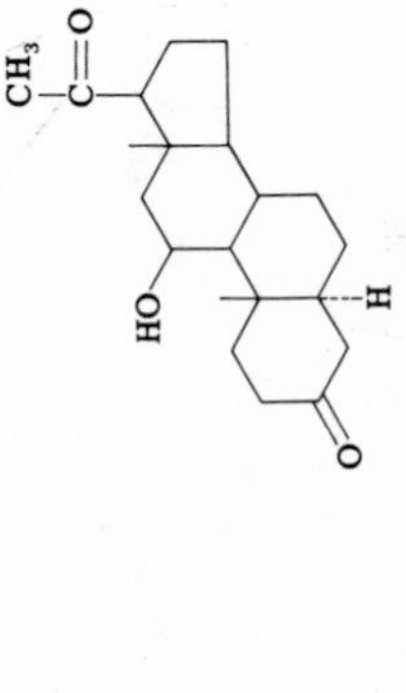

16

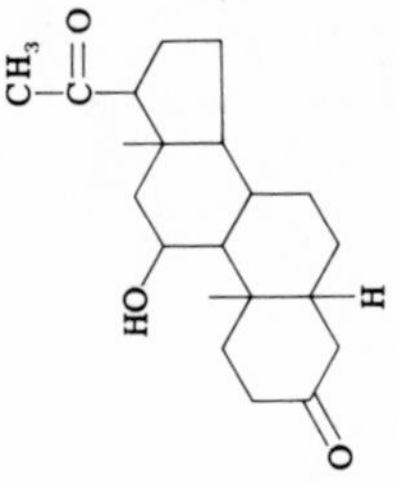

17

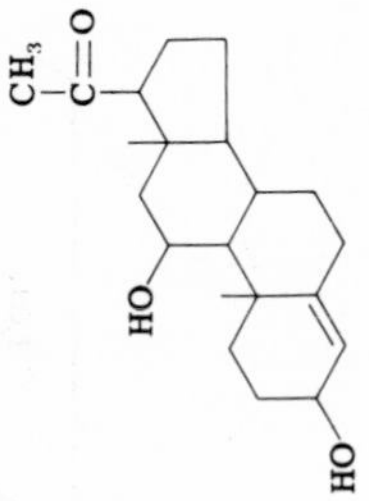

7

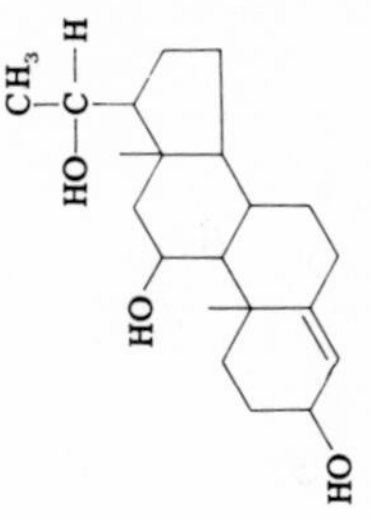

9

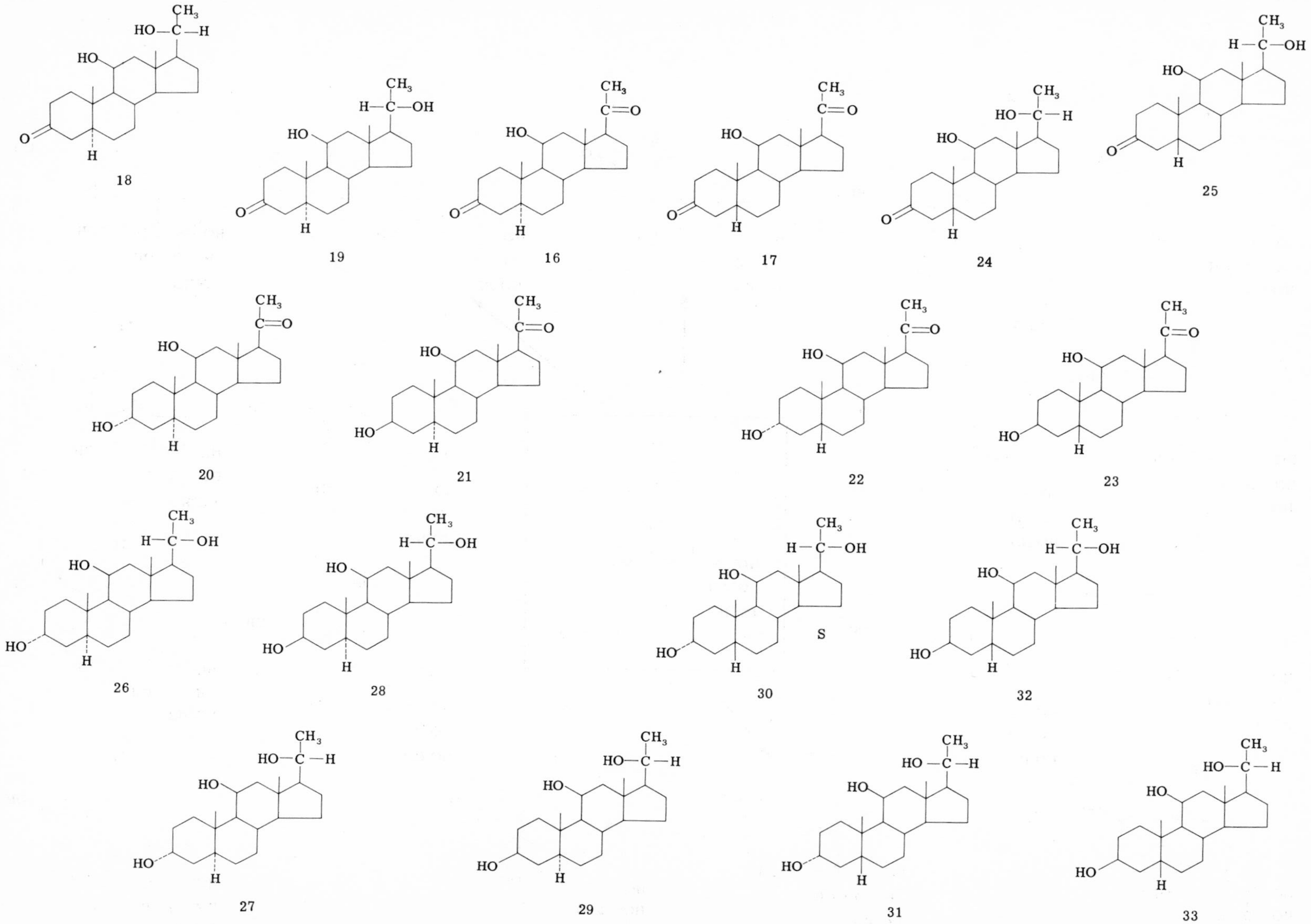

18 19 16 17 24 25

20 21 22 23

26 28 30 S 32

27 29 31 33

FIG. 35. C_{21}-15-1: 11β-Hydroxyprogesterone and related metabolites.

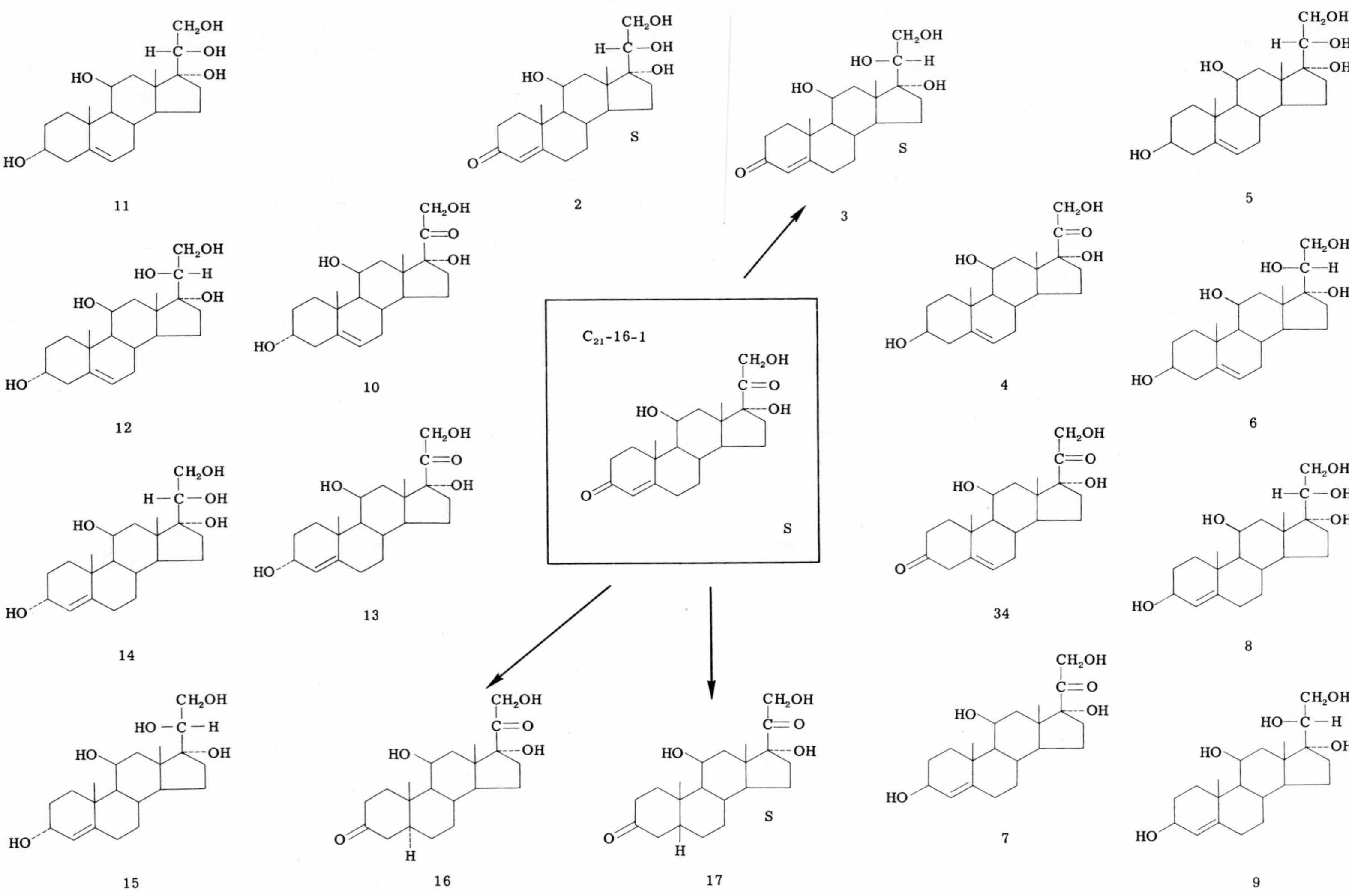
C$_{21}$-16-1
S
11
2
3
5
12
10
4
6
14
13
34
8
15
16
17
7
9

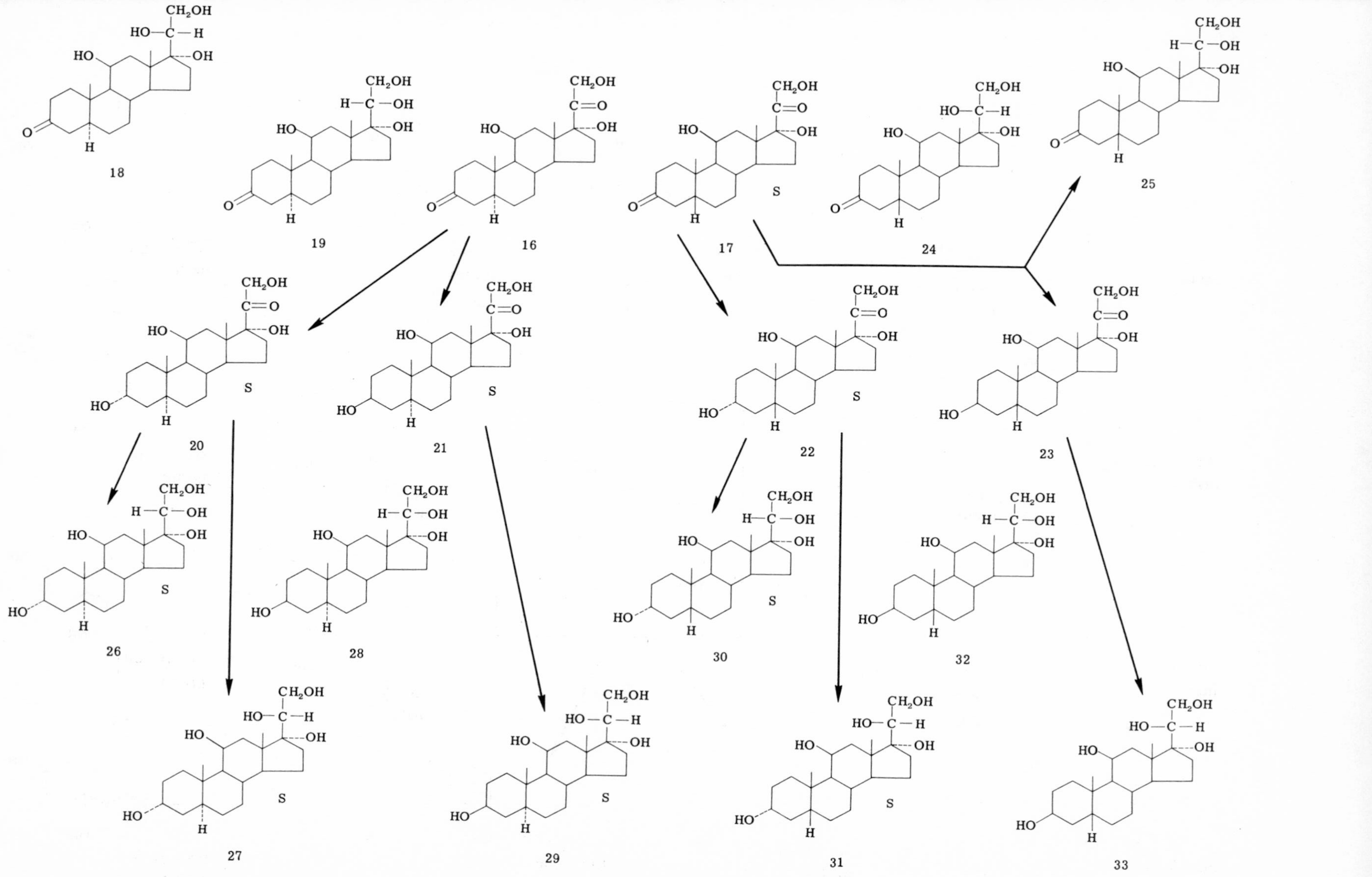

FIG. 36. C_{21}-16-1: Cortisol and related metabolites.

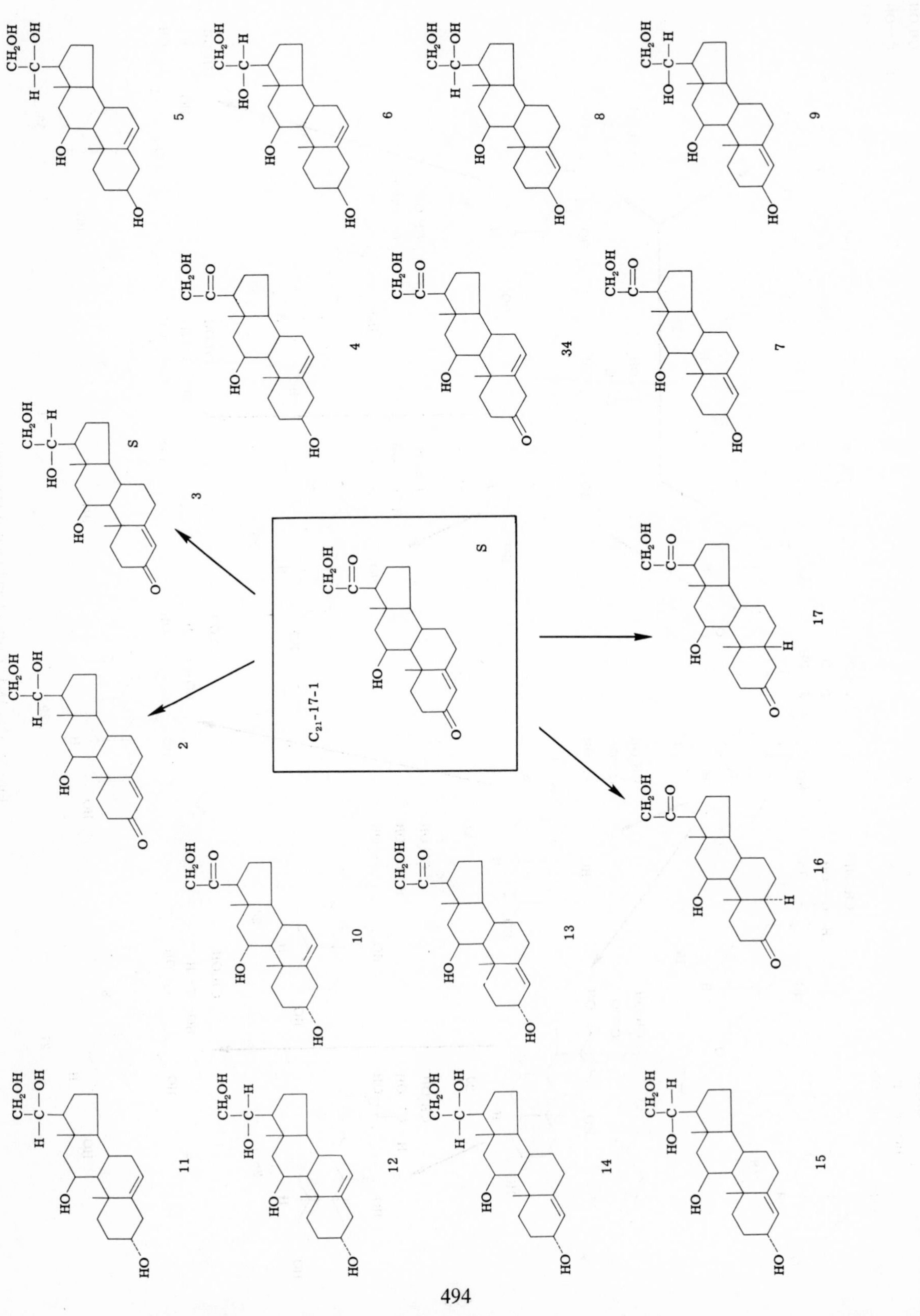

C_{21}-17-1

S

11 2 3 5

12 10 4 6

14 13 34 8

15 16 17 7 9

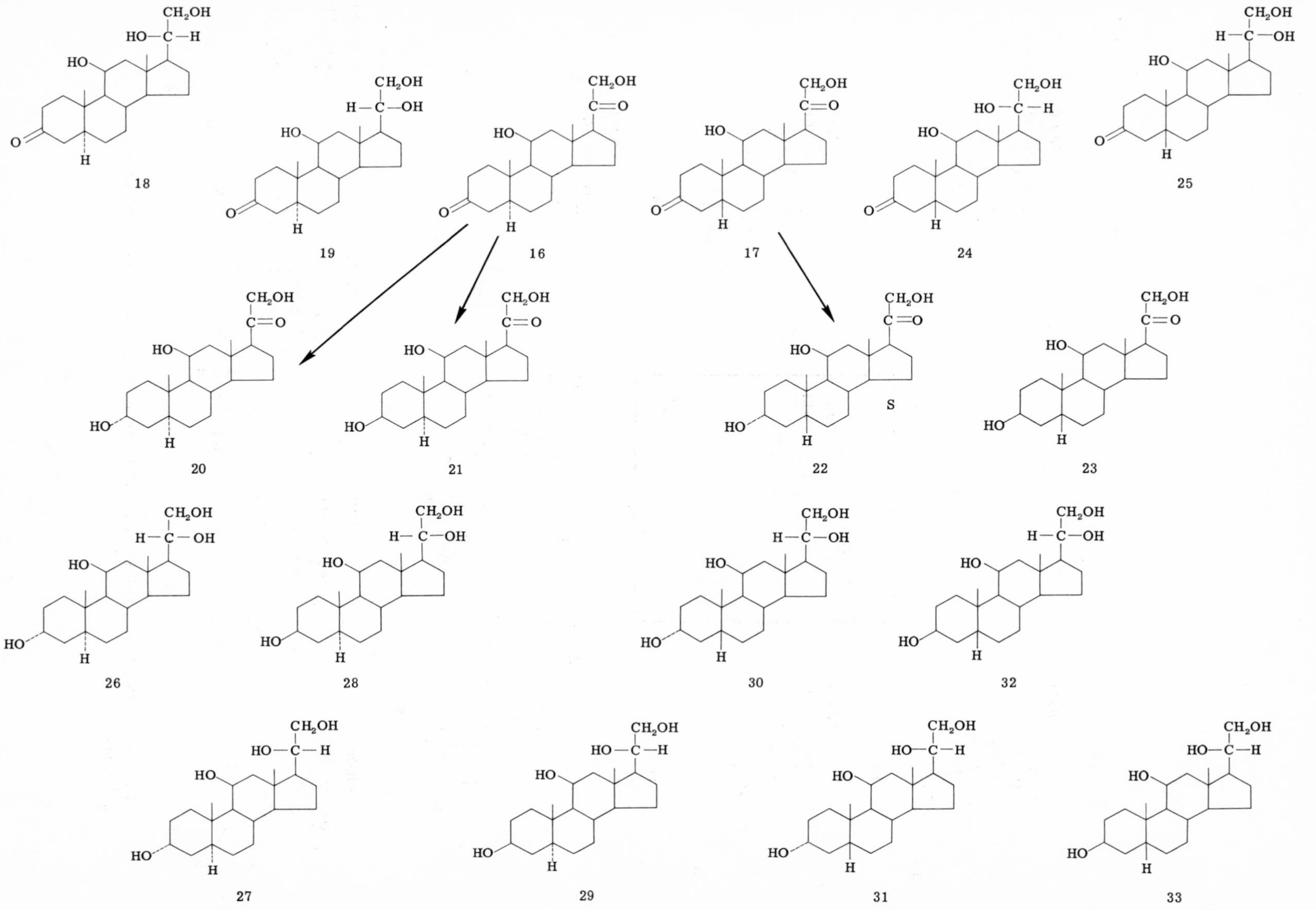

Fig. 37. C_{21}-17-1: Corticosterone and related metabolites.

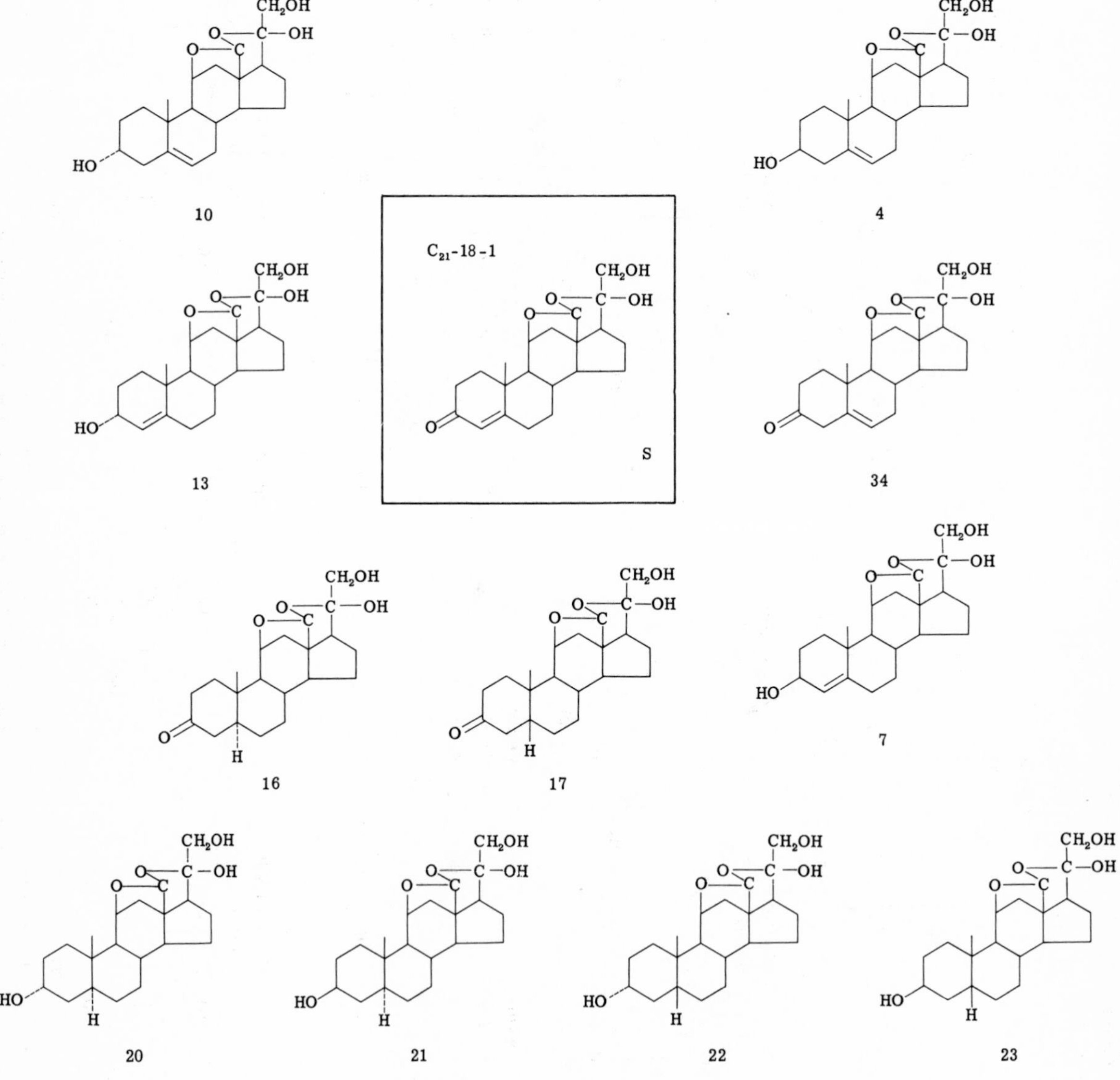

FIG. 38. C_{21}-18-1: 20α,21-Dihydroxy-11β,18;18, 20β-diepoxypregn-4-en-3-one and related metabolites.

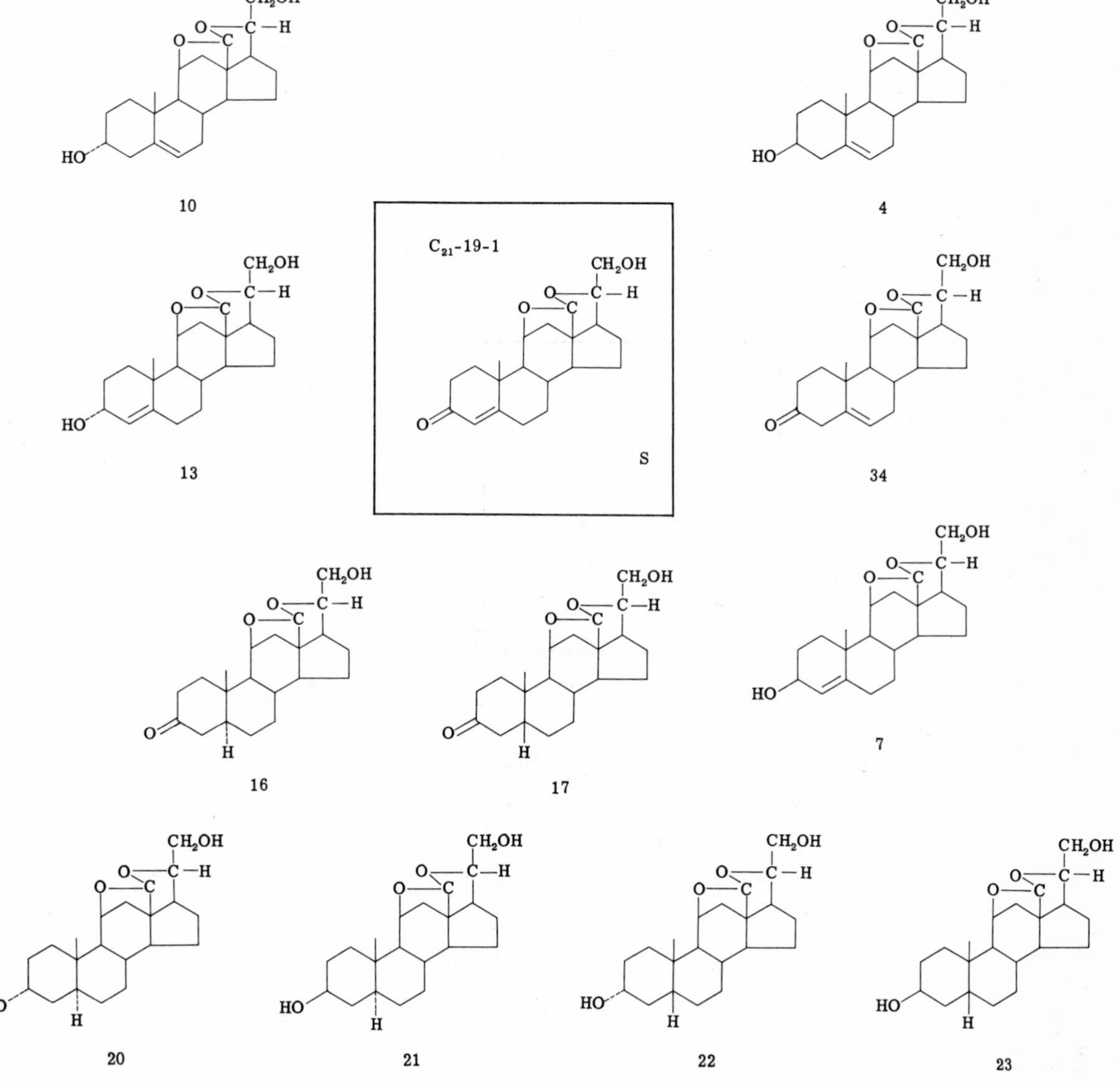

FIG. 39. C_{21}-19-1: 21-Hydroxy-11β,18;18,20β-diepoxypregn-4-en-3-one and related metabolites.

C_{21}-20-1

2 3 4 5 6 7 8 9 10 11 12 13 14 15 16 17 34

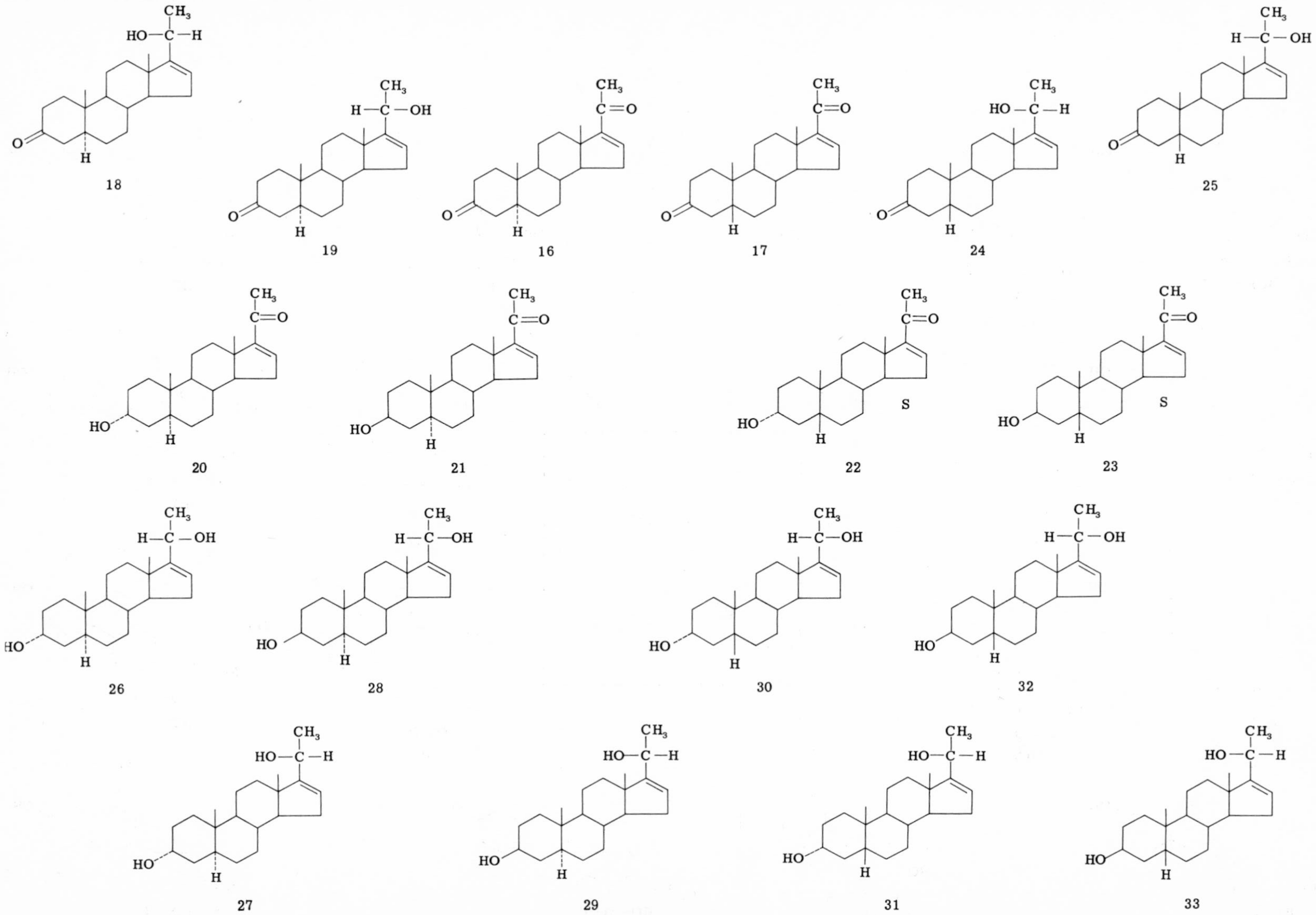

FIG. 40. C_{21}-20-1: Pregna-4,16-diene-3,20-dione and related metabolites.

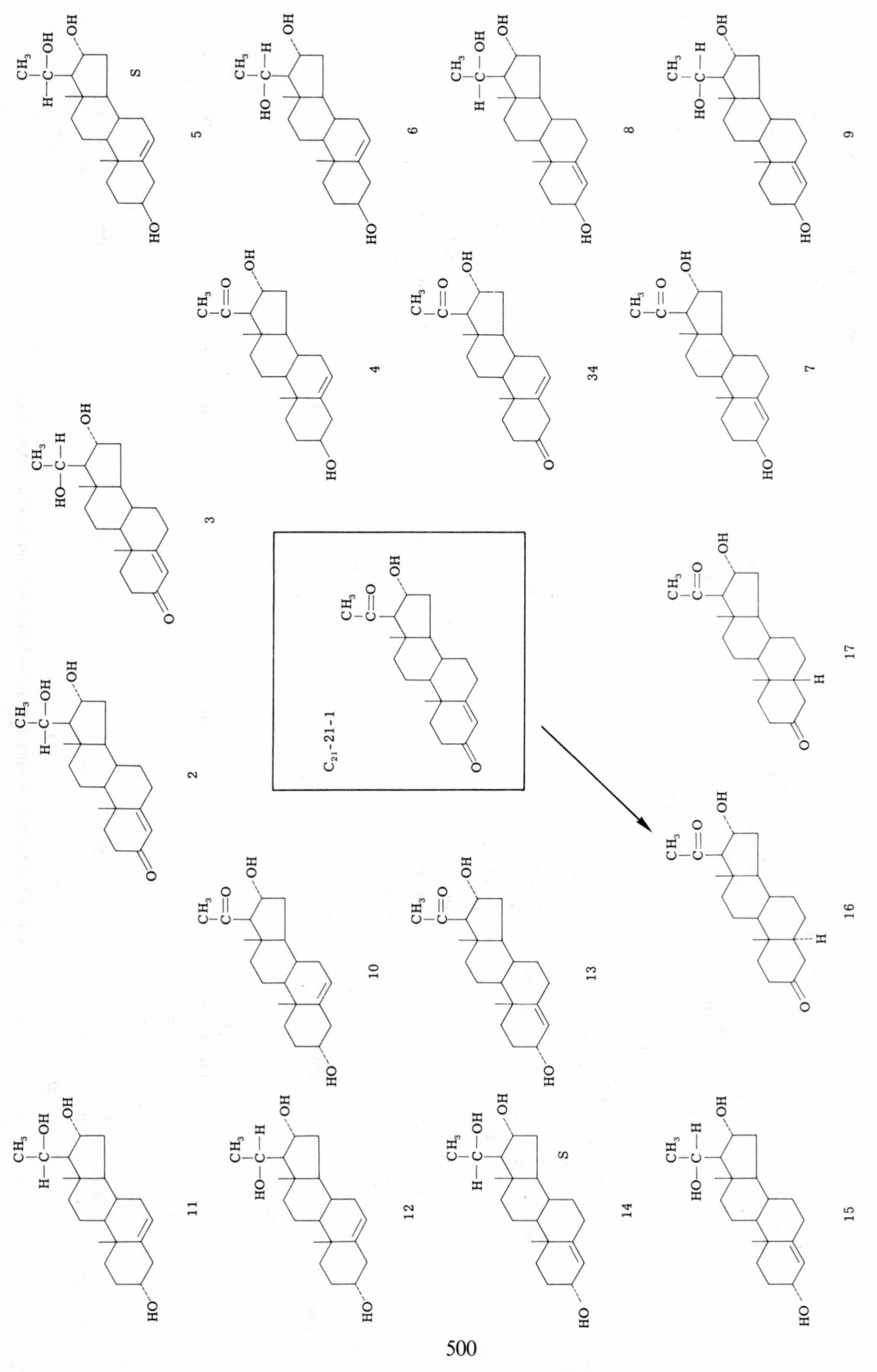

C_{21}-21-1

2 3 4 5 6 7 8 9 10 11 12 13 14 15 16 17 34

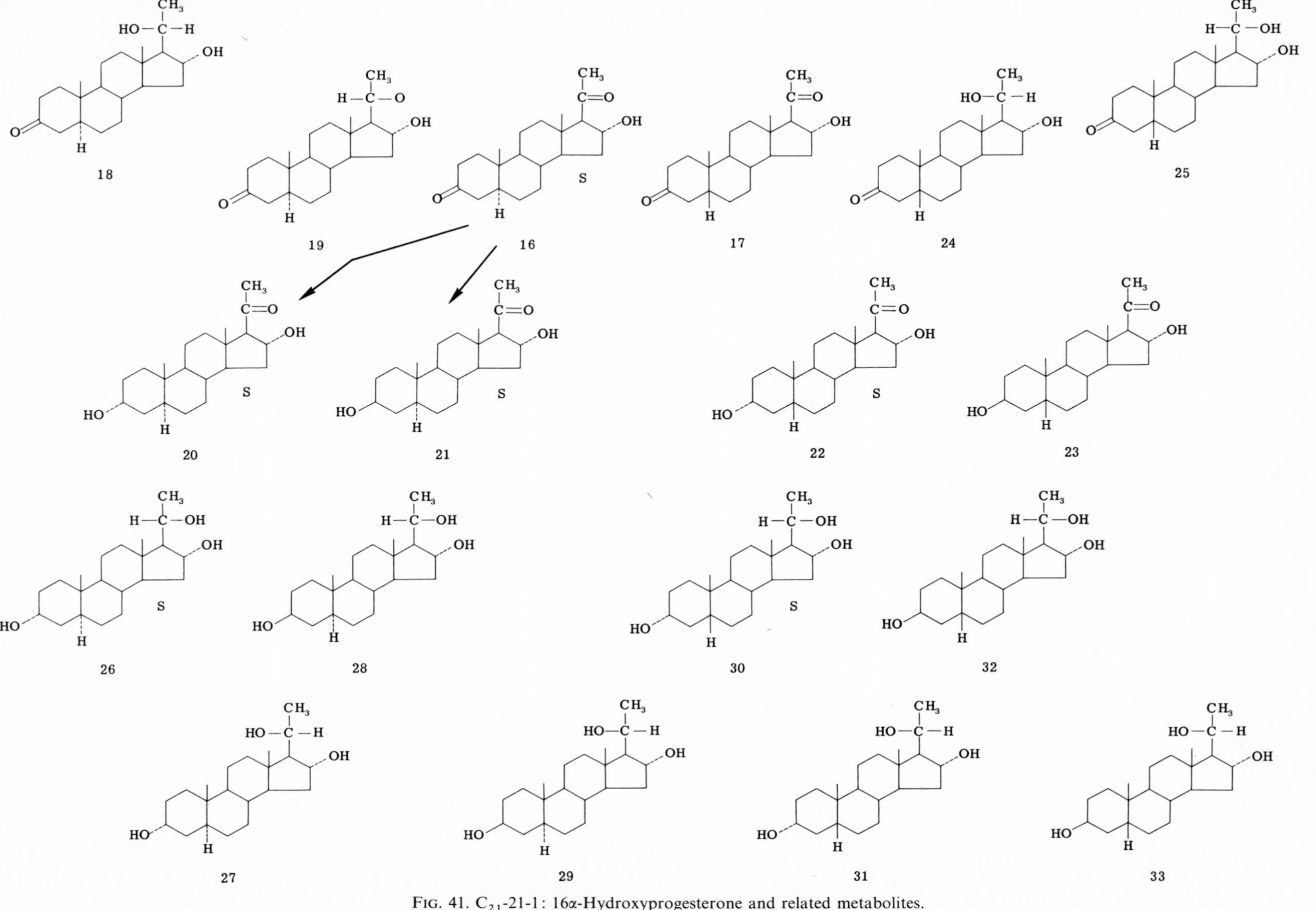

FIG. 41. C_{21}-21-1: 16α-Hydroxyprogesterone and related metabolites.

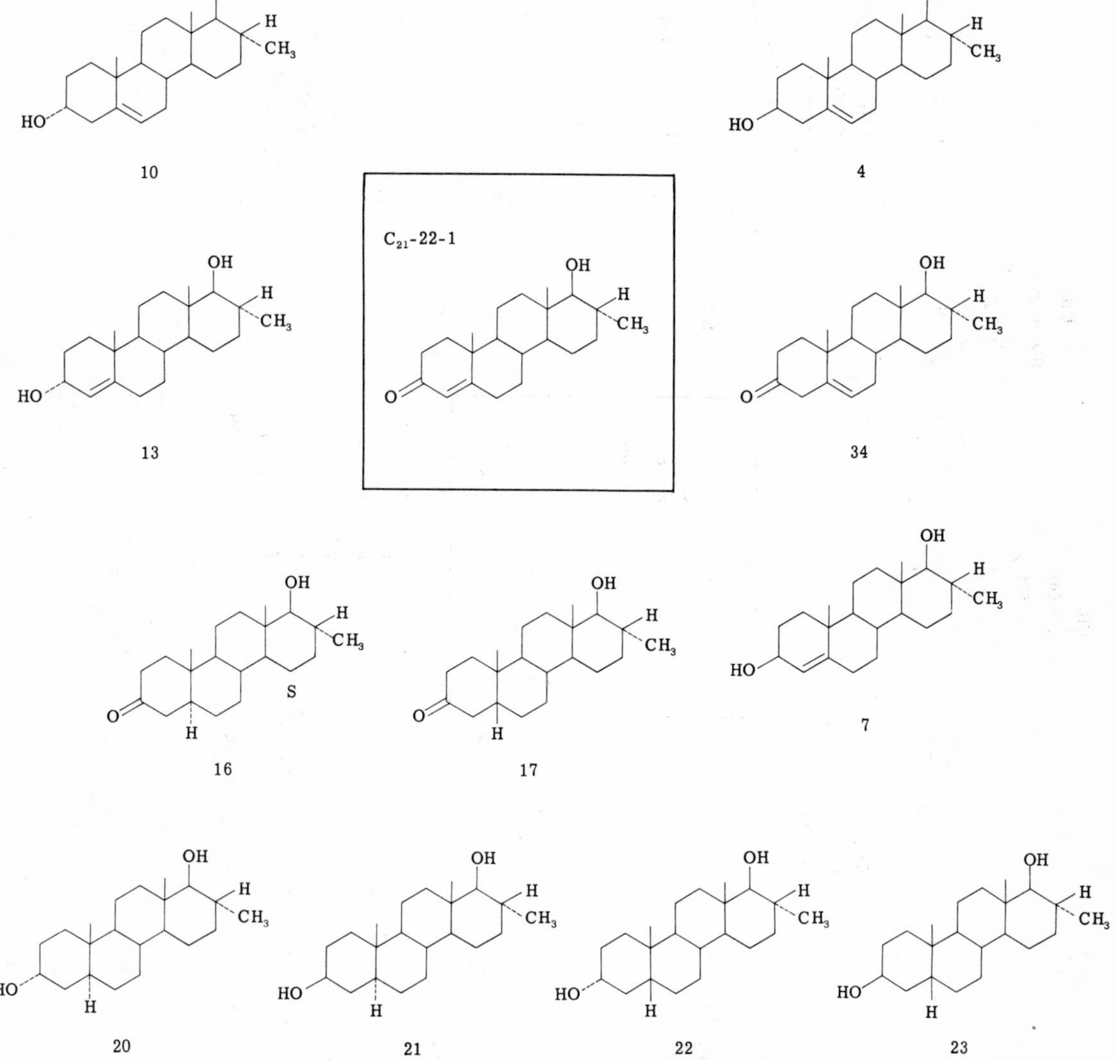

FIG. 42. C_{21}-22-1: 17α-Methyl-17a,β-hydroxy-*D*-homoandrost-4-en-3-one (uranolone) and related metabolites.

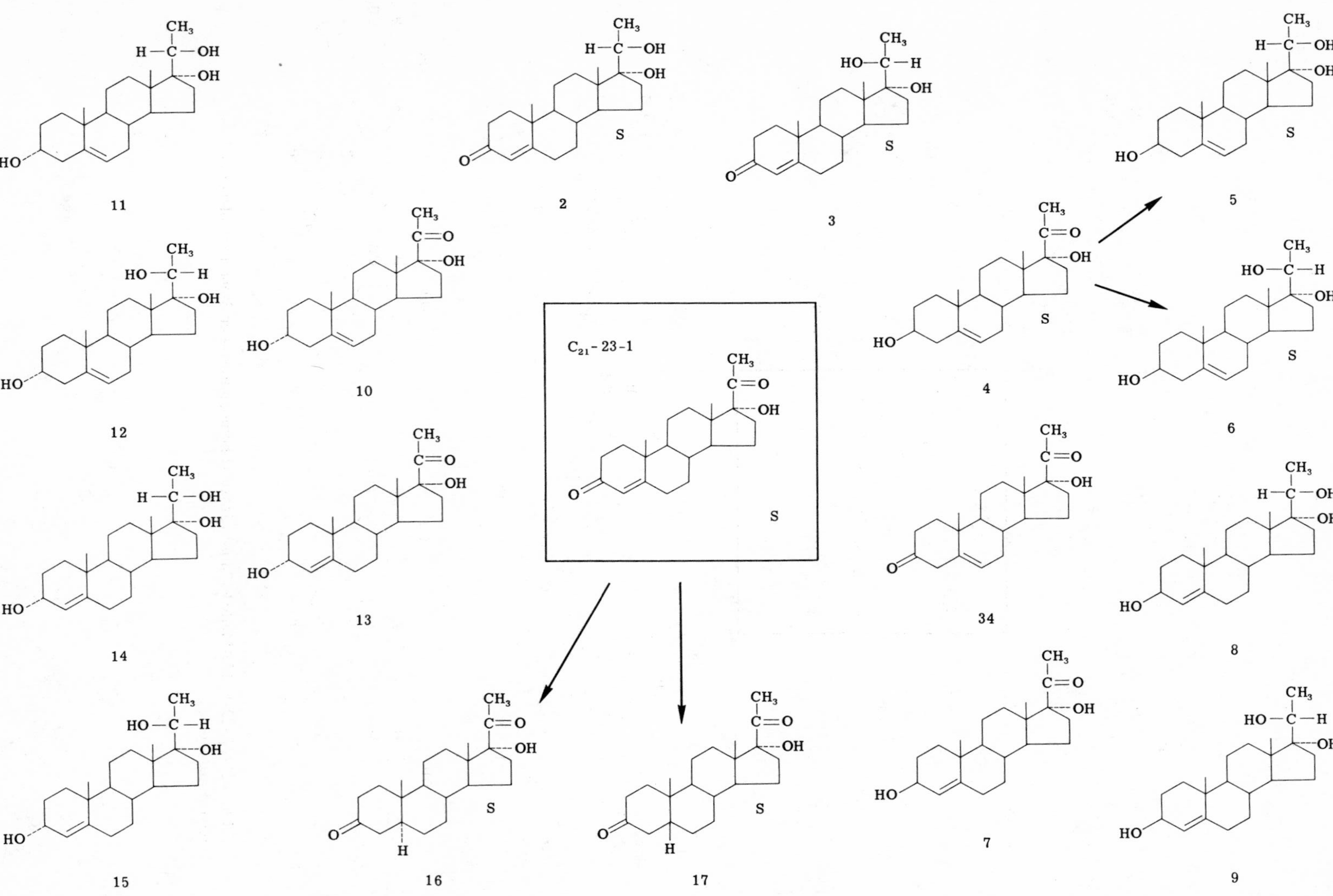
C21 - 23 - 1
11
2
3
5
12
10
4
6
14
13
34
8
15
16
17
7
9

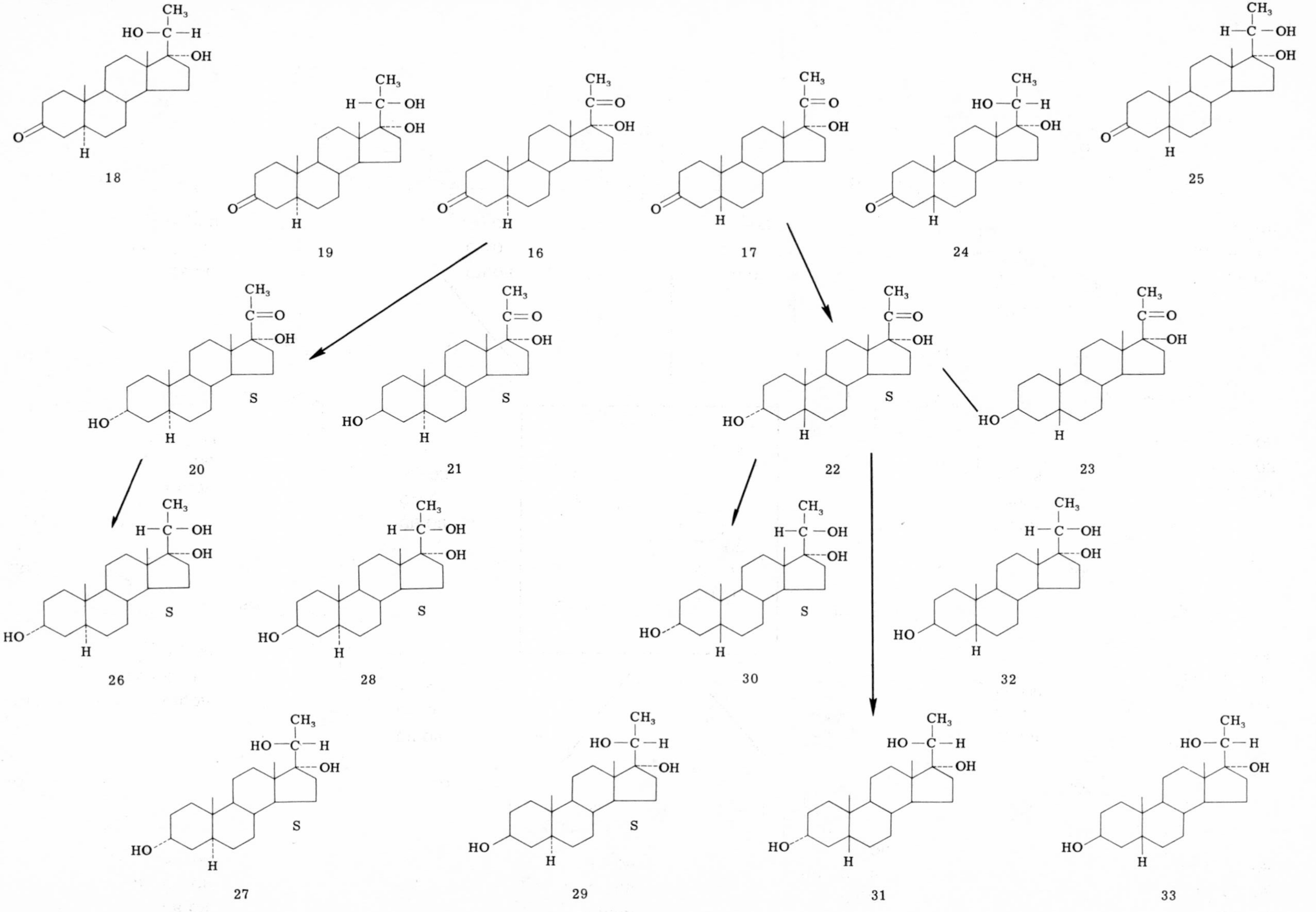

FIG. 43. C_{21}-23-1: 17α-Hydroxyprogesterone and related metabolites.

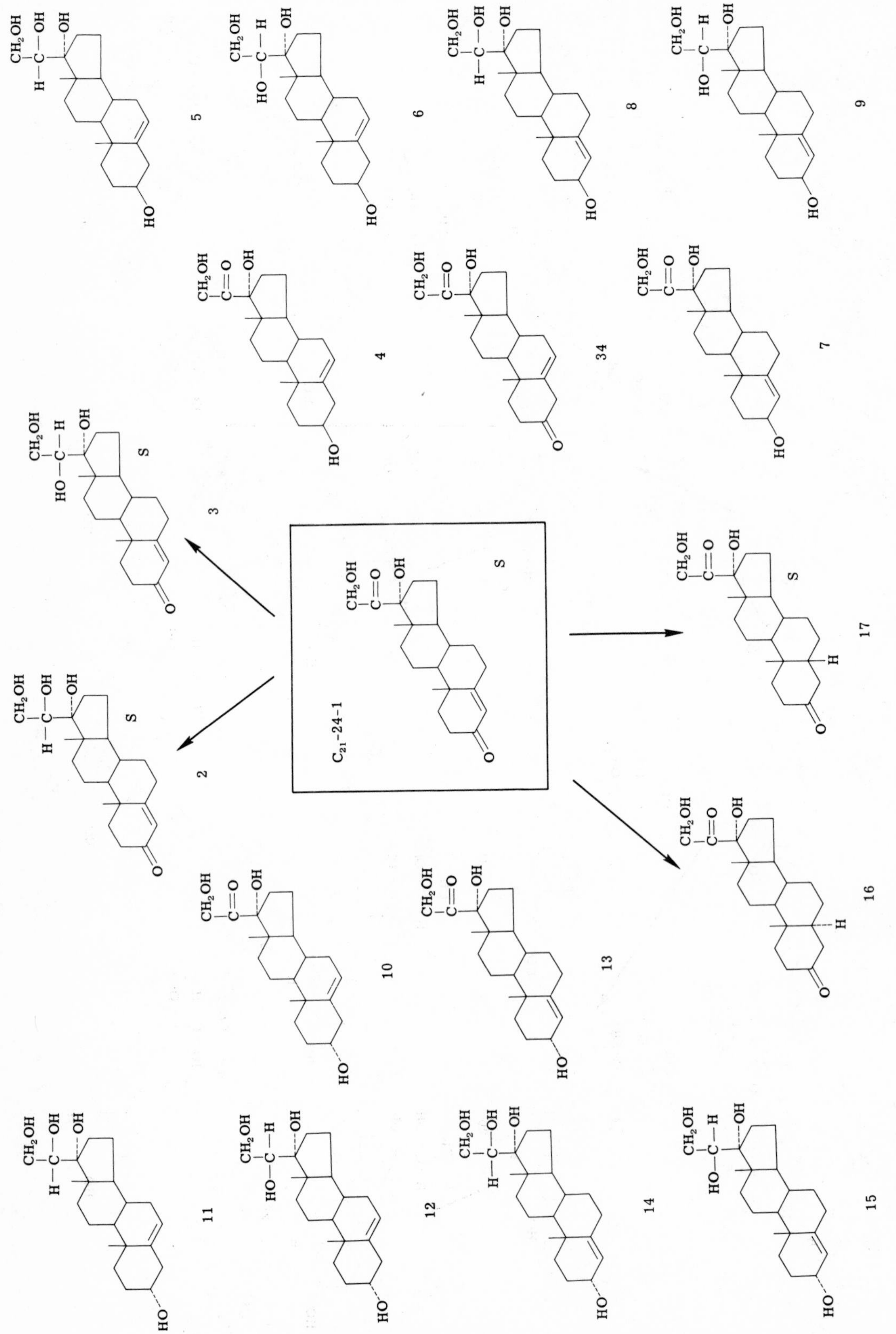

C_{21}-24-1

S

2

3

4

5

6

7

8

9

10

11

12

13

14

15

16

17

34

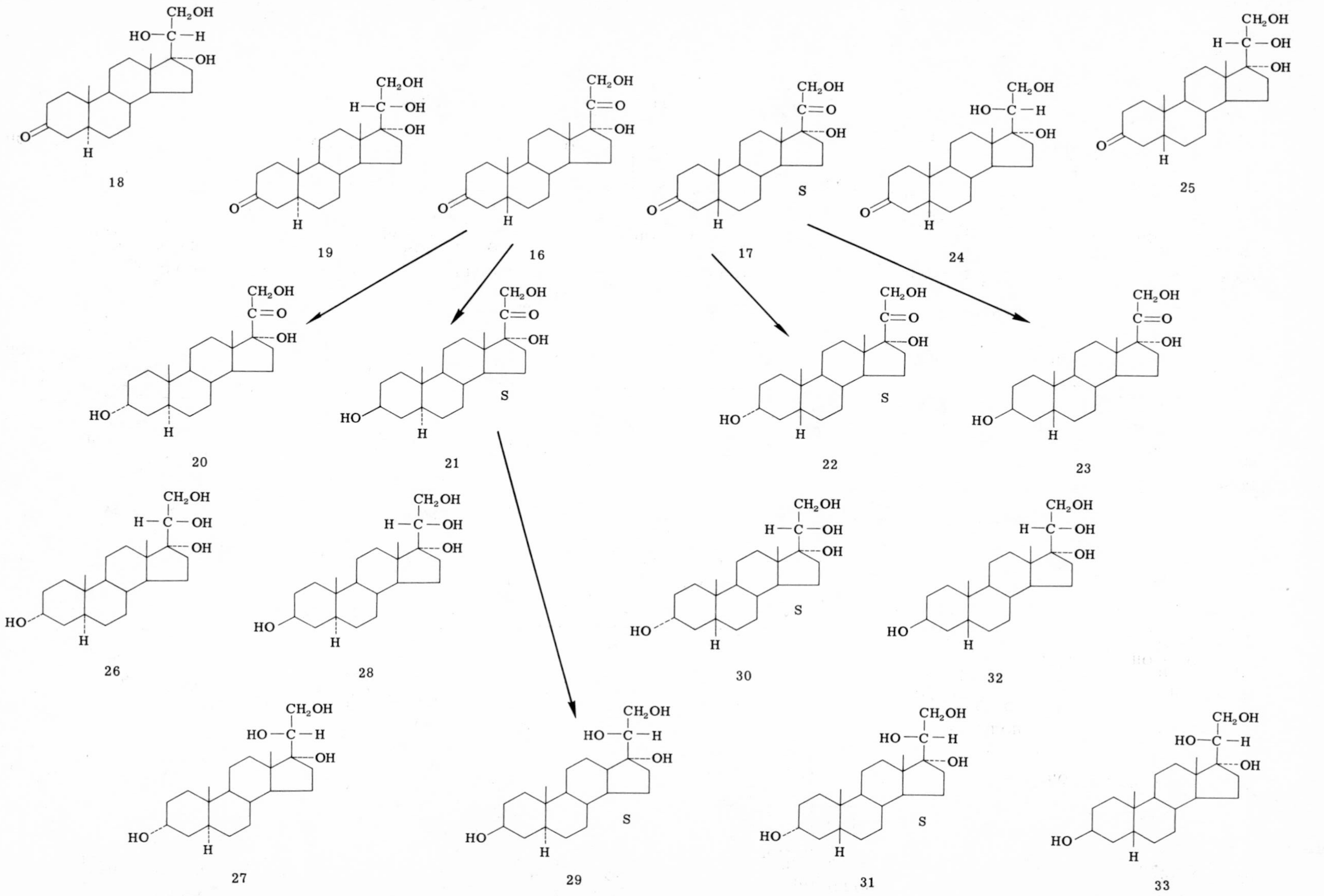

18 19 16 17 24 25

20 21 22 23

26 28 30 32

27 29 31 33

FIG. 44. C_{21}-24-1: 11-Deoxycortisol and related metabolites.

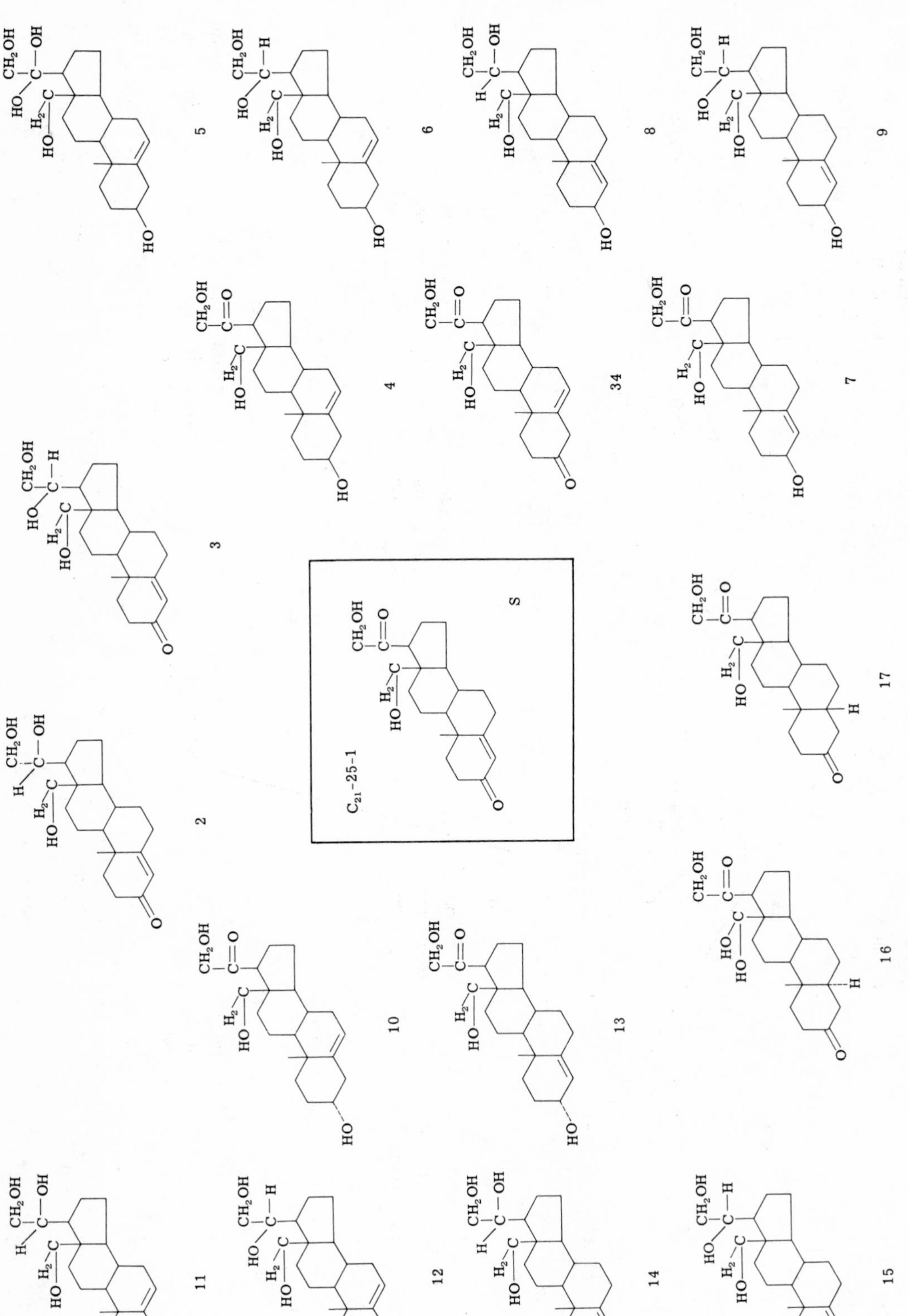

11 2 3 5

12 10 4 6

C_{21}-25-1

S

14 13 34 8

15 16 17 7 9

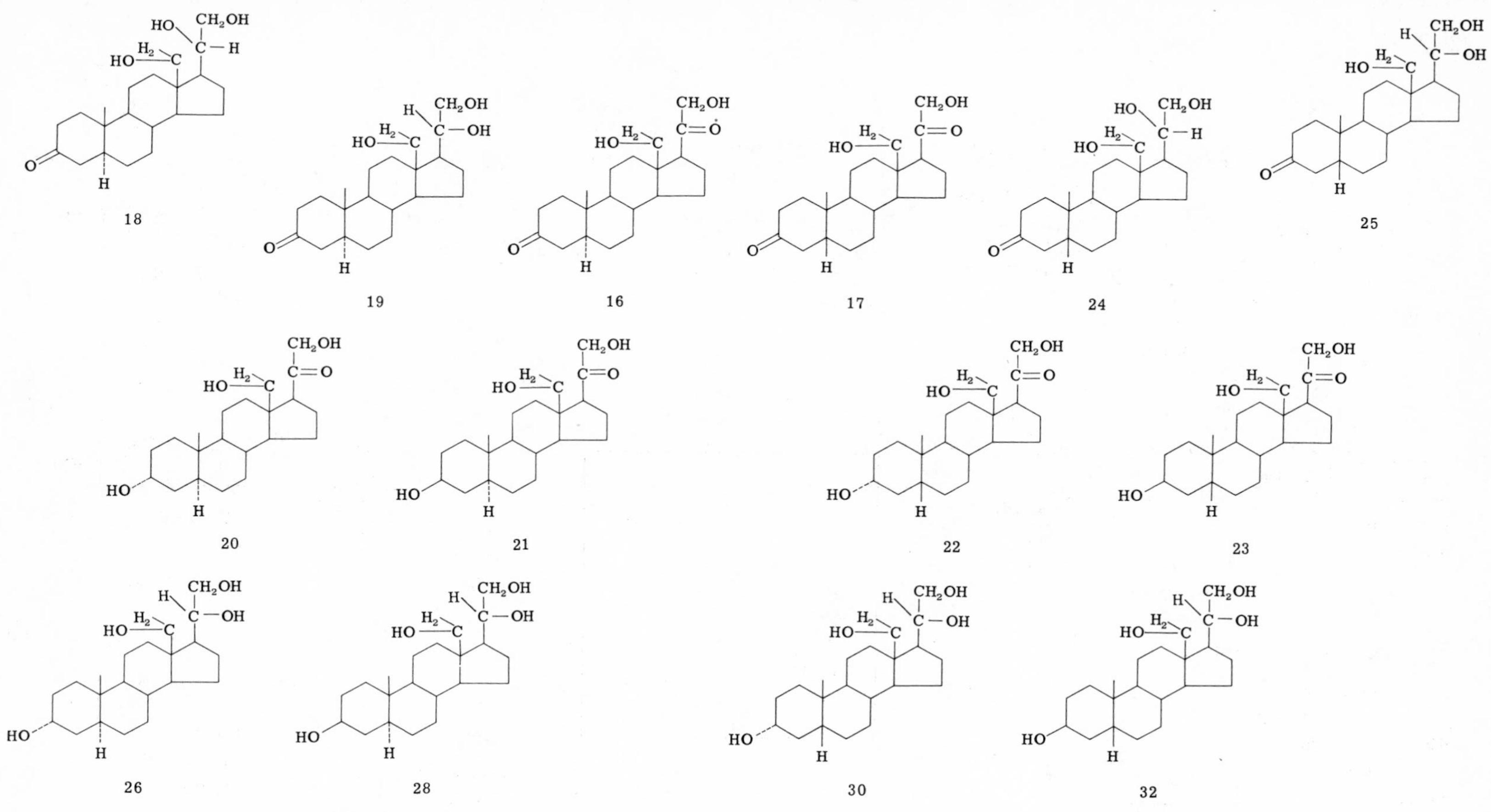

FIG. 45. C_{21}-25-1: 18, 21-Dihydroxyprogesterone and related metabolites.

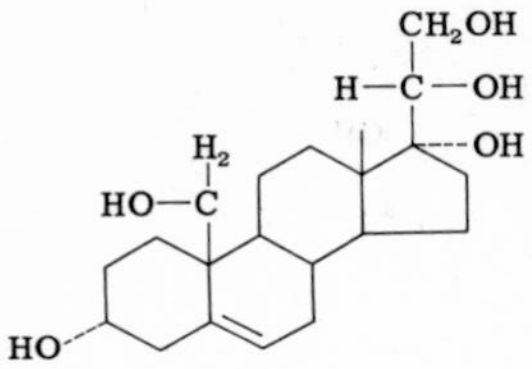

C_{21}-26-1

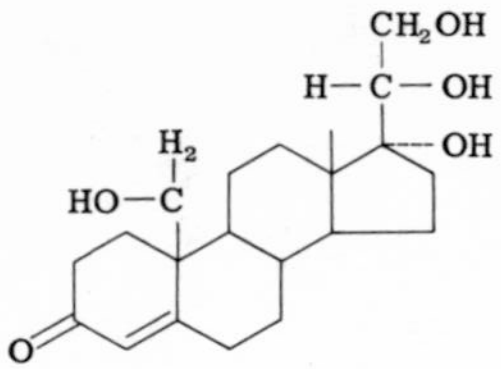

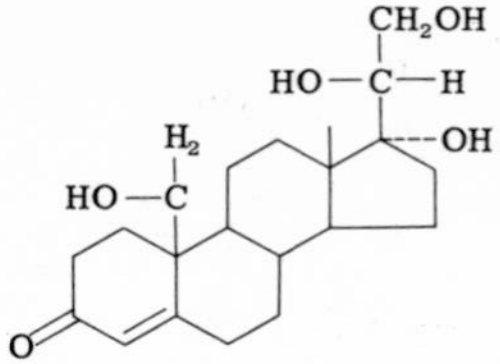

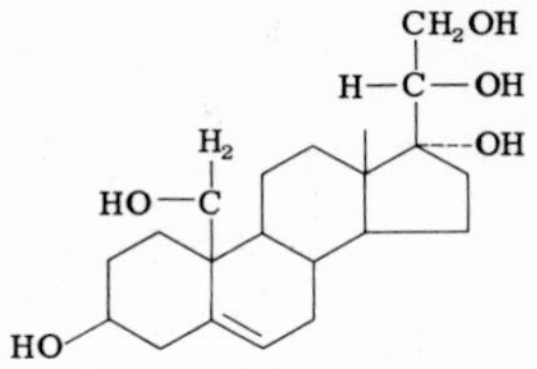

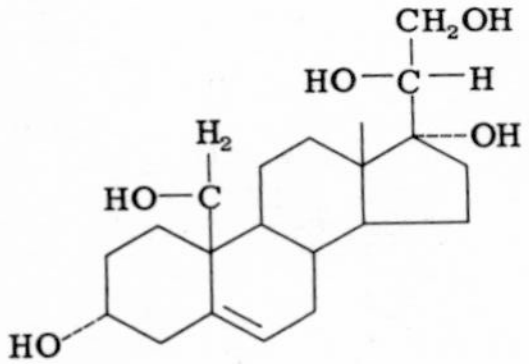

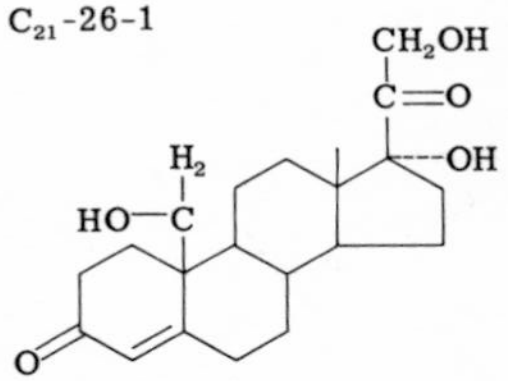

S

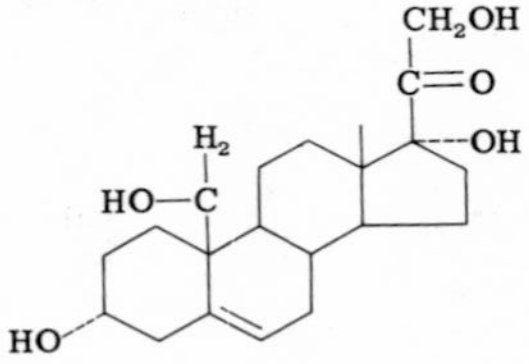

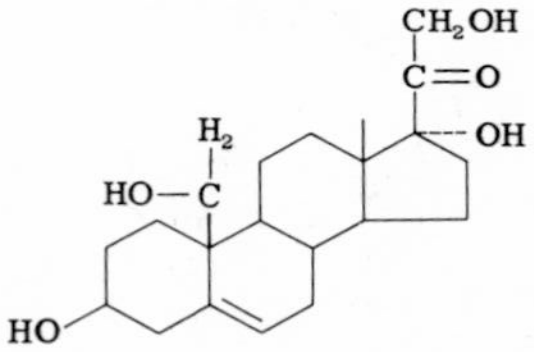

2

3

4

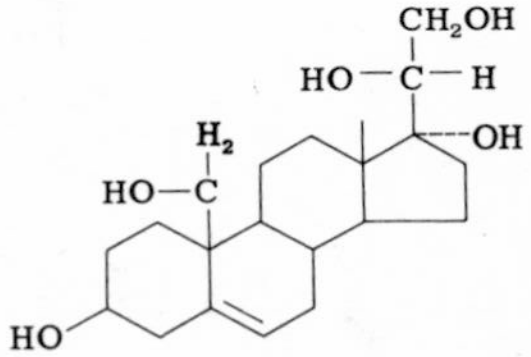

5

6

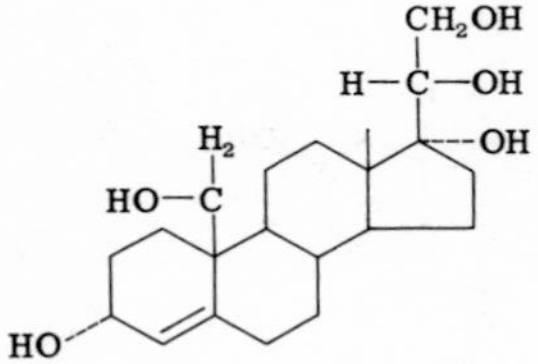

7

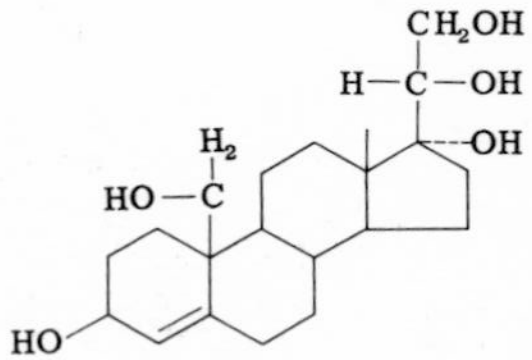

8

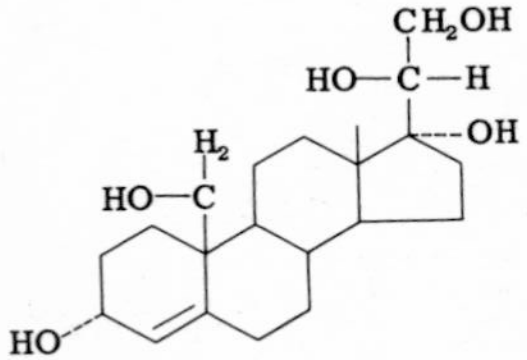

9

10

11

12

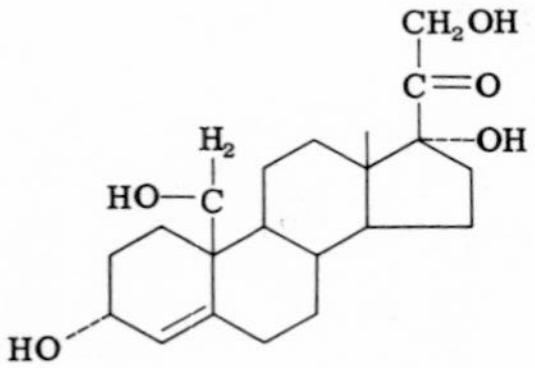

13

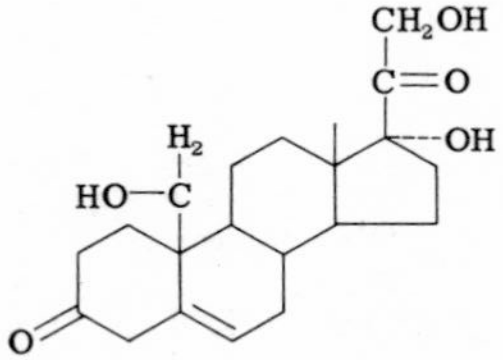

14

15

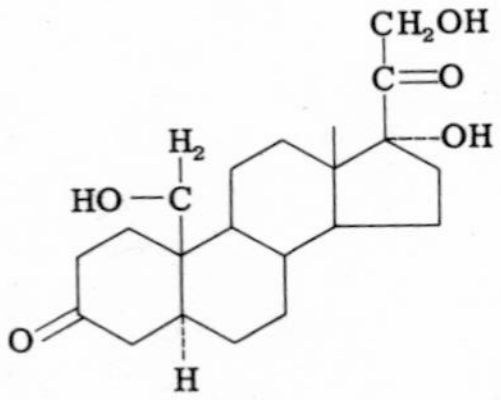

16

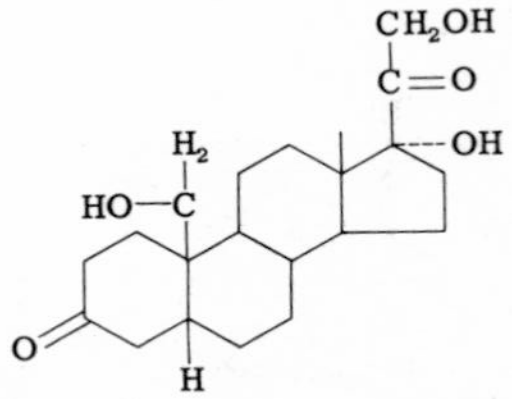

17

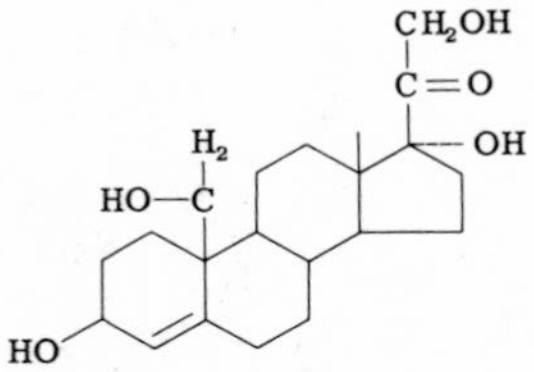

34

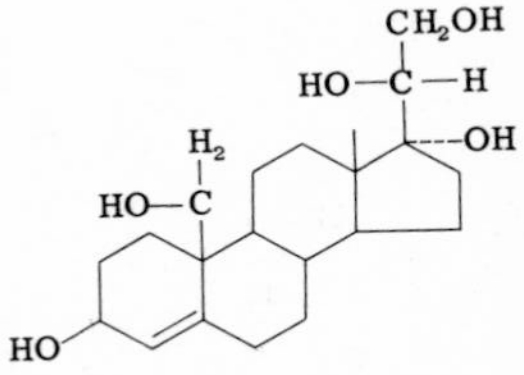

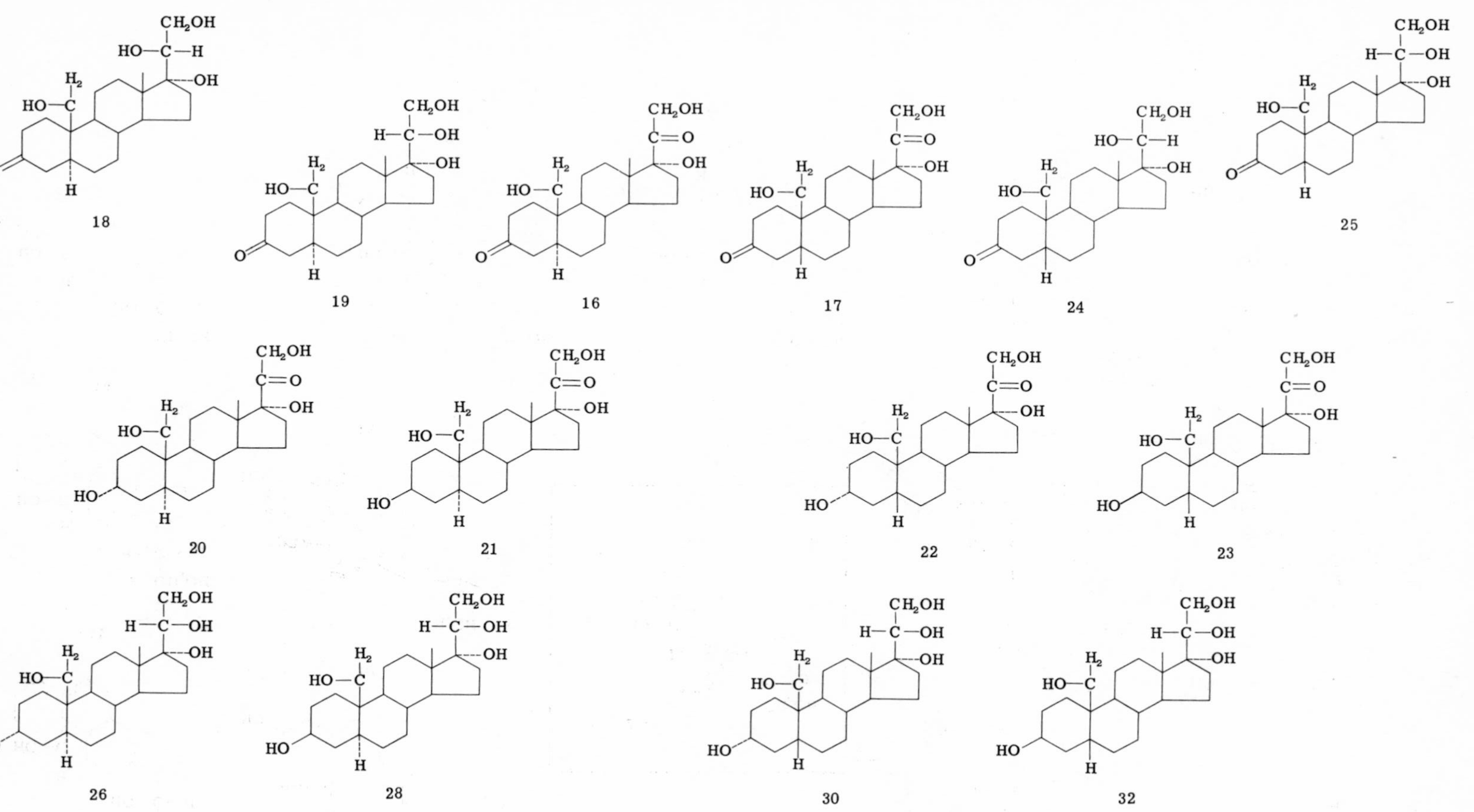

FIG. 46. C_{21}-26-1 : 17α,19,21-Trihydroxyprogesterone and related metabolites.

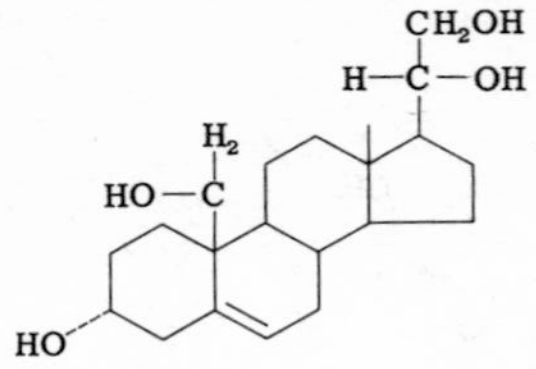

C_{21}-27-1

S

11 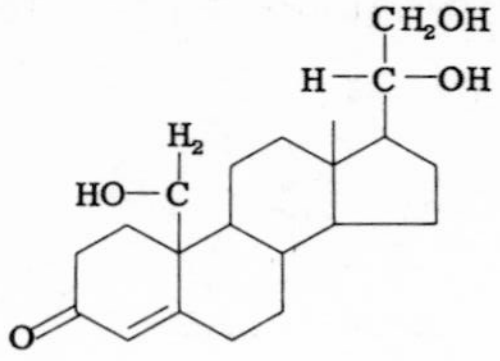 2 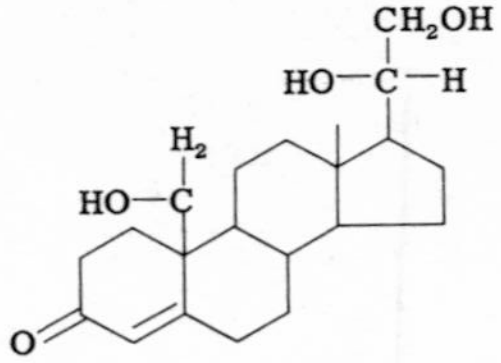 3 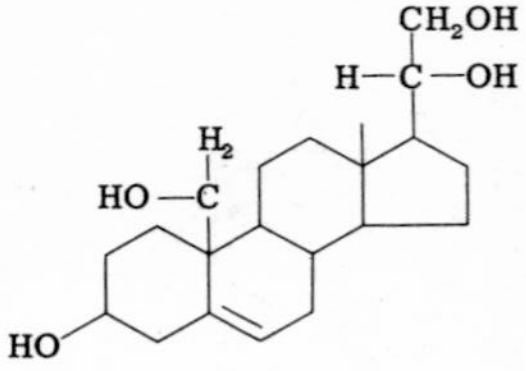 5

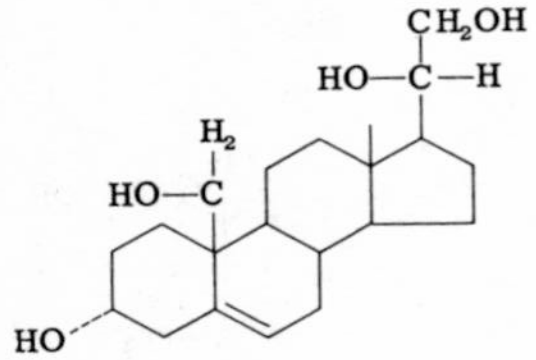

12 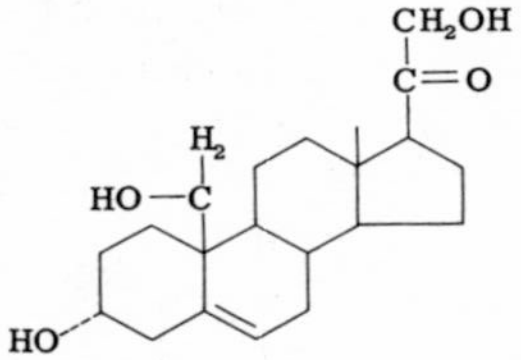 10 4 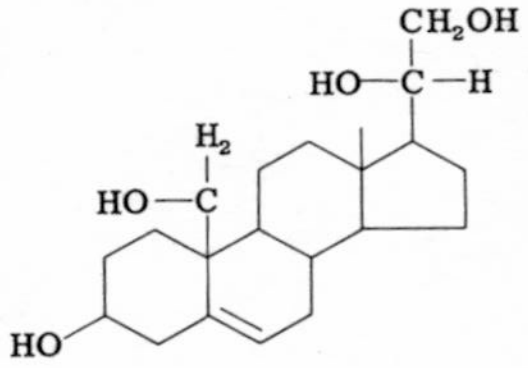 6

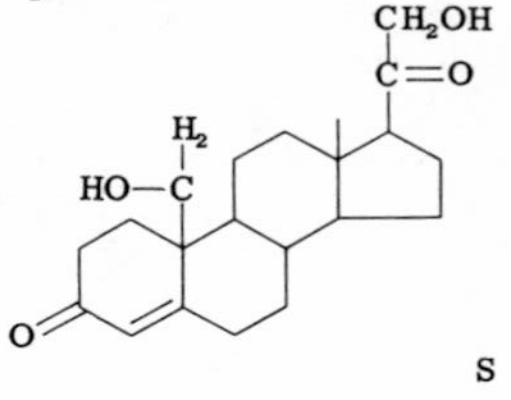

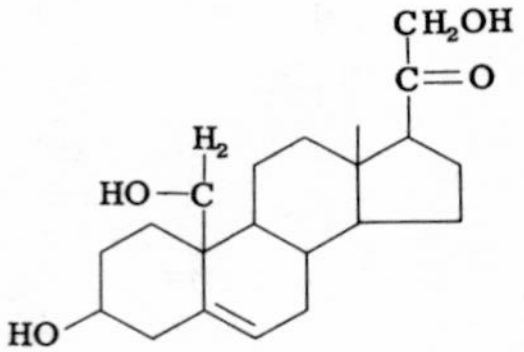

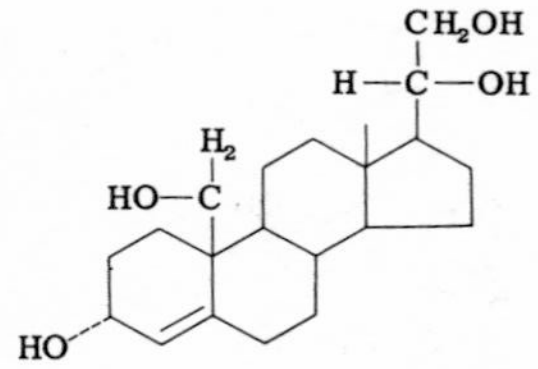

14 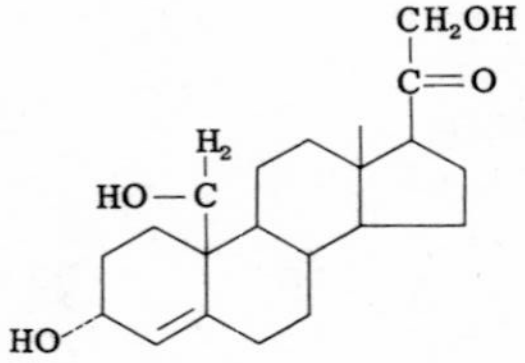 13 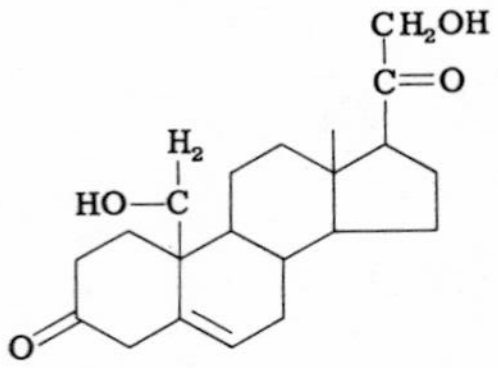 34 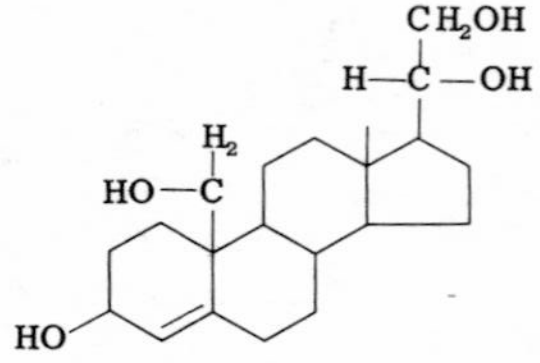 8

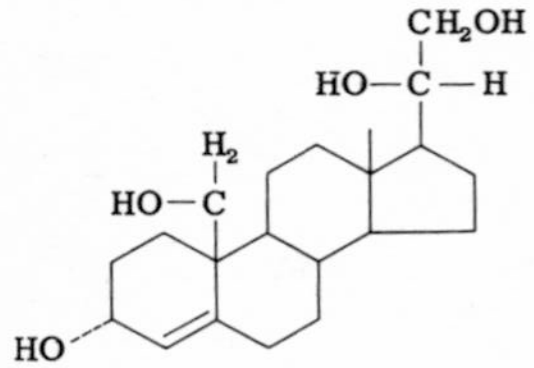

15 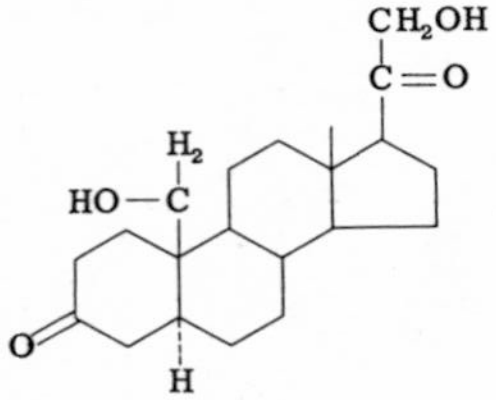 16 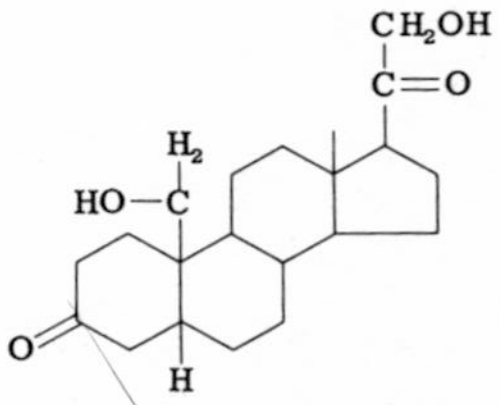 17 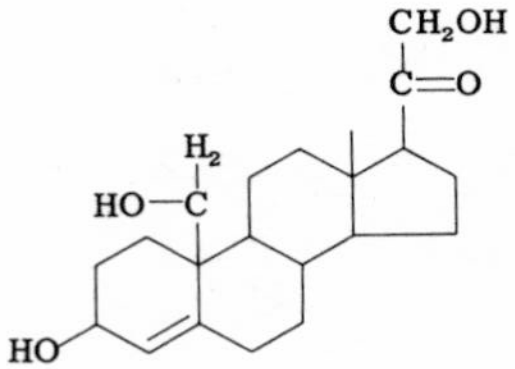 7 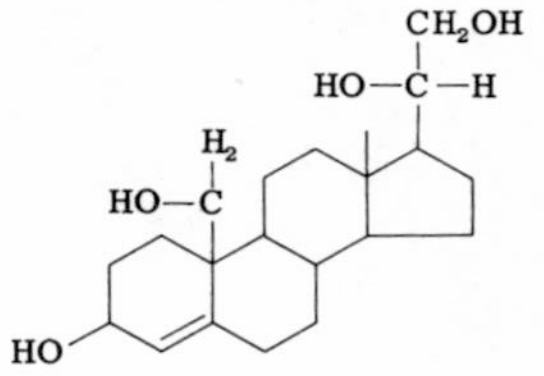 9

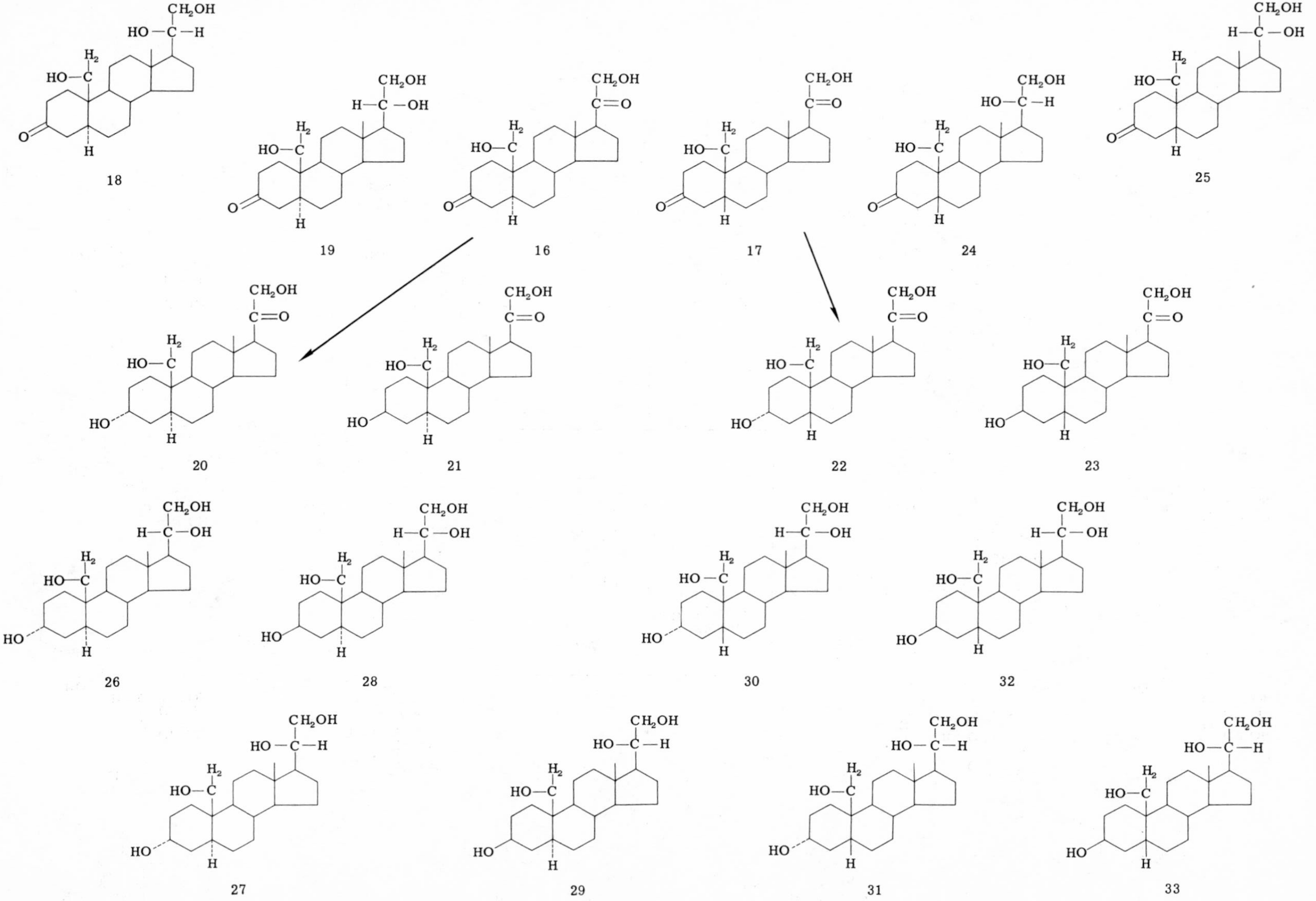

FIG. 47. C_{21}-27-1: 19,21-Dihydroxyprogesterone and related metabolites.

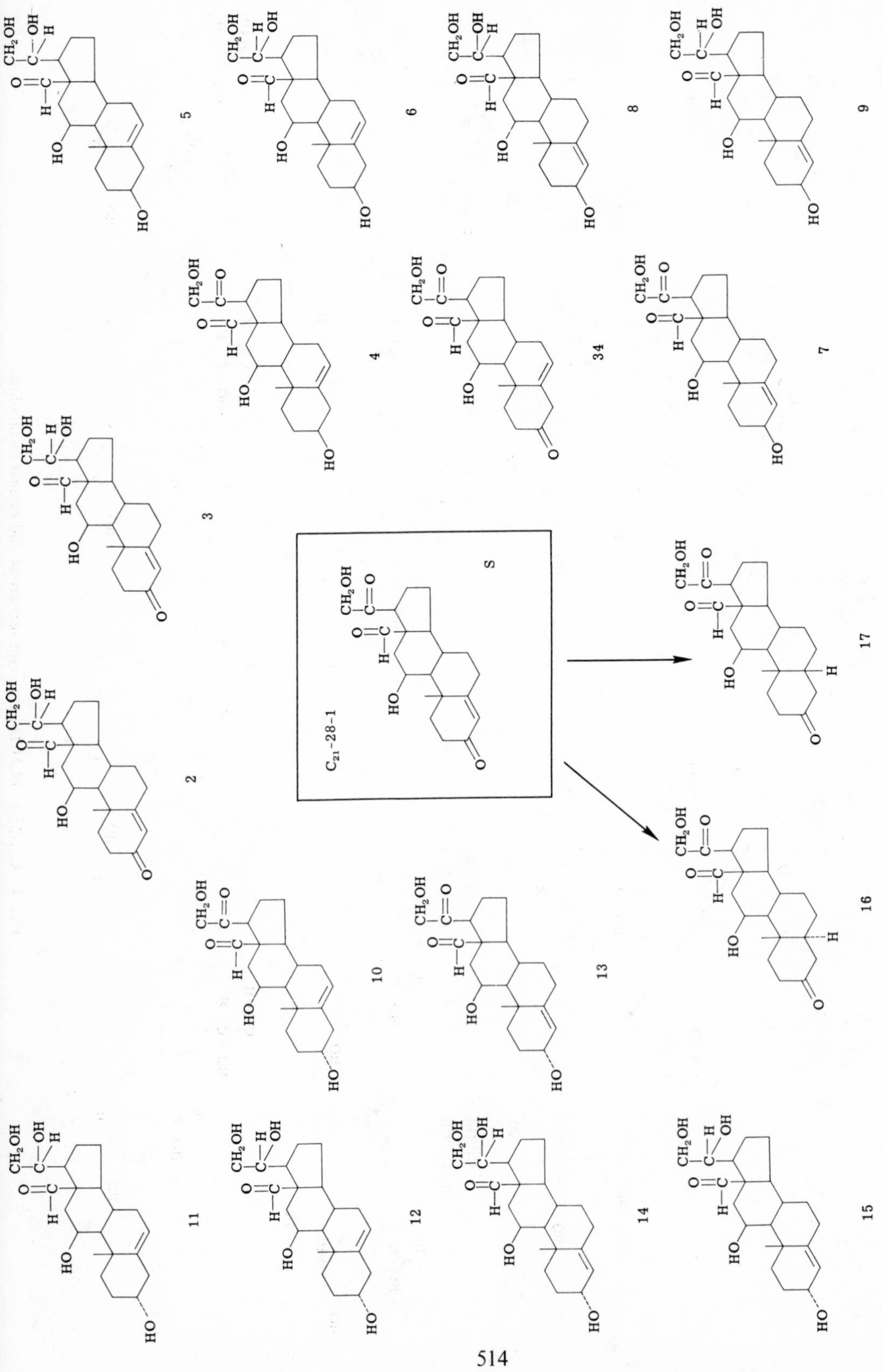

5

6

8

9

4

34

7

3

C_{21}-28-1

S

17

2

16

10

13

11

12

14

15

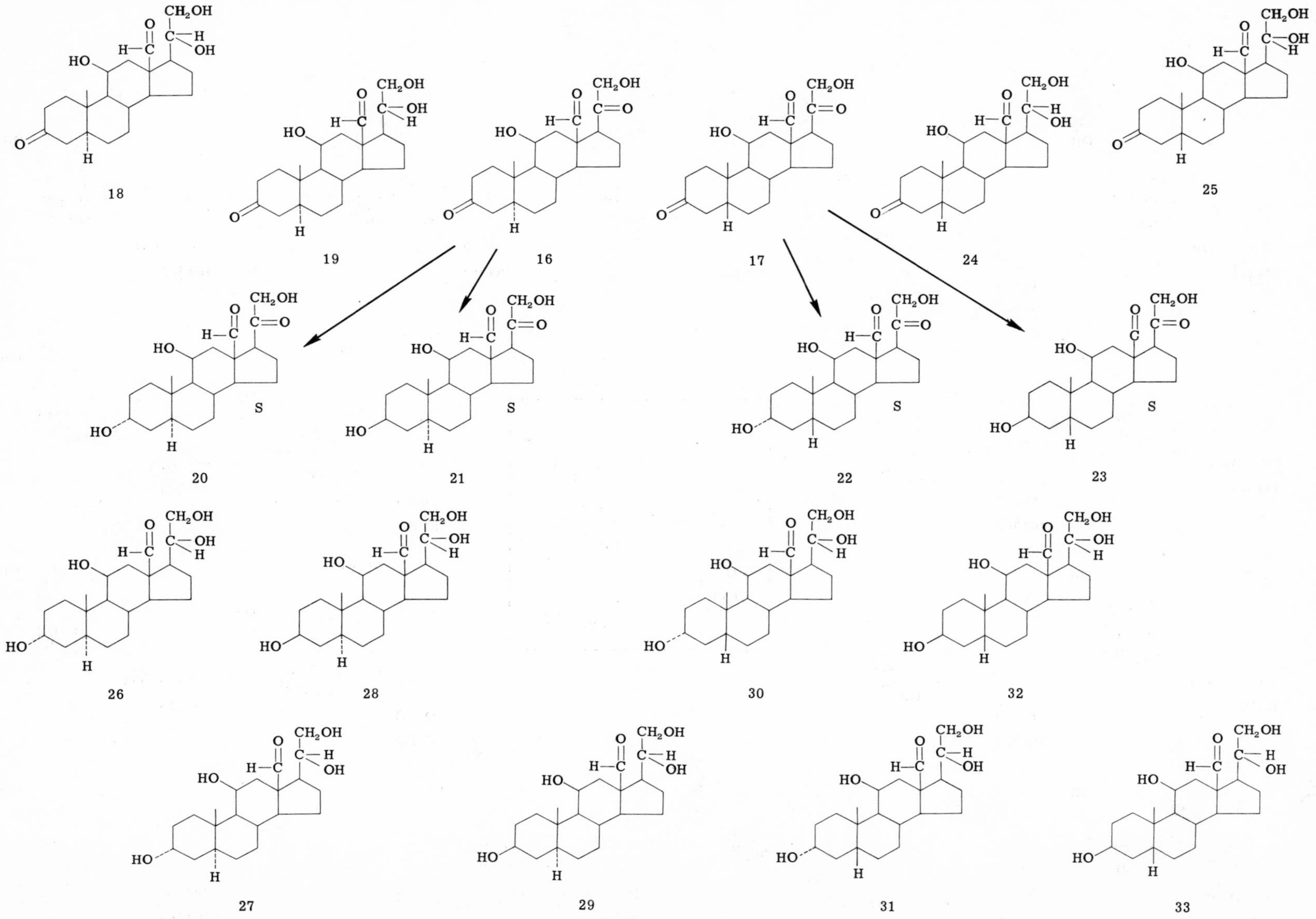

FIG. 48. C_{21}-28-1: Aldosterone and related metabolites.

C_{21}-29-1

S

2

3

4

5

6

7

8

9

10

11

12

13

14

15

16

17

34

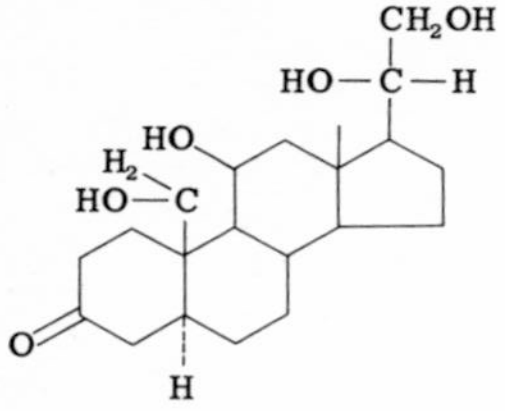

18 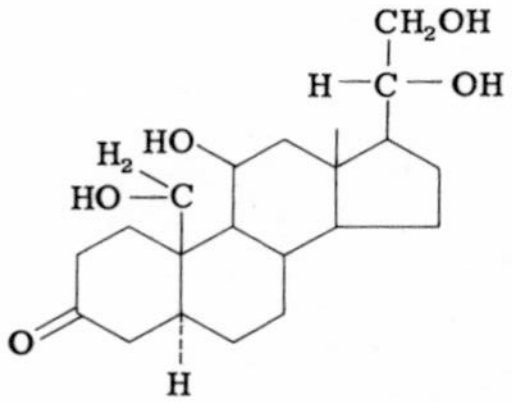 19 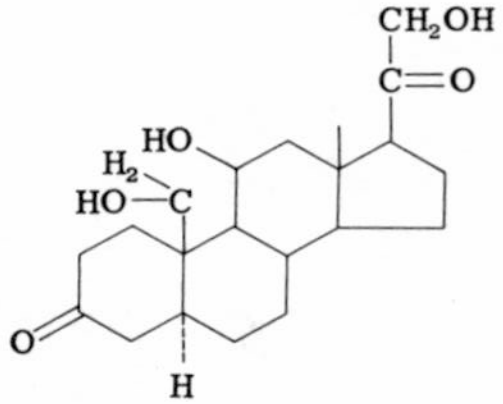 16 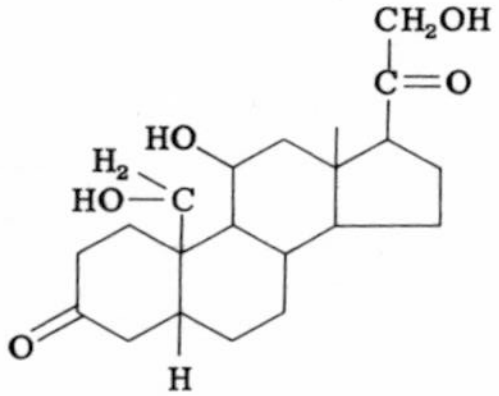 17 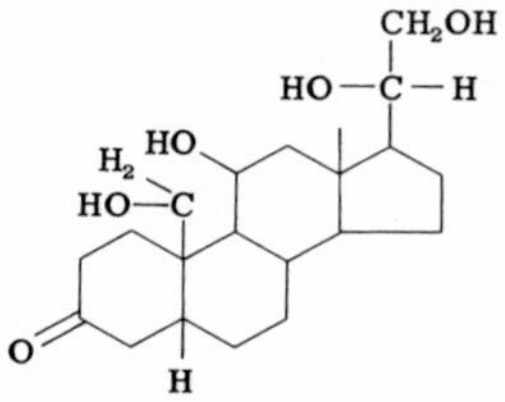 24 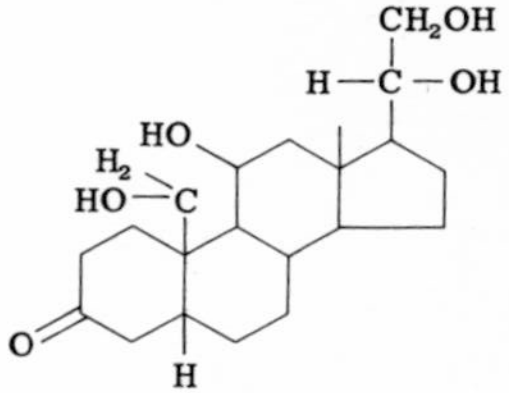 25

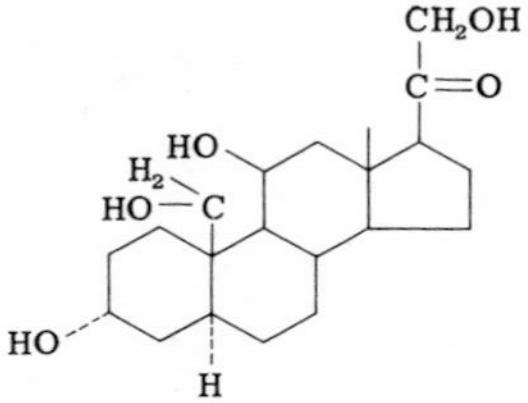

20 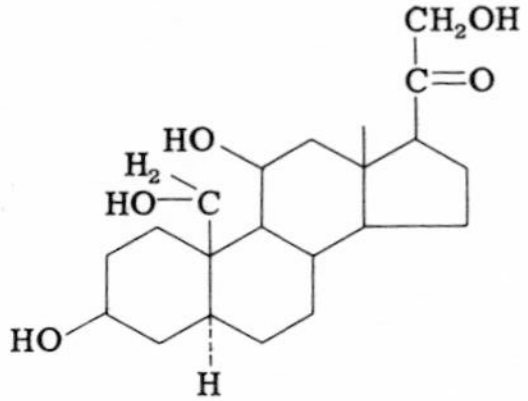 21 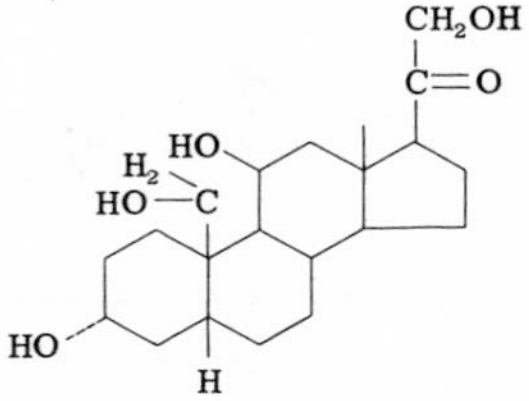 22 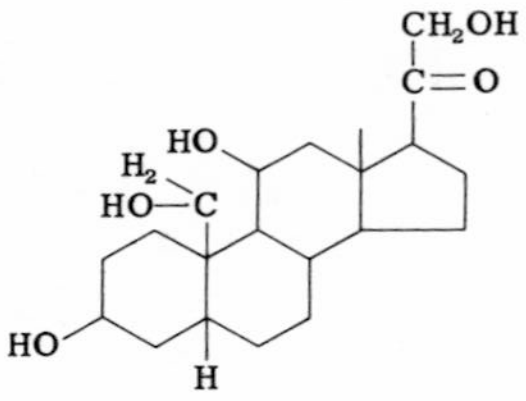 23

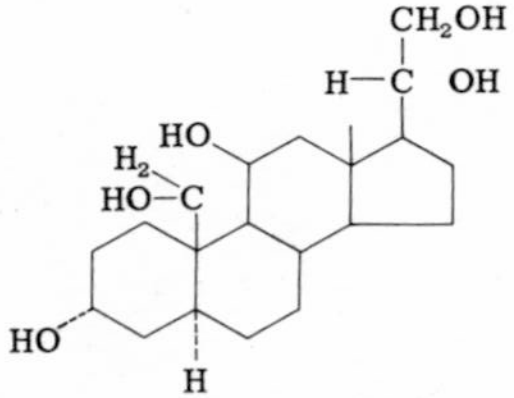

26 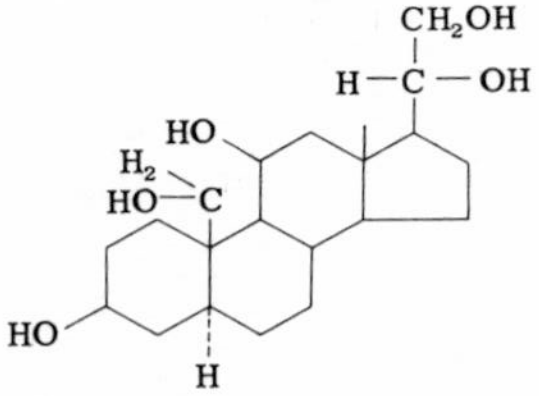 28 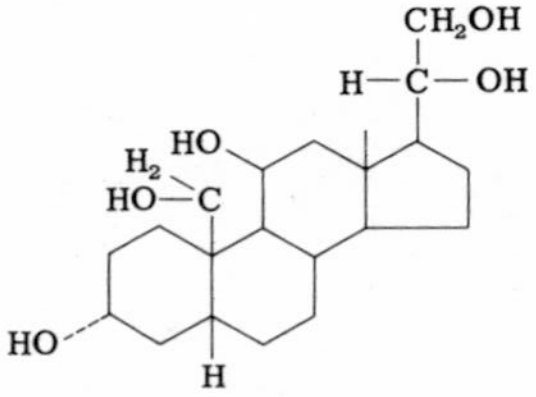 30 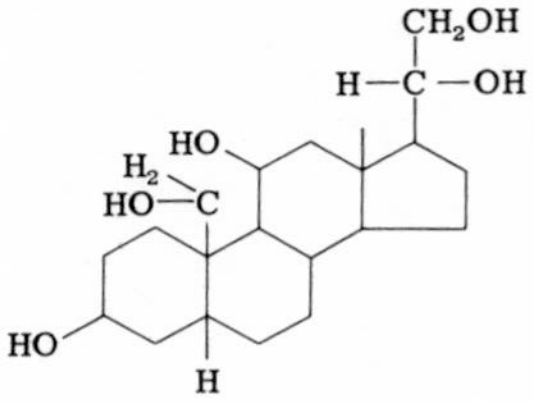 32

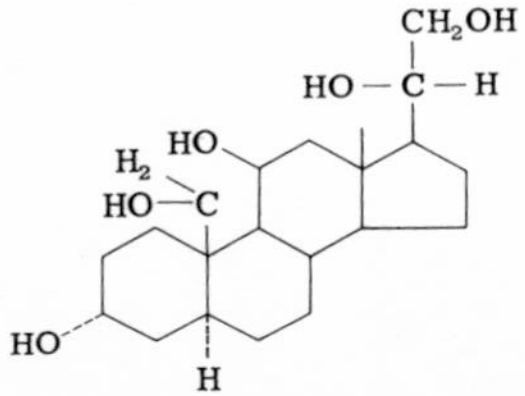

27 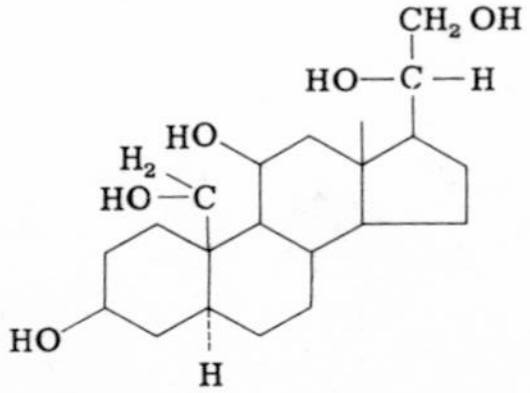 29 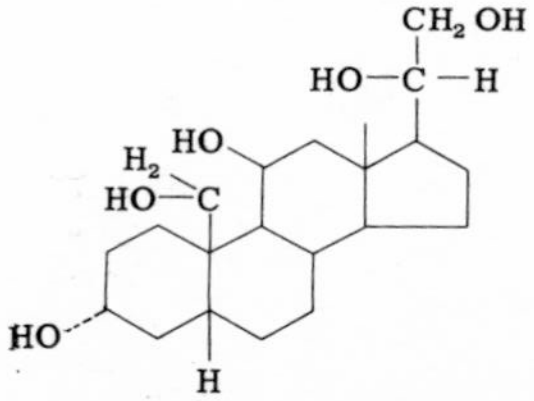 31 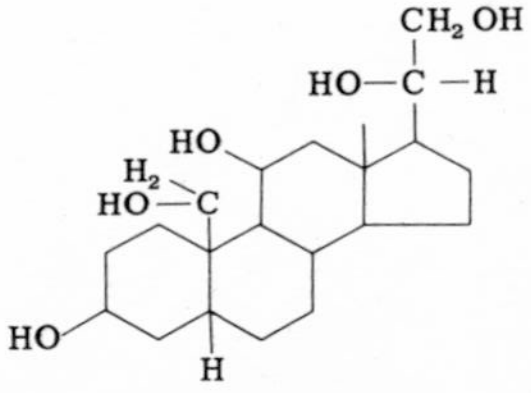 33

FIG. 49. C_{21}-29-1: 19-Hydroxycorticosterone and related metabolites.

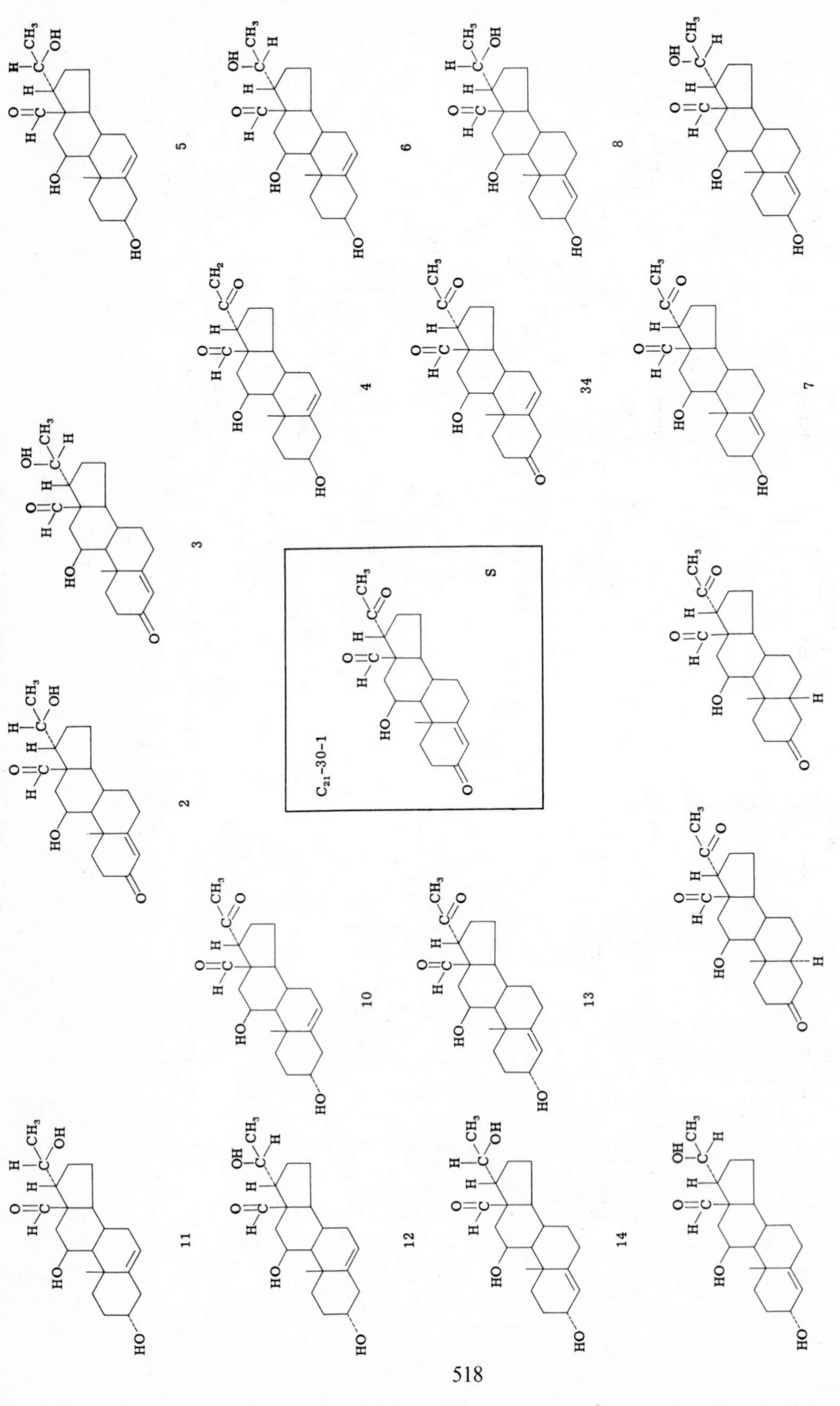

C_{21}–30–1

S

2

3

4

5

6

34

7

8

9

10

11

12

13

14

15

16

17

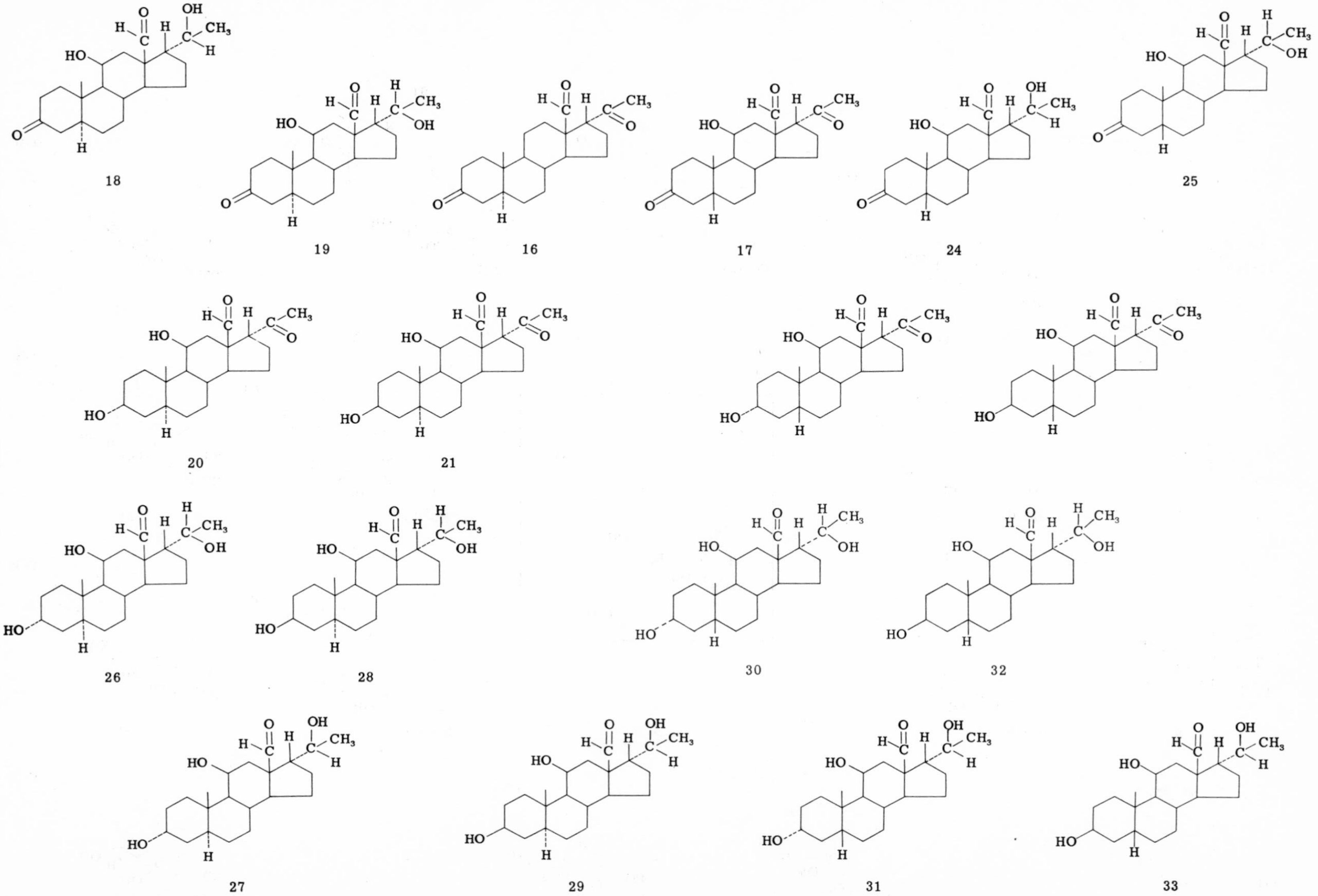

18 19 16 17 24 25

20 21

26 28 30 32

27 29 31 33

FIG. 50. C_{21}-30-1: Isoaldosterone and related metabolites.

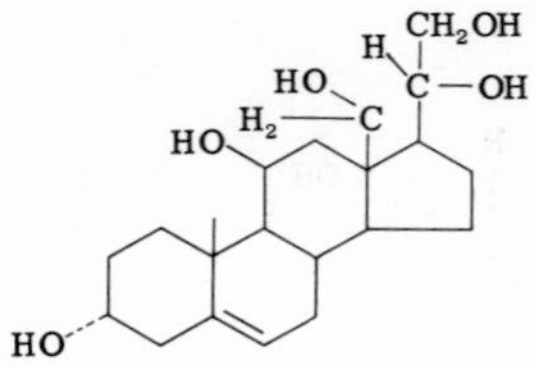

C_{21}-31-1

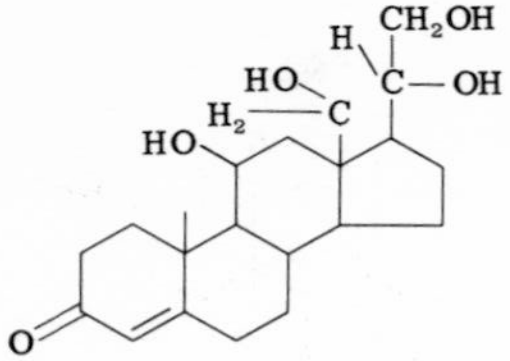

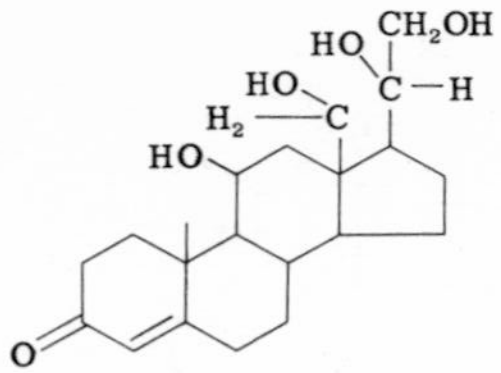

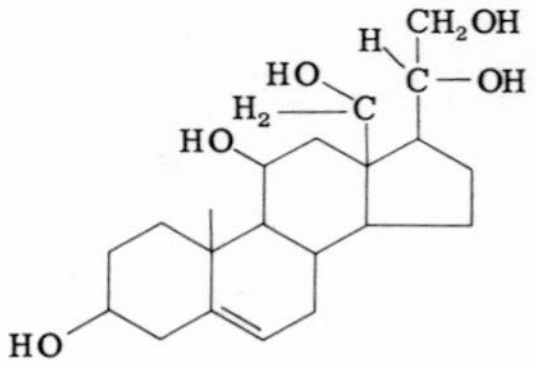

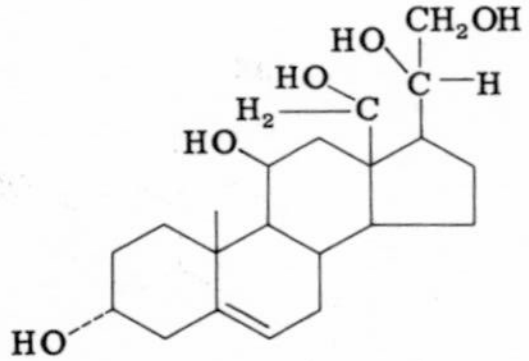

S

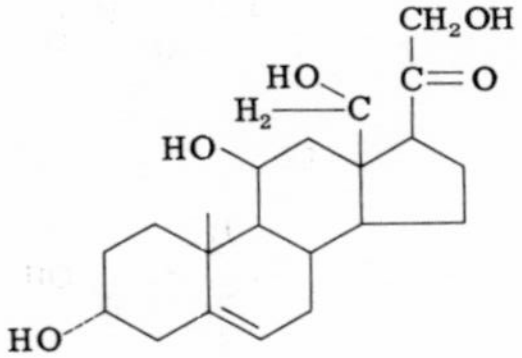

2 3 4 5 6 7 8 9 10 11 12 13 14 15 16 17 34

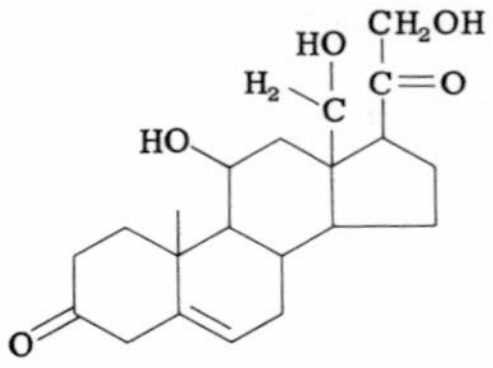

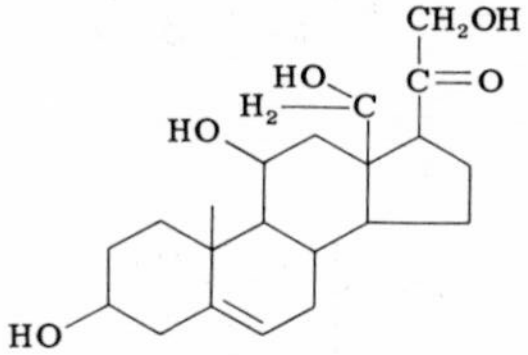

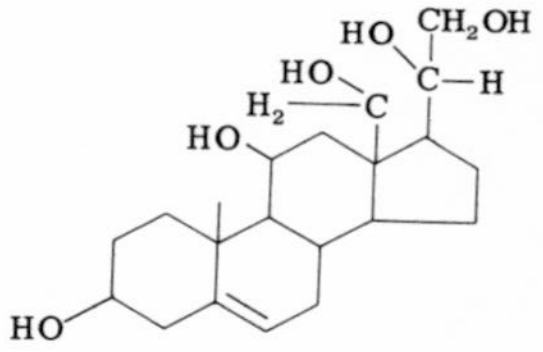

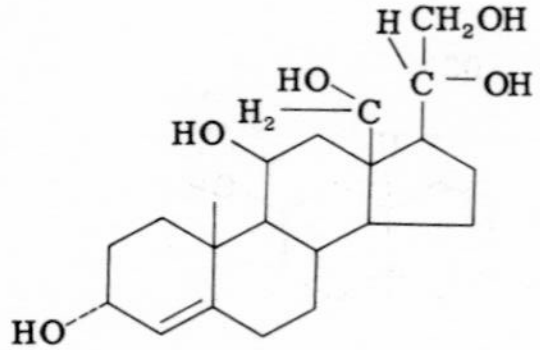

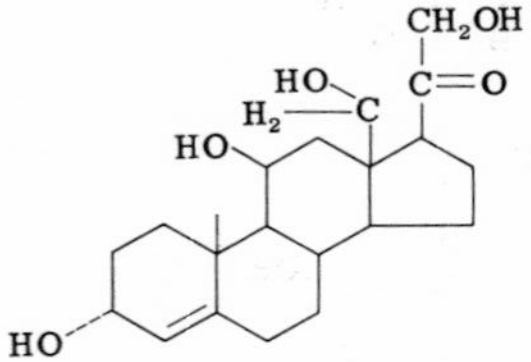

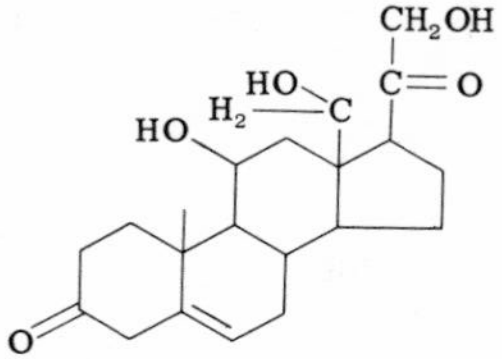

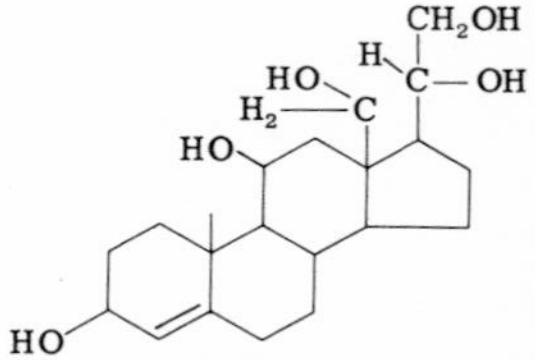

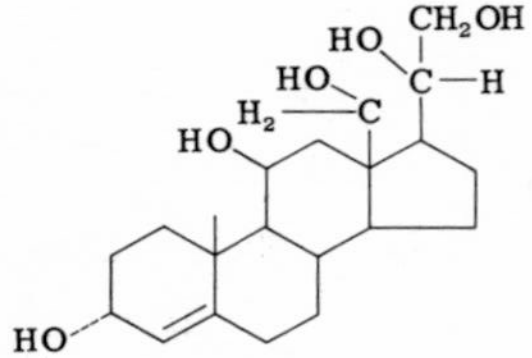

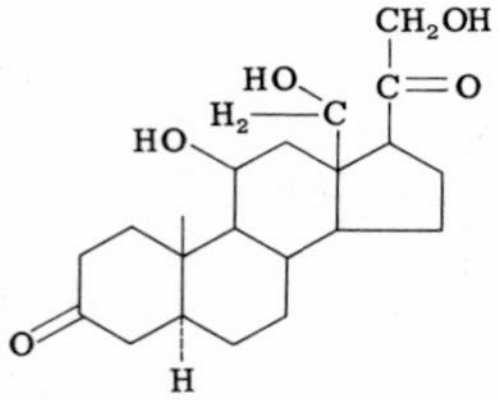

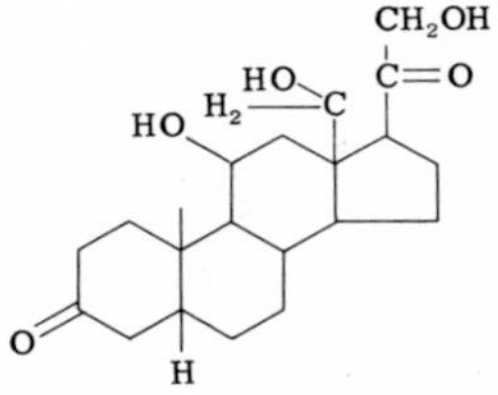

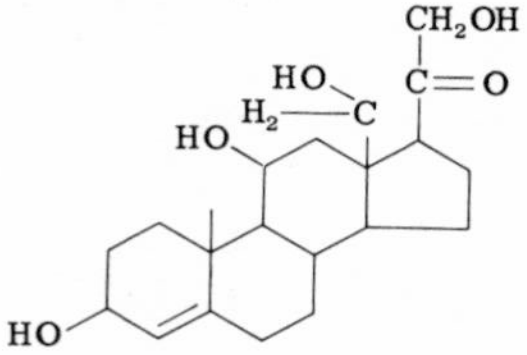

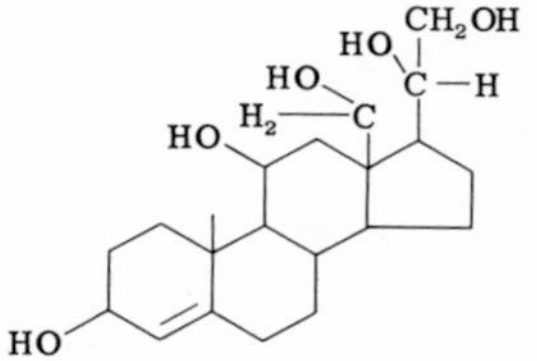

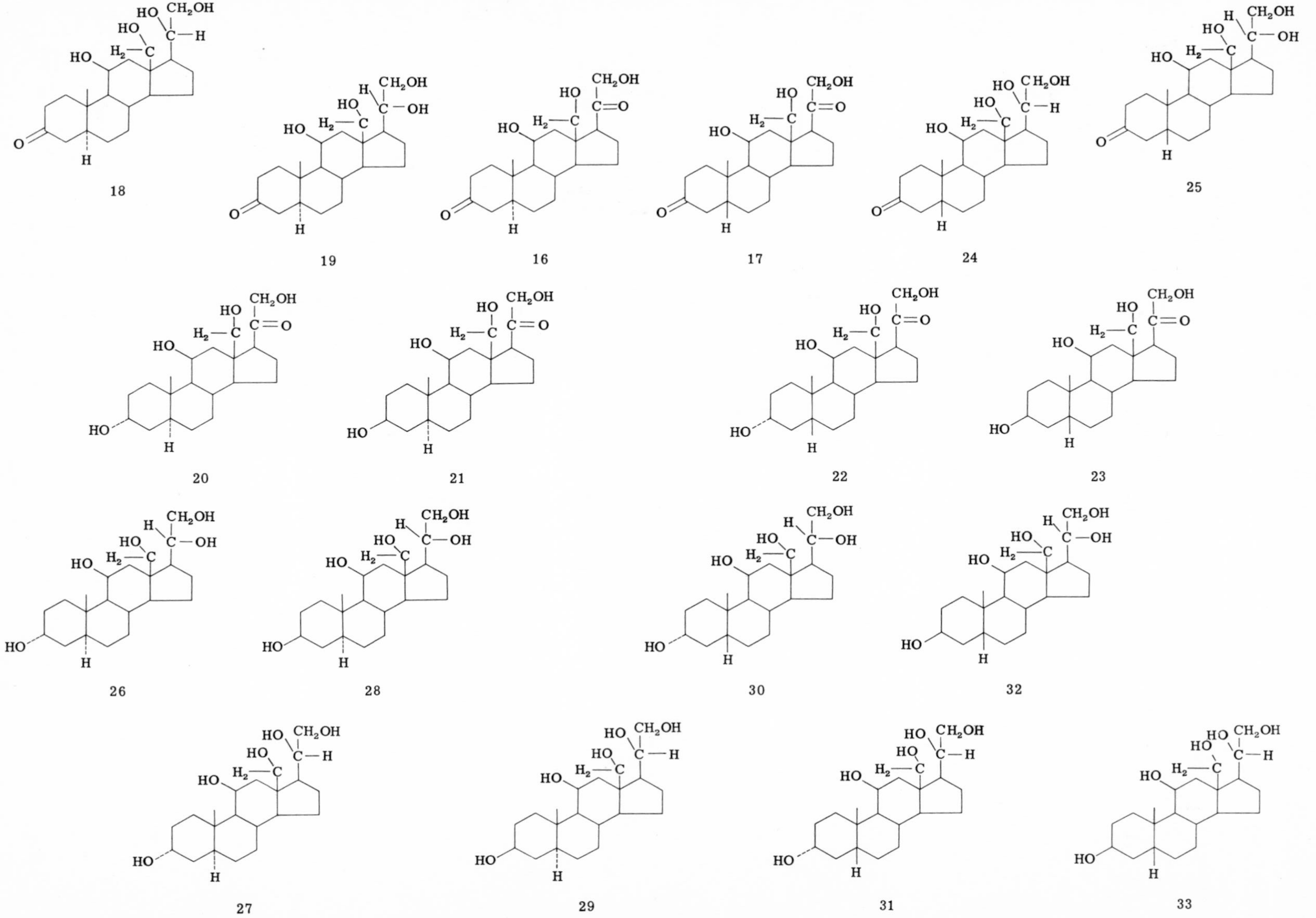

FIG. 51. C_{21}-31-1: 18-Hydroxycorticosterone and related metabolites.

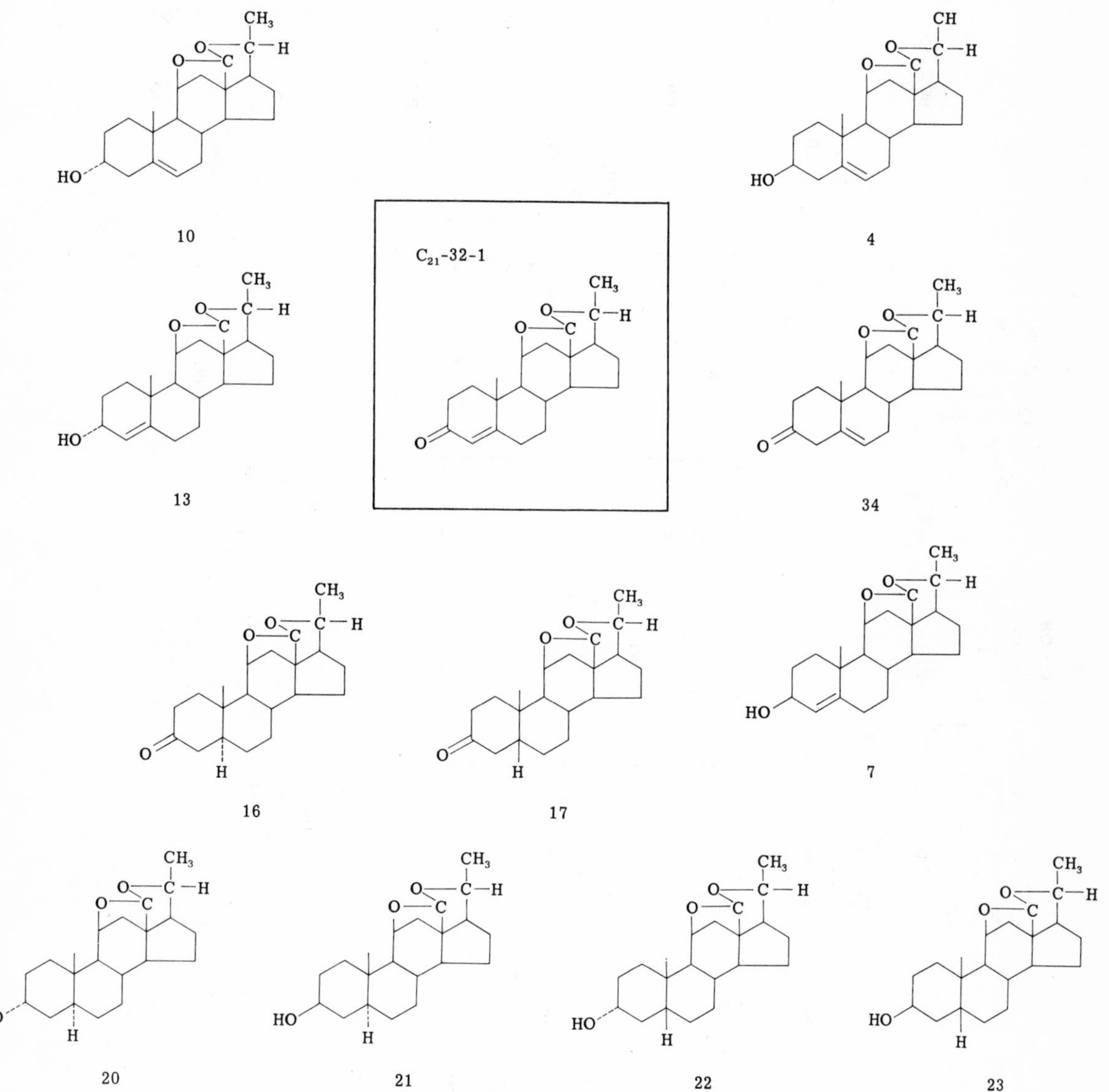

FIG. 52. C_{21}-32-1: 11β,18;18,20β-Diepoxypregn-4-en-3-one and related metabolites.

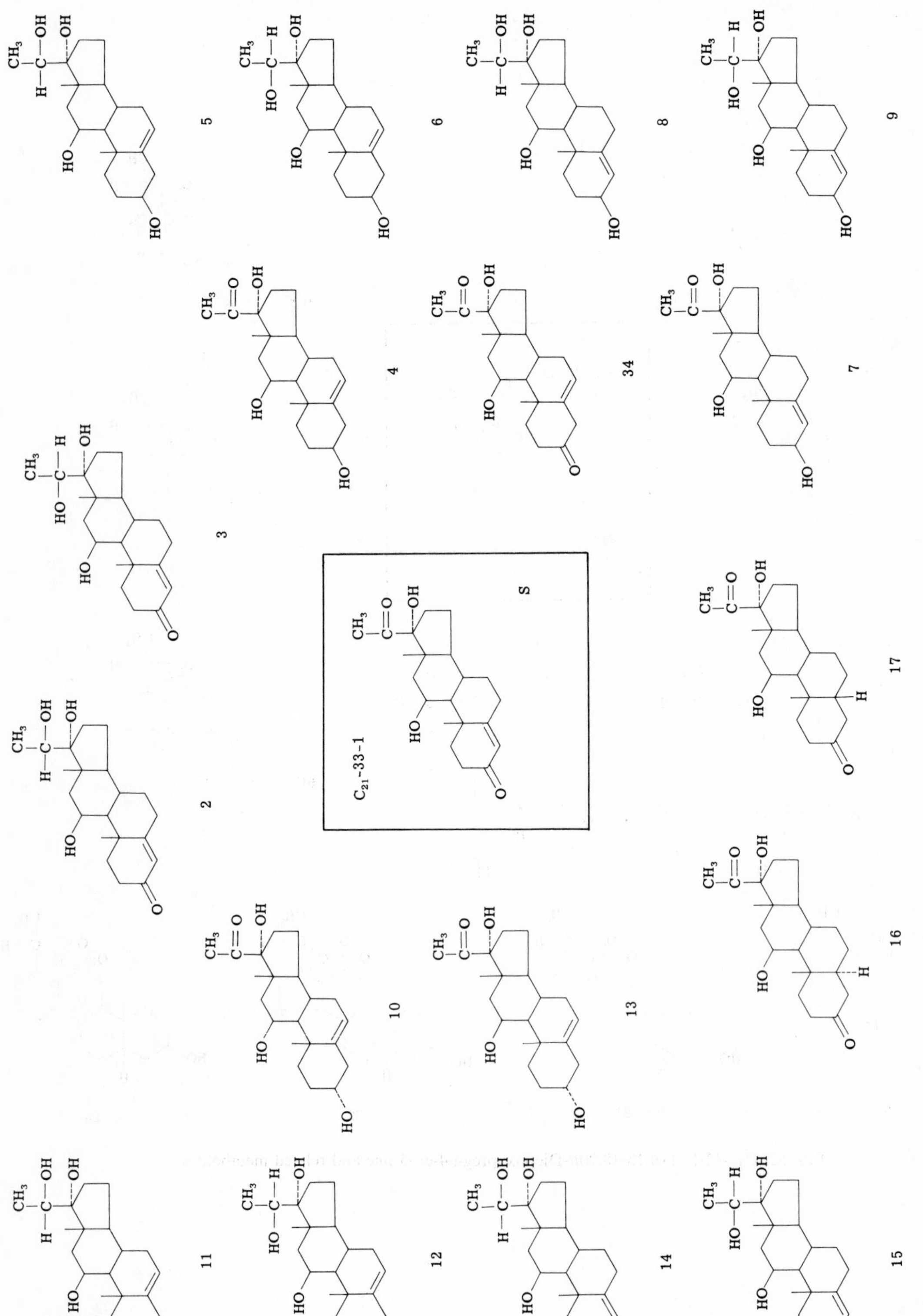

11

2

3

5

12

10

C_{21}-33-1

S

4

6

14

13

34

8

15

16

17

7

9

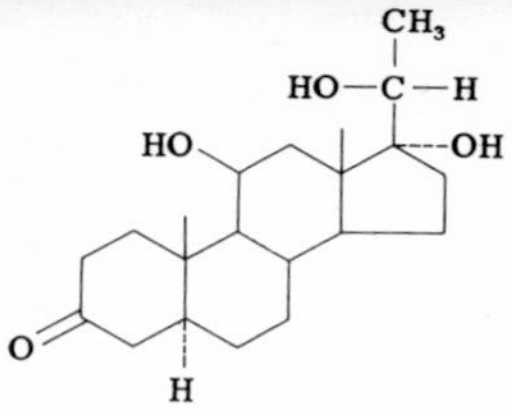

FIG. 53. C_{21}-33-1: 21-Deoxycortisol and related metabolites.

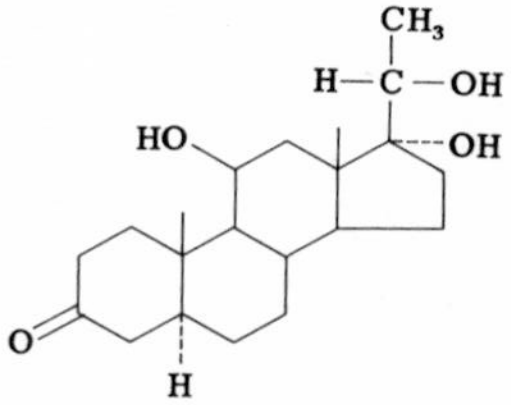

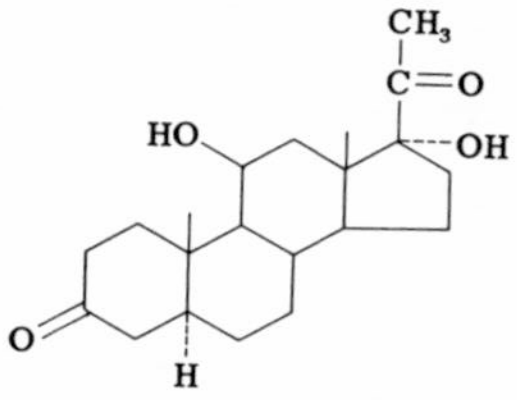

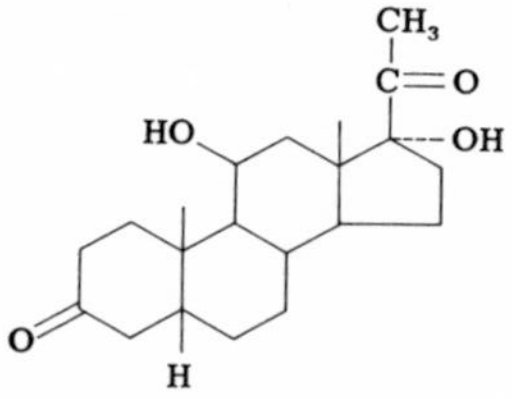

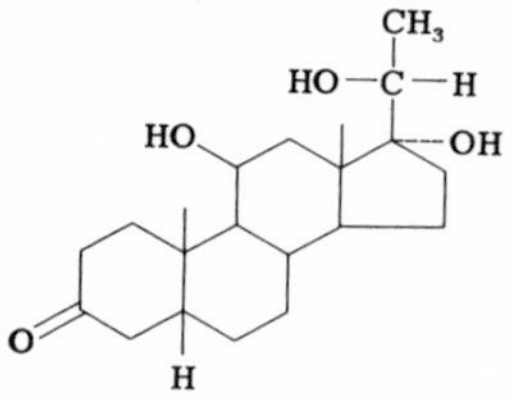

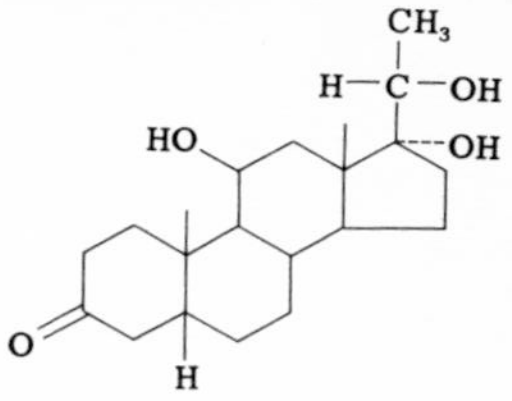

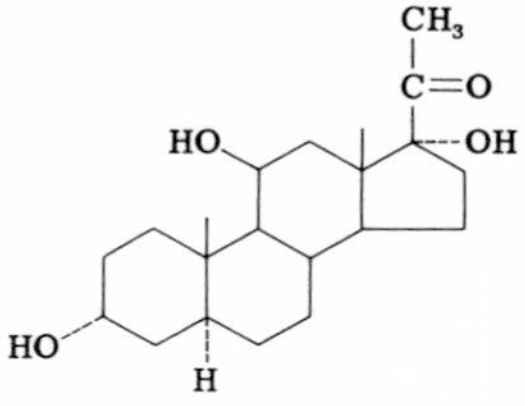

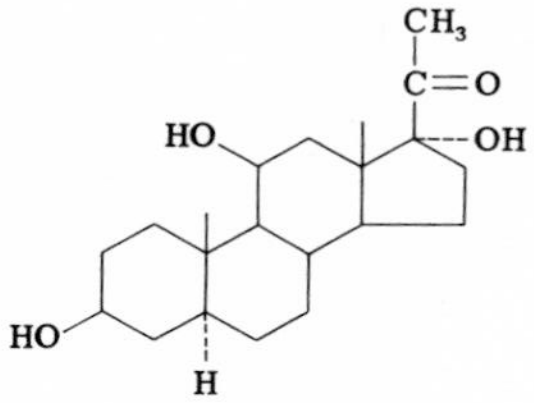

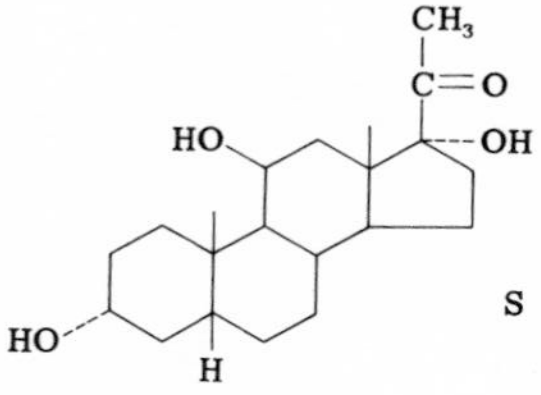

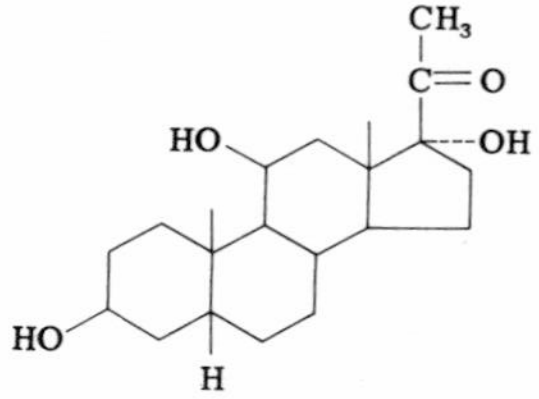

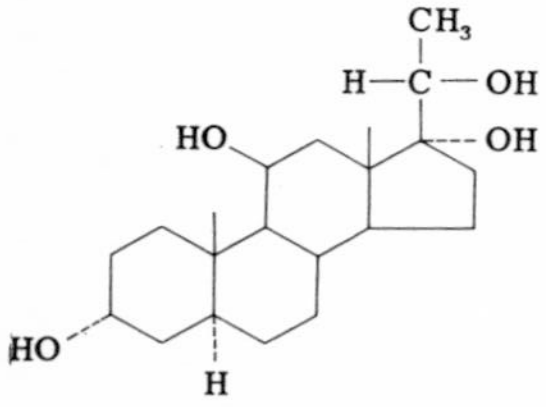

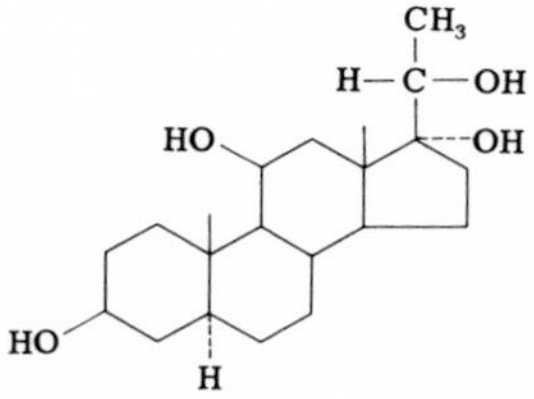

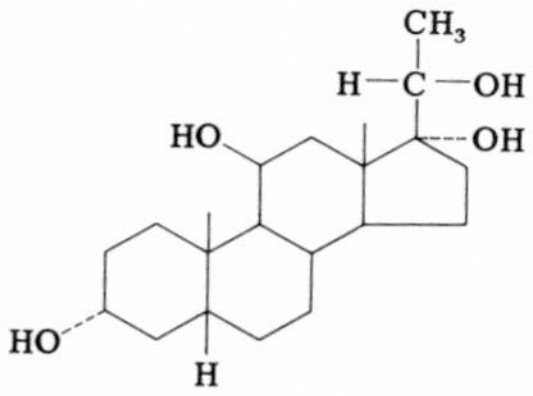

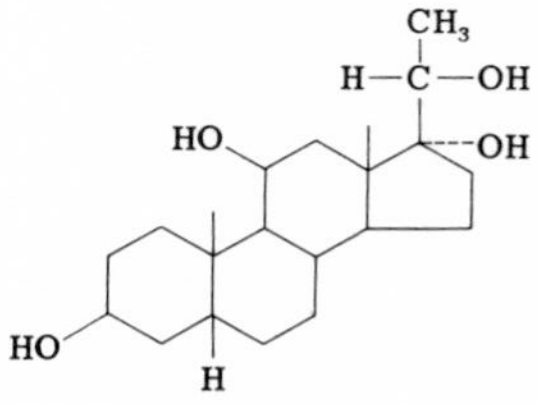

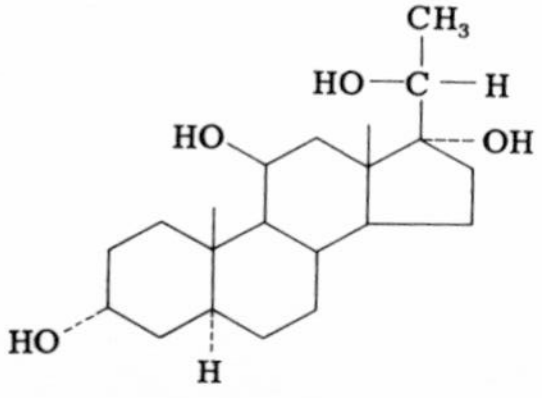

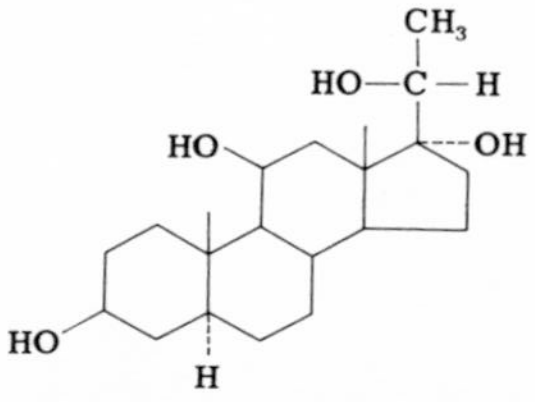

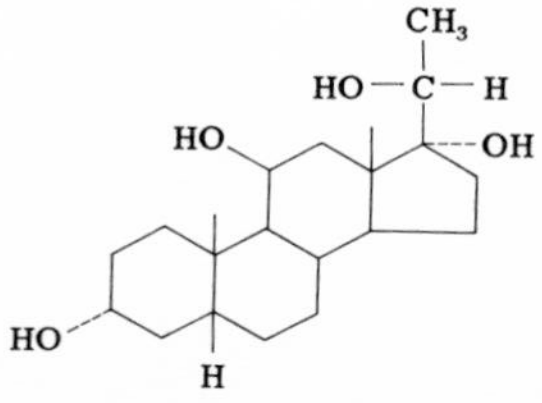

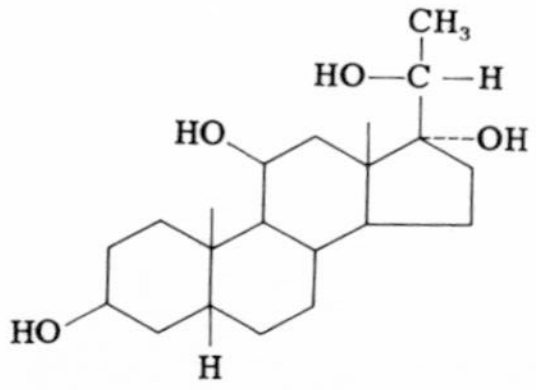

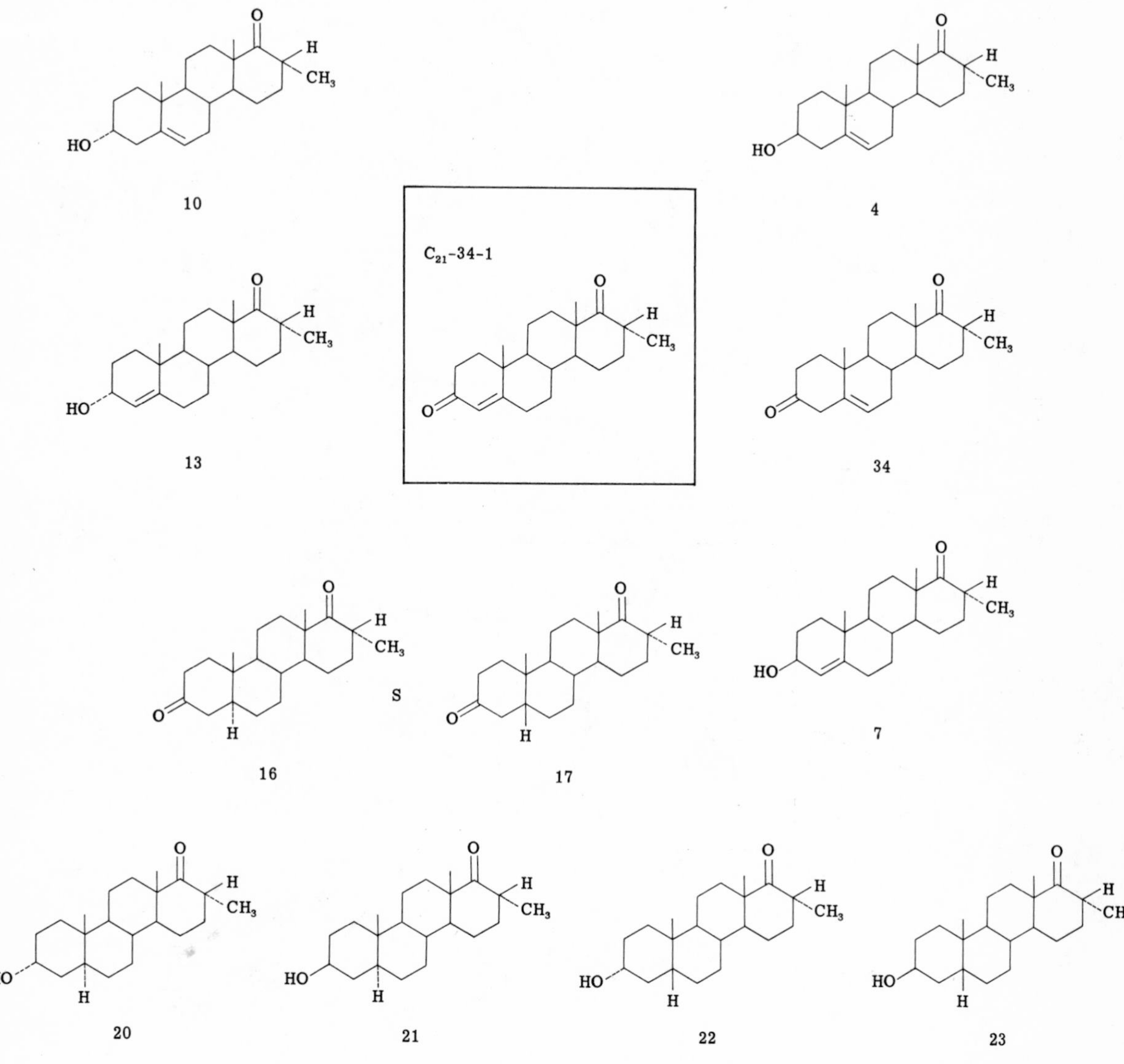

FIG. 54. C_{21}-34-1: *D*-Homo-17α-methylandrost-4-ene-3,17a-dione and related metabolites.

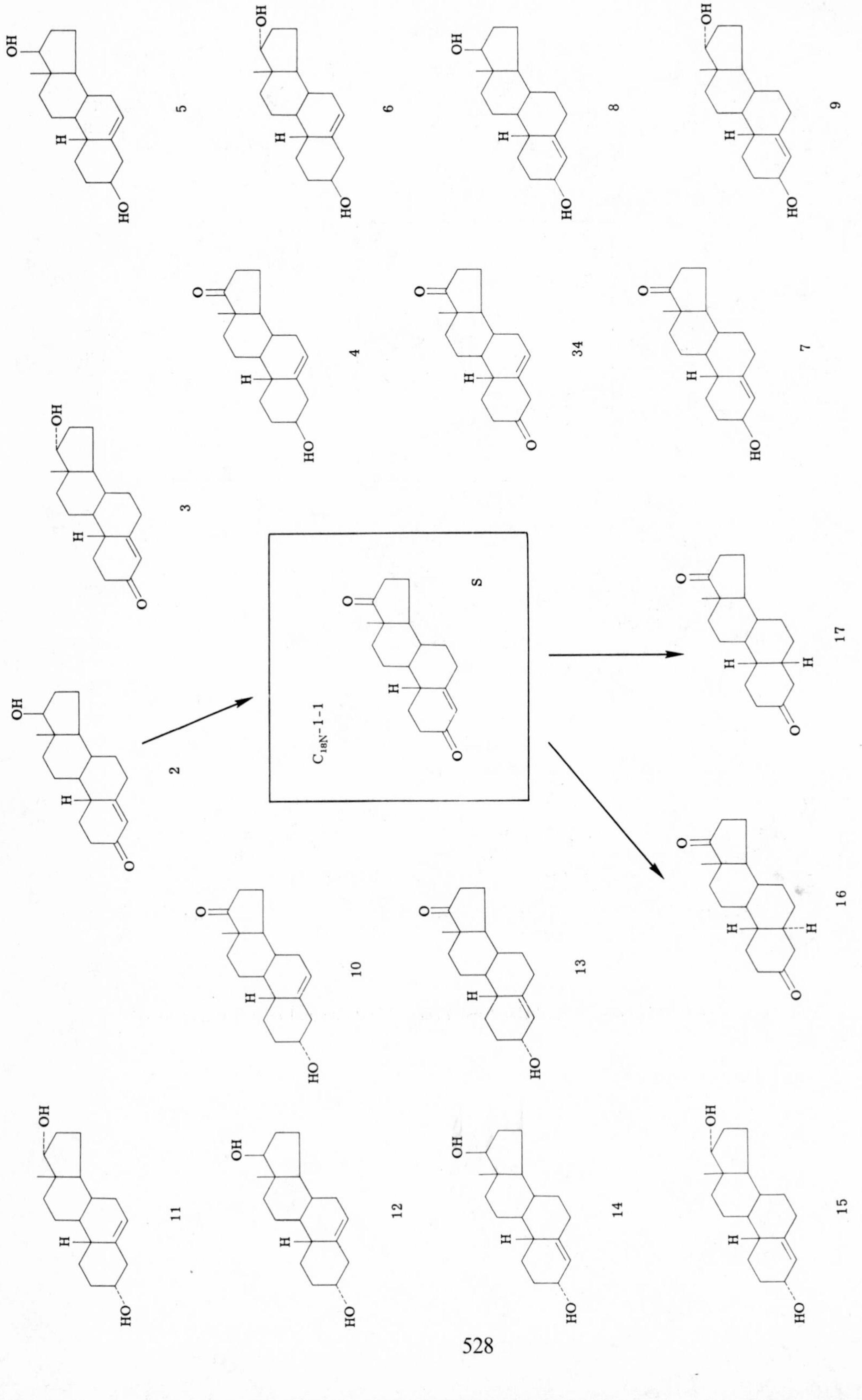

C_{18N}-1-1

S

11 2 3 5

12 10 4 6

14 13 34 8

15 16 17 7 9

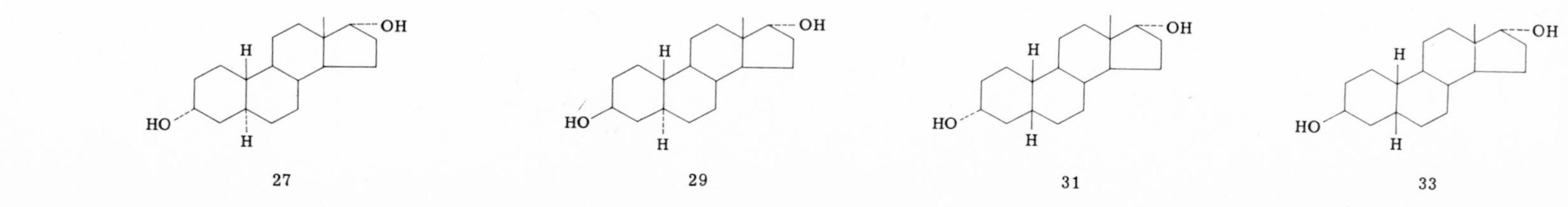

Fig. 55. C_{18N}-1-1: 19-Norandrost-4-ene-3,17-dione and related metabolites.

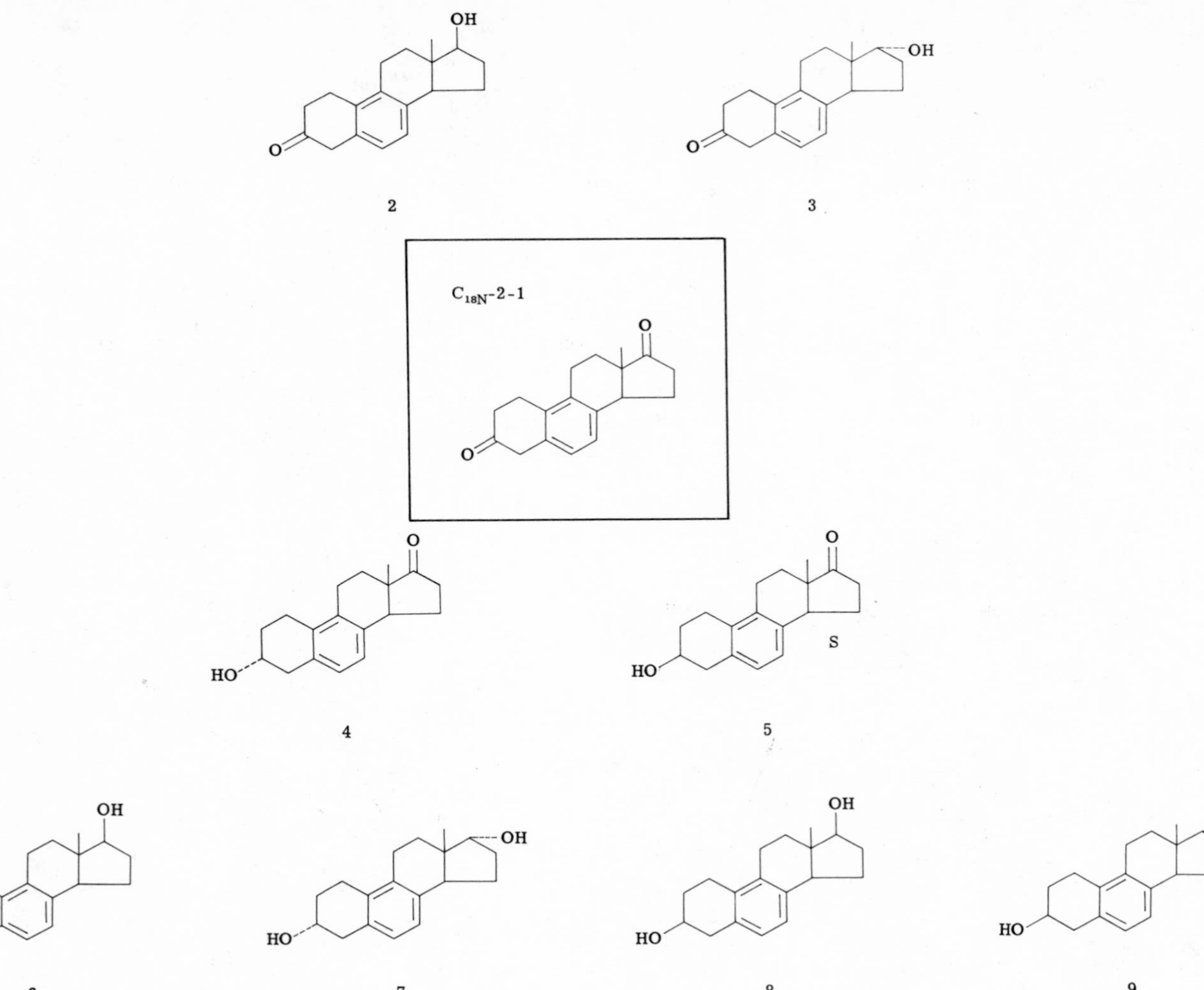

FIG. 56. C_{18N}-2-1: 19-Norandrosta-5,7,9-triene-3,17-dione and related metabolites.

C_{20}-1-1

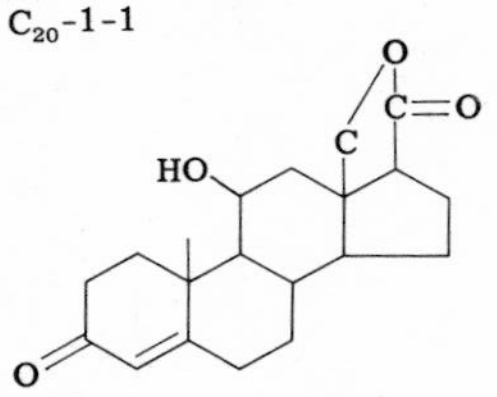

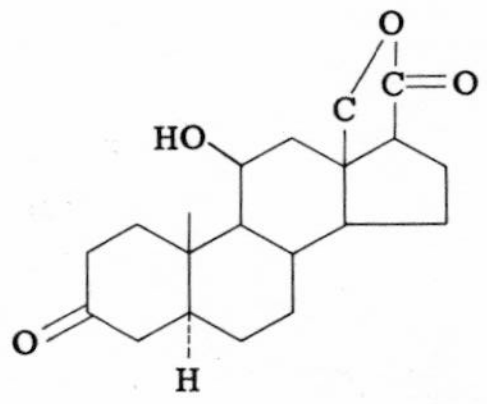

2

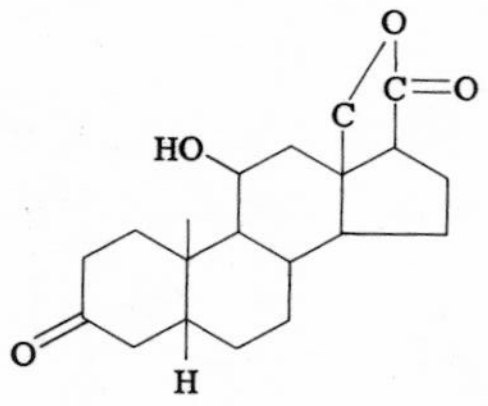

3

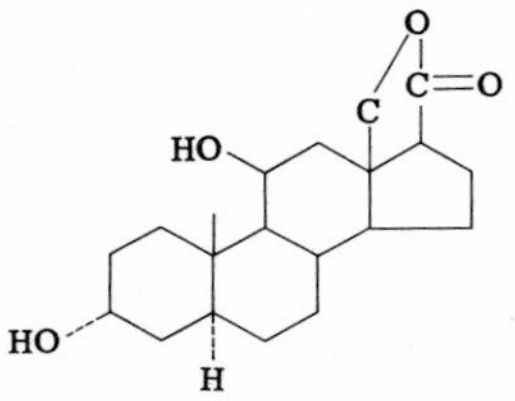

4

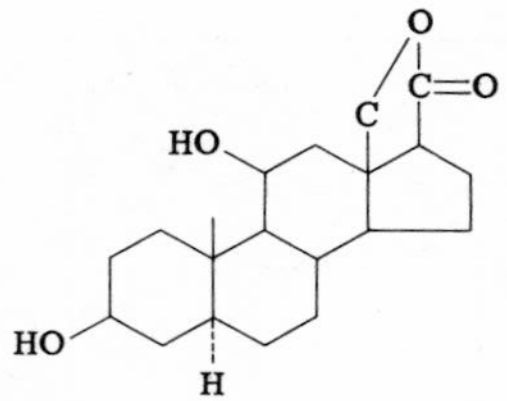

5

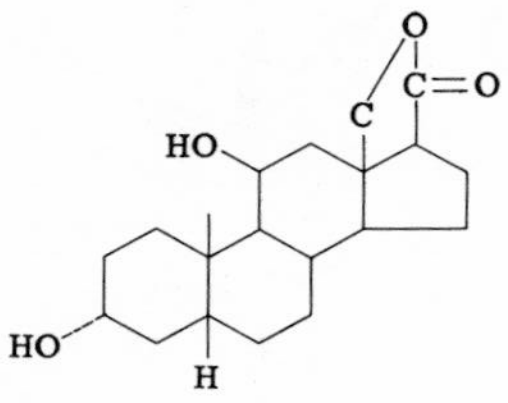

6

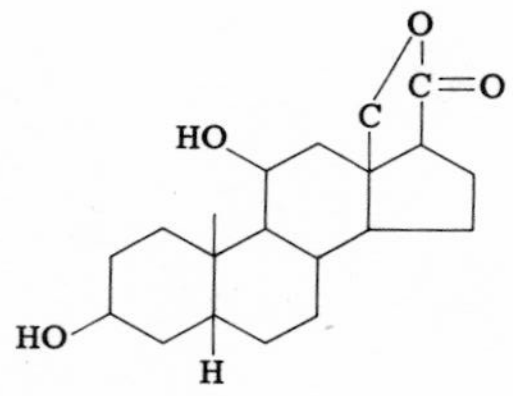

7

FIG. 57. C_{20}-1-1: 11β,18-Dihydroxy-3-ketoandrost-4-ene-17β-carboxylic acid 18 → 20 ester and related metabolites.

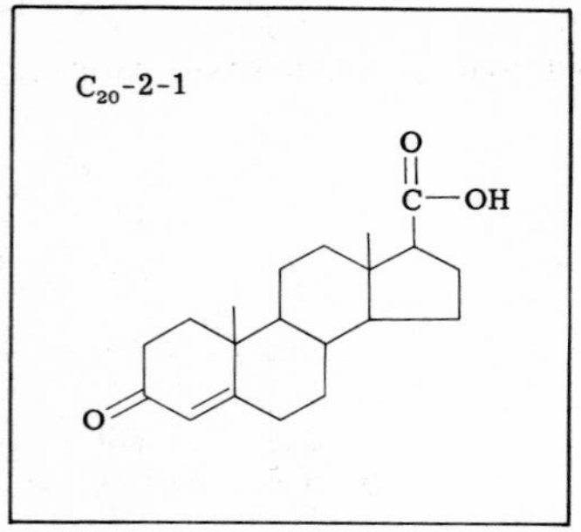

C_{20}-2-1

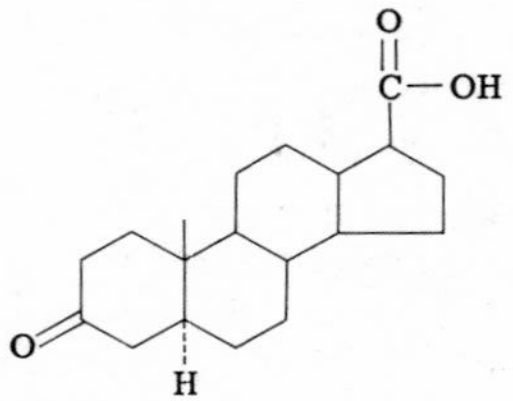

2

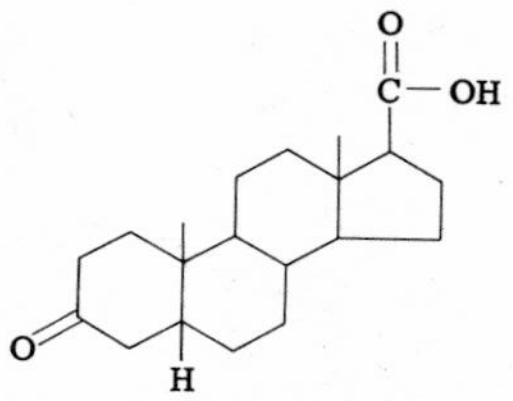

3

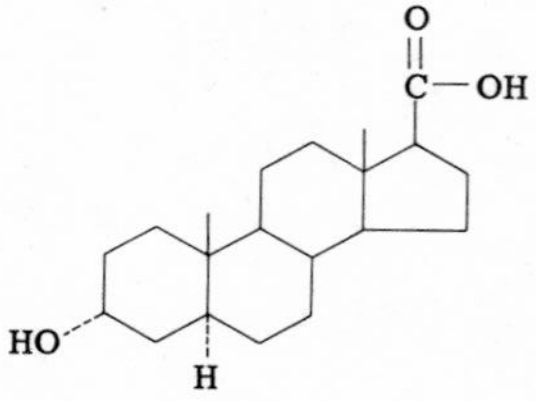

4

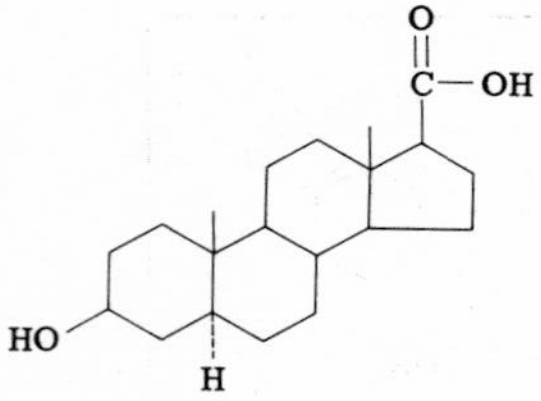

5

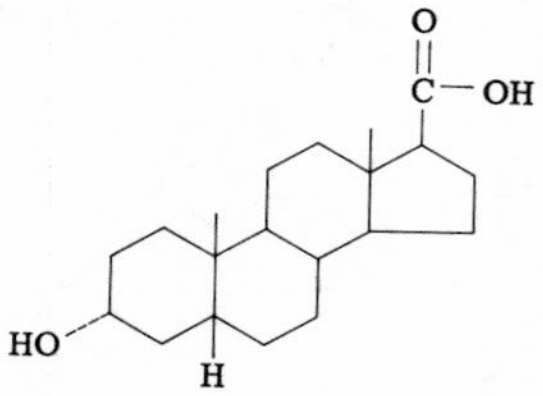

6

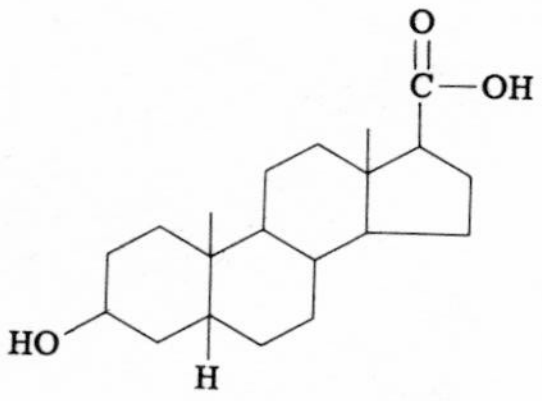

7

FIG. 58. C_{20}-2-1: 3-Ketoandrost-4-ene-17β-carboxylic acid and related metabolites.

C_{20}-3-1

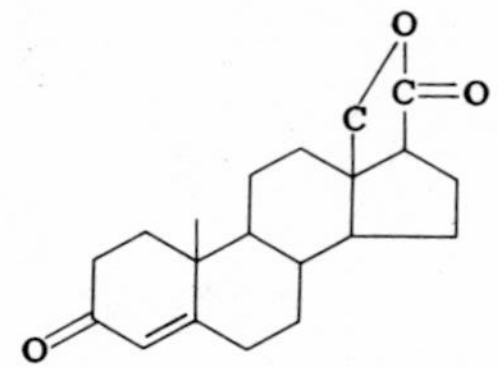

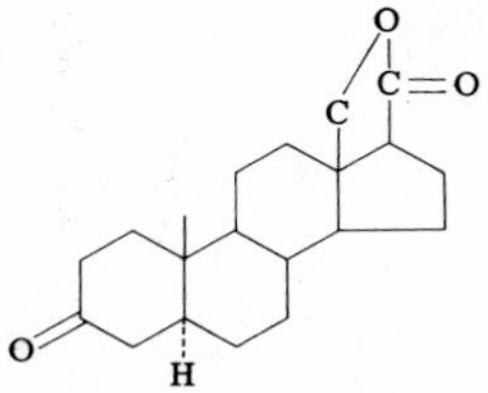

2

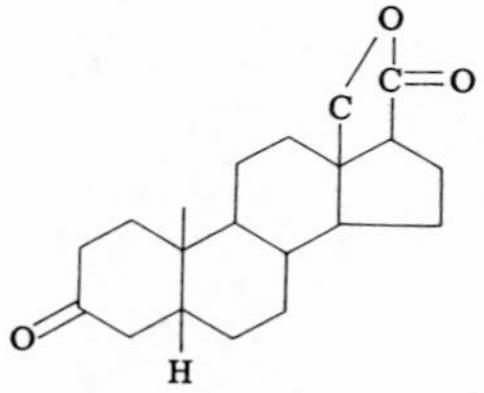

3

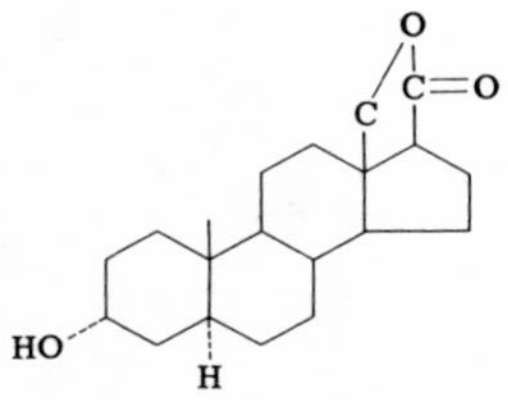

4

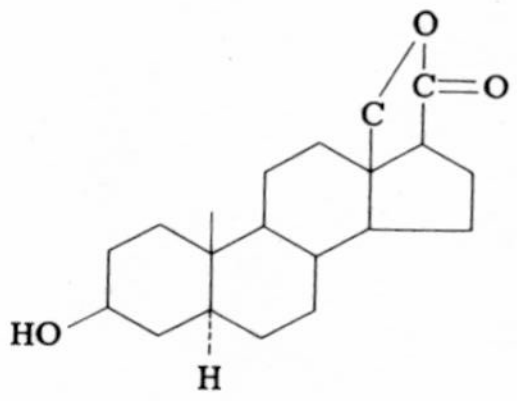

5

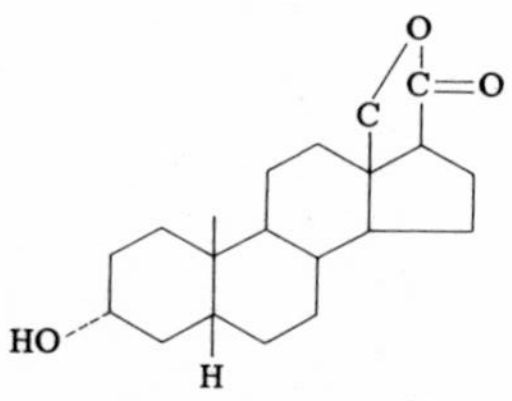

6

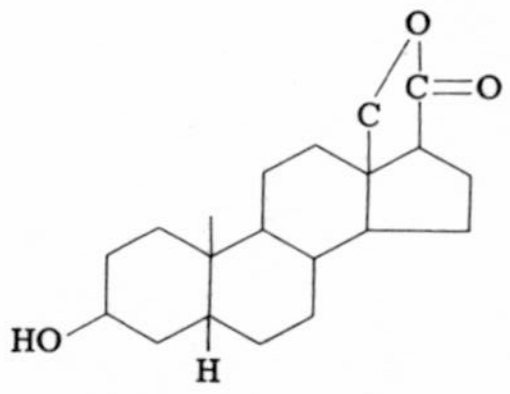

7

FIG. 59. C_{20}-3-1: 19-Hydroxy-3-ketoandrost-4-ene-17β-carboxylic acid 18 → 20 ester and related metabolites.

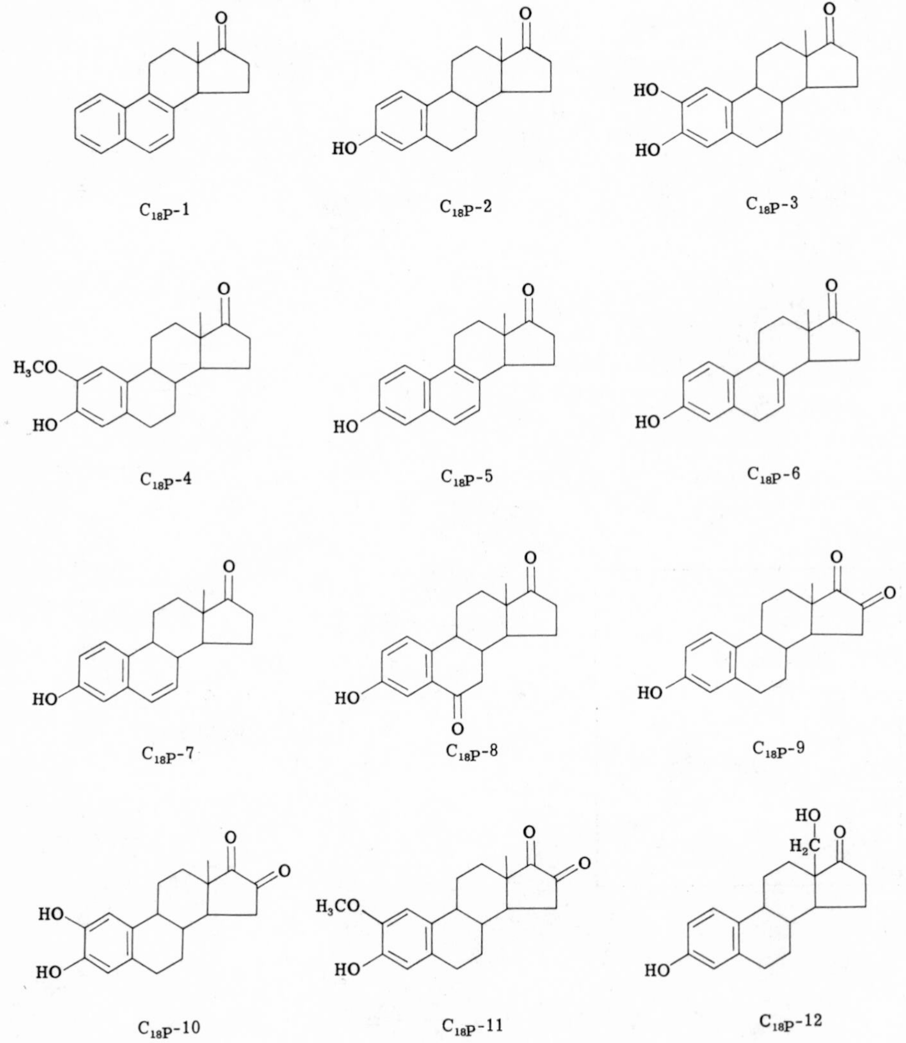

FIG. 60. C_{18}: Key phenolic steroids.

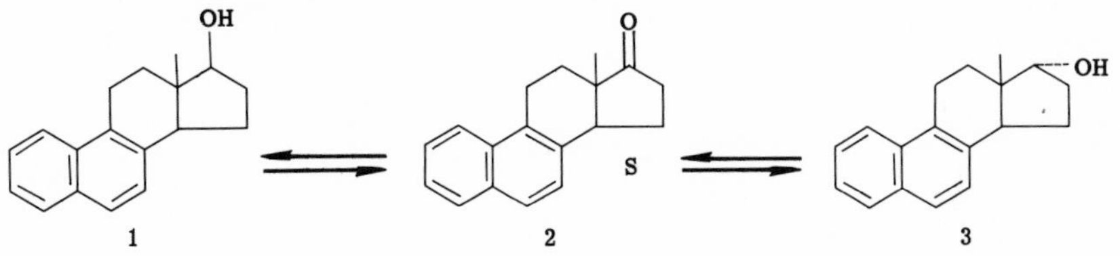

OH O OH
1 2 S 3

$C_{18}P$-1

FIG. 61. $C_{18\,P}$-1: 3-Deoxyequilenin (2) and related metabolites.

OH O OH
HO 1 HO 2 S HO 3

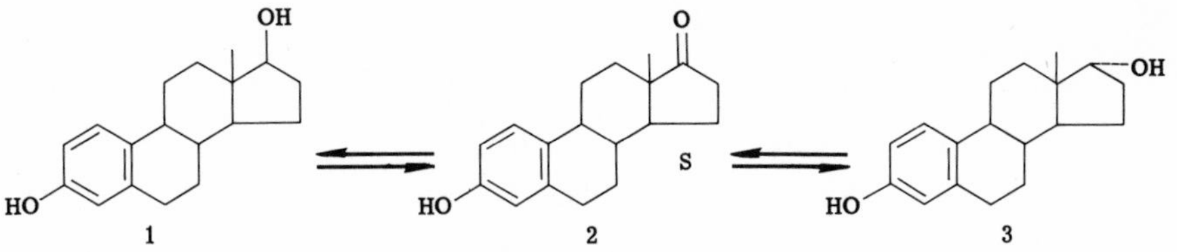

$C_{18}P$-2

FIG. 62. $C_{18\,P}$-2: Estrone (2) and related metabolites.

OH O OH
HO HO HO
HO 1 HO 2 S HO 3

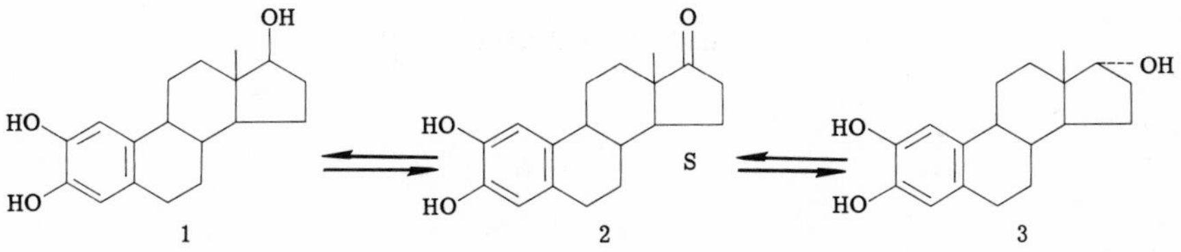

$C_{18}P$-3

FIG. 63. $C_{18\,P}$-3: 2-Hydroxyestrone (2) and related metabolites.

OH O OH
H_3CO H_3CO H_3CO
HO 1 HO 2 S HO 3

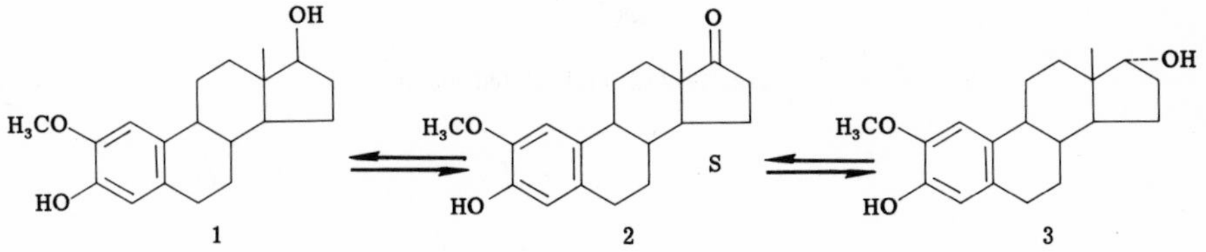

$C_{18}P$-4

FIG. 64. $C_{18\,P}$-4: 2-Methoxyestrone (2) and related metabolites.

OH O OH
HO 1 HO 2 S HO 3

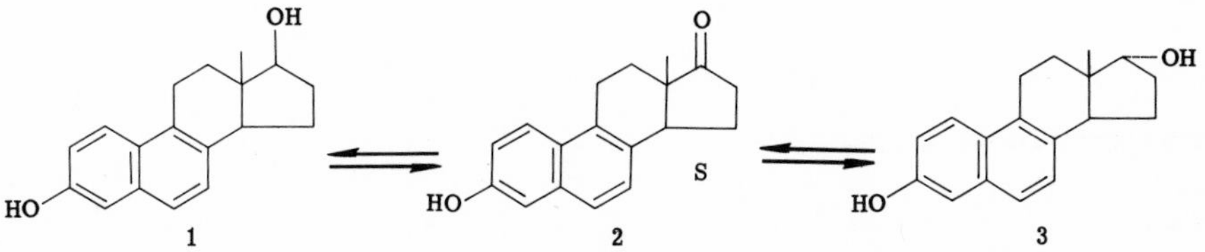

$C_{18}P$-5

FIG. 65. $C_{18\,P}$-5: Equilenin (2) and related metabolites.

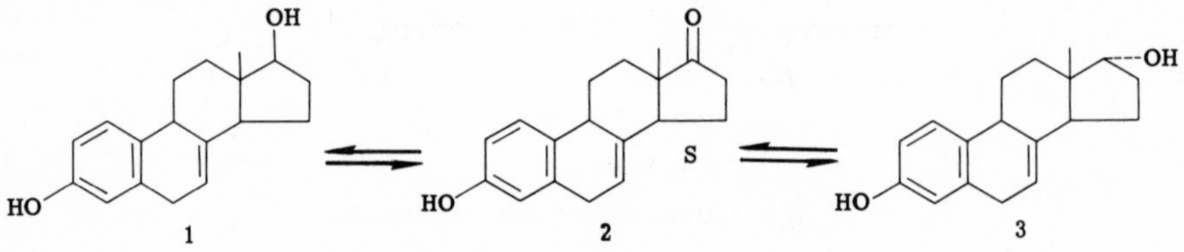

C_{18P}-6

FIG. 66. C_{18P}-6: Equilin (2) and related metabolites.

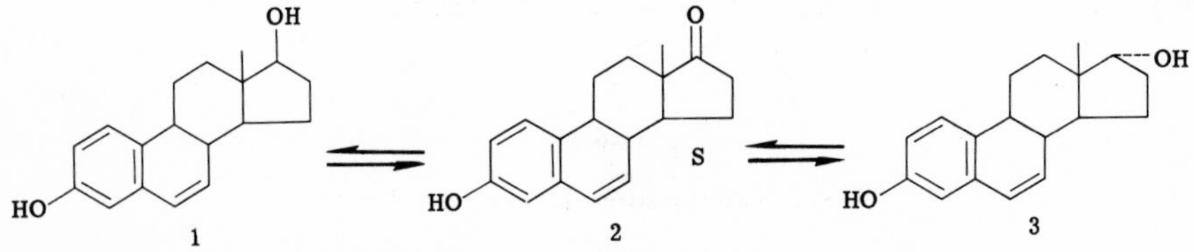

C_{18P}-7

FIG. 67. C_{18P}-7: Hippulin (2) and related metabolites.

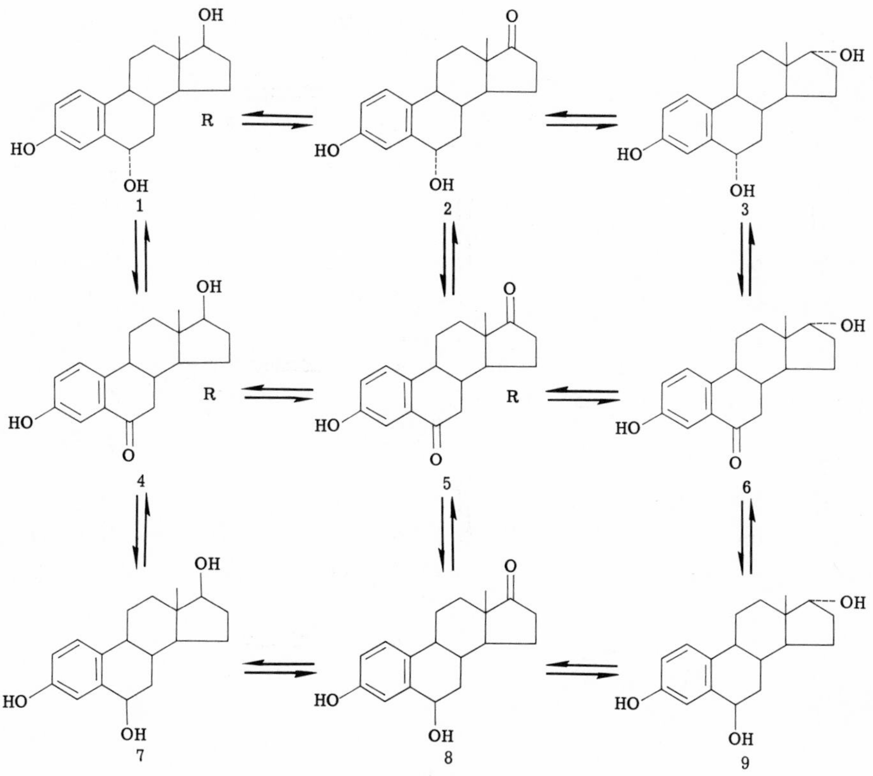

C$_{18P}$-8

FIG. 68. C_{18P}-8: 6-Ketoestrone (5) and related metabolites.

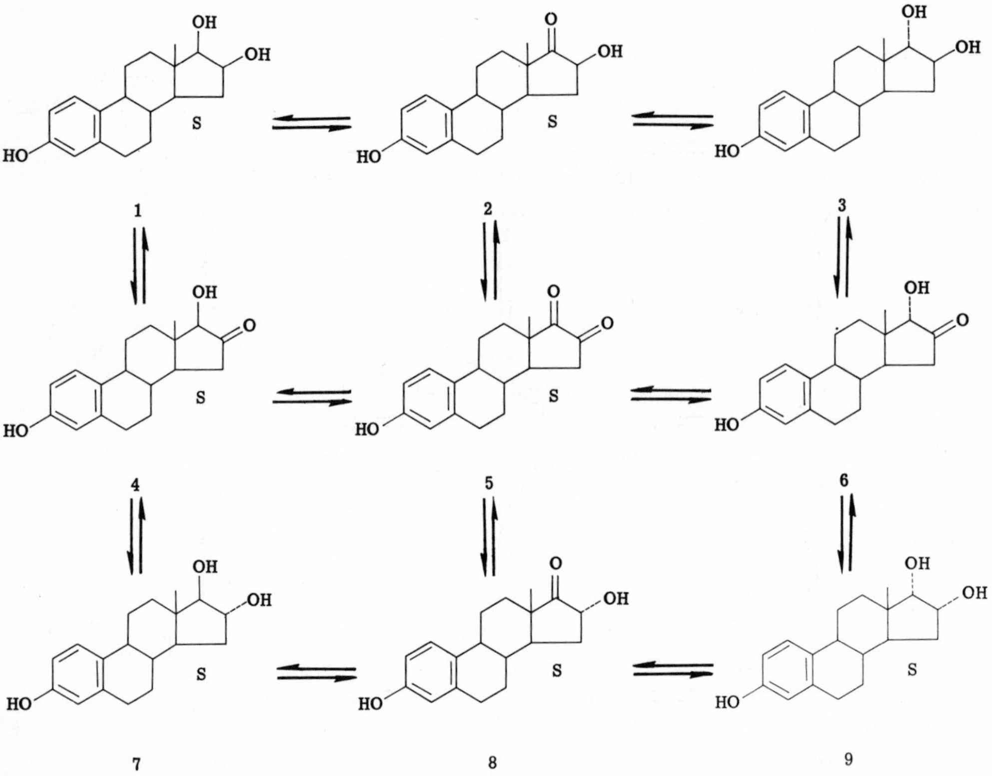

C_{18P}-9

FIG. 69. C_{18P}-9: 16-Ketoestrone (5) and related metabolites.

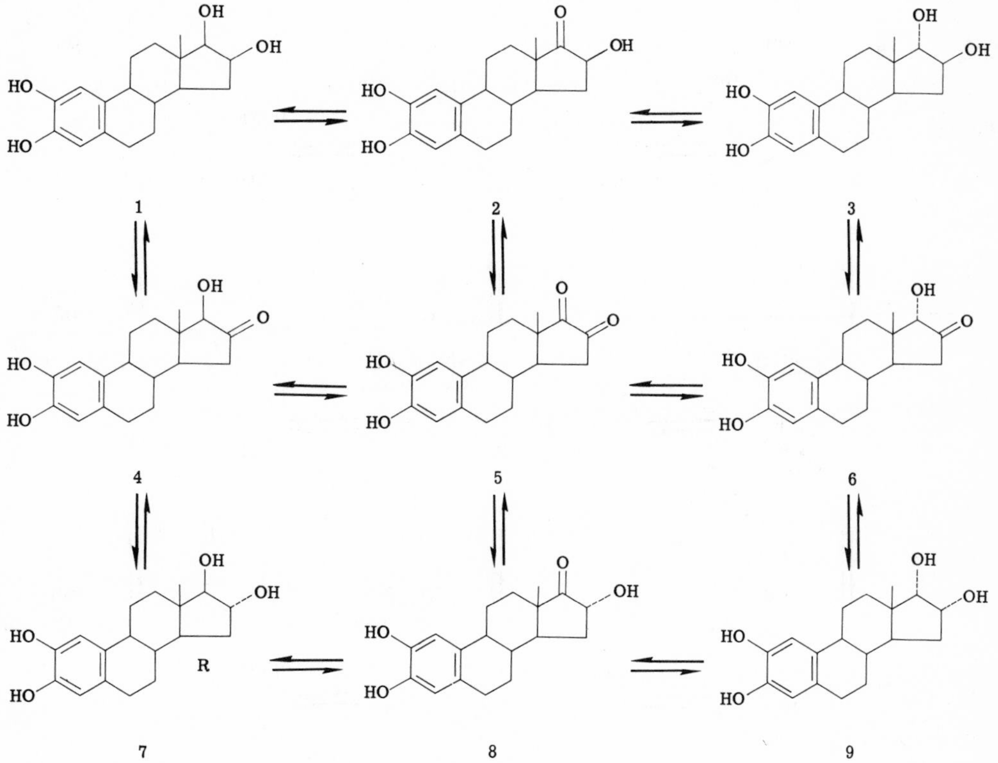

$C_{18}P$-10

FIG. 70. C_{18P}-10: 2-Hydroxy-16-ketoestrone (5) and related metabolites.

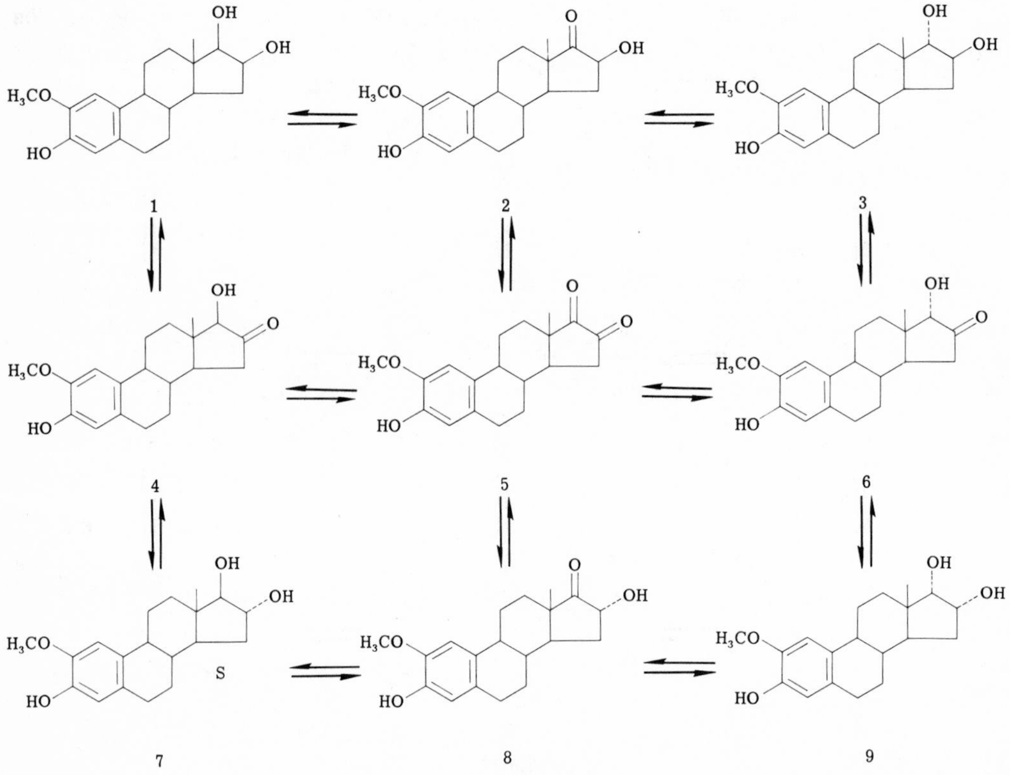

C_{18P}-11

FIG. 71. C_{18P}-11: 2-Methoxy-16-ketoestrone (5) and related metabolites.

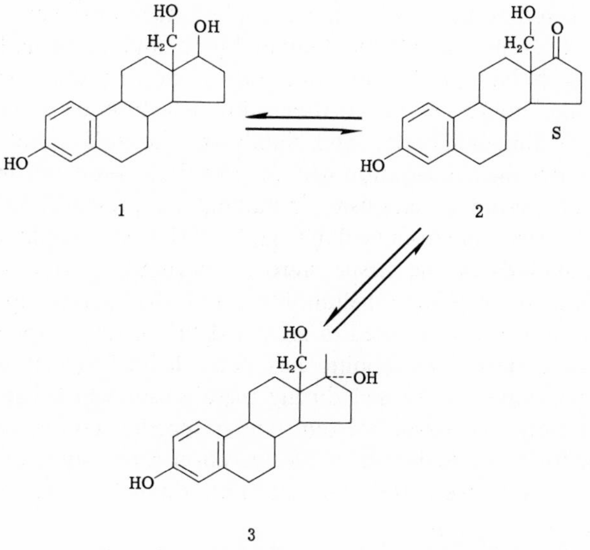

C_{18P}-12

FIG. 72. C_{18P}-12: 18-Hydroxyestrone (2) and related metabolites.

CHAPTER VIII

Relationships between Tissue Steroids and Metabolites in Blood and Urine

Considerable effort has been expended in the past to relate the compounds formed in steroid-producing tissues with their metabolites in blood and in urine. Various approaches to the study of the metabolism of tissue steroids have included: (a) a search for steroids in the various steroid-forming tissues, including the testes, adrenals, placentae, and ovaries; (b) isolation of steroids from animal and human blood and urine and, to a limited extent, other biological fluids, bile, saliva, etc.; (c) the isolation of tissue steroid metabolites in urine after administration of certain steroids to animals or human subjects; and, finally, (d) the isolation of metabolites of steroids after their incubation with *in vitro* tissue preparations. The general aspects of steroid metabolism, including the presentation of a possible complete system, are discussed in Chapter VII. Certain individual hormones and metabolites of the tissue steroids, particularly those which can be considered to be unique metabolites, and the factors involved in their metabolism will be examined in greater detail in this chapter.

A unique steroid metabolite has been defined (Dorfman, 1961) as a steroid persisting or formed during metabolism which can be related to one and only one tissue steroid. These specific, unique metabolites are essential for the calculation of the secretion rates, since they provide the definitive link between the tissue hormones and their derived products in body fluids.

The interrelationships between the tissue steroids and their metabolites are summarized here as a series of figures that are based on data taken from mammalian studies treated as a group. Although considerable advances have recently been made in comparative endocrinology, conclusions based on available data concerning steroid metabolism in various mammalian species are dangerous, since differences in steroid metabolism that can be cited for different species of animals at the present time may be due only to incomplete and fragmentary information. Where sufficient studies have been made among species, the differences that have been found are quantitative rather than qualitative.

Estrogenic Hormones and Their Metabolites

Estradiol-17β, the most active naturally occurring estrogen, undergoes a variety of metabolic transformations, which result in the formation, at the present count, of fifteen metabolites (Fig. 1). Actually, of the various types of transformations represented, no single metabolite could be called unique in the sense that a given metabolite is derived from secreted estradiol-17β and only from this compound. It is true that estrone may be derived from estradiol-17β, but estrone also may be secreted as such and, conversely, estradiol-17β may be derived from secreted estrone.

It should be re-emphasized that Fig. 1, as with the other figures in this series, represents pooled information from many *in vivo* and *in vitro* experiments involving studies in various species of mammals. It is assumed, since there is little evidence to the contrary, that all such transformations can take place in any and all given species. Estradiol-17β and its transformation products are arranged in Fig. 1 in an ordered sequence which, based on the available evidence, seems to be reasonable. The sequence represented is only one of several possible arrangements, and it should not be inferred that other pathways have been excluded or necessarily have a minor role.

The various transformations of estradiol-17β serve as a model for the fate of the other phenolic steroids. The oxidation of estradiol-17β to estrone has been described. The sequence of conversion of estradiol-17β to 2-hydroxyestradiol-17β and finally to the 2-methoxy derivative appears to be established. Some question remains about the stereoisomerism of the 6-hydroxy-substituted metabolites. The C_{16}-oxygenated derivatives are well established, and six such derivatives are represented. Estradiol-17α has been detected in a few species and may be expected to be present in many more.

Figure 2 summarizes the pool of information, obtained from *in vivo* and *in vitro* experiments, known about the metabolites of estrone, the second most active naturally occurring estrogen. Eight metabolites of estrone have been identified. The ninth compound, 16α-hydroxyestrone, is represented inside brackets since it has not been isolated but, as a possible intermediate, it permits a logical transformation from estrone to estriol. Fishman *et al.* (1961) presented evidence that estriol is formed from estrone but not from estradiol. This suggests a preferential biological sequence of the 16α-hydroxylation of a 17-ketone rather than a reaction on the 17β-hydroxy compound.

The interrelationships of estrone metabolism are essentially the same as those encountered for estradiol-17β, including the acquired substituents at position 16, the introduction of the 6-oxygen function, and the formation of estradiol-17α. One metabolite, which at the moment is unique for estrone, is 18-hydroxyestrone. Further studies of this transformation should be particularly interesting since, at the present time, 18-hydroxylation seems to be a specific property of the adrenal cortex.

Six metabolites of estriol containing the 16-oxygen function are recognized (Fig. 3). So far as is known, the 16-oxygen function cannot be removed, except by disruption of the steroid molecule. Catabolites of estriol include modifications at carbons 2, 16, and 17. As yet, no 6-oxygen substituted derivatives of estriol have been isolated.

The metabolic fate of 16-ketoestrone is illustrated in Fig. 4. The six known metabolites with an oxygen function at position 16 include both the 16α- and 16β-hydroxy derivatives which have been isolated as metabolic products of the original 16-ketoestrone substrate. A similar situation is seen at the 17 position, where both the 17α- and 17β-reduced derivatives are known. All six metabolites of 16-ketoestrone and the principal steroid are extremely weak estrogens.

Figures 5–7 deal with catabolism of additional 16,17 dioxygenated steroids involving dehydrogenase reactions at carbons 16 and 17. 16-Keto-estradiol-17β has yielded five metabolites and, for continuity, 16-keto-estradiol-17α has been included as a theoretical intermediate (Fig. 5).

Figure 6 records the three isolated metabolites of 16β-hydroxyestrone and, again for convenience in presentation, 16-ketoestrone, a theoretically possible intermediate, is represented within brackets. Figure 7 illustrates the three known catabolites of 16α-hydroxyestrone and the theoretical metabolite, 16-ketoestrone.

The catabolism of 2-hydroxyestradiol-17β is shown in Fig. 8. Two transformation products are known, both resulting from a transmethylation reaction. The conversion of 2-hydroxyestradiol-17β to the 2-methoxy-estradiol-17β probably proceeds directly and the product, in turn, could be oxidized to 2-methoxyestrone. A second approach to this last compound is through 2-hydroxyestrone (not isolated), which in turn could be methylated.

The first eight figures have summarized the known catabolic reactions involving phenolic estrogens. The concept of unique steroid metabolites introduced earlier in this chapter cannot be applied to the estrogens because of the complex interrelationships that exist among members of this group.

Δ^5-3β-Hydroxy Steroids

In Fig. 9, dehydroepiandrosterone is shown along with its immediate catabolities. In this figure, and in others that follow, those neutral steroid catabolites are presented that have been isolated as a result of direct metabolic studies by either the *in vitro* or *in vivo* method. Eleven catabolites of dehydroepiandrosterone have been so described. Three metabolites have an additional oxygen group at carbon 7, indicating the action of a 7α-hydroxylase and the oxidation of the 7α-hydroxy group to the 7-ketone. Hydroxylation at position 16 in the α position has been documented.

In considering the question of a unique metabolite of dehydroepiandro-sterone, it is obvious that any reaction which involves an oxidation of the Δ^5-3β-hydroxy group to the Δ^4-3-ketone leads to products that are confused with androst-4-ene-3,17-dione and testosterone metabolites. This would be true of the following dehydroepiandrosterone catabolites shown in Fig. 9: testosterone, androst-4-ene-3,17-dione, and their respective reduction products numbered 6, 7, 8, 9, and 10. Unique metabolites of dehydroepiandrosterone would include only those catabolites still possessing the Δ^5-3β-hydroxy group.

Androst-5-ene-3β,17β-diol metabolism (Fig. 10) must be considered with the pathways discussed for dehydroepiandrosterone. The smaller number of known catabolites from androst-5-ene-3β,17β-diol is due to the limited number of studies that have been reported, and these were executed by older, rather inadequate methods. The fact that the diol is convertible to dehydroepiandrosterone suggests that many more catabolites could be established.

Specific catabolites of pregnenolone, a precursor for all the steroid hormones, are shown in Fig. 11. The oxidation of pregnenolone to progesterone illustrates the problem of confusing the catabolites of this compound with those of progesterone. To date, the most significant and most important catabolite of pregnenolone appears to be pregn-5-ene-3β, 20α-diol. This compound could, in fact, be referred to as the unique catabolite of pregnenolone. It is obvious that the diol itself may be secreted and that any measure of the diol would, therefore, include production representing the two simple C_{21} Δ^5-3β-hydroxy compounds.

Figure 12 deals with the specific metabolites of 17α-hydroxypregnenolone. This compound, also an intermediate in the biosynthesis of the steroid hormones, could be an important indicator of certain abnormalities in steroid biosynthesis; this would apply to two or possibly three compounds which would be considered unique catabolites of 17α-hydroxypregnenolone. The formation of dehydroepiandrosterone from 17α-hydroxypregnenolone occurs peripherally to only a limited extent and obviously the dehydroepiandrosterone formed would not be of any real importance as an indicator of 17α-hydroxypregnenolone. However, the two reduced compounds, the 20α-hydroxy and 20β-hydroxy compounds, could serve as unique catabolites. No other compounds could be responsible for these materials. It is also possible that a considerable concentration of 17α-hydroxypregnenolone itself could be obtained under abnormal conditions. Thus, it may be concluded that there are three possible unique catabolites, the compound itself, plus the two C-20 reduced compounds (Fig. 12).

There is no unique metabolite derived exclusively from androst-4-ene-3, 17-dione (Fig. 13) since the catabolic products listed can arise from the metabolism of testosterone and dehydroepiandrosterone, as well as from certain C_{21}-steroids which also yield common C_{19}-metabolites. The limited number of metabolites of androst-4-ene-3, 17-dione that have been detected reflects the less intensive interest as compared with that shown in testosterone metabolism, where a larger number of compounds have been isolated.

Testosterone (Fig. 14) is catabolized to a variety of compounds, including two Δ^{16}-17-deoxysteroids. Conversion of testosterone to the Δ^{16}-derivative occurs only to a limited extent and, perhaps significantly, only in steroid-producing tissues. Administration of 50 mg to 1 gm per day of testosterone to a normal man did not result in a significant excretion of the Δ^{16}-compound. Negative results also have been reported after testosterone-C^{14} was administered. For these reasons, one is skeptical about the Δ^{16}-catabolites being useful for the indirect measurement of testosterone circulating peripherally, although there is a strong possibility that Δ^{16}-compounds are, in fact, produced by the gonads and/or the adrenals during testosterone formation.

Catabolism of 11β-hydroxy and 11-keto derivatives of androst-4-ene-3, 17-dione is represented in Figs. 15 and 16. Figure 15 is concerned with 11β-hydroxyandrost-4-ene-3,17-dione and its six catabolites, including the 11-keto analog (Fig. 16). The reduced catabolites are identical for both the 11-keto and 11β-hydroxy series. The bulk of these ring A reduction products are of the 5α series, whether the original steroid was adrenosterone or the corresponding 11β-hydroxy product. When these same catabolites arise from cortisone or cortisol, there is a preferential reduction to the 5β form. 3β,11β-Dihydroxyandrost-4-en-17-one (Fig. 15) is the first naturally occurring representative of a Δ^4-3-hydroxy steroid, that is, an allyl alcohol derivative. This compound was not isolated, but its presence was surmised on the basis of the derived artifact (Neeman *et al.*, 1960). However, two naturally-occurring Δ^4-3-hydroxy metabolites have been established (Levy *et al.*, 1963; Thomas and Dorfman, 1964).

The most characteristic catabolic change in the neutral steroid series is the ring A reduction of the Δ^4-3-ketosteroids. Figure 17, which deals with the catabolism of deoxycorticosterone, illustrates this type of change. Of the 13 catabolites known from *in vitro* and *in vivo* studies, the single most important compound and a unique catabolite is 3α,21-dihydroxy-5β-pregnan-20-one. *In vitro* studies frequently yield a preponderance of the 5α-reduced compound. This point is considered in greater detail in the section dealing with the metabolism of deoxycortisol.

Progesterone is metabolized to at least nine steroids (Fig. 18). Of these, two may be considered as unique catabolites, pregnanolone (compound 11) and pregnanediol (compound 13). The diol, however, is more useful for analytical purposes, owing to the larger amounts present in urine. Actually, some 10 to 30% of the secreted amounts of progesterone are finally found as the urinary pregnanediol conjugate. The hydroxyketone is excreted in about 1–3%. The relationship of 16-hydroxyprogesterone and its metabolites to progesterone metabolism requires further investigation. The presence of 16-hydroxyprogesterone in fetal adrenal has been noted by Villee *et al.* (1961).

The metabolism of aldosterone is summarized in Fig. 19. Earlier reports indicated a catabolite with a reduced ring A and additional reduction at carbon 18 which has been shown by Ulick and Kusch Vetter (1962) to be exclusively a metabolite of 18-hydroxycorticosterone. From *in vitro* and *in vivo* studies, particularly through the efforts of Pechet and his collaborators (1961), five metabolites are known, including the dihydro derivative of aldosterone having the 5α orientation, 11β,21-dihydroxy-3-oxo-5α-pregnan-18-al. The steroid 11β,21-dihydroxy-3-oxo-5β-pregnan-18-al (compound 5), has not been isolated, but is included as a theoretical intermediate. 3α,11β-21-Trihydroxy-5β-pregnan-18-al (compound 8) is a unique catabolite of aldosterone and has been referred to as uroaldosterone.

The steroid 17α-hydroxyprogesterone, shown in Fig. 20, has played a significant role in considerations of the disease, congenital adrenal hyperplasia, and is well known through its unique catabolite, pregnanetriol (5β-pregnane-3α,17α,20α-triol). In this state of adrenal abnormality, the production and secretion of 17α-hydroxyprogesterone increases greatly, resulting in the high urinary levels of pregnanetriol conjugates.

Some confusion has been associated with the biological activity of 17α-hydroxyprogesterone owing to the early erroneous report that this C_{21}-steroid was an important androgen and, as a result, it and its C_{19}-metabolites could account for the high amounts of circulating androgens responsible for the intense masculinization in the adrenogenital syndrome. Actually, only a small portion of the secreted 17α-hydroxyprogesterone in the normal or diseased state is converted to the C_{19}-steroids, androsterone and etiocholanolone, with a preponderance of etiocholanolone, which is essentially devoid of androgenic activity.

11-Deoxycortisol (Fig. 21) is produced in the adrenal normally in small amounts. The formation of increased amounts is associated with a variant of congenital adrenal hyperplasia where there is a relative lack of 11β-hydroxylase, or following the administration of the 11β-hydroxylase inhibitor, SU-4885, and in some patients with adrenal cancer. In certain patients with Cushing's disease, the production of this steroid may be increased enormously. 11-Deoxycortisol is converted to the 20α- and 20β-reduced compounds (compounds 2 and 3) with the Δ^4-3-ketone group intact, and also to some extent to the 6β-hydroxy compound (compound 5). Androst-4-ene-3,17-dione may be formed particularly by *in vitro* techniques. By *in vivo* procedures, androsterone (compound 12) and etiocholanolone (compound 14) can be produced in low yields with the latter metabolite predominating. The unique catabolite for 11-deoxycortisol is the corresponding 3α-hydroxy-5β-reduced compound, 3α,17α,21-trihydroxy-5β-pregnan-20-one (compound 10, Fig. 21).

Corticosterone catabolism is illustrated by the fifteen metabolites shown in Fig. 22. Both 20α and 20β (compounds 2 and 3) side chain reduced derivatives of corticosterone have been detected and it is quite likely that these compounds may be converted to corticosterone. Two 21-deoxy derivatives (compounds 4 and 5) have been isolated. Compound 11 represents the 3α,5β-tetrahydro reduction product and is one of the unique metabolites. In any discussion of a unique catabolite, one must consider the relationship of 11-dehydrocorticosterone to corticosterone and that compounds 11 and 15 may arise from both corticosterone and 11-dehydrocorticosterone.

Corticosterone catabolites need not have an intact 11β-hydroxy group as seen by the presence of no less than five metabolites with the 11-ketone group in ring C. Compounds 6 and 16, for example, retain the Δ^4-3-ketones, one compound being 11-dehydrocorticosterone and the other being the corresponding 20β-reduced derivative. Compounds 13, 14, and 15 have the 11-ketone group while compound 14 in addition has the 21-deoxy grouping.

11-Dehydrocorticosterone and its metabolites are represented in Fig. 23. A relatively small group of metabolites is represented, probably due to the fact that there have been relatively few metabolic experiments attempted. Compound 4 has the 21-deoxy grouping and quantitatively is an important member of this group. The corresponding tetrahydro derivative (compound 6) is the same as the compound (compound 15) seen in Fig. 22 which can serve as a unique catabolite for corticosterone and 11-dehydrocorticosterone. The 3α,5α-tetrahydro derivative is present to a small extent. Compounds 2 and 3 represent the 20β-reduced derivatives of the 11β-hydroxy and 11-keto compounds, respectively. In spite of the fact that no isolation has yet been reported, it is not unlikely that 11-dehydrocorticosterone is also catabolized to the metabolite, 3α,11β,21-trihydroxy-5β-pregnan-20-one (compound 11, Fig. 22), as already indicated.

Cortisone and cortisol are metabolized to a great number of steroid compounds, presented in Figs. 24–27. Figure 24 deals with the 3-keto catabolites of cortisone having the 11-keto or 11β-hydroxy group. The 3-ketone forms are in combination with a ring A reduced at carbons 4,5 (dihydro form) or with the 4,5 double bond. Cortisone may be oxidatively degraded to adrenosterone (compound 2). This apparently occurs more often under *in vitro* conditions, since cortisone is rapidly reduced at C—4,5 under *in vivo* conditions. Later in this chapter describing the conversion of C_{21} to C_{19} steroids, the point is made that the reduction in ring A occurs first and then the two-carbon side chain is oxidatively removed.

Figure 24 illustrates five different compounds in which the Δ^4-3-ketone is still intact. In compounds 3 and 4, carbon 20 has been reduced to the corresponding 20α- and 20β-reduced forms. Cortisone is converted to cortisol and to the 20α- (compound 7) and 20β- (compound 5) reduced derivatives of cortisol. Cortisone is also reduced to the 5α- and 5β-dihydro derivatives. These latter compounds under normal conditions are only present in minute amounts, since they are quickly and efficiently transformed to the 3α-hydroxy form and to a lesser extent to the 3β-hydroxy derivatives. Figure 25 considers the 3-hydroxy catabolites of cortisone. For convenience, compounds 8 and 9, which appeared in Fig. 24, are repeated since these compounds are the intermediates for the formation of the 3-hydroxy steroids. Figure 25 also indicates unique catabolites of cortisone or, rather, unique catabolites of cortisone and cortisol since the two compounds are interconvertible and yield the same catabolites.

These unique catabolites have been called urocortisone (compound 19) and urocortisol (compound 20). The measurement of both compounds 19 and 20 is the logical choice for estimates of cortisone-plus-cortisol secretion.

Compounds 10 and 11, the 11-hydroxy and 11-keto derivatives of androsterone, have been discussed previously as catabolites of 11β-hydroxyandrost-4-ene-3,17-dione and adrenosterone. Similarly, compounds 13 and 14, 11-ketoetiocholanolone and 11β-hydroxyetiocholanolone, respectively, are not only catabolites of cortisone, and for that matter cortisol as well, but also of adrenosterone and 11β-hydroxyandrost-4-ene-3,17-dione.

Figure 26 corresponds to Fig. 24 in that only the 3-keto catabolites of cortisol are listed. Among these 3-keto catabolites of cortisol are 11β-hydroxyandrost-4-ene-3,17-dione, adrenosterone, cortisone, and the 20α- and 20β-reduced derivatives of both cortisone and cortisol. Although corticosterone is illustrated in the figure because its isolation was reported, its presence as a catabolite of cortisol is by no means firmly established. 6β-Hydroxycortisol (compound 4) formation has been suggested to be stimulated by estrogens. The 5β- and 5α-dihydro derivatives (compounds 11 and 12) are shown. Although the latter compound has not been isolated, on the basis of indirect evidence it is considered a likely candidate.

Figure 27 presents, among others, the compounds urocortisol and urocortisone, which are the unique catabolites of both cortisol and cortisone as discussed before. Five 11-oxygenated 17-ketosteroids have been established as catabolites of cortisol. The ring A dihydro steroids (compounds 11 and 12) are repeated from Fig. 26. These two compounds on further reduction yield the many reduced catabolites represented in Fig. 27. Cortisone and cortisol catabolism have yielded, at present count, a total of 34 catabolites.

Figure 28 deals with the catabolites of 21-deoxycortisol, a steroid normally present and produced in low concentrations. In certain variants of the congenital adrenal hyperplasia syndrome, the rate of production may be increased enormously. This is presumably owing to a lowered concentration of the enzyme 21-hydroxylase. The unique catabolite of 21-deoxycortisol is compound 3, pregnanetriolone, which has been shown to be increased in the urine of patients with congenital adrenal hyperplasia and with the Stein-Leventhal syndrome.

Influence of Nuclear Substitution on Reduction of the Δ^4-Group

Differences in the reduction of the Δ^4-double bond to the 5α and 5β forms *in vivo* have been observed which depend upon the nature of the substituent groups, particularly at carbon atoms 11 and 17. The *in vivo* catabolism of $C_{19}O_2$ steroids in humans, such as testosterone, androst-4-ene-3,17-dione, and dehydroepiandrosterone, leads to the formation and excretion of the major urinary 17-ketosteroids androsterone (5α) and etiocholanolone (5β). It has been shown that, in a variety of normal subjects and patients, the over-all ratio of the C_{19}-5α to -5β reduced derivatives is approximately one to one (Dorfman, 1954a,b; Schiller *et al.*, 1945; Dobriner, 1951; Dorfman *et al.*, 1950; Gallagher *et al.*, 1951; Ungar and Dorfman, 1954; Mason and Kepler, 1947; Miller *et al.*, 1950).

The catabolism of testosterone has been found to be significantly modified by the effective concentration of the thyroid hormone (Bradlow *et al.*, 1956; Hellman *et al.*, 1959). Endogenous production of androsterone was very low in myxedematous patients. When testosterone was administered to these patients, a much smaller fraction was converted to androsterone than in subjects with normal thyroid function. Administration of thyroid hormone to the myxedematous patient restored to essentially normal the androsterone production from endogenous and exogenous precursors. Triiodothyronine administered to euthyroid subjects increased androsterone production significantly. An effect on the specific enzyme systems involved was reported by McGuire and Tompkins (1959), who found, using cortisone as the substrate, that thyroxine increased the Δ^4-5α-reductase concentration of rat liver.

In vivo metabolism studies of adrenosterone, the C_{19}-steroid that possesses a ketone group at carbon 11, indicated a ratio of 5α- to 5β-reduced metabolites of 5.3 (Savard *et al.*, 1953). This ratio was significantly greater than the one-to-one ratios found for the $C_{19}O_2$ steroids such as testosterone, androst-4-ene-3,17-dione, and dehydroepiandrosterone. It appears, therefore, that the oxygen substitution at carbon 11 orients the reduction of the Δ^4-double bond to the 5α configuration. Two additional points in metabolism were learned from these studies. First, that the oxygen function at carbon 11 was not removed in metabolism, that is, no 11-deoxy C_{19}-steroids were formed. Second, the 11-keto group of adrenosterone was reduced in part to the 11β-hydroxy group. Actually, by far the greatest concentration of metabolites contained the 11β-hydroxy grouping.

Bradlow and Gallagher (1959) studied the metabolism of 11β-hydroxyandrost-4-ene-3,17-dione in a patient with congenital adrenal hyperplasia and found essentially the same ratio of excreted 5α/5β metabolites as reported previously by Savard *et al.* (1953) for adrenosterone. In their studies, 66 and 72% were excreted as a 5α-metabolite (11β-hydroxyandrosterone) and two 5β-metabolites yielded 6.3 and 8.5% for 11β-hydroxyetiocholanolone and 7.4 and 6.9% for 11-ketoetiocholanolone. The mean 5α/5β ratio was 4.8 and compared favorably with the ratio found for adrenosterone (Savard *et al.*, 1953). In another paper, Bradlow and Gallagher (1957) had obtained 5α/5β ratios of 3.1 and 4.8 for the urinary products of 11β-hydroxyandrost-4-ene-3,17-dione.

Metabolism of Δ^4-3-Keto C_{21}-Steroids to 5α- and 5β-Reduced Metabolites

The generalization has been made that Δ^4-3-keto C_{21}-steroids are primarily reduced *in vivo* in humans to the 5β form (Dorfman, 1954a,b). Ample verification of this rule is seen in the studies on progesterone (Ungar *et al.*, 1951; Dobriner and Lieberman, 1952; Kyle and Marrian, 1951), 11-ketoprogesterone (Savard and Dorfman, 1963), deoxycorticosterone (Horwitt *et al.*, 1944), 21-deoxycortisone (Burstein *et al.*, 1953a), cortisone (Burstein *et al.*, 1953b), cortisol (Burstein *et al.*, 1953c), and 17α-hydroxy-progesterone (Fukushima *et al.*, 1961; Brooks, 1960).

The metabolism of 21-deoxycortisol was investigated in detail by Fukushima *et al.* (1959) in a patient with adrenal hyperplasia and in a normal subject. Six pregnane metabolites of the 5β and none of the 5α series were isolated. The 5β compounds were: 5β-pregnane-3α,11β,17α,20α-tetrol, 5β-pregnane-3α,11β,17α,20β-tetrol, 3α,17α,20α-trihydroxy-5β-pregnan-11-one, 3α,17α,20β-trihydroxy-5β-pregnan-11-one, 3α,11β,17α-trihydroxy-5β-pregnan-20-one, and 3α,17α-dihydroxy-5β-pregnane-11,20-dione. Thus, the preponderance of the 5β form in the excreted metabolites was again confirmed for a compound possessing a normal two-carbon side chain.

The metabolism of corticosterone and 11-dehydrocorticosterone has been studied *in vivo* in humans by a variety of workers and in at least one of these investigations (Engel *et al.*, 1955), the amount of 5α-reduced derivatives was of about the same order as that of the 5β form. Mason's (1948) earlier studies on 11-dehydrocorticosterone yielded only the 5β derivative 3α,20α-dihydroxy-5β-pregnan-11-one. The report of Richardson *et al.* (1955) also indicated a preponderance of the 5β form.

The principal urinary metabolites of cortisol and cortisone are the 3α,5β-tetrahydro forms, 3α,11β,17α,21-tetrahydroxy-5β-pregnan-20-one (urocortisol) and 3α,17α,21-trihydroxy-5β-pregnane-11,20-dione (urocortisone) (Richardson *et al.*, 1955; Burstein *et al.*, 1953b; Dougherty *et al.*, 1958). A 5α-tetrahydro isomer, 3α,11β,17α,21-tetrahydroxy-5α-pregnan-20-one, is present in lesser amounts.

The one major urinary metabolite of aldosterone isolated is in the 3α,5β-tetrahydro isomeric form.

The two 11-deoxy C_{21}-adrenal steroids, 11-deoxycorticosterone and 11-deoxycortisol, would not normally be secreted in amounts large enough to be detected. Metabolites have been isolated from urine, however, following the administration of these compounds *in vivo*, or in certain types of adrenal abnormality, where greater than normal amounts are excreted. The principal urinary metabolites of deoxycorticosterone are the 5β compounds, pregnanediol (Fish *et al.*, 1943; Westphal, 1942) and 3α,21-dihydroxy-5β-pregnan-20-one (Richardson *et al.*, 1955). The principal urinary metabolites of 11-deoxycortisol are also 5β-metabolites, 3α,17α,21-trihydroxy-5β-pregnan-20-one (Richardson *et al.*, 1954) and 3α,17α,20α,

21-tetrahydroxy-5β-pregnan-20-one (Ungar and Dorfman, 1956; Fukushima *et al.*, 1959; Gandy *et al.*, 1960).

Metabolism of C_{21}-Steroids to 17-Ketosteroids

C_{21}-steroids possessing oxygen functions at carbons 17 and 20 are in part catabolized to 17-ketosteroids. When this occurs, the predominating 17-ketosteroids are of the 5β form, etiocholanolone, 11 keto- and 11β-hydroxyetiocholanolone. The conversion of C_{21}-steroids to 11β-hydroxyandrosterone and 11-ketoandrosterone is also indicated, but the quantity of 5α stereoisomers formed is definitely less. This was indicated in the early studies for cortisone (Burstein *et al.*, 1953b), for cortisol (Burstein *et al.*, 1953a), and for 21-deoxycortisone (Burstein *et al.*, 1953c). The metabolism of 21-deoxycortisol in a patient with congenital adrenal hyperplasia yielded a 5α/5β ratio of 0.9 for the 11-oxygenated 17-ketosteroids (Fukushima *et al.*, 1959). In the same report, the normal subject showed a ratio of 3 with an extremely low percentage of recovery. In another report (Gallagher, 1957), cortisol was metabolized to both 5α and 5β 11-oxygenated 17-ketosteroids with a 5α/5β ratio of 0.12.

Mechanism of the In Vivo *Conversion of C_{21}-Steroids to 17-Ketosteroids*

In the preceding sections, evidence was presented to show that C_{19}-steroids with a C-11 oxygen function were metabolized primarily to 5α-metabolites (11β-hydroxyandrosterone and 11-ketoandrosterone) and that the ratio of 5α/5β isomers was about 5.0. It was also shown that C_{21}-steroids such as cortisone and cortisol were metabolized primarily to the 5β form of 17-ketosteroids and that the 5α/5β ratio is of the order of 0.2 or less.

It is postulated, on the basis of available evidence, that a steroid such as cortisol is reduced primarily to the dihydro (or tetrahydro) pregnane (5β) derivative, and only after this reduction in ring A is accomplished is the side chain removed by oxidative means, to form the 17-ketosteroid. The alternative, that is, the oxidative removal of the side chain before reduction in ring A, is untenable as the principal pathway, since, if this were the case, the first product formed would be either adrenosterone in the case of cortisone or 11-hydroxyandrost-4-ene-3,17-dione in the case of cortisol. These $C_{19}O_3$ steroids, as has already been demonstrated, would in turn yield predominantly the 11-oxygenated 17-ketosteroids in the androstane series (5α), which is contrary to the observations. Actually, both cortisone and cortisol yield almost exclusively 5β-stereoisomers. It is, therefore, concluded that the bulk of C_{21} compounds converted to C_{19} 17-ketosteroids first undergo reduction in ring A before the side chain is removed.

Unfortunately, corroboratory *in vitro* evidence is lacking, since attempts to demonstrate 17-ketosteroid formation from C_{21} precursors under *in vitro* conditions have not been very successful. Apart from the well-documented biogenetic pathway of testosterone formation from C_{21} precursors in the testis gland (Lynn and Brown, 1958), the enzymes present in liver, adrenal, and other tissues which could split the C_{21} side chain have not been isolated or purified, and the reactions that have been demonstrated (Forchielli and Dorfman, 1956) proceed at a very low rate of several per cent at most. It may be of interest that the conversion of C_{21}-reduced compounds, 17α,21-dihydroxy-5β-pregnane-3,20-dione to etiocholane-3,17-dione and 3α,17α-dihydroxy-5β-pregnan-20-one to etiocholanolone could be demonstrated by incubation with human adrenal tissue mince preparations (Ungar *et al.*, 1962).

Predicted Relationship between Adrenocortical Steroids and 17-Ketosteroids

On the basis of evidence already reviewed, the interrelationship between certain steroids in the adrenal cortex and the urinary 17-ketosteroids can be suggested. Androsterone arises primarily from the metabolism of testosterone, androst-4-ene-3,17-dione, and dehydroepiandrosterone. 17-Hydroxyprogesterone and 11-deoxycortisol could contribute small amounts of androsterone. Etiocholanolone would also arise from various sources, including testosterone, androst-4-ene-3,17-dione, and dehydroepiandrosterone, in about the same magnitude as the formation of androsterone. However, greater amounts of etiocholanolone would also be expected to result from the metabolism of such compounds as 11-deoxycortisol and 17-hydroxyprogesterone.

The 11-oxygenated 17-ketosteroids include both the 11-keto and 11-hydroxy derivatives, as would be expected since the 11-keto and 11β-hydroxy groups are interchangeable in metabolism. The 11-oxygenated androsterone derivatives arise almost exclusively from 11-oxygenated Δ^4-3-keto-17-ketosteroids, such as adrenosterone and 11β-hydroxyandrost-4-ene-3,17-dione. These two compounds may also contribute some 11-oxygenated etiocholane derivatives to the catabolic pool. However, the bulk of the 11-oxygenated etiocholane derivatives would be expected to be products of the metabolism of such substances as cortisol and cortisone.

Influence of Thyroid Hormone on Adrenal Steroid Production and Catabolism

According to several lines of evidence, the level of thyroxine in man and in animals controls at least in part the formation and metabolism of cortisol and estrogens (Tomkins and McGuire, 1960). Elevated levels of thyroid hormone increased the oxidation of the 11β-hydroxy group of cortisol to the 11-ketone, and also increased the endogenous production of cortisol. Conversely, a decreased level of thyroid hormone was associated with an increased level of 11β-hydroxy steroids and with a decreased formation of cortisol (Hellman *et al.*, 1961). Increased cortisol production and catabolism have been demonstrated *in vivo* with excess thyroid administration (Melby *et al.*, 1960; Timiras and Woodbury, 1955). Jao and Koritz (1962), using whole rat adrenal homogenates, obtained an inhibiting effect by the *in vitro* addition of thyroxine (10^{-5} *M*) or its analogs on the conversion of steroid precursors to corticosterone.

Increasing the thyroid hormone circulatory levels in man decreased the conversion of estradiol-17β to estriol and increased the formation of 2-methoxyestrone with no observable change in the levels of estrone (Fishman *et al.*, 1962).

Biologically Active Steroids in Plasma

It may be argued that the effective hormonal steroids are those present in plasma in a free, easily available form. If this were so, then the analysis of this fraction may, if all other factors remain constant, be a guide to the physiological hormonal stimulation imposed on the individual. The biologically active compounds in this category are relatively few, on the basis of our present knowledge, and may be reviewed here. The list at the present time includes cortisol, corticosterone (to a minor extent), aldosterone, deoxycorticosterone, 17α-hydroxyprogesterone, progesterone, testosterone, androsterone, etiocholanolone, dehydroepiandrosterone sulfate, pregnanolone, estradiol-17β, and estrone.

Cortisol in Plasma

Cortisol is the most important single corticoid of the glycogenic group. The free "available" cortisol in plasma would appear to be the important measure, and good analytical methods are available (Péron, 1962; Gray *et al.*, 1961).

Cortisol assays of the most extreme sensitivities are available with isotopic methods. Alkali fluorescent methods are sensitive to 0.01 μg of cortisol (Bush and Mahesh, 1959; Abelson and Bondy, 1955) and an acid fluorescence method has been described by Sweat (1954) which is claimed to detect 0.005 μg of cortisol.

Normal plasma values for free "available" cortisol have been reported to be of the order of 9–14 μg per 100 ml of plasma (summarized by Gray *et al.*, 1961), using fluorescence and isotope dilution methods (Bondy and Upton, 1957; Ely *et al.*, 1958; Sweat, 1955; Lewis, 1957; Peterson, 1957a). Plasma cortisol levels have also been reported in various clinical states such as: adrenal hyperplasia, 38–60 μg/100 ml (Peterson, 1957b), 135 μg/100 ml (Sweat, 1955); adrenal tumors, 21–33 μg (Peterson *et al.*, 1957); congenital adrenal hyperplasia, 1–4 μg (Peterson, 1957b); Bayliss *et al.*, 1954; Bush and Willoughby, 1957). Cortisol levels of 0–3 μg/100 ml were reported in Addison's disease and in hypopituitarism (Peterson, 1957b).

In shock stress due to infection, Melby and Spink (1958) found values of 30–160 μg in twelve samples from patients who succumbed and, in nonfatal cases, values of 40–78 μg/100 ml.

Corticosterone in Plasma

Good sensitive methods have been developed for the determination of corticosterone in human and animal plasma (Péron, 1962). The procedure of Bush and Mahesh (1959) is sensitive to 0.01 μg of corticosterone by alkali fluorescence, and Peterson (1957a,b) has determined quantities at the level of 0.005 μg by acid fluorescence and isotope dilution. Other methods have been reported by Silber *et al.* (1958), Péron and Dorfman (1958), and Moncloa *et al.* (1959).

The various studies on the concentration of corticosterone in human plasma show some low values: 1.3 ± 2.5 SD (Bondy and Upton, 1957), 1.2 μg/100 ml of plasma (Lewis, 1957), and 1.1 ± 0.4 per 100 ml (Peterson, 1957a); and high values: 3.0 ± 0.2 SD μg per 100 ml (Ely *et al.*, 1958), and 4.3 ± 2.3 SD μg/100 ml plasma (Sweat, 1955).

Corticosterone has been determined in patients with various endocrine abnormalities. Peterson (1957b) found no increase in adrenal hyperplasia in patients who appeared to have had cortisol increases of the order of three to five times normal. Sweat (1955), on the other hand, found a fourfold increase in a patient who had a twelvefold increase in cortisol.

Aldosterone and Deoxycorticosterone in Plasma

Aldosterone and deoxycorticosterone are primarily concerned with the regulation of salt and water metabolism, the latter steroid playing only a minor role. Physiological effective concentrations of deoxycorticosterone in plasma are probably reached only under grossly abnormal conditions. A precise plasma method for deoxycorticosterone determination is not available, but could be of value in the study of variants of congenital adrenal hyperplasia with a relative lack of 11β-hydroxylase.

Under most normal and abnormal circumstances, salt or Na^+ balance appears to be regulated primarily by aldosterone, and the concentration of "available" plasma aldosterone may be the important physiological constituent.

Sensitive methods for determination of aldosterone have been devised (Neher and Wettstein, 1956; Kalant, 1958; Bojeson, 1956, 1958; Moolenaar, 1957; Gornall and MacDonald, 1953; Gornall and Gwilliam, 1957; Flood *et al.*, 1961; Ayres *et al.*, 1957).

Plasma methods have been developed for the determination of aldosterone and are playing a most important role in experimental biology. Bojeson and Degn (1960) developed a method for aldosterone in 20–30 ml of plasma employing S^{35}-*p*-iodophenylsulfonylic anhydride and aldosterone I^{131}-*p*-iodophenylsulfonate as an indicator. Normal human subjects had values of 0.030, 0.025, and 0.016 μg/100 ml of plasma. Kliman and Peterson

(1960) and Davis *et al.* (1958) used tritiated acetic anhydride as the reagent and C^{14}-labeled aldosterone diacetate as the indicator. The report by Peterson (1959) set the value for normal plasma between 0.04 and 0.08 μg/100 ml; this is thought to be too high at the present time.

Progesterone in Plasma

The determination of progesterone in plasma has been reviewed by Zander (1962) and by Short (1961). Progesterone, even that bound to albumin, may be extracted from plasma by organic solvents. Progesterone is essentially confined to the plasma, with the red cells containing only insignificant amounts (Short, 1958).

Data of Zander (1955) and Oertel *et al.* (1959) indicate that human peripheral blood from normal women contains progesterone in the amount of 1–5 μg/100 ml of plasma. During the first half of pregnancy, values range from 5.0–10 μg/100 ml of plasma, and during the second half of pregnancy values of 5–40 μg/100 ml have been reported (Zander, 1954, 1955; Short, 1958, 1960b; Futterweit *et al.*, 1963a).

Futterweit *et al.* (1963a) reported a quantitative method for measuring progesterone in peripheral plasma of pregnant humans by gas chromatographic technics (see Horning *et al.*, 1959). Table 1 contains the retention times for progesterone, relative to cholestane, in the three chromatographic columns packed with silicone SE-30, neopentyl glycol succinate (NGS), and polydiethylene glycol adipate (PGA). In each instance, the extract of pregnancy plasma showed a peak identical in retention time to that of authentic progesterone. An augmented symmetrical peak was obtained when 0.03–0.1 μg of progesterone was added to an aliquot of plasma presumed to contain a similar quantity of progesterone.

The use of PGA resulted in less sensitivity than that obtainable with SE-30, presumably owing to excessive steroidal adsorption. By use of the PGA column, three plasma samples yielded the following values for progesterone (μg/100 ml of plasma): fourth month of pregnancy, 6.9; fifth month of pregnancy, 11.6 eighth month of pregnancy, 29.7.

20α-Hydroxypregn-4-en-3-one is present in the peripheral plasma of pregnant women (Short, 1960a). This progestationally active steroid is not efficiently separated on the preferable SE-30 phase, but preliminary purification on silica gel G affords a rapid way of separating this steroid from progesterone and other closely related compounds such as pregnenolone. Kumar *et al.* (1962) isolated progesterone from human pregnant myometrium. Their procedure included preliminary purification on a silicic acid column and final gas chromatographic separation with a 2% SE-30 phase.

The results of these investigations indicate that a method for gas chromatographic analysis of plasma progesterone is feasible, especially when coupled with the advantages of capacity, speed, and resolution afforded by preliminary purification on thin-layer adsorption chromatography.

17α-Hydroxyprogesterone in Plasma

Plasma levels of 17α-hydroxyprogesterone have not been studied in any detail, and quantitative methods for its determination in plasma are not available. The measurement of 17α-hydroxyprogesterone in plasma may be of some value since Jacobs *et al.* (1961) suggested that this compound should be considered as an inhibitor of aldosterone in its effect on salt retention. Apart from this consideration, the measurement of 17α-hydroxyprogesterone will be valuable in the diagnosis of the adrenogenital syndrome, a condition in which this steroid is often secreted in excessive amounts.

Testosterone in Plasma

Finkelstein *et al.* (1961) described a method for the estimation of free testosterone in the peripheral plasma from normal men and women. Plasma from men and virilized females contained significantly more testosterone than plasma obtained from normal women. Since the appearance of the preliminary communication, Oertel (1961) has reported on a method for measuring testosterone levels, and Oertel and Kaiser (1961) have measured levels of this androgen in the plasma of young male subjects. Sorcini *et al.* (1962) used the method of Finkelstein *et al.* (1961) to determine plasma testosterone and found a mean of 0.69 μg/100 ml of plasma in four normal men 21–30 years of age, 0.11 μg/100 ml of plasma in four normal women over 25 years of age, and 0.32 μg/100 ml of plasma in ten women with the Stein-Leventhal syndrome who had a mean excretion of only 8.7 mg of 17-ketosteroids per day. In a more recent communication, Forchielli *et al.* (1963) reported improvements in the assay procedure, and testosterone values were obtained in a larger series of normal men and women, hirsute women, and virilized women. The values obtained for testosterone in plasma for normal men and women and various patients with hirsutism and virilism are presented in Table 2. The difference in plasma levels between men and women was better than fourfold. One group had proven polycystic ovaries and were classed as having the Stein-Leventhal syndrome. The mean 17-ketosteroid value for this group of six women, ranging in age from 18 to 41 years, was 12.2 (7–24) mg per 24 hours. The blood testosterone values ranged from 0.25–0.42 μg/100 ml with a mean of 0.33 μg. The second group of four women were hirsute but the diagnosis was not established. The mean testosterone value for this group was 0.25 (0.11–0.32) μg per 100 ml of plasma, and the mean 17-ketosteroid values were 13.7 mg/day.

Five subjects had the stigma of virilization, and the blood testosterone values were considerably elevated. The mean value of 0.49 μg/100 ml of plasma was quite similar to that found for the normal men. Of particular interest is the fact that the 17-ketosteroid mean value for this group was only 10.9 mg per day. Actually in only one patient, who had a value of 20 mg per day, were the 17-ketosteroids increased.

Plasma testosterone levels were studied in four women bearing virilizing adrenal adenomas (Table 2). All had greatly elevated 17-ketosteroids, and three of the patients had very high testosterone levels. One subject had a value of 0.22 μg/100 ml, which was in the normal range, which decreased to 0.02 μg after the tumor was removed. Of further interest was the relative lack of virilism but the presence of severe hirsutism in this subject.

The influence of ovariectomy, adrenalectomy, wedge resection, prednisone, and human chorionic gonadotropin on plasma testosterone as reported by Forchielli *et al.* (1963) is listed in Table 3. Ovariectomy of hirsute women produced a decrease in blood testosterone; the extent, however, varied from subject to subject. In one virilized Stein-Leventhal patient who had an excessive plasma testosterone level of 0.71 μg, bilateral ovariectomy decreased this value to 0.22 μg. The mean value for all five ovariectomized women was 0.11 μg, which was not different from the plasma testosterone value of normal women. Wedge resection caused a net testosterone decrease of 0.41 μg/100 ml of plasma, from a mean of 0.63 μg to 0.22 μg. Prednisolone treatment lowered testosterone from 0.34 to 0.07 μg.

The adrenalectomized subject (Table 3) was treated once daily for three days with 3000 IU of human chorionic gonadotropin. The change from 0.08 to 0.09 μg per 100 ml of plasma as a result of this stimulation was not significant, but stimulation of plasma estrogens was definite.

Using a double isotope-derivative assay involving testosterone-C^{14} and acetic anhydride-H^3, Burger *et al.* (1963) reported the following testosterone levels (μg/100 ml of human plasma): normal men (19–30 years), 0.62 (0.32–0.94); normal women, 0.14 (0.06–0.36); adrenalectomized-ovariectomized females, 0.01–0.17; an untreated patient with congenital adrenal hyperplasia, 0·59. In a normal man whose free testosterone was 0.56 μg/100 ml of plasma, a value of 1.31 mg/100 ml was found after β-glucuronidase hydrolysis indicated that the bulk of the plasma testosterone is present in plasma as the glucuronic acid conjugate.

Testosterone in Urine

Steroids of the C_{19} series possessing an α,β-unsaturated ketone have been isolated from urine. Androst-4-ene-3,17-dione was isolated from the urine of virilized and hirsute patients by Miller *et al.* (1953) and by Lieberman *et al.* (1948).

More recently, Schubert and Wehrberger (1960) isolated testosterone from the urine of a healthy man. The urine was incubated with β-glucuronidase and extracted with ethyl acetate, subjected to a Girard fractionation, and chromatographed on a Al_2O_3 column using gradient elution. Further purification was accomplished by paper chromatography and filtration through activated Al_2O_3. With this technic, these investigators reported a daily excretion of 50 μg for a normal man.

Futterweit *et al.* (1963b) have developed a urinary testosterone procedure using thin-layer chromatography and gas chromatography. For this analysis, a Research Specialties Co. model 600 apparatus equipped with a model 660-1B hydrogen flame ionization detector was employed. Samples were introduced using a solids injector designed by McNiven *et al.* (1963).

Typical results (given in Table 4) illustrate that this method holds considerable promise as a means of evaluating the effective testosterone levels in body fluids. A reasonable correlation is indicated between the plasma and urine testosterone levels, and the latter method appears to be a more practical approach to evaluation of effective androgens in body fluids.

Camacho and Migeon (1963) have reported a method for the isolation and determination of testosterone in human urine. After β-glucuronidase hydrolysis and extraction with ether, the extract was subjected to Florisil column chromatography and paper chromatography in two systems, and the eluted material from the testosterone zone was quantitatively determined by use of the ultraviolet absorption spectrum of testosterone in sulfuric acid (Bernstein and Lenhard, 1953). Five normal men varying in age from 27 to 34 years had urine testosterone values of 46.1–106 μg per day, whereas four normal women had values of 7.5 μg or less. A boy with a virilizing hepatoma had a testosterone excretion of 695 μg per day before and 12.5 μg per day after surgery.

Androsterone in Plasma

Androsterone is present in plasma both as the sulfate conjugate and as the free compound. The hypothesis that the concentration of free androsterone in plasma is in part related to cholesterol levels in the plasma has considerable support. The studies of Bradlow *et al.* (1956) and Hellman *et al.* (1959) clearly indicated that androsterone treatment of subjects with normal thyroid function and in patients with myxedema resulted in the lowering of plasma cholesterol. These observations were confirmed by various investigators (Furman and Howard, 1960, 1962). The plasma cholesterol of a highly virilized woman suffering from an adrenal adenoma producing excessive androgens had an extremely low plasma cholesterol level which was significantly increased when the benign tumor was removed. Other studies have indicated that the level of free androsterone in plasma may determine in part the level of cholesterol in plasma. Methods being developed for the measurement of free androsterone in plasma may be of value for the eventual understanding of coronary disease.

Dehydroepiandrosterone Sulfate in Plasma

Dehydroepiandrosterone sulfate is present in plasma in a concentration of 50–150 μg/100 ml. The measurement of this compound may have added interest since Sharma *et al.* (1963) reported that 11β-hydroxylation of deoxycorticosterone to corticosterone is inhibited by the conjugate as well as by the free dehydroepiandrosterone and by androst-4-ene-3,17-dione. Several methods for the measurement of free dehydroepiandrosterone are available, as is the method for the determination of dehydroepiandrosterone sulfate (reviewed by Dorfman, 1962).

Etiocholanolone in Plasma

Etiocholanolone (3α-hydroxy-5β-androstan-17-one) and 5β-pregnane derivatives in adequate concentrations in plasma may cause temperature elevation. The original demonstration was reported by Segaloff *et al.* (1957), who injected 50 mg per day of 17β-hydroxy-5β-androstan-3-one and observed a significant elevation in body temperature in eight of eighteen patients. Etiocholanolone, when administered to normal subjects, produced the same effect, whereas androsterone, epiandrosterone, and 3β-hydroxy-5β-androstan-17-one did not produce this effect (Kappas *et al.*, 1957). Bondy and co-workers (1958, 1960) described a syndrome in which excessive plasma concentration of free etiocholanolone appears to cause fever, malaise, nausea, and myalgia (periodic disease). Cara and Gardner (1960) observed a similar relationship between elevated plasma etiocholanolone and periodic fever. An efficient plasma etiocholanolone method is needed to promote further studies in this area.

Temperature regulation may also be affected by 5β-pregnane compounds. The rise in body temperature at about the time of progesterone secretion during the menstrual cycle is well known. Administration of relatively high doses of progesterone will also produce significant temperature changes (Vignos and Dorfman, 1951; Kappas *et al.*, 1957).

Estradiol-17β and Estrone in Plasma

Two plasma methods for estrogens have been developed which appear to approach the required sensitivity needed to analyze plasma of non-pregnant women and men. One was developed by Svendsen (1960) and had a sensitivity of about 0.002 μg for estrone and estradiol-17β in plasma. The method is based on the double isotopic derivative principle using S^{35} and I^{131}. Plasma is extracted with chloroform, the estrone and estradiol-17β are esterified with *p*-iodobenzenesulphonyl chloride, and the esters are purified by paper chromatography before radioactivities are determined. Using this method, preliminary plasma values are given for normal women, patients with primary and secondary amenorrhea, and pregnant women.

A second method developed by Ichii *et al.* (1963) is briefly described. Plasma, after addition of a tracer dose of estrone-6,7-H^3 and estradiol-17β,6,7-H^3, was extracted with a mixture of chloroform:ether (3:1). The residue, after solvent distillation, was dissolved in 70% methanol, placed in a deep freeze overnight, centrifuged, and the supernatant partitioned against petroleum ether. The phenolic material of the 70% methanol fraction was subjected to paper chromatography in a Bush B3 system. The zones containing estrone and estradiol-17β were rechromatographed in Bush A and B1 systems, respectively. The quantity of estrogens was determined by a fluorescence method, and the radioactivity (for recovery correction) in a scintillation counter.

The recovery of estradiol-17β and estrone was 62% on a weight basis and 66% on the basis of H^3. The sensitivity of the method with 50 ml of plasma was of the order of 0.002 μg for each of the estrogens.

Estrone and estradiol-17β values obtained from plasma by this method are given in Table 5. The mean estrone values for men and women were of the same order in the small number of subjects tested, but the mean value of 0.032 μg for estradiol-17β for women was considerably higher than the mean value of 0.003 μg for the men. Svendsen (1960) reported on estrone and estradiol-17β titers in the plasma of normal women by the double isotope method employing S^{35} and I^{131}. These investigators found slightly more estradiol-17β than estrone, and the mean of five samples was 0.024 μg of estrone and 0.037 μg of estradiol-17β. On a preliminary basis, there appears to be a reasonable correspondence between the two methods.

The expected increases in both estrogens were found in the two pregnancy samples (Table 5) and on two samples from a patient who had a granulosa cell tumor. Steer adrenal vein plasma from two different animals indicated estrone at the levels of 0.100 and 0.020 μg and estradiol-17β at the 0.028 and 0.032 μg levels.

Two adrenal adenoma patients were studied, one with an elevated value for the estrogens and a second with normal values. The one patient with values in the normal range showed a drop from 0.035 to 0.005 μg per 100 ml of plasma for estrone and a decrease from 0.012 and 0.004 μg for estradiol-17β after removal of the adenoma.

Seven subjects with hirsutism owing to polycystic ovaries had a mean estradiol-17β concentration of 0.021 μg/100 ml of plasma (range 0.015–0.044) which did not seem to vary significantly from that found for the limited observations for normal women, but the estrone value of 0.070 μg/100 ml of plasma for the hirsute women appeared to be significantly higher than that for normal women.

In addition to the plasma estrogen methods of Svendsen (1960) and Ichii *et al.* (1963), a method has been proposed by Roy (1962) that utilizes the fluorescence reaction of Ittrich (1958) and the blood preparation method of Roy and Brown (1960). Preedy and Aitken (1957) also employed a fluorescence reaction and studied estrogens in women's plasma during the luteal phase of the cycle.

Table 1

RELATIVE RETENTION TIMES[a]

Compound	SE-30[b] 240°	PGA[c] 213°	NGS[d] 213°
Cholestane	1.00	1.00	1.00
Progesterone	0.94	7.90	10.05

[a] Data from Futterweit *et al.* (1963a).

[b] Column, 6.8% SE-30 on 110–120-mesh Anakrom ABS U-tube (3 ft × 1.9 mm); 47.5 psi; cholestane time, 6.0 min.

[c] Column, 1.1% polydiethylene glycol adipate (PGA) on 130–140-mesh Anakrom ABC U-tube ($2\frac{1}{3}$ ft × 2.0 mm); 55.5 psi; cholestane time, 1.36 min.

[d] Column, 1.34% neopentyl glycol adipate (NGS) on 130–140-mesh Anakrom ABS U-tube (3 ft × 2 mm); 45.5 psi; cholestane time, 1.9 min.

Table 2

TESTOSTERONE IN HUMAN PLASMA[a]

Subject (age range)	No. of subjects	17-Ketosteroids produced per day	Mean testosterone value (μg/100 ml) (range)
Normal men (23–74)	9	—	0.56 (0.1–0.98)
Normal women (22–35)	10	—	0.12 (0.02–0.26)
Hirsute women, polycystic ovaries (Stein–Leventhal type) (18–41)	6	12.2 (7–24)	0.33 (0.25–0.42)
Hirsute women (diagnosis not established) (14–47)	4	13.7 (8–18)	0.25 (0.11–0.32)
Virilized women, polycystic ovaries (Stein–Leventhal type) (14–36)	5	10.9 (6.4–20)	0.49 (0.30–0.74)
Ovarian hilus cell tumor (68)	1	2–4	2.0[b] 0.02[c] 0.05[c] 0.04[c]

Continued on following page

Table 2 (*continued*)

TESTOSTERONE IN HUMAN PLASMA[a]

Subject (age range)	No. of subjects	17-Ketosteroids produced per day	Mean testosterone value (μg/100 ml) (range)
Women with adrenal adenoma	4	1000	1.3
		250–1000	1.4
		308	0.22[b]
			0.02[c]
		200–272	0.79[d]

[a] Data of Forchielli *et al.* (1963).
[b] Before surgery.
[c] After surgery.
[d] Also bilateral polycystic ovaries.

Table 3

INFLUENCE OF SURGERY AND TREATMENT ON TESTOSTERONE IN PLASMA[a]

Subjects (no.)	Treatment	Mean testosterone value (μg/100 ml)	
Hirsute women (5)	Ovariectomy	0.11 (0.04–0.22)	
Bilaterally adrenalectomized women	Cortisone (25 mg) plus fluoxymestrone (1 mg) daily	0.08	
		0.09[b]	
Hirsute women (3)	Wedge resection	*Before*	*After*
		0.53	0.11
		0.77	0.34
		0.58	0.22
Hirsute women (4)	Prednisone treatment (10–20 mg/day)	0.48	0.13
		0.44	0.07
		0.1	0.02
		—	0.16

[a] Data of Forchielli *et al.* (1963).
[b] During treatment with 3000 IU of human chorionic gonadotropin.

Table 4

CONCENTRATION OF TESTOSTERONE IN THE URINE OF HUMAN SUBJECTS[a]

Subject (status)	Age range (yr)	No. of subjects	Mean value for testosterone in urine (range) (μg/day)
Normal boy	4	1	<13
Normal men	19–24	5	195 (82–290)
Normal men	29–34	4	97 (69–129)
Normal man	57	1	88
Normal women	16–26	4	<37 (20–57)
Normal woman	42	1	<22
Adrenogenital syndrome male	50	1	115
Adrenogenital syndrome female	49	1	709
Adrenal adenoma and polycystic ovaries	28	1	390

[a] Data of Futterweit *et al.* (1963b).

Table 5

CONCENTRATION OF ESTRONE AND ESTRADIOL-17β IN VARIOUS PLASMAS[a]

Subject or patient	Age range	No. of subjects	Concentration (μg/100 ml) Estrone	Estradiol-17β
Normal women	18–33	9	0.032	0.032
			(0.008–0.106)	(0.008–0.056)
			Mid-cycle	
Normal women	19–22	3	0.058	0.026
			Day of end of menstrual flow	
			0.023	0.010
Normal men	22–28	5	0.023	0.003
			(0.010–0.036)	(<0.002–0.006)
Pregnancy				
7th month		1	1.03	0.55
9th month		1	0.57	0.98
Granulosa cell tumor	30	1	0.33–0.37	0.18–0.19
Adrenal adenoma			0.128	0.076
Hirsutism; polycystic ovaries		7	0.070	0.021
			(0.004–0.134)	(0.015–0.044)
Steer adrenal vein plasma (lyophilized)		2	0.100	0.028
			0.020	0.032
Women with ovarian dermoid cyst			0.998	0.085
			Before surgery	
Adrenal adenoma			0.035	0.012
			After surgery	
			0.005	0.004

[a] Data of Ichii *et al.* (1963).

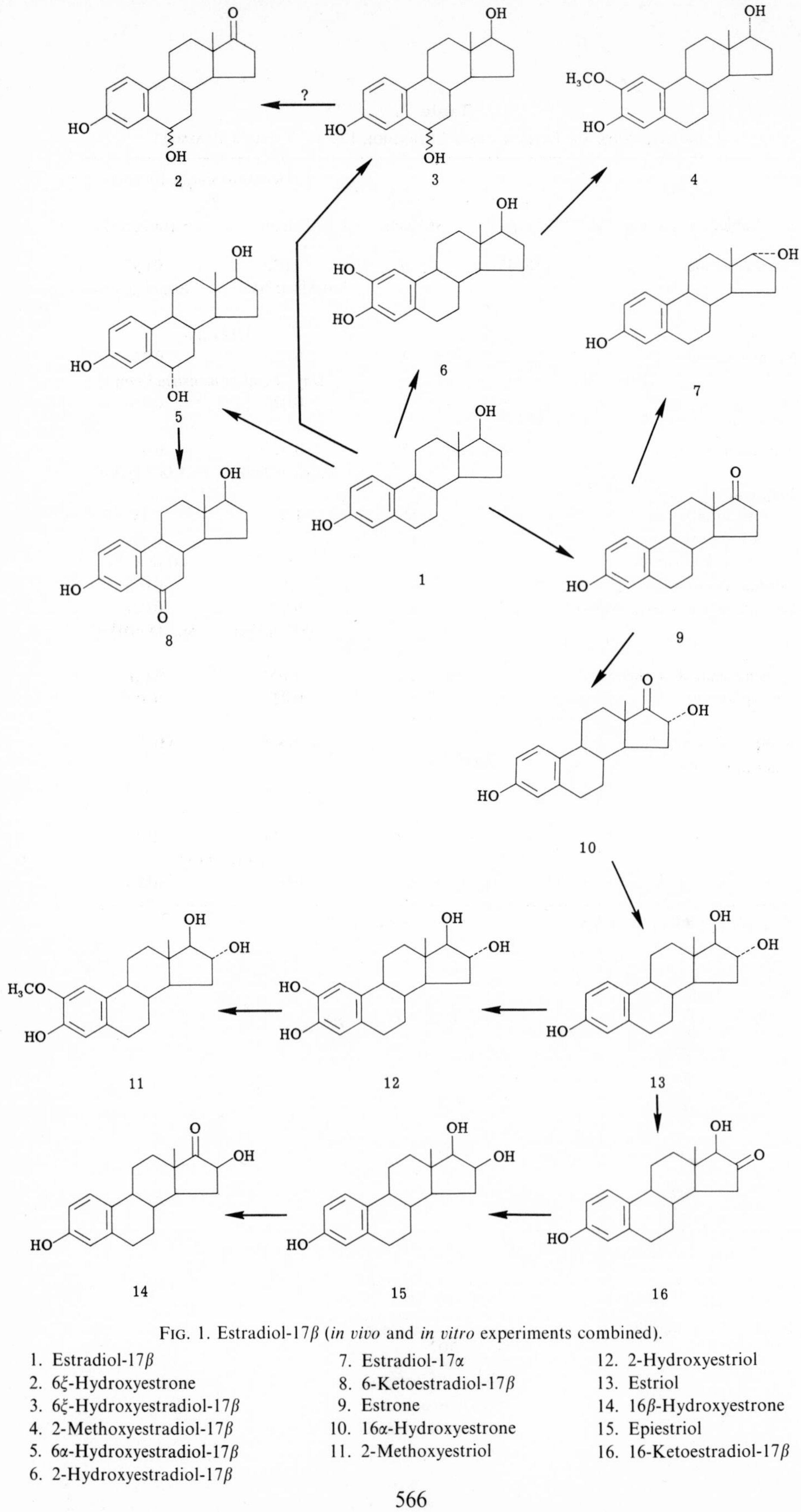

FIG. 1. Estradiol-17β (*in vivo* and *in vitro* experiments combined).

1. Estradiol-17β
2. 6ξ-Hydroxyestrone
3. 6ξ-Hydroxyestradiol-17β
4. 2-Methoxyestradiol-17β
5. 6α-Hydroxyestradiol-17β
6. 2-Hydroxyestradiol-17β
7. Estradiol-17α
8. 6-Ketoestradiol-17β
9. Estrone
10. 16α-Hydroxyestrone
11. 2-Methoxyestriol
12. 2-Hydroxyestriol
13. Estriol
14. 16β-Hydroxyestrone
15. Epiestriol
16. 16-Ketoestradiol-17β

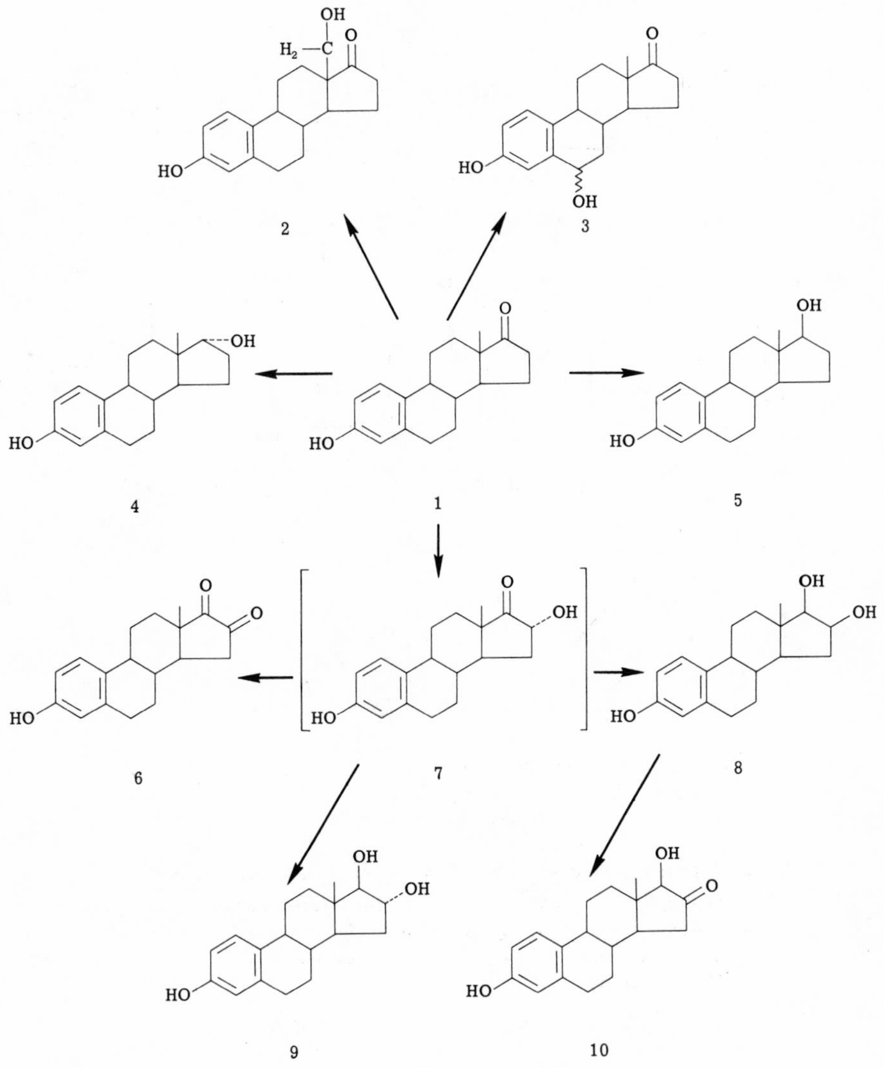

FIG. 2. Estrone metabolites (*in vivo* and *in vitro* experiments combined).

1. Estrone
2. 18-Hydroxyestrone
3. 6ξ-Hydroxyestrone
4. Estradiol-17α
5. Estradiol-17β
6. 16-Ketoestrone
7. 16α-Hydroxyestrone
8. Epiestriol
9. Estriol
10. 16-Ketoestradiol-17β

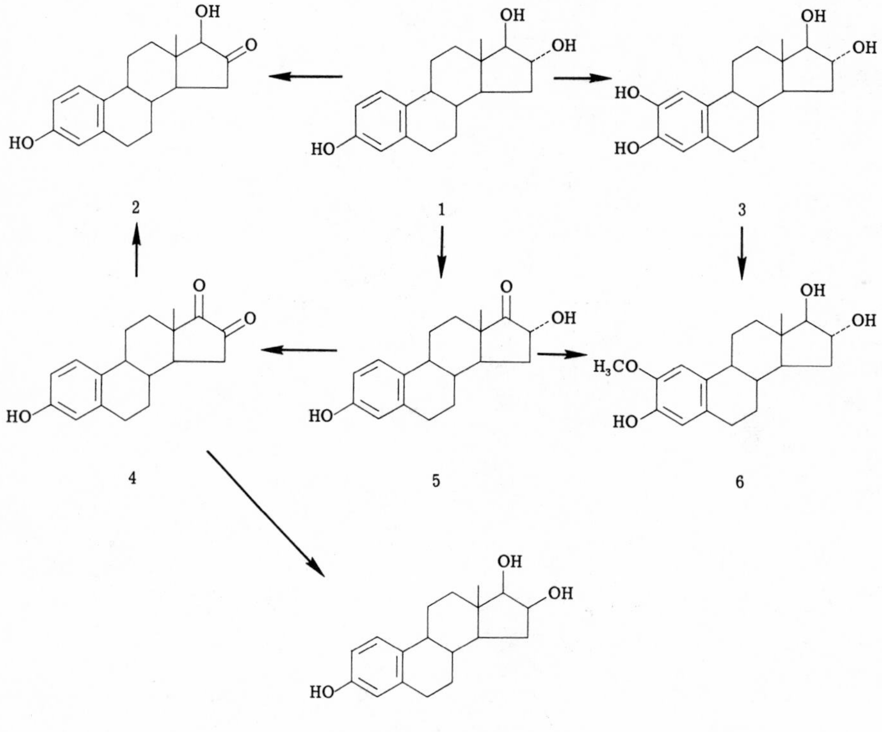

FIG. 3. Estriol metabolites (*in vivo* and *in vitro* experiments combined).

1. Estriol
2. 16-Ketoestradiol-17β
3. 2-Hydroxyestriol
4. 16-Ketoestrone
5. 16α-Hydroxyestrone
6. 2-Methoxyestriol
7. Epiestriol

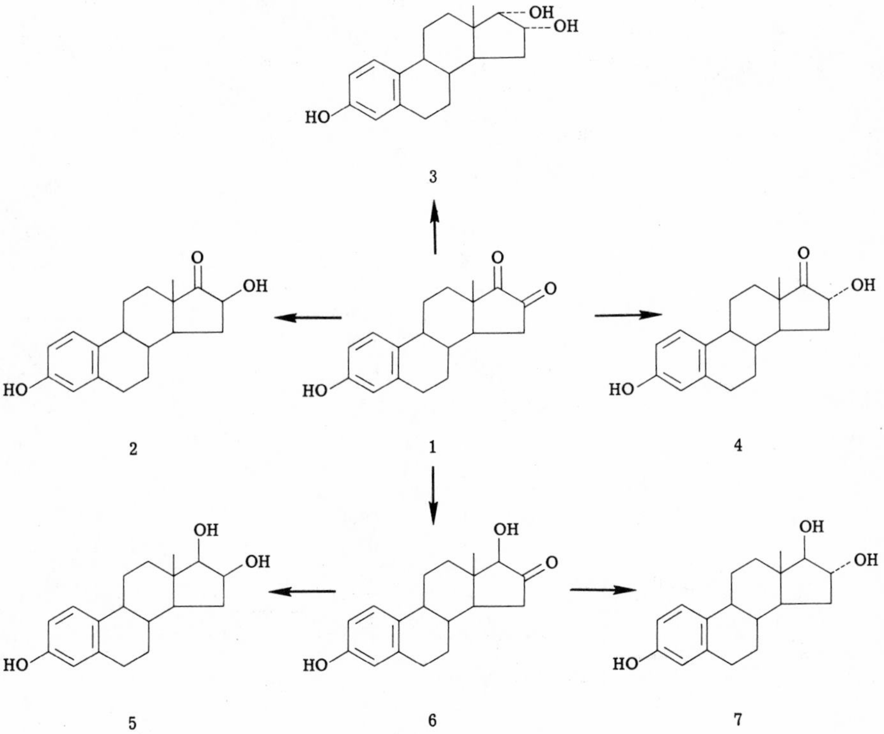

FIG. 4. 16-Ketoestrone metabolites (*in vivo* and *in vitro* experiments combined).

1. 16-Ketoestrone
2. 16β-Hydroxyestrone
3. 17-Epiestriol
4. 16α-Hydroxyestrone
5. 16-Epiestriol
6. 16-Ketoestradiol-17β
7. Estriol

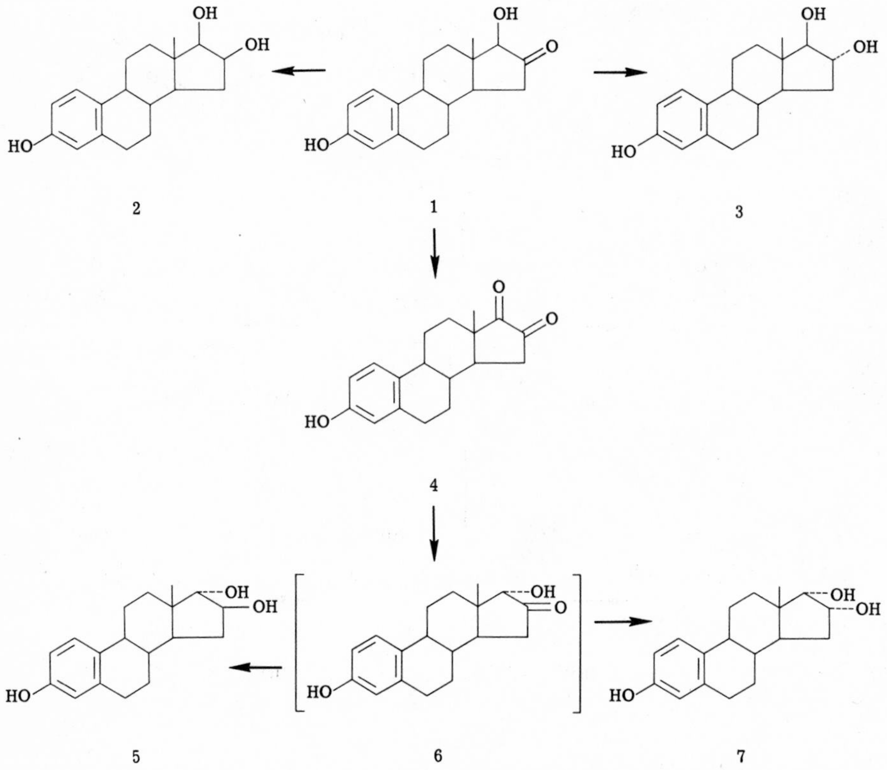

OH
OH
OH
O
OH
OH
HO
HO
HO
2
1
3
O
O
HO
4
OH
OH
OH
O
OH
OH
HO
HO
HO
5
6
7

FIG. 5. 16-Ketoestradiol-17β metabolites (*in vivo* and *in vitro* experiments combined).

1. 16-Ketoestradiol-17β
2. Epiestriol
3. Estriol
4. 16-Ketoestrone
5. 16,17-Epiestriol
6. 16-Ketoestradiol-17α
7. 17-Epiestriol

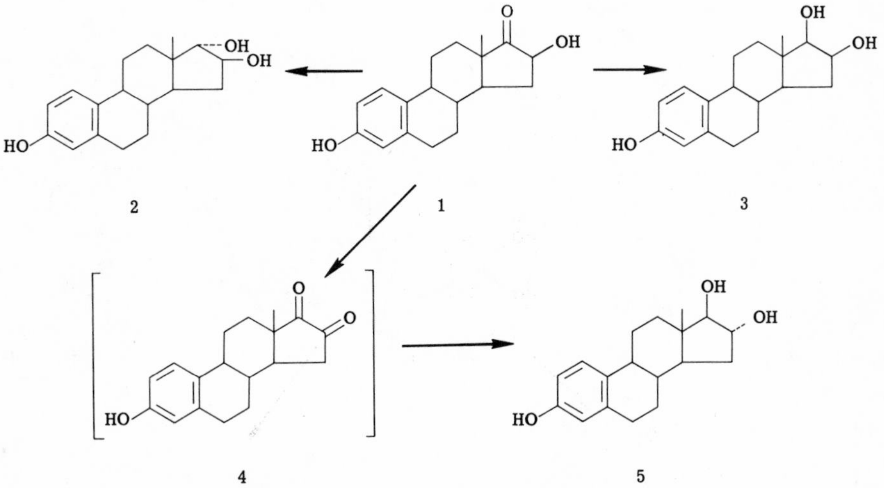

FIG. 6. 16β-Hydroxyestrone (*in vivo* and *in vitro* experiments combined).

1. 16β-Hydroxyestrone
2. 16,17-Epiestriol
3. 16-Epiestriol
4. 16-Ketoestrone
5. Estriol

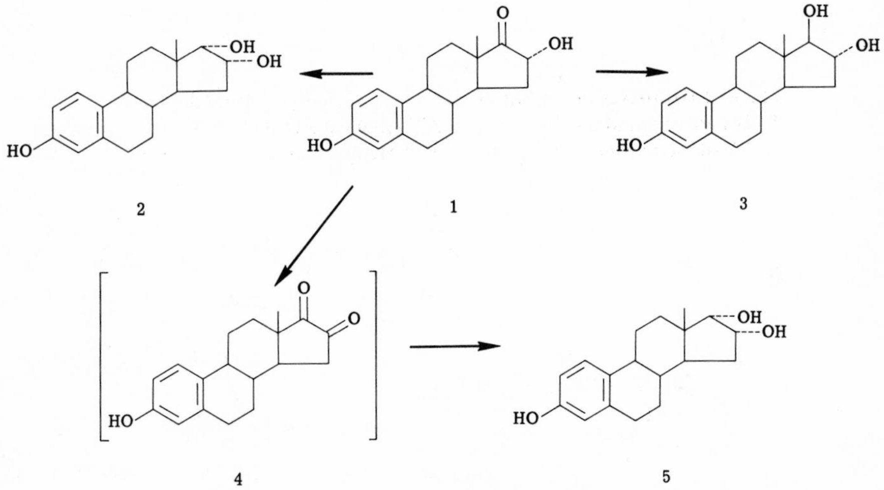

FIG. 7. 16α-Hydroxyestrone (*in vivo* and *in vitro* experiments combined).

1. 16α-Hydroxyestrone
2. 17-Epiestriol
3. Estriol
4. 16-Ketoestrone
5. 17-Epiestriol

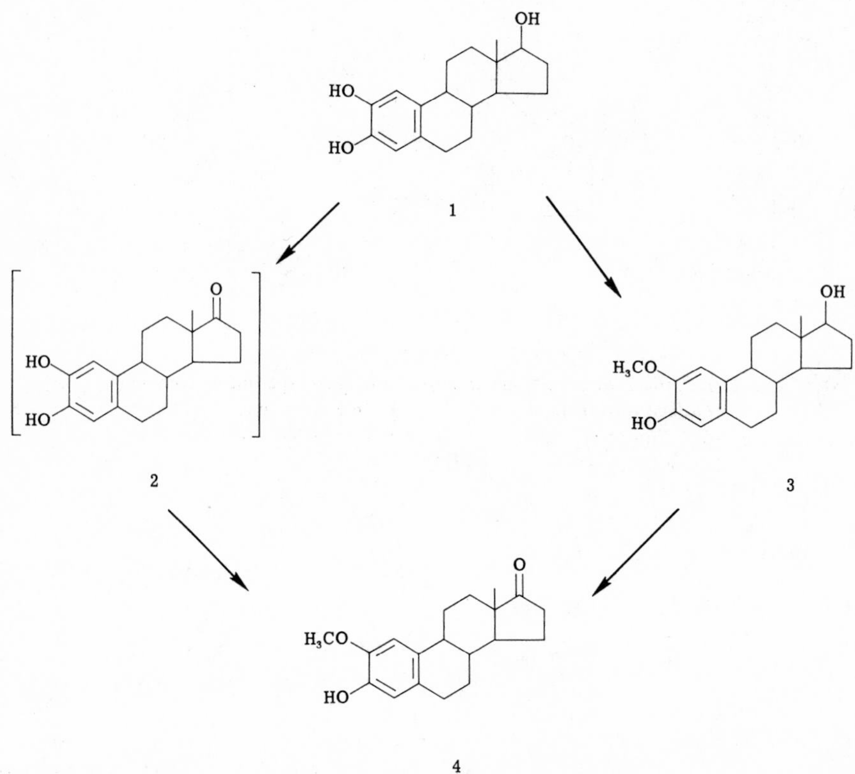

FIG. 8. 2-Hydroxyestradiol-17β (*in vivo* and *in vitro* experiments combined).

1. 2-Hydroxyestradiol-17β
2. 2-Hydroxyestrone
3. 2-Methoxyestradiol-17β
4. 2-Methoxyestrone

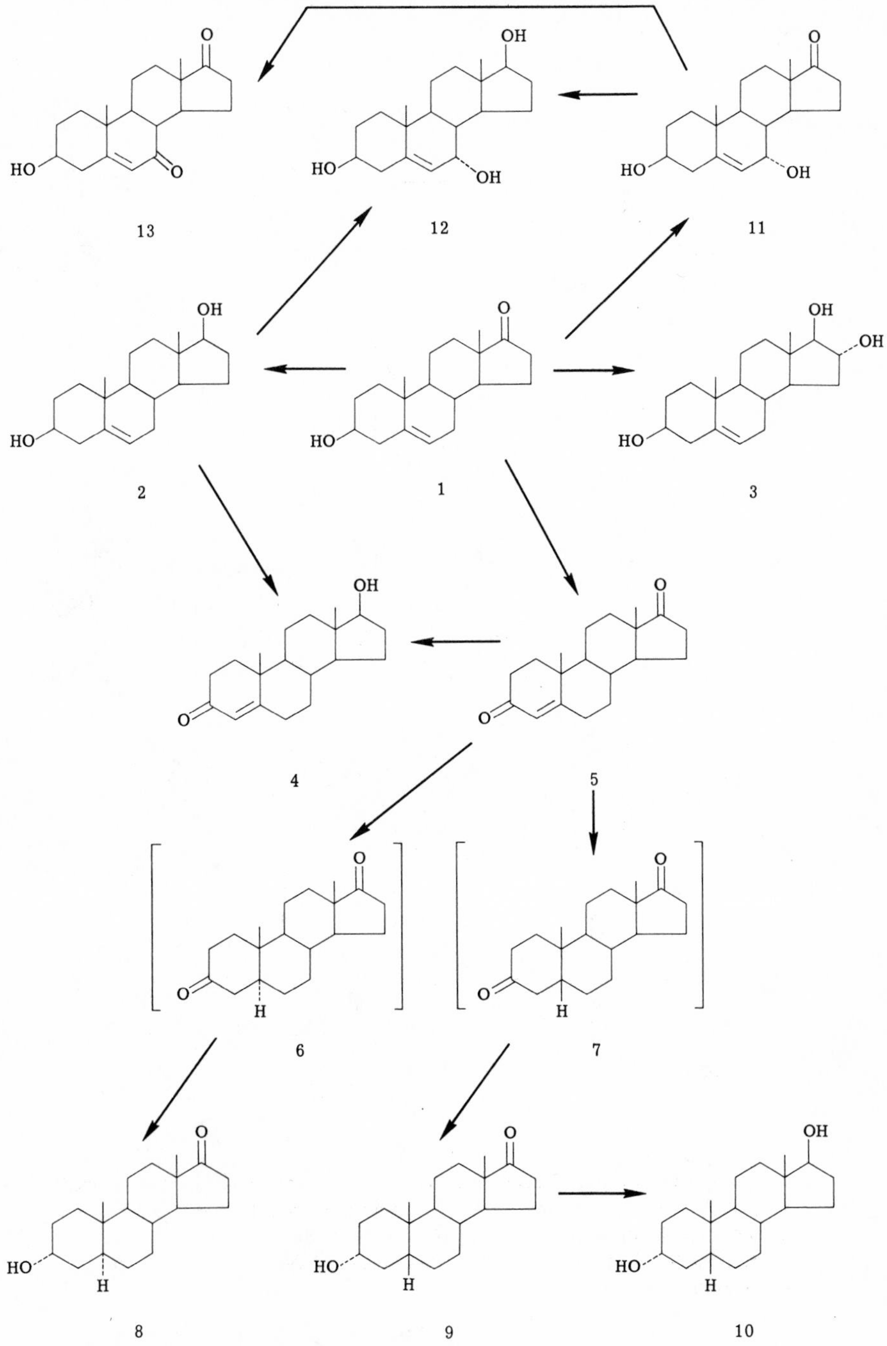

FIG. 9. Dehydroepiandrosterone metabolites (*in vivo* and *in vitro* experiments combined).

1. Dehydroepiandrosterone
2. Androst-5-ene-3β,17β-diol
3. Androst-5-ene-3β,16α,17β-triol
4. Testosterone
5. Androst-4-ene-3,17-dione
6. 5α-Androstane-3,17-dione
7. 5β-Androstane-3,17-dione
8. Androsterone
9. Etiocholanolone
10. 5β-Androstane-3α,17β-diol
11. 3β,7α-Dihydroxyandrost-5-en-17-one
12. Androst-5-ene-3β,7α,17β-triol
13. 3β-Hydroxyandrost-5-ene-7,17-dione

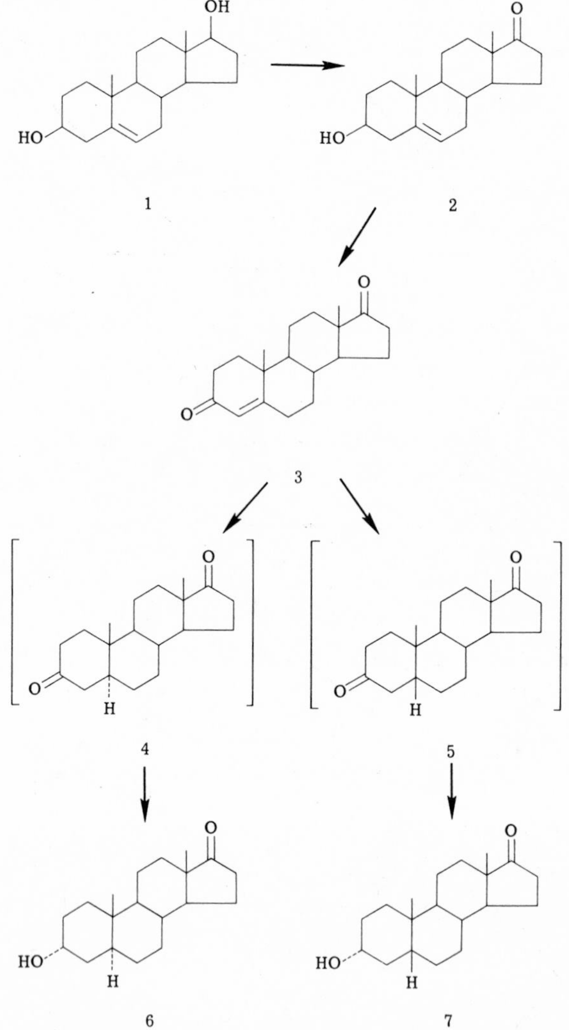

FIG. 10. Androst-5-ene-3β,17β-diol metabolites (*in vivo* and *in vitro* experiments combined).

1. Androst-5-ene-3β,17β-diol
2. Dehydroepiandrosterone
3. Androst-4-ene-3,17-dione
4. 5α-Androstane-3,17-dione
5. 5β-Androstane-3,17-dione
6. Androsterone
7. Etiocholanolone

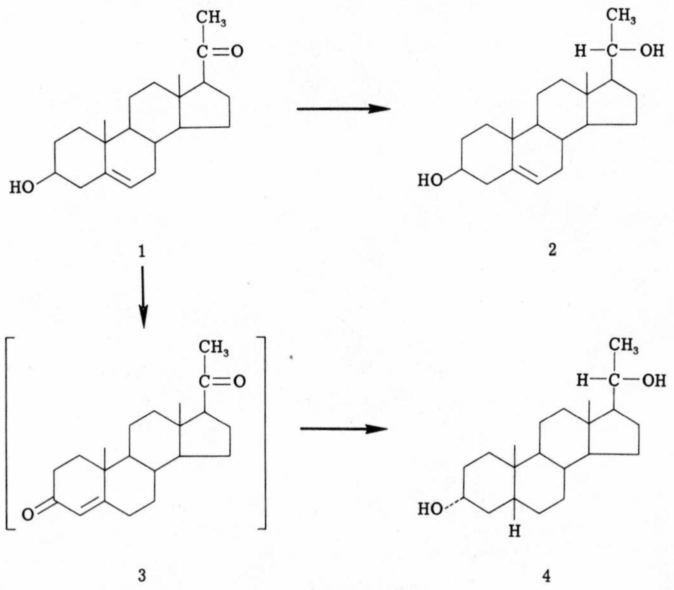

FIG. 11. Pregnenolone metabolites (*in vivo* and *in vitro* experiments combined).

1. Pregnenolone
2. Pregn-5-ene-3β,20α-diol
3. Progesterone
4. Pregnanediol

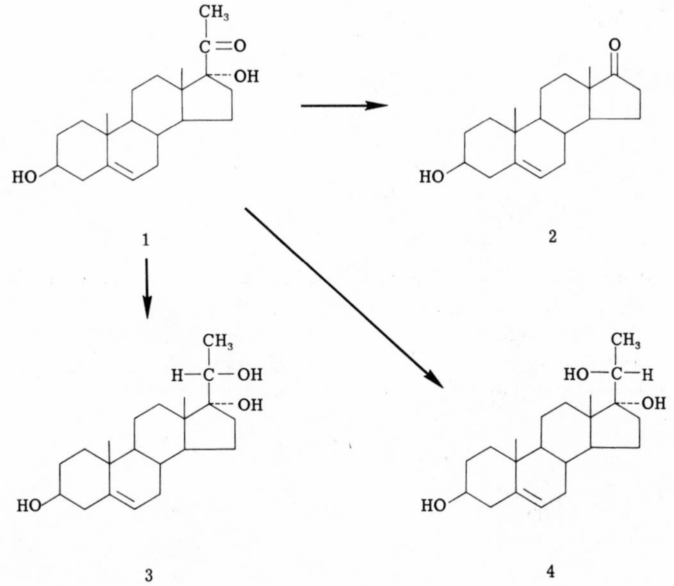

FIG. 12. 17α-Hydroxypregnenolone metabolites (*in vivo* and *in vitro* experiments combined).

1. 17α-Hydroxypregnenolone
2. Dehydroepiandrosterone
3. Pregn-5-ene-3β,17α,20α-triol
4. Pregn-5-ene-3β,17α,20β-triol

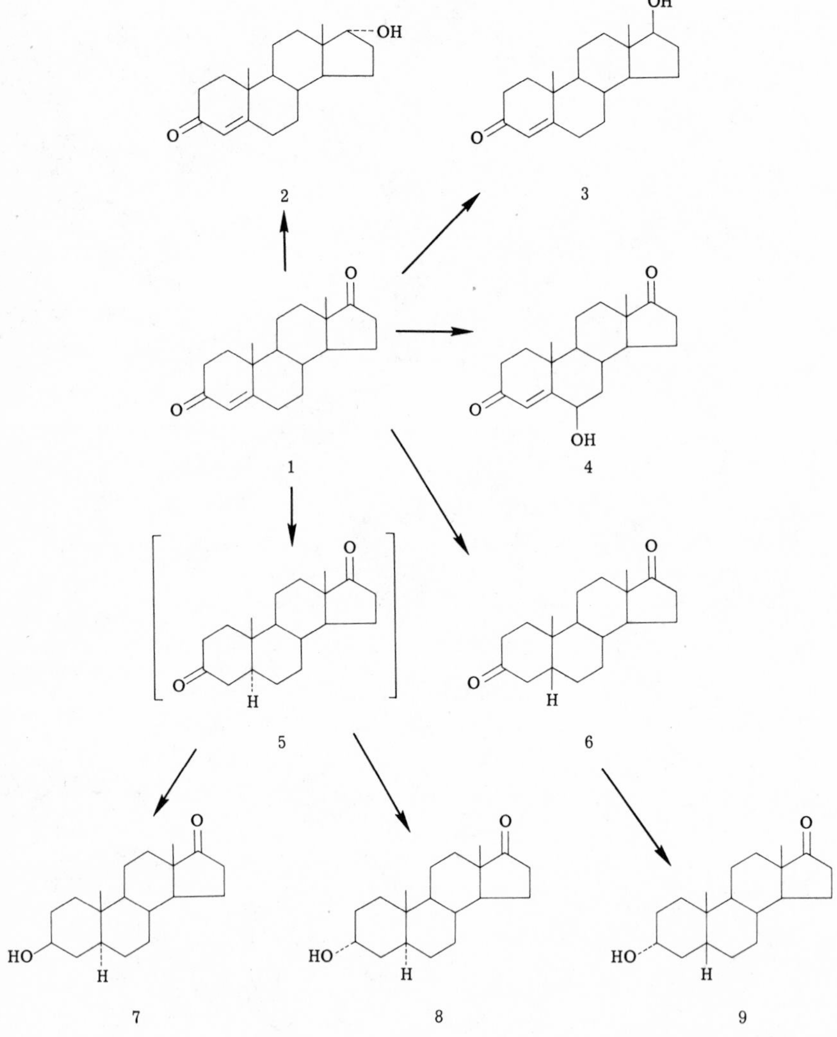

FIG. 13. Androst-4-ene-3,17-dione metabolites (*in vivo* and *in vitro* experiments combined).

1. Androst-4-ene-3,17-dione
2. Epitestosterone
3. Testosterone
4. 6β-Hydroxyandrost-4-ene-3,17-dione
5. 5α-Androstane-3,17-dione
6. 5β-Androstane-3,17-dione
7. Epiandrosterone
8. Androsterone
9. Etiocholanolone

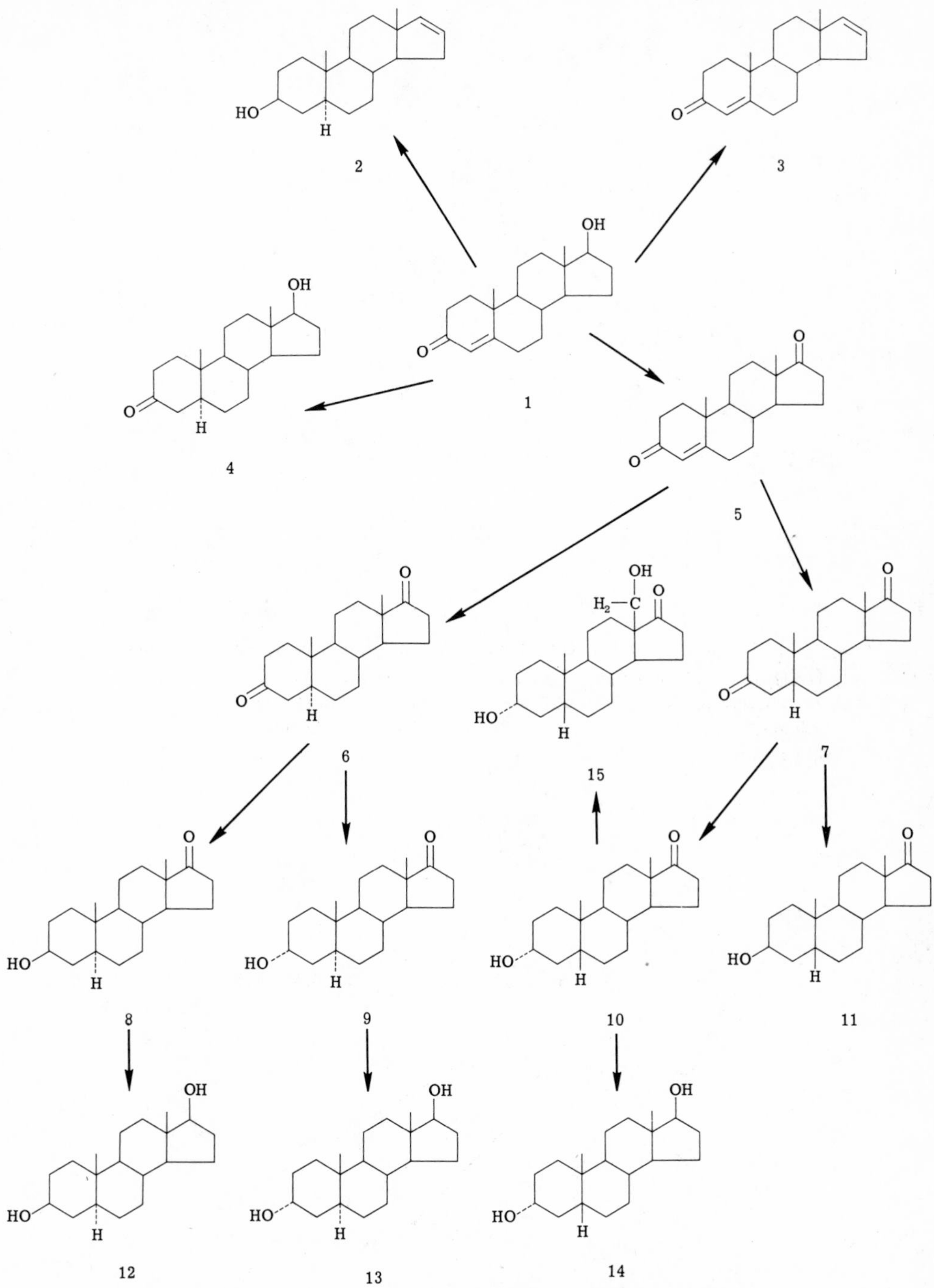

FIG. 14. Testosterone metabolites (*in vivo* and *in vitro* experiments combined).

1. Testosterone
2. 5α-Androst-16-en-3β-ol
3. Androsta-4,16-dien-3-one
4. 17β-Hydroxy-5α-androstan-3-one
5. Androst-4-ene-3,17-dione
6. 5α-Androstane-3,17-dione
7. 5β-Androstane-3,17-dione
8. Epiandrosterone
9. Androsterone
10. Etiocholanolone
11. 3β-Hydroxy-5β-androstan-17-one
12. 5α-Androstane-3β,17β-diol
13. 5α-Androstane-3α,17β-diol
14. 5β-Androstane-3α,17β-diol
15. 3α,18-Dihydroxy-5β-androstan-17-one

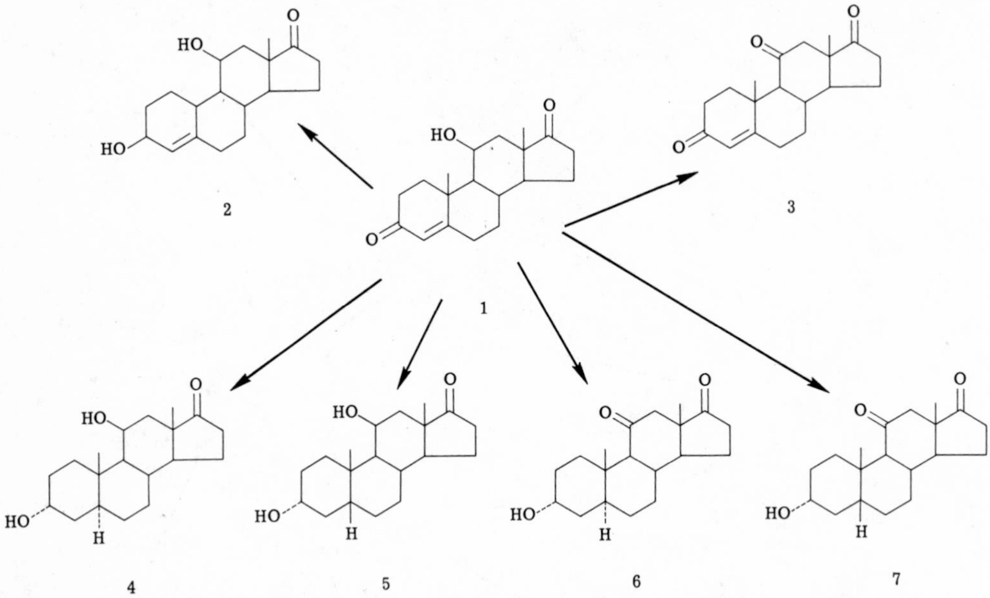

FIG. 15. 11β-Hydroxyandrost-4-ene-3,17-dione (*in vivo* and *in vitro* experiments combined).

1. 11β-Hydroxyandrost-4-ene-3,17-dione
2. 3β,11β-Dihydroxyandrost-4-en-17-one
3. Adrenosterone
4. 11β-Hydroxyandrosterone
5. 11β-Hydroxyetiocholanolone
6. 11-Ketoandrosterone
7. 11-Ketoetiocholanolone

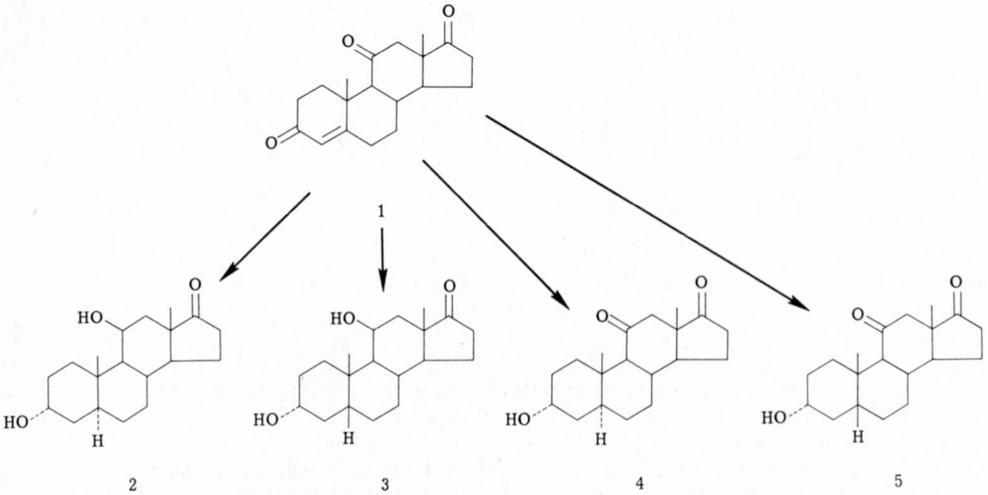

FIG. 16. Adrenosterone metabolites (*in vivo* and *in vitro* experiments combined).

1. Andrenosterone
2. 11β-Hydroxyandrosterone
3. 11β-Hydroxyetiocholanolone
4. 11-Ketoandrosterone
5. 11-Ketoetiocholanolone

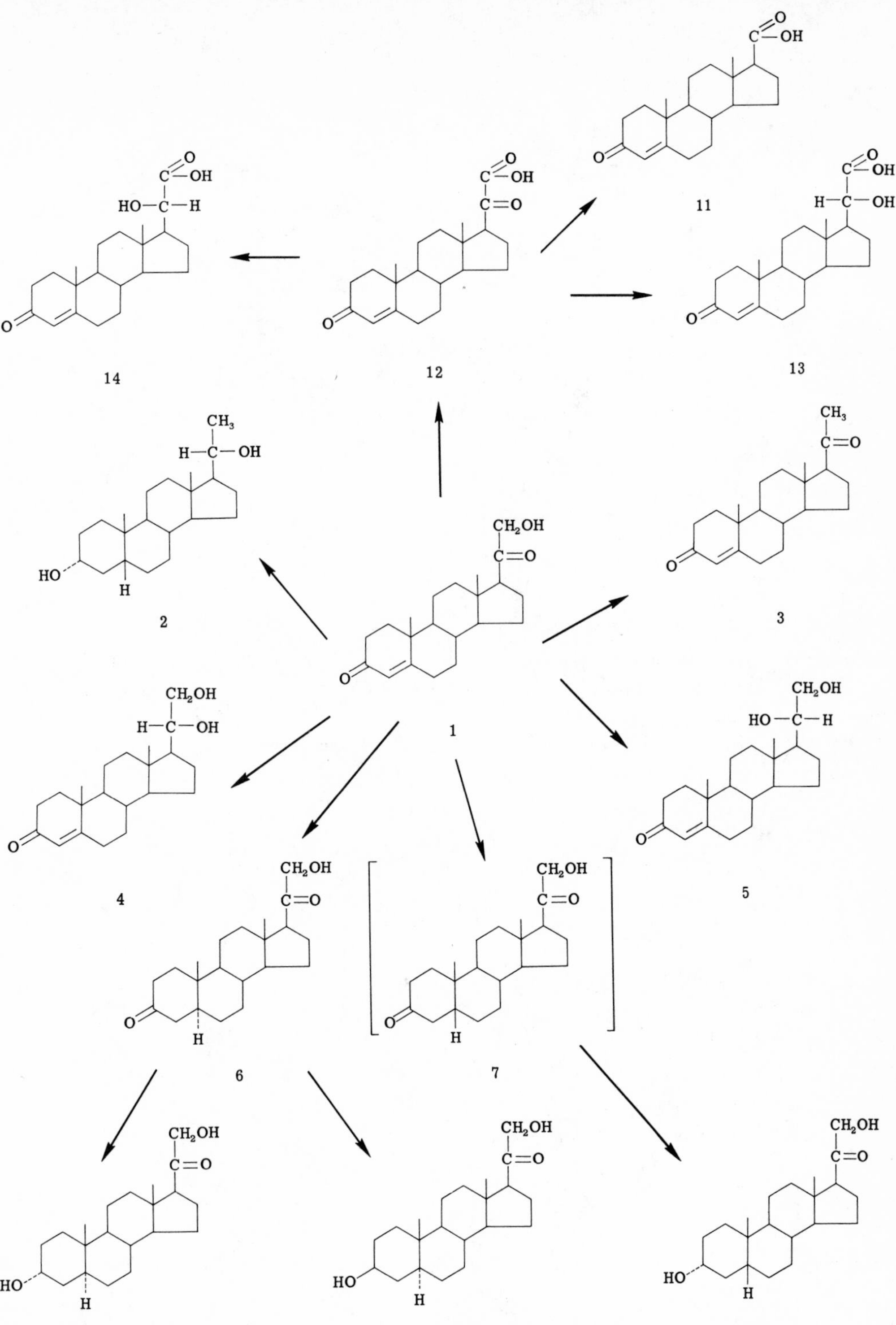

FIG. 17. Deoxycorticosterone metabolites (*in vivo* and *in vitro* experiments combined).

1. Deoxycorticosterone
2. Pregnanediol
3. Progesterone
4. 20α,21-Dihydroxypregn-4-en-3-one
5. 20β,21-Dihydroxypregn-4-en-3-one
6. 21-Hydroxy-5α-pregnane-3,20-dione
7. 21-Hydroxy-5β-pregnane-3,20-dione
8. 3α,21-Dihydroxy-5α-pregnan-20-one
9. 3β,21-Dihydroxy-5α-pregnan-20-one
10. 3α,21-Dihydroxy-5β-pregnan-20-one
11. 3-Keto-4-etienic acid
12. 3,20-Diketopregn-4-en-21-oic acid
13. 20α-Hydroxy-3-ketopregn-4-en-21-oic acid
14. 20β-Hydroxy-3-ketopregn-4-en-21-oic acid

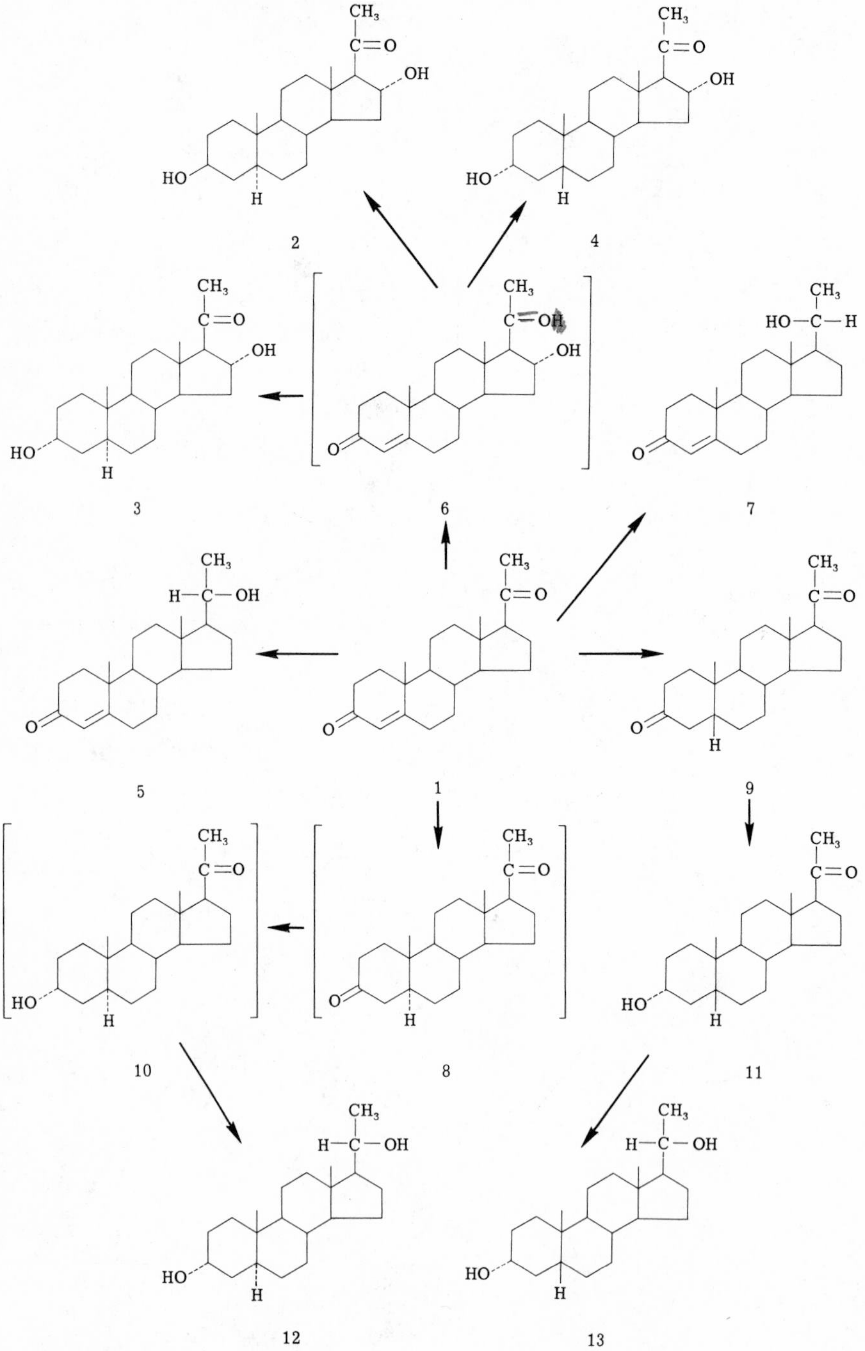

FIG. 18. Progesterone metabolites (*in vivo* and *in vitro* experiments combined).

1. Progesterone
2. 3β,16α-Dihydroxy-5α-pregnan-20-one
3. 3α,16α-Dihydroxy-5α-pregnan-20-one
4. 3α,16α-Dihydroxy-5β-pregnan-20-one
5. 20α-Hydroxypregn-4-en-3-one
6. 16α-Hydroxypregn-4-ene-3,20-dione
7. 20β-Hydroxypregn-4-en-3-one
8. 5α-Pregnane-3,20-dione
9. 5β-Pregnane-3,20-dione
10. 3α-Hydroxy-5α-pregnan-20-one
11. 3α-Hydroxy-5β-pregnan-20-one
12. 5α-Pregnane-3α,20α-diol
13. Pregnanediol

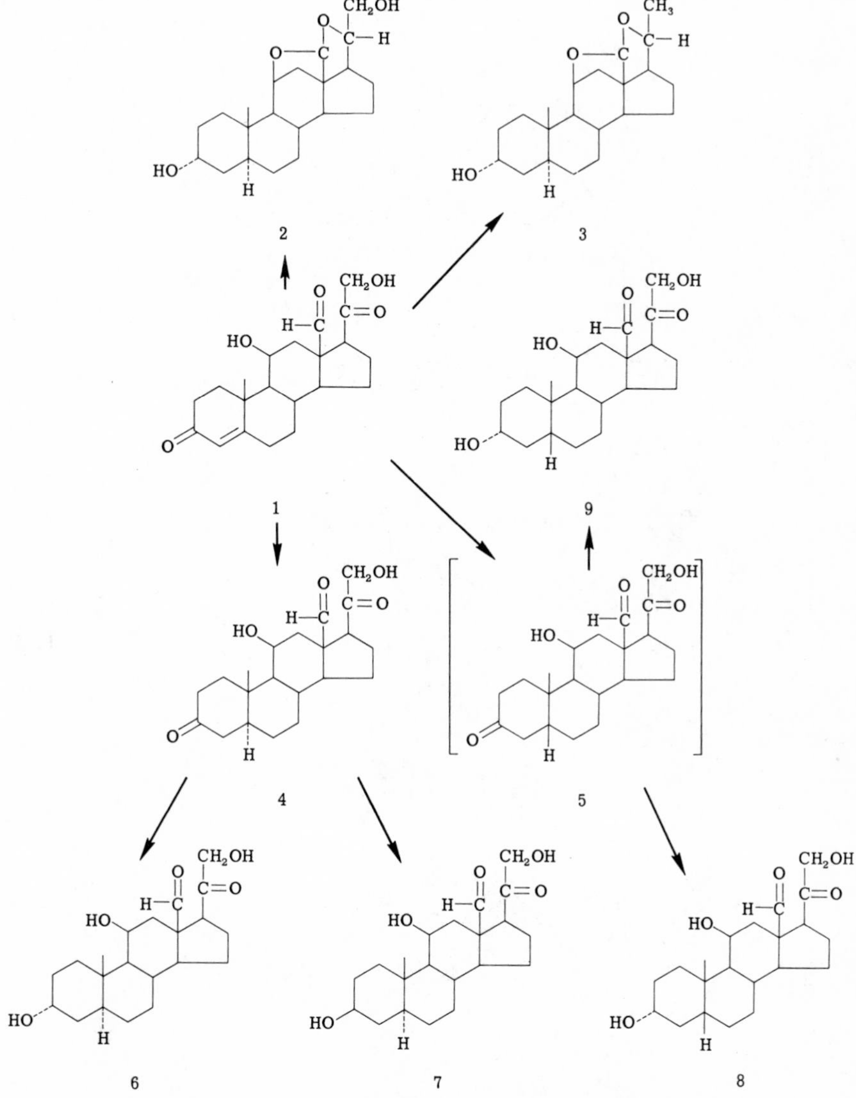

FIG. 19. Aldosterone metabolites (*in vivo* and *in vitro* experiments combined).

1. Aldosterone
2. 3α,21-Dihydroxy-5α-pregnane-(11β-18), (18-20) dioxide
3. 3α-Hydroxy-5α-pregnane-(11β-18), (18-20) dioxide
4. 11β,21-Dihydroxy-3-oxo-5α-pregnan-18-al
5. 11β,21-Dihydroxy-3-one-5β-pregnan-18-al
6. 3α,11β,21-Trihydroxy-5α-pregnan-18-al
7. 3β,11β,21-Trihydroxy-5α-pregnan-18-al
8. 3α,11β,21-Trihydroxy-5β-pregnan-18-al
9. 3β,11β,21-Trihydroxy-5β-pregnan-18-al

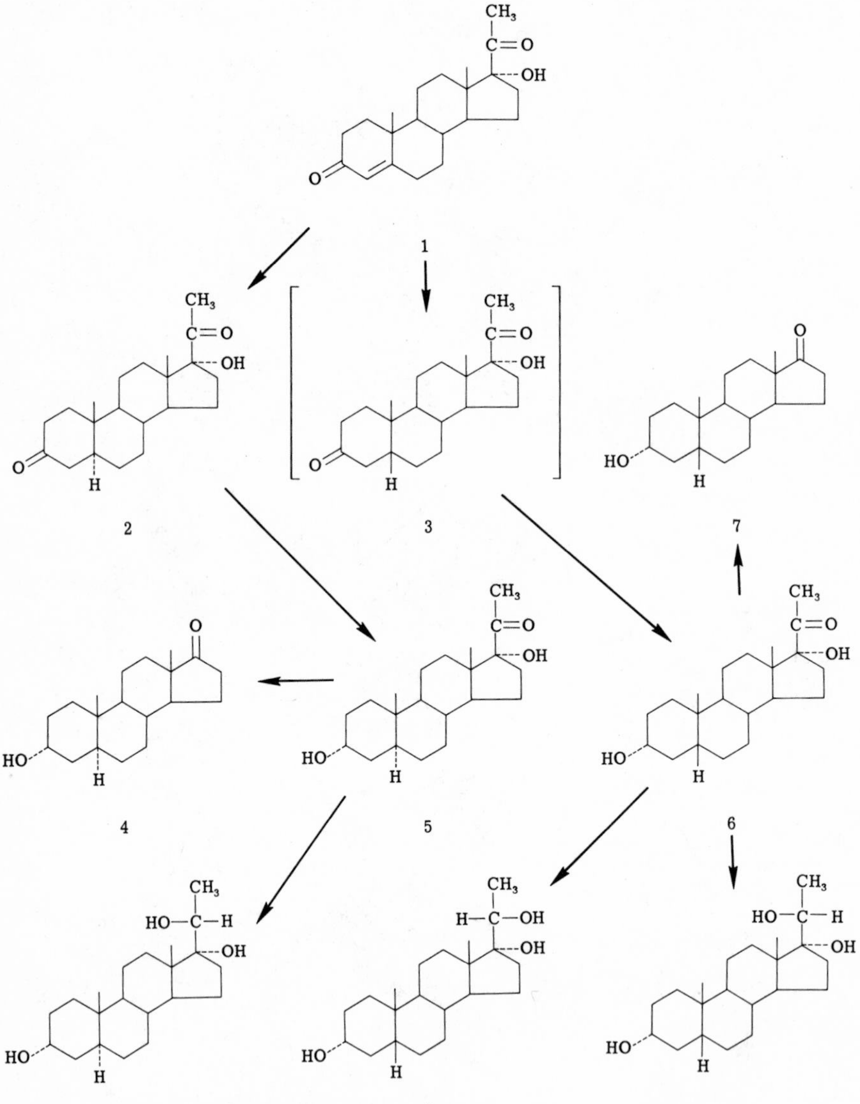

CH_3 C=O OH O 1
CH_3 C=O OH O H 2
CH_3 C=O OH O H 3
O HO H 7
O HO H 4
CH_3 C=O OH HO H 5
CH_3 C=O OH HO H 6
CH_3 HO—C—H OH HO H 8
CH_3 H—C—OH OH HO H 9
CH_3 HO—C—H OH HO H 10

FIG. 20. 17α-Hydroxyprogesterone (*in vivo* and *in vitro* experiments combined).

1. 17α-Hydroxyprogesterone
2. 17α-Hydroxy-5α-pregnane-3,20-dione
3. 17α-Hydroxy-5β-pregnane-3,20-dione
4. Androsterone
5. 3α,17α-Dihydroxy-5α-pregnan-20-one
6. 3α,17α-Dihydroxy-5β-pregnan-20-one
7. Etiocholanolone
8. 5α-Pregnane-3α,17α,20β-triol
9. 5β-Pregnane-3α,17α,20α-triol
10. 5β-Pregnane-3α,17α,20β-triol

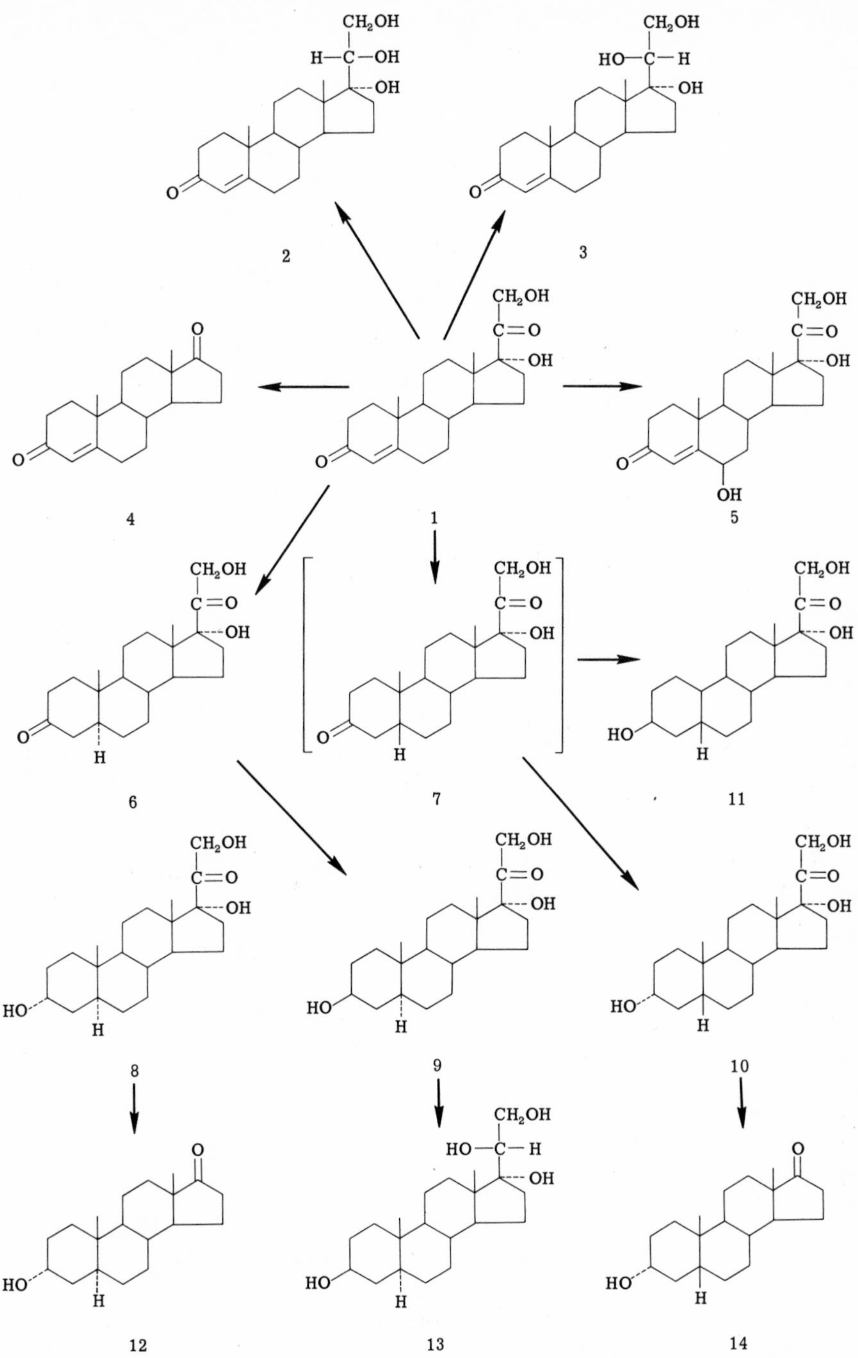

FIG. 21. 11-Deoxycortisol metabolites (*in vivo* and *in vitro* experiments combined).

1. 11-Deoxycortisol
2. 17α,20α,21-Trihydroxypregn-4-en-3-one
3. 17α,20β,21-Trihydroxypregn-4-en-3-one
4. Androst-4-ene-3,17-dione
5. 6β,17α,21-Trihydroxypregn-4-ene-3,20-dione
6. 17α,21-Dihydroxy-5α-pregnane-3,20-dione
7. 17α,21-Dihydroxy-5β-pregnane-3,20-dione
8. 3α,17α,21-Trihydroxy-5α-pregnan-20-one
9. 3β,17α,21-Trihydroxy-5α-pregnan-20-one
10. 3α,17α,21-Trihydroxy-5β-pregnan-20-one
11. 3β,17α,21-Trihydroxy-5β-pregnan-20-one
12. Androsterone
13. 5α-Pregnane-3β,17α,20β,21-tetrol
14. Etiocholanolone

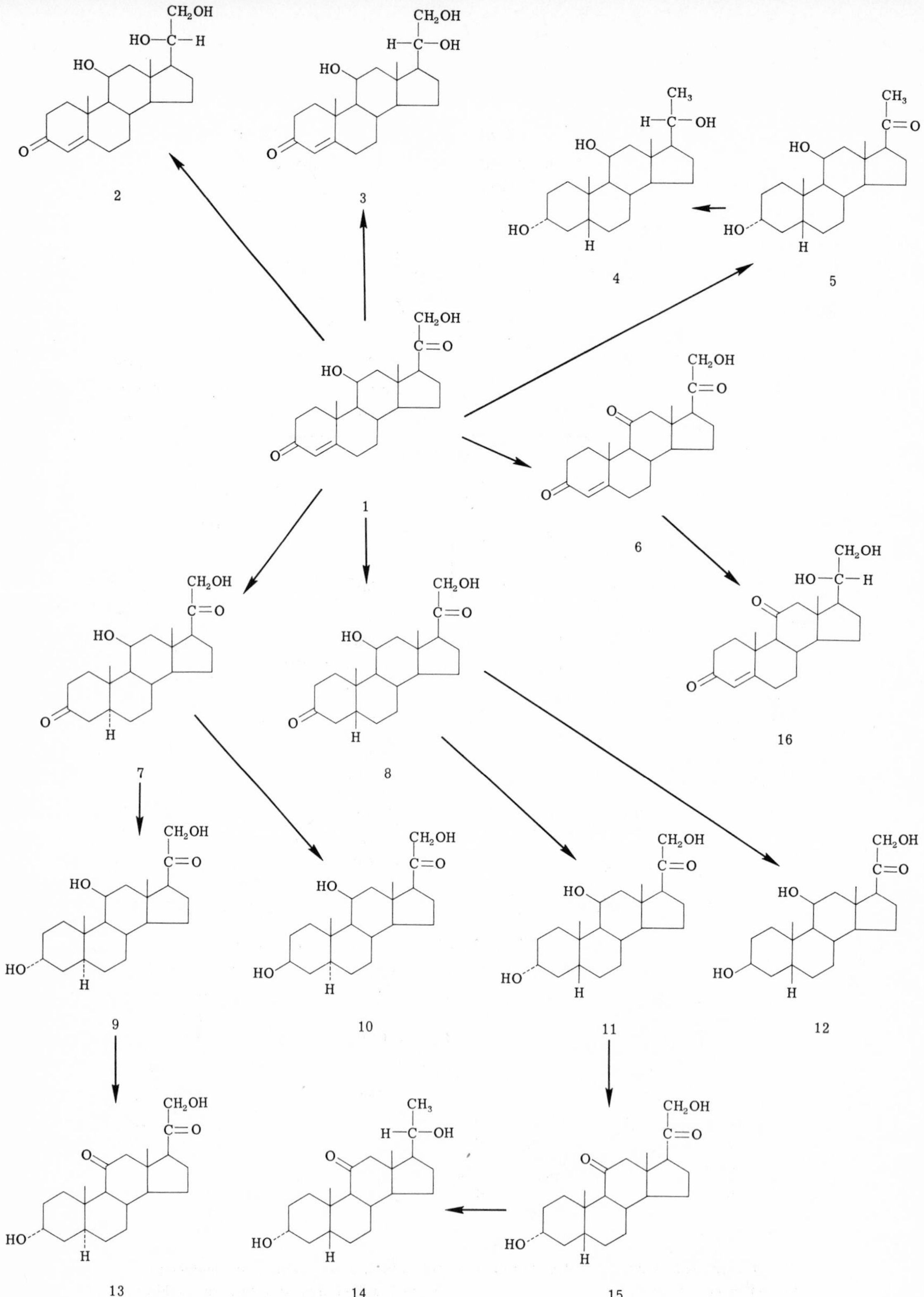

FIG. 22. Corticosterone metabolites (*in vivo* and *in vitro* experiments combined).

1. Corticosterone
2. 11β,20β,21-Trihydroxypregn-4-en-3-one
3. 11β,20α,21-Trihydroxypregn-4-en-3-one
4. 5β-Pregnane-3α,11β,20α-triol
5. 3α,11β-Dihydroxy-5β-pregnan-20-one
6. 21-Hydroxypregn-4-ene-3,11,20-trione
7. 11β,21-Dihydroxy-5α-pregnane-3,20-dione
8. 11β,21-Dihydroxy-5β-pregnane-3,20-dione
9. 3α,11β,21-Trihydroxy-5α-pregnan-20-one
10. 3β,11β,21-Trihydroxy-5α-pregnan-20-one
11. 3α,11β,21-Trihydroxy-5β-pregnan-20-one
12. 3β,11β,21-Trihydroxy-5β-pregnan-20-one
13. 3α,21-Dihydroxy-5α-pregnane-11,20-dione
14. 3α,20α-Dihydroxy-5β-pregnan-11-one
15. 3α,21-Dihydroxy-5β-pregnane-11,20-dione
16. 20β,21-Dihydroxypregn-4-ene-3,11-dione

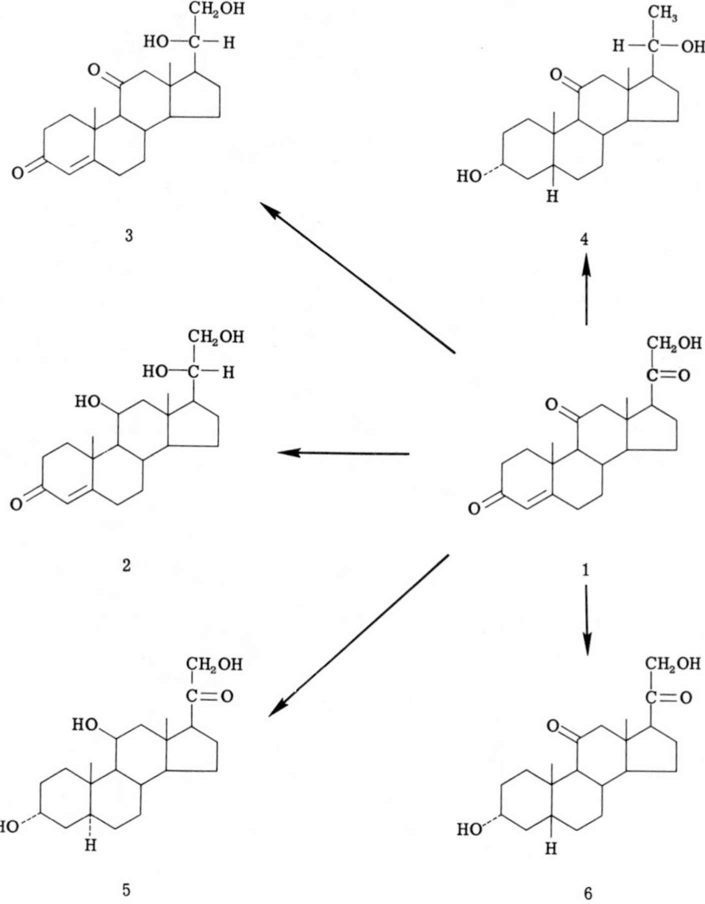

FIG. 23. 11-Dehydrocorticosterone metabolites (*in vivo* and *in vitro* experiments combined).

1. 11-Dehydrocorticosterone
2. 11β,20β,21-Trihydroxypregn-4-en-3-one
3. 20β,21-Dihydroxypregn-4-ene-3,11-dione
4. 3α,20α-Dihydroxy-5β-pregnan-11-one
5. 3α,11β,21-Trihydroxy-5α-pregnan-20-one
6. 3α,21-Dihydroxy-5β-pregnane-11,20-dione

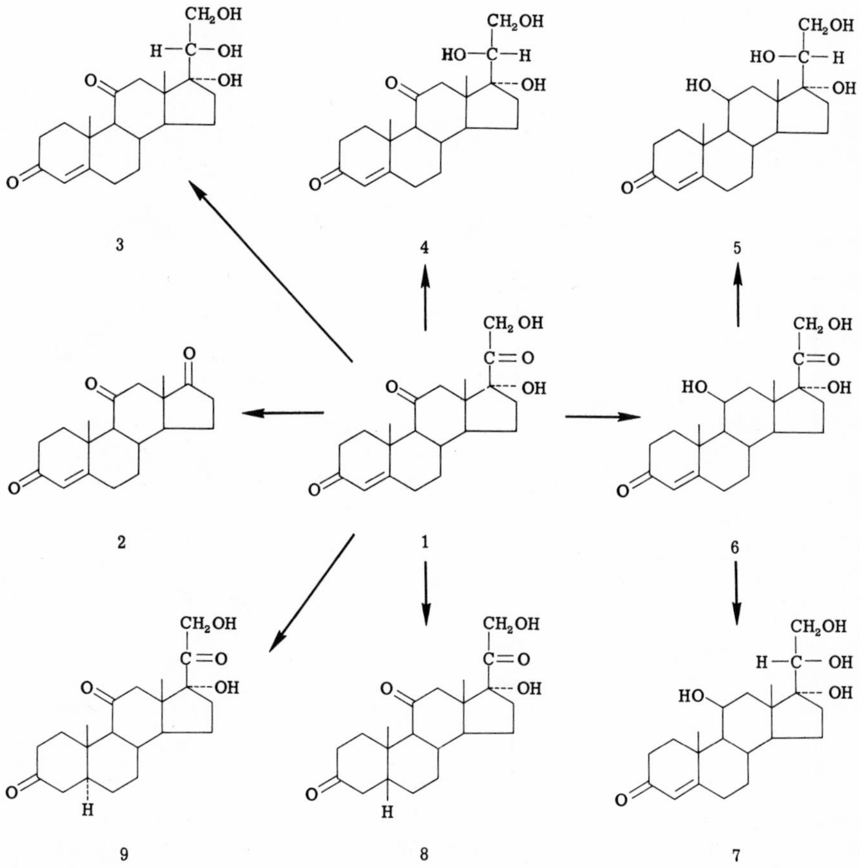

FIG. 24. 3-Keto metabolites of cortisone (*in vivo* and *in vitro* experiments combined).

1. Cortisone
2. Adrenosterone
3. 17α,20α,21-Trihydroxypregn-4-ene-3,11-dione
4. 17α,20β,21-Trihydroxypregn-4-ene-3,11-dione
5. 11β,17α,20β,21-Tetrahydroxypregn-4-en-3-one
6. Cortisol
7. 11β,17β,20α,21-Tetrahydroxypregn-4-en-3-one
8. 17α,21-Dihydroxy-5β-pregnane-3,11,20-trione
9. 17α,21-Dihydroxy-5α-pregnane-3,11,20-trione

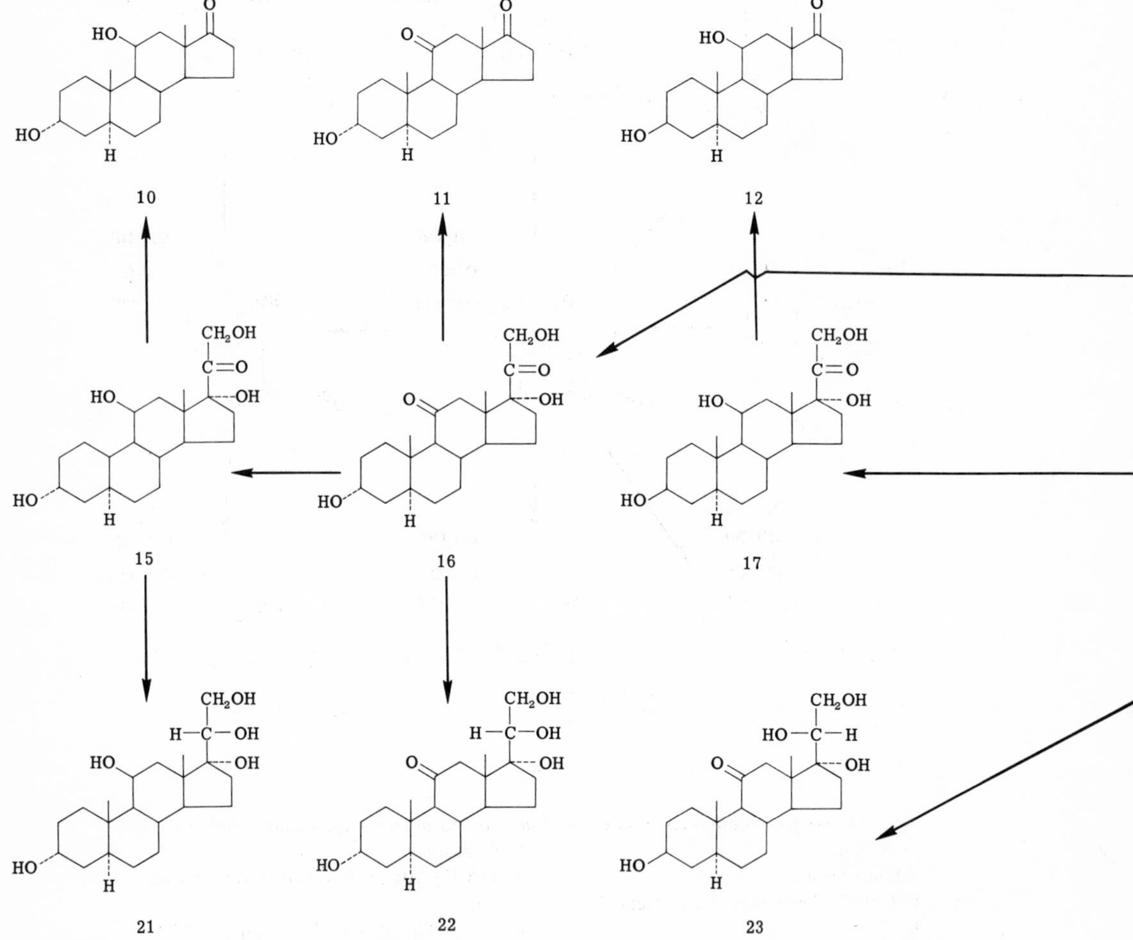

FIG. 25. 3-Hydroxy metabolites of cortisone (*in vivo* and *in vitro* experiments combined). Compounds 8 and 9 are repeated from Fig. 24 for continuity.

8. 17α,21-Dihydroxy-5β-pregnane-3,11, 20-trione
9. 17α,21-Dihydroxy-5α-pregnane-3,11, 20-trione
10. 11β-Hydroxyandrosterone
11. 11-Ketoandrosterone
12. 11β-Hydroxyepiandrosterone
13. 11-Ketoetiocholanolone
14. 11β-Hydroxyetiocholanolone
15. 3α,11β,17α,21-Tetrahydroxy-5α-pregnan-20-one
16. 3α,17α,21-Trihydroxy-5α-pregnane-11,20-dione
17. 3β,11β,17α,21-Tetrahydroxy-5α-pregnan-20-one
18. 3β,17α,21-Trihydroxy-5α-pregnane-11, 20-dione
19. Urocortisone
20. Urocortisol
21. Allocortol
22. Allocortolone
23. 3β,17α,20β,21-Tetrahydroxy-5α-pregnan-11-one
24. Cortolone

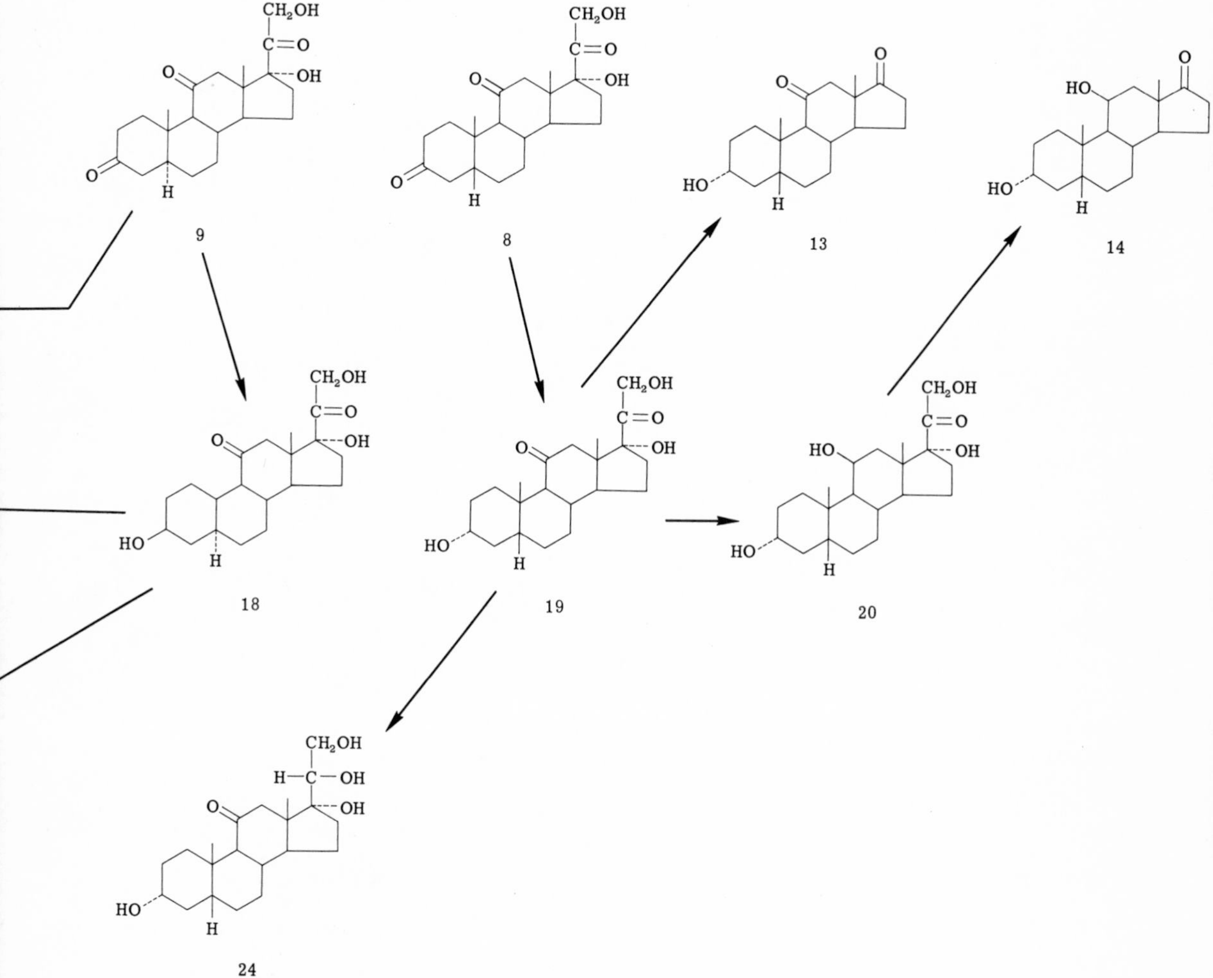

FIG. 25. Continued.

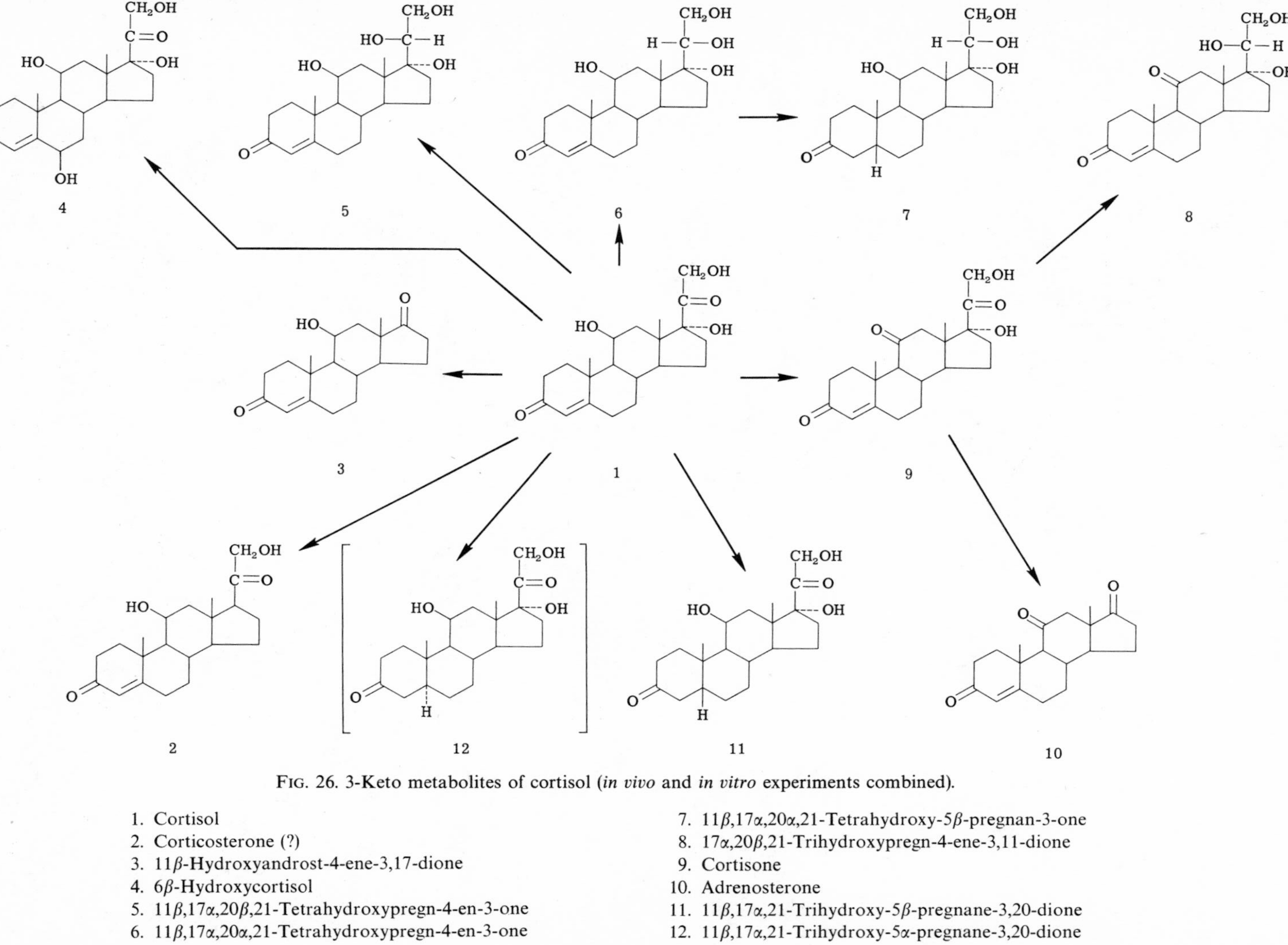

FIG. 26. 3-Keto metabolites of cortisol (*in vivo* and *in vitro* experiments combined).

1. Cortisol
2. Corticosterone (?)
3. 11β-Hydroxyandrost-4-ene-3,17-dione
4. 6β-Hydroxycortisol
5. 11β,17α,20β,21-Tetrahydroxypregn-4-en-3-one
6. 11β,17α,20α,21-Tetrahydroxypregn-4-en-3-one
7. 11β,17α,20α,21-Tetrahydroxy-5β-pregnan-3-one
8. 17α,20β,21-Trihydroxypregn-4-ene-3,11-dione
9. Cortisone
10. Adrenosterone
11. 11β,17α,21-Trihydroxy-5β-pregnane-3,20-dione
12. 11β,17α,21-Trihydroxy-5α-pregnane-3,20-dione

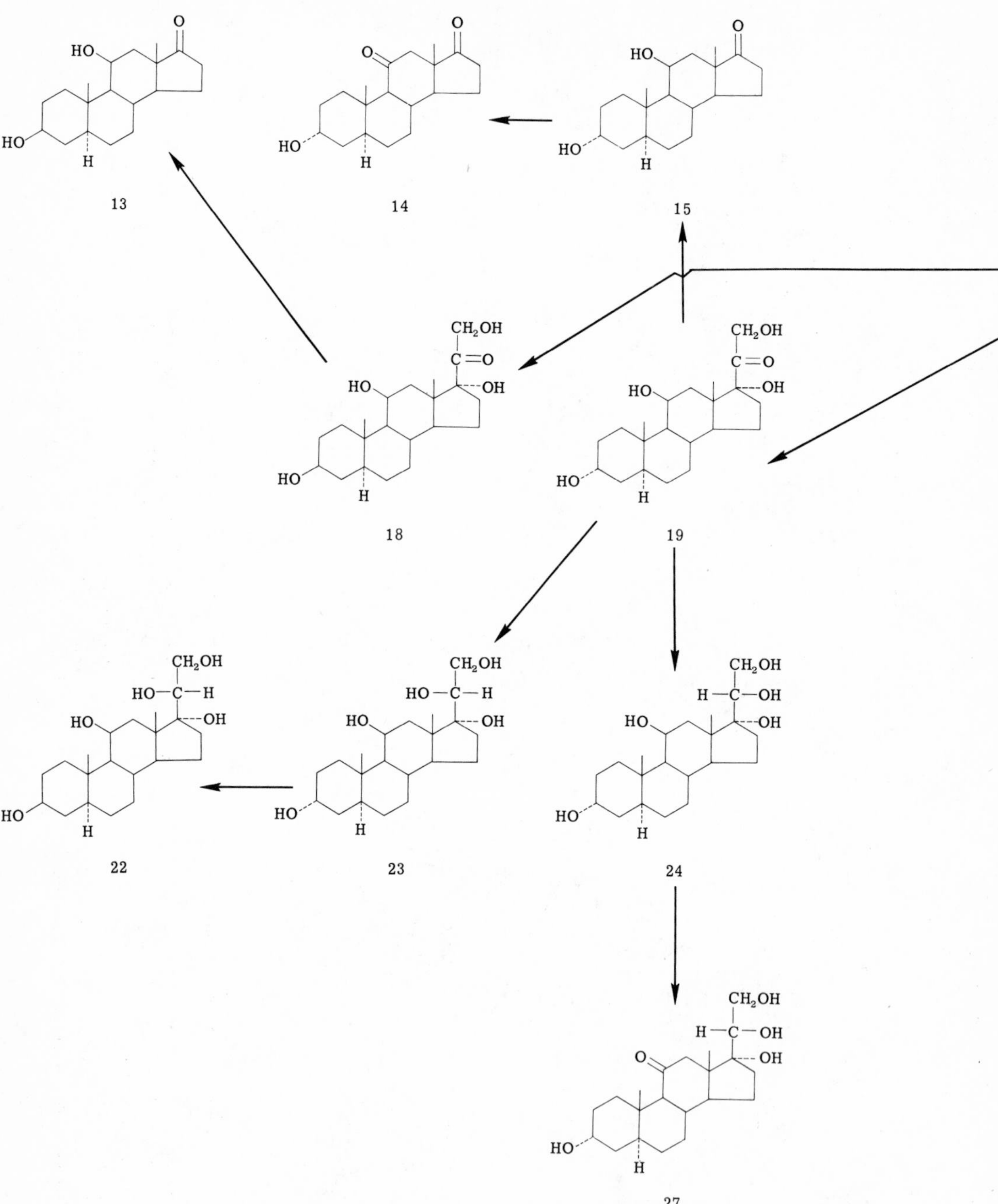

FIG. 27. 3-Hydroxy metabolites of cortisol (*in vivo* and *in vitro* experiments combined). Compounds 11 and 12 are repeated from Fig. 26 for continuity.

11. 11β,17α,21-Trihydroxy-5β-pregnane-3, 20-dione
12. 11β,17α,21-Trihydroxy-5α-pregnane-3, 20-dione
13. 11β-Hydroxyepiandrosterone
14. 11-Ketoandrosterone
15. 11β-Hydroxyandrosterone
16. 11β-Hydroxyetiocholanolone
17. 11-Ketoetiocholanolone
18. 3β,11β,17α,21-Tetrahydroxy-5α-pregnan-20-one
19. 3α,11β,17α,21-Tetrahydroxy-5α-pregnan-20-one

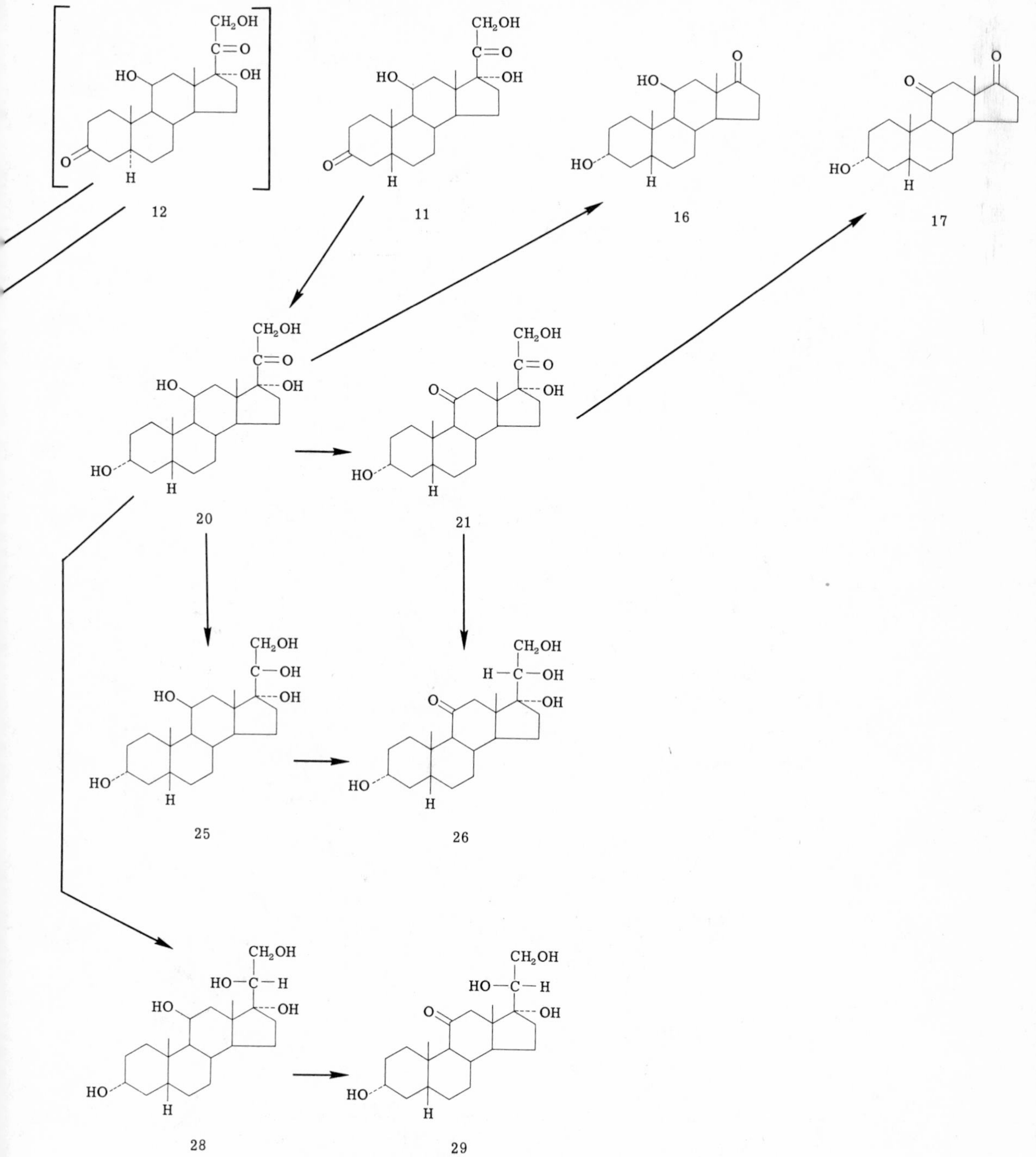

CH$_2$OH
C=O
HO
OH
O
H
12

CH$_2$OH
C=O
HO
OH
O
H
11

O
HO
HO
H
16

O
O
HO
H
17

CH$_2$OH
C=O
HO
OH
HO
H
20

CH$_2$OH
C=O
O
OH
HO
H
21

CH$_2$OH
C—OH
HO
OH
HO
H
25

CH$_2$OH
H—C—OH
O
OH
HO
H
26

CH$_2$OH
HO—C—H
HO
OH
HO
H
28

CH$_2$OH
HO—C—H
O
OH
HO
H
29

FIG. 27. Continued.

20. Urocortisol
21. Urocortisone
22. 5α-Pregnane-3β,11β,17α,20β,21-pentol
23. β-Allocortol
24. Allocortol
25. Cortol
26. Cortolone
27. Allocortolone
28. β-Cortol
29. β-Cortolone

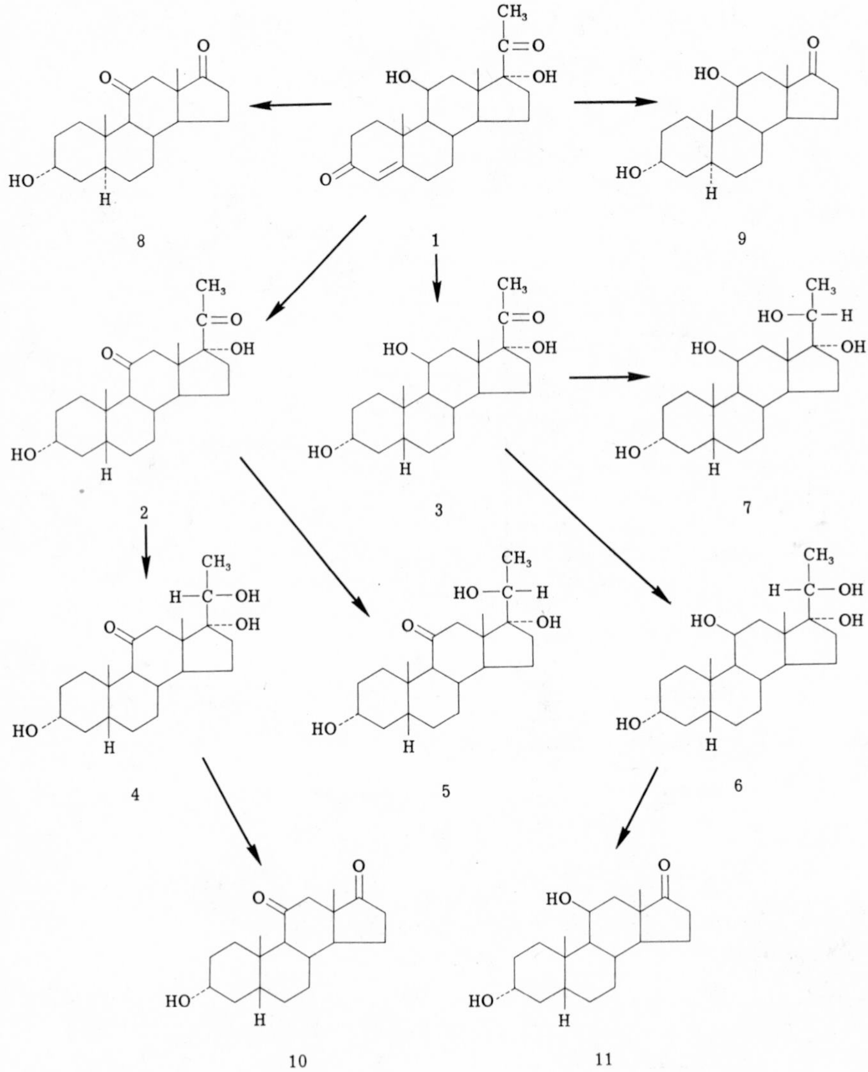

FIG. 28. 21-Deoxycortisol metabolites (*in vivo* and *in vitro* experiments combined).

1. 21-Deoxycortisol
2. $3\alpha,17\alpha$-Dihydroxy-5β-pregnane-11,20-dione
3. $3\alpha,11\beta,17\alpha$-Trihydroxy-5β-pregnan-20-one
4. $3\alpha,17\alpha,20\alpha$-Trihydroxy-$5\beta$-pregnan-11-one
5. $3\alpha,17\alpha,20\beta$-Trihydroxy-5β-pregnan-11-one
6. 5β-Pregnane-$3\alpha,11\beta,17\alpha,20\alpha$-tetrol
7. 5β-Pregnane-$3\alpha,11\beta,17\alpha,20\beta$-tetrol
8. 11-Ketoandrosterone
9. 11β-Hydroxyandrosterone
10. 11-Ketoetiocholanolone
11. 11β-Hydroxyetiocholanolone

References

Abelson, D., and Bondy, P. K. (1955) *Arch. Biochem. Biophys.* **57**: 208.

Ayers, P. J., Simpson, S. A., and Tait, J. F. (1957) *Biochem. J.* **65**: 647.

Bayliss, R. I. S., Broadbent, I. E., and Steinbeck, A. W. (1954) *Lancet* **i**, 434.

Bernstein, S., and Lenhard, R. H. (1953) *J. Org. Chem.* **18**: 1146.

Bojeson, E. (1956) *Scand. J. Clin. Lab. Invest.* **8**: 55.

Bojeson, E. (1958) *Abstr. Intern. Congr. Biochem., 4th, Vienna, 1958* Section 9, No. 118.

Bojeson, E., and Degn, H. (1960) *Abstr. Intern. Congr. Endocrinol., 1st, Copenhagen, 1960* p. 1057.

Bondy, P. K., and Upton, G. V. (1957) *Proc. Soc. Exptl. Biol. Med.* **94**: 585.

Bondy, P. K., Cohen, G. L., Hermann, W., and Crispell, K. R. (1958) *Yale J. Biol. Med.* **30**: 395.

Bondy, P. K., Cohn, G. L., and Catiglione, C. (1960) *Trans. Assoc. Am. Physicians* **73**: 186.

Bradlow, H. L., and Gallagher, T. F. (1957) *J. Biol. Chem.* **229**: 505.

Bradlow, H. L., and Gallagher, T. F. (1959) *J. Clin. Endocrinol. Metab.* **19**: 1575.

Bradlow, H. L., Hellman, L., Zumoff, B., and Gallagher, T. F. (1956) *Science* **124**: 1206.

Brooks, R. V. (1960) *J. Endocrinol.* **21**: 277.

Burger, H. G., Kent, J. R., and Kellie, A. E. (1963) *Proc. 45th Endocrine Soc. Meeting Atlantic City, N.J.* p. 41.

Burstein, S., Savard, K., and Dorfman, R. I. (1953a) *Endocrinology* **53**: 448.

Burstein, S., Savard, K., and Dorfman, R. I. (1953b) *Endocrinology* **53**: 88.

Burstein, S., Savard, K., and Dorfman, R. I. (1953c) *Endocrinology* **53**: 267.

Bush, I. E., and Mahesh, V. B. (1959) *J. Endocrinol.* **18**: 1.

Bush, I. E., and Willoughby, M. (1957) *Biochem. J.* **67**: 689.

Camacho, A. M., and Migeon, C. J. (1963) *J. Clin. Endocrinol. Metab.* **23**: 301.

Cara, J., and Gardner, L. I. (1960) *Pediatrics* **57**: 461.

Davis, J. O., Kliman, B., Yankopoulos, N. A., and Peterson, R. E. (1958) *J. Clin. Invest.* **37**: 1783.

Dobriner, K. (1951) *Symp. Steroids Exptl. Clin. Practice, 1st Conf., Cuernevaca, Mex., 1951* p. 130.

Dobriner, K., and Lieberman, S. (1952) *Ciba Found. Colloq. Endocrinol.* **2**: 81.

Dorfman, R. I. (1954a) *Recent Progr. Hormone Res.* **9**: 5.

Dorfman, R. I. (1954b) *J. Clin. Endocrinol. Metab.* **14**: 318.

Dorfman, R. I. (1961) *Metabolism* **10**: 902.

Dorfman, R. I. (1962) *In* "Methods in Hormone Research" (R. I. Dorfman, ed.), Vol. I, p. 54. Academic Press, New York.

Dorfman, R. I., Wise, J., and Shipley, R. A. (1950) *Endocrinology* **46**: 127.

Dougherty, T. F., Brown, H. E., and Berliner, D. L. (1958) *Endocrinology* **62**: 455.

Ely, R. S., Huges, E. R., and Kelley, V. C. (1958) *J. Clin. Endocrinol. Metab.* **18**: 190.

Engel, L. L., Carter, P., and Fielding, L. L. (1955) *J. Biol. Chem.* **213**: 99.

Finkelstein, M., Forchielli, E., and Dorfman, R. I. (1961) *J. Clin. Endocrinol. Metab.* **21**: 98.

Fish, W. R., Horwitt, B. N., and Dorfman, R. I. (1943) *Science* **97**: 227.

Fishman, J., Bradlow, H. L., Zumoff, B., Hellman, L., and Gallagher, T. F. (1961) *Acta Endocrinol.* **37**: 57.

Fishman, J., Hellman, L., Zumoff, B., and Gallagher, T. F. (1962) *J. Clin. Endocrinol. Metab.* **22**: 389.

Flood, C., Layne, D., Ramcharan, S., Rossipal, E., Tait, J. F., and Tait, S. A. S. (1961) *Acta Endocrinol.* **36**: 237.

Forchielli, E., and Dorfman, R. I. (1956) *J. Biol Chem.* **223**: 443.

Forchielli, E., Sorcini, G., Nightingale, M., Brust, N., Dorfman, R. I., Perloff, W. H., and Jacobson, G. (1963) *Anal. Biochem.* **5**: 416.

Fukushima, D. K., Bradlow, H. L., Hellman, L., and Gallagher, T. F. (1959) *J. Clin. Endocrinol. Metab.* **19**: 393.

Fukushima, D. K., Bradlow, H. L., Hellman, L., Zumoff, B., and Gallagher, T. F. (1961) *J. Clin. Endocrinol. Metab.* **21**: 765.

Furman, R. H., and Howard, R. P. (1960) *Circulation* **22**: 659.

Furman, R. H., and Howard, R. P. (1962) *Metabolism* **11**: 76.

Futterweit, W., McNiven, N. L., and Dorfman, R. I. (1963a) *Biochim. Biophys. Acta* **71**: 474.

Futterweit, W., McNiven, N. L., Narcus, L., Lantos, C., Drosdowsku, M., and Dorfman, R. I. (1963b) *Steroids* **1**: 628.

Gallagher, T. F. (1957) *Cancer Res.* **17**: 520.

Gallagher, T. F., Fukushima, D. K., Barry, M. C., and Dobriner, K. (1951) *Recent Progr. Hormone Res.* **6**: 131.

Gandy, H. M., Keutmann, E. H., and Izzo, A. J. (1960) *J. Clin. Invest.* **39**: 364.

Goldzieher, J. W., Baker, R. A., and Riha, E. C. (1961) *J. Clin. Endocrinol. Metab.* **21**: 62.

Gornall, A. G., and Gwilliam, C. (1957) *Can. J. Biochem. Physiol.* **35**: 71.

Gornall, A. G., and MacDonald, M. P. (1953) *J. Biol. Chem.* **201**: 279.

Gray, C. H., Greenaway, J. M., and Holness, N. J. (1961) *In* "Hormones in Blood" (C. H. Gray and A. L. Bacharach, eds.), p. 439. Academic Press, New York.

Hellman, L., Bradlow, H. L., Zumoff, B., Fukushima, D. K., and Gallagher, T. F. (1959) *J. Clin. Endocrinol. Metab.* **19**: 936.

Hellman, L., Bradlow, H. L., Zumoff, B., and Gallagher, T. F. (1961) *J. Clin. Endocrinol. Metab.* **21**: 1231.

Horning, E. C., Moscatelli, E. A., and Sweeley, C. C. (1959) *Chem. Ind.* (*London*) p. 751.

Horwitt, B. N., Dorfman, R. I., Shipley, R. A., and Fish, W. R. (1944) *J. Biol. Chem.* **155**: 213.

Ichii, S., Forchielli, E., Perloff, W. H., and Dorfman, R. I. (1963) *Anal. Biochem.* **5**: 422.

Ittrich, G. (1958) *Z. Physiol. Chem.* **312**: 1.

Jao, J., and Koritz, S. B. (1962) *Metabolism* **11**: 1302.

Jacobs, D. R., Van der Poll, J., Gabrilove, J. L., and Soffer, L. J. (1961) *J. Clin. Endocrinol. Metab.* **21**: 909.

Kalant, H. (1958) *Biochem. J.* **69**: 93.

Kappas, A., Hellman, L., Fukushima, D., and Gallagher, T. F. (1957) *J. Clin. Endocrinol.* **17**: 451.

Kliman, B., and Peterson, R. E. (1960) *J. Biol. Chem.* **235**: 1639.

Kumar, P., Soodno, J. A., and Barnes, A. C. (1962) *Nature* **195**: 1204.

Kyle, T. I., and Marrian, G. F. (1951) *Biochem. J.* **49**: 80.

Levy, H., Saito, T., Takeyama, S., Merrill, A. P., and Schepis, J. P. (1963) *Biochem. Biophys. Acta* **69**: 198.

Lewis, B. (1957) *J. Clin. Pathol.* **10**: 148.

Lieberman, S., Dobriner, K., Hill, B. R., Fieser, L. F., and Rhoads, C. P. (1948) *J. Biol. Chem.* **172**: 263.

Lieberman, S., Praetz, B., Humphries, P., and Dobriner, K. (1953) *J. Biol. Chem.* **204**: 491.

Lynn, W. S., Jr., and Brown, R. H. (1958) *J. Biol. Chem.* **232**: 1015.

McGuire, J. S. Jr., and Tomkins, G. M. (1959) *J. Biol. Chem.* **234**: 791.

McNiven, N. L., Futterweit, W., and Berenkey, K. M. (1963) Unpublished data.

Mason, H. L. (1948) *J. Biol. Chem.* **172**: 783.

Mason, H. L., and Kepler, E. J. (1947) *J. Biol. Chem.* **167**: 73.

Melby, J. C., and Spink, W. W. (1958) *J. Clin. Invest.* **37**: 1791.

Melby, J. C., Egdahl, R. H., Story, J. L., and Spink, W. W. (1960) *Endocrinology* **67**: 389.

Miller, A. M., Dorfman, R. I., and Miller, M. (1950) *Endocrinology* **46**: 127.
Miller, A. M., Rosenkrantz, H., and Dorfman, R. I. (1953) *Endocrinology* **53**: 238.
Moncloa, F., Péron, F. G., and Dorfman, R. I. (1959) *Endocrinology* **65**: 717.
Moolenaar, A. J. (1957) *Acta Endocrinol.* **25**: 161.
Neeman, M., Slaunwhite, W. R., Jr., Neely, L. M., Colson, J. G., and Sandberg, A. A. (1960) *J. Biol. Chem.* **235**: PC58.
Neher, R., and Wettstein, A. (1956) *J. Clin. Invest.* **35**: 800.
Oertel, G. W. (1961) *Acta Endocrinol.* **37**: 237.
Oertel, G. W., and Kaiser, E. (1961) *Klin. Wochschr.* **39**: 1146.
Oertel, G. W., Weiss, S. P., and Eik-Nes, K. B. (1959) *J. Clin. Endocrinol. Metab.* **19**: 213.
Pechet, M. M., Hesse, R. H., and Kohler, H. (1961) *J. Am. Chem. Soc.* **82**: 5251.
Péron, F. G. (1962) *In* "Methods in Hormone Research" (R. I. Dorfman, ed.), Vol. I, p. 199. Academic Press, New York.
Péron, F. G., and Dorfman, R. I. (1958) *Endocrinology* **62**: 1.
Peterson, R. E. (1957a) *J. Biol. Chem.* **225**: 25.
Peterson, R. E. (1957b) *J. Clin. Endocrinol. Metab.* **17**: 1150.
Peterson, R. E. (1959) *Recent Progr. Hormone Res.* **15**: 231.
Peterson, R. E., Karrer, A., and Guerra, S. L. (1957) *Anal. Chem.* **29**: 144.
Preedy, J. R. K., and Aitken, E. H. (1957) *Lancet* **i**: 191.
Richardson, E. M., Touchstone, J. C., and Dohan, F. C. (1954) *Federation Proc.* **13**: 118.
Richardson, E. M., Touchstone, J. C., and Dohan, F. C. (1955) *J. Clin. Invest.* **34**: 285.
Roy, E. J. (1962) *J. Endocrinol.* **25**: 361.
Roy, E. J., and Brown, J. B. (1960) *J. Endocrinol.* **21**: 9.
Savard, K., and Dorfman, R. I. (1963) Unpublished data.
Savard, K., Bernstein, S., Rosenkrantz, H., and Dorfman, R. I. (1953) *J. Biol. Chem.* **202**: 717.
Schiller, S., Dorfman, R. I., and Miller, M. (1945) *Endocrinology* **36**: 355.
Schubert, K., and Wehrberger, K. (1960) *Naturwissenschaften* **47**: 281.
Segaloff, A., Bowers, C. Y., Gordon, D. L., Schlosser, J. V., and Murison, P. J. (1957) *Cancer* **10**: 1116.
Sharma, D. C., Forchielli, E., and Dorfman, R. I. (1963) *J. Biol. Chem.* **238**: 572.
Short, R. V. (1958) *J. Endocrinol.* **16**: 415.
Short, R. V. (1960a) *J. Endocrinol.* **20**: XV.
Short, R. V. (1960b) *Mem. Soc. Endocrinol.* **8**: 86.
Short, R. V. (1961) *In* "Hormones in Blood" (C. H. Gray and A. L. Bacharach, eds.), p. 411. Academic Press, New York.
Silber, R. H., Busch, R. D., and Oslapas, R. (1958) *Clin. Chem.* **4**: 278.
Sorcini, G., Sciavri, F., Concolino, G., and Capone, M. (1962) *Folia Endocrinol.* (*Pisa*) **15**: 696.
Svendsen, R. (1960) *Acta Endocrinol.* **35**: 161.
Sweat, M. L. (1954) *Anal. Chem.* **26**: 1964.
Sweat, M. L. (1955) *J. Clin. Endocrinol. Metab.* **15**: 1043.
Thomas, P. Z., and Dorfman, R. I. (1964) *J. Biol. Chem.* **239**: 766.
Timiras, P. S., and Woodbury, D. M. (1955) *J. Pharmacol. Exptl. Therap.* **115**: 144.
Tomkins, G. M., and McGuire, J. S., Jr. (1960) *Ann. N.Y. Acad. Sci.* **86**: 600.
Ulick, S., and Kusch Vetter, K. (1962) *J. Biol. Chem.* **237**: 3364.
Ungar, F., and Dorfman, R. I. (1954) *J. Biol. Chem.* **205**: 125.
Ungar, F., and Dorfman, R. I. (1956) *Proc. 38th Ann. Endocrine Soc. Meeting 1956, Chicago* p. 20.
Ungar, F., Dorfman, R. I., Stecher, R. M., and Vignos, P. J., Jr. (1951) *Endocrinology* **49**: 440.
Ungar, F., Doe, R. P., and Moran, W. H. (1962) *Proc. 44th Endocrine Soc. Meeting 1962, Chicago* p. 87.

Vignos, P. J. Jr., and Dorfman, R. I. (1951) *Am. J. Med. Sci.* **222**: 29.
Villee, D. B., Engel, L. L., Loring, J. M., and Villee, C. A. (1961) *Endocrinology* **69**: 354.
Westphal, U. (1942) *Z. Physiol. Chem.* **273**: 13.
Zander, J. (1954) *Nature* **174**: 406.
Zander, J. (1955) *Klin. Wochschr.* **33**: 697.
Zander, J. (1962) *In* "Methods in Hormone Research" (R. I. Dorfman, ed.), Vol. II, p. 132. Academic Press, New York.

CHAPTER IX

Steroid Hormone Production Rates

The production and secretion of the steroid hormones have been estimated by both direct and indirect measurements. Since the steroid-producing endocrine glands do not store appreciable amounts of the hormones at any one time, it has been generally assumed, as a first approximation, that their rates of formation and of release are equivalent. Estimates of the rate of steroid formation obtained by *in vitro* techniques are extremely low, on the order of 10% or less of those obtained under *in vivo* conditions where normal balance of hormonal, circulatory, and nervous influences are maintained. For this and other reasons, *in vitro* estimates are of limited value in the assessment of normal production rates of these substances in the body.

Direct measurement of steroid production rates under *in vivo* conditions is difficult to obtain. Such direct measurements usually involve rather drastic conditions of major surgery, as is the case when the venous effluent of an endocrine organ is collected (Lindner, 1961a,b) for a period of time in the normal or abnormal animal. The indwelling permanent adrenal cannula technic of Nelson and Hume (1955) in the dog and the adrenal preparation of Blair-West *et al.* (1963), where the adrenal gland of the sheep is transplanted in the more accessible neck region, have been fairly successful for obtaining secretion rates in the normal unanesthetized animal.

Indirect procedures for the measurement of secretion or production rates were among the earliest used in attempts to answer these problems. Crude estimates of production rates were based on the amounts of pure hormone required for replacement therapy after the removal of an endocrine organ. The daily requirement of 20–30 mg of cortisol in an adrenalectomized human, for example, approximates the daily secretion rates obtained by other procedures. Fairly successful attempts to measure endogenous hormone secretion were based on the measurement of urinary excretion of steroid metabolites. With some knowledge of the metabolic pathways involved and of the fate of exogenously administered hormone, an estimate could be made. The procedures utilizing blood and urine concentrations, with radioactive labeling on the steroid molecule as a tracer, have become the most versatile and exact of the indirect procedures presently employed. In the following sections, the various approaches to the estimation of steroid production and secretion, particularly by these indirect procedures, are presented.

Cortisol Production

The production rate of cortisol is illustrated in summary form in Figs. 1–3. Men and women have about equal production rates. The values in these figures represent a composite of those found in the literature. Aging in women tends to cause decreases of the order of one-third, whereas the changes in men are of the order of a $\frac{1}{3}$–$\frac{1}{2}$ decrease. Figure 2 deals with conditions that cause decreases in production rates. The most intense decreases were found with Addison's disease, hypopituitarism, and corticoid inhibition. The changes from the normal production rate in cirrhosis and hypothyroidism were of the order of one-third decreases. Figure 3 presents data on increases in production. Maximal ACTH stimulation, in two different laboratories, was of the order of a ninefold increase. Obesity in men and hyperthyroidism showed 50% increases, and Cushing's disease patients produced 250% of the normal value.

Dorfman (1954) used the proportionate excretion of 5α and 5β reduced 11-oxygenated 17-ketosteroids in urine, with the value for percentage recovery after the administration of cortisol as a means of assessing cortisol production in humans. By this method, men were found to produce 21 mg of cortisol per day, and women elaborated 18 mg per day (Table 1). Bondy and Altrock (1953) used a renal vein catheterization method and reported a value of 21 mg per day. On the basis of Porter–Silber chromogens in urine, Silber (1955) reported values of 30–60 mg per day for normal subjects. Peterson and Wyngaarden (1956) used cortisol-4-C^{14}, and in nine normal subjects found a production rate of 17–29 mg per day, which increased to 160 mg per day with ACTH.

The studies of Flood *et al.* (1961) indicated a mean production (secretion) rate of 17.2 mg per 24 hours calculated on the basis of the specific activity of urocortisone and allourocortisol. The authors pointed out that, depending upon the metabolite chosen, variations up to 100% could be encountered. In the case of one subject (Table 2), the production rate was found to be 15.2 mg/day when the specific activity was based on the recovery, from the urine, of urocortisone plus allourocortisol, but only 7.7 mg on the basis of the specific activity of recovered cortisol alone, and 10.7 mg on the basis of cortisone recovery.

The question of cortisol secretion rate in obese individuals was studied by Melymaryk *et al.* (1962). They used a technic essentially similar to that described by Cope and Black (1958a,b). They injected about 1 μc of cortisol-4-C^{14}, using material with specific activity of 13.5–25 μc/mg. These investigators found an increased secretion rate in obese men, but when the data were calculated on a body weight basis, normal values were 0.214 ± 0.067 mg per kilogram per 24 hours, as compared with the values for the obese subjects of 0.222 ± 0.058 mg per kilogram per 24 hours.

Cost (1962) studied the normal excretion for THF + AlloTHF + THE + E + F, which was found to be 4.2 mg per 24 hours; total THB + AlloTHB + THA + A + B was 0.6 mg for the same time period. The ratio of F to B metabolites on this basis is 7. If we include THS values, it means that 1.5% of 11-deoxycortisol is normally secreted before 11-hydroxylation takes place.

Aldosterone Production Rates

Table 3 shows the extensive studies on aldosterone production rates. Figures 4 and 5 summarize the many reports. The production rate of aldosterone reported by Flood *et al.* (1961) was calculated from the specific activity of aldosterone released by extraction at pH 1. The production rate calculated from the mean per cent of dosage in this fraction and the concentration in the urine was 77 μg per day. Normal men and women on a normal diet produce about 150 μg of aldosterone with no apparent sex difference. Low Na diets call forth an important response, and the mean value of almost 1800 μg that is obtained illustrates the dramatic increase. But this change was only a portion of the value of 5700 μg found for the combination of a low Na and a high K diet. High levels of K increased aldosterone about 100% and high levels of Na resulted in a secretion of the order of one-third that of normal. Various other conditions are illustrated in Fig. 5. Nephrosis, hypertension, and congestive heart disease may cause dramatic increases. Pregnancy (last trimester) was highly effective, with values increased about 900%.

Progesterone

Pearlman (1957a) presented a procedure for relating the amount of circulating hormone to that produced under conditions in the body in which it is assumed that a steady state has been obtained. Under these conditions, the expression:

$$\frac{M}{r} = T$$

holds where:

T = Turnover time

M = Total amount of hormone in the circulation

r = Production rate

Since M is a product of the blood volume concentration (C) and the blood volume (V), the expression may be written as:

$$T = \frac{CV}{r}$$

Using progesterone-16-H^3, Pearlman (1957b) determined by this method the endogenous production rate of 0.25 gm of progesterone per day in late pregnancy.

Zander and Münstermann (1956) estimated a production of 190–280 mg per day toward the end of pregnancy, on the basis of earlier studies of the progesterone content of uterine vein blood (Zander and Münstermann, 1954).

Progesterone administered by intramuscular injection (50 mg/day) to men and postmenopausal women over a 2-week period resulted in 12.2% of the hormone being excreted as pregnanediol (Marrian *et al.*, 1954). Romanoff (1962), using a tracer dose of progesterone-4-C^{14}, obtained a value in men of 14% excretion as pregnenediol. Since men excrete about 0.3–0.9 mg (mean 0.6 mg) of pregnanediol per day (Romanoff, 1962), a daily secretion rate of 2.4–7.2 mg (mean 4.8 mg) may be calculated. This calculated value agrees well with the secretion rate calculated by isotope dilution.

Progesterone production rates calculated by recovery procedures and by isotope dilution methods are recorded in Table 4. The data are summarized in Figs. 6 and 7. Men produce about 4.6 mg of progesterone per day, a value equivalent to that found in women in the follicular phase. Since an ovariectomized woman has a value of 1.3 mg (the adrenal contribution) and the balance is produced by the ovary, then the value of 4.6 mg for men represents a reasonable composite figure of testis and adrenal production.

In the luteal phase, progesterone production by the corpus luteum is eight times the follicular phase value. With pregnancy, the value increases to 92 mg and in late pregnancy mean values of 270 mg may be observed (Fig. 7).

Androgen Production Rates

Table 5 summarizes the data on the secretion rate of various androgens in man. Among the earlier studies is the method suggested and employed by Dorfman (1954) that makes use of the value of the conversion percentage, that is, the fraction of administered steroid that appears in urine. Fukushima *et al.* (1954) also used this method and reported, in an early study, that testosterone production in men was of the order of 17–36 mg per day. The authors suggested that this value was for the total $C_{19}O_2$ production rate, assuming, quite reasonably, that conversion of C_{21} to C_{19} steroids was of a negligible order. The earlier studies measured groups of steroids or used group reactions in their analysis. More recently, emphasis has shifted to an analysis of individual components.

Vande Wiele and Lieberman (1960) studied the secretory rate of dehydroepiandrosterone, using the formula:

$$\text{Secretory rate (mg/day)} = \frac{\text{cpm of radioactive precursor injected}}{\text{Specific activity of urinary metabolite}}$$

These workers found values of dehydroepiandrosterone secretion of 15, 22, and 23 mg per day for men, and 18 and 25 mg per day for women. In the course of these studies, it soon became apparent that the dehydroepiandrosterone was being diluted by another source, thought to be the sulfate conjugate of dehydroepiandrosterone. Baulieu (1960) had first demonstrated dehydroepiandrosterone sulfate, in a concentration above that present in peripheral plasma, in the adrenal venous effluent of a woman with an adrenal tumor. This and subsequent studies by others suggest that dehydroepiandrosterone sulfate, rather than the free dehydroepiandrosterone, is a primary secretory product of the adrenal. A sulfatase active on dehydroepiandrosterone sulfate has been demonstrated in rat adrenals, suggesting that the free and sulfate forms of the steroid are interconvertible.

Hudson *et al.* (1962) reported that normal men have a testosterone production rate of 4.1–8.8 mg per day. The values reported by Lieberman *et al.* (1962) were for testosterone and androst-4-ene-3,17-dione; since intense corticoid suppression was employed, it is likely that a mechanism involving dehydroepiandrosterone (from adrenal) to androst-4-ene-3,17-dione to testosterone is seriously impaired and that the values reported are only minimal (Table 5).

The daily testosterone production by the testes of various species, calculated in kilograms of body weight, is shown in Table 6.

Estrogen Production Rates

Pearlman's initial studies in the field, using isotope dilution methods, indicated estrone production rates in late pregnancy to be 20 mg per day on the basis of estrone, 5 mg per day on the basis of estradiol-17β, and 85 mg per day on the basis of estriol (Table 7). Similar data were found by Gurpide *et al.* (1962) and by Fishman *et al.* (1962).

Gurpide *et al.* (1962) used the isotopic dilution technic in an attempt to measure the production rate of estradiol in a pregnant woman; he concluded that the pattern of metabolism of the endogenously secreted estradiol cannot be estimated from the recovery of radioactivity in the urinary estrogens. Unless the pattern of metabolism in the fetal compartment is known, the relationship between the production of estradiol by the placenta and the excretion of urinary estrogens remains undefined. Alterations in the excretion of urinary estrogens during pregnancy may reflect a change in metabolism of estradiol in the fetal (or maternal) compartment as well as a change in the amount of estradiol synthesized by the placenta.

Physiological significance could be assigned to data derived from the cumulative specific activities of urinary estrone and estradiol if the situation in pregnancy is such that the rate of transfer of estradiol from the maternal to the fetal compartment is small as compared with the rate of metabolism of estradiol in the maternal compartment, and if estrone and estradiol conjugates are not significantly transferred from the fetal to the maternal compartment. Indirect evidence suggests that this is actually the case and that the secretion of estradiol into the maternal compartment would be measured, rather than the total endogenous production.

Preedy *et al.* (1962) studied estrone production rates of normal and gynecomastia males and reported that the latter individuals had production rates three times greater than the normal subjects (Table 7).

Fragmentary reports of the production rates of corticosterone, 18-hydroxycorticosterone, and 16α-hydroxyprogesterone are presented in Tables 8 and 9. The fact that 18-hydroxycorticosterone is produced at such high rates (up to 4 mg per day) indicates that, in the pathway from this steroid to aldosterone, the 18-dehydrogenase is present only in limited amounts or that the pathway is in fact not operating. The reports by Ulick and Kusch Vetter (1962a) indicate that 18-hydroxycorticosterone is not a precursor of aldosterone.

Tables 1–9 have considered production rates in humans in some detail; Table 10 provides a summary of these data.

Table 11 considers production rates of steroids in various animals. The cortisol data in four species (Fig. 8) indicate the relatively large discrepancies among species when production rates are expressed as milligrams per kilogram per day.

Tait and Burstein (1964) dealt in considerable detail with the *in vivo* studies of steroid dynamics in man, including a discussion of the assumptions required for mathematical analysis of the data. These workers have drawn on the concepts of production and metabolic clearance rates for an approach to their problems of steroid dynamics. Metabolic clearance rate is defined by them as "the volume of blood from which the steroid hormone is completely and irreversibly removed in unit time."

The steady state relationship has been developed as follows. If P^I is defined as the production rate, i as the blood nonisotopic steroid concentration, and MCR as the metabolic clearance rate, then

$$P^I = \text{MCR} \times i$$

If MCR is expressed as liters per day and plasma concentration as micrograms per liter, P^I will be evaluated as micrograms per day.

Tait and Burstein (1964) related the MCR, which they believe "provides the most direct measure of the metabolism of a steroid," to the removal-rate coefficient (Yates and Urquhart, 1962), which appears to have the dimensions of a clearance rate and which represents the load on the control system in cybernetic terminology.

The MCR may be estimated after a single injection or constant infusion of a labeled steroid. The constant infusion method has the advantage that few samples need be analyzed, that a smaller quantity of radioactivity is needed to attain the same accuracy in the determination of MCR, and that estimation of errors is simpler than in the single-injection procedure.

An important factor influencing the metabolic clearance rate is hepatic blood flow. Preliminary experiments have been published by Tait *et al.*

(1962), who showed that the placing of subjects in the upright from the reclining position decreased the aldosterone clearance rate in a manner parallel to the change in hepatic blood flow previously described (Culbertson *et al.*, 1951).

Conditions contributing to lowered metabolic clearance rate of cortisol have been summarized by Tait and Burstein (1964) as estrogen treatment, pregnancy, cirrhosis, hepatitis, hypothyroidism, surgical stress, aging, uremia, and it probably occurs in the newborn. Increased clearance rates appear to occur in hyperthyroidism and obesity.

The volumes of distribution of steroids are cited by Tait and Burstein (1964). The total volume of distribution of cortisol is estimated to be about 11 liters, with an inner pool of 6 liters. Owing to rapid equilibrium, a single pool of 12 liters appears to be a practical value. The ratio of mean tissue values to total plasma steroid is calculated as $5/30 = 0.17$.

The inner pool for aldosterone in normal women is about 25 liters, and the total volume is 40 liters.

Steroids are bound to plasma albumin and, as pointed out by Tait and Burnstein (1964), the "less polar the steroid the stronger the binding." Transcortin, another plasma protein, also has a limited capacity for steroid binding, but binds cortisol intensively. By comparison, plasma albumin has a high capacity for binding cortisol, but the affinity is low. The high affinity of transcortin to bind cortisol is shared by corticosterone, 11-deoxycortisol, and 17-hydroxyprogesterone, but other steroids tend to be bound only weakly. There exists the possibility of non-albumin proteins having specific affinity of hormones other than cortisol, but this field has yet to be developed. Chen *et al.* (1961) believe that testosterone may be bound to a protein other than albumin.

Mills *et al.* (1960) reported that the ratio of bound to unbound cortisol is constant. Over a range of cortisol concentrations, Tait and Burstein (1964) report a value of 1.3 ± 0.2 (SE) for this ratio.

Typical data for a normal subject are illustrated in Table 4 of the review of Tait and Burstein (1964). With a secretory rate of 28.5 mg of cortisol per day, estrogen treatment decreased the rate to 15.6 mg. The unbound cortisol remained constant at 1.5 μg/100 ml of plasma; the albumin-bound cortisol was constant at 2.0 μg/100 ml, but transcortin-bound cortisol changed from 12.5 to 36.5 μg. The total cortisol in plasma increased from 16 to 40 μg/100 ml and the metabolic clearance rate decreased from 178 to 39 liters/day.

Table I

CORTISOL PRODUCTION RATE IN HUMANS

Subject	Method	Mean production rate (mg/day)		Reference
Men	Catabolism to $C_{19}O_3$ and urinary recovery	Normal adult: 21 Aged (70–88 yr): 11.4		Dorfman (1954)
Women	Catabolism to $C_{19}O_3$ and urinary recovery	Normal adult: 18 Aged (74–78 yr): 14.1		Dorfman (1954)
Stressed normal	Vein catherization	21		Bondy and Altrock (1953)
Normal	Silber–Porter chromogens in urine	30–60		Silber (1955)
Normal	Cortisol-4-C^{14} administration	17–29		Peterson and Wyngaarden (1956)
ACTH stimulation	Cortisol-4-C^{14} administration	Up to 60 mg		Peterson and Wyngaarden (1956)
Normal	—	36		Samuels *et al.* (1957)
Normal adults	Cortisol-4-C^{14} SA[a] of urocortisone	15–57		Geyer (1956)
5 normal women 1 normal man	Isotope dilution (SA of urocortisone and allourocortisol)	17.2 (12.2-26.2)		Flood *et al.* (1961)
Cushing's syndrome (suspected)	Isotope dilution	24–111		Brooks and Prunty (1960)
12 normal men (25–54 yr)	Cortisol-4-C^{14}; urocortisone	16.1 ± 6.5		Melynaryk *et al.* (1962)
22 obese men (22–70 yr)	Cortisol-4-C^{14}; urocortisone	23.9 ± 6.0		Melynaryk *et al.* (1962)
Normal human	Recovery of administered material	30		Hellman *et al.* (1954)
Adrenalectomized patient receiving cortisol	Isotope dilution	Predicted	Calculated	Lazarus (1962)
		138	150	
		86	85	
		40	43	
		31	36	
		134	150	
		133	144	

Continued on following page

Table I (*continued*)

CORTISOL PRODUCTION RATE IN HUMANS

Subject	Method	Mean production rate (mg/day)		Reference
Leukemic patients	Isotope dilution	*On basis of*		Garren and Lipsett (1961)
		Urocortisol	Urocortisone	
		17	16	
		(5.7–31)	(4.3–27)	
Men	Isotope dilution	Young males (21–31 yr): 8 (15.9-31.1) Aged males (65–73 yr): 8 (12.3-23.0)		Romanoff *et al.* (1961)
Adult male	Isotope dilution	15–57		Geyer (1956)
Stressed individual	Adrenal vein cortisol	34		Hardy and Turner (1957)
Men	Metabolite excretion	9–49 (17-KGS[b]) 14–45 (17-OHCS[c])		Moxham and Nabarro (1956)
Women	Metabolite excretion	6–40 (17-KGS) 10–36 (17-OHCS)		Moxham and Nabarro (1956)
Normal (23–55 yr)	Isotope dilution	Normal	ACTH test (maximal)	Samuels *et al.* (1957)
		36	252	
Normal (66–92 yr)	Isotope dilution	23	196	
Cirrhosis	Isotope dilution	23	165	
Hypothyroid (12 patients)	Isotope dilution	22	182	
Hyperthyroid	Isotope dilution	42	376	
Normal resting convalescent	Isotope dilution	11.3 4.2–24		Cope and Black (1958a)
Congenital adrenal hyperplasia (Female, 22 yr)	Isotope dilution	24–23		Cope (1959)
12 normal	Isotope dilution	12.8–14.5		Cope and Black (1958b)
12 normal plus ACTH	Isotope dilution	99–127		
Addison's disease	Isotope dilution	0.7–0.8		
Hypopituitary	Isotope dilution	1.0–1.1		
		0.6–0.8		
		1.0–1.2		

Continued on following page

Table I (*continued*)

CORTISOL PRODUCTION RATE IN HUMANS

Subject	Method	Mean production rate (mg/day)	Reference
Pseudohermaphrodite	Isotope dilution	0.9–1.1	
Inhibition with 9α-fluorocortisol	Isotope dilution	2.3–2.8	
Inhibition with prednisone	Isotope dilution	2.4–2.6 1.6–2.2	
Hyperthyroidism (3 subjects)	Isotope dilution	21.9–25.3	
Hepatic cirrhosis with endocrine changes	Isotope dilution	6.7–9.5	
Normal men	Isotope dilution	15.9–30.9 (21.4)	Van der Straetaem *et al.* (1963)
Cushing's syndrome Idiopathic hirsutism	Isotope dilution	Increased	De Witt *et al.* (1962)
Congenital adrenal hyperplasia (hypertensive form)	Isotope dilution	2 (before ACTH) 1.8 (after ACTH)	Reynolds and Ulstrom (1963)
Man (30 yr)	Isotope dilution	19 (control) 130 (ACTH) 19 (20 mg of dehydroepiandrosterone infused)	MacDonald and Reich (1959)
Women	Adrenal vein cannulation	1214 (before ACTH) 20 (after ACTH)	

[a] SA: specific activity.

[b] KGS: ketogenic steroids.

[c] OHCS: hydroxycorticosteroids.

Table 2

CALCULATION OF CORTISOL PRODUCTION BY VARIOUS METHODS[a]

Method and end point		Production rate (mg/day)
Cortisol-C^{14} administration	SA[b] of urocortisone plus allocortisol	15.2
Cortisol-C^{14} administration	SA of cortisone	10.7
Cortisol-C^{14} administration	SA of cortisol	7.7
Determination of cortisone and mean recovery (%) of cortisol in urine		11.7
Determination of cortisol and mean recovery (%) of cortisol in urine		11.7
Determination of urocortisone and allourocortisol and mean recovery (%) of cortisol in urine		14.7
Determination of urocortisone, urocortisol, and allourocortisol and mean recovery (%) of these constituents in urine		13.8

[a] Data on Subject A from Flood *et al.* (1961).
[b] SA: specific activity.

Table 3

ALDOSTERONE PRODUCTION RATE IN HUMANS

Subject	Method	Production rate (μg/day)	Reference
6 normal women	Aldosterone-H^3 (SA[a] of urinary aldosterone released at pH 1)	77 (50–118)	Flood *et al.* (1961)
6 normal women (21–33 yr; follicular phase of cycle)	Aldosterone-H^3 (SA[a] of urinary aldosterone released at pH 1)	192 (72–315)	Jones *et al.* (1959)
6 pregnant women (week 32–38; 23–33 yr)		582 (248–1100)	
Normal men (22–39 yr)		114 (82–190)	
Normal man (Normal diet)		154 (116–190)	
Normal man (Low Na diet)		780	
Pregnancy (near term)	Isotope dilution	2000	Solomon *et al.* (1962)

Continued on following page

Table 3 (*continued*)
ALDOSTERONE PRODUCTION RATE IN HUMANS

Subject	Method	Production rate (μg/day)	Reference
Pregnancy	Isotope dilution	140–190	Solomon *et al.* (1962)
Severe toxemia and nonpregnancy			
11 normal women	Injection of aldosterone-16-H^3 (or *d*-aldosterone-7α-H^3) and SA of 3-oxo-conjugate of aldosterone	140 (50–315)	Laumas *et al.* (1961)
Normal subjects	*dl*-Aldosterone-H^3	360 (330–400)	Peterson (1959)
	d-Aldosterone-H^3 (ring A reduced metabolite)	150–3000	Ulick *et al.* (1958)
Normal subjects (Normal diet)	Isotope dilution	230 (150–330)	Laragh *et al.* (1960)
Normal subjects (Normal diet)	Isotope dilution	ca. 200	Muller *et al.* (1959)
Normal subjects (Normal diet)	Isotope dilution	128 (45–255)	Tait *et al.* (1961)
Normal subjects (Normal diet)	Isotope dilution	147 (62–300)	Cope *et al.* (1961); Mills (1962)
Normal subjects (Normal diet)	Isotope dilution	70 (14–185)	Mills (1962)
Normal	Isotope dilution	156 (62–250) (6 observations)	Summary of Mills (1962)
High Na		29 (11–50) (3 observations)	
Low Na		564 (224–930) (4 observations)	
High K		330 (288–370) (2 observations)	
Depletion of Na and K	Isotope dilution	5700	Mills (1962)
Repletion with Na and K after depletion of both	Isotope dilution	Decreased to 1850 then to 600	Mills (1962)
Nephrosis	Isotope dilution	6600	Ulick *et al.* (1958)
Hepatic cirrhosis	Isotope dilution	Increased	Ulick *et al.* (1958)
Hepatic cirrhosis	Isotope dilution	Normal	Hurter and Nabarro (1960)
Hematemesis	Isotope dilution	1130	Hurter and Nabarro (1960)

Continued on following page

Table 3 (*continued*)

ALDOSTERONE PRODUCTION RATE IN HUMANS

Subject	Method	Production rate (μg/day)	Reference
33 cases of hypertension	Isotope dilution	130–10,000 (higher values in more severe hypertension)	Laragh *et al.* (1960)
Congestive heart	Isotope dilution	One normal Other, 500	Ulick *et al.* (1958)
Congestive heart (4 patients)	Isotope dilution	75–280	Cope *et al.* (1961)
During chlorothiazide treatment (4 patients)	Isotope dilution	111–620	Cope *et al.* (1961)
Normal diet	Isotope dilution	180 (170–190)	Ayres *et al.* (1957)
Low sodium	Isotope dilution	780	Ayres *et al.* (1957)
Normal diet (6 subjects)	Isotope dilution	144 (62–275)	Cope *et al.* (1961)
High Na (1 subject)	Isotope dilution	55	Cope *et al.* (1961)
Low Na (2 subjects)	Isotope dilution	1348 (880–1817)	Cope *et al.* (1961)

[a] SA: specific activity.

Table 4

PROGESTERONE PRODUCTION RATE IN HUMANS

Subject	Method	Production rate (mg/day)	Reference
Late pregnancy	Uterine vein blood content	190–280	Zander and Münstermann (1954, 1956)
Late pregnancy	Isotope dilution (progesterone-16-H^3)	250	Pearlman (1957a)
Pregnancy (3rd trimester)	Isotope dilution	322 (188–563)	Solomon *et al.* (1962)
Pregnancy (27–31 weeks)	Isotope dilution	263	
Pregnancy (15 weeks)	Isotope dilution	92	
Normal young men (8 subjects)	Isotope dilution	4.5 (3.2–5.6)	Romanoff (1962)

Continued on following page

Table 4 (*continued*)

PROGESTERONE PRODUCTION RATE IN HUMANS

Subject	Method	Production rate (mg/day)	Reference
Normal men	Isotope dilution (pregnanediol)	3.6	Little *et al.* (1962)
Ovariectomized women	Isotope dilution	1.3	Little *et al.* (1962)
Normal men	Isotope dilution (pregnanediol)	3.9–6.8	Dominguez *et al.* (1962)
Normal women (Follicular phase)	Isotope dilution (pregnanediol)	2.3–5.4	
Normal women (Luteal phase)	Isotope dilution (pregnanediol)	22–43	
Pregnancy (50 subjects; 27–40 weeks)	Isotope dilution (pregnanediol)	188–563 (76% of data: 200–400 μg)	
Normal men	Recovery data ($\frac{1}{8}$ excreted in urine)	4.8 (2.4–7.2)	Romanoff (1962); Marrian *et al.* (1954)
Elderly men (68–80 yr)	Isotope dilution	1.8(0.6–2.7)	Romanoff *et al.* (1963)
Young men (23–39 yr)	Isotope dilution	4.5 (3.2–5.6)	Romanoff *et al.* (1963)
Pregnant women (Mid-term)	Isotope dilution	76 (70% placenta; 30% extra-placental sources)	Ejarque and Bengtsson (1962)

Table 5

PRODUCTION RATE OF C_{19} STEROIDS IN HUMANS

Subject	Method	Production rate (mg/day)	Reference
Men	Conversion percentage	Normal adult: 18 Aged: 3 Testosterone + androst-4-ene-3,17-dione + dehydroepiandrosterone	Dorfman (1954)
Women	Conversion percentage	Normal adult: 17 Aged: 6	

Continued on following page

Table 5 *(continued)*

PRODUCTION RATE OF C_{19} STEROIDS IN HUMANS

Subject	Method	Production rate (mg/day)	Reference
		Testosterone + androst-4-ene-3,17-dione + dehydroepiandrosterone	
Men	Conversion percentage	Normal adult: 7.4 Aged: 2.2 Adrenosterone 11β-Hydroxyandrost-4-ene-3,17-dione	
Women	Conversion percentage	Normal adult: 7.0 Aged: 3.4 Adrenosterone 11β-Hydroxyandrost-4-ene-3,17-dione	
Normal man	Amount of conversion	17–36 mg of testosterone (Authors really meant testosterone or equivalent, which would include primarily other $C_{19}O_2$ steroids)	Fukushima *et al.* (1954)
Men (30–36 yr)	Isotope dilution	15; 22; 23 (dehydroepiandrosterone)	Vande Wiele and Lieberman (1960)
Women (18–32 yr)	Isotope dilution	18; 25 (dehydroepiandrosterone)	Vande Wiele and Lieberman (1960)
Addisonian receiving 15 mg of dehydroepiandrosterone and 15 mg of androst-4-ene-3,17-dione	Administration of dehydroepiandrostene-H^3 and androst-4-ene-3,17-dione-C^{14}	No data listed	Brooks and Prunty (1962)
Corticoid-suppressed men	Isotope dilution	2.5–4.5 (Testosterone + androst-4-ene-3,17-dione)	Lieberman *et al.* (1962)
Corticoid-suppressed women	Isotope dilution	0–1.6 (Testosterone + androst-4-ene-3,17-dione)	Lieberman *et al.* (1962)
Normal men	Isotope dilution	4.1–8.8 Testosterone	Hudson *et al.* (1962)
Arrhenoblastoma	Isotope dilution	700 ("androgens")	Gallagher *et al.* (1962)

Continued on following page

Table 5 (*continued*)

PRODUCTION RATE OF C_{19} STEROIDS IN HUMANS

Subject	Method	Production rate (mg/day)	Reference
Man (30 yr)	Isotope dilution	Dehydroepiandro-sterone (D) 32 (control) 51 (20 mg; 1 day of D) 70 (ACTH)	MacDonald *et al.* (1962b)
Men (27–31 yr)	Isotope dilution	Dehydroepiandro-sterone 30 (19–40)	MacDonald *et al.* (1962a)
Humans	Isotope dilution	Dehydroepiandro-sterone 10 Men; 29 (15–32) 15 Women: 19 (12–25) Man (adrenal suppressed): 5 Testosterone + androst-4-ene-3,17-dione: 3	Vande Wiele *et al.* (1962)

Table 6

TESTOSTERONE PRODUCTION RATE BY TESTIS OF VARIOUS SPECIES

Species	Testosterone production μg/kg/day)
Human	70
Dog	70
Bull	40
Boar	10
Stallion	20
Calf	2

Table 7

Estrogen Production Rate in Humans

Subject	Method	Production rate (mg/day)			Reference
Late pregnancy	Estrone-6,17-H^3 Isotope dilution	Estrone: 20			Pearlman *et al.* (1954)
Late pregnancy	Recovery percentage of administered hormone	Estriol: 85 Estradiol-17β: 5			Pearlman *et al.* (1954)
Nonpregnant women	Isotope dilution	Estradiol-17β: 0.2; 0.5 (Calculated from estrone, estradiol-17β, and estriol)			Gurpide *et al.* (1962)
Pregnant		*Calculated from*			Gurpide *et al.* (1962)
Month		Estrone	Estradiol-17β	Estriol	
4 (1 subject)	Isotope dilution	7	7	83	
5 (2 subjects)		9.5 (9–10)	8.5 (7–10)	86 (62–110)	
9 (2 subjects)		31 (26–36)	26 (24–28)	230 (190–270)	
Normal female	Isotope dilution	Estrone: 0.097 Estradiol-17β: 0.045 Estriol: 0.140			Fishman *et al.* (1962)
Pregnancy (6 months)	Isotope dilution	Estrone: 6–14 Estradiol-17β: 7–14 Estriol: 58–247			
		Basis	Estrone production rate		Preedy *et al.* (1962)
Normal men	Isotope dilution	Estrone conjugates	0.048 (0.034–0.078)		
Gynecomastia	Isotope dilution	Estrone conjugates	0.181 (0.136–0.226)		

Table 8

RATE OF PRODUCTION OF VARIOUS STEROIDS IN HUMANS

Steroid	Subject	Method	Production rate (mg/day)	Reference
18-Hydroxy-corticosterone	Normal	Isotope dilution on basis of specific activity of 3α,18,21-trihydroxy-5β-pregnane-11,20-dione	Up to 4	Ulick and Kusch Vetter (1962)
16α-Hydroxy-progesterone	Normal man	Isotope dilution on basis of activity of 17-isopregnanolone	1–2	Calvin and Lieberman (1962)
3β,17α-Dihydroxy-pregn-5-en-20-one	Adrenal adenoma	Isotope dilution	154–2000	Fukushima *et al.* (1962)

Table 9

CORTICOSTERONE PRODUCTION RATE IN HUMANS

Subject	Method	Mean production rate (mg/day)	Reference
Normal men and women	Isotope dilution	1.5–4.0(2.3)	Peterson and Pierce (1960)
Normal men	Isotope dilution	1.6–5.5(3.4)	Van der Straetaem *et al.* (1963)
Normal	Isotope dilution	0.84	Ayres *et al.* (1957)
Women	Adrenal venous blood	Before ACTH (mean): 4.8 μg/min After ACTH (mean): 3.6 μg/min	Grant *et al.* (1957)

Table 10

Production Rates of Various Steroids in Humans

Steroid	Subject	Rate (mg/day)
Cortisol	Men and women	25
Corticosterone	Men and women	1
Aldosterone	Men and women	0.15
18-Hydroxycorticosterone		Up to 4
16α-Hydroxyprogesterone	Man	1–2
Progesterone	Man	4
	Women (follicular phase)	4
	Women (luteal phase)	30
	Early pregnancy	100
	Late pregnancy	300
Testosterone	Man	6
	Women	1

Table 11

Steroid Production Rate Studies in Animals

Steroid	Species	Method	Production rate	Reference
Cortisol	Cebus monkey	Direct adrenal vein collection	*Males* 16.1 ± 1.4 μg/gm of gland/min 368.8 ± 17 μg/kg of body weight/hr *Females* 15.9 ± 2.0 μg/gm of gland/min 339.0 ± 35 μg/kg of body weight/hr	Aires *et al.* (1962)
Cortisol	Guinea pig (500 gm)	Direct adrenal vein collection	9.1 ± 0.4 μg/gm of gland/min 161 ± 12 μg/kg of body weight/hr	Fajer and Vogt (1962)
Cortisol	Guinea pig (870 gm)	Direct vein collection	3.7 ± 0.3 μg/gm of gland/min 87 ± 8 μg/kg of body weight/hr	Fajer and Vogt (1962)
Testosterone	Anesthetized dog	Direct vein collection	0.68 mg/day Stimulation by: LH, FSH No stimulation by: ACTH, synthetic vasopressor	Eik-Nes (1962)

Continued on following page

Table II (*continued*)

STEROID PRODUCTION RATE STUDIES IN ANIMALS

Steroid	Species	Method	Production rate		Reference
Testosterone	Calves	Direct	Body wt.	mg/day	Lindner (1961a)
			89	0.6	
			123	1.5	
			128	1.8	
			137	9.4	
			175	4.0	
			178	11.1	
			200	2.6	
Androst-4-ene-3,17-dione	Calves	Direct	89	3.0	
			123	10.4	
			128	0.6	
			137	4.1	
			175	1.2	
			178	0.7	
			200	0.2	
Testosterone	Boar and ram (3½ months)		0.34–0.49 mg/day		Lindner (1961b)
Testosterone	Mature boar		4.3–14.8 mg/day		Lindner (1961b)
Progesterone	Dog		48(5–270) μg/hr 2.6(0.3–9.8) μg/hr/gm of ovary/kg of body wt		Telegdy and Endröczi (1961)
Progesterone	Cow (non-pregnant)		3 mg/day		Short (1962)
Testosterone	Young boar (3½ months)		0.36–0.50 mg/day		Lindner (1960)
	Stallion (3 yr)		6.2 mg/day		
Androst-4-ene-3,17-dione	Stallion (3 yr)		1.6 mg/day		
Testosterone	Bull (17 yr)		0.8 mg/hr After HCG: Up to 11.8 mg/hr		
Testosterone	Calves		0.03 mg/hr After GH: 0.04 mg/hr		Lindner (1959)
Androst-4-ene-3,17-dione	Calves		0.12 mg/hr After GH: 1.08 mg/hr		Lindner (1959)

Continued on following page

Table II (*continued*)

STEROID PRODUCTION RATE STUDIES IN ANIMALS

Steroid	Species	Method	Production rate	Reference
				From review of Yates and Urquhart (1962)
			mg/kg of body wt/hr	Specific references
Cortisol	Dog		12	Endröczi *et al.* (1958a)
			40	Zaffaroni and Burton (1953)
			63	Farrell *et al.* (1955)
			75	Hechter *et al.* (1955)
			21	Rosnagle and Farrell (1956)
Corticosterone	Dog		20	Zaffaroni and Burton (1953)
			2	Endröczi *et al.* (1958b)
			27	Farrell *et al.* (1955)
			20	Hechter *et al.* (1955)
Aldosterone	Dog		0.16	Yankopoulos *et al.* (1959)
			0.66	Farrell *et al.* (1955)
			0.39	Rosnagle and Farrell (1956)
11-Deoxycortisol	Dog		7.4	Farrell *et al.* (1955)
			0.56	
Corticosterone	Rabbit		49	Vogt (1954)
Cortisol	Hamster		42	Schindler and Knigge (1959)
Cortisol	Cat		50	Endröczi *et al.* (1958b)
Corticosterone	Cat		10	Endröczi *et al.* (1958b)
Cortisol	Sheep		15	MacDonald and Reich (1959)
Corticosterone	Sheep		5	MacDonald and Reich (1959)
Cortisol	Sheep		5–50	MacDonald and Reich (1959)
Corticosterone	Sheep		0.5–5	MacDonald and Reich (1959)
Cortisol	Guinea pig		0.01–0.07	Telegdy *et al.* (1960)

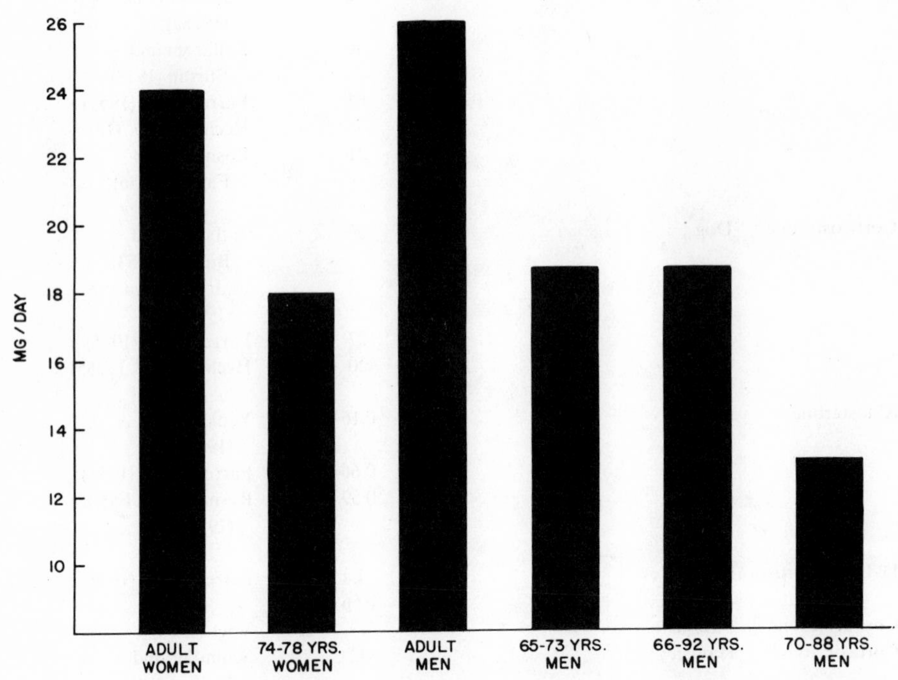

FIG. 1. Cortisol production rates in normal men and women.

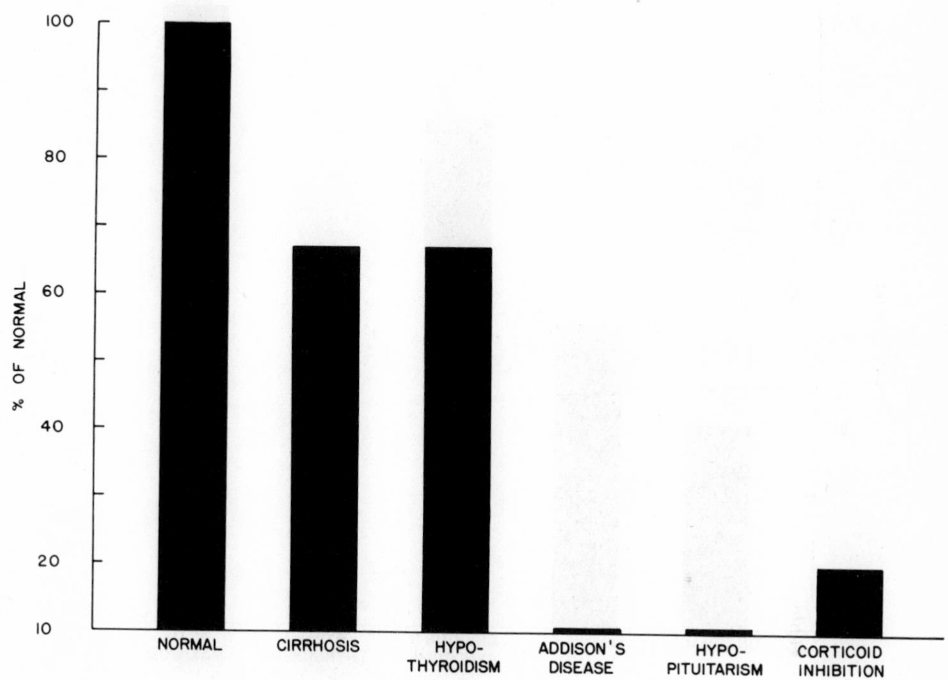

FIG. 2. Conditions of decreased cortisol production.

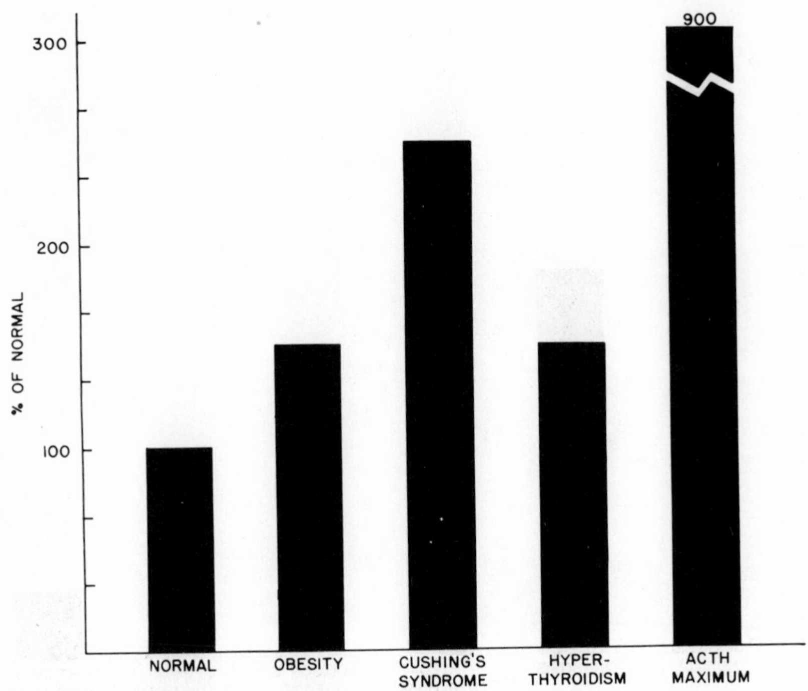

FIG. 3. Conditions of increased cortisol production.

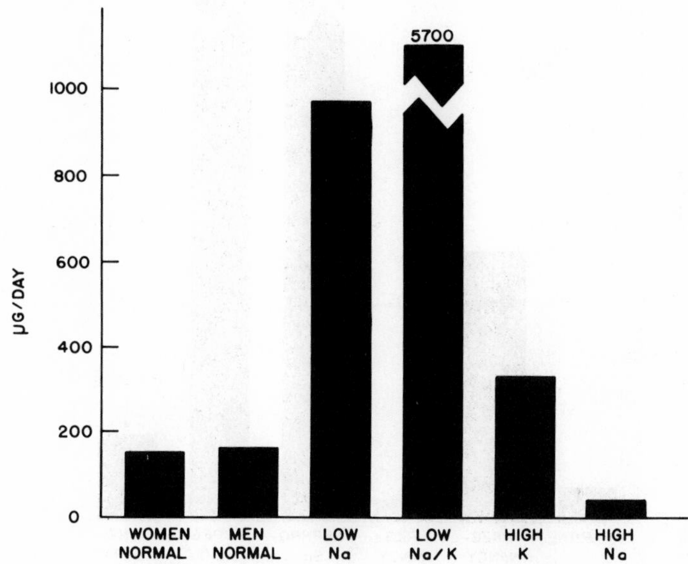

FIG. 4. Aldosterone production rates in normal and abnormal states.

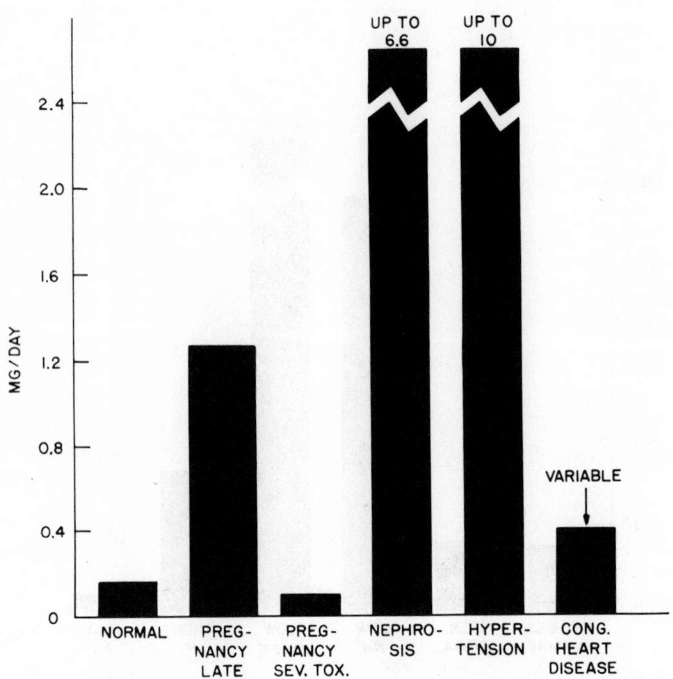

FIG. 5. Aldosterone production rates in normal and abnormal states (continued from Fig. 4).

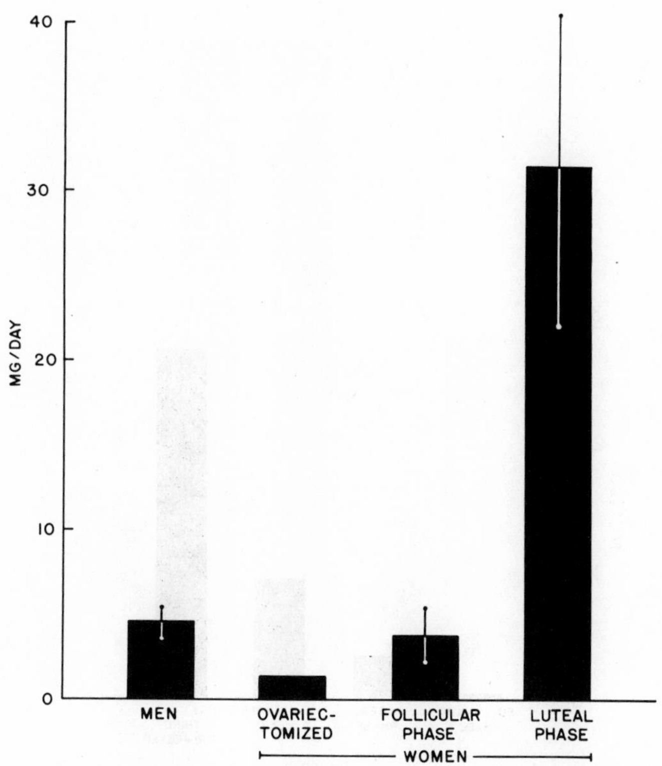

FIG. 6. Progesterone secretion rates in men and women.

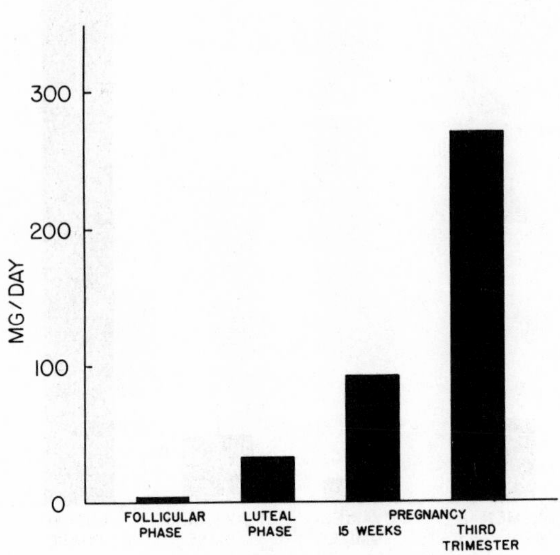

FIG. 7. Progesterone secretion rates in pregnant and nonpregnant women.

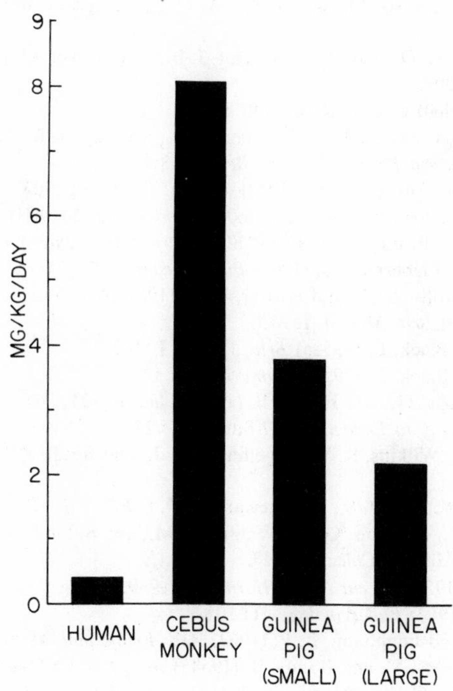

FIG. 8. Cortisol production rates in various animals.

References

Aires, M. M., Kadekaro, M., and Fajer, A. (1962) *Excerpta Med. Intern. Congr. Ser.* **51**: 141.

Ayres, P. J., Garrod, O., Tait, S. A. S., Tait, J. F., and Walker, G. (1957) *Ciba Found. Colloq. Endocrinol.* **2**: 309.

Baulieu, E. E. (1960) *Compt. Rend.* **248**: 1421.

Blair-West, J. R., Coghlan, J. P., Denton, D. A., Goding, J. R., Wintour, M., and Wright, R. D. (1963) *Recent Progr. Hormone Res.* **19**: 311.

Bondy, P. K., and Altrock, J. R. (1953) *J. Clin. Invest.* **32**: 703.

Brooks, R. V., and Prunty, F. T. G. (1960) *J. Endocrinol.* **20**: XIII.

Brooks, R. V., and Prunty, F. T. G. (1962) *Excerpta Med. Intern. Congr. Ser.* **51**: 174.

Calvin, H. I., and Lieberman, S. (1962) *Biochemistry* **1**: 639.

Chen, P. S., Jr., Mills, I. H., and Bartter, F. C. (1961) *J. Endocrinol.* **23**: 129.

Cope, C. L. (1959) *Brit. Med. J.* **I**: 815.

Cope, C. L., and Black, E. (1958a) *Brit. Med. J.* **I**: 1020.

Cope, C. L., and Black, E. (1958b) *Clin. Sci.* **17**: 147.

Cope, C. L., Nicolis, G., and Fraser, B. (1961) *Clin. Sci.* **21**: 367.

Cost, W. S. (1962) *Acta Endocrinol.* **27** Suppl. 67: 27.

Culbertson, J. W., Wilkins, R. W., Ingelfinger, F. J., and Bradley, S. E. (1951). *J. Clin. Invest.* **30**: 305.

De Witt, G. F., Robson, J. S., and Stewart, C. P. (1962) *Clin. Chim. Acta* **7**: 664.

Dominguez, O. V., Francois, G. D., Watanabe, M., and Solomon, S. (1962) *Abstr. Endocrine Soc. 44th Ann. Meeting Chicago.* p. 17.

Dorfman, R. I. (1954) *Recent Progr. Hormone Res.* **9**: 5.

Eik-Nes, K. B. (1962) *Endocrinology* **71**: 101.

Ejarque, P. M., and Bengtsson, L. P. (1962) *Acta Endocrinol.* **41**: 521.

Endröczi, E., Kovács, S., and Bohus, B. (1958a) *Acta Physiol. Acad. Sci. Hung.* **14**: 39.

Endröczi, E., Batu, G., and Martin, J. (1958b) *Endokrinologie* **35**: 280.

Fajer, A., and Vogt, M. (1962) *Excerpta Med. Intern. Congr. Ser.* **51**: 141.

Farrell, G. L., Rauschkolb, E. W., and Royce, P. C. (1955) *Am. J. Physiol.* **182**: 269.

Fishman, J., Brown, J. B., Hellman, L., Zumoff, B., and Gallagher, T. F. (1962) *J. Biol. Chem.* **237**: 1489.

Flood, C., Layne, D. S., Ramacharan, S., Rossipal, E., Tait, J. F., and Tait, S. A. S. (1961) *Acta Endocrinol.* **36**: 237.

Fukushima, D. K., Bradlow, H. L., Dobriner, K., and Gallagher, T. F. (1954) *J. Biol. Chem.* **206**: 863.

Fukushima, D. K., Bradlow, H. L., Hellman, L., and Gallagher, T. F. (1962) *J. Clin. Endocrinol. Metab.* **22**: 765.

Gallagher, T. F., Spencer, H., Bradlow, T. F., Allen, L., and Hellman, L. (1962) *J. Clin. Endocrinol. Metab.* **22**: 970.

Garren, L. D., and Lipsett, M. B. (1961) *J. Clin. Endocrinol. Metab.* **21**: 1248.

Geyer, G. (1956) *Verhandl. Deut. Ges. Inn. Med.* **62**: 476.

Grant, J. K., Forrest, A. P. M., and Symington, T. (1957) *Acta Endocrinol.* **26**: 195.

Gurpide, E., Angers, M., Vande Wiele, R. L., and Lieberman, S. (1962) *J. Clin. Endocrinol. Metab.* **22**: 935.

Hardy, J. D., and Turner, M. D. (1957) *Am. J. Med.* **22**: 967.

Hechter, O., Macchi, I. A., Korman, H., Frank, E. D., and Frank, H. A. (1955) *Am. J. Physiol.* **182**: 29.

Hellman, L., Bradlow, H. L., Adesman, J., Fukushima, D. K., Kulp, J. L., and Gallagher, T. F. (1954) *J. Clin. Invest.* **33**: 1106.

Hudson, B., Coghlan, J., Dulmanis, A., and Ekkel, I. (1962) *Abstr. Endocrine Soc. 44th Ann. Meeting Chicago*, p. 16.

Hurter, R., and Nabarro, J. D. N. (1960) *Acta Endocrinol.* **33**: 168.

Jones, K. M., Lloyd-Jones, R., Riondel, A., Tait, J. F., Tait, S. A. S., Bulbrook, R. D., and Greenwood, F. C. (1959) *Acta Endocrinol.* **30**: 321.

Laragh, J. H., Ulick, S., Januszewicz, V., Deming, Q. B., Kelly, W. G., and Lieberman, S. (1960) *J. Clin. Invest.* **39**: 1091.

Laumas, K. R., Tait, J. F., and Tait, S. A. S. (1961) *Acta Endocrinol.* **36**: 265.

Lazarus, L. (1962) *J. Clin. Endocrinol. Metab.* **22**: 581.

Lieberman, S., MacDonald, P. C., and Vande Wiele, R. L. (1962) *Excerpta Med. Intern. Congr. Ser.* **51**: 16.

Lindner, H. R. (1959) *Nature* **183**: 1605.

Lindner, H. R. (1960) *J. Endocrinol.* **20**: V.

Lindner, H. R. (1961a) *J. Endocrinol.* **23**: 139.

Lindner, H. R. (1961b) *J. Endocrinol.* **23**: 171.

Little, B., Tait, J. F., Black, W. P. and Tait, S. A. S. (1962) *Abstr. Endocrine Soc. 44th Ann. Meeting Chicago* p. 17.

MacDonald, I. R., and Reich, M. (1959) *J. Physiol.* (*London*) **147**: 33.

MacDonald, P. C., Vande Wiele, R. L., and Lieberman, S. (1962a) *J. Clin. Endocrinol. Metab.* **22**: 1229.

MacDonald, P. C., Vande Wiele, R. L., and Lieberman, S. (1962b) *J. Clin. Endocrinol. Metab.* **22**: 1222.

Marrian, G. F., Russell, M. E., and Atherden, S. M. (1954) *J. Endocrinol.* **10**: 351.

Melymaryk, P., Gillies, R. R., Murphy, B., and Pattee, C. J. (1962) *J. Clin. Endocrinol. Metab.* **22**: 587.

Mills, I. H., Schedl, H. P., Chen, P. S., Jr., and Bartter, F. C. (1960) *J. Clin. Endocrinol. Metab.* **20**: 515.

Mills, J. N. (1962) *Brit. Med. Bull.* **18**: 170.

Moxham, A., and Nabarro, J. D. N. (1956) *J. Clin. Pathol.* **9**: 351.

Muller, A. F., Veyrat, R., and Manning, E. L. (1959) *Helv. Med. Acta.* **26**: 714.

Nelson, D. H., and Hume, D. M. (1955) *Endocrinology* **57**: 184.

Pearlman, W. H. (1957a) *Ciba Found. Colloq. Endocrinol.* **11**: 233.

Pearlman, W. H. (1957b) *Biochem. J.* **65**: 7P.

Pearlman, W. H., Pearlman, M. R. J., and Rakoff, A. E. (1954) *J. Biol. Chem.* **209**: 803.

Peterson, R. E. (1959) *Recent Progr. Hormone Res.* **15**: 231.

Peterson, R. E., and Pearce, C. E. (1960) *J. Clin. Invest.* **39**: 741.

Peterson, R. E., and Wyngaarden, J. B. (1956) *J. Clin. Invest.* **35**: 552.

Preedy, J. R. K., Crowell, G. C., Kosola, W., and Maner, F. D. (1962) *Abstr. Endocrine Soc. 44th Ann. Meeting Chicago* p. 14.

Reynolds, J. W., and Ulstrom, R. A. (1963) *J. Clin. Endocrinol. Metab.* **23**: 191.

Romanoff, L. P. (1962) *Excerpta Med. Intern. Congr. Ser.* **51**: 194.

Romanoff, L. P., Morris, C. W., Welch, P., Rodriguez, R. M., and Pincus, G. (1961) *J. Clin. Endocrinol. Metab.* **21**: 1413.

Romanoff, L. P., Morris, C. W., Welch, P., Grace, M. P., and Pincus, G. (1963) *J. Clin. Endocrinol. Metab.* **23**: 286.

Rosnagle, R. S., and Farrell, G. L. (1956) *Am. J. Physiol.* **187**: 7.

Samuels, L. T., Brown, H., Eik-Nes, K., Tyler, F. H., and Dominguez, O. V. (1957) *Ciba Found. Colloq. Endocrinol.* **11**: 208.

Schindler, W. J., and Knigge, K. M. (1959) *Endocrinology* **65**: 739.

Short, R. V. (1962) *J. Endocrinol.* **23**: 401.

Silber, R. H. (1955) *Clin. Chem.* **1**: 234.

Solomon, S., Watanabe, M., Dominguez, O. V., Gray, M. J., Meeker, C. I., and Sims, E. A. H. (1962) *Excerpta Med. Intern. Congr. Ser.* **51**: 267.

Tait, J. F., and Burstein, S. (1964) *In* "The Hormones" (G. Pincus, E. B. Astwood, and K. V. Thimann, eds.), Vol. 4, Academic Press, New York, in preparation.

Tait, J. F., Tait, S. A. S., Little, B., and Laumas, K. R. (1961) *J. Clin. Invest.* **40**: 72.

Tait, J. F., Little, B., Tait, S. A. S., and Flood, C. (1962) *J. Clin. Invest.* **4**: 2093.

Telegdy, G., and Endröczi, E. (1961) *Acta Physiol. Acad. Sci. Hung.* **20**: 277.

Telegdy, G., Endröczi, E., and Lissák, K. (1960) *Acta Physiol. Acad. Sci. Hung.* **18**: 211.

Ulick, S., and Kusch Vetter, K. (1962) *Excerpta Med. Intern. Congr. Ser.* **51**: 172.

Ulick, S., and Kusch Vetter, K. (1962a) *J. Biol. Chem.* **237**: 3364.

Ulick, S., Laragh, S. H., and Lieberman, S. (1958) *Trans. Assoc. Am. Physicians* **71**: 225.

Vande Wiele, R. L., and Lieberman, S. (1960) *In* "Biological Activities of Steroids in Relation to Cancer" (G. Pincus and E. P. Vollmer, eds.), p. 93. Academic Press, New York.

Vande Wiele, R. L., MacDonald, P. C., Bolte, E., and Lieberman, S. (1962) *J. Clin. Endocrinol. Metab.* **22**: 1207.

Van der Straetaem, M., Vermeulen, A., and Orie, N. (1963) *Acta Endocrinol.* **43**: 430.

Vogt, M. (1954) *J. Physiol.* (*London*) **130**: 601.

Yankopoulos, N. A., Davis, J. O., Kliman, B., and Peterson, R. E. (1959) *J. Clin. Invest.* **38**: 1278.

Yates, F. E., and Urquhart, J. (1962) *Physiol. Rev.* **42**: 359.

Zaffaroni, A., and Burton, R. B. (1953) *Arch. Biochem. Biophys.* **42**: 1.

Zander, J., and Münstermann, A. M. V. (1954) *Klin. Wochschr.* **32**: 894.

Zander, J., and Münstermann, A. M. V. (1956) *Klin. Wochschr.* **34**: 944.

Author Index

C

G

H

I

J

L

M

R

S

U

V

W

Subject Index

A

D

E

G

H

N

O

Q

R

T

U

V